S0-BSL-585

The Radio Amateur's Handbook

By the HEADQUARTERS STAFF

of the

AMERICAN RADIO RELAY LEAGUE

NEWINGTON, CONN., U.S.A. 06111

Editor
Robert Myers, W1FBY

Assistant Editors:
Laird Campbell, W1CUT
Tony Dorbuck, W1YNC
Gerald Hall, K1PLP
George Hart, W1NJM
Lewis McCoy, W1ICP
Thomas McMullen, W1SL
Perry Williams, W1UED

1975

Fifty-Second Edition

Library of Congress Catalog Card Number: 41-3345

Fifty-Second Edition

$5.50 in the U.S.A. and Possessions, $6.00 in Canada, $7.00 elsewhere.

Clothbound edition $8.50 U.S.A., Possessions and Canada, $9.00 elsewhere.

Errata

Pg. 128: Fig. 2, U1 should be CA3085 rather than CA3055. This change also applies to the text.

Pg. 299: Fig. 1, RFC1 is 3 turns, No. 28 enam. on ferrite bead. A 220-ohm resistor may be substituted. In Table I, L1 for 144 MHz should be on a 1/4 ID form.

Pg. 318: Fig. 9-7, identification for L10 and L11 should be transposed.

Pg. 440: The template shown in Fig. 2 is no longer available from ARRL Hq.

Pg. 535: CR1 should be reversed.

FOREWORD

If ever evidence were needed of the continued absorption of radio amateurs with improvement of their technical knowledge and operating skills, it surely rests in the more than four and a half million copies of *The Radio Amateur's Handbook* distributed since the first edition a half century ago.

That unique publishing record is attributable in large part to the fact that the *Handbook* is, and always has been, just that – a practical, useful manual rather than a theoretical textbook. Its continuing purpose is to present the necessary fundamentals, as well as changing technology and applications, to serve the varied interests of the experimenter, the home builder, the DXer, the contester, and the ragchewer.

It has for some time been the custom to bring out each annual edition shortly after the first of the calendar year. To correlate its appearance more closely with the commencement of the peak activity season, however, this year the publication date has been advanced to the autumn months. Future schedules will depend on comments from amateurs as to the usefulness of this change.

The present volume is the product of the efforts and the skills of many talented amateurs. We hope you will find it of value in the pursuit of your goals and your interests.

JOHN HUNTOON, W1RW
General Manager

Newington, Conn.
November, 1974

SCHEMATIC SYMBOLS USED IN CIRCUIT DIAGRAMS

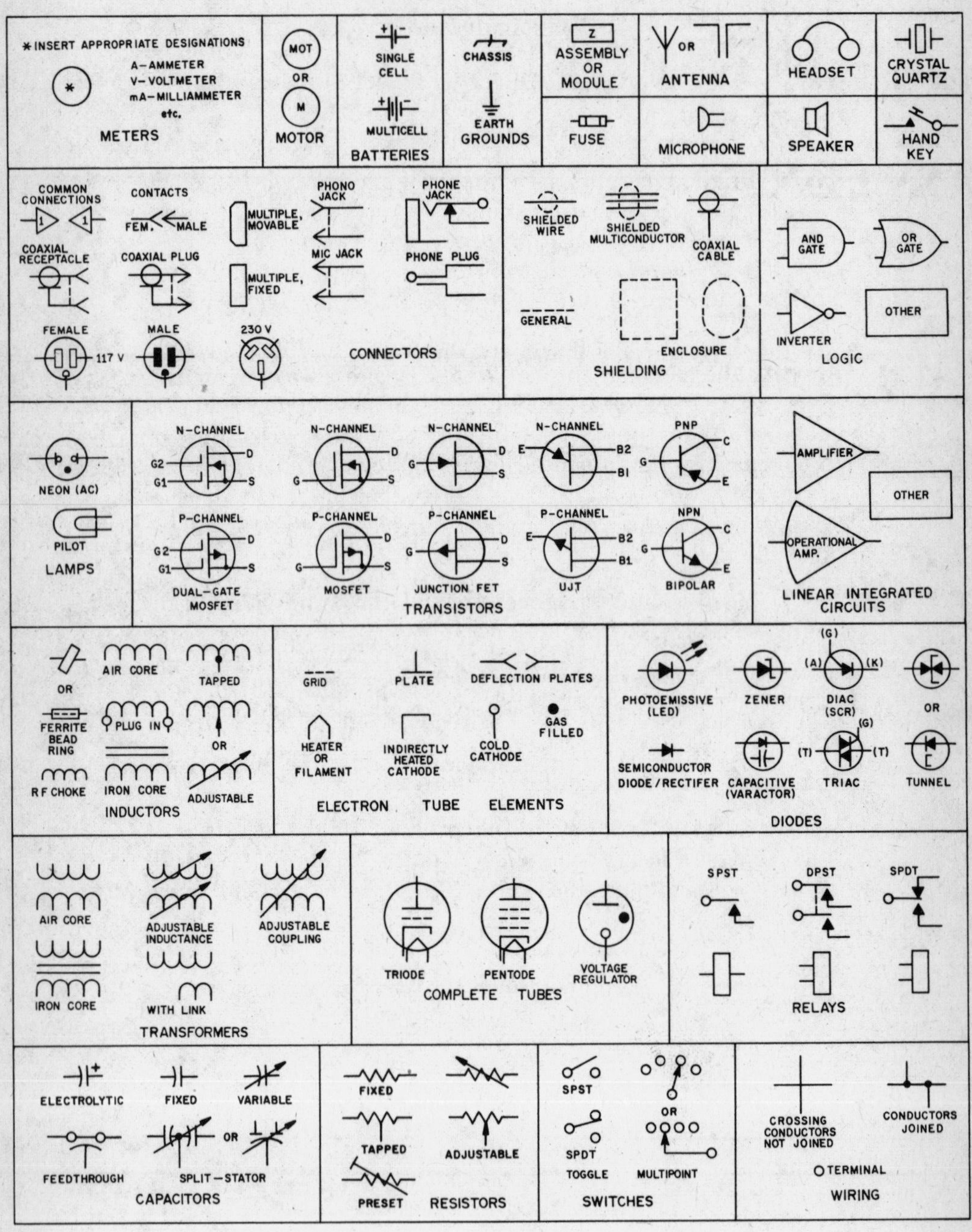

CONTENTS

The Amateur's Code

ONE

The Amateur is considerate . . .He never knowingly uses the air in such a way as to lessen the pleasure of others.

TWO

The Amateur is Loyal . . .He offers his loyalty, encouragement and support to his fellow radio amateurs, his local club and to the American Radio Relay League, through which amateur radio is represented.

THREE

The Amateur is Progressive . . .He keeps his station abreast of science. It is well built and efficient. His operating practice is above reproach.

FOUR

The Amateur is Friendly . . .Slow and patient sending when requested, friendly advice and counsel to the beginner, kindly assistance, cooperation and consideration for the interests of others; these are marks of the amateur spirit.

FIVE

The Amateur is Balanced . . .Radio is his hobby. He never allows it to interfere with any of the duties he owes to his home, his job, his school, or his community.

SIX

The Amateur is Patriotic . . . His knowledge and his station are always ready for the service of his country and his community.

– PAUL M. SEGAL

Amateur Radio

Amateur radio is a scientific hobby, a means of gaining personal skill in the fascinating art of electronics and an opportunity to communicate with fellow citizens by private short-wave radio. Scattered over the globe are over 700,000 amateur radio operators who perform a service defined in international law as one of "self-training, intercommunication and technical investigations carried on by . . . duly authorized persons interested in radio technique solely with a personal aim and without pecuniary interest."

From a humble beginning at the turn of the century, amateur radio has grown to become an established institution. Today the American followers of amateur radio number over 250,000, trained communicators from whose ranks will come the professional communications specialists and executives of tomorrow – just as many of today's radio leaders were first attracted to radio by their early interest in amateur radio communication. A powerful and prosperous organization now provides a bond between amateurs and protects their interests; an internationally respected magazine is published solely for their benefit. The military services seek the cooperation of the amateur in developing communications reserves. Amateur radio supports a manufacturing industry which, by the very demands of amateurs for the latest and best equipment, is always up-to-date in its designs and production techniques – in itself a national asset. Amateurs have won the gratitude of the nation for their heroic performances in times of natural disaster; traditional amateur skills in emergency communication are also the stand-by system for the nation's civil defense. Amateur radio is, indeed, a magnificently useful institution.

Although as old as the art of radio itself, amateur radio did not always enjoy such prestige. Its first enthusiasts were private citizens of an experimental turn of mind whose imaginations went wild when Marconi first proved that messages actually could be sent by wireless. They set about learning enough about the new scientific marvel to build homemade spark transmitters. By 1912 there were numerous Government and commercial stations, and hundreds of amateurs; regulation was needed, so laws, licenses and wavelength specifications appeared. There was then no amateur organization nor spokesman. The official viewpoint toward amateurs was something like this:

"Amateurs? . . . Oh, yes . . . Well, stick 'em on 200 meters and below; they'll never get out of their backyards with that."

But as the years rolled on, amateurs found out how, and DX (distance) jumped from local to 500-mile and even occasional 1000-mile two-way contacts. Because all long-distance messages had to be relayed, relaying developed into a fine art – an ability that was to prove invaluable when the Government suddenly called hundreds of skilled amateurs into war service in 1917. Meanwhile U.S. amateurs began to wonder if there were amateurs in other countries across the seas and if, some day, we might not span the Atlantic on 200 meters.

Most important of all, this period witnessed the birth of the American Radio Relay League, the amateur radio organization whose name was to be virtually synonymous with subsequent amateur progress and short-wave development. Conceived and formed by the famous inventor, the late Hiram Percy Maxim, ARRL was formally launched in early 1914. It had just begun to exert its full force in amateur activities when the United States declared war in 1917, and by that act sounded the knell for amateur radio for the next two and a half years. There were then over 6000 amateurs. Over 4000 of them served in the armed forces during that war.

Today, few amateurs realize that World War I not only marked the close of the first phase of amateur development but came very near marking its end for all time. The fate of amateur radio was in the balance in the days immediately following the signing of the Armistice. The Government, having had a taste of supreme authority over communications in wartime, was more than half inclined to keep it. The war had not been ended a month before Congress was considering legislation that would have made it impossible for the

HIRAM PERCY MAXIM
President ARRL, 1914–1936

amateur radio of old ever to be resumed. ARRL's President Maxim rushed to Washington, pleaded, argued, and the bill was defeated. But there was still no amateur radio; the war ban continued. Repeated representations to Washington met only with silence. The League's offices had been closed for a year and a half, its records stored away. Most of the former amateurs had gone into service; many of them would never come back. Would those returning be interested in such things as amateur radio? Mr. Maxim, determined to find out, called a meeting of the old Board of Directors. The situation was discouraging: amateur radio still banned by law, former members scattered, no organization, no membership, no funds. But those few determined men financed the publication of a notice to all the former amateurs that could be located, hired Kenneth B. Warner as the League's first paid secretary, floated a bond issue among old League members to obtain money for immediate running expenses, bought the magazine *QST* to be the League's official organ, started activities, and dunned officialdom until the wartime ban was lifted and amateur radio resumed again, on October 1, 1919. There was a headlong rush by amateurs to get back on the air. Gangway for King Spark! Manufacturers were hard put to supply radio apparatus fast enough. Each night saw additional dozens of stations crashing out over the air. Interference? It was bedlam!

But it was an era of progress. Wartime needs had stimulated technical development. Vacuum tubes were being used both for receiving and transmitting. Amateurs immediately adapted the new gear to 200-meter work. Ranges promptly increased and it became possible to bridge the continent with but one intermediate relay.

TRANSATLANTICS

As DX became 1000, then 1500 and then 2000 miles, amateurs began to dream of transatlantic work. Could they get across? In December, 1921, ARRL sent abroad an expert amateur, Paul F. Godley, 2ZE, with the best receiving equipment available. Tests were run, and *thirty* American stations were heard in Europe. In 1922 another transatlantic test was carried out and 315 American calls were logged by European amateurs and one French and two British stations were heard on this side.

Everything now was centered on one objective: two-way amateur communication across the Atlantic! It must be possible – but somehow it couldn't quite be done. More power? Many already were using the legal maximum. Better receivers? They had superheterodynes. Another wavelength? What about those undisturbed wavelengths *below* 200 meters? The engineering world thought they were worthless – but they had said that about 200 meters. So, in 1922, tests between Hartford and Boston were made on 130 meters with encouraging results. Early in 1923, ARRL-sponsored tests on wavelengths down to 90 meters were successful. Reports indicated that *as the wavelength dropped the results were better.* Excitement began to spread through amateur ranks.

Finally, in November, 1923, after some months of careful preparation, two-way amateur transatlantic communication was accomplished, when Fred Schnell, 1MO (now W4CF) and the late John Reinartz, 1XAM (later K6BJ) worked for several hours with Deloy, 8AB, in France, with all three stations on 110 meters! Additional stations dropped down to 100 meters and found that they, too, could easily work two-way across the Atlantic. The exodus from the 200-meter region had started. The "short-wave" era had begun!

By 1924 dozens of commercial companies had rushed stations into the 100-meter region. Chaos threatened, until the first of a series of national and international radio conferences partitioned off various bands of frequencies for the different services. Although thought still centered around 100 meters, League officials at the first of these frequency-determining conferences, in 1924, wisely obtained amateur bands not only at 80 meters but at 40, 20, and even 5 meters.

Eighty meters proved so successful that "forty" was given a try, and QSOs with Australia, New Zealand and South Africa soon became commonplace. Then how about 20 meters? This new band revealed entirely unexpected possibilities when 1XAM worked 6TS on the West Coast, direct, at high noon. The dream of amateur radio – daylight DX! – was finally true.

PUBLIC SERVICE

Amateur radio is a grand and glorious hobby but this fact alone would hardly merit such wholehearted support as is given it by our Government at international conferences. There are other reasons. One of these is a thorough appreciation by the military and civil defense authorities of the value of the amateur as a source of skilled radio personnel in time of war. Another asset is best described as "public service."

About 4000 amateurs had contributed their skill and ability in '17-'18. After the war it was only natural that cordial relations should prevail between the Army and Navy and the amateur. These relations strengthened in the next few years and, in gradual steps, grew into cooperative activities which resulted, in 1925, in the establishment of the Naval Communications Reserve and the Army-Amateur Radio System (now the Military

A view of the ARRL laboratory.

Affiliate Radio System). In World War II thousands of amateurs in the Naval Reserve were called to active duty, where they served with distinction, while many other thousands served in the Army, Air Forces, Coast Guard and Marine Corps. Altogether, more than 25,000 radio amateurs served in the armed forces of the United States. Other thousands were engaged in vital civilian electronic research, development and manufacturing. They also organized and manned the War Emergency Radio Service, the communications section of OCD.

The "public-service" record of the amateur is a brilliant tribute to his work. These activities can be roughly divided into two classes, expeditions and emergencies. Amateur cooperation with expeditions began in 1923 when a League member, Don Mix, 1TS, of Bristol, Conn. (from 1933 to 1968 a member of the *QST* technical staff), accompanied MacMillan to the Arctic on the schooner *Bowdoin* with an amateur station. Amateurs in Canada and the U.S. provided the home contacts. The success of this venture was so outstanding that other explorers followed suit. During subsequent years a total of perhaps two hundred voyages and expeditions were assisted by amateur radio, the several explorations of the Antarctic being perhaps the best known.

Since 1913 amateur radio has been the principal, and in many cases the only, means of outside communication in several hundred storm, flood and earthquake emergencies in this country. The earthquakes which hit Alaska in 1964, Peru in 1970 and California in 1971, the Dakota floods and the aftermath of Tropical Storm Agnes in 1972, respectively, called for the amateur's greatest emergency effort. In these disasters and many others – tornados, sleet storms, forest fires, blizzards – amateurs played a major role in the relief work and earned wide commendation for their resourcefulness in effecting communication where all other means had failed. The League's Emergency Corps, now a part of the Amateur Radio Public Service Corps (APRSC), was formalized in 1938, and a program of close cooperation with the American Red Cross was adopted. Since 1947, there has been a staff member at headquarters whose primary job is coordination of public service activities.

After World War II, it became evident that the international situation was destined to be tense and the need for some civil defense measures was apparent. In the discussions with government agencies that followed, the League got two points across: first, that amateur radio had a potential for and capability of playing a major role in this program; and second, that our participation should, this time as never before, be in our own name, as an *amateur radio service*, even if and after war should break out. These principles were included into the planning by the formulation of regulations creating a new branch of the amateur service, the Radio Amateur Civil Emergency Services, RACES. As an *amateur* service, its frequency segments are shared with the regular amateur service during peacetime. In the event of war, it is planned that regular (i.e., casual) amateur radio will cease and RACES will continue to operate under certain restrictions. In peacetime emergencies (such as natural disasters), RACES will operate closely with ARPSC.

TECHNICAL DEVELOPMENTS

The amateur is constantly in the forefront of technical progress. His incessant curiosity, his eagerness to try anything new, are two reasons. Another is that ever-growing amateur radio continually overcrowds its frequency assignments, spurring amateurs to the development and adoption of new techniques to permit the accommodation of more stations.

During World War II, thousands of skilled amateurs contributed their knowledge to the development of secret radio devices, both in Government and private laboratories. Equally as important, the prewar technical progress by amateurs provided the keystone for the development of modern military communications equipment.

From this work, amateurs have moved on to satellites of their own, launched piggyback on regular space shots at no cost to the taxpayer. Project Oscar Inc., an ARRL affiliate, designed and constructed the first four, with launch dates of December 12, 1961; June 2, 1962; March 9, 1965; and December 21, 1965. Australis-Oscar 5 was built in Australia and launched by NASA under the auspices of Radio Amateur Satellite Corporation (Amsat); it went aloft on January 23, 1970. Amsat-Oscar 6 was orbited October 15, 1972 and is expected to remain usable throughout 1973. It contains beacons operating on 435.10 and 29.45; a repeater with input from 145.9 to 146 MHz and output from 29.45 to 29.55. Ground stations using the satellite should not exceed 100 watts effective radiated power. Incidentally, Oscar stands for: "Orbital Satellite Carrying Amateur Radio."

Another space-age field in which amateurs are currently working is that of long-range communication using the moon as a passive reflector. The amateur bands from 50 to 2450 MHz are being used for this work. Moonbounce communications have been carried out, for instance, between Sweden and New Zealand on 144 MHz and between California and England on both 432 and 1296 MHz.

THE AMERICAN RADIO RELAY LEAGUE

The ARRL is today not only the spokesman for amateur radio in the U.S. and Canada but it is the largest amateur organization in the world. It is strictly of, by and for amateurs, is noncommercial and has no stockholders. The members of the League are the owners of the ARRL and *QST*.

The League is pledged to promote interest in two-way amateur communication and experimentation. It is interested in the relaying of messages by amateur radio. It is concerned with the advancement of the radio art. It stands for the maintenance of fraternalism and a high standard of conduct. It represents the amateur in legislative matters.

One of the League's principal purposes is to keep amateur activities so well conducted that the amateur will continue to justify his existence. Amateur radio offers its followers countless pleasures and unending satisfaction. It also calls for the shouldering of responsibilities – the maintenance of high standards, a cooperative loyalty to the traditions of amateur radio, a dedication to its ideals and principles, so that the institution of amateur radio may continue to operate "in the public interest, convenience and necessity."

The operating territory of ARRL is divided into one Canadian and fifteen U.S. divisions. The affairs of the League are managed by a Board of Directors. One director is elected every two years by the membership of each U.S. division, and one by the Canadian membership. These directors then choose the president and three vice-presidents, who are also members of the Board. The secretary and treasurer are also appointed by the Board. The directors, as representatives of the amateurs in their divisions, meet annually to examine current amateur problems and formulate ARRL policies thereon. The directors appoint a general manager to supervise the operations of the League and its headquarters, and to carry out the policies and instructions of the Board.

ARRL owns and publishes the monthly magazine, *QST*. Acting as a bulletin of the League's organized activities, *QST* also serves as a medium for the exchange of ideas and fosters amateur spirit. Its technical articles are renowned. It has grown to be the "amateur's bible," as well as one of the foremost radio magazines in the world. Membership dues include a subscription to *QST*.

ARRL maintains a model headquarters amateur station, known as the Hiram Percy Maxim Memorial Station, in Newington, Conn. Its call is W1AW, the call held by Mr. Maxim until his death and later transferred to the League station by a special government action. Separate transmitters of maximum legal power on each amateur band have permitted the station to be heard regularly all over the world. More important, W1AW transmits on regular schedules bulletins of general interest to amateurs, conducts code practice as a training feature, and engages in two-way work on all popular bands with as many amateurs as time permits.

At the headquarters of the League in Newington, Conn., is a well-equipped laboratory to assist staff members in preparation of technical material for *QST* and the *Radio Amateur's Handbook*. Among its other activities, the League maintains a Communications Department concerned with the operating activities of League members. A large field organization is headed by a Section Communications Manager in each of the League's seventy-four sections. There are appointments for qualified members in various fields, as outlined in Chapter 24. Special activities and contests promote operating skill. A special place is reserved each month in *QST* for amateur news from every section.

AMATEUR LICENSING IN THE UNITED STATES

Pursuant to the law, the Federal Communications Commission (FCC) has issued detailed regulations for the amateur service.

A radio amateur is a duly authorized person interested in radio technique solely with a personal aim and without pecuniary interest. Amateur operator licenses are available to most permanent residents who can pass an examination on operation, apparatus, and regulations affecting amateurs, and who can demonstrate ability to send and receive code. There are five available classes of amateur license – Novice, Technician, General ("Conditional" if taken by mail), Advanced, and Amateur Extra Class. Each has different requirements, the first two being the simplest and consequently conveying limited privileges as to frequencies available. Extra Class licensees have exclusive use of the frequencies 3.5-3.525, 3.775-3.8, 7.0-7.025, 14.0-14.025, 21.0-21.025 and 21.25-21.270 MHz. Advanced and Extra have exclusive use of the frequencies 3.8-3.890, 7.15-7.225, 14.2-14.275, 21.270-21.35 and 50.0-50.1 MHz. Exams for Novice, Technician and Conditional classes are taken by mail under the supervision of a volunteer examiner. Station licenses are granted only to licensed operators. An amateur station may not be used for material compensation of any sort nor for broadcasting. Narrow bands of frequencies are allocated exclusively for use by amateur stations. Transmissions may be on any frequency within the assigned bands. All the frequencies may be used for cw telegraphy; some are available for radiotelephone, others for special forms of transmission such as teletype, facsimile amateur television or radio control. The input to the final stage of amateur stations is limited to 1000 watts (with lower limits in some cases; see the table on page 14) and on frequencies below 144 MHz must be adequately filtered direct current. Emissions must be free from spurious radiations. The licensee must provide for measurement of the transmitter frequency and establish a procedure for checking it regularly. A complete log of station operation must be maintained, with specified data. The station license also authorizes the holder to operate portable and mobile stations subject to further regulations. All radio licenses are subject to penalties for violation of regulations.

Amateur licenses are issued without regard to the applicant's age or physical condition. A fee of $9.00 (payable to the Federal Communications Commission) must accompany applications for new and renewed licenses. The fee for license modification is $4.00 (except Novices: no fee). When you are able to copy code at the required speed, have studied basic transmitter theory and are familiar with the law and amdteur regulations, you are ready to give serious thought to securing the Government amateur licenses which are issued you, after examination by an FCC engineer (or by a volunteer, depending on the license class), through the FCC Licensing Unit, Gettysburg, Pa., 17325. A complete up-to-the-minute discussion of license requirements, the FCC regulations for the amateur service, and study guides for those preparing for the examinations, are to be found in *The Radio Amateur's License Manual*, available from the American Radio Relay League, Newington, Conn. 06111, for $1.00, postpaid.

AMATEUR LICENSING IN CANADA

The agency responsible for amateur radio in Canada is the Department of Communications, with its principal offices in Ottawa. Prospective amateurs, no longer restricted as to age, may take the examination for an Amateur Radio Operator Certificate at one of the regional offices of the DOC. The test is in three parts: a Morse code test at ten words per minute, a written technical exam and an oral examination. Upon passing the examination, the amateur may apply for a station license, the fee for which is $10 per year. At this point, the amateur is permitted to use cw on all authorized amateur bands (see table on page 13) and phone on those bands above 50MHz.

After six months, during which the station has been operated on cw on frequencies below 29.7 MHz, the Canadian amateur may have his certificate endorsed for phone operation in the 28.0-29.7 MHz band. The amateur may take a 15 wpm code test and more-difficult oral and written examinations for the Advanced Amateur Radio Operator Certificate, which permits phone operations on portions of all authorized amateur bands. Holders of First or Second Class or Special Radio Operator's Certificates may enjoy the privileges of Advanced class without further examinations. The maximum input power to the final stage of an amateur transmitter is limited to 1,000 watts.

Prospective amateurs living in remote areas may obtain a provisional station license after signing a statement that they can meet the technical and operating requirements. A provisional license is valid for a maximum of twelve consecutive months only; by then, a provisional licensee should have taken the regular examination.

Licenses are available to citizens of Canada, to citizens of other countries in the British Commonwealth, and to non-citizens who qualify as "landed immigrants" within the meaning of Canadian immigration law. The latter status may be enjoyed for only six years, incidentally. A U.S. citizen who obtained a Canadian license as a "landed immigrant" would have to become a Canadian citizen at the end of six years or lose his Canadian license.

Copies of the Radio Act and of the General Radio Regulations may be obtained for a nominal fee from the Queen's Printer, Ottawa, and its dealers. An extract of the amateur rules, Form AR-5-80, is available at DOC offices. Other books include: *The Canadian Amateur Radio Regulations Handbook,* $2.55 from CARF, Box 356, Kingston, K7L 4W2, Ontario; the *Ham Handbook for Beginners* and the *Ham Handbook for Advanced*, each $5.30 from ARTA Publishing Co., P.O. Box 571 Don Mills, Ont.; *Radio Amateur Licensing Handbook* $4.95, ALH Distributors, P.O. Box 27, Vancouver 1, B.C.; and *Comment Devenir Amateur,* $2.50 from Guy Cadieux, VE2BTG, 924 20th Ave. S., Ville de St. Antoine, P.Q.

RECIPROCAL OPERATING

U.S. amateurs may operate their amateur stations while visiting in Argentina, Australia, Austria, Barbados, Belgium, Bolivia, Brazil, Canada, Chile, Colombia, Costa Rica, Dominican Republic, Ecuador, El Salvador, Finland, France*, Germany, Guatemala, Guyana, Honduras, India, Indonesia, Ireland, Israel, Jamaica, Kuwait, Luxembourg, Monaco, Netherlands,* New Zealand, Nicaragua, Norway, Panama, Paraguay, Peru, Portugal, Sierre Leone, Sweden, Switzerland, Trinidad & Tobago, the United Kingdom*,Uruguay and Venezuela and vice versa. For the latest information, write to ARRL headquarters..

LEARNING THE CODE

In starting to learn the code, you should consider it simply another means of conveying information. The spoken word is one method, the printed page another, and typewriting and shorthand are additional examples. Learning the code is as easy – or as difficult – as learning to type.

The important thing in beginning to study code is to think of it as a language of *sound*, never as combinations of dots and dashes. It is easy to "speak" code equivalents by using "dit" and *"dah,"* so that A would be "di*dah*" (the "t" is dropped in such combinations). The sound "di" should be staccato; a code character such as "5" should sound like a machinegun burst: dididididit! Stress each *"dah"* equally; they are underlined or italicized in this text because they should be slightly accented and drawn out.

Take a few characters at a time. Learn them thoroughly in di*dah* language before going on to new ones. If someone who is familiar with code can be found to "send" to you, either by whistling or by means of a buzzer or code oscillator, enlist his cooperation. Learn the code by *listening* to it. Don't think about speed to start; the first requirement is to learn the characters to the point where you can recognize each of them without hesitation. Concentrate on any difficult letters. Learning the code is not at all hard; a simple booklet treating the subject in detail is another of the beginner publications available from the League, and is entitled, *Learning the Radiotelegraph Code,* 50 cents, postpaid.

Code-practice transmissions are sent by W1AW every evening at 0030 and 0230 GMT (0130 and 2330 May through October). Code is also sent, Monday-Friday, at 1400 GMT (1300 GMT, May through October). See Chapter 24, "Code Proficiency."

A Code-Practice Set

A simple oscillator circuit like the one shown in Fig. 1-2 may be built using a Signetics NE555

* Includes overseas entities.

A	didah	N	dahit
B	dahdididit	O	dahdahdah
C	dahdidahdit	P	didahdahdit
D	dahdidit	Q	dahdahdidah
E	dit	R	didahdit
F	dididahdit	S	dididit
G	dahdahdit	T	dah
H	didididit	U	dididah
I	didit	V	didididah
J	didahdahdah	W	didahdah
K	dahdidah	X	dahdididah
L	didahdidit	Y	dahdidahdah
M	dahdah	Z	dahdahdidit
1	didahdahdahdah	6	dahdidididit
2	dididahdahdah	7	dahdahdididit
3	didididahdah	8	dahdahdahdidit
4	dididididah	9	dahdahdahdahdit
5	dididididit	0	dahdahdahdahdah

Period: didahdidahdidah. Comma: dahdahdididahdah. Question mark: dididahdahdidit. Error: dididididididit. Double dash: dahdididididah. Colon: dahdahdahdididit. Semicolon: dahdidahdidahdit. Parenthesis: dahdidahdahdidah. Fraction bar: dahdididahdit. Wait: didahdididit. End of message: didahdidahdit. Invitation to transmit: dahdidah. End of work: didididahdidah.

Fig. 1-1 — The Continental (International Morse) code.

A cw code-practice oscillator along with a speaker may be mounted inside a homemade aluminum box. If desired, the battery could be mounted inside the enclosure also, thereby allowing easy portability of the unit.

timer and a few extra parts. The printed circuit for the oscillator is made from a 2-inch square piece of pc material but the IC could have been placed on Masonite, Formica or some other insulating material. Point-to-point wiring may be used. The circuit is housed in a homemade enclosure that provides room for a battery of almost any value between 4-1/2 and 18 volts. The speaker is attached to the front of the enclosure with caulking compound. Any speaker in the range of 4 to 50 ohms will work well and may be salvaged from a discarded transistor pocket radio.

The circuit shown costs approximately five dollars to build. R2 is made from one fixed-value resistor chosen to give a pleasant tone. The volume control could be removed altogether (placing the speaker at the negative side of C3) or be replaced with a pair of resistors equalling about 10,000 ohms. The speaker should be connected between the junction of these resistors and ground. An on-off switch should be used to disable the oscillator when it is not in use.

The audio pitch is determined by the values of R1, C2 and the setting of R2. The cost of the oscillator may be reduced somewhat by replacing R2 with a fixed value of resistance; R3 could be replaced by a fixed-value resistor. If this is done, the speaker lead must be connected to the junction of C3 and R3.

When power is applied the oscillator runs continuously and the audio output is keyed on and off. This circuit gives a degree of freedom from chirps or whoop-like sounds when rapidly keyed. However, the circuit always draws about 6 mA of current when operated. If used with a small battery, such as those used in transistor portable radios, the battery could quickly be discharged, so a means of disconnecting the power should be used, such as a spst switch, as shown at S1.

If facilities are not available for etching a board, point-to-point wiring will work just as well, and perforated board stock is a suitable material to be used. If a builder does not want to solder directly to the IC leads an 8-pin IC socket can be used, making all connections to the socket.

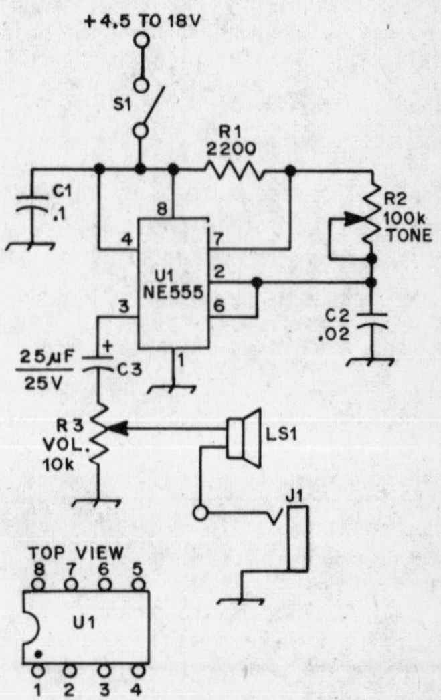

Fig. 1-2 — Schematic diagram for the code oscillator. Resistance is in ohms, k = 1000. The 0.1-µF capacitor is a disk ceramic. U1 is a Signetics NE555 IC timer.

INTRODUCTION TO RADIO THEORY

As you start your studies for an amateur license, you may wish to have the additional help available in *How to Become a Radio Amateur* ($1.00). It features an elementary description of radio theory and constructional details on a simple receiver and transmitter.

Another aid is *A Course in Radio Fundamentals* ($2.00). There are experiments, discussions, and quizzes to help you learn radio fundamentals.

A League publication, *Understanding Amateur Radio*, explains radio theory and practice in greater detail than is found in *How to Become a Radio Amateur*, but is at a more basic level than this *Handbook*. *Understanding Amateur Radio* contains 304 pages, and is priced at $2.50.

These booklets are available postpaid from ARRL, Newington, Connecticut 06111.

THE AMATEUR BANDS

Amateurs are assigned bands of frequencies at approximate harmonic intervals throughout the spectrum. Like assignments to all services, they are subject to modification to fit the changing picture of world communications needs. Modifications of rules to provide for domestic needs are also occasionally issued by FCC and DOC, and in that respect each amateur should keep himself informed by W1AW bulletins, *QST* reports, or by communication with ARRL Hq. concerning a specific point.

On this page and page 14 are summaries of the Canadian and U.S. amateur bands on which operation is permitted as of our press date. AØ and FØ mean unmodulated carriers. A1 means cw telegraphy, A2 is tone-modulated cw telegraphy, A3 is amplitude-modulated phone, A4 is facsimile, A5 is television, F1 is frequency-shift keying, F2 is frequency-modulated tone keying (Morse or teletype), F3 is fm phone, F4 is fm facsimile and F5 is fm television.

CANADIAN AMATEUR BANDS

Band	From	To	Emission
80 meters	3.500–	3.725 MHz	A1, F1
1) 3) 4) 5)	3.725–	4.000 MHz	A1, A3, F3
40 meters	7.000–	7.150 MHz	A1, F1,
1) 3) 4) 5)	7.150–	7.300 MHz	A1, A3, F3
20 meters	14.000–	14.100 MHz	A1, F1
1) 3) 4) 5)	14.100–	14.350 MHz	A1, A3, F3
15 meters	21.000–	21.100 MHz	A1, F1
1) 3) 4) 5)	21.100–	21.450 MHz	A1, A3, F3
10 meters	28.000–	28.100 MHz	A1, F1
2) 3) 4) 5)	28.100–	29.700 MHz	A1, A3, F3
6 meters	50.000–	50.050 MHz	A1
3) 4)	50.050–	51.000 MHz	A1, A2, A3, F1 F2, F3
	51.000–	54.000 MHz	AØ, A1, A2, A3 A4, F1, F2, F3, F4
2 meters	144.000–	144.100 MHz	A1
3) 4)	144.100–	148.000 MHz	AØ, A1, A2, A3 A4, F1, F2, F3 F4
3) 4)	220.000–	225.000 MHz	AØ, A1, A2, A3, A4, F1, F2, F3, F4
4) 6)	420.000–	450.000 MHz)	AØ, A1, A2, A3 A4, A5, F1, F2 F3, F4
	1215.000–	1300.000 MHz)	
	2300.000–	2450.000 MHz)	
	3300.000–	3500.000 MHz)	
	5650.000–	5925.000 MHz)	
	10000.000–	10500.000 MHz)	
	21000.000–	22000.000 MHz)	

1) Phone privileges are restricted to holders of Advanced Amateur Radio Operator Certificates, and of Commercial Certificates.

2) Phone privileges are restricted as in footnote 1), and to holders of Amateur Radio Operators Certificates, whose certificates have been endorsed for operation on phone in these bands.

3) Amplitude modulation (A2, A3, A4) shall not exceed ± 3 kHz (6A3).

4) Frequency modulation (F2, F3, F4) shall not produce a carrier deviation exceeding ±3 kHz, (6F3) except that in the 52–54 MHz and 146–148 MHz bands and higher the carrier deviation shall not exceed ±15 kHz (30F3).

5) Slow Scan television (A5), permitted by special authorization, shall not exceed a bandwidth greater than that occupied by a normal single sideband voice transmission.

6) Television (A5), permitted by special authorization, shall employ a system of standard interlace and scanning with a bandwidth of not more than 4 MHz.

Operation in frequency band 1.800–2.000 MHz shall be limited to the areas as indicated in the following table and shall be limited to the indicated maximum dc power input to the anode of the final radio frequency stage of the transmitter during day and night hours respectively; for the purpose of this table "day" means the hours between sunrise and sunset, and "night" means the hours between sunset and sunrise. A1, A3 and F3 emission are permitted.

	A	*B*	*C*	*D*	*E*	*F*	*G*	*H*
British Columbia	3[1)]	3	3	1	0	0	0	0
Alberta	3[1)]	3	3	3	1	0	0	1
Saskatchewan	3[1)]	3	3	3	3	1	1	3
Manitoba	3[1)]	2	2	2	2	2	2	3[1)]
Ontario North of 50° N. Lat.	3	1	1	1	1	0	0	2
Ontario South of 50° N. Lat.	3[1)]	2	1	0	0	0	0	1
Province of Quebec North of 52° N. Lat.	1	0	0	1	1	0	0	2
Province of Quebec South of 52° N. Lat.	3	2	1	0	0	0	0	0
New Brunswick	3	2	1	0	0	0	0	0
Nova Scotia	3	2	1	0	0	0	0	0
Prince Edward Island	3	2	1	0	0	0	0	0
Newfoundland (Island)	3	1	1	0	0	0	0	0
Newfoundland (Labrador)	2	0	0	0	0	0	0	0
Yukon Territory	3[1)]	3	3	1	0	0	0	0
District of MacKenzie	3[1)]	3	3	3	1	0	0	1
District of Keewatin	3	1	1	3	2	0	0	2
District of Franklin	0	0	0	0	1	0	0	1

1) The power levels 500 day – 100 night may be increased to 1000 day – 200 night when authorized by a Radio Inspector of the Department of Communications.

Frequency Band

A 1.800–1.825 MHz	E 1.900–1.925 MHz
B 1.825–1.850 MHz	F 1.925–1.950 MHz
C 1.850–1.875 MHz	G 1.950–1.975 MHz
D 1.875–1.900 MHz	H 1.975–2.000 MHz

Power Level – Watts

0 – Operation not permitted
1 – 25 night 125 day
2 – 50 night 250 day
3 – 100 night 500 day

U.S. AND POSSESSIONS AMATEUR BANDS

	kHz	EMISSIONS
160 m.*	1800–2000	A1,A3
80 m.**	3500–4000	A1
	3500–3775	F1
	3775–3890	A5[1], F5[1]
	3775–4000	A3, F3[2]
40 m.**	7000–7300	A1
	7000–7150	F1
	7150–7225	A5[1], F5[1]
	7150–7300	A3, F3[2]
20 m.**	14000–14350	A1
	14000–14200	F1
	14200–14275	A5[1], F5[1]
	14200–14350	A3, F3[2]

	MHz	EMISSIONS
15 m.**	21.00–21.45	A1
	21.00–21.25	F1
	21.25–21.35	A5[1], F5[1]
	21.25–21.45	A3, F3[2]
10 m.	28.0–29.7	A1
	28.0–28.5	F1
	28.5–29.7	A3, A5[1], F3[2], F5[1]
	29.0–29.7	F3

NOTE: Frequencies from 3.9-4.0 MHz and 7.1-7.3 MHz are not available to amateurs on Baker, Canton, Enderbury, Guam, Howland, Jarvis, Palmyra, American Samoa, and Wake Islands.

When operating from points outside ITU Region 2 (roughly, the Western Hemisphere extended to include Hawaii), licensees of Conditional Class and higher may operate A3 and F3 from 7075-7100 kHz; Novice licensees may operate A1 from 7050-7075 kHz.

REPEATERS:

The frequency ranges (in MHz) available for repeater inputs and outputs are as follows:

52.0 – 54.0
146.0 – 148.0
222.0 – 225.0
442.0 – 450.0
any amateur frequency above 1215 MHz.

The frequency band 29.5 – 29.7 MHz may be authorized upon a special showing of need for repeater station operation in this band.

	MHz	EMISSIONS
6 m.**	50.0–54.0	A1
	50.1–54.0	A2, A3, A4, A5[3], F1, F2, F3[2], F5[1]
	51.0–54.0	AØ
	52.5–54.0	F3
2 m.	144-148	A1
	144.1–148	AØ, A2, A3, A4, A5[3], FØ, F1, F2, F3, F5[1]
	220–225	AØ, A1, A2, A3, A4, A5[3], FØ, F1, F2, F3, F4, F5[1]
	420–450[4] 1,215–1,300	AØ, A1, A2, A3, A4, A5[3], FØ, F1, F2, F3, F4, F5
	2,300–2,450 3,300–3,500 5,650–5,925 10,000–10,500[5] 24,000–24,050	AØ, A1, A2, A3, A4, A5 FØ, F1, F2, F3, F4, F5, pulse

The bands 220 through 10,500 MHz are shared with the Government Radio Positioning Service, which has priority.

[1] Slow-scan television no wider than a single-sideband voice signal may be used; on A5 if voice is simultaneously used, the total signal can be no wider than a standard a-m signal.

[2] Narrow-band frequency- or phase-modulation no wider than standard a-m voice signal.

[3] Slow-scan television no wider than a standard a-m voice signal.

[4] Input power must not exceed 50 watts in Fla., Ariz., and parts of Ga., Ala., Miss., N. Mex., Tex., Nev., and Ca. See the *License Manual* or write ARRL for further details.

[5] No pulse permitted in this band.

Novice licensees may use A1 emission and a maximum power input of 75 watts on the following frequencies:

3.700–3.750 MHz	21.100–21.200 MHz
7.100–7.150 MHz	28.100–28.200 MHz

Technician licensees are permitted all amateur privileges in 50.1-54 MHz, 145-148 MHz and in the bands 220 MHz and above.

Except as otherwise specified, the maximum amateur power input is 1000 watts.

*To minimize interference to radionavigation systems sharing the 160 meter band, amateurs are required to observe frequency and power restrictions according to their geographic location. Exact limitations are contained in Section 97.61(b)(2) of the FCC Amateur Regulations. This information also appears in the ARRL *License Manual*, available for $1.00 postpaid. A chart of U.S. 160 meter limitations is available from ARRL Headquarters; send a stamped, addressed envelope and request form S-15(a).

**See page 10 for restrictions on usage of parts of these bands.

Chapter 2

Electrical Laws and Circuits

ELECTRIC AND MAGNETIC FIELDS

When something occurs at one point in space because something else happened at another point, with no visible means by which the "cause" can be related to the "effect," we say the two events are connected by a **field**. In radio work, the fields with which we are concerned are the **electric** and **magnetic**, and the combination of the two called the **electromagnetic** field.

A field has two important properties, intensity (magnitude) and direction. The field exerts a *force* on an object immersed in it; this force represents potential (ready-to-be-used) energy, so the **potential** of the field is a measure of the **field intensity**. The **direction** of the field is the direction in which the object on which the force is exerted will tend to move.

An electrically charged object in an electric field will be acted on by a force that will tend to move it in a direction determined by the direction of the field. Similarly, a magnet in a magnetic field will be subject to a force. Everyone has seen demonstrations of magnetic fields with pocket magnets, so intensity and direction are not hard to grasp.

A "static" field is one that neither moves nor changes in intensity. Such a field can be set up by a stationary electric charge (**electrostatic field**) or by a stationary magnet (**magnetostatic field**). But if either an electric or magnetic field is moving in space or changing in intensity, the motion or change sets up the other kind of field. That is, a changing electric field sets up a magnetic field, and a changing magnetic field generates an electric field. This interrelationship between magnetic and electric fields makes possible such things as the electromagnet and the electric motor. It also makes possible the **electromagnetic waves** by which radio communication is carried on, for such waves are simply traveling fields in which the energy is alternately handed back and forth between the electric and magnetic fields.

Lines of Force

Although no one knows what it is that composes the field itself, it is useful to invent a picture of it that will help in visualizing the forces and the way in which they act.

A field can be pictured as being made up of **lines of force** or **flux lines**. These are purely imaginary threads that show, by the direction in which they lie, the direction the object on which the force is exerted will move. The *number* of lines in a chosen cross section of the field is a measure of the *intensity* of the force. The number of lines per unit of area (square inch or square centimeter) is called the **flux density**.

ELECTRICITY AND THE ELECTRIC CURRENT

Everything physical is built up of atoms, particles so small that they cannot be seen even through the most powerful microscope. But the atom in turn consists of several different kinds of still smaller particles. One is the **electron**, essentially a small particle of electricity. The quantity or **charge** of electricity represented by the electron is, in fact, the smallest quantity of electricity that can exist. The kind of electricity associated with the electron is called **negative.**

An ordinary atom consists of a central core called the **nucleus**, around which one or more electrons circulate somewhat as the earth and other planets circulate around the sun. The nucleus has an electric charge of the kind of electricity called **positive**, the amount of its charge being just exactly equal to the sum of the negative charges on all the electrons associated with that nucleus.

The important fact about these two "opposite" kinds of electricity is that they are strongly attracted to each other. Also, there is a strong force of repulsion between two charges of the *same* kind. The positive nucleus and the negative electrons are attracted to each other, but two electrons will be repelled from each other and so will two nuclei.

In a normal atom the positive charge on the nucleus is exactly balanced by the negative charges on the electrons. However, it is possible for an atom to lose one of its electrons. When that happens the atom has a little less negative charge than it should – that is, it has a net positive charge. Such an atom is said to be **ionized**, and in this case the atom is a **positive ion**. If an atom picks up an extra electron, as it sometimes does, it has a net negative charge and is called a **negative ion**. A positive ion will attract any stray electron in the vicinity, including the extra one that may be attached to a nearby negative ion. In this way it is possible for electrons to travel from atom to atom. The movement of ions or electrons constitutes the **electric current.**

The **amplitude** of the current (its intensity or magnitude) is determined by the rate at which electric charge – an accumulation of electrons or ions of the same kind – moves past a point in a circuit. Since the charge on a single electron or ion is extremely small, the number that must move as a group to form even a tiny current is almost inconceivably large.

Conductors and Insulators

Atoms of some materials, notably metals and acids, will give up an electron readily, but atoms of other materials will not part with any of their electrons even when the electric force is extremely strong. Materials in which electrons or ions can be moved with relative ease are called **conductors**, while those that refuse to permit such movement are called **nonconductors** or **insulators**. The following list shows how some common materials are classified:

Conductors	*Insulators*	
Metals	Dry Air	Glass
Carbon	Wood	Rubber
Acids	Porcelain	Resins
	Textiles	

Electromotive Force

The electric force or potential (called **electromotive force**, and abbreviated **emf**) that causes current flow may be developed in several ways. The action of certain chemical solutions on dissimilar metals sets up an emf; such a combination is called a **cell**, and a group of cells forms an electric **battery**. The amount of current that such cells can carry is limited, and in the course of current flow one of the metals is eaten away. The amount of electrical energy that can be taken from a battery consequently is rather small. Where a large amount of energy is needed it is usually furnished by an electric **generator**, which develops its emf by a combination of magnetic and mechanical means.

Direct and Alternating Currents

In picturing current flow it is natural to think of a single, constant force causing the electrons to move. When this is so, the electrons always move in the same direction through a path or **circuit** made up of conductors connected together in a continuous chain. Such a current is called a **direct current**, abbreviated **dc**. It is the type of current furnished by batteries and by certain types of generators.

It is also possible to have an emf that periodically reverses. With this kind of emf the current flows first in one direction through the circuit and then in the other. Such an emf is called an alternating emf, and the current is called an **alternating current** (abbreviated **ac**). The reversals (alternations) may occur at any rate from a few per second up to several billion per second. Two reversals make a **cycle**; in one cycle the force acts first in one direction, then in the other, and then returns to the first direction to begin the next cycle. The number of cycles in one second is called the **frequency** of the alternating current.

The difference between direct current and alternating current is show in Fig. 2-1. In these graphs the horizontal axis measures time, increasing toward the right away from the vertical axis. The vertical axis represents the amplitude or strength of the current, increasing in either the up or down direction away from the horizontal axis. If the graph is *above* the horizontal axis the current is flowing in one direction through the circuit (indicated by the + sign) and if it is *below* the horizontal axis the current is flowing in the reverse direction through the circuit (indicated by the – sign). Fig. 2-1A shows that, if we close the circuit – that is, make the path for the current complete – at the time indicated by *X*, the current instantly takes the amplitude indicated by the height *A*. After that, the current continues at the same amplitude as time goes on. This is an ordinary *direct* current.

In Fig. 2-1B, the current starts flowing with the amplitude *A* at time *X*, continues at that amplitude until time *Y* and then instantly ceases. After an interval *YZ* the current again begins to flow and the same sort of start-and-stop performance is repeated. This is an *intermittent* direct current. We could get it by alternately closing and opening a switch in the circuit. It is a *direct* current because the *direction* of current flow does not change; the graph is always on the + side of the horizontal axis.

In Fig. 2-1C the current starts at zero, increases in amplitude as time goes on until it reaches the amplitude *A1* while flowing in the + direction, then decreases until it drops to zero amplitude once more. At that time (*X*) the *direction* of the current flow reverses; this is indicated by the fact that the next part of the graph is below the axis. As time goes on the amplitude increases, with the current now flowing in the – direction, until it reaches amplitude *A2*. Then the amplitude

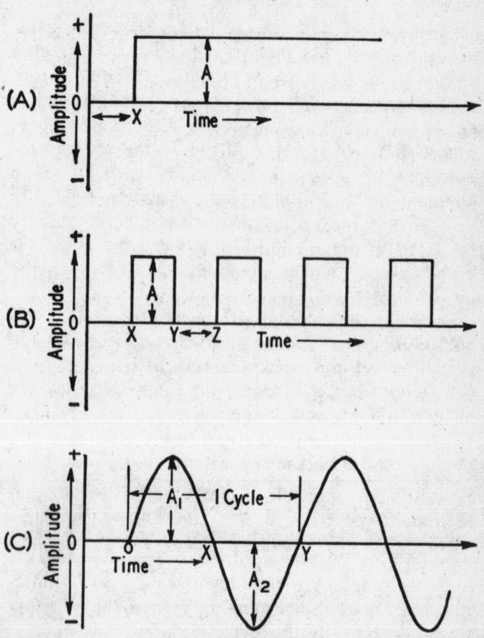

Fig. 2-1 – Three types of current flow. A – direct current; B – intermittent direct current; C – alternating current.

decreases until finally it drops to zero (*Y*) and the direction reverses once more. This is an *alternating* current.

Waveforms

The type of alternating current shown in Fig. 2-1C is known as a **sine wave**. The variations in many ac waves are not so smooth, nor is one half-cycle necessarily just like the preceding one in shape. However, these **complex waves** can be shown to be the sum of two or more sine waves of frequencies that are exact integral (whole-number) multiples of some lower frequency. The lowest frequency is called the **fundamental**, and the higher frequencies are called **harmonics**.

Fig. 2-2 shows how a fundamental and a second harmonic (twice the fundamental) might add to form a complex wave. Simply by changing the relative amplitudes of the two waves, as well as the times at which they pass through zero amplitude, an infinite number of waveshapes can be constructed from just a fundamental and second harmonic. More complex waveforms can be constructed if more harmonics are used.

Frequency multiplication, the generation of second, third and higher-order harmonics, takes place whenever a fundamental since wave is passed through a nonlinear device. The distorted output is made up of the fundamental frequency plus harmonics; a desired harmonic can be selected through the use of tuned circuits. Typical nonlinear devices used for frequency multiplication include rectifiers of any kind and amplifiers that distort an applied signal.

Electrical Units

The unit of electromotive force is called the **volt.** An ordinary flashlight cell generates and emf of about 1.5 volts. The emf commonly supplied for domestic lighting and power is 117 volts ac at a frequency of 60 cycles per second.

The flow of electric current is measured in **amperes**. One ampere is equivalent to the movement of many billions of electrons past a point in the circuit in one second. The *direct* currents used in amateur radio equipment usually are not large, and it is customary to measure such currents in **milliamperes**. One milliampere is equal to one one-thousandth of an ampere.

A "dc ampere" is a measure of a *steady* current, but the "ac ampere" must measure a current that is continually varying in amplitude and periodically reversing direction. To put the two on the same basis, an ac ampere is defined as the current that will cause the same heating effect as one ampere of steady direct current. For sine-wave ac, this **effective** or (**rms**, for *root mean square*, the mathematical derivation) **value** is equal to the *maximum* (or **peak**) amplitude (*A1* or *A2* in Fig. 2-1C) multiplied by 0.707. The **instantaneous value** is the value that the current (or voltage) has at any selected instant in the cycle. If all the instantaneous values in a sine wave are averaged over a *half*-cycle, the resulting figure is the **average** value. It is equal to 0.636 times the maximum amplitude.

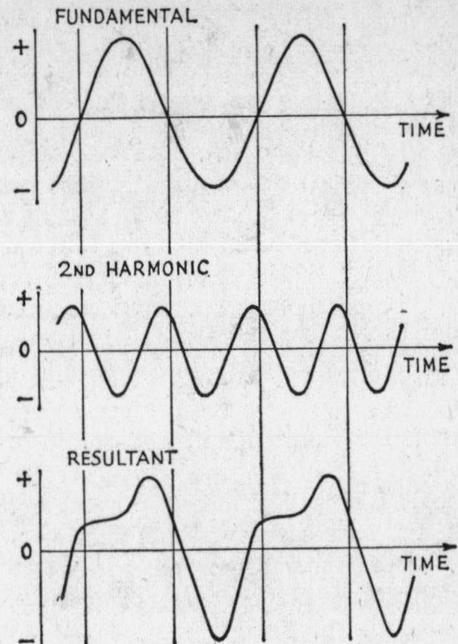

Fig. 2-2 — A complex waveform. A fundamental (top) and second harmonic (center) added together, point by point at each instant, result in the waveform shown at the bottom. When the two components have the same polarity at a selected instant, the resultant is the simple sum of the two. When they have opposite polarities, the resultant is the *difference*; if the negative-polarity component is larger, the resultant is negative at that instant.

FREQUENCY AND WAVELENGTH

Frequency Spectrum

Frequencies ranging from about 15 to 15,000 cycles per second (cps ,Hertz, or Hz) are called **audio** frequencies, because the vibrations of air particles that our ears recognize as sounds occur at a similar rate. Audio frequencies (abbreviated **af**) are used to actuate loudspeakers and thus create sound waves.

Frequencies above about 15,000 cps are called **radio** frequencies (**rf**) because they are useful in radio transmission. Frequencies all the way up to and beyond 10,000,000,000 cps have been used for radio purposes. At radio frequencies it becomes convenient to use a larger unit than the cycle. Two such units are the **kilohertz**, which is equal to 1000 cycles (or hz), and is abbreviated to **kHz**, and the **megahertz**, which is equal to 1,000,000 hertz or 1000 kilohertz, and is abbreviated **MHz.**

The various radio frequencies are divided off into classifications. These classifications, listed below, constitute the **frequency spectrum** so far as it extends for radio purposes at the present time.

Frequency	*Classification*	*Abbrev*
10 to 30 kHz	Very-low frequencies	vlf
30 to 300 kHz	Low frequencies	lf
300 to 3000 kHz	Medium frequencies	mf
3 to 30 MHz	High frequencies	hf
30 to 300 MHz	Very-high frequencies	vhf
300 to 3000 MHz	Ultrahigh frequencies	uhf
3000 to 30,000 MHz	Superhigh frequencies	shf

Wavelength

Radio waves travel at the same speed as light – 300,000,000 meters or about 186,000 miles a second in space. They can be set up by a radio-frequency current flowing in a circuit, because the rapidly changing current sets up a magnetic field that changes in the same way, and the varying magnetic field in turn sets up a varying electric field. And whenever this happens, the two fields move outward at the speed of light.

Suppose an rf current has a frequency of 3,000,000 cycles per second. The field will go through complete reversals (one cycle) in 1/3,000,000 second. In that same period of time the fields – that is, the wave – will move 300,000,000/3,000,000 meters, or 100 meters. By the time the wave has moved that distance the next cycle has begun and a new wave has started out. The first wave, in other words, covers a distance of 100 meters before the beginning of the next, and so on. This distance is the **wavelength**.

The longer the time of one cycle – that is, the lower the frequency – the greater the distance occupied by each wave and hence the longer the wavelength. The relationship between wavelength and frequency is shown by the formula

$$\lambda = \frac{300{,}000}{f}$$

where λ = Wavelength in meters
f = Frequency in kilohertz

or

$$\lambda = \frac{300}{f}$$

where λ = Wavelength in meters
f = Frequency in megahertz

Example: The wavelength corresponding to a frequency of 3650 kilohertz is

$$\lambda = \frac{300{,}000}{3650} = 82.2 \text{ meters}$$

RESISTANCE

Given two conductors of the same size and shape, but of different materials, the amount of current that will flow when a given emf is applied will be found to vary with what is called the **resistance** of the material. The lower the resistance, the greater the current for a given value of emf.

Resistance is measured in **ohms**. A circuit has a resistance of one ohm when an applied emf of one volt causes a current of one ampere to flow. The **resistivity** of a material is the resistance, in ohms, of a cube of the material measuring one centimeter on each edge. One of the best conductors is copper, and it is frequently convenient, in making resistance calculations, to compare the resistance of the material under consideration with that of a copper conductor of the same size and shape. Table 2-I gives the ratio of the resistivity of various conductors to that of copper.

The longer the path through which the current flows the higher the resistance of that conductor. For direct current and low-frequency alternating currents (up to a few thousand cycles per second) the resistance is *inversely* proportional to the cross-sectional area of the path the current must travel; that is, given two conductors of the same material and having the same length, but differing in cross-sectional area, the one with the larger area will have the lower resistance.

TABLE 2-1

Relative Resistivity of Metals

Materials	*Resistivity Compared to Copper*
Aluminum (pure)	1.6
Brass	3.7–4.9
Cadmium	4.4
Chromium	1.8
Copper (hard-drawn)	1.03
Copper (annealed)	1.00
Gold	1.4
Iron (pure)	5.68
Lead	12.8
Nickel	5.1
Phosphor Bronze	2.8–5.4
Silver	0.94
Steel	7.6–12.7
Tin	6.7
Zinc	3.4

Resistance of Wires

The problem of determining the resistance of a round wire of given diameter and length – or its opposite, finding a suitable size and length of wire to supply a desired amount of resistance – can be easily solved with the help of the copper-wire table given in a later chapter. This table gives the resistance, in ohms per thousand feet, of each standard wire size.

Example: Suppose a resistance of 3.5 ohms is needed and some No. 28 wire is on hand. The wire table in Chapter 18 shows that No. 28 has a resistance of 66.17 ohms per thousand feet. Since the desired resistance is 3.5 ohms, the length of wire required will be

$$\frac{3.5}{66.17} \times 1000 = 52.89 \text{ feet.}$$

Or, suppose that the resistance of the wire in the circuit must not exceed 0.05 ohm and that the length of wire required for making the connections totals 14 feet. Then

$$\frac{14}{1000} \times R = 0.05 \text{ ohm}$$

where R is the maximum allowable resistance in ohms per thousand feet. Rearranging the formula gives

$$R = \frac{0.05 \times 1000}{14} = 3.57 \text{ ohms/1000 ft.}$$

Reference to the wire table shows that No. 15 is the smallest size having a resistance less than this value.

When the wire is not copper, the resistance values given in the wire table should be multiplied by the ratios given in Table 2-I to obtain the resistance.

Types of resistors used in radio equipment. Those in the foreground with wire leads are carbon types, ranging in size from 1/2 watt at the left to 2 watts at the right. The larger resistors use resistance wire wound on ceramic tubes; sizes shown range from 5 watts to 100 watts. Three are the adjustable type, having a sliding contact on an exposed section of the resistance winding.

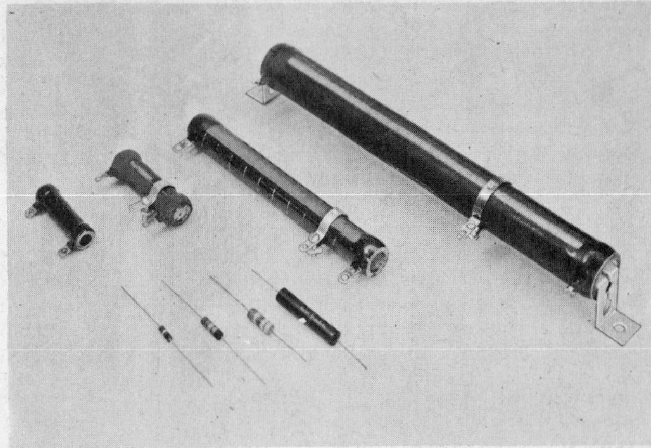

Example: If the wire in the first example were nickel instead of copper the length required for 3.5 ohms would be

$$\frac{3.5}{66.17 \times 5.1} \times 1000 = 10.37 \text{ feet}$$

Temperature Effects

The resistance of a conductor changes with its temperature. Although it is seldom necessary to consider temperature in making resistance calculations for amateur work, it is well to know that the resistance of practically all metallic conductors increases with increasing temperature. Carbon, however, acts in the opposite way; its resistance *decreases* when its temperature rises. The temperature effect is important when it is necessary to maintain a constant resistance under all conditions. Special materials that have little or no change in resistance over a wide temperature range are used in that case.

Resistors

A "package" of resistance made up into a single unit is called a **resistor.** Resistors having the same resistance value may be considerably different in size and construction. The flow of current through resistance causes the conductor to become heated; the higher the resistance and the larger the current, the greater the amount of heat developed. Resistors intended for carrying large currents must be physically large so the heat can be radiated quickly to the surrounding air. If the resistor does not get rid of the heat quickly it may reach a temperature that will cause it to melt or burn.

Skin Effect

The resistance of a conductor is not the same for alternating current as it is for direct current. When the current is alternating there are internal effects that tend to force the current to flow mostly in the outer parts of the conductor. This decreases the effective cross-sectional area of the conductor, with the result that the resistance increases.

For low audio frequencies the increase in resistance is unimportant, but at radio frequencies this **skin effect** is so great that practically all the current flow is confined within a few thousandths of an inch of the conductor surface. The rf resistance is consequently many times the dc resistance, and increases with increasing frequency. In the rf range a conductor of thin tubing will have just as low resistance as a solid conductor of the same diameter, because material not close to the surface carries practically no current.

Conductance

The reciprocal of resistance (that is, $1/R$) is called **conductance.** It is usually represented by the symbol G. A circuit having large conductance has low resistance, and vice versa. In radio work the term is used chiefly in connection with vacuum-tube characteristics. The unit of conductance is the **mho.** A resistance of one ohm has a conductance of one mho, a resistance of 1000 ohms has a conductance of .001 mho, and so on. A unit frequently used in connection with vacuum tubes is the **micromho,** or one-millionth of a mho. It is the conductance of a resistance of one megohm.

OHM'S LAW

The simplest form of electric circuit is a battery with a resistance connected to its terminals, as shown by the symbols in Fig. 2-3. A complete circuit must have an unbroken path so current can flow out of the battery, through the apparatus connected to it, and back into the battery. The circuit is **broken,** or **open,** if a connection is removed at any point. A **switch** is a device for making and breaking connections and thereby closing or opening the circuit, either allowing current to flow or preventing it from flowing.

The values of current, voltage and resistance in a circuit are by no means independent of each

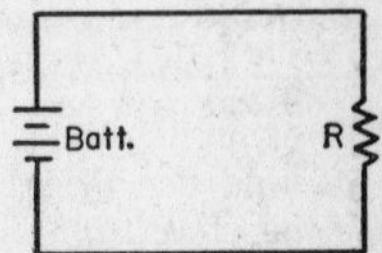

Fig. 2-3 — A simple circuit consisting of a battery and resistor.

TABLE 2-II

Conversion Factors for Fractional and Multiple Units

Change From	*To*	*Divide by*	*Multiply by*
Units	Micro-units		1,000,000
	Milli-units		1,000
	Kilo-units	1,000	
	Mega-units	1,000,000	
Micro-units	Milli-units	1,000	
	Units	1,000,000	
Milli-units	Micro-units		1,000
	Units	1,000	
Kilo-units	Units		1,000
	Mega-units	1,000	
Mega-units	Units		1,000,000
	Kilo-units		1,000

other. The relationship between them is known as **Ohm's Law.** It can be stated as follows: The current flowing in a circuit is directly proportional to the applied emf and inversely proportional to the resistance. Expressed as an equation, it is

$$I \text{ (amperes)} = \frac{E \text{ (volts)}}{R \text{ (ohms)}}$$

The equation above gives the value of current when the voltage and resistance are known. It may be transposed so that each of the three quantities may be found when the other two are known:

$$E = IR$$

(that is, the voltage acting is equal to the current in amperes multiplied by the resistance in ohms) and

$$R = \frac{E}{I}$$

$R = \frac{V}{A}$

(or, the resistance of the circuit is equal to the applied voltage divided by the current).

All three forms of the equation are used almost constantly in radio work. It must be remembered that the quantities are in *volts, ohms* and *amperes*; other units cannot be used in the equations without first being converted. For example, if the current is in milliamperes it must be changed to the equivalent fraction of an ampere before the value can be substituted in the equations.

Table 2-II shows how to convert between the various units in common use. The prefixes attached to the basic-unit name indicate the nature of the unit. These prefixes are:

micro – one-millionth (abbreviated μ)
milli – one-thousandth (abbreviated *m*)
kilo – one thousand (abbreviated *k*)
mega – one million (abbreviated *M*)

For example, one microvolt is one-millionth of a volt, and one megohm is 1,000,000 ohms. There are therefore 1,000,000 microvolts in one volt, and 0.000001 megohm in one ohm.

The following examples illustrate the use of ohm's law:

The current flowing in a resistance of 20,000 ohms is 150 milliamperes. What is the voltage? Since the voltage is to be found, the equation to use is $E = IR$. The current must first be converted from milliamperes to amperes, and reference to the table shows that to do so it is necessary to divide by 1000. Therefore,

$$E = \frac{150}{1000} \times 20{,}000 = 3000 \text{ volts}$$

When a voltage of 150 is applied to a circuit the current is measured at 2.5 amperes. What is the resistance of the circuit? In this case R is the unknown, so

$$R = \frac{E}{I} = \frac{150}{2.5} = 60 \text{ ohms}$$

No conversion was necessary because the voltage and current were given in volts and amperes.

How much current will flow if 250 volts is applied to a 5000-ohm resistor? Since I is unknown

$$I = \frac{E}{R} = \frac{250}{5000} = 0.05 \text{ ampere}$$

Milliampere units would be more convenient for the current, and 0.05 amp. × 1000 = 50 milliamperes.

SERIES AND PARALLEL RESISTANCES

Very few actual electric circuits are as simple as the illustration in the preceding section. Commonly, resistances are found connected in a variety of ways. The two fundamental methods of connecting resistances are shown in Fig. 2-4. In the upper drawing, the current flows from the source of emf (in the direction shown by the arrow, let us say) down through the first resistance, *R1*, then through the second, *R2*, and then back to the source. These resistors are connected in **series.** The current everywhere in the circuit has the same value.

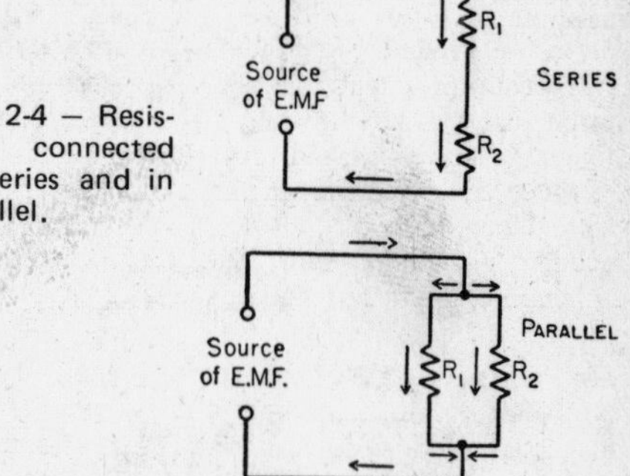

Fig. 2-4 – Resistors connected in series and in parallel.

In the lower drawing the current flows to the common connection point at the top of the two resistors and then divides, one part of it flowing through *R1* and the other through *R2*. At the lower connection point these two currents again combine; the total is the same as the current that flowed into the upper common connection. In this case the two resistors are connected in **parallel.**

Resistors in Series

When a circuit has a number of resistances connected in series, the total resistance of the circuit is the sum of the individual resistances. If these are numbered *R1, R2, R3,* etc., then

$R \text{ (total)} = R1 + R2 + R3 + R4 + \ldots\ldots\ldots$

where the dots indicate that as many resistors as necessary may be added.

Example: Suppose that three resistors are connected to a source of emf as shown in Fig. 2-5. The emf is 250 volts. R1 is 5000 ohms, R2 is 20,000 ohms, and R3 is 8000 ohms. The total resistance is then

$$R = R1 + R2 + R3 = 5000 + 20{,}000 + 8000 = 33{,}000 \text{ ohms}$$

The current flowing in the circuit is then

$$I = \frac{E}{R} = \frac{250}{33{,}000} = 0.00757 \text{ amp.} = 7.57 \text{ mA.}$$

(We need not carry calculations beyond three significant figures, and often two will suffice because the accuracy of measurements is seldom better than a few percent.)

Voltage Drop

Ohm's Law applies to *any part* of a circuit as well as to the whole circuit. Although the current is the same in all three of the resistances in the example, the total voltage divides among them. The voltage appearing across each resistor (the **voltage drop**) can be found from Ohm's Law.

Example: If the voltage across R1 (Fig. 2-5) is called E1, that across R2 is called E2, and that across R3 is called E3, then

$$E1 = IR1 = 0.00757 \times 5000 = 37.9 \text{ volts}$$
$$E2 = IR2 = 0.00757 \times 20{,}000 = 151.4 \text{ volts}$$
$$E3 = IR3 = 0.00757 \times 8000 = 60.6 \text{ volts}$$

The applied voltage must equal the sum of the individual voltage drops:

$$E = E1 + E2 + E3 = 37.9 + 151.4 + 60.6 = 249.9 \text{ volts}$$

The answer would have been more nearly exact if the current had been calculated to more decimal places, but as explained above a very high order of accuracy is not necessary.

In problems such as this considerable time and trouble can be saved, when the current is small enough to be expressed in milliamperes, if the resistance is expressed in kilohms rather than ohms. When resistance in kilohms is substituted directly in Ohm's Law the current will be milliamperes if the emf is in volts.

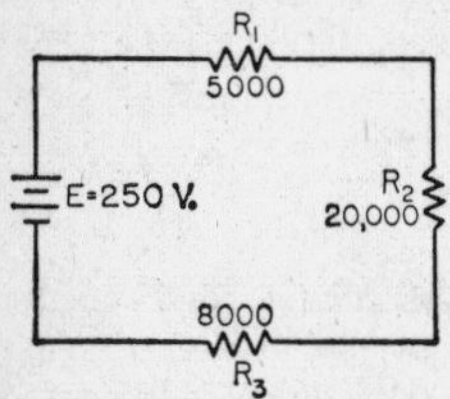

Fig. 2-5 – An example of resistors in series. The solution of the circuit is worked out in the text.

Resistors in Parallel

In a circuit with resistances in parallel, the total resistance is *less* than that of the *lowest* value of resistance present. This is because the total current is always greater than the current in any individual resistor. The formula for finding the total resistance of resistances in parallel is

$$R = \frac{1}{\frac{1}{R1} + \frac{1}{R2} + \frac{1}{R3} + \frac{1}{R4} + \cdots\cdots}$$

where the dots again indicate that any number of resistors can be combined by the same method. For only two resistances in parallel (a very common case) the formula becomes

$$R = \frac{R1R2}{R1 + R2}$$

Example: If a 500-ohm resistor is paralleled with one of 1200 ohms, the total resistance is

$$R = \frac{R1R2}{R1 + R2} = \frac{500 \times 1200}{500 + 1200} = \frac{600{,}000}{1700} = 353 \text{ ohms}$$

It is probably easier to solve practical problems by a different method than the "reciprocal of reciprocals" formula. Suppose the three resistors of the previous example are connected in parallel as shown in Fig. 2-6. The same emf, 250 volts, is applied to all three of the resistors. The current in each can be found from Ohm's Law as shown below, *I1*, being the current through *R1*, *I2* the current through *R2* and *I3* the current through *R3*.

For convenience, the resistance will be expressed in kilohms so the current will be in milliamperes.

$$I1 = \frac{E}{R1} = \frac{250}{5} = 50 \text{ mA}$$

$$I2 = \frac{E}{R2} = \frac{250}{20} = 12.5 \text{ mA}$$

$$I3 = \frac{E}{R3} = \frac{250}{8} = 31.25 \text{ mA}$$

The total current is

$$I = I1 + I2 + I3 = 50 + 12.5 + 31.25 = 93.75 \text{ mA}$$

The total resistance of the circuit is therefore

$$R = \frac{E}{I} = \frac{250}{93.75} = 2.66 \text{ kilohms } (= 2660 \text{ ohms})$$

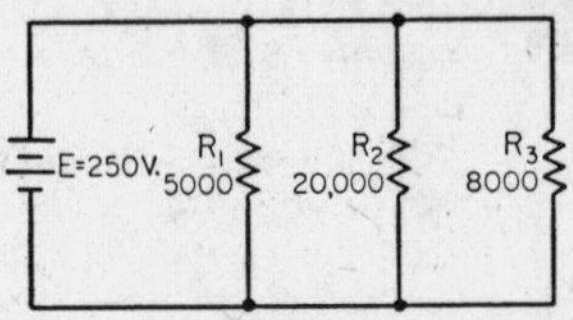

Fig. 2-6 – An example of resistors in parallel. The solution is worked out in the text.

Resistors in Series-Parallel

An actual circuit may have resistances both in parallel and in series. To illustrate, we use the same three resistances again, but now connected as in Fig. 2-7. The method of solving a circuit such as Fig. 2-7 is as follows: Consider *R2* and *R3* in parallel as through they formed a single resistor. Find their equivalent resistance. Then this resistance in series with *R1* forms a simple series circuit, as shown at the right in Fig. 2-7. An example of the arithmetic is given under the illustration.

Using the same principles, and staying within the practical limits, a value for *R2* can be computed that will provide a given voltage drop across *R3* or a given current through *R1*. Simple algebra is required.

Example: The first step is to find the equivalent resistance of R2 and R3. From the formula for two resistances in parallel,

$$R_{eq.} = \frac{R2R3}{R2 + R3} = \frac{20 \times 8}{20 + 8} = \frac{160}{28} = 5.71 \text{ kilohms}$$

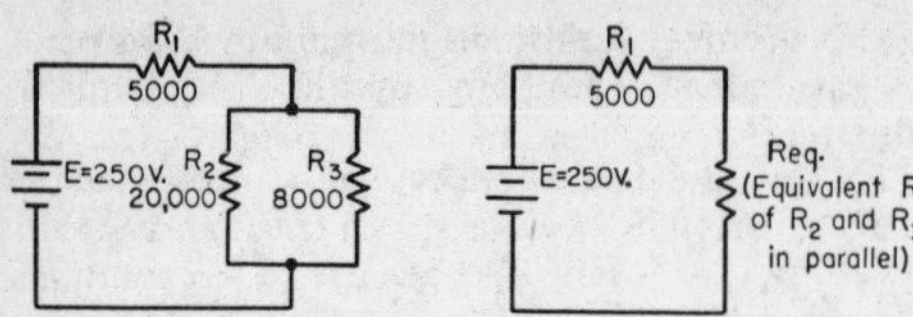

Fig. 2-7 – An example of resistors in series-parallel. The equivalent circuit is at the right. The solution is worked out in the text.

The total resistance in the circuit is then

$$R = R1 + Req. = 5 + 5.71 \text{ kilohms} = 10.71 \text{ kilohms}$$

The current is

$$I = \frac{E}{R} = \frac{250}{10.71} = 23.3 \text{ mA}$$

The voltage drops across R1 and Req are

$$E1 = IR1 = 23.3 \times 5 = 117 \text{ volts}$$
$$E2 = IReq = 23.3 \times 5.71 = 133 \text{ volts}$$

with sufficient accuracy. These total 250 volts, thus checking the calculations so far, because the sum of the voltage drops must equal the applied voltage. Since E2 appears across both R2 and R3,

$$I2 = \frac{E2}{R2} = \frac{133}{20} = 6.65 \text{ mA}$$

$$I3 = \frac{E2}{R3} = \frac{133}{8} = 16.6 \text{ mA}$$

where I2 = Current through R2
I3 = Current through R3

The total is 23.25 mA, which checks closely enough with 23.3 mA, the current through the whole circuit.

POWER AND ENERGY

Power – the rate of doing work – is equal to voltage multiplied by current. The unit of electrical power, called the **watt**, is equal to one volt multiplied by one ampere. The equation for power therefore is

$P = EI$ where P = Power in watts
E = Emf in volts
I = Current in amperes

Common fractional and multiple units for power are the **milliwatt**, one one-thousandth of a watt, and the **kilowatt**, or one thousand watts.

Example: The plate voltage on a transmitting vacuum tube is 2000 volts and the plate current is 350 milliamperes. (The current must be changed to amperes before substitution in the formula, and so is 0.35 amp.) Then

$$P = EI = 2000 \times 0.35 = 700 \text{ watts}$$

By substituting the Ohm's Law equivalent for E and I, the following formulas are obtained for power:

$$P = \frac{E^2}{R} \qquad P = I^2R$$

These formulas are useful in power calculations when the resistance and either the current or voltage (but not both) are known.

Example: How much power will be used up in a 4000-ohm resistor if the voltage applied to it is 200 volts? From the equation

$$P = \frac{E^2}{R} = \frac{(200)^2}{4000} = \frac{40,000}{4000} = 10 \text{ watts}$$

Or, suppose a current of 20 milliamperes flows through a 300-ohm resistor. Then

$$P = I^2R = (0.02)^2 \times 300 = 0.0004 \times 300 = 0.12 \text{ watt}$$

Note that the current was changed from milliamperes to amperes before substitution in the formula.

Electrical power in a resistance is turned into heat. The greater the power the more rapidly the heat is generated. Resistors for radio work are made in many sizes, the smallest being rated to "dissipate" (or carry safely) about 1/8 watt. The largest resistors commonly used in amateur equipment will dissipate about 100 watts.

Generalized Definition of Resistance

Electrical power is not always turned into heat. The power used in running a motor, for example, is converted to mechanical motion. The power supplied to a radio transmitter is largely converted into radio waves. Power applied to a loudspeaker is changed into sound waves. But in every case of this kind the power is completely "used up" – it cannot be recovered. Also, for proper operation of the device the power must be supplied at a definite ratio of voltage to current. Both these features are characteristics of resistance, so it can be said that any device that dissipates power has a definite value of "resistance." This concept of resistance as something that absorbs power at a definite voltage/current ratio is very useful, since it permits substituting a simple resistance for the **load** or power-consuming part of the device receiving power, often with considerable simplification of calculations. Of course, every electrical device has some resistance of its own in the more narrow sense, so a part of the power supplied to it is dissipated in that resistance and hence appears as heat even though the major part of the power may be converted to another form.

Efficiency

In devices such as motors and vacuum tubes, the object is to obtain power in some other form than heat. Therefore power used in heating is considered to be a loss, because it is not the *useful* power. The **efficiency** of a device is the useful power output (in its converted form) divided by the power input to the device. In a vacuum-tube transmitter, for example, the object is to convert power from a dc source into ac power at some radio frequency. The ratio of the rf power output to the dc input is the efficiency of the tube. That is,

$$Eff. = \frac{P_o}{P_i}$$

where $Eff.$ = Efficiency (as a decimal)
P_o = Power output (watts)
P_i = Power input (watts)

Example: If the dc input to the tube is 100 watts, and the rf power output is 60 watts, the efficiency is

$$Eff. = \frac{P_o}{P_i} = \frac{60}{100} = 0.6$$

Efficiency is usually expressed as a percentage; that is, it tells what percent of the input power will be available as useful output. The efficiency in the above example is 60 percent.

Energy

In residences, the power company's bill is for electrical **energy**, not for power. What you pay for is the *work* that electricity does for you, not the *rate* at which that work is done. Electrical work is equal to power multiplied by time; the common unit is the **watt-hour**, which means that a power of one watt has been used for one hour. That is,

$W = PT$ where W = Energy in watt-hours
P = Power in watts
T = Time in hours

Other energy units are the **kilowatt-hour** and the **watt-second**. These units should be self-explanatory.

Energy units are seldom used in amateur practice, but it is obvious that a small amount of power used for a long time can eventually result in a "power" bill that is just as large as though a large amount of power had been used for a very short time.

CAPACITANCE

Suppose two flat metal plates are placed close to each other (but not touching) and are connected to a battery through a switch, as shown in Fig. 2-8. At the instant the switch is closed, electrons will be attracted from the upper plate to the positive terminal of the battery, and the same number will be repelled into the lower plate from the negative battery terminal. Enough electrons move into one plate and out of the other to make the emf between them the same as the emf of the battery.

If the switch is opened after the plates have been **charged** in this way, the top plate is left with a deficiency of electrons and the bottom plate with an excess. The plates remain charged despite the fact that the battery no longer is connected. However, if a wire is touched between the two plates (**short-circuiting** them) the excess electrons on the bottom plate will flow through the wire to the upper plate, thus restoring electrical neutrality. The plates have then been **discharged**.

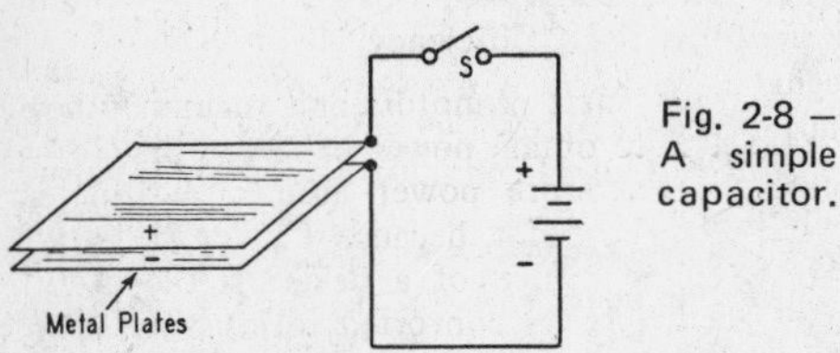

Fig. 2-8 – A simple capacitor.

The two plates constitute an electrical **capacitor**; a capacitor possesses the property of storing electricity. (The energy actually is stored in the electric field between the plates.) During the time the electrons are moving – that is, while the capacitor is being charged or discharged – a current is flowing in the circuit even though the circuit is "broken" by the gap between the capacitor plates. However, the current flows only during the time of charge and discharge, and this time is usually very short. There can be no continuous flow of direct current "through" a capacitor, but an alternating current can pass through easily if the frequency is high enough.

The **charge** or quantity of electricity that can be placed on a capacitor is proportional to the applied voltage and to the **capacitance** of the capacitor. The larger the plate area and the smaller the spacing between the plate the greater the capacitance. The capacitance also depends upon the kind of insulating material between the plates; it is smallest with air insulation, but substitution of other insulating materials for air may increase the capacitance many times. The ratio of the capacitance with some material other than air between the plates, to the capacitance of the same capacitor with air insulation, is called the **dielectric constant** of that particular insulating material. The material itself is called a **dielectric**. The dielectric constants of a number of materials commonly used as dielectrics in capacitors are given in Table 2-III. If a sheet of polystyrene is substituted for air between the plates of a capacitor, for example, the capacitance will be increased 2.6 times.

Units

The fundamental unit of capacitance is the **farad**, but this unit is much too large for practical work. Capacitance is usually measured in **microfarads** (abbreviated μF) or **picofarads** (pF). The microfarad is one-millionth of a farad, and the picofarad (formerly micromicrofarad) is one-millionth of a microfarad. Capacitors nearly always have more than two plates, the alternate plates being connected together to form two sets as shown in Fig. 2-9. This makes it possible to attain a fairly large capacitance in a small space, since several plates of smaller individual area can be

TABLE 2-III
Dielectric Constants and Breakdown Voltages

Material	*Dielectric Constant**	*Puncture Voltage***
Air	1.0	
Alsimag 196	5.7	240
Bakelite	4.4–5.4	300
Bakelite, mica-filled	4.7	325–375
Cellulose acetate	3.3–3.9	250–600
Fiber	5–7.5	150–180
Formica	4.6–4.9	450
Glass, window	7.6–8	200–250
Glass, Pyrex	4.8	335
Mica, ruby	5.4	3800–5600
Mycalex	7.4	250
Paper, Royalgrey	3.0	200
Plexiglass	2.8	990
Polyethylene	2.3	1200
Polystyrene	2.6	500–700
Porcelain	5.1–5.9	40–100
Quartz, fuxed	3.8	1000
Steatite, low-loss	5.8	150–315
Teflon	2.1	1000–2000

*** At 1 MHz ** In volts per mil (0.001 inch)**

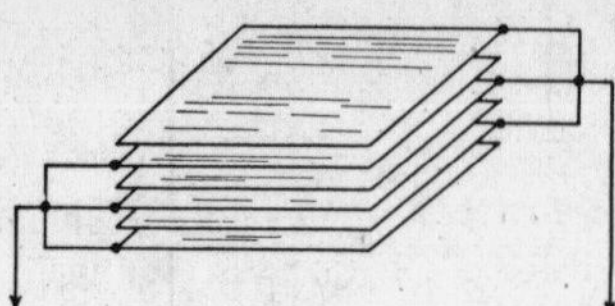

Fig. 2-9 – A multiple-plate capacitor. Alternate plates are connected together.

stacked to form the equivalent of a single large plate of the same total area. Also, all plates, except the two on the ends, are exposed to plates of the other group on *both sides*, and so are twice as effective in increasing the capacitance.

The formula for calculating capacitance is:

$$C = 0.224 \frac{KA}{d} (n - 1)$$

where C = Capacitance in pF.
K = Dielectric constant of material between plates
A = Area of one side of *one* plate in square inches
d = Separation of plate surfaces in inches
n = Number of plates

If the plates in one group do not have the same area as the plates in the other, use the area of the *smaller* plates.

Capacitors in Radio

The types of capacitors used in radio work differ considerably in physical size, construction, and capacitance. Some representative types are shown in the photograph. In **variable** capacitors (almost always constructed with air for the dielectric) one set of plates is made movable with respect to the other set so that the capacitance can be varied. **Fixed** capacitors – that is, assemblies having a single, non-adjustable value of capacitance – also can be made with metal plates and with air as the dielectric, but usually are constructed from plates of metal foil with a thin solid or liquid dielectric sandwiched in between, so that a relatively large capacitance can be secured in a small unit. The solid dielectrics commonly used are mica, paper and special ceramics. An example of a liquid dielectric is mineral oil. The **electrolytic** capacitor uses aluminum-foil plates with a semiliquid conducting chemical compound between them; the actual dielectric is a very thin film of insulating material that forms on one set of plates through electrochemical action when a dc voltage is applied to the capacitor. The capacitance obtained with a given plate area in an electrolytic capacitor is very large, compared with capacitors having other dielectrics, because the film is so thin – much less than any thickness that is practicable with a solid dielectric.

The use of electrolytic and oil-filled capacitors is confined to power-supply filtering and audio bypass applications. Mica and ceramic capacitors are used throughout the frequency range from audio to several hundred megacycles.

Voltage Breakdown

When a high voltage is applied to the plates of a capacitor, a considerable force is exerted on the electrons and nuclei of the dielectric. Because the dielectric is an insulator the electrons do not become detached from atoms the way they do in conductors. However, if the force is great enough the dielectric will "break down"; usually it will puncture and may char (if it is solid) and permit current to flow. The **breakdown voltage** depends upon the kind and thickness of the dielectric, as shown in Table 2-III. It is not directly proportional to the thickness; that is, doubling the thickness does not quite double the breakdown voltage. If the dielectric is air or any other gas, breakdown is evidenced by a spark or arc between the plates, but if the voltage is removed the arc ceases and the capacitor is ready for use again. Breakdown will occur at a lower voltage between pointed or sharp-edged surfaces than between rounded and polished surfaces; consequently, the breakdown voltage between metal plates of given spacing in air can be increased by buffing the edges of the plates.

Since the dielectric must be thick to withstand high voltages, and since the thicker the dielectric the smaller the capacitance for a given plate area, a high-voltage capacitor must have more plate area than a low-voltage one of the same capacitance. High-voltage high-capacitance capacitors are physically large.

Fixed and variable capacitors. The large unit at the left is a transmitting-type variable capacitor for rf tank circuits. To its right are other air-dielectric variables of different sizes ranging from the midget "air padder" to the medium-power tank capacitor at the top center. The cased capacitors in the top row are for power-supply filters, the cylindrical-can unit being an electrolytic and the rectangular one a paper-dielectric capacitor. Various types of mica, ceramic, and paper-dielectric capacitors are in the foreground.

CAPACITORS IN SERIES AND PARALLEL

The terms "parallel" and "series" when used with reference to capacitors have the same circuit meaning as with resistances. When a number of capacitors are connected in parallel, as in Fig. 2-10, the total capacitance of the group is equal to the sum of the individual capacitances, so

$C\text{ (total)} = C1 + C2 + C3 + C4 + \ldots\ldots\ldots\ldots$

However, if two or more capacitors are connected in series, as in the second drawing, the total capacitance is less than that of the smallest capacitor in the group. The rule for finding the capacitance of a number of series-connected capacitors is the same as that for finding the resistance of a number of *parallel*-connected resistors. That is,

$$C\text{ (total)} = \frac{1}{\frac{1}{C1} + \frac{1}{C2} + \frac{1}{C3} + \frac{1}{C4} + \ldots\ldots\ldots\ldots}$$

and, for only two capacitors in series,

$$C\text{ (total)} = \frac{C1C2}{C1 + C2}$$

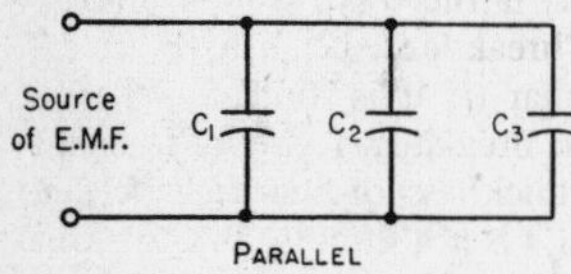

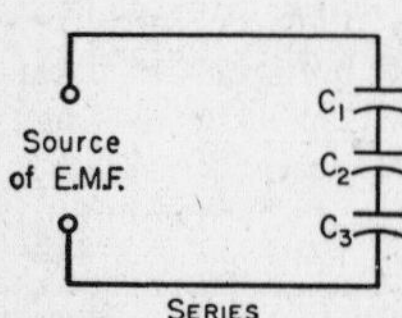

Fig. 2-10 — Capacitors in parallel and in series.

The same units must be used throughout; that is, all capacitances must be expressed in either μF or pF; both kinds of units cannot be used in the same equation.

Capacitors are connected in parallel to obtain a larger total capacitance than is available in one unit. The largest voltage that can be applied safely to a group of capacitors in parallel is the voltage that can be applied safely to the one having the *lowest* voltage rating.

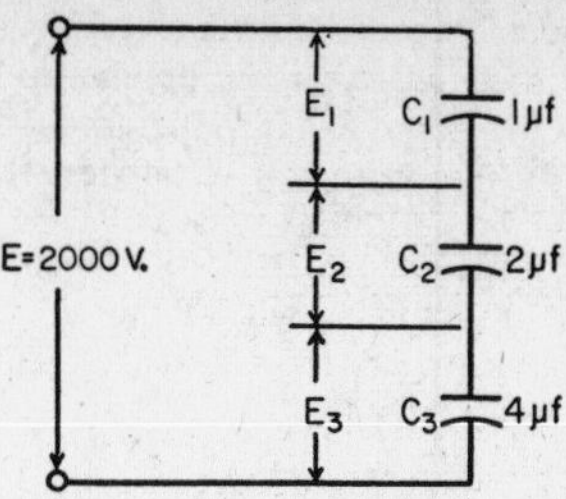

Fig. 2-11 — An example of capacitors connected in series. The solution to this arrangement is worked out in the text.

When capacitors are connected in series, the applied voltage is divided up among them, the situation is much the same as when resistors are in series and there is a voltage drop across each. However, the voltage that appears across each capacitor of a group connected in series is in *inverse* proportion to its capacitance, as compared with the capacitance of the whole group.

Example: Three capacitors having capacitances of 1, 2 and 4 μF, respectively, are connected in series as shown in Fig. 2-11. The total capacitance is

$$C = \frac{1}{\frac{1}{C1} + \frac{1}{C2} + \frac{1}{C3}} = \frac{1}{\frac{1}{1} + \frac{1}{2} + \frac{1}{4}} = \frac{1}{\frac{7}{4}} = \frac{4}{7}$$

$$= 0.571\ \mu F$$

The voltage across each capacitor is proportional to the *total* capacitance divided by the capacitance of the capacitor in question, so the voltage across C1 is

$$E1 = \frac{0.571}{1} \times 2000 = 1142 \text{ volts}$$

Similarly, the voltages across C2 and C3 are

$$E2 = \frac{0.571}{2} \times 2000 = 571 \text{ volts}$$

$$E3 = \frac{0.571}{4} \times 2000 = 286 \text{ volts}$$

totaling approximately 2000 volts, the applied voltage.

Capacitors are frequently connected in series to enable the group to withstand a larger voltage (at the expense of decreased total capacitance) than any individual capacitor is rated to stand. However, as shown by the previous example, the applied voltages does not divide equally among the capacitors (except when all the capacitances are the same) so care must be taken to see that the voltage rating of no capacitor in the group is exceeded.

INDUCTANCE

It is possible to show that the flow of current through a conductor is accompanied by magnetic effects; a compass needle brought near the conductor, for example, will be deflected from its normal north-south position. The current, in other words, sets up a magnetic field.

The transfer of energy to the magnetic field represents work done by the source of emf. Power is required for doing work, and since power is equal to current multiplied by voltage, there must be a voltage drop in the circuit during the time in which energy is being stored in the field. This voltage "drop" (which has nothing to do with the voltage drop in any resistance in the circuit) is the result of an opposing voltage "induced" in the circuit while the field is building up to its final value. When the field becomes constant the **induced emf** or **back emf** disappears, since no further energy is being stored.

Since the induced emf opposes the emf of the source, it tends to prevent the current from rising rapidly when the circuit is closed. The amplitude of the induced emf is proportional to the rate at which the current is changing and to a constant associated with the circuit itself, called the **inductance** of the circuit.

Inductance depends on the physical characteristics of the conductor. If the conductor is formed into a coil, for example, its inductance is increased. A coil of many turns will have more inductance than one of few turns, if both coils are otherwise physically similar. Also, if a coil is placed on an iron core its inductance will be greater than it was without the magnetic core.

The polarity of an induced emf is always such as to oppose any change in the current in the circuit. This means that when the current in the circuit is increasing, work is being done against the induced emf by storing energy in the magnetic field. If the current in the circuit tends to decrease, the stored energy of the field returns to the circuit, and thus adds to the energy being supplied by the source of emf. This tends to keep the current flowing even though the applied emf may be decreasing or be removed entirely.

The unit of inductance is the **henry**. Values of inductance used in radio equipment vary over a wide range. Inductance of several henrys is required in power-supply circuits (see chapter on Power Supplies) and to obtain such values of inductance it is necessary to use coils of many turns wound on iron cores. In radio-frequency circuits, the inductance values used will be measured in **millihenrys** (a **mH**, one one-thousandth of a henry) at low frequencies, and in **microhenrys** (**μH**, one one-millionth of a henry) at medium frequencies and higher. Although coils for radio frequencies may be wound on special iron cores (ordinary iron is not suitable) most rf coils made and used by amateurs are of the "air-core" type; that is, wound on an insulating support consisting of nonmagnetic material.

Every conductor has inductance, even though the conductor is not formed into a coil. The inductance of a short length of straight wire is small, but it may not be negligible because if the current through it changes its intensity rapidly enough the induced voltage may be appreciable. This will be the case in even a few inches of wire when an alternating current having a frequency of the order of 100 MHz. or higher is flowing. However, at much lower frequencies the inductance of the same wire could be ignored because the induced voltage would be negligibly small.

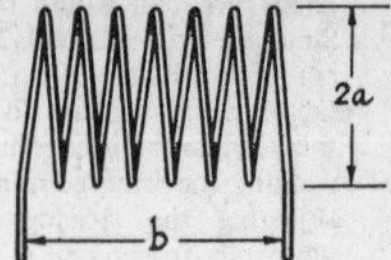

Fig. 2-12 – Coil dimensions used in the inductance formula. The wire diameter does not enter into the formula.

Calculating Inductance

The approximate inductance of single-layer air-core coils may be calculated from the simplified formula

$$L\ (\mu\text{H}) = \frac{a^2n^2}{9a + 10b}$$

where L = Inductance in microhenrys
a = Coil radius in inches
b = Coil length in inches
n = Number of turns

The notation is explained in Fig. 2-12. This formula is a close approximation for coils having a length equal to or greater than $0.8a$

Example: Assume a coil having 48 turns wound 32 turns per inch and a diameter of 3/4 inch. Thus $a = 0.75 \div 2 = 0.375$, $b = 48 \div 32 = 1.5$, and $n = 48$. Substituting,

$$L = \frac{.375 \times .375 \times 48 \times 48}{(9 \times .375) + (10 \times 1.5)} = 17.6\ \mu\text{H}$$

To calculate the number of turns of a single-layer coil for a required value of inductance,

$$n = \sqrt{\frac{L\,(9a + 10b)}{a^2}}$$

Example: Suppose an inductance of 10 μH is required. The form on which the coil is to be wound has a diameter of one inch and is long enough to accommodate a coil of 1 1/4 inches. Then $a = 0.5$, $b = 1.25$, and $L = 10$. Substituting,

$$n = \sqrt{\frac{10\,(4.5 + 12.5)}{.5 \times .5}} = \sqrt{680} = 26.1 \text{ turns}$$

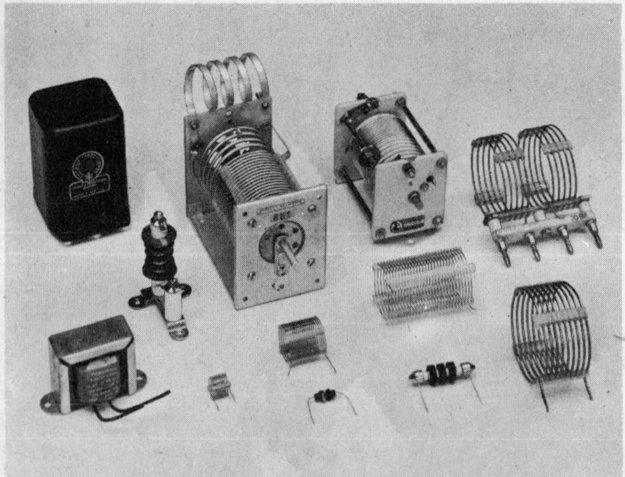

Inductors for power and radio frequencies. The two iron-core coils at the left are "chokes" for power-supply filters. The mounted air-core coils at the top center are adjustable inductors for transmitting tank circuits. The "pie-wound" coils at the left and in the foreground are radio-frequency choke coils. The remaining coils are typical of inductors used in rf tuned circuits, the larger sizes being used principally for transmitters.

A 26-turn coil would be close enough in practical work. Since the coil will be 1.25 inches long, the number of turns per inch will be 26.1 ÷ 1.25 =20.8. Consulting the wire table, we find that No. 17 enameled wire (or anything smaller) can be used. The proper inductance is obtained by winding the required number of turns on the form and then adjusting the spacing between the turns to make a uniformly-spaced coil 1.25 inches long.

Inductance Charts

Most inductance formulas lose accuracy when applied to small coils (such as are used in vhf work and in low-pass filters built for reducing harmonic interference to television) because the conductor thickness is no longer negligible in comparison with the size of the coil. Fig. 2-13 shows the measured inductance of vhf coils, and may be used as a basis for circuit design. Two curves are given: curve A is for coils wound to an inside diameter of 1/2 inch; curve B is for coils of 3/4-inch inside diameter. In both curves the wire size is No. 12, winding pitch 8 turns to the inch (1/8 inch center-to-center turn spacing). The inductance values given include leads 1/2 inch long.

The charts of Figs. 2-14 and 2-15 are useful for rapid determination of the inductance of coils of the type commonly used in radio-frequency circuits in the range 3-30 MHz. They are of sufficient accuracy for most practical work. Given the coil length in inches, the curves show the multiplying factor to be applied to the inductance value given in the table below the curve for a coil of the same diameter and number of turns per inch.

Example: A coil 1 inch in diameter is 1 1/4 inches long and has 20 turns. Therefore it has 16 turns per inch, and from the table under Fig. 2-15 it is found that the reference inductance for a coil of this diameter and number of turns per inch is 16.8 μH. From curve B in the figure the multiplying factor is 0.35, so the inductance is

$$16.8 \times 0.35 = 5.9\ \mu H$$

The charts also can be used for finding suitable dimensions for a coil having a required value of inductance.

Example: A coil having an inductance of 12 μH is required. It is to be wound on a form having a diameter of 1 inch, the length available for the winding being not more than 1 1/4 inches. From Fig. 2-15, the multiplying factor for a 1-inch diameter coil (curve B) having the maximum possible length of 1 1/4 inches is 0.35. Hence the number of turns per inch must be chosen for a reference inductance of at least 12/0.35, or 34 μH. From the Table under Fig. 2-15 it is seen that 16 turns per inch (reference inductance 16.8 μH) is too small. Using 32 turns per inch, the multiplying factor is 12/68, or 0.177, and from curve B this corresponds to a coil length of 3/4 inch. There will be 24 turns in this length, since the winding "pitch" is 32 turns per inch.

Machine-wound coils with the diameters and turns per inch given in the tables are available in many radio stores, under the trade names of "B&W Miniductor" and "Illumitronic Air Dux."

IRON-CORE COILS

Permeability

Suppose that the coil in Fig. 2-16 is wound on an iron core having a cross-sectional area of 2 square inches. When a certain current is sent through the coil it is found that there are 80,000 lines of force in the core. Since the area is 2 square inches, the flux density is 40,000 lines per square inch. Now suppose that the iron core is removed and the same current is maintained in the coil, and that the flux density without the iron core is found to be 50 lines per square inch. The ratio of the flux density with the given core material to the flux density (with the same coil and same current) with an air core is called the **permeability** of the material. In this case the permeability of the iron is 40,000/50 = 800. The inductance of the coil is increased 800 times by inserting the iron core since, other things being equal, the inductance will be proportional to the magnetic flux through the coil.

The permeability of a magnetic material varies with the flux density. At low flux densities (or with an air core) increasing the current through the coil will cause a proportionate increase in flux, but at very high flux densities, increasing the current may cause no appreciable change in the flux. When this is so, the iron is said to be **saturated**. Saturation causes a rapid decrease in permeability, because it decreases the ratio of flux lines to those obtainable with the same current and an air core. Obviously, the inductance of an iron-core inductor is highly dependent upon the current flowing in the coil. In an air-core coil, the inductance is independent of current because air does not saturate.

Iron core coils such as the one sketched in Fig. 2-16 are used chiefly in power-supply equipment. They usually have direct current flowing through the winding, and the variation in inductance with current is usually undesirable. It may be overcome by keeping the flux density below the saturation point of the iron. This is done by opening the core so that there is a small "air gap," as indicated by the dashed lines. The magnetic "resistance" introduced by such a gap is so large – even though the gap is only a small fraction of an inch – compared with that of the iron that the gap, rather than the iron, controls the flux density. This reduces the inductance, but makes it practically constant regardless of the value of the current.

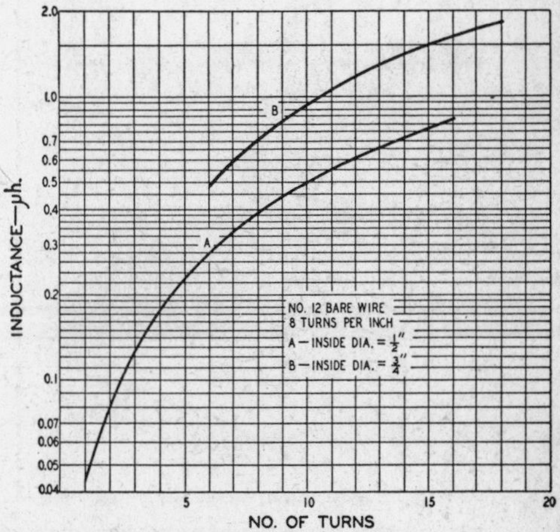

Fig. 2-13 – Measured inductance of coils wound with No. 12 bare wire, 8 turns to the inch. The values include half-inch leads.

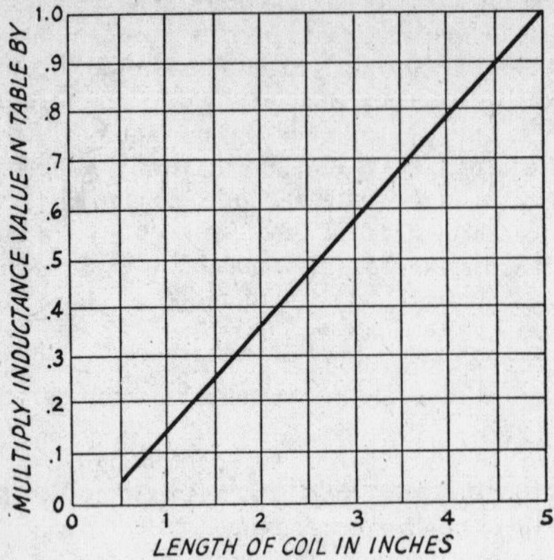

Fig. 2-14 – Factor to be applied to the inductance of coils listed in the table below, for coil lengths up to 5 inches.

Eddy Currents and Hysteresis

When alternating current flows through a coil wound on an iron core an emf will be induced, as previously explained, and since iron is a conductor a current will flow in the core. Such currents (called **eddy currents**) represent a waste of power because they flow through the resistance of the iron and thus cause heating. Eddy-current losses can be reduced by **laminating** the core; that is, by cutting it into thin strips. These strips or **laminations** must be insulated from each other by painting them with some insulating material such as varnish or shellac.

There is also another type of energy loss: the iron tends to resist any change in its magnetic state, so a rapidly-changing current such as ac is forced continually to supply energy to the iron to overcome this "inertia." Losses of this sort are called **hysteresis** losses.

Eddy-current and hysteresis losses in iron increase rapidly as the frequency of the alternating current is increased. For this reason, ordinary iron cores can be used only at power and audio frequencies – up to, say, 15,000 cycles. Even so, a very good grade of iron or steel is necessary if the core is to perform well at the higher audio frequencies. Iron cores of this type are completely useless at radio frequencies.

Coil dia, Inches	*No. of tpi*	*Inductance in μH*
1 1/4	4	2.75
	6	6.3
	8	11.2
	10	17.5
	16	42.5
1 1/2	4	3.9
	6	8.8
	8	15.6
	10	24.5
	16	63
1 3/4	4	5.2
	6	11.8
	8	21
	10	33
	16	85
2	4	6.6
	6	15
	8	26.5
	10	42
	16	108
2 1/2	4	10.2
	6	23
	8	41
	10	64
3	4	14
	6	31.5
	8	56
	10	89

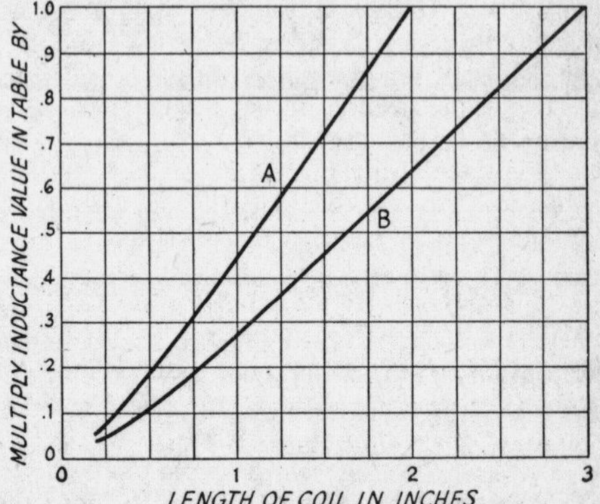

Fig. 2-15 – Factor to be applied to the inductance of coils listed in the table below, as a function of coil length. Use curve A for coils marked *A*, and curve B for coils marked *B*.

Coil dia, Inches	*No. of tpi*	*Inductance in μH*
1/2 (A)	4	0.18
	6	0.40
	8	0.72
	10	1.12
	16	2.9
	32	12
5/8 (A)	4	0.28
	6	0.62
	8	1.1
	10	1.7
	16	4.4
	32	18
3/4 (B)	4	0.6
	6	1.35
	8	2.4
	10	3.8
	16	9.9
	32	40
1 (B)	4	1.0
	6	2.3
	8	4.2
	10	6.6
	16	16.9
	32	68

For radio-frequency work, the losses in iron cores can be reduced to a satisfactory figure by grinding the iron into a powder and then mixing it with a "binder" of insulating material in such a way that the individual iron particles are insulated from each other. By this means cores can be made that will function satisfactorily even through the vhf range – that is, at frequencies up to perhaps 100 MHz. Because a large part of the magnetic path is through a nonmagnetic material, the permeability of the iron is low compared with the values

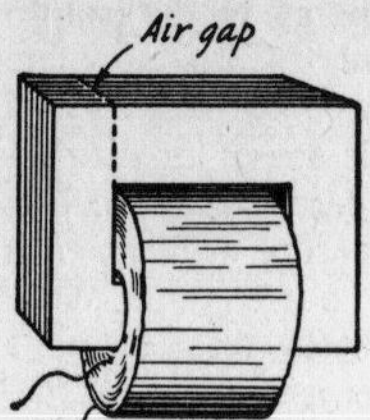

Fig. 2-16 – Typical construction of an iron-core inductor. The small air gap prevents magnetic saturation of the iron and thus maintains the inductance at high currents.

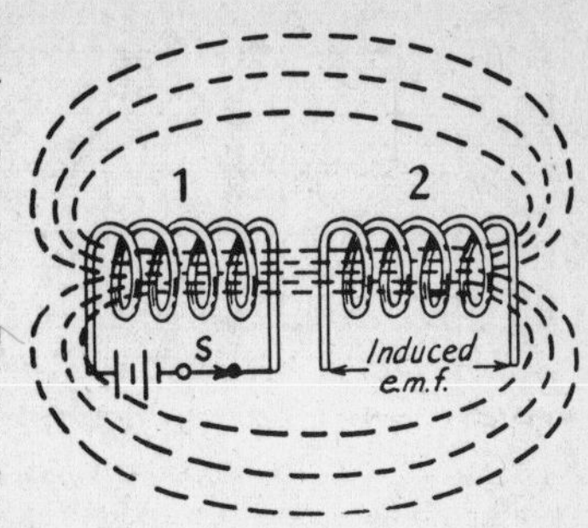

Fig. 2-18 – Mutual inductance. When the switch, *S*, is closed current flows through coil No. 1, setting up a magnetic field that induces an emf in the turns of coil No. 2.

obtained at power-supply frequencies. The core is usually in the form of a "slug" or cylinder which fits inside the insulating form on which the coil is wound. Despite the fact that, with this construction, the major portion of the magnetic path for the flux is in air, the slug is quite effective in increasing the coil inductance. By pushing the slug in and out of the coil the inductance can be varied over a considerable range.

INDUCTANCES IN SERIES AND PARALLEL

When two or more inductors are connected in series (Fig. 2-17, left) the total inductance is equal to the sum of the individual inductances, *provided the coils are sufficiently separated so that no coil is in the magnetic field of another*.

That is,

$$L_{total} = L1 + L2 + L3 + L4 + \ldots\ldots\ldots\ldots$$

If inductors are connected in parallel (Fig. 2-17, right) – and the coils are separated sufficiently, the total inductance is given by

$$L_{total} = \frac{1}{\frac{1}{L1} + \frac{1}{L2} + \frac{1}{L3} + \frac{1}{L4} + \ldots\ldots}$$

and for two inductances in parallel,

$$L = \frac{L1L2}{L1 + L2}$$

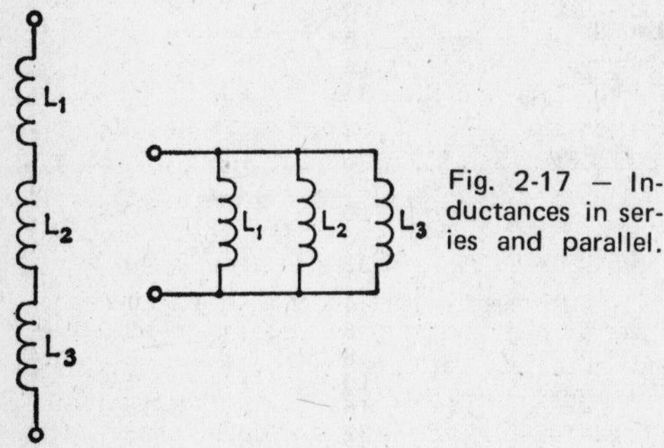

Fig. 2-17 – Inductances in series and parallel.

Thus the rules for combining inductances in series and parallel are the same for resistances, *if* the coils are far enough apart so that each is unaffected by another's magnetic field. When this is not so the formulas given above cannot be used.

MUTUAL INDUCTANCE

If two coils are arranged with their axes on the same line, as shown in Fig. 2-18, a current sent through Coil 1 will cause a magnetic field which "cuts" Coil 2. Consequently, an emf will be induced in Coil 2 whenever the field strength is changing. This induced emf is similar to the emf of self-induction, but since it appears in the *second* coil because of current flowing in the *first*, it is a "mutual" effect and results from the **mutual inductance** between the two coils.

If all the flux set up by one coil cuts all the turns of the other coil the mutual inductance has its maximum possible value. If only a small part of the flux set up by one coil cuts the turns of the other the mutual inductance is relatively small. Two coils having mutual inductance are said to be **coupled**.

The ratio of actual mutual inductance to the maximum possible value that could theoretically be obtained with two given coils is called the **coefficient of coupling** between the coils. It is frequently expressed as a percentage. Coils that have nearly the maximum possible (coefficient = 1 or 100%) mutual inductance are said to be **closely**, or **tightly**, coupled, but if the mutual inductance is relatively small the coils are said to be **loosely** coupled. The degree of coupling depends upon the physical spacing between the coils and how they are placed with respect to each other. Maximum coupling exists when they have a common axis and are as close together as possible (one wound over the other). The coupling is least when the coils are far apart or are placed so their axes are at right angles.

The maximum possible coefficient of coupling is closely approached only when the two coils are wound on a closed iron core. The coefficient with air-core coils may run as high as 0.6 or 0.7 if one coil is wound over the other, but will be much less if the two coils are separated.

TIME CONSTANT

Capacitance and Resistance

Connecting a source of emf to a capacitor causes the capacitor to become charged to the full emf practically instantaneously, if there is no resistance in the circuit. However, if the circuit contains resistance, as in Fig. 2-19A, the resistance limits the current flow and an appreciable length of time is required for the emf between the capacitor

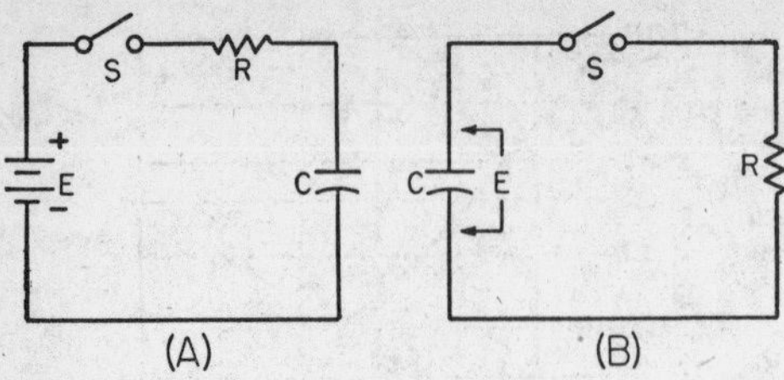

Fig. 2-19 – Illustrating the time constant of an *RC* circuit.

plates to build up to the same value as the emf of the source. During this "building-up" period the current gradually decreases from its initial value, because the increasing emf stored on the capacitor offers increasing opposition to the steady emf of the source.

Theoretically, the charging process is never really finished, but eventually the charging current drops to a value that is smaller than anything that can be measured. The **time constant** of such a circuit is the length of time, in seconds, required for the voltage across the capacitor to reach 63 per cent of the applied emf (this figure is chosen for mathematical reasons). The voltage across the capacitor rises with time as shown by Fig. 2-20.

The formula for time constant is

$$T = RC$$

where T = Time constant in seconds
C = Capacitance in farads
R = Resistance in ohms

Example: The time constant of a 2-μF capacitor and a 250,000-ohm (0.25 megohm) resistor is

$$T = RC = 0.25 \times 2 = 0.5 \text{ second}$$

If the applied emf is 1000 volts, the voltage between the capacitor plates will be 630 volts at the end of 1/2 second.

If C is in microfarads and R in megohms, the time constant also is in seconds. These units usually are more convenient.

If a charged capacitor is *discharged* through a resistor, as indicated in Fig. 2-19B, the same time constant applies. If there were no resistance, the capacitor would discharge instantly when S was closed. However, since R limits the current flow the capacitor voltage cannot instantly go to zero, but it will decrease just as rapidly as the capacitor can rid itself of its charge through R. When the capacitor is discharging through a resistance, the time constant (calculated in the same way as above) is the time, in seconds, that it takes for the capacitor to *lose* 63 percent of its voltage; that is, for the voltage to drop to 37 percent of its initial value.

Example: If the capacitor of the example above is charged to 1000 volts, it will discharge to 370 volts in 1/2 second through the 250,000-ohm resistor.

Inductance and Resistance

A comparable situation exists when resistance and inductance are in series. In Fig. 2-21, first consider L to have no resistance and also assume that R is zero. Then closing S would tend to send a current through the circuit. However, the instantaneous transition from no current to a finite value,

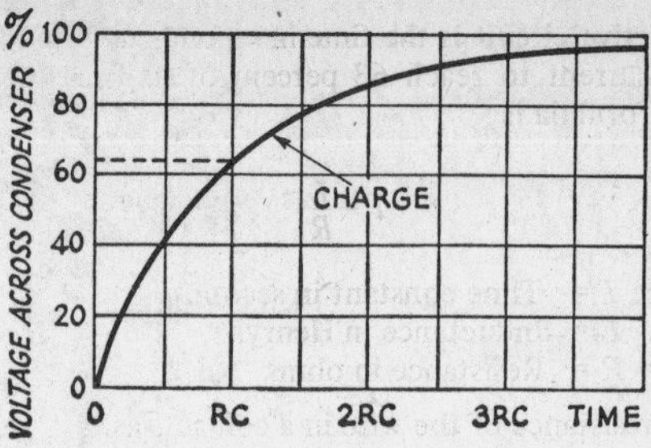

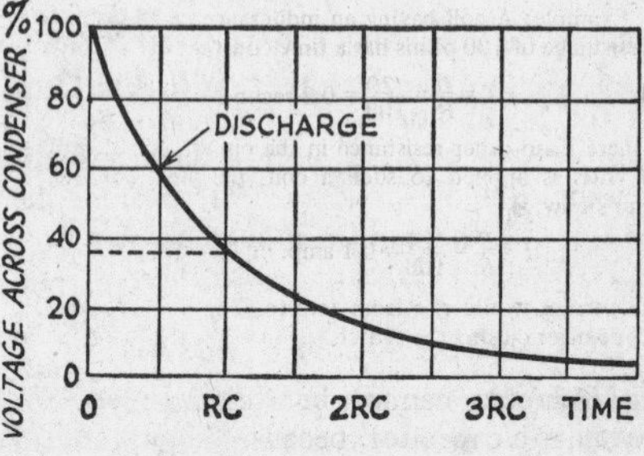

Fig. 2-20 – How the voltage across a capacitor rises, with time, when charged through a resistor. The lower curve shows the way in which the voltage decreases across the capacitor terminals on discharging through the same resistor.

however small, represents a very rapid *change* in current, and a *back emf* is developed by the self-inductance of L that is practically equal and opposite to the applied emf. The result is that the initial current is very small.

The back emf depends upon the *change* in current and would cease to offer opposition if the current did not continue to increase. With no resistance in the circuit (which would lead to an infinitely large current, by Ohm's Law) the current would increase forever, always growing just fast enough to keep the emf of self-induction equal to the applied emf.

When resistance is in series, Ohm's Law sets a limit to the value that the current can reach. The back emf generated in L has only to equal the *difference* between E and the drop across R, because that difference is the voltage actually applied to L. This difference becomes smaller as the current approaches the final Ohm's Law value. Theoretically, the back emf never quite disappears and so the current never quite reaches the Ohm's Law value, but practically the differences becomes unmeasurable after a time. The time constant of an

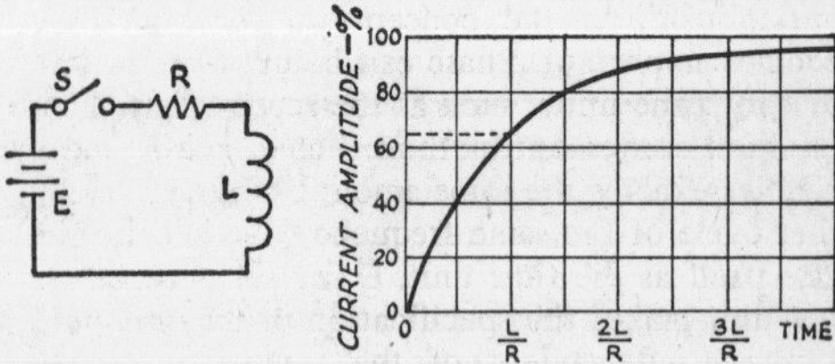

Fig. 2-21 – Time constant of an *LR* circuit.

inductive circuit is the time in seconds required for the current to reach 63 percent of its final value. The formula is

$$T = \frac{L}{R}$$

where T = Time constant in seconds
L = Inductance in Henrys
R = Resistance in ohms

The resistance of the wire in a coil acts as if it were in series with the inductance.

Example: A coil having an inductance of 20 henrys and a resistance of 100 ohms has a time constant of

$$T = \frac{L}{R} = \frac{20}{100} = 0.2 \text{ second}$$

if there is no other resistance in the circuit. If a dc emf of 10 volts is applied to such a coil, the final current, by Ohm's Law, is

$$I = \frac{E}{R} = \frac{10}{100} = 0.1 \text{ amp. or } 100 \text{ mA}$$

The current would rise from zero to 63 milliamperes in 0.2 second after closing the switch.

An inductor cannot be "discharged" in the same way as a capacitor, because the magnetic field disappears as soon as current flow ceases. Opening S does not leave the inductor "charged." The energy stored in the magnetic field instantly returns to the circuit when S is opened. The rapid disappearance of the field causes a very large voltage to be induced in the coil – ordinarily many times larger than the voltage applied, because the induced voltage is proportional to the *speed* with which the field changes. The common result of opening the switch in a circuit such as the one shown is that a spark or arc forms at the switch contacts at the instant of opening. If the inductance is large and the current in the circuit is high, a great deal of energy is released in a very short period of time. It is not at all unusual for the switch contacts to burn or melt under such circumstances. The spark or arc at the opened switch can be reduced or suppressed by connecting a suitable capacitor and resistor in series across the contacts.

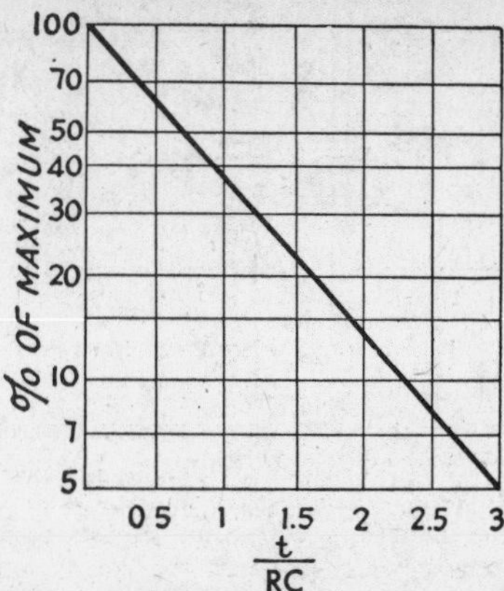

Fig. 2-22 – Voltage across capacitor terminals in a discharging RC circuit, in terms of the initial charged voltage. To obtain time in seconds, multiply the factor t/RC by the time constant of the circuit.

Time constants play an important part in numerous devices, such as electronic keys, timing and control circuits, and shaping of keying characteristics by vacuum tubes. The time constants of circuits are also important in such applications as automatic gain control and noise limiters. In nearly all such applications a resistance-capacitance (RC) time constant is involved, and it is usually necessary to know the voltage across the capacitor at some time interval larger or smaller than the actual time constant of the circuit as given by the formula above. Fig. 2-22 can be used for the solution of such problems, since the curve gives the voltage across the capacitor, in terms of percentage of the initial charge, for percentages between 5 and 100, at any time after discharge begins.

Example: A 0.01-μF capacitor is charged to 150 volts and then allowed to discharge through a 0.1-megohm resistor. How long will it take the voltage to fall to 10 volts? In percentage, 10/150 = 6.7%. From the chart, the factor corresponding to 6.7% is 2.7. The time constant of the circuit is equal to RC = 0.1 X .01 = .001. The time is therefore 2.7 X 0.001 = .0027 second, or 2.7 milliseconds.

ALTERNATING CURRENTS

PHASE

The term **phase** essentially means "time," or the *time interval* between the instant when one thing occurs and the instant when a second related thing takes place. The later event is said to *lag* the earlier, while the one that occurs first is said to *lead*. In ac circuits the current amplitude changes continuously, so the concept of phase or time becomes important. Phase can be measured in the ordinary time units, such as the second, but there is a more convenient method: Since each ac cycle occupies exactly the same amount of time as every other cycle of the same frequency, we can use the cycle itself as the time unit. Using the cycle as the time unit makes the specification or measurement of phase independent of the frequency of the current, so long as only one frequency is under consideration at a time. When two or more frequencies are to be considered, as in the case where harmonics are present, the phase measurements are made with respect to the lowest, or fundamental, frequency.

The time interval or "phase difference" under consideration usually will be less than one cycle. Phase difference could be measured in decimal parts of a cycle, but it is more convenient to divide the cycle into 360 parts or **degrees**. A phase degree is therefore 1/360 of a cycle. The reason for this choice is that with sine-wave alternating current the value of the current at any instant is proportional to the sine of the angle that corresponds to the number of degrees – that is, length of time – from the instant the cycle began. There is no actual "angle" associated with an alternating current. Fig. 2-23 should help make this method of measurement clear.

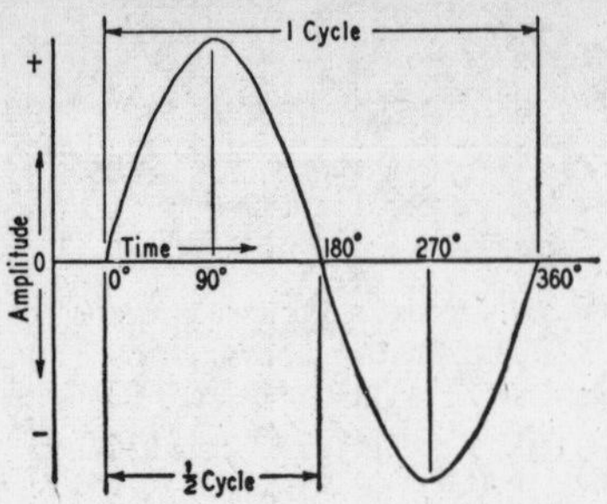

Fig. 2-23 – An ac cycle is divided off into 360 degrees that are used as a measure of time or phase.

Measuring Phase

The phase difference between two currents of the same frequency is the time or angle difference between corresponding parts of cycles of the two currents. This is shown in Fig. 2-24. The current labeled *A* leads the one marked *B* by 45 degrees, since *A*'s cycles begin 45 degrees earlier in time. It is equally correct to say that *B lags A* by 45 degrees.

Two important special cases are shown in Fig. 2-25. In the upper drawing *B* lags 90 degrees behind *A*; that is, its cycle begins just one-quarter cycle later than that of *A*. When one wave is passing through zero, the other is just at its maximum point.

In the lower drawing *A* and *B* are 180 degrees out of phase. In this case it does not matter which one is considered to lead or lag. *B* is always positive while *A* is negative, and vice versa. The two waves are thus *completely* out of phase.

The waves shown in Figs. 2-24 and 2-25 could represent current, voltage, or both. *A* and *B* might be two currents in separate circuits, or *A* might represent voltage and *B* current in the same circuit. If *A* and *B* represent two currents in the *same* circuit (or two voltages in the same circuit) the total or **resultant** current (or voltage) also is a sine wave, because adding any number of sine waves of the same frequency always gives a sine wave also of the same frequency.

Phase in Resistive Circuits

When an alternating voltage is applied to a resistance, the current flows exactly in step with the voltage. In other words, the voltage and current are **in phase**. This is true at any frequency if the resistance is "pure" – that is, is free from the reactive effects discussed in the next section. Practically, it is often difficult to obtain a purely resistive circuit at radio frequencies, because the reactive effects become more pronounced as the frequency is increased.

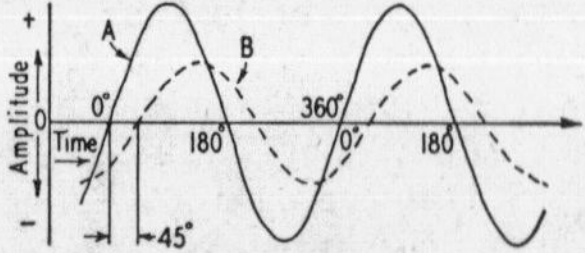

Fig. 2-24 – When two waves of the same frequency start their cycles at slightly different times, the time difference or phase difference is measured in degrees. In this drawing wave *B* starts 45 degrees (one-eighth cycle) later than wave *A*, and so lags 45 degrees behind *A*.

In a purely resistive circuit, or for purely resistive parts of circuits, Ohm's Law is just as valid for ac of any frequency as it is for dc.

REACTANCE

Alternating Current in Capacitance

In Fig. 2-26 a sine-wave ac voltage having a maximum value of 100 volts is applied to a capacitor. In the period *OA*, the applied voltage increases from zero to 38 volts; at the end of this period the capacitor is charged to that voltage. In interval *AB* the voltage increases to 71 volts; that is, 33 volts additional. In this interval a *smaller* quantity of charge has been added than in *OA*, because the voltage rise during interval *AB* is smaller. Consequently the average current during

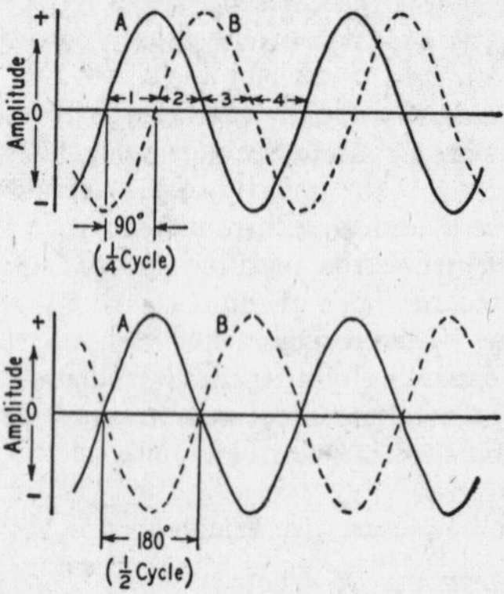

Fig. 2-25 – Two important special cases of phase difference. In the upper drawing, the phase difference between *A* and *B* is 90 degrees; in the lower drawing the phase difference is 180 degrees.

AB is smaller than during *OA*. In the third interval, *BC*, the voltage rises from 71 to 92 volts, an increase of 21 volts. This is less than the voltage increase during *AB*, so the quantity of electricity added is less; in other words, the average current during interval *BC* is still smaller. In the fourth interval, *CB*, the voltage increases only 8 volts; the charge added is smaller than in any preceding interval and therefore the current also is smaller.

By dividing the first quarter cycle into a very large number of intervals it could be shown that the current charging the capacitor has the shape of a sine wave, just as the applied voltage does. The current is largest at the beginning of the cycle and becomes zero at the maximum value of the voltage, so there is a phase difference of 90 degrees between the voltage and current. During the first quarter cycle the current is flowing in the normal direction through the circuit, since the capacitor is being charged. Hence the current is positive, as indicated by the dashed line in Fig. 2-26.

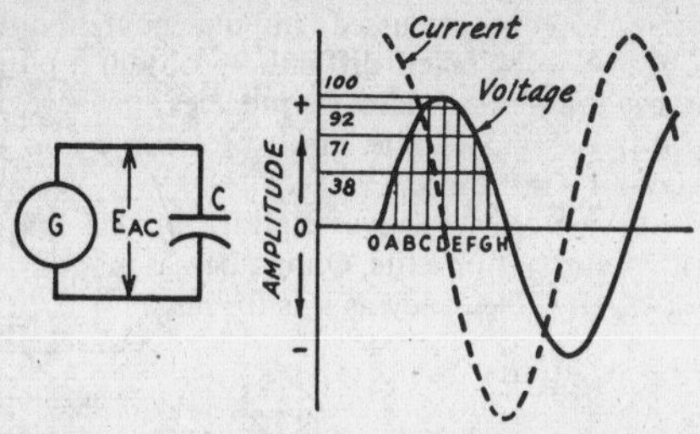

Fig. 2-26 – Voltage and current phase relationships when an alternating voltage is applied to a capacitor.

In the second quarter cycle – that is, in the time from D to H, the voltage applied to the capacitor decreases. During this time the capacitor *loses* its charge. Applying the same reasoning, it is plain that the current is small in interval DE and continues to increase during each succeeding interval. However, the current is flowing *against* the applied voltage because the capacitor is discharging into the circuit. The current flows in the *negative* direction during this quarter cycle.

The third and fourth quarter cycles repeat the events of the first and second, respectively, with this difference – the polarity of the applied voltage has reversed, and the current changes to correspond. In other words, an alternating current flows in the circuit because of the alternate charging and discharging of the capacitance. As shown by Fig. 2-26, the current starts its cycle 90 degrees before the voltage, so the current in a capacitor leads the applied voltage by 90 degrees.

Capacitive Reactance

The quantity of electric charge that can be placed on a capacitor is proportional to the applied emf and the capacitance. This amount of charge moves back and forth in the circuit once each cycle, and so the *rate* of movement of charge – that is, the current – is proportional to voltage, capacitance and frequency. If the effects of capacitance and frequency are lumped together, they form a quantity that plays a part similar to that of resistance in Ohm's Law. This quantity is called **reactance**, and the unit for it is the ohm, just as in the case of resistance. The formula for it is

$$X_C = \frac{1}{2\pi fC}$$

where X_C = Capacitive reactance in ohms
f = Frequency in cycles per second
C = Capacitance in farads
π = 3.14

Although the unit of reactance is the ohm, there is no power dissipation in reactance. The energy stored in the capacitor in one quarter of the cycle is simply returned to the circuit in the next.

The fundamental units (cycles per second, farads) are too large for practical use in radio circuits. However, if the capacitance is in microfarads and the frequency is in megacycles, the reactance will come out in ohms in the formula.

Example: The reactance of a capacitor of 470 pF (0.00047 μF) at a frequency of 7150 kHz (7.15 MHz) is

$$X = \frac{1}{2\pi fC} = \frac{1}{6.28 \times 7.15 \times .00047} = 47.4 \text{ ohms}$$

Inductive Reactance

When an alternating voltage is applied to a *pure* inductance (one with no resistance – all *practical* inductors have resistance) the current is again 90 degrees out of phase with the applied voltage. However, in this case the current *lags* 90 degrees behind the voltage – the opposite of the capacitor current-voltage relationship.

The primary cause for this is the *back emf* generated in the inductance, and since the amplitude of the back emf is proportional to the rate at which the current changes, and this in turn is proportional to the frequency, the amplitude of the current is inversely proportional to the applied frequency. Also, since the back emf is proportional to inductance for a given rate of current change, the current flow is inversely proportional to inductance for a given applied voltage and frequency. (Another way of saying this is that just enough current flows to generate an induced emf that equals and opposes the applied voltage.)

The combined effect of inductance and frequency is called **inductive reactance**, also expressed in ohms, and the formula for it is

$$X_L = 2\pi fL$$

where X_L = Inductive reactance in ohms
f = Frequency in cycles per second
L = Inductance in henrys
π = 3.14

Example: The reactance of a 15-microhenry coil at a frequency of 14 MHz is

$$X_L = 2\pi fL = 6.28 \times 14 \times 15 = 1319 \text{ ohms}$$

In radio-frequency circuits the inductance values usually are small and the frequencies are large. If the inductance is expressed in millihenrys and the frequency in kilocycles, the conversion factors for the two units cancel, and the formula for reactance may be used without first converting to fundamental units. Similarly, no conversion is necessary if the inductance is in microhenrys and the frequency is in megacycles.

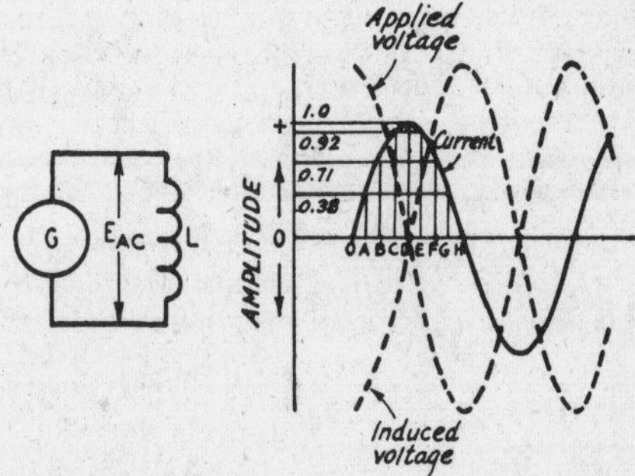

Fig. 2-27 – Phase relationships between voltage and current when an alternating voltage is applied to an inductance.

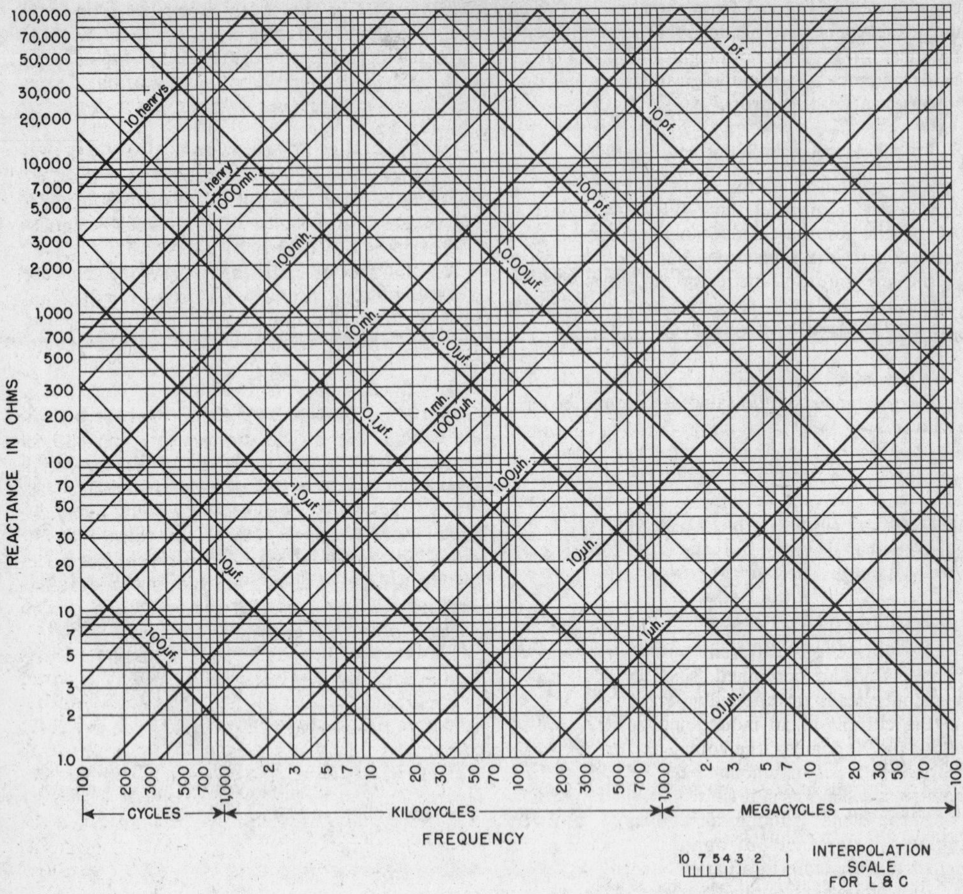

Fig. 2-28 — Inductive and capacitive reactance vs. frequency. Heavy lines represent multiples of 10, intermediate light lines multiples of 5; e.g., the light line between 10 µH and 100 µH represents 50 µH, the light line between 0.1 µF and 1 µF represents 0.5 µF, etc. Intermediate values can be estimated with the help of the interpolation scale.

Reactances outside the range of the chart may be found by applying appropriate factors to values within the chart range. For example, the reactance of 10 henrys at 60 cycles can be found by taking the reactance to 10 henrys at 600 cycles and dividing by 10 for the 10-times decrease in frequency.

Example: The reactance of a coil having an inductance of 8 henrys, at a frequency of 120 cycles, is

$$X_L = 2\pi f L = 6.28 \times 120 \times 8 = 6029 \text{ ohms}$$

The resistance of the wire of which the coil is wound has no effect on the reactance, but simply acts as though it were a separate resistor connected in series with the coil.

Ohm's Law for Reactance

Ohm's Law for an ac circuit containing *only* reactance is

$$I = \frac{E}{X}$$

$$E = IX$$

$$X = \frac{E}{I}$$

where E = Emf in volts
I = Current in amperes
X = Reactance in ohms

The reactance in the circuit may, of course, be either inductive or capacitive.

Example: If a current of 2 amperes is flowing through the capacitor of the earlier example (reactance = 47.4 ohms) at 7150 kHz, the voltage drop across the capacitor is

$$E = IX = 2 \times 47.4 = 94.8 \text{ volts}$$

If 400 volts at 120 hertz is applied to the 8-henry inductor of the earlier example, the current through the coil will be

$$I = \frac{E}{X} = \frac{420}{6029} = 0.0663 \text{ amp. (66.3 mA)}$$

Reactance Chart

The accompanying chart, Fig. 2-28, shows the reactance of capacitances from 1 pF to 100 µF, and the reactance of inductances from 0.1 µH to 10 henrys, for frequencies between 100 hertz and 100 megahertz per second. The approximate value of reactance can be read from the chart or, where more exact values are needed, the chart will serve as a check on the order of magnitude of reactances calculated from the formulas given above, and thus avoid "decimal-point errors."

Reactances in Series and Parallel

When reactances of the same kind are connected in series or parallel the resultant reactance is that of the resultant inductance or capacitance. This leads to the same rules that are used when determining the resultant resistance when resistors are combined. That is, for series reactances of the same kind the resultant reactance is

$$X = X1 + X2 + X3 + X4$$

and for reactances of the same kind in parallel the resultant is

$$X = \frac{1}{\frac{1}{X1} + \frac{1}{X2} + \frac{1}{X3} + \frac{1}{X4}}$$

or for two in parallel,

$$X = \frac{X1X2}{X1 + X2}$$

The situation is different when reactances of opposite kinds are combined. Since the current in a capacitance leads the applied voltage by 90 degrees and the current in an inductance lags the applied voltage by 90 degrees, the voltages at the terminals of opposite types of reactance are 180 degrees out of phase in a series circuit (in which the current has to be the same through all elements), and the currents in reactances of opposite types are 180 degrees out of phase in a parallel circuit (in which the same voltage is applied to all elements). The 180-degree phase relationship means that the currents or voltages are of opposite polarity, so in the series circuit of Fig. 2-29A the voltage *EL* across the inductive reactance *XL* is of opposite polarity to the voltage *EC* across the capacitive reactance *XC*. Thus if we call *XL* "positive" and *XC* "negative" (a common convention) the applied voltage *EAC* is *EL* – *EC*. In the parallel circuit at *B* the total current, *I*, is equal to *IL* – *IC*, since the currents are 180 degrees out of phase.

In the series case, therefore, the resultant reactance of *XL* and *XC* is

$$X = X_L - X_C$$

and in the parallel case

$$X = \frac{-X_L X_C}{X_L - X_C}$$

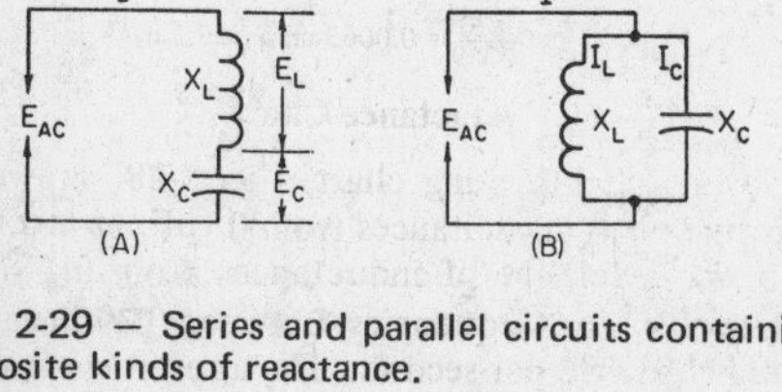

Fig. 2-29 – Series and parallel circuits containing opposite kinds of reactance.

Note that in the series circuit the total reactance is negative if *XC* is larger than *XL*; this indicates that the total reactance is capacitive in such a case. The resultant reactance in a series circuit is always smaller than the larger of the two individual reactances.

In the parallel circuit, the resultant reactance is negative (i.e., capacitive) if *XL* is larger than *XC*, and positive (inductive) if *XL* is smaller than *XC*, but in every case is always larger than the smaller of the two individual reactances.

In the special case where *XL* = *XC* the total reactance is zero in the series circuit and infinitely large in the parallel circuit.

Reactive Power

In Fig. 2-29A the voltage drop across the inductor is larger than the voltage applied to the circuit. This might seem to be an impossible condition, but it is not; the explanation is that while energy is being stored in the inductor's magnetic field, energy is being returned to the circuit from the capacitor's electric field, and vice versa. This stored energy is responsible for the fact that the voltages across reactances in series can be larger than the voltage applied to them.

In a resistance the flow of current causes heating and a power loss equal to I^2R. The power in a reactance is equal to I^2X, but is not a "loss"; it is simply power that is transferred back and forth between the field and the circuit but not used up in heating anything. To distinguish this "nondissipated" power from the power which is actually consumed, the unit of reactive power is called the **volt-ampere-reactive**, or **var**, instead of the watt. Reactive power is sometimes called "wattless" power.

IMPEDANCE

When a circuit contains both resistance and reactance the combined effect of the two is called **impedance**, symbolized by the letter *Z*. (Impedance is thus a more general term than either resistance or reactance, and is frequently used even for circuits that have only resistance or reactance, although usually with a qualification – such as "resistive impedance" to indicate that the circuit has only resistance, for example.)

The reactance and resistance comprising an impedance may be connected either in series or in parallel, as shown in Fig. 2-30. In these circuits the reactance is shown as a box to indicate that it may be either inductive or capacitive. In the series circuit the current is the same in both elements, with (generally) different voltages appearing across the resistance and reactance. In the parallel circuit the same voltage is applied to both elements, but different currents flow in the two branches.

Since in a resistance the current is in phase with the applied voltage while in a reactance it is 90 degrees out of phase with the voltage, the phase relationship between current and voltage in the circuit as a whole may be anything between zero and 90 degrees, depending on the relative amounts of resistance and reactance.

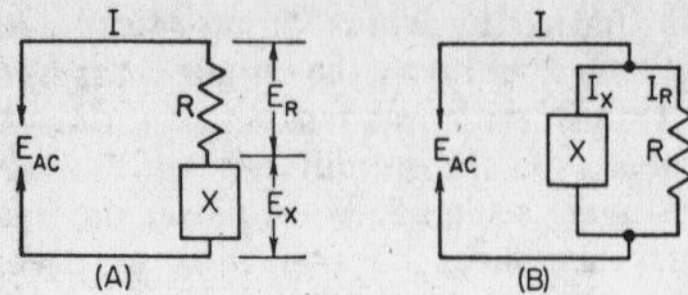

Fig. 2-30 – Series and parallel circuits containing resistance and reactance.

Series Circuits

When resistance and reactance are in series, the impedance of the circuit is

$$Z = \sqrt{R^2 + X^2}$$

where Z = Impedance in ohms
R = Resistance in ohms
X = Reactance in ohms

The reactance may be either capacitive or inductive. If there are two or more reactances in the circuit they may be combined into a resultant by the rules previously given, before substitution into the formula above; similarly for resistances.

The "square root of the sum of the squares" rule for finding impedance in a series circuit arises from the fact that the voltage drops across the resistance and reactance are 90 degrees out of phase, and so combine by the same rule that applies in finding the hypothenuse of a right-angled triangle when the base and altitude are known.

Parallel Circuits

With resistance and reactance in parallel, as in Fig. 2-30B, the impedance is

$$Z = \frac{RX}{\sqrt{R^2 + X^2}}$$

where the symbols have the same meaning as for series circuits.

Just as in the case of series circuits, a number of reactances in parallel should be combined to find the resultant reactance before substitution into the formal above; similarly for a number of resistances in parallel.

Equivalent Series and Parallel Circuits

The two circuits shown in Fig. 2-30 are equivalent if the same current flows when a given voltage of the same frequency is applied, and if the phase angle between voltage and current is the same in both cases. It is in fact possible to "transform" any given series circuit into an equivalent parallel circuit, and vice versa.

Transformations of this type often lead to simplification in the solution of complicated circuits. However, from the standpoint of practical work the usefulness of such transformations lies in the fact that the impedance of a circuit may be modified by the addition of *either* series or parallel elements, depending on which happens to be most convenient in the particular case. Typical applications are considered later in connection with tuned circuits and transmission lines.

Ohm's Law for Impedance

Ohm's Law can be applied to circuits containing impedance just as readily as to circuits having resistance or reactance only. The formulas are

$$I = \frac{E}{Z}$$

$$E = IZ$$

$$Z = \frac{E}{I}$$

where E = Emf in volts
I = Current in amperes
Z = Impedance in ohms

Fig. 2-31 shows a simple circuit consisting of a resistance of 75 ohms and a reactance of 100 ohms in series. From the formula previously given, the impedance is

$$Z = \sqrt{R^2 + X_L{}^2} = \sqrt{(75)^2 + (100)^2} = 125$$

If the applied voltage is 250 volts, then

$$I = \frac{E}{Z} = \frac{250}{125} = 2 \text{ amperes}$$

This current flows through both the resistance and reactance, so the voltage drops are

$$E_R = IR = 2 \times 75 = 150 \text{ volts}$$

$$E_{XL} = IX_L = 2 \times 100 = 200 \text{ volts}$$

The simple arithmetical sum of these two drops, 350 volts, is greater than the applied voltage because the two voltages are 90 degrees out of phase. Their actual resultant, when phase is taken into account, is

$$\sqrt{(150)^2 + (200)^2} = 250 \text{ volts}$$

Power Factor

In the circuit of Fig. 2-31 an applied emf of 250 volts results in a current of 2 amperes, giving an apparent power of 250 X 2 = 500 watts. However, only the resistance actually consumes power. The power in the resistance is

$$P = I^2R = (2)^2 \times 75 = 300 \text{ watts}$$

The ratio of the power consumed to the apparent power is called the **power factor** of the circuit, and in this example the power factor would be 300/500 = 0.6. Power factor is frequently expressed as a percentage; in this case, it would be 60 percent.

"Real" or dissipated power is measured in watts; apparent power, to distinguish it from real power, is measured in volt-amperes. It is simply the product of volts and amperes and has no direct relationship to the power actually used up or dissipated unless the power factor of the circuit is known. The power factor of a purely resistive circuit is 100 percent or 1, while the power factor of a pure reactance is zero. In this illustration, the reactive power is $VAR = I2X$ = (2)2 X 100 = 400 volt-amperes.

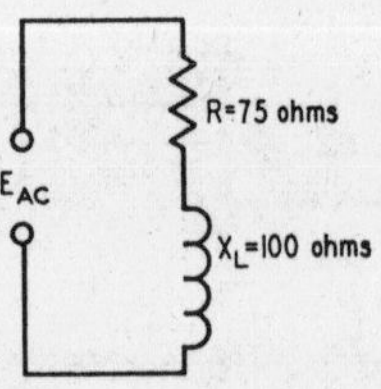

Fig. 2-31 – Circuit used as an example for impedance calculations.

Reactance and Complex Waves

It was pointed out earlier in this chapter that a complex wave (a "nonsinusoidal" wave) can be resolved into a fundamental frequency and a series of harmonic frequencies. When such a complex voltage wave is applied to a circuit containing reactance, the current through the circuit will not have the same wave shape as the applied voltage. This is because the reactance of an inductor and capacitor depend upon the applied frequency. For the second-harmonic component of a complex wave, the reactance of the inductor is twice and the reactance of the capacitor one-half their respective values at the fundamental frequency; for the third harmonic the inductor reactance is three times and the capacitor reactance one-third, and so on. Thus the circuit impedance is different for each harmonic component.

Just what happens to the current wave shape depends upon the values of resistance and reactance involved and how the circuit is arranged. In a simple circuit with resistance and inductive reactance in series, the amplitudes of the harmonic currents will be reduced because the inductive reactance increases in proportion to frequency. When capacitance and resistance are in series, the harmonic current is likely to be accentuated because the capacitive reactance becomes lower as the frequency is raised. When both inductive and capacitive reactance are present the shape of the current wave can be altered in a variety of ways, depending upon the circuit and the "constants," or the relative values of *L*, *C*, and *R*, selected.

This property of nonuniform behavior with respect to fundamental and harmonics is an extremely useful one. It is the basis of "filtering," or the suppression of undesired frequencies in favor of a single desired frequency or group of such frequencies.

TRANSFORMERS FOR AUDIO FREQUENCIES

Two coils having mutual inductance constitute a **transformer**. The coil connected to the source of energy is called the **primary** coil, and the other is called the **secondary** coil.

The usefulness of the transformer lies in the fact that electrical energy can be transferred from one circuit to another without direct connection, and in the process can be readily changed from one voltage level to another. Thus, if a device to be operated requires, for example, 115 volts ac and only a 440-volt source is available, a transformer can be used to change the source voltage to that required. A transformer can be used only with ac, since no voltage will be induced in the secondary if the magnetic field is not changing. If dc is applied to the primary of a transformer, a voltage will be induced in the secondary only at the instant of closing or opening the primary circuit, since it is only at these times that the field is changing.

THE IRON-CORE TRANSFORMER

As shown in Fig. 2-32, the primary and secondary coils of a transformer may be wound on a core of magnetic material. This increases the inductance of the coils so that a relatively small number of turns may be used to induce a given value of voltage with a small current. A **closed core** (one having a continuous magnetic path) such as that shown in Fig. 2-32 also tends to insure that practically all of the field set up by the current in the primary coil will cut the turns of the secondary coil. However, the core introduces a power loss because of hysteresis and eddy currents so this type of construction is normally practicable only at power and audio frequencies. The discussion in this section is confined to transformers operating at such frequencies.

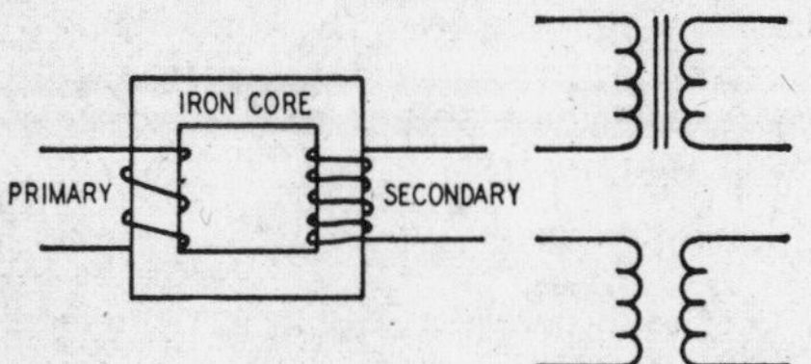

Fig. 2-32 — The transformer. Power is transferred from the primary coil to the secondary by means of the magnetic field. The upper symbol at right indicates an iron-core transformer, the lower one an air-core transformer.

Voltage and Turns Ratio

For a given varying magnetic field, the voltage induced in a coil in the field will be proportional to the number of turns in the coil. If the two coils of a transformer are in the same field (which is the case when both are wound on the same closed core) it follows that the induced voltages will be proportional to the number of turns in each coil. In the primary the induced voltage is practically equal to, and opposes, the applied voltage, as described earlier. Hence,

$$E_s = \frac{n_s}{n_p} E_p$$

where E_s = Secondary voltage
E_p = Primary applied voltage
n_s = Number of turns on secondary
n_p = Number of turns on primary

The ratio, ns/np is called the secondary-to-primary **turns ratio** of the transformer.

Example: A transformer has a primary of 400 turns and a secondary of 2800 turns, and an emf of 115 volts is applied to the primary.

$$E_s = \frac{n_s}{n_p} E_p = \frac{2800}{400} \times 115 = 7 \times 115$$
$$= 805 \text{ volts}$$

Also, if an emf of 805 volts is applied to the 2800-turn winding (which then becomes the primary) the output voltage from the 400-turn winding will be 115 volts.

Either winding of a transformer can be used as the primary, providing the winding has enough turns (enough inductance) to induce a voltage equal to the applied voltage without requiring an excessive current flow.

Effect of Secondary Current

The current that flows in the primary when no current is taken from the secondary is called the **magnetizing current** of the transformer. In any properly-designed transformer the primary inductance will be so large that the magnetizing current will be quite small. The power consumed by the transformer when the secondary is "open" – that is, not delivering power – is only the amount necessary to supply the losses in the iron core and in the resistance of the wire with which the primary is wound.

When power is taken from the secondary winding, the secondary current sets up a magnetic field that opposes the field set up by the primary current. But if the induced voltage in the primary is to equal the applied voltage, the original field must be maintained. Consequently, the primary must draw enough additional current to set up a field exactly equal and opposite to the field set up by the secondary current.

In practical calculations on transformers it may be assumed that the entire primary current is caused by the secondary "load." This is justifiable because the magnetizing current should be very small in comparison with the primary "load" current at rated power output.

If the magnetic fields set up by the primary and secondary currents are to be equal, the primary current multiplied by the primary turns must equal the secondary current multiplied by the secondary turns. From this it follows that

$$I_p = \frac{n_s}{n_p} I_s$$

where I_p = Primary current
I_s = Secondary current
n_p = Number of turns on primary
n_s = Number of turns on secondary

Example: Suppose that the secondary of the transformer in the previous example is delivering a current of 0.2 ampere to a load. Then the primary current will be

$$I_p = \frac{n_s}{n_p} I_s = \frac{2800}{400} \times 0.2 = 7 \times 0.2 = 1.4 \text{ amp.}$$

Although the secondary voltage is higher than the primary voltage, the secondary *current* is *lower* than the primary current, and by the same ratio.

Power Relationships; Efficiency

A transformer cannot create power; it can only transfer it and change the emf. Hence, the power taken from the secondary cannot exceed that taken by the primary from the source of applied emf. There is always some power loss in the resistance of the coils and in the iron core, so in all practical cases the power taken from the source will exceed that taken from the secondary. Thus,

$$P_o = nP_i$$

where P_o = Power output from secondary
P_i = Power input to primary
n = Efficiency factor

The efficiency, n, always is less than 1. It is usually expressed as a percentage; if n is 0.65, for instances, the efficiency is 65 percent.

Example: A transformer has an efficiency of 85 percent at its full-load output of 150 watts. The power input to the primary at full secondary load will be

$$P_i = \frac{P_o}{n} = \frac{150}{0.85} = 176.5 \text{ watts}$$

A transformer is usually designed to have its highest efficiency at the power output for which it is rated. The efficiency decreases with either lower or higher outputs. On the other hand, the *losses* in the transformer are relatively small at low output but increase as more power is taken. The amount of power that the transformer can handle is determined by its own losses, because these heat the wire and core. There is a limit to the temperature rise that can be tolerated, because too-high temperature either will melt the wire or cause the insulation to break down. A transformer can be operated a reduced output, even though the efficiency is low,because the actual loss will be low under such conditions.

The full-load efficiency of small power transformers such as are used in radio receivers and transmitters usually lies between about 60 and 90 percent, depending upon the size and design.

Leakage Reactance

In a practical transformer not all of the magnetic flux is common to both windings, although in well-designed transformers the amount of flux that "cuts" one coil and not the other is only a small percentage of the total flux. This **leakage flux** causes an emf of self-induction; consequently, there are small amounts of **leakage inductance** associated with both windings of the transformer. Leakage inductance acts in exactly the same way as an equivalent amount of ordinary inductance inserted in series with the circuit. It has, therefore, a certain reactance, depending upon the amount of leakage inductance and the frequency. This reactance is called **leakage reactance**.

Current flowing through the leakage reactance causes a voltage drop. This voltage drop increases with increasing current, hence it increases as more power is taken from the secondary. Thus, the greater the secondary current, the smaller the secondary terminal voltage becomes. The resistances of the transformer windings also cause voltage drops when current is flowing; although these voltage drops are not in phase with those caused by leakage reactance, together they result in a lower secondary voltage under load than is indicated by the turns ratio of the transformer.

At power frequencies (60 cycles) the voltage at the secondary, with a reasonably well-designed transformer, should not drop more than about 10 percent from open-circuit conditions to full load. The drop in voltage may be considerably more than this in a transformer operating at audio frequencies because the leakage reactance increases directly with the frequency.

Impedance Ratio

In an ideal transformer – one without losses or leakage reactance – the following relationship is true:

$$Z_p = Z_s \left[\frac{N_p}{N_s}\right]^2$$

where Z_p = Impedance looking into primary terminals from source of power
Z_s Impedance of load connected to secondary
N_p/N_s = Turns ratio, primary to secondary

That is, a load of any given impedance connected to the secondary of the transformer will be transformed to a different value "looking into" the primary from the source of power. The impedance transformation is proportional to the square of the primary-to-secondary turns ratio.

Example: A transformer has a primary-to-secondary turns ratio of 0.6 (primary has 6/10 as many turns as the secondary) and a load of 3000 ohms is connected to the secondary. The impedance looking into the primary then will be

$$Z_p = Z_s\left[\frac{N_p}{N_s}\right] = 3000 \times (0.6)^2 = 3000 \times 0.36$$
$$= 1080 \text{ ohms}$$

By choosing the proper turns ratio, the impedance of a fixed load can be transformed to any desired value, within practical limits. If transformer losses can be neglected, the transformed or "reflected" impedance has the same phase angle as the actual load impedance; thus if the load is a pure resistance the load presented by the primary to the source of power also will be a pure resistance.

The above relationship may be used in practical work even though it is based on an "ideal" transformer. Aside from the normal design requirements of reasonably low internal losses and low leakage reactance, the only requirement is that the primary have enough inductance to operate with low magnetizing current at the voltage applied to the primary.

The primary impedance of a transformer – *as it appears to the source of power* – is determined wholly by the load connected to the secondary and by the turns ratio. If the characteristics of the transformer have an appreciable effect on the impedance presented to the power source, the transformer is either poorly designed or is not suited to the voltage and frequency at which it is being used. Most transformers will operate quite well at voltages from slightly above to well below the design figure.

Impedance Matching

Many devices require a specific value of load resistance (or impedance) for optimum operation.

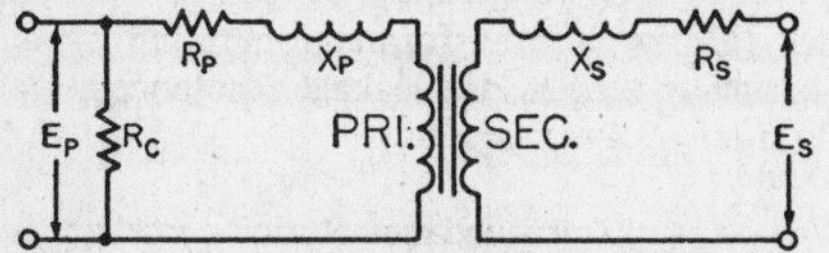

Fig. 2-33 – The equivalent circuit of a transformer includes the effects of leakage inductance and resistance of both primary and secondary windings. The resistance R_c is an equivalent resistance representing the core losses, which are essentially constant for any given applied voltage and frequency. Since these are comparatively small, their effect may be neglected in many approximate calculations.

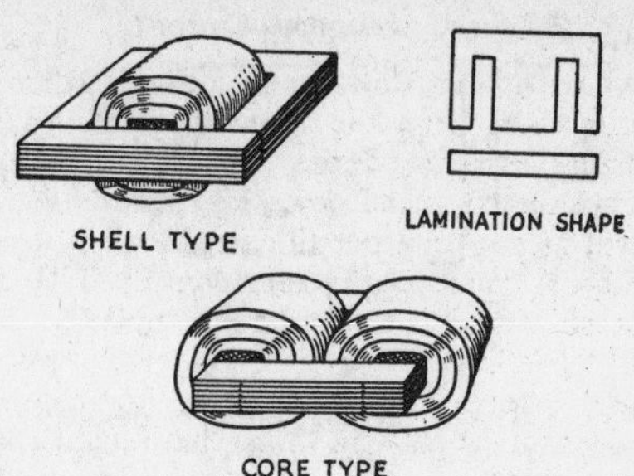

Fig. 2-34 – Two common types of transformer construction. Core pieces are interleaved to provide a continuous magnetic path.

The impedance of the actual load that is to dissipate the power may differ widely from this value, so a transformer is used to change the actual load into an impedance of the desired value. This is called **impedance matching**. From the preceding,

$$\frac{N_p}{N_s} = \sqrt{\frac{Z_p}{Z_s}}$$

where N_p/N_s = Required turns ratio, primary to secondary
Z_p = Primary impedance required
Z_s = Impedance of load connected to secondary

Example: A vacuum-tube af amplifier requires a load of 5000 ohms for optimum performance, and is to be connected to a loud-speaker having an impedance of 10 ohms. The turns ratio, primary to secondary, required in the coupling transformer is

$$\frac{N_p}{N_s} = \sqrt{\frac{Z_p}{Z_s}} = \sqrt{\frac{5000}{10}} = \sqrt{500} = 22.4$$

The primary therefore must have 22.4 times as many turns as the secondary.

Impedance matching means, in general, adjusting the load impedance – by means of a transformer or otherwise – to a desired value. However, there is also another meaning. It is possible to show that any source of power will deliver its maximum possible output when the impedance of the load is equal to the internal impedance of the source. The impedance of the source is said to be "matched" under this condition. The efficiency is only 50 percent in such a case; just as much power is used up in the source as is delivered to the load. Because of the poor efficiency, this type of impedance matching is limited to cases where only a small amount of power is available and heating from power loss in the source is not important.

Transformer Construction

Transformers usually are designed so that the magnetic path around the core is as short as possible. A short magnetic path means that the transformer will operate with fewer turns, for a given applied voltage, than if the path were long. A short path also helps to reduce flux leakage and therefore minimizes leakage reactance.

Two core shapes are in common use, as shown in Fig. 2-34. In the shell type both windings are placed on the inner leg, while in the core type the

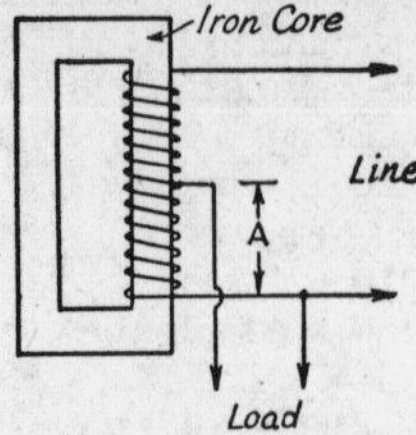

Fig. 2-35 – The autotransformer is based on the transformer principle, but uses only one winding. The line and load currents in the common winding *(A)* flow in opposite directions, so that the resultant current is the difference between them. The voltage across A is proportional to the turns ratio.

primary and secondary windings may be placed on separate legs, if desired. This is sometimes done when it is necessary to minimize capacitive effects between the primary and secondary, or when one of the windings must operate at very high voltage.

Core material for small transformers is usually silicon steel, called "transformer iron." The core is built up of laminations, insulated from each other (by a thin coating of shellac, for example) to prevent the flow of eddy currents. The laminations are interleaved at the ends to make the magnetic path as continuous as possible and thus reduce flux leakage.

The number of turns required in the primary for a given applied emf is determined by the size, shape and type of core material used, and the frequency. The number of turns required is inversely proportional to the cross-sectional area of the core. As a rough indication, windings of small power transformers frequently have about six to eight turns per volt on a core of 1-square-inch cross section and have a magnetic path 10 or 12 inches in length. A longer path or smaller cross section requires more turns per volt, and vice versa.

In most transformers the coils are wound in layers, with a thin sheet of treated-paper insulation between each layer. Thicker insulation is used between coils and between coils and core.

Autotransformers

The transformer principle can be utilized with only one winding instead of two, as shown in Fig. 2-35; the principles just discussed apply equally well. A one-winding transformer is called an **autotransformer**. The current in the common section (A) of the winding is the difference between the line (primary) and the load (secondary) currents, since these currents are out of phase. Hence if the line and load currents are nearly equal the common section of the winding may be wound with comparatively small wire. This will be the case only when the primary (line) and secondary (load) voltages are not very different. The autotransformer is used chiefly for boosting or reducing the power-line voltage by relatively small amounts. Continuously-variable autotransformers are commercially available under a variety of trade names; "Variac" and "Powerstat" are typical examples.

THE DECIBEL

In most radio communication the received signal is converted into sound. This being the case, it is useful to appraise signal strengths in terms of relative loudness as registered by the ear. A peculiarity of the ear is that an increase or decrease in loudness is responsive to the *ratio* of the amounts of power involved, and is practically independent of absolute value of the power. For example, if a person estimates that the signal is "twice as loud" when the transmitter power is increased from 10 watts to 40 watts, he will also estimate that a 400-watt signal is twice as loud as a 100-watt signal. In other words, the human ear has a *logarithmic* response.

This fact is the basis for the use of the relative-power unit called the **decibel** (abbreviated **dB**). A change of one decibel in the power level is just detectable as a change in loudness under ideal conditions. The number of decibels corresponding to a given power ratio is given by the following formula:

$$dB = 10 \log \frac{P_2}{P_1}$$

Common logarithms (base 10) are used.

Voltage and Current Ratios

Note that the decibel is based on *power* ratios. Voltage or current ratios can be used, but only when the impedance is the same for both values of voltage, or current. The gain of an amplifier cannot be expressed correctly in dB if it is based on the ratio of the output voltage to the input voltage unless both voltages are measured across the same value of impedance. When the impedance at both points of measurement is the same, the following formula may be used for voltage or current ratios:

$$dB = 20 \log \frac{V_2}{V_1} \quad \text{or } 20 \log \frac{I_2}{I_1}$$

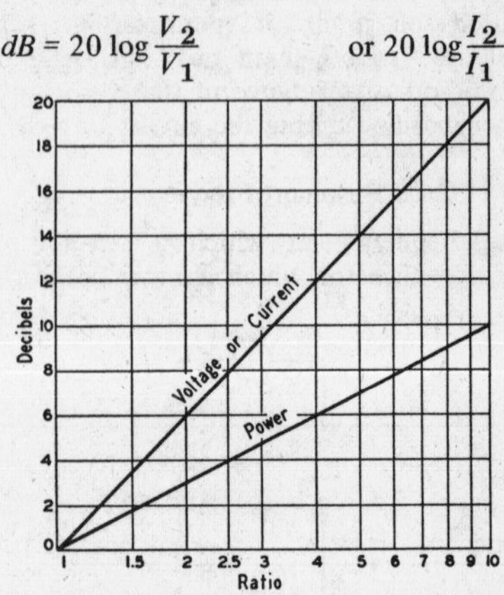

Fig. 2-36 – Decibel chart for power, voltage and current ratios for power ratios of 1:1 and 10:1. In determining decibels for current or voltage ratios the currents (or voltages) being compared must be referred to the same value of impedance.

Decibel Chart

The two formulas are shown graphically in Fig. 2-36 for ratios from 1 to 10. Gains (increases) expressed in decibels may be added arithmetically; losses (decreases) may be subtracted. A power decrease is indicated by prefixing the decibel figure with a minus sign. Thus +6 dB means that the power has been multiplied by 4, while −6 dB means that the power has been divided by 4.

The chart may be used for other ratios by adding (or subtracting, if a loss) 10 dB each time the ratio scale is multiplied by 10, for power ratios; or by adding (or subtracting) 20 dB each time the scale is multiplied by 10 for voltage or current ratios. For example, a power ratio of 2.5 is 4 dB (from the chart). A power ratio of 10 times 2.5, or 25, is 14 dB (10 + 4), and a power ratio of 100 times 2.5, or 250, is 24 dB (20 + 4). A voltage or current ratio of 4 is 12 dB, a voltage or current ratio of 40 is 32 dB (20 + 12), and one of 400 is 52 dB (40 + 12).

RADIO-FREQUENCY CIRCUITS

RESONANCE IN SERIES CIRCUITS

Fig. 2-37 shows a resistor, capacitor and inductor connected in series with a source of alternating current, the frequency of which can be varied over a wide range. At some *low* frequency the capacitive reactance will be much larger than the resistance of R, and the inductive reactance will be small compared with either the reactance of C or the resistance of R. (R is assumed to be the same at all frequencies.) On the other hand, at some very *high* frequency the reactance of C will be very small and the reactance of L will be very large. In either case the current will be small, because the net reactance is large.

At some intermediate frequency, the reactances of C and L will be equal and the voltage drops across the coil and capacitor will be equal and 180 degrees out of phase. Therefore they cancel each other completely and the current flow is determined wholly by the resistance, R. At that frequency the current has its largest possible value, assuming the source voltage to be constant regardless of frequency. A series circuit in which the inductive and capacitive reactances are equal is said to be **resonant.**

The principle of resonance finds its most extensive application in radio-frequency circuits. The reactive effects associated with even small inductances and capacitances would place drastic limitations on rf circuit operation if it were not possible to "cancel them out" by supplying the right amount of reactance of the opposite kind – in other words, "tuning the circuit to resonance."

Resonant Frequency

The frequency at which a series circuit is resonant is that for which $XL = XC$. Substituting the formulas for inductive and capacitive reactance gives

$$f = \frac{1}{2\pi\sqrt{LC}}$$

where f = Frequency in cycles per second
L = Inductance in henrys
C = Capacitance in farads
π = 3.14

These units are inconveniently large for radio-frequency circuits. A formula using more appropriate units is

$$f = \frac{10^6}{2\pi\sqrt{LC}}$$

where f = Frequency in kilohertz (kHz)
L = Inductance in microhenrys (μH)
C = Capacitance in picofarads (pF)
π = 3.14

Example: The resonant frequency of a series circuit containing a 5-μH inductor and a 35-pF capacitor is

$$f = \frac{10^6}{2\pi\sqrt{LC}} = \frac{10^6}{6.28 \times \sqrt{5 \times 35}}$$

$$= \frac{10^6}{6.28 \times 13.2} = \frac{10^6}{83} = 12{,}050 \text{ kHz}$$

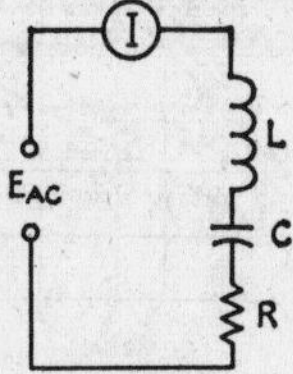

Fig. 2-37 – A series circuit containing L, C and R is "resonant" at the applied frequency when the reactance of C is equal to the reactance of L.

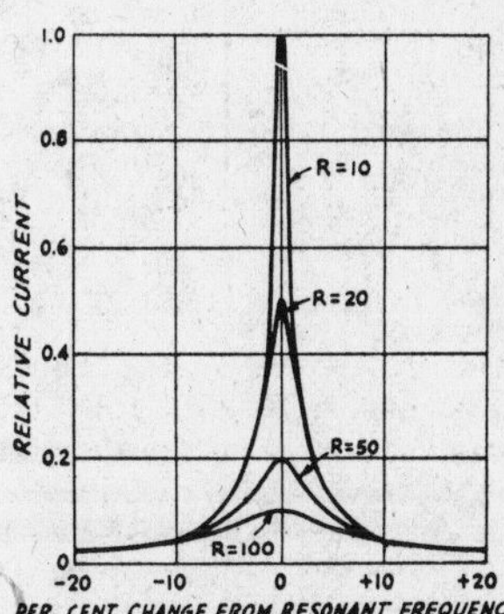

Fig. 2-38 – Current in a series-resonant circuit with various values of series resistance. The values are arbitrary and would not apply to all circuits, but represent a typical case. It is assumed that the reactances (at the resonant frequency) are 1000 ohms. Note that at frequencies more than plus or minus ten percent away from the resonant frequency the current is substantially unaffected by the resistance in the circuit.

The formula for resonant frequency is not affected by resistance in the circuit.

Resonance Curves

If a plot is drawn on the current flowing in the circuit of Fig. 2-37 as the frequency is varied (the applied voltage being constant) it would look like one of the curves in Fig. 2-38. The shape of the **resonance curve** at frequencies near resonance is determined by the ratio of reactance to resistance.

If the reactance of either the coil or capacitor is of the same order of magnitude as the resistance, the current decreases rather slowly as the frequency is moved in either direction away from resonance. Such a curve is said to be **broad**. On the other hand, if the reactance is considerably larger than the resistance the current decreases rapidly as the frequency moves away from resonance and the circuit is said to be **sharp**. A sharp circuit will respond a great deal more readily to the resonant frequency than to frequencies quite close to resonance; a broad circuit will respond almost equally well to a group or band of frequencies centering around the resonant frequency.

Both types of resonance curves are useful. A sharp circuit gives good **selectivity** – the ability to respond strongly (in terms of current amplitude) at one desired frequency and discriminate against others. A broad circuit is used when the apparatus must give about the same response over a band of frequencies rather than to a single frequency alone.

Q

Most diagrams of resonant circuits show only inductance and capacitance; no resistance is indicated. Nevertheless, resistance is always present. At frequencies up to perhaps 30 MHz this resistance is mostly in the wire of the coil. Above this frequency energy loss in the capacitor (principally in the solid dielectric which must be used to form an insulating support for the capacitor plates) also becomes a factor. This energy loss is equivalent to resistance. When maximum sharpness or selectivity is needed the object of design is to reduce the inherent resistance to the lowest possible value.

The value of the reactance of either the inductor or capacitor at the resonant frequency of a series-resonant circuit, divided by the *series* resistance in the circuit, is called the Q (quality factor) of the circuit, or

$$Q = \frac{X}{r}$$

where Q = Quality factor
X = Reactance of either coil or capacitor in ohms
r = Series resistance in ohms

Example: The inductor and capacitor in a series circuit each have a reactance of 350 ohms at the resonant frequency. The resistance is 5 ohms. Then the Q is

$$Q = \frac{X}{r} = \frac{350}{5} = 70$$

The effect of Q on the sharpness of resonance of a circuit is shown by the curves of Fig. 2-39. In these curves the frequency change is shown in percentage above and below the resonant frequency. Qs of 10, 20, 50 and 100 are shown; these values cover much of the range commonly used in radio work. The **unloaded Q** of a circuit is determined by the inherent resistances associated with the components.

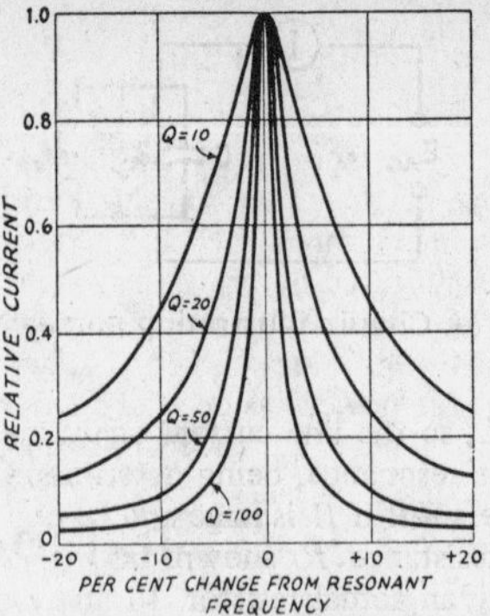

Fig. 2-39 – Current in series-resonant circuits having different Qs. In this graph the current at resonance is assumed to be the same in all cases. The lower the Q, the more slowly the current decreases as the applied frequency is moved away from resonance.

Voltage Rise at Resonance

When a voltage of the resonant frequency is inserted in series in a resonant circuit, the voltage that appears across either the inductor or capacitor is considerably higher than the applied voltage. The current in the circuit is limited only by the resistance and may have a relatively high value; however, the same current flows through the high reactances of the inductor and capacitor and causes large voltage drops. The ratio of the reactive voltage to the applied voltage is equal to the ratio of reactance to resistance. This ratio is also the Q of the circuit. Therefore, the voltage across either the inductor or capacitor is equal to QE where E is the voltage inserted in series. This fact accounts for the high voltages developed across the components of series-tuned antenna couplers (see chapter on "Transmission Lines").

RESONANCE IN PARALLEL CIRCUITS

When a variable-frequency source of constant voltage is applied to a parallel circuit of the type shown in Fig. 2-40 there is a resonance effect similar to that in a series circuit. However, in this case the "line" current (measured at the point indicated) is *smallest* at the frequency for which the inductive and capacitive reactances are equal. At that frequency the current through L is exactly canceled by the out-of-phase current through C, so that only the current taken by R flows in the line. At frequencies *below* resonance the current through L is larger than that through C, because the reactance of L is smaller and that of C higher at low frequencies; there is only partial cancellation of the two reactive currents and the line current therefore is larger than the current taken by R alone. At frequencies *above* resonance the situation is reversed and more current flows through C than

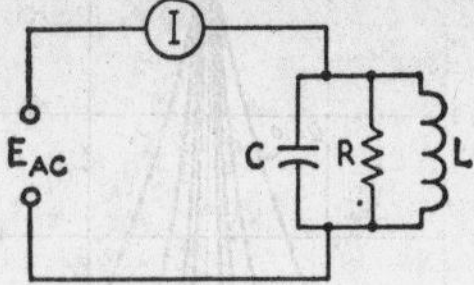

Fig. 2-40 – Circuit illustrating parallel resonance.

through L, so the line current again increases. The current at resonance, being determined wholly by R, will be small if R is large and large if R is small.

The resistance R shown in Fig. 2-40 is not necessarily an actual resistor. In many cases it will be the series resistance of the coil "transformed" to an equivalent parallel resistance (see later). It may be antenna or other load resistance coupled into the tuned circuit. In all cases it represents the total effective resistance in the circuit.

Parallel and series resonant circuits are quite alike in some respects. For instance, the circuits given at A and B in Fig. 2-41 will behave identically, when an external voltage is applied, if (1) L and C are the same in both cases; and (2) R multiplied by r, equals the square of the reactance (at resonance) of either L or C. When these conditions are met the two circuits will have the same Q. (These statements are approximate, but are quite accurate if the Q is 10 or more.) The circuit at A is a *series* circuit if it is viewed from the "inside" – that is, going around the loop formed by L, C and r – so its Q can be found from the ratio of X to r.

Thus a circuit like that of Fig. 2-41A has an equivalent **parallel impedance** (at resonance) of $R = \frac{X^2}{r}$; X is the reactance of either the inductor or the capacitor. Although R is not an actual resistor, to the source of voltage the parallel-resonant circuit "looks like" a pure resistance of that value. It is "pure" resistance because the inductive and capacitive currents are 180 degrees out of phase and are equal; thus there is no reactive current in the line. In a practical circuit with a high-Q capacitor, at the resonant frequency the parallel impedance is

$$Z_r = QX$$

where Z_r = Resistive impedance at resonance
Q = Quality factor of inductor
X = Reactance (in ohms) of either the inductor or capacitor

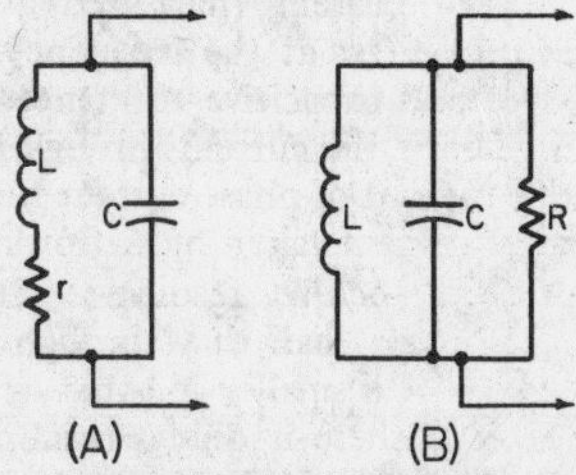

Fig. 2-41 – Series and parallel equivalents when the two circuits are resonant. The series resistance, r, in A is replaced in B by the equivalent parallel resistance $(R = X^2_C/r = X^2_L/r)$ and vice versa.

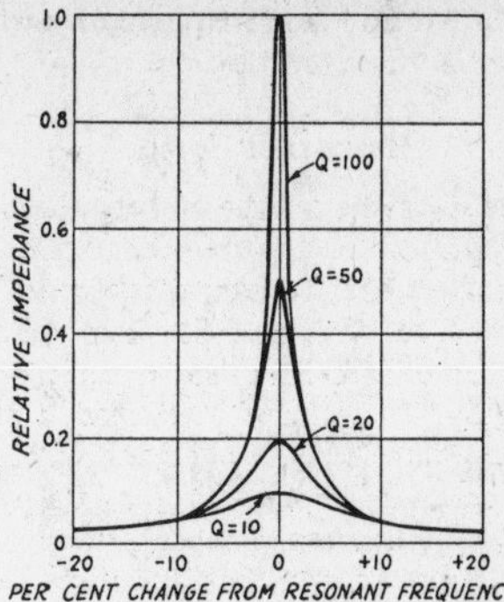

Fig. 2-42 – Relative impedance of parallel-resonant circuits with different Qs. These curves are similar to those in Fig. 2-39 for current in a series-resonant circuit. The effect of Q on impedance is most marked near the resonant frequency.

Example: The parallel impedance of a circuit with a coil Q of 50 and having inductive and capacitive reactance of 300 ohms will be

$$Z_r = QX = 50 \times 300 = 15{,}000 \text{ ohms}$$

At frequencies off resonance the impedance is no longer purely resistive because the inductive and capacitive currents are not equal. The off-resonant impedance therefore is complex, and is lower than the resonant impedance for the reasons previously outlined.

The higher the Q of the circuit, the higher the parallel impedance. Curves showing the variation of impedance (with frequency) of a parallel circuit have just the same shape as the curves showing the variation of current with frequency in a series circuit. Fig. 2-42 is a set of such curves. A set of curves showing the relative response as a function of the departure from the resonant frequency would be similar to Fig. 2-39. The –3 dB bandwidth (bandwidth at 0.707 relative response) is given by

$$\textit{Bandwidth} \ -3 \text{ dB} = f_o/Q$$

where fo is the resonant frequency and Q the circuit Q. It is also called the "half-power" bandwidth, for ease of recollection.

Parallel Resonance in Low-Q Circuits

The preceding discussion is accurate only for Qs of 10 or more. When the Q is below 10, resonance in a parallel circuit having resistance in series with the coil, as in Fig. 2-41A, is not so easily defined. There is a set of values for L and C that will make the parallel impedance a pure resistance, but with these values the impedance does not have its maximum possible value. Another set of values for L and C will make the parallel impedance a maximum, but this maximum value is not a pure resistance. Either condition could be called "resonance," so with low-Q circuits it is necessary to distinguish between **maximum impedance** and **resistive impedance** parallel resonance. The difference between these L and C values and the equal reactances of a series-resonant circuit is appreciable when the Q is in the vicinity of 5, and becomes more marked with still lower Q values.

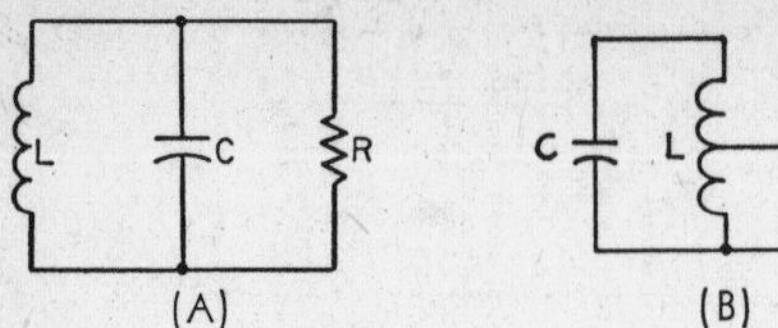

Fig. 2-43 – The equivalent circuit of a resonant circuit delivering power to a load. The resistor *R* represents the load resistance. At B the load is tapped across part of *L*, which by transformer action is equivalent to using a higher load resistance across the whole circuit.

Q of Loaded Circuits

In many applications of resonant circuits the only power lost is that dissipated in the resistance of the circuit itself. At frequencies below 30 MHz most of this resistance is in the coil. Within limits, increasing the number of turns in the coil increases the reactance faster than it raises the resistance, so coils for circuits in which the Q must be high are made with relatively large inductance for the frequency.

However, when the circuit delivers energy to a load (as in the case of the resonant circuits used in transmitters) the energy consumed in the circuit itself is usually negligible compared with that consumed by the load. The equivalent of such a circuit is shown in Fig. 2-43A, where the parallel resistor represents the load to which power is delivered. If the power dissipated in the load is at least ten times as great as the power lost in the inductor and capacitor, the parallel impedance of the resonant circuit itself will be so high compared with the resistance of the load that for all practical purposes the impedance of the combined circuit is equal to the load resistance. Under these conditions the Q of a parallel resonant circuit loaded by a resistive impedance is

$$Q = \frac{R}{X}$$

where R = Parallel load resistance (ohms)
X = Reactance (ohms)

Example: A resistive load of 3000 ohms is connected across a resonant circuit in which the inductive and capacitive reactances are each 250 ohms. The circuit Q is then

$$Q = \frac{R}{X} = \frac{3000}{250} = 12$$

The "effective" Q of a circuit loaded by a parallel resistance becomes higher when the reactances are decreased. A circuit loaded with a relatively low resistance (a few thousand ohms) must have low-reactance elements (large capacitance and small inductance) to have reasonably high Q.

Impedance Transformation

An important application of the parallel-resonant circuit is as an impedance-matching device in the output circuit of a vacuum-tube rf power amplifier. As described in the chapter on vacuum tubes, there is an optimum value of load resistance for each type of tube and set of operating conditions. However, the resistance of the load to which the tube is to deliver power usually is considerably lower than the value required for proper tube operation. To transform the actual load resistance to the desired value the load may be tapped across part of the coil, as shown in Fig. 2-43B. This is equivalent to connecting a higher value of load resistance across the whole circuit, and is similar in principle to impedance transformation with an iron-core transformer. In high-frequency resonant circuits the impedance ratio does not vary exactly as the square of the turns ratio, because all the magnetic flux lines do not cut every turn of the coil. A desired reflected impedance usually must be obtained by experimental adjustment.

When the load resistance has a very low value (say below 100 ohms) it may be connected in series in the resonant circuit (as in Fig. 2-41A, for example), in which case it is transformed to an equivalent parallel impedance as previously described. If the Q is at least 10, the equivalent parallel impedance is

$$Z_r = \frac{X^2}{r}$$

where Z_r = Resistive parallel impedance at resonance
X = Reactance (in ohms) of either the coil or capacitor
r = Load resistance inserted in series

If the Q is lower than 10 the reactance will have to be adjusted somewhat, for the reasons given in the discussion of low-Q circuits, to obtain a resistive impedance of the desired value.

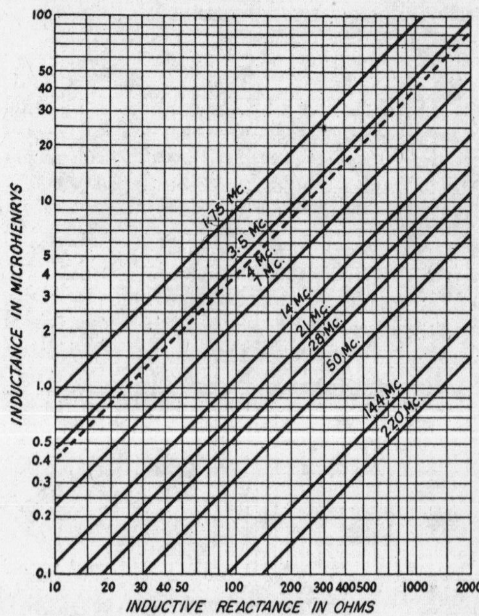

Fig. 2-44 – Reactance chart for inductance values commonly used in amateur bands from 1.75 to 220 MHz.

Reactance Values

The charts of Figs. 2-44 and 2-45 show reactance values of inductances and capacitances in the range commonly used in rf tuned circuits for the amateur bands. With the exception of the 3.5-4 MHz band, limiting values for which are shown on the charts, the change in reactance over a band, for either inductors or capacitors, is small enough so that a single curve gives the reactance with sufficient accuracy for most practical purposes.

L/C Ratio

The formula for resonant frequency of a circuit shows that the same frequency always will be obtained so long as the *product* of *L* and *C* is constant. Within this limitation, it is evident that *L* can be large and *C* small, *L* small and *C* large, etc. The relation between the two for a fixed frequency is called the **L/C ratio.** A **high-C** circuit is one that has more capacitance than "normal" for the frequency; a **low-C** circuit is one that has less than normal capacitance. These terms depend to a considerable extent upon the particular application considered, and have no exact numerical meaning.

LC Constants

It is frequently convenient to use the numerical value of the **LC constant** with a number of calculations have to be made involving different *L*/*C* ratios for the same frequency. The constant for any frequency is given by the following equation:

$$LC = \frac{25{,}330}{f^2}$$

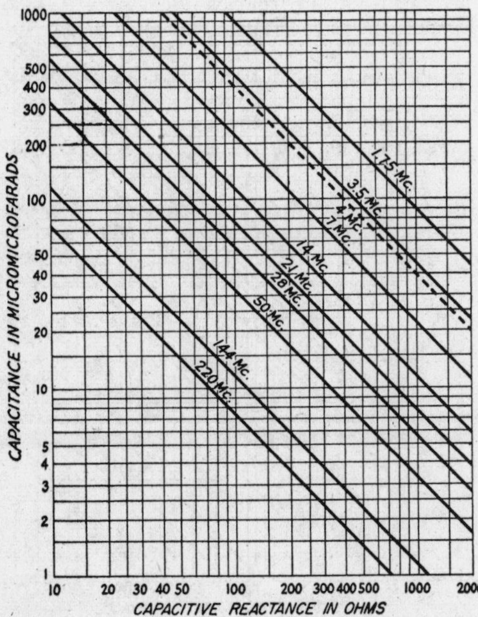

Fig. 2-45 – Reactance chart for capacitance values commonly used in amateur bands from 1.75 to 220 MHz.

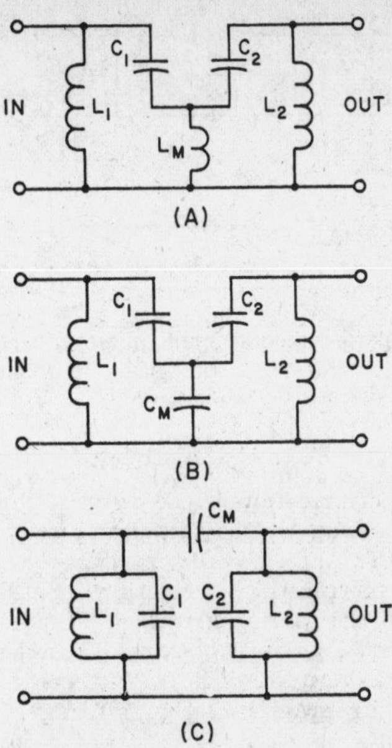

Fig. 2-46 – Three methods of circuit coupling.

where L = Inductance in microhenrys (μH)
C = Capacitance in picofarads (pF)
f = Frequency in megahertz

Example: Find the inductance required to resonate at 3650 kHz (3.65 MHz) with capacitances of 25, 50, 100 and 500 pF. The *LC* constant is

$$LC = \frac{25{,}330}{(3.65)^2} = \frac{25{,}330}{13.35} = 1900$$

With 25 pF $L = 1900/C = 1900/25 = 76$ μH
50 pF $L = 1900/C = 1900/50 = 38$ μH
100 pF $L = 1900/C = 1900/100 = 19$ μH
500 pF $L = 1900/C = 1900/500 = 3.8$ μH

COUPLED CIRCUITS

Energy Transfer and Loading

Two circuits are **coupled** when energy can be transferred from one to the other. The circuit delivering power is called the **primary** circuit; the one receiving power is called the **secondary** circuit. The power may be practically all dissipated in the secondary circuit itself (this is usually the case in receiver circuits) or the secondary may simply act as a medium through which the power is transferred to a load. In the latter case, the coupled circuits may act as a radio-frequency impedance-matching device. The matching can be accomplished by adjusting the loading on the secondary and by varying the amount of coupling between the primary and secondary.

Coupling by a Common Circuit Element

One method of coupling between two resonant circuits is through a circuit element common to both. The three common variations of this type of coupling are shown in Fig. 2-46; the circuit element common to both circuits carries the subscript *M*. At A and B current circulating in

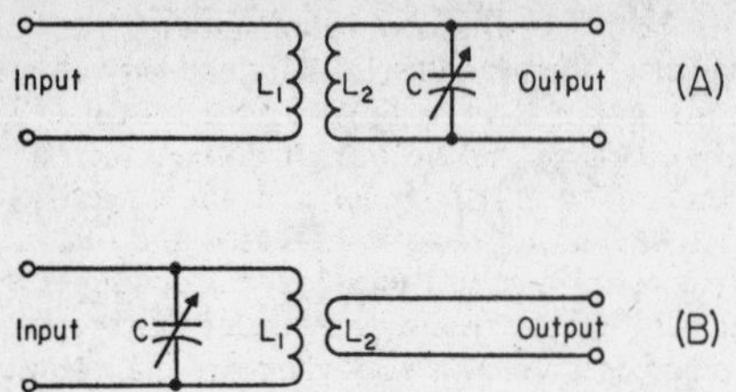

Fig. 2-47 — Single-tuned inductively coupled circuits.

L1C1 flows through the common element, and the voltage developed across this element causes current to flow in *L2C2*. At *C*, *CM* and *C2* form a capacitive voltage divider across *L1C1*, and some of the voltage developed across *L1C1* is applied across *L2C2*.

If both circuits are resonant to the same frequency, as is usually the case, the value of coupling reactance required for maximum energy transfer can be approximated by the following, based on $L1 = L2$, $C1 = C2$ and $Q1 = Q2$:

$$(A)\ L_M \approx L1/Q1;\quad (B)\ C_M \approx Q1C1;\quad (C)\ C_M \approx C1/Q1$$

The coupling can be increased by increasing the above coupling elements in A and C and decreasing the value in B. When the coupling is increased, the resultant bandwidth of the combination is increased, and this principle is sometimes applied to "broad-band" the circuits in a transmitter or receiver. When the coupling elements in A and C are decreased, or when the coupling element in B is increased, the coupling between the circuits is decreased below the *critical coupling* value on which the above approximations are based. Less than critical coupling will decrease the bandwidth and the energy transfer; the principle is often used in receivers to improve the selectivity.

Inductive Coupling

Figs. 2-47 and 2-48 show inductive coupling, or coupling by means of the mutual inductance between two coils. Circuits of this type resemble the iron-core transformer, but because only a part of the magnetic flux lines set up by one coil cut the turns of the other coil, the simple relationships between turns ratio, voltage ratio and impedance ratio in the iron-core transformer do not hold.

Two types of inductively-coupled circuits are shown in Fig. 2-47. Only one circuit is resonant. The circuit at A is frequently used in receivers for coupling between amplifier tubes when the tuning of the circuit must be varied to respond to signals of different frequencies. Circuit B is used principally in transmitters, for coupling a radio-frequency amplifier to a resistive load.

In these circuits the coupling between the primary and secondary coils usually is "tight" — that is, the coefficient of coupling between the coils is large. With very tight coupling either circuit operates nearly as though the device to which the untuned coil is connected were simply tapped across a corresponding number of turns on the tuned-circuit coil, thus either circuit is approximately equivalent to Fig. 2-43B.

By proper choice of the number of turns on the untuned coil, and by adjustment of the coupling, the parallel impedance of the tuned circuit may be adjusted to the value required for the proper operation of the device to which it is connected. In any case, the maximum energy transfer possible for a given coefficient of coupling is obtained when the reactance of the untuned coil is equal to the resistance of its load.

The *Q* and parallel impedance of the tuned circuit are reduced by coupling through an untuned coil in much the same way as by the tapping arrangement shown in Fig. 2-43B.

Coupled Resonant Circuits

When the primary and secondary circuits are both tuned, as in Fig. 2-48, the resonance effects in both circuits make the operation somewhat more complicated than in the simpler circuits just considered. Imagine first that the two circuits are not coupled and that each is independently tuned to the resonant frequency. The impedance of each will be purely resistive. If the primary circuit is connected to a source of rf energy of the resonant frequency and the secondary is then loosely coupled to the primary, a current will flow in the secondary circuit. In flowing through the resistance of the secondary circuit and any load that may be connected to it, the current causes a power loss. This power must come from the energy source through the primary circuit, and manifests itself in the primary as an increase in the equivalent resistance in series with the primary coil. Hence the *Q* and parallel impedance of the primary circuit are decreased by the coupled secondary. As the coupling is made greater (without changing the tuning of either circuit) the coupled resistance becomes larger and the parallel impedance of the primary continues to decrease. Also, as the coupling is made tighter the amount of power transferred from the primary to the secondary will

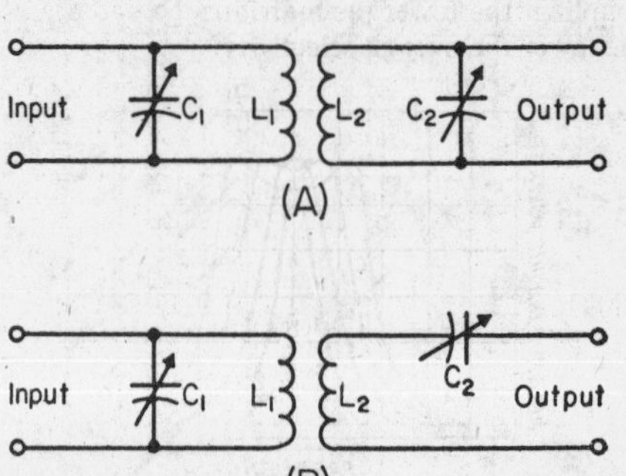

Fig. 2-48 — Inductively-coupled resonant circuits. Circuit A is used for high-resistance loads (load resistance much higher than the reactance of either L2 or C2 at the resonant frequency). Circuit B is suitable for low resistance loads (load resistance much lower than the reactance of either L2 or C2 at the resonant frequency).

increase to a maximum of one value of coupling, called **critical coupling**, but then decreases if the coupling is tightened still more (still without changing the tuning).

Critical coupling is a function of the *Q*s of the two circuits. A higher coefficient of coupling is required to reach critical coupling when the *Q*s are low; if the *Q*s are high, as in receiving applications, a coupling coefficient of a few per cent may give critical coupling.

With loaded circuits such as are used in transmitters the *Q* may be too low to give the desired power transfer even when the coils are coupled as tightly as the physical construction permits. In such case, increasing the *Q* of either circuit will be helpful, although it is generally better to increase the *Q* of the lower-*Q* circuit rather than the reverse. The *Q* of the parallel-tuned primary (input) circuit can be increased by decreasing the *L/C* ratio because, as shown in connection with Fig. 2-43, this circuit is in effect loaded by a parallel resistance (effect of coupled-in resistance). In the parallel-tuned secondary circuit, Fig. 2-48A, the *Q* may be increased by *increasing* the *L/C* ratio. There will generally be no difficulty in securing sufficient coupling, with practicable coils, if the product of the *Q*s of the two tuned circuits is 10 or more. A smaller product will suffice if the coil construction permits tight coupling.

Selectivity

In Fig. 2-47 only one circuit is tuned and the selectivity curve will be essentially that of a single resonant circuit. As stated, the effective *Q* depends upon the resistance connected to the untuned coil.

In Fig. 2-48, the selectivity is increased. It approaches that of a single tuned circuit having a *Q* equalling the sum of the individual circuit *Q*s – *if* the coupling is well below critical (this is not the condition for optimum power transfer discussed immediately above) and both circuits are tuned to resonance. The *Q*s of the individual circuits are affected by the degree of coupling, because each couples resistance into the other; the tighter the coupling, the lower the individual *Q*s and therefore the lower the over-all selectivity.

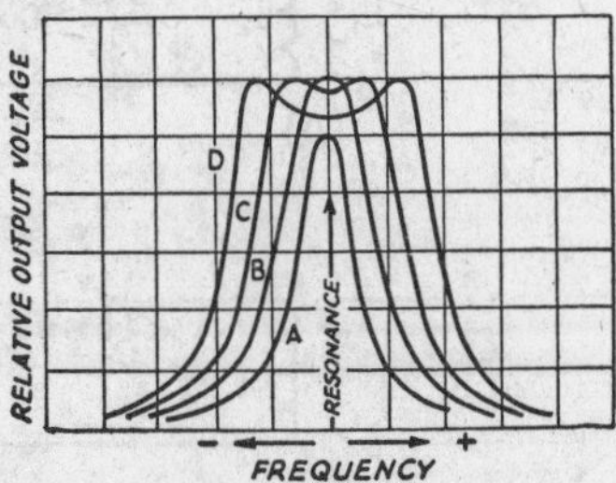

Fig. 2-49 – Showing the effect on the output voltage from the secondary circuit of changing the coefficient of coupling between two resonant circuits independently tuned to the same frequency. The voltage applied to the primary is held constant in amplitude while the frequency is varied, and the output voltage is measured across the secondary.

If both circuits are independently tuned to resonance, the over-all selectivity will vary about as shown in Fig. 2-49 as the coupling is varied. With loose coupling, *A*, the output voltage (across the secondary circuit) is small and the selectivity is high. As the coupling is increased the secondary voltage also increases until critical coupling, *B*, is reached. At this point the output voltage at the resonant frequency is maximum but the selectivity is lower than with looser coupling. At still tighter coupling, *C*, the output voltage at the resonant frequency decreases, but as the frequency is varied either side of resonance it is found that there are two "humps" to the curve, one on either side of resonance. With very tight coupling, *D*, there is a further decrease in the output voltage at resonance and the "humps" are farther away from the resonant frequency. Curves such as those at *C* and *D* are called **flat-topped** because the output voltage does not change much over an appreciable band of frequencies.

Note that the off-resonance humps have the same maximum value as the resonant output voltage at critical coupling. These humps are caused by the fact that at frequencies off resonance the secondary circuit is reactive and couples reactance as well as resistance into the primary. The coupled resistance decreases off resonance, and each hump represents a new condition of critical coupling at a frequency to which the primary is tuned by the additional coupled-in reactance from the secondary.

Fig. 2-50 shows the response curves for various degrees of coupling between two circuits tuned to a frequency f_o. Equal *Q*s are assumed in both circuits, although the curves are representative if the *Q*s differ by ratios up to 1.5 or even 2 to 1. In these cases, a value of $Q = \sqrt{Q1\,Q2}$ should be used.

Band-Pass Coupling

Over-coupled resonant circuits are useful where substantially uniform output is desired over a continuous band of frequencies, without readjustment of tuning. The width of the flat top of the resonance curve depends on the *Q*s of the two circuits as well as the tightness of coupling; the frequency separation between the humps will increase, and the curve become more flat-topped, as the *Q*s are lowered.

Band-pass operation also is secured by tuning the two circuits to slightly different frequencies, which gives a double-humped resonance curve even with loose coupling. This is called **stagger tuning.** To secure adequate power transfer over the frequency band it is usually necessary to use tight coupling and experimentally adjust the circuits for the desired performance.

Link Coupling

A modification of inductive coupling, called **link coupling**, is shown in Fig. 2-51. This gives the effect of inductive coupling between two coils that have no mutual inductance; the link is simply a means for providing the mutual inductance. The total mutual inductance between two coils coupled

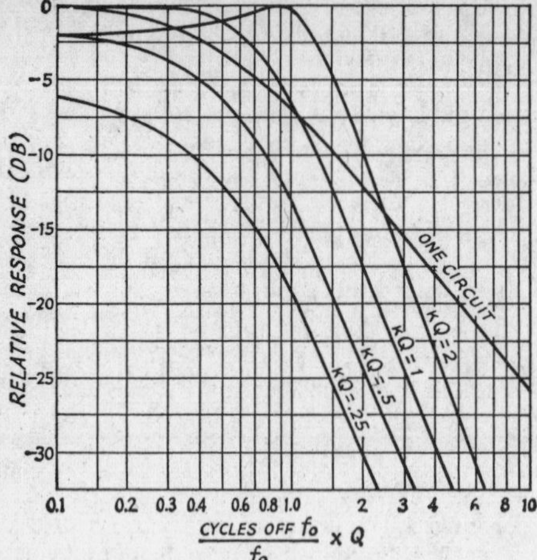

Fig. 2-50 – Relative response for a single tuned circuit and for coupled circuits. For inductively-coupled circuits (Figs. 2-46A and 2-48A),

$$k = \frac{M}{\sqrt{L1L2}}$$

where M is the mutual inductance. For capacitance-coupled circuits (Figs. 2-46B and 2-46C),

$$k \approx \frac{\sqrt{C1C2}}{C_M} \text{ and } k \approx \frac{C_M}{\sqrt{C1C2}}$$

respectively.

by a link cannot be made as great as if the coils themselves were coupled. This is because the coefficient of coupling between air-core coils is considerably less than 1, and since there are two coupling points the over-all coupling coefficient is less than for any *pair* of coils. In practice this need not be disadvantageous because the power transfer can be made great enough by making the tuned circuits sufficiently high-Q. Link coupling is convenient when ordinary inductive coupling would be impracticable for constructional reasons.

The link coils usually have a small number of turns compared with the resonant-circuit coils. The number of turns is not greatly important, because the coefficient of coupling is relatively independent of the number of turns on either coil; it is more important that both link coils should have about the *same* inductance. The length of the link between the coils is not critical if it is very small compared with the wavelength, but if the length is more than about one-twentieth of a wavelength the link operates more as a transmission line than as a means for providing mutual inductance. In such case it should be treated by the methods described in the chapter on Transmission Lines.

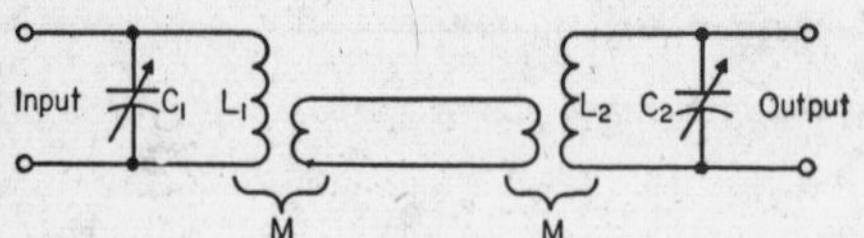

Fig. 2-51 – Link coupling. The mutual inductances at both ends of the link are equivalent to mutual inductance between the tuned circuits, and serve the same purpose.

IMPEDANCE-MATCHING CIRCUITS

Various combinations of L and C can be used to transform one impedance level to another and provide desirable selectivity to unwanted energy at the same time. While the simpler matching circuits use fewer components and are relatively easy to design, they lack the flexibility that is possible with more sophisticated networks.

The L network shown in Fig. 2-52 is the simplest possible impedance-matching circuit. It closely resembles an ordinary resonant circuit with the load resistance, R, either in series or parallel. The arrangement shown in Fig. 2-52A is used when the desired impedance, R_{in}, is larger than the actual load resistance, R while Fig. 2-52B is used in the opposite case. The design equations for each case are given in the figure, in terms of the circuit reactances. The reactances may be converted to inductance and capacitance by means of the formulas previously given or taken directly from the charts of Figs. 2-44 and 2-45.

The Q of an L network is found in the same way as for simple resonant circuits. That is, it is equal to XL/R or R_{IN}/XC in Fig. 2-52A, and to XL/R_{IN} or R/XC in Fig. 2-52B. The value of Q is determined by the ratio of the impedances to be matched, and cannot be selected independently. In the equations of Fig. 2-52 it is assumed that both R and R_{in} are pure resistances.

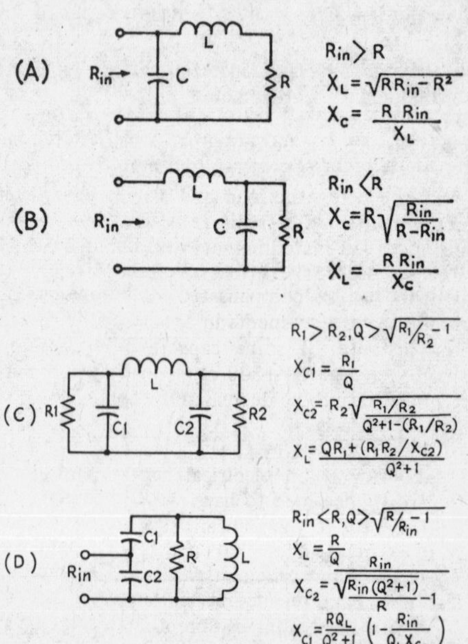

Fig. 2-52 – Impedance-matching networks adaptable to amateur work. (A) L network for matching to a lower value of resistance. (B) L network for matching to a higher resistance value. (C) pi network. (D) Versatile circuit often used in transistor- and antenna-matching networks.

The pi network shown in Fig. 2-52C is often used in the final stage of a transmitter. Different values of L are switched in for the appropriate band of frequencies while C1 and C2 are usually continuously variable.

In its principal application as a "tank" circuit matching a transmission line to a power amplifier tube, the load $R2$ will generally have a fairly low value of resistance (up to a few hundred ohms) while $R1$, the required load for the tube, will be of the order of a few thousand ohms.

Graphical solutions for practical cases are given in the chapter on transmitter design in the discussion of plate tank circuits. The L and C values may be calculated from the reactances or read from the charts of Figs. 2-44 and 2-45.

While the pi network can be used to match a high resistance to a low one, the circuit shown in Fig. 2-52D has some attractive features. With C1 and C2 ganged and L variable, it is often used in matching an antenna to a transmitter (Transmatch). The inductor can be tapped to provide impedance transformation between resistances that are low in value, but nearly equal. This is often the case with many transistor circuits.

Example: Find a circuit that will match an antenna with a resistance of 1500 ohms, to a transmitter with a resistance of 50 ohms. Using the circuit shown in Fig. 2-52D, we see that Q has to be greater than $\sqrt{1500/50 - 1}$ or 5.38. A Q of 10 will satisfy this condition and a guess is made that it will also give reasonable component values. XL will be 1500/10 or 150 ohms.

$$XC2 = 50\sqrt{\frac{50(101)}{1500} - 1} \text{ or } 76.9 \text{ ohms.}$$

$$XC1 = \frac{1500\,(10)}{101}\left(1 - \frac{50}{10\,(76.9)}\right) \text{ or } 138.85 \text{ ohms.}$$

If the frequency of operation was 3.7 MHz, the component values would be: $L = 6.4$ µH, C1 = 309 pF, and C2 = 559.3 pF. The guess was good since C2 is becoming large and higher values of Q would make this situation worse.

Quite often the load and source have reactive components along with resistance but in many instances the matching networks just discussed can still be used. The effect of these reactive components can be compensated for by changing one of the reactive elements in the matching network. For instance, if some capacitive reactance was shunted across the 1500 ohms in the last example, L would have to be decreased to cancel it.

FILTERS

A **filter** is an electrical circuit configuration (**network**) designed to have specific characteristics with respect to the transmission or attenuation of various frequencies that may be applied to it. There are four general types of filters: **low-pass, high-pass, band-reject,** and **band-pass.**

A low-pass filter is one that will permit all frequencies below a specified one, called the **cut-off frequency,** to be transmitted with little or no loss, but that will attenuate all frequencies above the cut-off frequency.

A high-pass filter similarly has a cut-off frequency, above which there is little or no loss in transmission, but below which there is considerable attenuation. Its behavior is the opposite of that of the low-pass filter.

A band-pass filter is one that will transmit a selected band of frequencies with substantially no loss, but that will attenuate all frequencies either higher or lower than the desired band.

A band-reject filter attenuates a selected band of frequencies, but allows others to be transmitted. The types that amateurs frequently encounter are commonly called traps .

The **pass band** of a filter is the frequency spectrum that is transmitted with little or no loss. The transmission characteristic is not necessarily perfectly uniform in the pass band, but the variations usually are small.

The **stop band** is the frequency region in which attenuation is desired. The attenuation may vary in the stop band, and in a simple filter usually is least near the cut-off frequency, rising to high values at frequencies considerably removed from the cut-off frequency.

Filters are designed for a specific value of purely resistive impedance (the **terminating impedance** of the filter). When such an impedance is connected to the output terminals of the filter, the impedance looking into the input terminals has essentially the same value throughout most of the pass band. Simple filters do not give perfectly uniform performance in this respect, but the input impedance of a properly-terminated filter can be made fairly constant, as well as closer to the design value, over the pass band by using **m-derived** filter sections.

A discussion of filter design principles is beyond the scope of this *Handbook*, but it is not difficult to build satisfactory filters from the circuits and formulas given in Fig. 2-53. Filter circuits are built up from elementary sections as shown in the figure. These sections can be used alone or, if greater attenuation and sharper cut-off (that is, more rapid rate of rise of attenuation with frequency beyond the cut-off frequency) are required, several sections can be connected in series. In the low- and high-pass filters, fc represents the cut-off frequency, the highest (for the low-pass) or the lowest (for the high-pass) frequency transmitted without attenuation. In the band-pass filter designs, $f1$ is the low-frequency cut-off and $f2$ the high-frequency cut-off. The units for L, C, R and f are microhenrys, picofarads, ohms and megahertz, respectively.

All of the types shown are "unbalanced" (one side grounded). For use in balanced circuits (e.g., 300-ohm transmission line, or push-pull audio circuits), the series reactances should be equally divided between the two legs. Thus the balanced constant-k π-section low-pass filter would use two inductors of a value equal to $L_k/2$, while the balanced constant-k π-section high-pass filter would use two capacitors each equal to $2C_k$.

If several low- (or high-) pass sections are to be used, it is advisable to use m-derived end sections on either side of a constant-k center section, although an m-derived center section can be used. The factor m determines the ratio of the cut-off

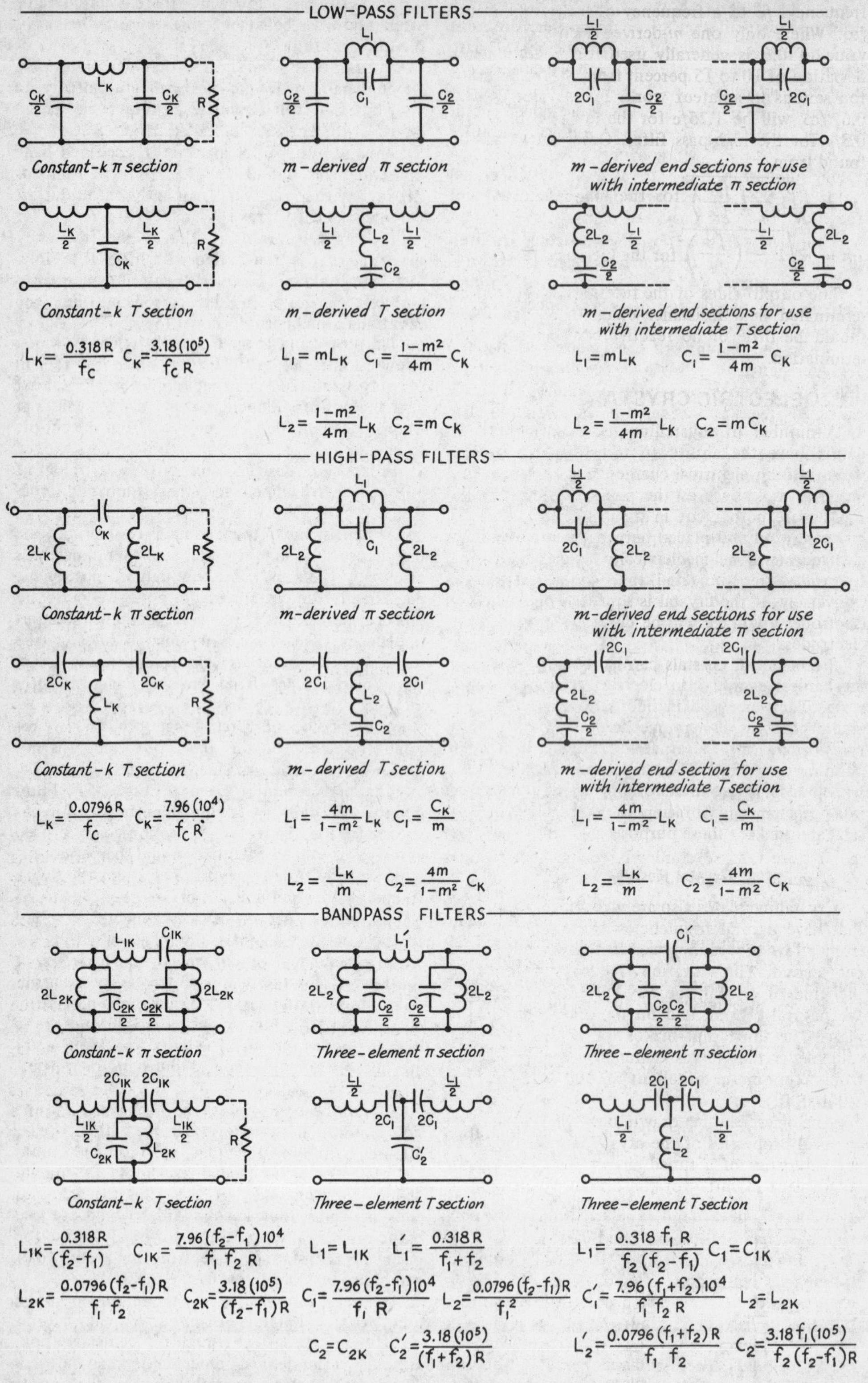

Fig. 2-53 – Basic filter sections and design formulas. In the above formulas R is in ohms, C in farads, L in henrys, and f in cycles per second.

frequency, fc to a frequency of high attenuation, $f\infty$. Where only one m-derived section is used, a value of 0.6 is generally used for m, although a deviation of 10 to 15 percent from this value is not too serious in amateur work. For a value of m = 0.6, $f\infty$ will be 1.25fc for the low-pass filter and 0.8fc for the high-pass filter. Other values can be found from

$$m = \sqrt{1 - \left(\frac{f_c}{f_\infty}\right)^2}$$ for the low-pass filter and

$$m = \sqrt{1 - \left(\frac{f_\infty}{f_c}\right)^2}$$ for the high-pass filter.

The output sides of the filters shown should be terminated in a resistance equal to R, and there should be little or no reactive component in the termination.

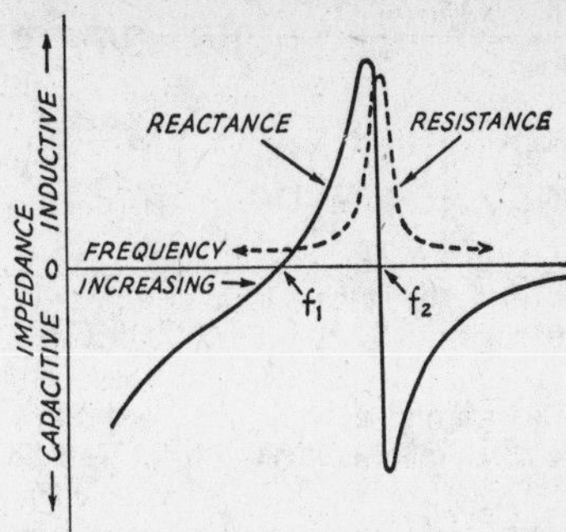

Fig. 2-55 — Reactance and resistance vs. frequency of a circuit of the type shown in Fig. 2-54. Actual values of reactance, resistance and the separation between the series- and parallel-resonant frequencies, f_1, and f_2, respectively, depend on the circuit constants.

PIEZOELECTRIC CRYSTALS

A number of crystalline substances found in nature have the ability to transform mechanical strain into an electrical charge, and *vice versa*. This property is known as the **piezoelectric effect.** A small plate or bar cut in the proper way from a quartz crystal and placed between two conducting electrodes will be mechanically strained when the electrodes are connected to a source of voltage. Conversely, if the crystal is squeezed between two electrodes a voltage will be developed between the electrodes.

Piezoelectric crystals can be used to transform mechanical energy into electrical energy, and vice versa. They are used in microphones and phonograph pick-ups, where mechanical vibrations are transformed into alternating voltages of corresponding frequency. They are also used in headsets and loudspeakers, transforming electrical energy into mechanical vibration. Crystals of Rochelle salts are used for these purposes.

Crystal Resonators

Crystalline plates also are mechanical resonators that have natural frequencies of vibration ranging from a few thousand cycles to tens of megacycles per second. The vibration frequency depends on the kind of crystal, the way the plate is cut from the natural crystal, and on the dimensions of the plate. The thing that makes the **crystal resonator** valuable is that it has extremely high Q, ranging from a minimum of about 20,000 to as high as 1,000,000.

Analogies can be drawn between various mechanical properties of the crystal and the electrical characteristics of a tuned circuit. This leads to an "equivalent circuit" for the crystal. The electrical coupling to the crystal is through the holder plates between which it is sandwiched; these plates form, with the crystal as the dielectric, a small capacitor like any other capacitor constructed of two plates with a dielectric between. The crystal itself is equivalent to a series-resonant circuit, and together with the capacitance of the holder forms the equivalent circuit shown in Fig. 2-54. At frequencies of the order of 450 kHz, where crystals are widely used as resonators, the equivalent L may be several henrys and the equivalent C only a few hundredths of a picofarad. Although the equivalent R is of the order of a few thousand ohms, the reactance at resonance is so high that the Q of the crystal likewise is high.

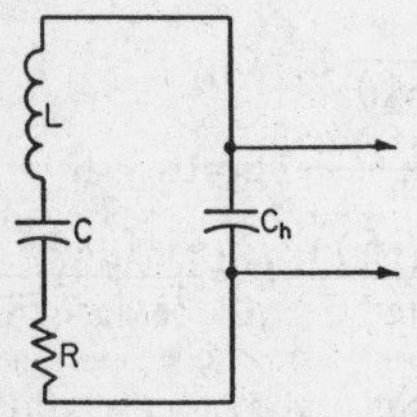

Fig. 2-54 — Equivalent circuit of a crystal resonator. L, C and R are the electrical equivalents of mechanical properties of the crystal; Ch is the capacitance of the holder plates with the crystal plate between them.

A circuit of the type shown in Fig. 2-54 has a series-resonant frequency, when viewed from the circuit terminals indicated by the arrowheads, determined by L and C only. At this frequency the circuit impedance is simply equal to R, providing the reactance of Ch is large compared with R (this is generally the case). The circuit also has a parallel-resonant frequency determined by L and the equivalent capacitance of C and Ch in series. Since this equivalent capacitance is smaller than C alone, the parallel-resonant frequency is higher than the series-resonant frequency. The separation between the two resonant frequencies depends on the ratio of Ch to C, and when this ratio is large (as in the case of a crystal resonator, where Ch will be a few pF, in the average case) the two frequencies will be quite close together. A separation of a kilocycle or less at 455 kHz is typical of a quartz crystal.

Fig. 2-55 shows how the resistance and reactance of such a circuit vary as the applied frequency is varied. The reactance passes through zero at both resonant frequencies, but the resistance rises to a large value at parallel resonance, just as in any tuned circuit.

Quartz crystals may be used either as simple resonators for their selective properties or as the frequency-controlling elements in oscillators as described in later chapters. The series-resonant frequency is the one principally used in the former case, while the more common forms of oscillator circuit use the parallel-resonant frequency.

PRACTICAL CIRCUIT DETAILS

COMBINED AC AND DC

Most radio circuits are built around vacuum tubes, and it is the nature of these tubes to require direct current (usually at a fairly high voltage) for their operation. They convert the direct current into an alternating current (and sometimes the reverse) at frequencies varying from well down in the audio range to well up in the super-high range. The conversion process almost invariably requires that the direct and alternating currents meet somewhere in the circuit.

In this meeting, the ac and dc are actually combined into a single current that "pulsates" (at the ac frequency) about an average value equal to the direct current. This is shown in Fig. 2-56. It is convenient to consider that the alternating current is **superimposed** on the direct current, so we may look upon the actual current as having two components, one dc and the other ac.

In an alternating current the positive and negative alternations have the same average amplitude, so when the wave is superimposed on a direct current the latter is alternately increased and decreased by the same amount. There is thus no *average* change in the direct current. If a dc instrument is being used to read the current, the reading will be exactly the same whether or not the ac is superimposed.

However, there is actually more power in such a combination current than there is in the direct current alone. This is because power varies as the square of the instantaneous value of the current, and when all the instantaneous squared values are averaged over a cycle the total power is greater than the dc power alone. If the ac is a sine wave having a peak value just equal to the dc, the power in the circuit is 1.5 times the dc power. An instrument whose readings are proportional to power will show such an increase.

Series and Parallel Feed

Fig. 2-57 shows in simplified form how dc and ac may be combined in a vacuum-tube circuit. In this case, it is assumed that the ac is at radio frequency, as suggested by the coil-and-capacitor tuned circuit. It is also assumed that rf current can easily flow through the dc supply; that is, the impedance of the supply at radio frequencies is so small as to be negligible.

In the circuit at the left, the tube, tuned circuit, and dc supply all are connected in series. The direct current flows through the rf coil to get to

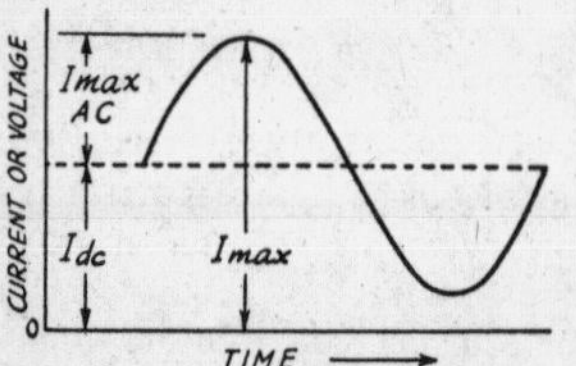

Fig. 2-56 — Pulsating dc, composed of an alternating current or voltage superimposed on a steady direct current or voltage.

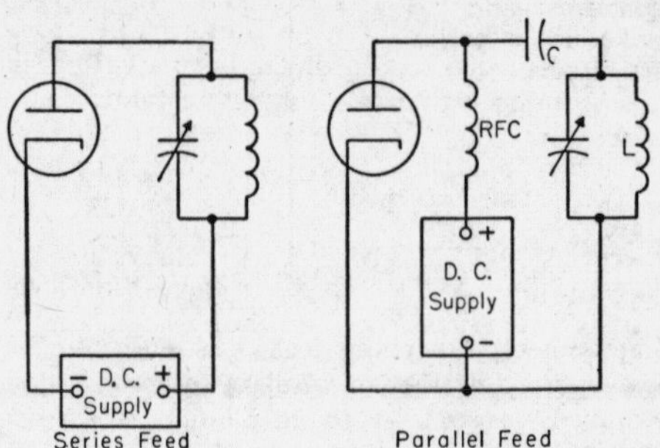

Fig. 2-57 — Illustrating series and parallel feed.

the tube; the rf current generated by the tube flows through the dc supply to get to the tuned circuit. This is **series feed.** It works because the impedance of the dc supply at radio frequencies is so low that it does not affect the flow of *rf* current, because the dc resistance of the coil is so low that it does not affect the flow of *direct* current.

In the circuit at the right the direct current does not flow through the rf tuned circuit, but instead goes to the tube through a second coil, *RFC* **(radio-frequency choke).** Direct current cannot flow through *L* because a **blocking capacitance,** *C*, is placed in the circuit to prevent it. (Without *C*, the dc supply would be short-circuited by the low resistance of *L*.) On the other hand, the rf current generated by the tube can easily flow through *C* to the tuned circuit because the capacitance of *C* is intentionally chosen to have low reactance (compared with the impedance of the tuned circuit) at the radio frequency. The rf current cannot flow through the dc supply because the inductance of *RFC* is intentionally made so large that it has a very high reactance at the radio frequency. The resistance of *RFC*, however, is too low to have an appreciable effect on the flow of direct current. The two currents are thus in *parallel*, hence the name **parallel feed.**

Either type of feed may be used for both af and rf circuits. In parallel feed there is no dc voltage on the ac circuit, a desirable feature from the viewpoint of safety to the operator, because the voltages applied to tubes – particularly transmitting tubes – are dangerous. On the other hand, it is somewhat difficult to make an rf choke work well over a wide range of frequencies. Series feed is often preferred, therefore, because it is relatively easy to keep the impedance between the ac circuit and the tube low.

Bypassing

In the series-feed circuit just discussed, it was assumed that the dc supply had very low impedance at radio frequencies. This is not likely to be true in a practical power supply, partly because the normal physical separation between the supply and the rf circuit would make it necessary to use rather

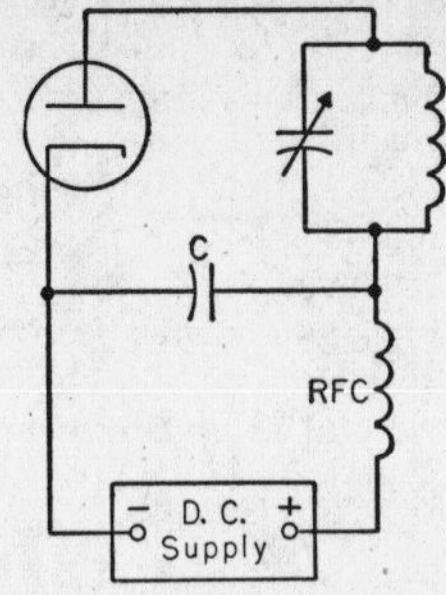

Fig. 2-58 – Typical use of a bypass capacitor and rf choke in a series-feed circuit.

long connecting wires or leads. At radio frequencies, even a few feet of wire can have fairly large reactance – too large to be considered a really "low-impedance" connection.

An actual circuit would be provided with a **bypass capacitor**, as shown in Fig. 2-58. Capacitor *C* is chosen to have low reactance at the operating frequency, and is installed right in the circuit where it can be wired to the other parts with quite short connecting wires. Hence the rf current will tend to flow through it rather than through the dc supply.

To be effective, the reactance of the bypass capacitor should not be more than one-tenth of the impedance of the bypassed part of the circuit. Very often the latter impedance is not known, in which case it is desirable to use the largest capacitance in the bypass that circumstances permit. To make doubly sure that rf current will not flow through a non-rf circuit such as a power supply, an rf choke may be connected in the lead to the latter, as shown in Fig. 2-58.

The same type of bypassing is used when audio frequencies are present in addition to rf. Because the reactance of a capacitor changes with frequency, it is readily possible to choose a capacitance that will represent a very low reactance at radio frequencies but that will have such high reactance at audio frequencies that it is practically an open circuit. A capacitance of .001 μF is practically a short circuit for rf, for example, but is almost an open circuit at audio frequencies. (The actual value of capacitance that is usable will be modified by the impedances concerned.) Capacitors also are used in audio circuits to carry the audio frequencies around a dc supply.

Distributed Capacitance and Inductance

In the discussions earlier in this chapter it was assumed that a capacitor has only capacitance and that an inductor has only inductance. Unfortunately, this is not strictly true. There is always a certain amount of inductance in a conductor of any length, and a capacitor is bound to have a little inductance in addition to its intended capacitance. Also, there is always capacitance between two conductors or between parts of the same conductor, and thus there is appreciable capacitance between the turns of an inductance coil.

This **distributed inductance** in a capacitor and the **distributed capacitance** in an inductor have important practical effects. Actually, every capacitor is in effect a series-tuned circuit, resonant at the frequency where its capacitance and inductance have the same reactance. Similarly, every inductor is in effect a parallel tuned circuit, resonant at the frequency where its inductance and distributed capacitance have the same reactance. At frequencies well below these **natural resonances**, the capacitor will act like a capacitor and the coil will act like an inductor. Near the natural resonance points, the inductor will have its highest impedance and the capacitor will have its lowest impedance. At frequencies above resonance, the capacitor acts like an inductor and the inductor acts like a capacitor. Thus there is a limit to the amount of capacitance that can be used at a given frequency. There is a similar limit to the inductance that can be used. At audio frequencies, capacitances measured in microfarads and inductances measured in henrys are practicable. At low and medium radio frequencies, inductances of a few mH and capacitances of a few thousand pF are the largest practicable. At high radio frequencies, usable inductance values drop to a few μH and capacitances to a few hundred pF.

Distributed capacitance and inductance are important not only in rf tuned circuits, but in bypassing a choking as well. It will be appreciated that a bypass capacitor that actually acts like an inductance, or an rf choke that acts like a low-reactance capacitor, cannot work as it is intended they should.

Grounds

Throughout this book there are frequent references to **ground** and **ground potential.** When a connection is said to be "grounded" it does not necessarily mean that it actually goes to earth. What it means that an actual earth connection to that point in the circuit should not disturb the operation of the circuit in any way. The term also is used to indicate a "common" point in the circuit where power supplies and metallic supports (such as a metal chassis) are electrically tied together. It is general practice, for example, to "ground" the filament or heater power supplies for vacuum tubes. Since the cathode of a vacuum tube is a junction point for grid and plate voltage supplies, and since the various circuits connected to the tube elements have at least one point connected to cathode, these points also are "returned to ground." Ground is therefore a common reference point in the radio circuit. "Ground potential" means that there is no "difference of potential" – no voltage – between the circuit point and the earth.

Single-Ended and Balanced Circuits

With reference to ground, a circuit may be either **single-ended** (unbalanced) or **balanced.** In a single-ended circuit, one side of the circuit (the **cold** side) is connected to ground. In a balanced circuit, the electrical midpoint is connected to ground, so that the circuit has two "hot" ends each at the same voltage "above" ground.

Typical single-ended and balanced circuits are shown in Fig. 2-59. Rf circuits are shown in the

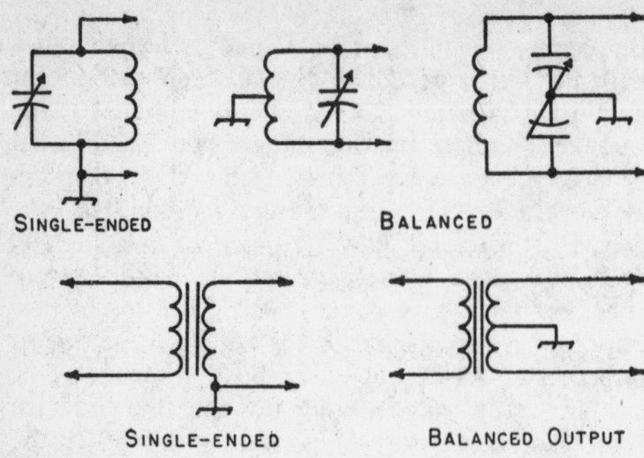

Fig. 2-59 – Single-ended and balanced circuits.

upper row, while iron-core transformers (such as are used in power-supply and audio circuits) are shown in the lower row. The rf circuits may be balanced either by connecting the center of the coil to ground or by using a "balanced" or "split-stator" capacitor and connecting its rotor to rf ground. In the iron-core transformer, one or both windings may be tapped at the center of the winding to provide the ground connection.

Shielding

Two circuits that are physically near each other usually will be coupled to each other in some degree even though no coupling is intended. The metallic parts of the two circuits form a small capacitance through which energy can be transferred by means of the electric field. Also, the magnetic field about the coil or wiring of one circuit can couple that circuit to a second through the latter's coil and wiring. In many cases these unwanted couplings must be prevented if the circuits are to work properly.

Capacitive coupling may readily be prevented by enclosing one or both of the circuits in grounded low-resistance metallic containers, called **shields**. The electric field from the circuit components does not penetrate the shield. A metallic plate, called a **baffle shield**, inserted between two components also may suffice to prevent electrostatic coupling between them. It should be large enough to make the components invisible to each other.

Similar metallic shielding is used at radio frequencies to prevent magnetic coupling. The shielding effect for magnetic fields increases with frequency and with the conductivity and thickness of the shielding material.

A closed shield is required for good magnetic shielding; in some cases separate shields, one about each coil, may be required. The baffle shield is rather ineffective for magnetic shielding, although it will give partial shielding if placed at right angles to the axes of, and between, the coils to be shielded from each other.

Shielding a coil reduces its inductance, because part of its field is canceled by the shield. Also, there is always a small amount of resistance in the shield, and there is therefore an energy loss. This loss raises the effective resistance of the coil. The decrease in inductance and increase in resistance lower the Q of the coil, but the reduction in inductance and Q will be small if the spacing between the sides of the coil and the shield is at least half the coil diameter, and if the spacing at the ends of the coil is at least equal to the coil diameter. The higher the conductivity of the shield material, the less the effect on the inductance and Q. Copper is the best material, but aluminum is quite satisfactory.

For good magnetic shielding at audio frequencies it is necessary to enclose the coil in a container of high-permeability iron or steel. In this case the shield can be quite close to the coil without harming its performance.

UHF CIRCUITS

RESONANT LINES

In resonant circuits as employed at the lower frequencies it is possible to consider each of the reactance components as a separate entity. The fact that an inductor has a certain amount of self-capacitance, as well as some resistance, while a capacitor also possesses a small self-inductance, can usually be disregarded.

At the very-high and ultrahigh frequencies it is not readily possible to separate these components. Also, the connecting leads, which at lower frequencies would serve merely to join the capacitor and coil, now may have more inductance than the coil itself. The required inductance coil may be no more than a single turn of wire, yet even this single turn may have dimensions comparable to a wavelength at the operating frequency. Thus the energy in the field surrounding the "coil" may in part be radiated. At a sufficiently high frequency the loss by radiation may represent a major portion of the total energy in the circuit.

For these reasons it is common practice to utilize resonant sections of transmission line as tuned circuits at frequencies above 100 MHz or so.

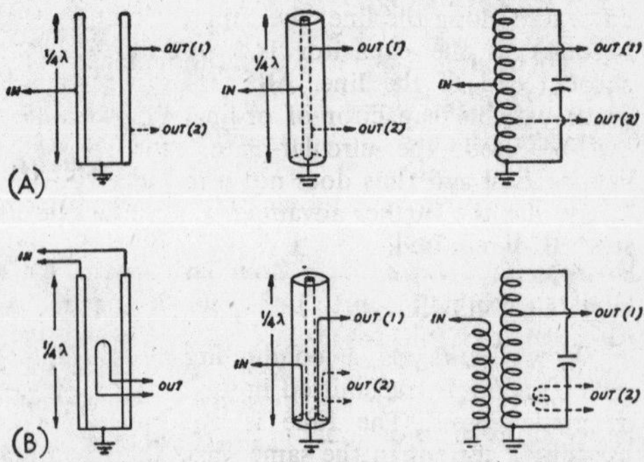

Fig. 2-60 – Equivalent coupling circuits for parallel-line, coaxial-line and conventional resonant circuits.

A quarter-wavelength line, or any odd multiple thereof, shorted at one end and open at the other exhibits large standing waves, as described in the section on transmission lines. When a voltage of the frequency at which such a line is resonant is applied to the open end, the response is very similar to that of a parallel resonant circuit. The equivalent relationships are shown in Fig. 2-60. At frequencies off resonance the line displays qualities comparable with the inductive and capacitive reactances of a conventional tuned circuit, so sections of transmission line can be used in much the same manner as inductors and capacitors.

To minimize radiation loss the two conductors of a parallel-conductor line should not be more than about one-tenth wavelength apart, the spacing being measured between the conductor axes. On the other hand, the spacing should not be less than about twice the conductor diameter because of "proximity effect," which causes eddy currents and an increase in loss. Above 300 MHz it is difficult to satisfy both these requirements simultaneously, and the radiation from an open line tends to become excessive, reducing the Q. In such case the coaxial type of line is to be preferred, since it is inherently shielded.

Representative methods for adjusting coaxial lines to resonance are shown in Fig. 2-61. At the left, a sliding shorting disk is used to reduce the effective length of the line by altering the position of the short-circuit. In the center, the same effect is accomplished by using a telescoping tube in the end of the inner conductor to vary its length and thereby the effective length of the line. At the right, two possible methods of using parallel-plate capacitors are illustrated. The arrangement with the loading capacitor at the open end of the line has the greatest tuning effect per unit of capacitance; the alternative method, which is equivalent to tapping the capacitor down on the line, has less effect on the Q of the circuit. Lines with capacitive "loading" of the sort illustrated will be shorter, physically, than unloaded lines resonant at the same frequency.

Two methods of tuning parallel-conductor lines are shown in Fig. 2-62. The sliding short-circuiting strap can be tightened by means of screws and nuts to make good electrical contact. The parallel-plate capacitor in the second drawing may be placed anywhere along the line, the tuning effect becoming less as the capacitor is located nearer the shorted end of the line. Although a low-capacitance variable capacitor of ordinary construction can be used, the circular-plate type shown is symmetrical and thus does not unbalance the line. It also has the further advantage that no insulating material is required.

WAVEGUIDES

A waveguide is a conducting tube through which energy is transmitted in the form of electromagnetic waves. The tube is not considered as carrying a current in the same sense that the wires of a two-conductor line do, but rather as a *boundary* which confines the waves to the enclosed space. Skin effect prevents any electromagnetic effects from being evident outside the guide. The energy is injected at one end, either through capacitive or inductive coupling or by radiation, and is received at the other end. The waveguide then merely confines the energy of the fields, which are propagated through it to the receiving end by means of reflections against its inner walls.

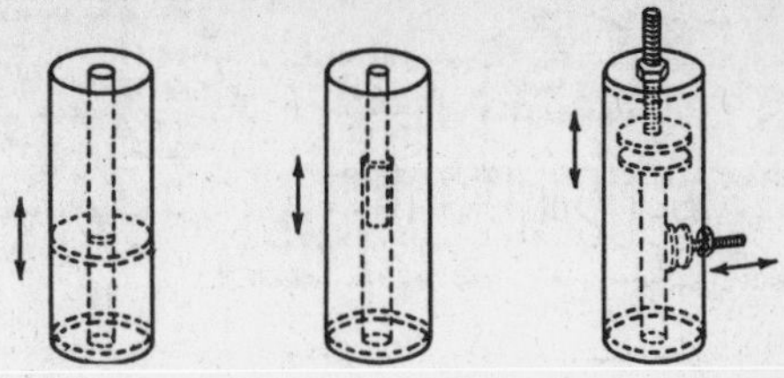

Fig. 2-61 — Methods of tuning coaxial resonant lines.

Analysis of waveguide operation is based on the assumption that the guide material is a perfect conductor of electricity. Typical distributions of electric and magnetic fields in a rectangular guide are shown in Fig. 2-63. It will be observed that the intensity of the electric field is greatest (as indicated by closer spacing of the lines of force) at the center along the x dimension, Fig. 2-63(B), diminishing to zero at the end walls. The latter is a necessary condition, since the existence of any electric field parallel to the walls at the surface would cause an infinite current to flow in a perfect conductor. This represents an impossible situation.

Modes of Propagation

Fig. 2-63 represents a relatively simple distribution of the electric and magnetic fields. There is in general an infinite number of ways in which the fields can arrange themselves in a guide so long as there is no upper limit to the frequency to be transmitted. Each field configuration is called a **mode**. All modes may be separated into two general groups. One group, designated *TM* (**transverse magnetic**), has the magnetic field entirely transverse to the direction of propagation, but has a component of electric field in that direction. The other type, designated *TE* (**transverse electric**) has the electric field entirely transverse, but has a component of magnetic field in the direction of propagation. *TM* waves are sometimes called *E* waves, and *TE* waves are sometimes called *H* waves, but the *TM* and *TE* designations are preferred.

The particular mode of transmission is identified by the group letters followed by two subscript

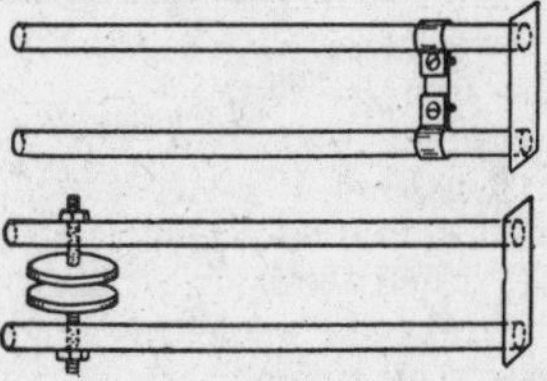

Fig. 2-62 — Methods of tuning parallel-type resonant lines.

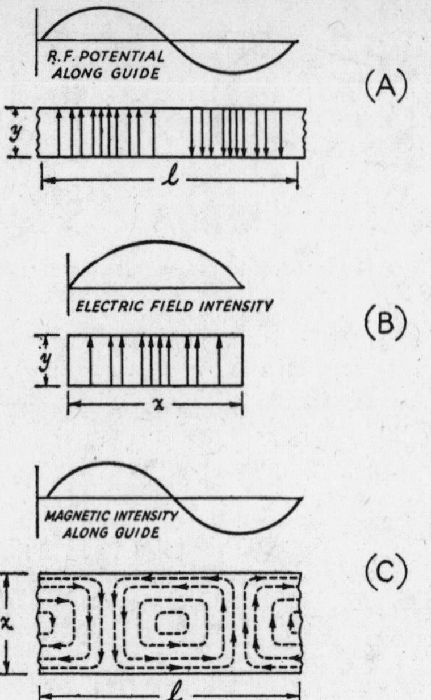

Fig. 2-63 – Field distribution in a rectangular waveguide. The $TE_{1,0}$ mode of propagation is depicted.

numerals; for example, $TE_{1,0}$, $TM_{1,1}$, etc. The number of possible modes increases with frequency for a given size of guide. There is only one possible mode (called the **dominant mode**) for the lowest frequency that can be transmitted. The dominant mode is the one generally used in practical work.

Waveguide Dimensions

In the rectangular guide the critical dimension is x in Fig. 2-63; this dimension must be more than one-half wavelength at the lowest frequency to be transmitted. In practice, the y dimension usually is made about equal to $1/2\,x$ to avoid the possibility of operation at other than the dominant mode.

Other cross-sectional shapes than the rectangle can be used, the most important being the circular pipe. Much the same considerations apply as in the rectangular case.

Wavelength formulas for rectangular and circular guides are given in the following table, where x is the width of a rectangular guide and r is the radius of a circular guide. All figures are in terms of the dominant mode.

	Rectangular	*Circular*
Cutoff wavelength	$2x$	$3.41r$
Longest wavelength transmitted with little attenuation	$1.6r$	$3.2r$
Shortest wavelength before next mode becomes possible	$1.1x$	$2.8r$

Cavity Resonators

Another kind of circuit particularly applicable at wavelengths of the order of centimeters is the **cavity resonator**, which may be looked upon as a section of a waveguide with the dimensions chosen so that waves of a given length can be maintained inside.

Typical shapes used for resonators are the cylinder, the rectangular box and the sphere, as shown in Fig. 2-64. The resonant frequency depends upon the dimensions of the cavity and the mode of oscillation of the waves (comparable to the transmission modes in a waveguide). For the lowest modes the resonant wavelengths are as follows:

Cylinder . . . . $2.61r$
Square box . . . . $1.41l$
Sphere . . . . $2.28r$

The resonant wavelengths of the cylinder and square box are independent of the height when the height is less than a half wavelength. In other modes of oscillation the height must be a multiple of a half wavelength as measured inside the cavity. A cylindrical cavity can be tuned by a sliding shorting disk when operating in such a mode. Other tuning methods include placing adjustable tuning paddles or "slugs" inside the cavity so that the standing-wave pattern of the electric and magnetic fields can be varied.

A form of cavity resonator in practical use is the re-entrant cylindrical type shown in Fig. 2-65. In construction it resembles a concentric line closed at both ends with capacitive loading at the top, but the actual mode of oscillation may differ considerably from that occuring in coaxial lines. The resonant frequency of such a cavity depends upon the diameters of the two cylinders and the distance d between the cylinder ends.

Compared with ordinary resonant circuits, cavity resonators have extremely high Q. A value of Q of the order of 1000 or more is readily obtainable, and Q values of several thousand can be secured with good design and construction.

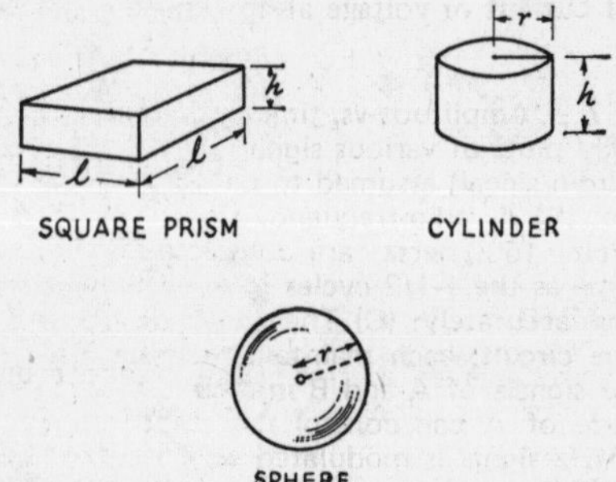

Fig. 2-64 – Forms of cavity resonators.

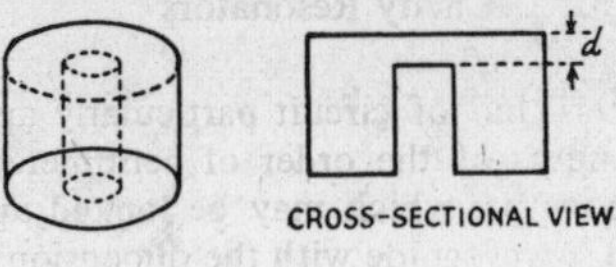

Fig. 2-65 – Re-entrant cylindrical cavity resonator.

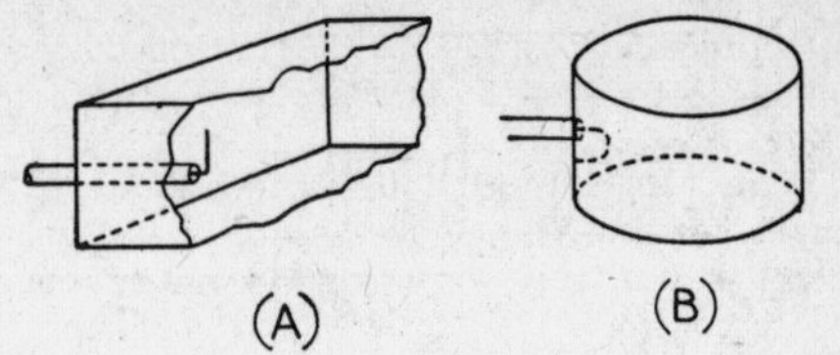

Fig. 2-66 – Coupling to waveguides and resonators.

Coupling to Waveguides and Cavity Resonators

Energy may be introduced into or abstracted from a waveguide or resonator by means of either the electric or magnetic field. The energy transfer frequently is through a coaxial line, two methods of coupling to which are shown in Fig. 2-66. The probe shown at A is simply a short extension of the inner conductor of the coaxial line, so oriented that it is parallel to the electric lines of force. The loop shown at B is arranged so that it encloses some of the magnetic lines of force. The point at which maximum coupling will be secured depends upon the particular mode of propagation in the guide or cavity; the coupling will be maximum when the coupling device is in the most intense field.

Coupling can be varied by turning the probe or loop through a 90-degree angle. When the probe is perpendicular to the electric lines the coupling will be minimum; similarly, when the plane of the loop is parallel to the magnetic lines the coupling will have its minimum value.

MODULATION, HETERODYNING, AND BEATS

Since one of the most widespread uses of radio frequencies is the transmission of speech and music, it would be very convenient if the audio spectrum to be transmitted could simply be shifted up to some radio frequency, transmitted as radio waves, and shifted back down to audio at the receiving point. Suppose the audio signal to be transmitted by radio is a pure 1000-hertz tone, and we wish to transmit the signal at 1 MHz (1,000,000 hertz. One possible way to do this might be to add 1.000 MHz and 1 kHz together, thereby obtaining a radio frequency of 1.001 MHz. No simple method for doing this directly has been devised, although the *effect* is obtained and used in "single-sideband transmission."

When two different frequencies are present simultaneously in an ordinary circuit (specifically, one in which Ohm's Law holds) each behaves as though the other were not there. The total or resultant voltage (or current) in the circuit will be the sum of the instantaneous values of the two at every instant. This is because there can be only one value of current or voltage at any single point in a circuit at any instant. Figs. 2-67A and B show two such frequencies, and C shows the resultant. The amplitude of the 1-MHz current is not affected by the presence of the 1-kHz current, but the axis is shifted back and forth at the 1-kHz rate. An attempt to transmit such a combination as a radio wave would result in only the radiation of the

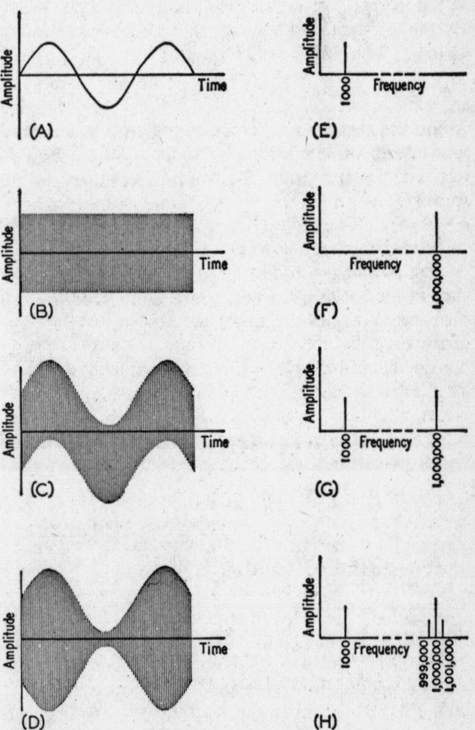

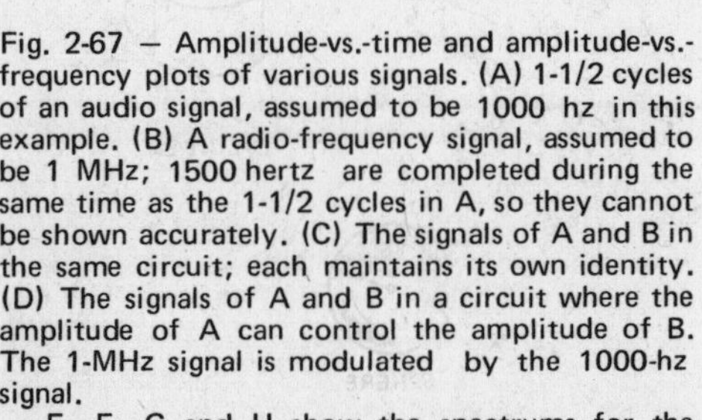

Fig. 2-67 – Amplitude-vs.-time and amplitude-vs.-frequency plots of various signals. (A) 1-1/2 cycles of an audio signal, assumed to be 1000 hz in this example. (B) A radio-frequency signal, assumed to be 1 MHz; 1500 hertz are completed during the same time as the 1-1/2 cycles in A, so they cannot be shown accurately. (C) The signals of A and B in the same circuit; each maintains its own identity. (D) The signals of A and B in a circuit where the amplitude of A can control the amplitude of B. The 1-MHz signal is modulated by the 1000-hz signal.

E, F, G and H show the spectrums for the signals in A, B, C and D, respectively. Note the new frequencies in H, resulting from the modulation process.

1-MHz frequency, since the 1-kHz frequency retains its identity as an audio frequency and will not radiate.

There are devices, however, which make it possible for one frequency to control the amplitude of the other. If, for example, a 1-kHz tone is used to control a 1-MHz signal, the maximum rf output will be obtained when the 1-kHz signal is at the peak of one alternation and the minimum will occur at the peak of the next alternation. The process is called **amplitude modulation**, and the effect is shown in Fig. 2-67D. The resultant signal is now entirely at radio frequency, but with its amplitude varying at the modulation rate (1 kHz). Receiving equipment adjusted to receive the 1-MHz rf signal can reproduce these changes in amplitude, and reveal what the audio signal is, through a process called **detection.**

It might be assumed that the only radio frequency present in such a signal is the original 1.000 MHz, but such is not the case. Two new frequencies have appeared. These are the sum (1.00 + .001) and the difference (1.000 – .001) of the two, and thus the radio frequencies appearing after modulation are 1.001, 1.000 and .999 MHz.

When an audio frequency is used to control the amplitude of a radio frequency, the process is generally called "amplitude modulation," as mentioned, but when a radio frequency modulates another radio frequency it is called **heterodyning.** The processes are identical. A general term for the sum and difference frequencies generated during heterodyning or amplitude modulation is **"beat frequencies,"** and a more specific one is **upper side frequency**, for the sum, and **lower side frequency** for the difference.

In the simple example, the modulating signal was assumed to be a pure tone, but the modulating signal can just as well be a *band* of frequencies making up speech or music. In this case, the side frequencies are grouped into the **upper sideband** and the **lower sideband.** Fig. 2-67H shows the side frequencies appearing as a result of the modulation process.

Amplitude modulation (**a-m**) is not the only possible type nor is it the only one in use. Such signal properties as phase and frequency can also be modulated. In every case the modulation process leads to the generation of a new set (or sets) of radio frequencies symmetrically disposed about the original radio **(carrier)** frequency.

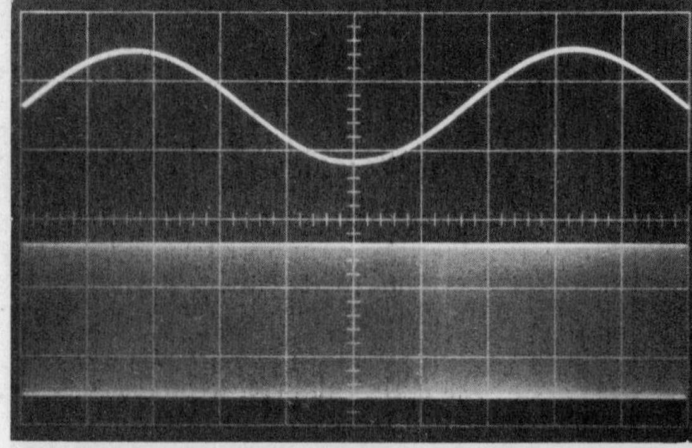

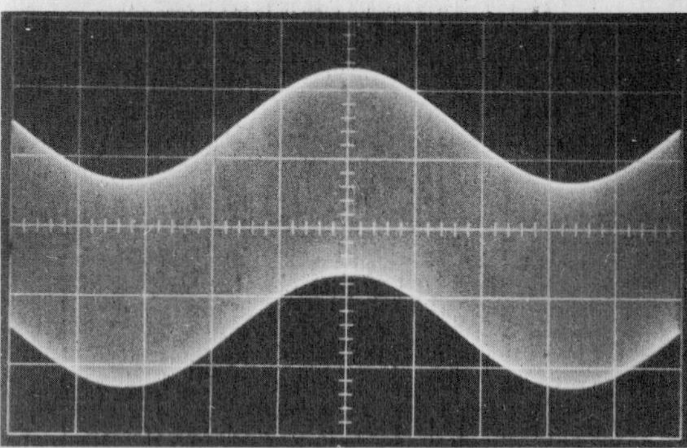

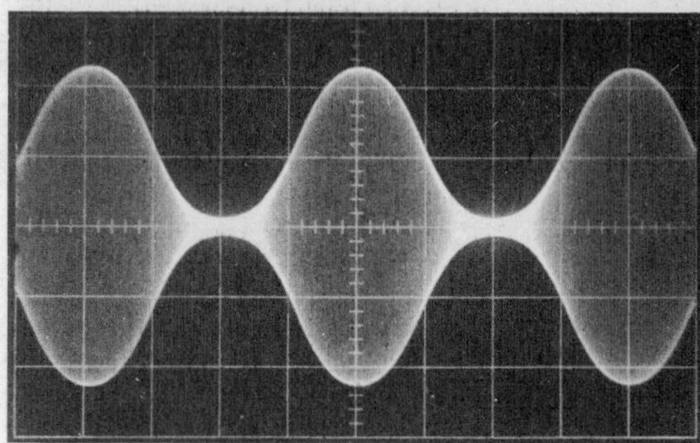

Fig. 2-68 – Actual oscilloscope photograph showing the signals described in the text and shown in the drawings of Fig. 2-67.

TOROIDAL INDUCTORS AND TRANSFORMERS

With many builders, miniaturization is the watchword. This is especially true when working with solid-state and etched-circuit projects. One of the deterrents encountered in designing small-volume equipment is the squeezing in of bulky inductors – slug-tuned or air wound – into a compact assembly. Toroids offer a practical solution to the problem of mass. The good points do not end there, however; toroidal-wound inductors not only fit into small places, they offer exceptionally high values of tuned-circuit *Q*, a definite attribute when selectivity in an important consideration in equipment performance. Ordinarily, air-wound inductors which provide comparable *Q* are many times larger than are their toroidal kinsmen. The correct type of core material must be used in order to realize the best possible *Q* at a particular frequency.

Minimum interaction between the tuned stages of a given piece of equipment is usually of paramount importance to the builder. Here is where the toroid performs well; a toroidal inductor is self-shielding. That is to say, its magnetic flux is very nearly all contained within the coil itself. This feature cuts down stray inductive coupling between adjacent circuits and permits the toroid to be mounted physically close to other components – including the chassis and cabinet walls – without impairment of its efficiency. The latter is not true of ordinary rf or af inductors. Because the flux is contained within the toroid coil, tighter coupling between windings, when a primary and secondary are used, is possible.

The high permeability of ferrite toroid cores permits the user to employ fewer turns in the tuned-circuit inductor. With fewer turns of wire required, larger wire gauges can be used, with a resultant reduction in heating and I^2R losses. This feature is especially beneficial in transistorized equipment where high collector currents are frequently required.

It is best to understand that the word "toroidal" refers to a physical format – doughnut shape – rather than to a specific device or type of material. Toroid cores come in a host of sizes, are manufactured by many firms (each with a different identifying code for the type of core material used), and are fashioned from a wide variety of materials. Some cores are made by rolling up great lengths of thin silicon steel tape (Hypersil) into a toroidal form. Such cores are held together by means of plastic covers, or are wrapped with glass tape which holds the core intact while insulating it from the wire which is wound on it. This type of core is commonly used for low-frequency power applications such as dc-to-dc, and dc-to-ac converters. For audio and rf applications powdered iron and ferrite (a newer type of ceramic) material are generally used. Ferrite acts like an insulating material, making it unnecessary in all instances to place a layer of tape between the core and the winding of the transformer or inductor.

Choosing a Core

There is no simple rule that can be used for selecting a toroid core for a particular job. Many things must be considered notably the intended frequency of operation, the operating frequency versus the physical size and permeability of the core, and whether or not the core will be used in a small- or large-signal tuned circuit. The higher the permeability rating of the material, the fewer will be the number of turns required to obtain a specific inductance value. For example: if a core of certain size has a permeability rating of 400, it might require, say, 25 turns of wire to give an inductance of 10 μH. Therefore, where minimum I^2R loss in the winding is desirable, the higher permeability is better. A core with a larger cross-sectional area (computed from inside diameter, outside diameter, and core height) will reduce the required number of turns also. These are but a few possibilites to consider when selecting a core. Q1 material is rated for rf applications up to 10 MHz, Q2 stock is good to 50 MHz, and Q3 ferrite is rated to 225 MHz. These three ranges handle most rf needs. [1] If the improper material is chosen for a given frequency of operation, the core material will not provide a high-*Q* inductor. In fact, the wrong material can completely ruin a tuned circuit. If too large a core (physical size) is used in the upper hf region, or at vhf, it may be impossible to wind a suitable coil on the toroid because so little wire will be required to provide the needed value of inductance. For this reason, the smaller cores, and those with low permeability ratings, should be used in the upper frequency range.

It is helpful to have some knowledge of the core types offered by the various companies before ordering a toroid for a particular project. Indiana General offers a specification sheet for each of their core materials (see Table I). Each sheet lists such data as permeability, flux density, residual magnetism, usable frequency range, and the loss factor at a specified frequency. Bulletin 101A lists the physical dimensions of their cores and also gives the cross-sectional area of each model in square inches. With this information one can calculate the required number of turns for a specific inductance value, using a selected core size. With the foregoing information at our disposal, the formula given here will enable the constructor to determine the inductance of a toroid when the number of turns is known:

$$L = \left(0.0046\, \mu N^2 h \,\log_{10} \frac{OD}{ID} \right) \mu H$$

Where L = inductance
μ = permeability of the material
N = number of turns
OD = outer diameter of core (cm.)
ID = inner diameter of core (cm.)
h = height of core (in cm.)

To obtain dimensions in centimeters, multiply inches by 2.54. The inductance nomogram given in Fig. 2-70 can be used when designing toroidal inductors which are to be wound on the standard cores offered by Indiana General.

Specific Applications

Because toroids can be used in circuits that handle anything from microwatts to kilowatts, they can be put to good use in almost any tuned-circuit or transformer application.

Most amateurs are familiar with balun transformers, having used them at one time or another in their antenna systems. Toroids find widespread use as balun transformers because they provide a broad-band transformer that is compact and offers good power-transfer efficiency. An article which describes how to contruct homemade toroidal baluns was published in August 1964 *QST*. Core size with respect to four different power levels – 150 to 1000 watts – is treated in the article.

Toroidal inductors are useful when applied to circuits in which a high degree of selectivity is desired. A high-*Q* toroidal tuned circuit in the rf and mixer stages of a communications receiver can aid image rejection more than is possible with conventional slug-tuned inductors.

---

[1] Q1, Q2, and Q3 designations used here are those assigned to cores made by Indiana General Corp., Keasbey, NJ 08832. Other manufactures of ferramic materials use different identifying codes.

Another application for toroidal inductors is in transistorized transmitting and receiving equipment – and in some vacuum-tube circuits – where broad-band input, interstage, or output rf transformers are desired. Toroids can be used in such circuits to provide good efficiency and small physical size. The broad-band transformer requires no tuning controls when properly designed for a given frequency range – a particularly useful feature in mobile equipment. It is not difficult to design a broad-band transformer [2] that will work over a range of 3 to 30 MHz, but one must take precautions against the radiation of harmonic energy when using this kind of transformer in the final stage of a transmitter.

Compact equipment calls for the close spacing of component parts, often requiring that the tuned circuits of several stages be in close physical proximity. This sort of requirement often leads to electrical instability of one or more of the stages, because of unwanted interstage coupling, thus impairing the performance of the equipment. Because the toroidal transformer or inductor is self-shielding, it is possible to place the tuned circuits much closer together than when using conventional inductors. The self-shielding feature also makes it possible to mount a toroid against a circuit board, or against a metal chassis or cabinet wall, without significantly affecting their *Q*. Normally, the most noticeable effect of moving a toroid closer to or farther away from a metal surface is a change in overall circuit capacitance, which in turn slightly affects the resonant frequency of the toroidal tuned circuit. Because fewer turns of wire are needed for a toroid coil than for ordinary ai-wound or slug-tuned inductors, the assembly can be made extremely compact – a much sought-after feature in miniaturized equipment.

Inductors and transformers which are wound on toroid cores are subject to the same general conditions that are common to the laminated iron-core types treated earlier in this chapter. A sufficient amount of cross-sectional area is necessary for a given amount of power in order to prevent saturation and heating. Either of these conditions will seriously impair the efficiencyof a circuit. When toroids are used in circuits where high pk-pk rf voltage is (or can be) present, the core should be wrapped with glass tape or some insulating material of similar characteristics. Teflon-insulated wire should be used to prevent flashover between turns, or between the winding and the core.

Additional design data and information on making one's own toroid cores are given in, "Toroidal-Wound Inductors," *QST* for January 1968, page 11. Industrial data files and application notes are available from the manufacturers of ferrite products.[3]

[2] C.L. Ruthroff, "Some Broadband Transformers", *Proc. IREs* Vol. 47, p. 137, Aug. 1959.

[3] Indiana General Corp., Electronics Div./Ferrites, Keasbey, NJ 08832. Also, Ferroxcube Corp. of America, Saugerties, NY 12477 and Amidon Associates, 12033 Otsego St., N. Hollywood, CA 91607.

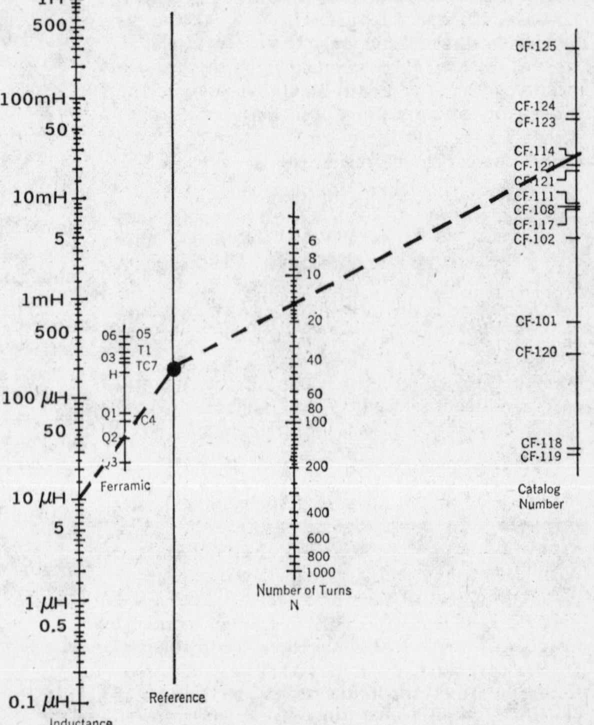

Fig. 2-69 – Nomograph which can be used to calculate the number of turns required for a specific inductance once the type of core (Indiana General) is known. Draw a line of inductance, L through the marker which indicates the core material being used, Q1, Q2, Q3, etc. Complete this line until it intersects the Reference line. Now draw a line from the intersect point on the Reference line to the catalog number line of the nomogram (CF number of the core). This line will cross the Number of Turns (N) line, indicating the number of turns needed. Example shown 15-turn winding required for 10μH inductance on CF-114 core of Q2 material. (Nomogram courtesy of Indiana General.)

Chapter 3

Vacuum-Tube Principles

CURRENT IN A VACUUM

The outstanding difference between the vacuum tube and most other electrical devices is that the electric current does not flow through a conductor but through empty space – a vacuum. This is only possible when "free" electrons – that is, electrons that are not attached to atoms – are somehow introduced into the vacuum. Free electrons in an evacuated space will be attracted to a positively charged object within the same space, or will be repelled by a negatively charged object. The movement of the electrons under the attraction or repulsion of such charged objects constitutes the current in the vacuum.

The most practical way to introduce a sufficiently large number of electrons into the evacuated space is by **thermionic emission.**

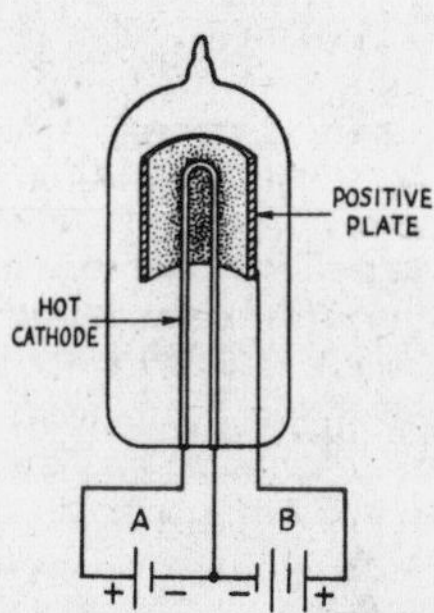

Fig. 3-1 – Conduction by thermionic emission in a vacuum tube. The A battery is used to heat the cathode to a temperature that will cause it to emit electrons. The B battery makes the plate positive with respect to the cathode, thereby causing the emitted electrons to be attracted to the plate. Electrons captured by the plate flow back through the B battery to the cathode.

Thermionic Emission

If a piece of metal is heated to incandescence in a vacuum, electrons near the surface are given enough energy of motion to fly off into the surrounding space. The higher the temperature, the greater the number of electrons emitted. The name for the emitting metal is **cathode.**

If the cathode is the only thing in the vacuum, most of the emitted electrons stay in its immediate vicinity, forming a "cloud" about the cathode. The reason for this is that the electrons in the space, being negative electricity, for a negative charge **(space charge)** in the region of the cathode. The space charge repels those electrons nearest the cathode, tending to make them fall back on it.

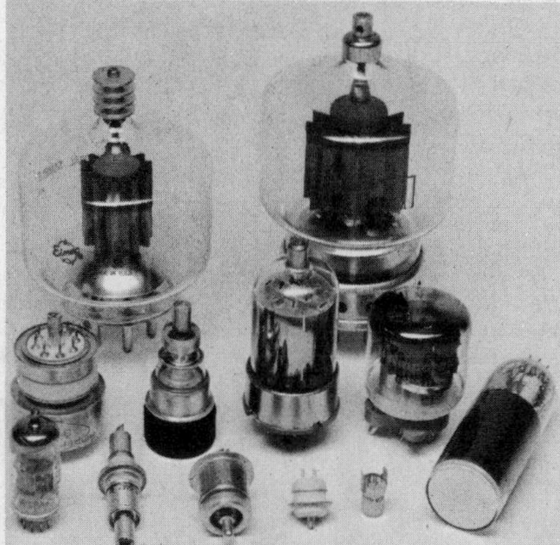

Transmitting tubes are in the back and center rows. Receiving tubes are in the front row (l. to r.): miniature, pencil, planar triode (two), Nuvistor and 1-inch diameter cathode-ray tube.

Now suppose a second conductor is introduced into the vacuum, but not connected to anything else inside the tube. If this second conductor is given a positive charge by connecting a voltage source between it and the cathode, as indicated in Fig. 3-1, electrons emitted by the cathode are attracted to the positively charged conductor. An electric current then flows through the circuit formed by the cathode, the charged conductor, and the voltage source. In Fig. 3-1 this voltage source is a battery (**"B" battery**); a second battery (**"A" battery**) is also indicated for heating the cathode to the proper operating temperature.

The positively charged conductor is usually a metal plate or cylinder (surrounding the cathode) and is called an **anode** or **plate.** Like the other working parts of a tube, it is a **tube element** or **electrode.** The tube shown in Fig. 3-1 is a **two-element** or **two-electrode** tube, one element being the cathode and the other the anode or plate.

Since electrons are negative electricity, they will be attracted to the plate *only* when the plate is positive with respect to the cathode. If the plate is given a negative charge, the electrons will be repelled back to the cathode and no current will flow. The vacuum tube therefore can conduct *only in one direction.*

Cathodes

Before electron emission can occur, the cathode must be heated to a high temperature. However, it is not essential that the heating current flow

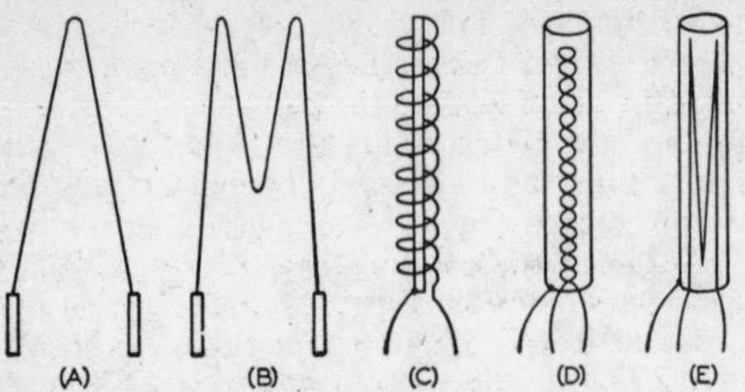

Fig. 3-2 – Types of cathode construction. Directly heated cathodes or "filaments" are shown at A, B, and C. The inverted V filament is used in small receiving tubes, the M in both receiving and transmitting tubes. The spiral filament is a transmitting tube type. The indirectly heated cathodes at D and E show two types of heater construction, one a twisted loop and the other bunched heater wires. Both types tend to cancel the magnetic fields set up by the current through the heater.

through the actual material that does the emitting; the filament or heater can be electrically separate from the emitting cathode. Such a cathode is called **indirectly heated**, while an emitting filament is called a **directly heated** cathode. Fig. 3-2 shows both types in the forms which they commonly take.

Much greater electron emission can be obtained, at relatively low temperatures, by using special cathode materials rather than pure metals. One of these is **thoriated tungsten** or tungsten in which thorium is dissolved. Still greater efficiency is achieved in the **oxide-coated** cathode, a cathode in which rare-earth oxides form a coating over a metal base.

Although the oxide-coated cathode has the highest efficiency, it can be used successfully only in tubes that operate at rather low plate voltages. Its use is therefore confined to receiving-type tubes and to the smaller varieties of transmitting tubes. The thoriated filament, on the other hand, will operate well in high-voltage tubes.

Plate Current

If there is only a small positive voltage on the plate, the number of electrons reaching it will be small because the space charge (which is negative) prevents those electrons nearest the cathode from being attracted to the plate. As the plate voltage is increased, the effect of the space charge is increasingly overcome and the number of electrons attracted to the plate becomes larger. That is, the **plate current** increases with increasing plate voltage.

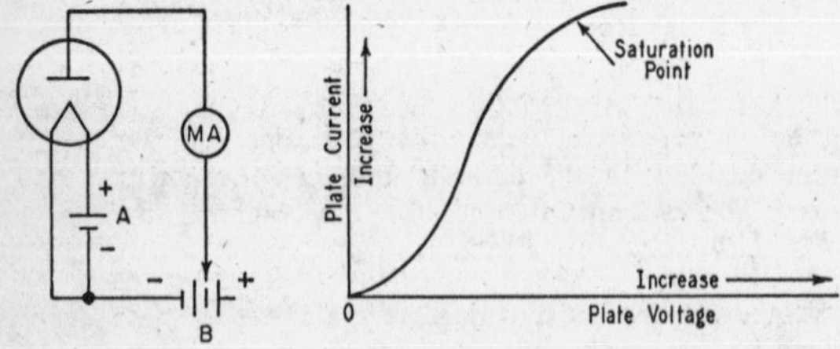

Fig. 3-3 – The diode, or two-element tube, and a typical curve showing how the plate current depends upon the voltage applied to the plate.

Fig. 3-3 shows a typical plot of plate current *vs.* plate voltage for a two-element tube or **diode.** A curve of this type can be obtained with the circuit shown, if the plate voltage is increased in small steps and a current reading taken (by means of the current-indicating instrument – a milliammeter) at each voltage. The plate current is zero with no plate voltage and the curve rises until a **saturation point** is reached. This is where the positive charge on the plate has substantially overcome the space charge and almost all the electrons are going to the plate. At higher voltages the plate current stays at practically the same value.

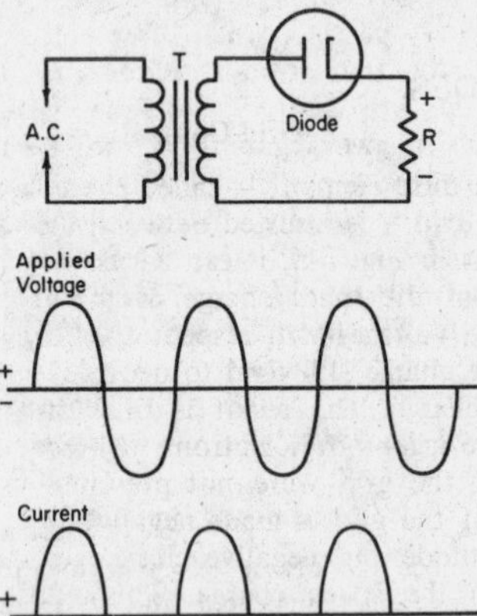

Fig. 3-4 – Rectification in a diode. Current flows only when the plate is positive with respect to the cathode, so that only half-cycles of current flow through the load resistor, *R*.

The plate voltage multiplied by the plate current is the **power input** to the tube. In a circuit like that of Fig. 3-3 this power is all used in heating the plate. If the power input is large, the plate temperature may rise to a very high value (the plate may become red or even white hot). The heat developed in the plate is radiated to the bulb of the tube, and in turn radiated by the bulb to the surrounding air.

RECTIFICATION

Since current can flow through a tube in only one direction, a diode can be used to change alternating current into direct current. It does this by permitting current to flow only when the anode is positive with respect to the cathode. There is no current flow when the plate is negative.

Fig. 3-4 shows a representative circuit. Alternating voltage from the secondary of the transformer, *T*, is applied to the diode tube in series with a **load resistor**, *R*. The voltage varies as is usual with ac, but current flows through the tube and *R* only when the plate is positive with respect to the cathode – that is, during the half-cycle when the upper end of the transformer winding is positive. During the negative half-cycle there is simply a gap in the current flow. This **rectified** alternating current therefore is an *intermittent* direct current.

The load resistor, *R*, represents the actual circuit in which the rectified alternating current does work. All tubes work with a load of one type or another; in this respect a tube is much like a generator or transformer. A circuit that did not provide a load for the tube would be like a short-circuit across a transformer; no useful purpose would be accomplished and the only result would be the generation of heat in the transformer. So it is with vacuum tubes; they must cause power to be developed in a load in order to serve a useful purpose. Also, to be *efficient* most of the power must do useful work in the load and not be used in heating the plate of the tube. Thus the voltage drop across the load should be much higher than the drop across the diode.

With the diode connected as shown in Fig. 3-4, the polarity of the current through the load is as indicated. If the diode were reversed, the polarity of the voltage developed across the load *R* would be reversed.

VACUUM-TUBE AMPLIFIERS

TRIODES

Grid Control

If a third element – called the **control grid**, or simply **grid** – is inserted between the cathode and plate as in Fig. 3-5, it can be used to control the effect of the space charge. If the grid is given a positive voltage with respect to the cathode, the positive charge will tend to neutralize the negative space charge. The result is that, at any selected plate voltage, more electrons will flow to the plate than if the grid were not present. On the other hand, if the grid is made negative with respect to the cathode the negative charge on the grid will add to the space charge. This will reduce the number of electrons that can reach the plate at any selected plate voltage.

The grid is inserted in the tube to control the space charge and not to attract electrons to itself, so it is made in the form of a wire mesh or spiral. Electrons then can go through the open spaces in the grid to reach the plate.

Characteristic Curves

For any particular tube, the effect of the grid voltage on the plate current can be shown by a set of **characteristic curves.** A typical set of curves is shown in Fig. 3-6, together with the circuit that is used for getting them. For each value of plate voltage, there is a value of negative grid voltage that will reduce the plate current to zero; that is, there is a value of negative grid voltage that will cut off the plate current.

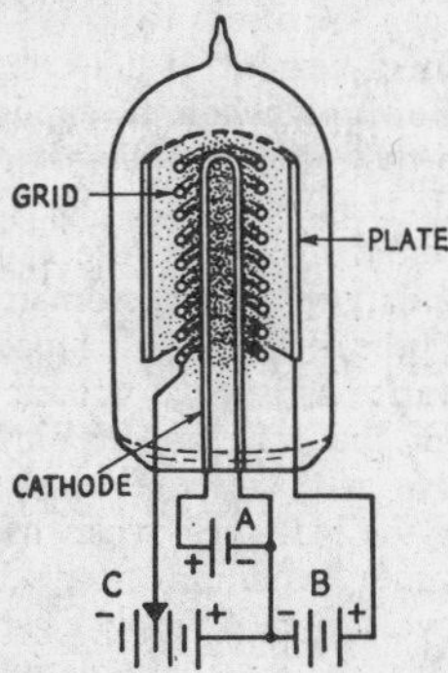

Fig. 3-5 – Construction of an elementary triode vacuum tube, showing the directly-heated cathode (filament), grid (with an end view of the grid wires) and plate. The relative density of the space charge is indicated roughly by the dot density.

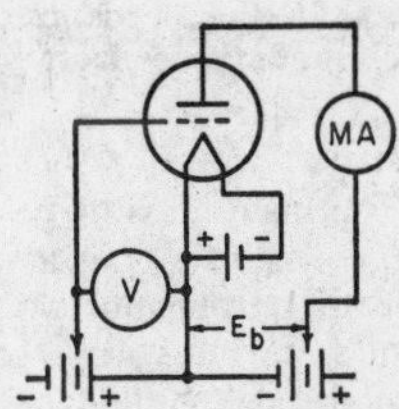

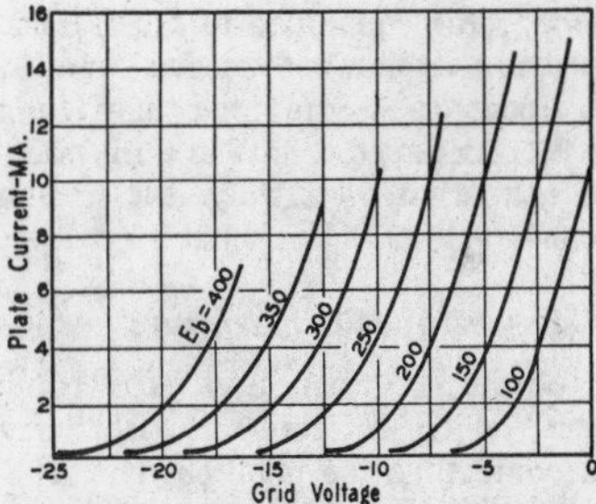

Fig. 3-6 – Grid-voltage-vs.-plate-current curves at various fixed values of plate voltage (E_b) for a typical small triode. Characteristic curves of this type can be taken by varying the battery voltages in the circuit at the right.

The curves could be extended by making the grid voltage positive as well as negative. When the grid is negative, it repels electrons and therefore none of them reaches it; in other words, no current flows in the grid circuit. However, when the grid is positive, it attracts electrons and a current (**grid current**) flows, just as current flows to the positive plate. Whenever there is grid current there is an accompanying power loss in the grid circuit, but so long as the grid is negative no power is used.

It is obvious that the grid can act as a valve to control the flow of plate current. Actually, the grid has a much greater effect on plate current flow than does the plate voltage. A small change in grid voltage is just as effective in bringing about a given change in plate current as is a large change in plate voltage.

The fact that a small voltage acting on the grid is equivalent to a large voltage acting on the plate indicates the possibility of **amplification** with the

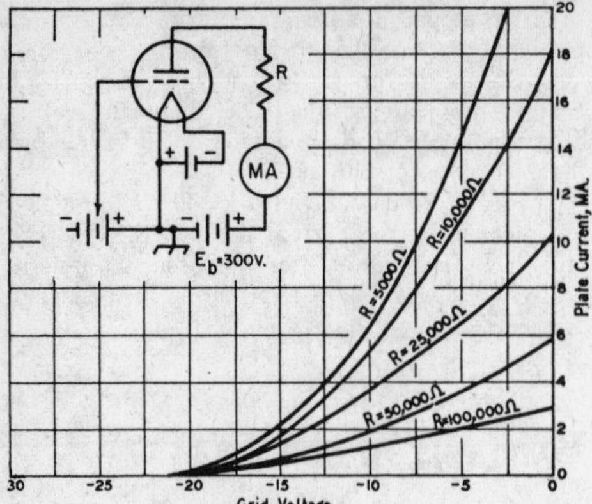

Fig. 3-7 – Dynamic characteristics of a small triode with various load resistances from 5000 to 100,000 ohms.

triode tube. The many uses of the electronic tube nearly all are based upon this amplifying feature. The amplified output is not obtained from the tube itself, but from the voltage source connected between its plate and cathode. The tube simply controls the power from this source, changing it to the desired form.

To utilize the controlled power, a load must be connected in the plate or "output" circuit, just as in the diode case. The load may be either a resistance or an impedance. The term "impedance" is frequently used even when the load is purely resistive.

Tube Characteristics

The physical construction of a triode determines the relative effectiveness of the grid and plate in controlling the plate current. The control of the grid is increased by moving it closer to the cathode or by making the grid mesh finer.

The **plate resistance** of a vacuum tube is the ac resistance of the path from cathode to plate. For a given grid voltage, it is the quotient of a small change in plate voltage divided by the resultant change in plate current. Thus if a 1-volt change in plate voltage caused a plate-current change of .01 mA (.00001 ampere), the plate resistance would be 100,000 ohms.

The **amplification factor** (usually designated by the Greek letter μ) of a vacuum tube is defined as the ratio of the change in plate voltage to the change in grid voltage to effect equal changes in plate current. If, for example, an increase of 10 plate volts raised the plate current 1.0 mA, and an increase in (negative) grid voltage of 0.1 volt were required to return the plate current to its original value, the amplification factors of triode tubes would be 100. The amplification factors of triode tubes range from 3 to 100 or so. A **high-μ** tube is one with an amplification of perhaps 30 or more, **medium-μ** tubes have amplification factors in the approximate range 8 to 30 and **low-μ** tubes in the range below 7 or 8. The μ of a triode is useful in computing stage gains.

The best all-around indication of the effectiveness of a tube as an amplifier is its grid-plate **transconductance** – also called **mutual conductance** or g_m. It is the change in plate current divided by the change in grid voltage that caused the change; it can be found by dividing the amplification factor by the plate resistance. Since current divided by voltage is conductance, transconductance is measured in the unit of conductance, the mho.

Practical values of transconductance are very small, so the micromho (one millionth of a mho) is the commonly used unit. Different types of tubes have transconductances ranging from a few hundred to several thousand. The higher the transconductance the greater the posible amplification.

AMPLIFICATION

The way in which a tube amplifies is best known by a type of graph called the **dynamic characteristic**. Such a graph, together with the circuit used for obtaining it, is shown in Fig. 3-7. The curves are taken with the plate-supply voltage fixed at the desired operating value. The difference between this circuit and the one shown in Fig. 3-6 is that in Fig. 3-7 a load resistance is connected in series with the plate of the tube. Fig. 3-7 thus shows how the plate current will vary, with different grid voltages, when the plate current is made to flow through a load and thus do useful work.

The several curves in Fig. 3-7 are for various values of load resistance. When the resistance is small (as in the case of the 5000-ohm load) the plate current changes rather rapidly with a given change in grid voltage. If the load resistance is high (as in the 100,000-ohm curve), the change in plate current for the same grid-voltage change is relatively small; also, the curve tends to be straighter.

Fig. 3-8 is the same type of curve, but with the circuit arranged so that a source of alternating voltage (**signal**) is inserted between the grid and the grid battery (**"C" battery**). The voltage of the grid battery is fixed at −5 volts, and from the curve it is seen that the plate current at this grid voltage is 2 milliamperes. This current flows when the load resistance is 50,000 ohms, as indicated in the circuit diagram. If there is no ac signal in the grid circuit, the voltage drop in the load resistor is 50,000 × .002 = 100 volts, leaving 200 volts between the plate and cathode.

When a sine-wave signal having a peak value of 2 volts is applied in series with the bias voltage in the grid circuit, the instantaneous voltage at the grid will swing to −3 volts at the instant the signal reaches its positive peak, and to −7 volts at the instant the signal reaches its negative peak. The maximum plate current will occur at the instant the grid voltage is −3 volts. As shown by the graph, it will have a value of 2.65 milliamperes. The minimum plate current occurs at the instant the grid voltage is −7 volts, and has a value of 1.35 mA. At intermediate values of grid voltage, intermdiate plate-current values will occur.

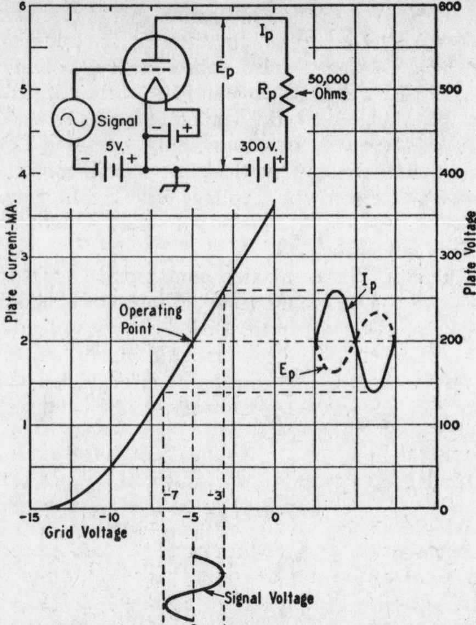

Fig. 3-8 – Amplifier operation. When the plate current varies in response to the signal applied to the grid, a varying voltage drop appears across the load, R_p, as shown by the dashed curve. E_p. I_p is the plate current.

The instantaneous voltage between the plate and cathode of the tube also is shown on the graph. When the plate current is maximum, the instantaneous voltage drop in R_p is 50,000 × .00265 = 132.5 volts; when the plate current is minimum the instantaneous voltage drop in R_p is 50,000 × .00135 = 67.5 volts. The actual voltage between plate and cathode is the difference between the plate-supply potential, 300 volts, and the voltage drop in the load resistance. The plate-to-cathode voltage is therefore 167.5 volts at maximum plate current and 232.5 volts at minimum plate current.

This varying plate voltage is an ac voltage superimposed on the steady plate-cathode potential of 200 volts (as previously determined for no-signal conditions). The peak value of this ac **output voltage** is the difference between either the maximum or minimum plate-cathode voltage and the no-signal value of 200 volts. In the illustration this difference is 232.5 – 200 or 200 – 167.5; that is, 32.5 volts in either case. Since the grid signal voltage has a peak value of 2 volts, the **voltage-amplification ratio** of the amplifier is 32.5/2 or 16.25. That is, approximately 16 times as much voltage is obtained from the plate circuit as is applied to the grid circuit.

As shown by the drawings in Fig. 3-8, the alternating component of the plate voltage swings in the *negative* direction (with reference to the no-signal value of plate-cathode voltage) when the grid voltage swings in the *positive* direction, and vice versa. This means that the alternating component of plate voltage (that is, the amplified signal) is 180 degrees out of phase with the signal voltage on the grid.

Bias

The fixed negative grid voltage (called **grid bias**) in Fig. 3-8 serves a very useful purpose. One object of the type of amplification shown in this drawing is to obtain, from the plate circuit, an alternating voltage that has the same wave shape as the signal voltage applied to the grid. To do so, an **operating point** on the straight part of the curve must be selected. The curve must be straight in both directions from the operating point at least far enough to accommodate the maximum value of the signal applied to the grid. If the grid signal swings the plate current back and forth over a part of the curve that is not straight, as in Fig. 3-9, the shape of the ac wave in the plate circuit will not be the same as the shape of the grid-signal wave. In such a case the output wave shape will be **distorted.**

A second reason for using negative grid bias is that any signal whose peak positive voltage does not exceed the fixed negative voltage on the grid cannot cause grid current to flow. With no current flow there is no power consumption, so the tube will amplify without taking any power from the signal source. (However, if the positive peak of the signal does exceed the negative bias, current will flow in the grid circuit during the time the grid is positive.)

Distortion of the output wave shape that results from working over a part of the curve that is not straight (that is, a **nonlinear** part of the curve) has the effect of transforming a sine-wave grid signal into a more complex waveform. As explained in an earlier chapter, a complex wave can be resolved into a fundamental and a series of harmonics. In other words, distortion from nonlinearity causes the generation of harmonic frequencies – frequencies that are not present in the signal applied to the

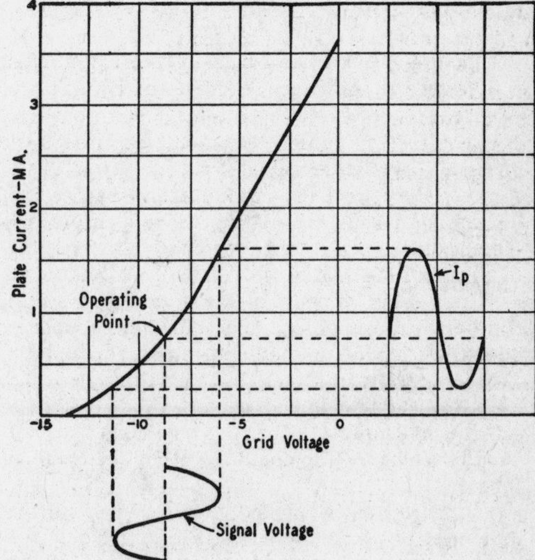

Fig. 3-9 – Harmonic distortion resulting from choice of an operating point on the curved part of the tube characteristic. The lower half-cycle of plate current does not have the same shape as the upper half-cycle.

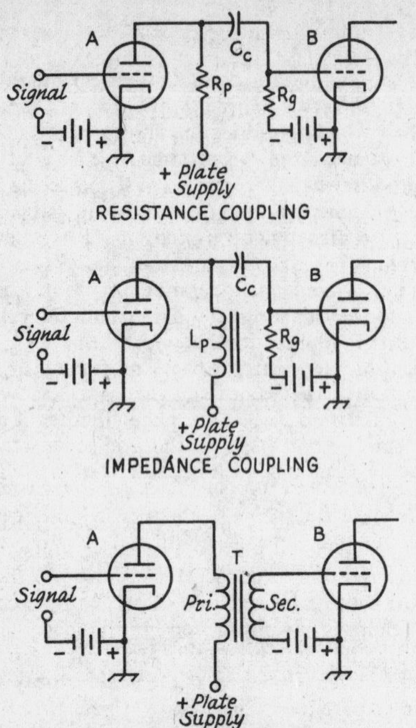

Fig. 3-10 – Three types of coupling are in common use at audio frequencies. These are resistance coupling, impedance coupling, and transformer coupling. In all three cases the output is shown coupled to the grid circuit of a subsequent amplifier tube, but the same types of circuits can be used to couple to other devices than tubes.

grid. Harmonic distortion is undesirable in most amplifiers, although there are occasions when harmonics are deliberately generated and used.

Audio Amplifier Output Circuits

The useful output of a vacuum-tube amplifier is the *alternating* component of plate current or plate voltage. The dc voltage on the plate of the tube is essential for the tube's operation, but it almost invariably would cause difficulties if it were applied, along with the ac output voltage, to the load. The output circuits of vacuum tubes are therefore arranged so that the ac is transferred to the load but the dc is not.

Three types of coupling are in common use at audio-frequencies. These are **resistance coupling, impedance coupling,** and **transformer coupling.** They are shown in Fig. 3-10. In all three cases the output is shown coupled to the grid circuit of a subsequent amplifier tube, but the same types of circuits can be used to couple to other devices than tubes.

In the resistance-coupled circuit, the ac voltage developed across the **plate resistor** R_p (that is, the ac voltage between the plate and cathode of the tube) is applied to a second resistor, R_g, through a **coupling capacitor,** C_c. The capacitor "blocks off" the dc voltage on the plate of the first tube and prevents it from being applied to the grid of tube *B*. The latter tube has negative grid bias supplied by the battery shown. No current flows on the grid circuit of tube *B* and there is therefore no dc voltage drop in R_g; in other words, the full voltage of the bias battery is applied to the grid of tube *B*.

The **grid resistor** R_g, usually has a rather high value (0.5 to 2 megohms). The reactance of the coupling capacitor, C_c, must be low enough compared with the resistance of R_g so that the ac voltage drop in C_c is negligible at the lowest frequency to be amplified. If R_g is at least 0.5 megohm, a 0.1-μF capacitor will be amply large for the usual range of audio frequencies.

So far as the alternating component of plate voltage is concerned, it will be realized that if the voltage drop in C_c is negligible then R_p and R_g are effectively in parallel (although they are quite separate so far as dc is concerned). The resultant parallel resistance of the two is therefore the actual load resistance for the tube. That is why R_g is made as high in resistance as possible; then it will have the least effect on the load represented by R_p.

The impedance-coupled circuit differs from that using resistance coupling only in the substitution of a high inductance (as high as several hundred henrys) for the plate resistor. The advantage of using an inductor rather than a resistor at this point is that the impedance of the inductor is high for audio frequencies, but its resistance, is relatively low. Thus it provides a higher value of load impedance for ac without an excessive dc voltage drop, and consequently the power-supply voltage does not have to be high for effective operation.

The transformer-coupled amplifier uses a transformer with its primary connected in the plate circuit of the tube and its secondary connected to the load (in the circuit shown, a following amplifier). There is no direct connection between the two windings, so the plate voltage on tube *A* is isolated from the grid of tube *B*. The transformer-coupled amplifier has the same advantage as the impedance-coupled circuit with respect to loss of dc voltage from the plate supply. Also, if the secondary has more turns than the primary, the output voltage will be "stepped up" in proportion to the turns ratio.

Resistance coupling is simple, inexpensive, and will give the same amount of amplification – or **voltage gain** – over a wide range of frequencies; it will give substantially the same amplification at any frequency in the audio range, for example. Impedance coupling will give somewhat more gain, with the same tube and same plate-supply voltage, than resistance coupling. However, it is not quite so good over a wide frequency range; it tends to "peak," or give maximum gain, over a comparatively narrow band of frequencies. With a good transformer the gain of a transformer-coupled amplifier can be kept fairly constant over the audio-frequency range. On the other hand, transformer coupling in voltage amplifiers (see below) is best suited to triodes having amplification factors of about 20 or less, for the reason that the primary inductance of a practicable transform-

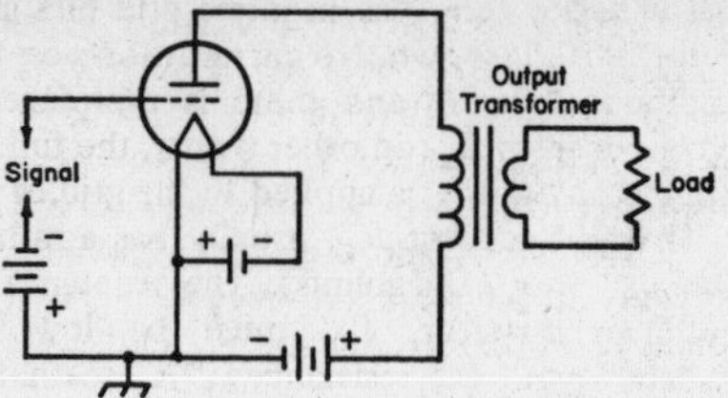

Fig. 3-11 — An elementary power-amplifier circuit in which the power-consuming load is coupled to the plate circuit through an impedance-matching transformer.

er cannot be made large enough to work well with a tube having high plate resistance.

Class A Amplifiers

An amplifier in which voltage gain is the primary consideration is called a **voltage amplifier.** Maximum voltage gain is secured when the load resistance or impedance is made as high as possible in comparison with the plate resistance of the tube. In such a case, the major portion of the voltage generated will appear across the load.

Voltage amplifiers belong to a group called **Class A amplifiers.** A Class A amplifier is one operated so that the wave shape of the output voltage is the same as that of the signal voltage applied to the grid. If a Class A amplifier is biased so that the grid is always negative, even with the largest signal to be handled by the grid, it is called a **Class A_1 amplifier.** Voltage amplifiers are always Class A_1 amplifiers, and their primary use is in driving a following Class A_1 amplifier.

Power Amplifiers

The end result of any amplification is that the amplified signal does some work. For example, an audio-frequency amplifier usually drives a loudspeaker that in turn produces sound waves. The greater the amount of af power supplied to the speaker the louder the sound it will produce.

Fig. 3-11 shows an elementary **power-amplifier** circuit. It is simply a transformer-coupled amplifier with the load connected to the secondary. Although the load is shown as a resistor, it actually would be some device, such as a loudspeaker, that employs the power usefully. Every power tube requires a specific value of load resistance from plate to cathode, usually some thousands of ohms, for optimum operation. The resistance of the actual load is rarely the right value for "matching" this optimum load resistance, so the transformer turns ratio is chosen to reflect the power value of resistance into the primary. The turns ratio may be either step-up or step-down, depending on whether the actual load resistance is higher or lower than the load the tube wants.

The **power-amplification ratio** of an amplifier is the ratio of the power output obtained from the plate circuit to the power required from the ac signal in the grid circuit. There is no power lost in the grid circuit of a Class A_1 amplifier, so such an amplifier has an infinitely large power-amplification ratio. However, it is quite possible to operate a Class A amplifier in such a way that current flows in its grid circuit during at least part of the cycle. In such a case power is used up in the grid circuit and the power amplification ratio is not infinite. A tube operated in this fashion is known as a **Class A_2 amplifier.** It is necessary to use a power amplifier to drive a Class A_2 amplifier, because a voltage amplifier cannot deliver power without serious distortion of the wave shape.

Another term used in connection with power amplifiers is **power sensitivity.** In the case of a Class A_1 amplifier, it means the ratio of power output to the grid signal voltage that causes it. If grid current flows, the term usually means the ratio of plate power output to grid power input.

The ac power that is delivered to a load by an amplifier tube has to be paid for in power taken from the source of plate voltage and current. In fact, there is always more power going into the plate circuit of the tube than is coming out as useful output. The difference between the input and output power is used up in heating the plate of the tube, as explained previously. The ratio of useful power output to dc plate input is called the **plate efficiency.** The higher the plate efficiency, the greater the amount of power that can be taken from a tube having a given plate-dissipation rating.

Parallel and Push-Pull

When it is necessary to obtain more power output than one tube is capable of giving, two or more similar tubes may be connected in **parallel.** In this case the similar elements in all tubes are connected together. This method is shown in Fig. 3-12 for a transformer-coupled amplifier. The power output is in proportion to the number of tubes used; the grid signal or **exciting voltage** required, however, is the same as for one tube.

If the amplifier operates in such a way as to consume power in the grid circuit, the grid power required is in proportion to the number of tubes used.

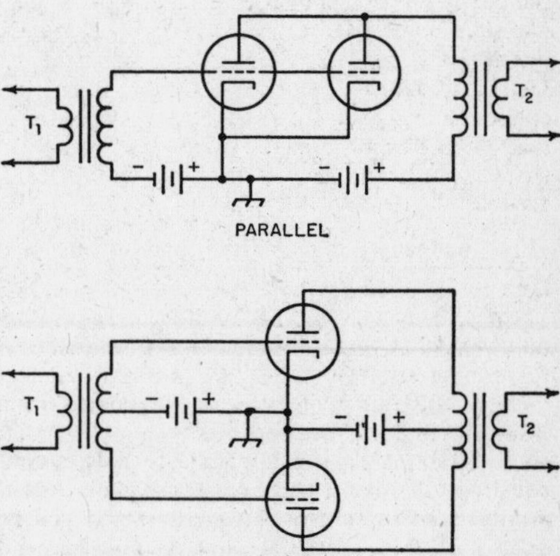

Fig. 3-12 — Parallel and push-pull af amplifier circuits.

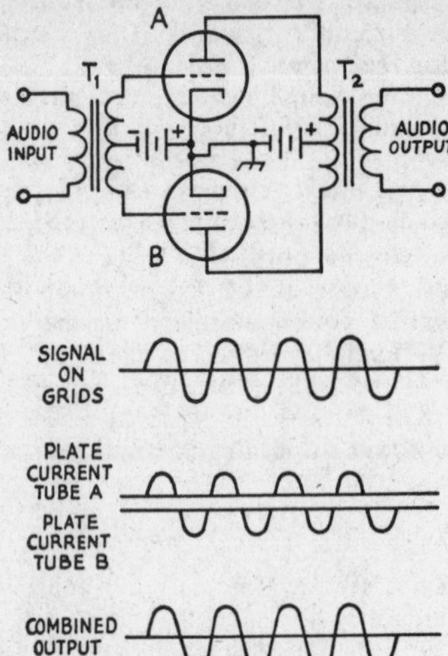

Fig. 3-13 – Class B amplifier operation.

An increase in power output also can be secured by connecting two tubes in **push-pull**. In this case the grids and plates of the two tubes are connected to opposite ends of a balanced circuit as shown in Fig. 3-12. At any instant the ends of the secondary winding of the input transformer, T_1, will be at opposite polarity with respect to the cathode connection, so the grid of one tube is swung positive at the same instant that the grid of the other is swung negative. Hence, in any push-pull-connected amplifier the voltages and currents of one tube are out of phase with those of the other tube.

In push-pull operation the even-harmonic (second, fourth, etc.) distortion is balanced out in the plate circuit. This means that for the same power output the distortion will be less than with parallel operation.

The exciting voltage measured between the two grids must be twice that required for one tube. If the grids consume power, the driving power for the push-pull amplifier is twice that taken by either tube alone.

Cascade Amplifiers

It is readily possible to take the output of one amplifier and apply it as a signal on the grid of a second amplifer, then take the second amplifier's output and apply it to a third, and so on. Each amplifier is called a **stage**, and stages used successively are said to be in **cascade**.

Class B Amplifiers

Fig. 3-13 shows two tubes connected in a push-pull circuit. If the grid bias is set at the point where (when no signal is applied) the plate current is just cut off, then a signal can cause plate current to flow in either tube only when the signal voltage applied to that particular tube is positive with respect to the cathode. Since in the balanced grid circuit the signal voltages on the grids of the two tubes always have opposite polarities, plate current flows only in one tube at a time.

The graphs show the operation of such an amplifier. The plate current of tube *B* is drawn inverted to show that it flows in the opposite direction, through the primary of the output transformer, to the plate current of tube *A*. Thus each half of the output-transformer primary works alternately to induce a half-cycle of voltage in the secondary. In the secondary of T2, the original waveform is restored. This type of operation is called **Class B amplification.**

The Class B amplifier has considerably higher plate efficiency than the Class A amplifier. Furthermore, the dc plate current of a Class B amplifier is proportional to the signal voltage on the grids, so the power input is small with small signals. The dc plate power input to a Class A amplifier is the same whether the signal is large, small, or absent altogether; therefore the maximum dc plate input that can be applied to a Class A amplifier is equal to the rated plate dissipation of the tube or tubes. Two tubes in a Class B amplifier can deliver approximately twelve times as much audio power as the same two tubes in a Class A amplifier.

A Class B amplifier usually is operated in such a way as to secure the maximum possible power output. This requires rather large values of plate current, and to obtain them the signal voltage must completely overcome the grid bias during at least part of the cycle, so grid current flows and the grid circuit consumes power. While the power requirements are fairly low (as compared with the power output), the fact that the grids are positive during only part of the cycle means that the load on the preceding amplifier or **driver stage** varies in magnitude during the cycle; the effective load resistance is high when the grids are not drawing current and relatively low when they do take current. This must be allowed for when designing the driver.

Certain types of tubes have been designed specifically for Class B service and can be operated without fixed or other form of grid bias **(zero-bias tubes)**. The amplification factor is so high that the plate current is small without signal. Because there is no fixed bias, the grids start drawing current immediately whenever a signal is applied, so the grid-current flow is continuous throughout the cycle. This makes the load on the driver much more constant than is the case with tubes of lower μ biased to plate-current cut off.

Class B amplifiers used at radio frequencies are known as **linear amplifiers** because they are adjusted to operate in such a way that the power output is proportional to the square of the rf exciting voltage. This permits amplification of a modulated rf signal without distortion. Push-pull is not required in this type of operation; a single tube can be used equally well.

Class AB Amplifiers

A **Class AB audio amplifier** is a push-pull amplifier with higher bias than would be normal for pure Class A operation, but less than the cut-off bias required for Class B. At low signal levels the tubes operate as Class A amplifiers, and the plate current is the same with or without signal. At higher signal levels, the plate current of one tube is cut off during part of the negative cycle of the signal applied to its grid, and the plate current of the other tube rises with the signal. The total plate current for the amplifier also rises above the no-signal level with a large signal is applied.

In a properly designed Class AB amplifier the distortion is as low as with a Class A stage, but the efficiency and power output are considerably higher than with pure Class A operation. A Class AB amplifier can be operated either with or without driving the grids into the positive region. A **Class AB_1 amplifier** is one in which the grids are never positive with respect to the cathode; therefore no driving power is required – only voltage. A **Class AB_2 amplifier** is one that has grid-current flow during part of the cycle if the applied signal is large; it takes a small amount of driving power. The Class AB_2 amplifier will deliver somewhat more power (using the same tubes) but the Class AB_1 amplifier avoids the problem of designing a driver that will deliver power, without distortion, into a load of highly variable resistance.

Operating Angle

Inspection of Fig. 3-13 shows that either of the two vacuum tubes is working for only half the ac cycle and idling during the other half. It is convenient to describe the amount of time during which plate current flows in terms of electrical degrees. In Fig. 3-13 each tube has "180-degree" excitation, a half-cycle being equal to 180 degrees. The number of degrees during which plate current flows is called the **operating angle** of the amplifier. From the descriptions given above, it should be clear that a Class A amplifier has 360-degree excitation, because plate current flows during the whole cycle. In a Class AB amplifier the operating angle is between 180 and 360 degrees (in each tube) depending on the particular operating conditions chosen. The greater the amount of negative grid bias, the smaller the operating angle becomes.

An operating angle of less than 180 degrees leads to a considerable amount of distortion, because there is no way for the tube to reproduce even a half-cycle of the signal on its grid. Using two tubes in push-pull, as in Fig. 3-13, would merely put together two distorted half-cycles. An operating angle of less than 180 degrees therefore cannot be used if distortionless output is wanted.

Class C Amplifiers

In power amplifiers operating at radio frequencies distortion of the rf wave form is relatively unimportant. For reasons described later in this chapter, an rf amplifier must be operated with tuned circuits, and the selectivity of such circuits "filters out" the rf harmonics resulting from distortion.

A radio-frequency power amplifier therefore can be used with an operating angle of less than 180 degrees. This is called **Class C** operation. The advantage is that the plate efficiency is increased, because the loss in the plate is proportional, among other things, to the amount of time during which the plate current flows, and this time is reduced by decreasing the operating angle.

Depending on the type of tube, the optimum load resistance for a Class C amplifier ranges from about 1500 to 5000 ohms. It is usually secured by using tuned-circuit arrangements, of the type described in the chapter on circuit fundamentals, to transform the resistance of the actual load to the value required by the tube. The grid is driven well into the positive region, so that grid current flows and power is consumed in the grid circuit. The smaller the operating angle, the greater the driving voltage and the larger the grid driving power required to develop full output in the load resistance. The best compromise between driving power, plate efficiency, and power output usually results when the minimum plate voltage (at the peak of the driving cycle, when the plate current reaches its highest value) is just equal to the peak positive grid voltage. Under these conditions the operating angle is usually between 120 and 150 degrees and the plate efficiency lies in the range of 60 to 80 percent. While higher plate efficiencies are possible, attaining them requires excessive driving power and grid bias, together with higher plate voltage than is "normal" for the particular tube type.

With proper design and adjustment, a Class C amplifier can be made to operate in such a way that the power input and output are proportional to the square of the applied plate voltage. This is an important consideration when the amplifier is to be plate-modulated for radiotelephony, as described in the chapter on amplitude modulation.

FEEDBACK

It is possible to take a part of the amplified energy in the plate circuit of an amplifier and insert it into the grid circuit. When this is done the amplifier is said to have **feedback.**

If the voltage that is inserted in the grid circuit is 180 degrees out of phase with the signal voltage acting on the grid, the feedback is called **negative**, or **degenerative.** On the other hand, if the voltage is fed back in phase with the grid signal, the feedback is called **positive**, or **regenerative.**

Negative Feedback

With negative feedback the voltage that is fed back opposes the signal voltage. This decreases the amplitude of the voltage acting between the grid and cathode and thus has the effect of reducing the voltage amplification. That is, a larger exciting voltage is required for obtaining the same output voltage from the plate circuit.

The greater the amount of negative feedback (when properly applied) the more independent the amplification becomes of tube characteristics and circuit conditions. This tends to make the frequency-response characteristic of the amplifier **flat** – that is, the amplification tends to be the same at all frequencies within the range for which the amplifier is designed. Also, any distortion generated in the plate circuit of the tube tends to

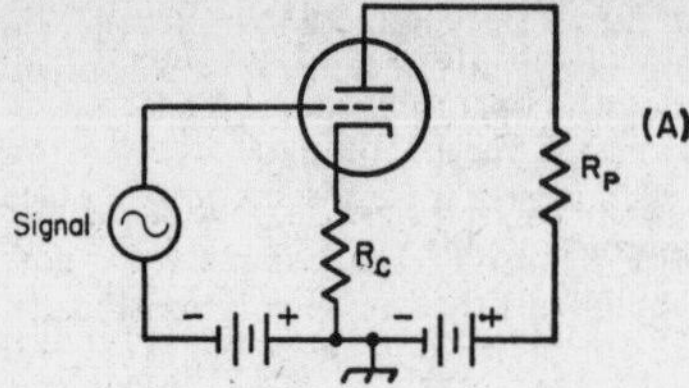

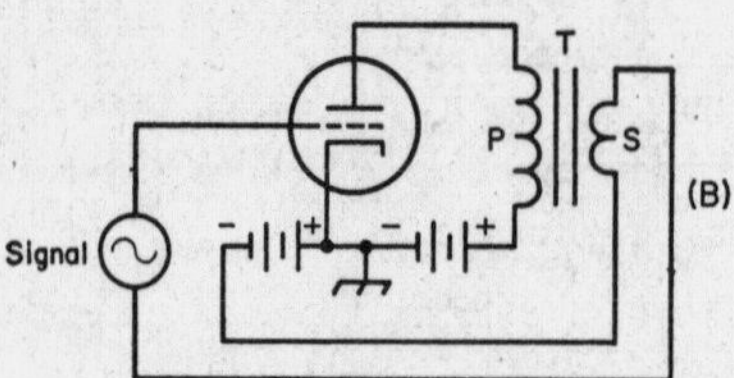

Fig. 3-14 – Simple circuits for producing feedback.

"buck itself out." Amplifiers with negative feedback are therefore comparatively free from harmonic distortion. These advantages are worth while if the amplifier otherwise has enough voltage gain for its intended use.

In the circuit shown at A in Fig. 3-14 resistor R_c is in series with the regular plate resistor, R_p and thus is a part of the load for the tube. Therefore, part of the output voltage will appear across R_c. However, R_c also is connected in series with the grid circuit, and so the output voltage that appears across R_c is in series with the signal voltage. The output voltage across R_c opposes the signal voltage, so the actual ac voltage between the grid and cathode is equal to the *difference* between the two voltages.

The circuit shown At B in Fig. 3-14 can be used to give either negative or positive feedback. The secondary of a transformer is connected back into the grid circuit to insert a desired amount of feedback voltage. Reversing the terminals of either transformer winding (but not both simultaneously) will reverse the phase.

Positive Feedback

Positive feedback increases the amplification because the feedback voltage adds to the original signal voltage and the resulting larger voltage on the grid causes a larger output voltage. The amplification tends to be greatest at one frequency (which depends upon the particular circuit arrangement) and harmonic distortion is increased. If enough energy is fed back, a self-sustaining **oscillation** – in which energy at essentially one frequency is generated by the tube itself – will be set up. In such case all the signal voltage on the grid can be supplied from the plate circuit; no external signal is needed because any small irregularity in the plate current – and there are always some irregularities – will be amplified and thus give the oscillation an opportunity to build up. Positive feedback finds a major application in such "oscillators," and in addition is used for selective amplification at both audio and radio frequencies, the feedback being kept below the value that causes self-oscillation.

INTERELECTRODE CAPACITANCES

Each pair of elements in a tube forms a small capacitor "plate." There are three such capacitances in a triode – that between the grid and cathode, that between the grid and plate, and that between the plate and cathode. The capacitances are very small – only a few picofarads at most – but they frequently have a very pronounced effect on the operation of an amplifier circuit.

Input Capacitance

It was explained previously that the ac grid voltage and ac plate voltage of an amplifier having a resistive load are 180 degrees out of phase, using the cathode of the tube as a reference point. However, these two voltages are *in* phase going around the circuit from plate to grid as shown in Fig. 3-15. This means that their sum is acting between the grid and plate; that is, across the grid-plate capacitance of the tube.

As a result, a capacitive current flows around the circuit, its amplitude being directly proportional to the sum of the ac grid and plate voltages and to the grid-plate capacitance. The source of the grid signal must furnish this amount of current, in addition to the capacitive current that flows in the grid-cathode capacitance. Hence the signal source "sees" an effective capacitance that is larger than the grid-cathode capacitance. This is known as the **Miller Effect.**

The greater the voltage amplification the greater the effective input capacitance. The input capacitance of a resistance-coupled amplifier is given by the formula

$$C_{input} = C_{gk} + C_{gp} (A + 1)$$

where C_{gk} is the grid-to-cathode capacitance, C_{gp} is the grid-to-plate capacitance, and A is the voltage amplification. The input capacitance may be as much as several hundred picofarads when the voltage amplification is large, even though the interelectrode capacitances are quite small.

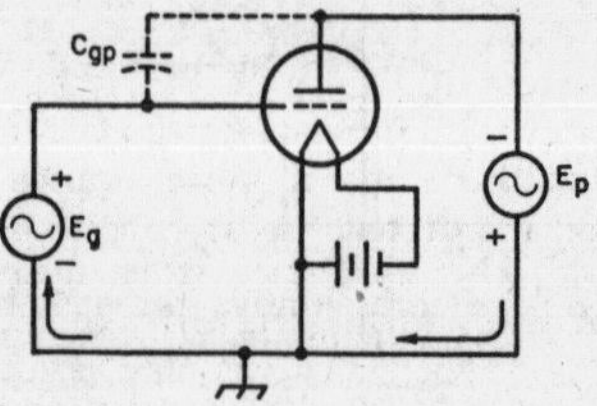

Fig. 3-15 – The ac voltage appearing between the grid and plate of the amplifier is the sum of the signal voltage and the output voltage, as shown by this simplified circuit. Instantaneous polarities are indicated.

Output Capacitance

The principal component of the output capacitance of an amplifier is the actual plate-to-cathode capacitance of the tube. The output capacitance usually need not be considered in audio amplifiers, but becomes of importance at radio frequencies.

Tube Capacitance at RF

At radio frequencies the reactances of even very small interelectrode capacitances drop to very low values. A resistance-coupled amplifier gives very little amplification at rf, for example, because the reactances of the interelectrode "capacitors" are so low that they practically short-circuit the input and output circuits and thus the tube is unable to amplify. This is overcome at radio frequencies by using tuned circuits for the grid and plate, making the tube capacitances part of the tuning capacitances. In this way the circuits can have the high resistive impedances necessary for satisfactory amplification.

The grid-plate capacitance is important at radio frequencies because its reactance, relatively low at rf, offers a path over which energy can be fed back from the plate to the grid. In practically every case the feedback is in the right phase and of sufficient amplitude to cause self-oscillation, so the circuit becomes useless as an amplifier.

Special "neutralizing" circuits can be used to prevent feedback but they are, in general, not too satisfactory when used in radio receivers. They are, however, used in transmitters.

SCREEN-GRID TUBES

The grid-plate capacitance can be reduced to a negligible value by inserting a second grid between the control grid and the plate, as indicated in Fig. 3-16. The second grid, called the **screen grid,** acts as an electrostatic shield to prevent capacitive coupling between the control grid and plate. It is made in the form of a grid or coarse screen so that electrons can pass through it.

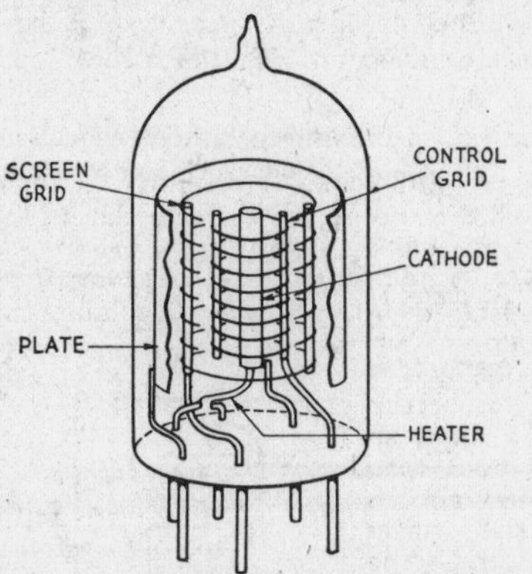

Fig. 3-16 — Representative arrangement of elements in a screen-grid tetrode, with part of plate and screen cut away. This is "single-ended" construction with a button base, typical of miniature receiving tubes. To reduce capacitance between control grid and plate the leads from these elements are brought out at opposite sides; actual tubes probably would have additional shielding between these leads.

Because of the shielding sction of the screen grid, the positively charged plate cannot attract electrons from the cathode as it does in a triode. In order to get electrons to the plate, it is necessary to apply a positive voltage (with respect to the cathode) to the screen. The screen then attracts electrons much as does the plate in a triode tube. In traveling toward the screen the electrons acquire such velocity that most of them shoot between the screen wires and then are attracted to the plate. A certain proportion do strike the screen, however, with the result that some current also flows in the screen-grid circuit.

To be a good shield, the screen grid must be connected to the cathode through a circuit that has low impedance at the frequency being amplified. A bypass capacitor from screen grid to cathode, having a reactance of not more than a few hundred ohms, is generally used.

A tube having a cathode, control grid, screen grid and plate (four elements) is called a **tetrode.**

Pentodes

When an electron traveling at appreciable velocity through a tube strikes the plate it dislodges other electrons which "splash" from the plate into the interelement space. This is called **secondary emission.** In a triode the negative grid repels the secondary electrons back into the plate and they cause no disturbance. In the screen-grid tube, however, the positively charged screen attracts the secondary electrons, causing a reverse current to flow between screen and plate.

To overcome the effects of secondary emission, a third grid, called the **suppressor grid,** may be inserted between the screen and plate. This grid acts as a shield between the screen grid and plate so the secondary electrons cannot be attracted by the screen grid. They are hence attracted back to the plate without appreciably obstructing the regular plate-current flow. A five-element tube of this type is called a **pentode.**

Although the screen grid in either the tetrode or pentode greatly reduces the influence of the plate upon plate-current flow, the control grid still can control the plate current in essentially the same way that it does in a triode. Consequently, the grid-plate transconductance (or mutual conductance) of a tetrode or pentode will be of the same order of value as in a triode of corresponding structure. On the other hand, since a change in plate voltage has very little effect on the plate-current flow, both the amplification factor and plate resistance of a pentode or tetrode are very high. In small receiving pentodes the amplification factor is of the order of 1000 or higher, while the plate resistance may be from 0.5 to 1 or more megohms. Because of the high plate resistance, the actual voltage amplification possible with a pentode is very much less than the large amplification factor might indicate. A voltage gain in the vicinity of 50 to 200 is typical of a pentode stage.

In practical screen-grid tubes the grid-plate capacitance is only a small fraction of a picofarad. This capacitance is too small to cause an appreciable increase in input capacitance as described in the preceding section, so the input capacitance of a screen-grid tube is equal to the capacitance between the plate and screen.

In addition to their applications as radio-frequency amplifiers, pentodes or tetrodes also are used for audio-frequency power amplification. In tubes designed for this purpose the chief function of the screen is to serve as an accelerator of the electrons, so that large values of plate current can be drawn at relatively low plate voltages. Such tubes have quite high power sensitivity compared with triodes of the same power output, although harmonic distortion is somewhat greater.

Beam Tubes

A **beam tetrode** is a four-element screen-grid tube constructed in such a way that the electrons are formed into concentrated beams on their way to the plate. Additional design features overcome the effects of secondary emission so that a suppressor grid is not needed. The "beam" construction makes it possible to draw large plate currents at relatively low plate voltages, and increases the power sensitivity.

For power amplification at both audio and radio frequencies beam tetrodes have largely supplanted the non beam types because large power outputs can be secured with very small amounts of grid driving power.

Variable-μ Tubes

The mutual conductance of a vacuum tube decreases when its grid bias is made more negative, assuming that the other electrode voltages are held constant. Since the mutual conductance controls the amount of amplification, it is possible to adjust the gain of the amplifier by adjusting the grid bias. This method of gain control is universally used in radio-frequency amplifiers designed for receivers.

The ordinary type of tube has what is known as a **sharp-cutoff** characteristic. The mutual conductance decreases at a uniform rate as the negative bias is increased. The amount of signal voltage that such a tube can handle without causing distortion is not sufficient to take care of very strong signals. To overcome this, some tubes are made with a **variable-μ** characteristic – that is, the amplification factor decreases with increasing grid bias. The variable-μ tube can handle a much larger signal than the sharp-cutoff type before the signal swings either beyond the zero grid-bias point or the plate-current cutoff point.

INPUT AND OUTPUT IMPEDANCES

The **input impedance** of a vacuum-tube amplifier is the impedance "seen" by the signal source when connected to the input terminals of the amplifier. In the types of amplifiers previously discussed, the input impedance is the impedance measured between the grid and cathode of the tube with operating voltages applied. At audio frequencies the input impedance of a Class A_1 amplifier is for all practical purposes the input impedance of the stage. If the tube is driven into the grid-current region there is in addition a resistance component in the input impedance, the resistance having an average value equal to E^2/P, where E is the rms driving voltage and P is the power in watts consumed in the grid. The resistance usually will vary during the ac cycle because grid current may flow only during part of the cycle; also, the grid-voltage/grid-current characteristic is seldom linear.

The **output impedance** of amplifiers of this type consists of the plate resistance of the tube shunted by the output capacitance.

At radio frequencies, when tuned circuits are employed, the input and output impedances are usually pure resistances; any reactive components are "tuned out" in the process of adjusting the circuits to resonance at the operating frequency.

OTHER TYPES OF AMPLIFIERS

In the amplifier circuits so far discussed, the signal has been applied between the grid and cathode and the amplified output has been taken from the plate-to-cathode circuit. That is, the cathode has been the meeting point for the input and output circuits. However, it is possible to use any one of the three principal elements as the common point. This leads to two additional kinds of amplifiers, commonly called the **grounded-grid amplifier** (or **grid-separation** circuit) and the **cathode follower.**

These two circuits are shown in simplified form in Fig. 3-17. In both circuits the resistor R represents the load into which the amplifier works; the actual load may be resistance-capacitance-coupled, transformer-coupled, may be a tuned circuit if the amplifier operates at radio frequencies, and so on. Also, in both circuits the batteries that supply grid bias and plate power are assumed to have such negligible impedance that they do not enter into the operation of the circuits.

Grounded-Grid Amplifier

In the grounded-grid amplifier the input signal is applied between the cathode and grid, and the

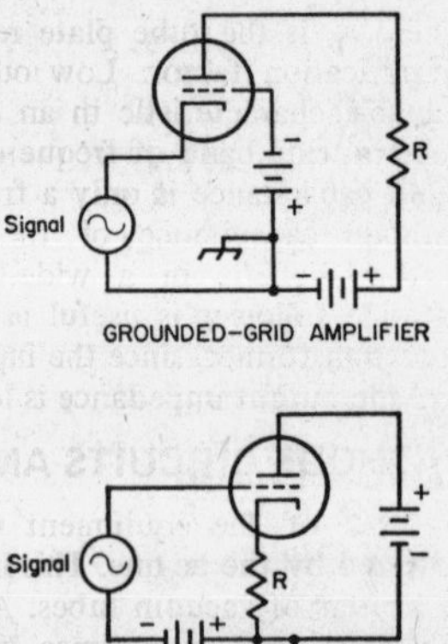

Fig. 3-17 – In the upper circuit, the grid is the junction point between the input and output circuits in the lower drawing, the plate is the junction. In either case the output is developed in the load resistor, R, and may be coupled to a following amplifier by the usual methods.

output is taken between the plate and grid. The grid is thus the common element. The ac component of the plate current has to flow through the signal source to reach the cathode. The source of signal is in series with the load through the plate-to-cathode resistance of the tube, so some of the power in the load is supplied by the signal source. In transmitting applications this fed-through power is of the order of 10 percent of the total power output, using tubes suitable for grounded-grid service.

The input impedance of the grounded-grid amplifier consists of a capacitance in parallel with an equivalent resistance representing the power furnished by the driving source of the grid and to the load. This resistance is of the order of a few hundred ohms. The output impedance, neglecting the interelectrode capacitances, is equal to the plate resistance of the tube. This is the same as in the case of the grounded-cathode amplifier.

The grounded-grid amplifier is widely used at vhf and uhf, where the more conventional amplifier circuit fails to work properly. With a triode tube designed for this type of operation, an rf amplifier can be built that is free from the type of feedback that causes oscillation. This requires that the grid act as a shield between the cathode and plate, reducing the plate-cathode capacitance to a very low value.

Cathode Follower

The cathode follower uses the plate of the tube as the common element. The input signal is applied between the grid and plate (assuming negligible impedance in the batteries) and the output is taken between cathode and plate. This circuit is degenerative; in fact, all of the output voltage is fed back into the input circuit out of phase with the grid signal. The input signal therefore has to be larger than the output voltage; that is, the cathode follower gives a loss in voltage, although it gives the same power gain as other circuits under equivalent operating conditions.

An important feature of the cathode follower is its low output impedance, which is given by the formula (neglecting interelectrode capacitances)

$$Z_{out} = \frac{r_p}{1 + \mu}$$

where r_p is the tube plate resistance and μ is the amplification factor. Low output impedance is a valuable characteristic in an amplifier designed to cover a wide band of frequencies. In addition, the input capacitance is only a fraction of the grid-to-cathode capacitance of the tube, a feature of further benefit in a wide-band amplifier. The cathode follower is useful as a step-down impedance transformer, since the input impedance is high and the output impedance is low.

CATHODE CIRCUITS AND GRID BIAS

Most of the equipment used by amateurs is powered by the ac line. This includes the filaments or heaters of vacuum tubes. Although supplies for the plate (and sometimes the grid) are usually rectified and filtered to give **pure dc** – that is, direct current that is constant and without a superimposed ac component – the relatively large currents required by filaments and heaters usually make a rectifier-type dc supply impracticable.

Filament Hum

Alternating current is just as good as direct current from the heating standpoint, but some of the ac voltage is likely to get on the grid and cause a low-pitched "ac hum" to be superimposed on the output.

Hum troubles are worst with directly-heated cathodes or filaments, because with such cathodes there has to be a direct connection between the source of heating power and the rest of the circuit. The hum can be minimized by either of the connections shown in Fig. 3-18. In both cases the grid- and plate-return circuits are connected to the electrical midpoint **(center tap)** of the filament supply. Thus, so far as the grid and plate are concerned, the voltage and current on one side of the filament are balanced by an equal and opposite voltage and current on the other side. The balance is never quite perfect, however, so filament-type tubes are never completely hum-free. For this reason directly-heated filaments are employed for the most part in power tubes, where the hum introduced is extremely small in comparison with the power-output level.

With indirectly heated cathodes the chief problem is the magnetic field set up by the heater. Occasionally, also, there is leakage between the heater and cathode, allowing a small ac voltage to get to the grid. If hum appears, grounding one side of the heater supply usually will help to reduce it, although sometimes better results are obtained if the heater supply is center-tapped and the center-tap grounded, as in Fig. 3-18.

Cathode Bias

In the simplified amplifier circuits discussed in this chapter, grid bias has been supplied by a battery. However, in equipment that operates from the power line, **cathode bias** is almost universally used for tubes that are operated in Class A (constant dc input).

The cathode-bias method uses a resistor **(cathode resistor)** connected in series with the cathode,

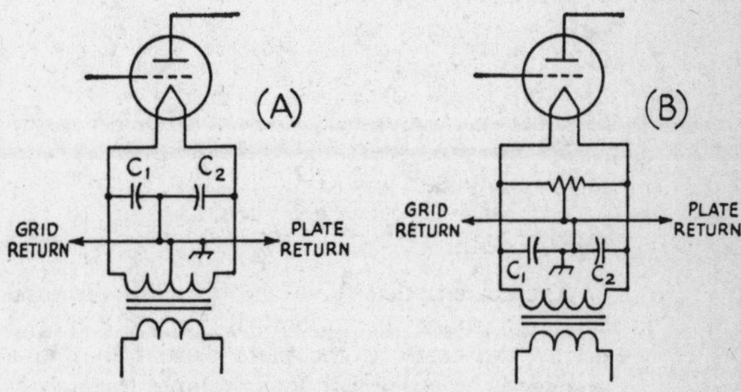

Fig. 3-18 – Filament center-tapping methods for use with directly heated tubes.

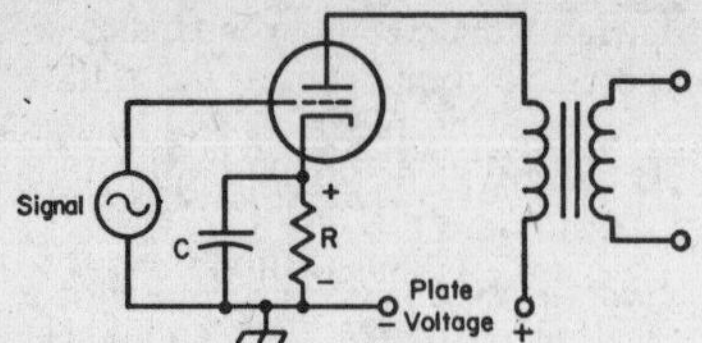

Fig. 3-19 – Cathode biasing. *R* is the cathode resistor and *C* is the cathode bypass capacitor.

as shown at *R* in Fig. 3-19. The direction of plate-current flow is such that the end of the resistor nearest the cathode is positive. The voltage drop across *R* therefore places a *negative* voltage on the grid. This negative bias is obtained from the steady dc plate current.

If the alternating component of plate current flows through *R* when the tube is amplifying, the voltage drop caused by the ac will be degenerative (note the similarity between this circuit and that of Fig. 3-14A). To prevent this the resistor is bypassed by a capacitor, *C*, that has very low reactance compared with the resistance of *R*. Depending on the type of tube and the particular kind of operation, *R* may be between about 100 and 3000 ohms. For good bypassing at the low audio frequencies, *C* should be 10 to 50 microfarads (electrolytic capacitors are used for this purpose). At radio frequencies, capacitances of about 100 pF to 0.1 μF are used; the small values are sufficient at very high frequencies and the largest at low and medium frequencies. In the range 3 to 30 megahertz a capacitance of .01 μF is satisfactory.

The value of cathode resistor for an amplifier having negligible dc resistance in its plate circuit (transformer or impedance coupled) can easily be calculated from the known operating conditions of the tube. The proper grid bias and plate current always are specified by the manufacturer. Knowing these, the required resistance can be found by applying Ohm's Law.

Example: It is found from tube tables that the tube to be used should have a negative grid bias of 8 volts and that at this bias the plate current will be 12 milliamperes (0.012 amp). The required cathode resistance is then

$$R = \frac{E}{I} = \frac{8}{012} = 667 \text{ ohms}$$

The nearest standard value, 680 ohms, would be close enough. The power used in the resistor is

$$P = EI = 8 \times .012 = 0.096 \text{ watt}$$

A 1/4-watt or 1/2-watt resistor would have ample rating.

The current that flows through *R* is the total cathode current. In an ordinary triode amplifier this is the same as the plate current, but in a screen-grid tube the cathode current is the sum of the plate and screen currents. Hence these two currents must be added when calculating the value of cathode resistor required for a screen-grid tube.

Example: A receiving pentode requires 3 volts negative bias. At this bias and the recommended plate and screen voltages, its plate current is 9 mA and its screen current is 2 mA. The cathode current is therefore 11 mA (0.011 amp). The required resistance is

$$R = \frac{E}{I} = \frac{3}{.011} = 272 \text{ ohms}$$

A 270-ohm resistor would be satisfactory. The power in the resistor is

$$P = EI = 3 \times 0.011 = .033 \text{ watt}$$

The cathode-resistor method of biasing is self-regulating, because if the tube characteristics vary slightly from the published values (as they do in practice) the bias will increase if the plate current is slightly high, or decrease if it is slightly low. This tends to hold the plate current at the proper value.

Calculation of the cathode resistor for a resistance-coupled amplifier is ordinarily not practicable by the method described above, because the plate current in such an amplifier is usually much smaller than the rated value given in the tube tables. However, representative data for the tubes commonly used as resistance-coupled amplifiers are given in the chapter on audio amplifiers, including cathode-resistor values.

"Contact Potential" Bias

In the absence of any negative bias voltage on the grid of a tube, some of the electrons in the space charge will have enough velocity to reach the grid. This causes a small current (of the order of microamperes) to flow in the external circuit between the grid and cathode. If the current is made to flow through a high resistance – a megohm or so – the resulting voltage drop in the resistor will give the grid a negative bias of the order of one volt. The bias so obtained is called contact-potential bias.

Contact-potential bias can be used to advantage in circuits operating at low signal levels (less than one volt peak) since it eliminates the cathode-bias resistor and bypass capacitor. It is principally used in low-level resistance-coupled audio amplifiers. The bias resistor is connected directly between grid and cathode, and must be isolated from the signal source by a blocking capacitor.

Screen Supply

In practical circuits using tetrodes and pentodes the voltage for the screen frequently is taken from the plate supply through a resistor. A typical circuit for an rf amplifier is shown in Fig. 3-20. Resistor *R* is the **screen dropping resistor**, and *C* is the **screen bypass capacitor.** In flowing through *R*, the screen current causes a voltage drop in *R* that reduces the plate-supply voltage to the proper value for the screen. When the plate-supply voltage and the screen current are known, the value of *R* can be caluclated from Ohm's Law.

Example: An rf receiving pentode has a rated screen current of 2 milliamperes (0.002 amp) at normal operating conditions. The rated screen voltage is 100 volts, and the plate supply gives 250 volts. To put 100 volts on the screen, the drop across *R* must be equal to the difference between the plate-supply voltage and the screen voltage; that is, 250 – 100 = 150 volts. Then

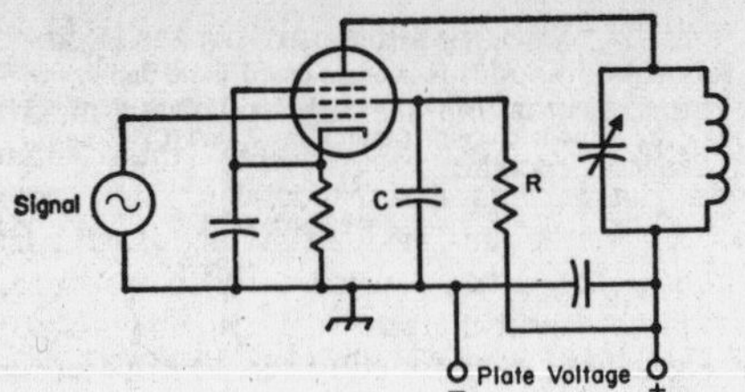

Fig. 3-20 — Screen-voltage supply for a pentode tube through a dropping resistor, *R*. The screen bypass capacitor, *C*, must have low enough reactance to bring the screen to ground potential for the frequency or frequencies being amplified.

$$R = \frac{E}{I} = \frac{150}{.002} = 75{,}000 \text{ ohms}$$

The power to be dissipated in the resistor is

$$P = EI = 150 \times .002 = 0.3 \text{ watt}$$

A 1/2- or 1-watt resistor would be satisfactory.

The reactance of the screen bypass capacitor, *C*, should be low compared with the screen-to-cathode impedance. For radio-frequency applications a capacitance in the vicinity of .01 μF is amply large.

In some vacuum-tube circuits the screen voltage is obtained from a voltage divider connected across the plate supply. The design of voltage dividers is discussed at length elsewhere in this book.

OSCILLATORS

It was mentioned earlier that if there is enough positive feedback in an amplifier circuit, self-sustaining oscillations will be set up. When an amplifier is arranged so that this condition exists it is called an **oscillator.**

Oscillations normally take place at only one frequency, and a desired frequency of oscillation can be obtained by using a resonant circuit tuned to that frequency. For example, in Fig. 3-21A the circuit *LC* is tuned to the desired frequency of oscillation. The cathode of the tube is connected to a tap on coil *L* and the grid and plate are connected to opposite ends of the tuned circuit. When an rf current flows in the tuned circuit there is a voltage drop across *L* that increases progressively along the turns. Thus the point at which the tap is connected will be at an intermediate potential with respect to the two ends of the coil. The amplified current in the plate circuit, which flows through the bottom section of *L*, is in phase with the current already flowing in the circuit and thus in the proper relationship for positive feedback.

The amount of feedback depends on the position of the tap. If the tap is too near the grid end the voltage drop between grid and cathode is too small to give enough feedback to sustain oscillation, and if it is too near, the plate end of the impedance between the cathode and plate is too small to permit good amplification. Maximum feedback usually is obtained when the tap is somewhere near the center of the coil.

The circuit of Fig. 3-21A is parallel-fed, C_b being the blocking capacitor. The value of C_b is not critical so long as its reactance is low (not more than a few hundred ohms) at the operating frequency.

Capacitor C_g is the **grid capacitor.** It and R_g (the **grid leak**) are used for the purpose of obtaining grid bias for the tube. In most oscillator circuits the tube generates its own bias. During the part of the cycle when the grid is positive with respect to the cathode, it attracts electrons. These electrons cannot flow through *L* back to the cathode because C_g "blocks" direct current. They therefore have to flow or "leak" through R_g to cathode, and in doing so cause a voltage drop in R_g that places a negative bias on the grid. The amount of bias so developed is equal to the grid current multiplied by the resistance of R_g (Ohm's Law). The value of grid-leak resistance required depends upon the kind of tube used and the purpose for which the oscillator is intended. Values range all the way from a few thousand to several hundred thousand ohms. The capacitance of C_g should be large enough to have low reactance (a few hundred ohms) at the operating frequency.

The circuit shown at B in Fig. 3-21 uses the voltage drops across two capacitors in series in the tuned circuit to supply the feedback. Other than this, the operation is the same as just described. The feedback can be varied by varying the ratio of the reactance of C1 and C2 (that is, by varying the ratio of their capacitances).

Another type of oscillator, called the **tuned-plate tuned-grid** circuit, is shown in Fig. 3-22. Resonant circuits tuned approximately to the same frequency are connected between grid and cathode and between plate and cathode. The two coils, L1

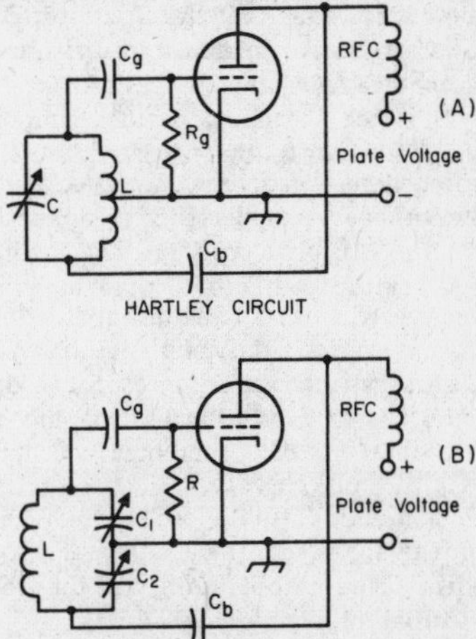

Fig. 3-21 — Basic oscillator circuits. Feedback voltage is obtained by tapping the grid and cathode across a portion of the tuned circuit. In the Hartley circuit the tap is on the coil, but in the Colpitts circuit the voltage is obtained from the drop across a capacitor.

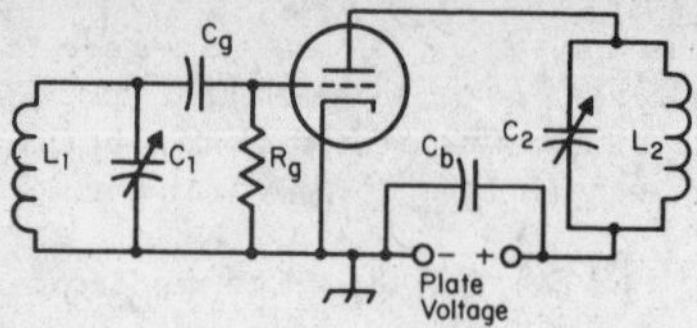

Fig. 3-22 – The tuned-plate tuned-grid oscillator.

and L2, are not magnetically coupled. The feedback is through the grid-plate capacitance of the tube, and will be in the right phase to be positive when the plate circuit, C2-L2, is tuned to a slightly higher frequency than the grid circuit, L1-C1. The amount of feedback can be adjusted by varying the tuning of either circuit. The frequency of oscillation is determined by the tuned circuit that has the higher *Q*. The grid leak and grid capacitor have the same functions as in the other circuits. In this case it is convenient to use series feed for the plate circuit, so C_b is a bypass capacitor to guide the rf current around the plate supply.

There are many oscillator circuits (examples of others will be found in later chapters) but the basic feature of all of them is that there is positive feedback in the proper amplitude and phase to sustain oscillation.

Oscillator Operating Characteristics

When an oscillator is delivering power to a load, the adjustment for proper feedback will depend on how heavily the oscillator is loaded – that is, how much power is being taken from the circuit. If the feedback is not large enough – **grid excitation** too small – a small increase in load may tend to throw the circuit out of oscillation. On the other hand, too much feedback will make the grid current excessively higher, with the result that the power loss in the grid circuit becomes larger than necessary. Since the oscillator itself supplies this grid power, excessive feedback lowers the over-all efficiency because whatever power is used in the grid circuit is not available as useful output.

One of the most important considerations in oscillator design is **frequency stability**. The principal factors that cause a change in frequency are (1) temperature, (2) plate voltage, (3) loading, (4) mechanical variations of circuit elements. Temperature changes will cause vacuum-tube elements to expand or contract slightly, thus causing variations in the interelectrode capacitances. Since these are unavoidably part of the tuned circuit, the frequency will change correspondingly. Temperature changes in the coil or the tuning capacitor will alter the inductance or capacitance slightly, again causing a shift in the resonant frequency. These effects are relatively slow in operation, and the frequency change caused by them is called **drift**.

A change in plate voltage usually will cause the frequency to change a small amount, an effect called **dynamic instability**. Dynamic instability can be reduced by using a tuned circuit of high effective *Q*. The energy taken from the circuit to supply grid losses, as well as energy supplied to a load, represent an increase in the effective resistance of the tuned circuit and thus lower its *Q*. For highest stability, therefore, the coupling between the tuned circuit and the tube and load must be kept as loose as possible. Preferably, the oscillator should not be required to deliver power to an external circuit, and a high value of grid leak resistance should be used since this helps to raise the tube grid and plate resistances as seen by the tuned circuit. Loose coupling can be effected in a variety of ways – one, for example, is by "tapping down" on the tank for the connections to the grid and plate. This is done in the "series-tuned" Colpitts circuit widely used in variable-frequency oscillators for amateur transmitters and described in a later chapter. Alternatively, the *L/C* ratio may be made as small as possible while sustaining stable oscillations **(high C)** with the grid and plate connected to the ends of the circuit as shown in Figs. 3-21 and 3-22. Using relatively high plate voltage and low plate current also is desirable.

In general, dynamic stability will be at maximum when the feedback is adjusted to the least value that permits reliable oscillation. The use of a tube having a high value of transconductance is desirable, since the higher the transconductance the looser the permissible coupling to the tuned circuit and the smaller the feedback required.

Load variations act in much the same way as plate-voltage variations. A temperature change in the load may also result in drift.

Mechanical variations, usually caused by vibrations, cause changes in inductance and/or capacitance that in turn cause the frequency to "wobble" in step with the vibration.

Methods of minimizing frequency variations in oscillators are taken up in detail in later chapters.

Ground Point

In the oscillator circuits shown in Figs. 3-21 and 3-22 the cathode is connected to ground. It is not actually essential that the radio-frequency circuit should be grounded at the cathode; in fact, there are many times when an *rf* ground on some other point in the circuit is desirable. The rf ground can be placed at any point so long as proper provisions are made for feeding the supply voltages to the tube elements.

Fig. 3-23 shows the Hartley circuit with the plate end of the circuit grounded. The cathode and control grid are "above ground," so far as the rf is concerned. An advantage of such a circuit is that the frame of the tuning capacitor can be grounded. The Colpitts circuit can also be used with the plate

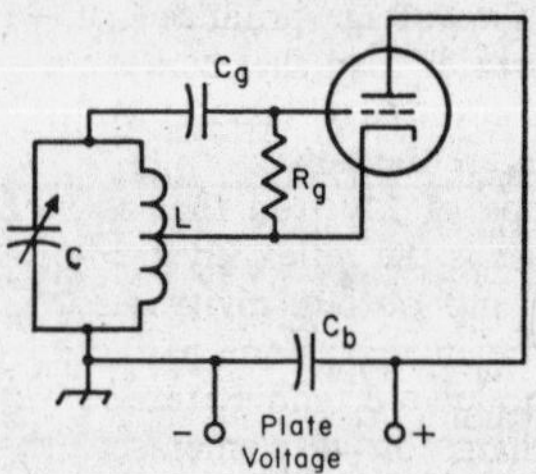

Fig. 3-23 – Showing how the plate may be grounded for rf in a typical oscillator circuit (Hartley).

grounded and the cathode above ground; it is only necessary to feed the dc to the cathode through an rf choke.

A tetrode or pentode tube can be used in any of the popular oscillator circuits. A common variation is to use the screen grid of the tube as the anode for the Hartley or Colpitts oscillator circuit. It is usually used in the grounded anode circuit, and the plate circuit of the tube is tuned to the second harmonic of the oscillator frequency.

VHF AND MICROWAVE TUBES

Until now, it has been assumed that the time it takes for the electrons to travel from the cathode to the plate does not affect the performance of vacuum-tube operation. As the frequency of operation is raised, this time, called the **transit time**, becomes increasingly important. The transit time depends upon the voltage from the cathode to the plate and the spacing between them. The higher the voltage and the smaller the spacing, the shorter the transit time. This is why tubes designed for vhf and uhf work have very small interelectrode spacings. However, the power handling capabilities also get smaller as the spacing decreases so there is a limit above which ordinary triode and pentode tubes cannot be operated efficiently.

Many different tubes have been developed which actually use transit-time effects to an advantage. **Velocity modulation** of the electron stream in a **klystron** is one example. A small voltage applied across the gap in a re-entrant cavity resonator either retards or accelerates an electron stream by means of the resultant electric field. Initially, all the electrons are traveling at the same velocity and the current in the beam is uniform. After the velocity fluctuations are impressed on the beam, the current is still uniform for awhile but then the electrons that were accelerated begin to catch up with the slower ones that passed through when the field was zero. The latter are also catching up with ones that passed through the gap earlier but were retarded. The result is that the current in the beam is no longer uniform but consists of a series of pulses. If the beam now passes through another cavity gap, a current will be induced in the cavity walls and an electric field also will be set up across the gap. If the phase of the electric field is right, the electron pulses or "bunches" pass through the gap and are retarded, thus giving up energy to the electric field. When the electric field reverses, it would normally accelerate the same number of electrons and give back the energy, but fewer electrons now pass through the gap and the energy given up is less. Thus, a net flow of energy is from the beam to the cavity. If the voltage produced across the output cavity is greater than that across the input cavity, amplification results (assuming the two cavity impedances are the same).

The type of klystron that amateurs are most likely to use is the reflex klystron oscillator. Here, the input and output cavity are the same. The electron stream makes one pass through, becomes velocity modulated, and is turned around by the negative charge on an element called the repeller. During the second pass through, the stream is now bunched and delivers some of its energy to the cavity. The dissipated beam is then picked up by the cavity walls and the circuit is completed. This is shown pictorially in Fig. 3-24.

Klystrons either have cavities external to the vacuum part of the tube or built in as an integral part of the tube structure. The 723 reflex klystron is of the latter type, and along with similar types can be purchased surplus. These tubes were used as local oscillators in radar receivers and can be used for the same purpose in amateur applications. They also may be used in low power transmitters.

Along with a heater supply (usually 6.3 volts), two other voltages are necessary for the operation of the reflex klystron. This is shown in Fig. 3-24. Vc is typically 300 volts dc and Vr will vary from 100 to 150 volts dc. The loaded Q of the reflex klystron cavity is quite low and oscillations will occur at different frequencies for various values of Vr. This can be used to advantage and either frequency modulation or automatic frequency control (afc) can be applied to the klystron by means of changes in Vr. As the repeller voltage is made more negative, it will be found that oscillations will occur, increase in amplitude, and then drop out. This will be repeated as the voltage is increased and each time the maximum amplitude of the output power will be less. However, the frequency range covered by each different set of oscillation conditions is approximately the same.

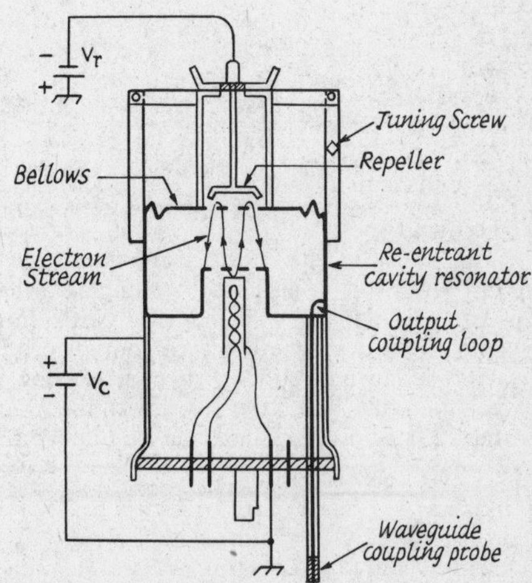

Fig. 3-24 — Cross-sectional view of a typical reflex klystron. The frequency of the cavity resonator is changed by varying the spacing between the grids using a tuning mechanism and a flexible bellows. Modification of this system may be necessary to get certain surplus klystrons into an appropriate amateur band.

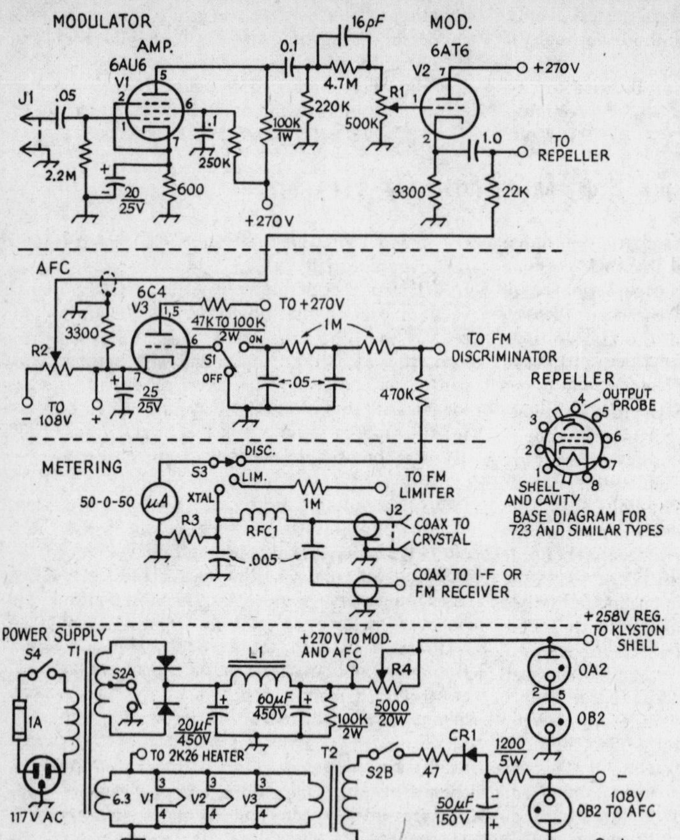

Fig. 3-25 – Schematic diagram and parts information for a power supply and control unit suitable for amateur microwave transceivers. Unless otherwise specified, capacitor values are in μF and resistors are 1/2-watt composition.

CR1 – 1000 PRV, 1-A.
F1 – 1-A fuse and holder.
J1 – Shielded microphone jack.
J2 – Coaxial chassis fitting.
L1 – 10-H 110-mA choke (Stancor C-1001).
R1 – 0.5-megohm potentiometer, audio taper.
R2 – 0.2-meghom potentiometer, carbon, linear taper.
R3 – Meter shunt; value to suit meter used, for 1-mA range.
R4 – 5000 ohms, 20 watts, with slider.
RFC1 – 15 turns No. 24 enamel on 1/2-inch form. (Any rf choke for 30 to 100 MHz is suitable.)
S1 – Toggle switch.
S2 – Toggle switch.
S3 – Single-pole 3-position wafer switch.
S4 – Toggle switch.
T1 – 270-0-270 volts at 70 mA min., 5 volts, 3 A. 6.3 volts, 3.5 A (Stancor PC-8405).
T2 – 6.3 volts, 1.2 A (Stancor P-6134).

Practical metering, afc, modulator, and power supply circuit diagrams are shown in Fig. 3-25 (*QST*, August, 1960) which are suitable for the 723 and 2K26 klystrons. One disadvantage of the system shown is that the shell of the klystron is at 260 volts above ground. An alternate method is to ground the shell and apply −260 volts to the cathode and −(260 + Vr) to the repeller. A 510-volt supply is needed for the repeller, but since the repeller draws negligible current, this should not be difficult.

As is the case with most microwave tubes, coupling power out from the klystron is somewhat more complicated than is the case with low-frequency tubes. A magnetic pickup loop placed in the cavity is connected either to a coaxial fitting or a waveguide probe. The latter (used with the 2K26 and the 723) is inserted into the middle of the waveguide and the coupling to the line is determined by the depth of the probe. Since klystrons (and other microwave tubes) are quite sensitive to variations in loading, some sort of attenuator or an isolator is often necessary to prevent malfunctions.

Other types of microwave tubes that the amateur may encounter are the traveling wave tube (TWT), and the backward wave oscillator (BWO). Here, an electromagnetic wave is slowed down below the speed of light in free space and allowed to interact continuously with an electron stream. While the latter two tubes use magnets for focusing the electron beam, the magnetron and other crossed-field amplifiers also use a magnetic field in conjunction with an electric field in their operation.

Chapter 4

Semiconductor Devices

Materials whose conductivity falls approximately midway between that of good conductors (e.g., copper) and good insulators (e.g., quartz) are called **semiconductors.** Some of these materials (primarily germanium and silicon) can, by careful processing, be used in **solid-state** electronic devices that perform many or all of the functions of thermionic tubes. In many applications their small size, long life and low power requirements make them superior to tubes.

The conductivity of a material is proportional to the number of free electrons in the material. Pure germanium and pure silicon crystals have relatively few free electrons. If, however, carefully controlled amounts of "impurities" (materials having a different atomic structure, such as arsenic or antimony) are added the number of free electrons, and consequently the conductivity, is increased. When certain other impurities are introduced (such as aluminum, gallium or indium), an electron deficiency, or **hole**, is produced. As in the case of free electrons, the presence of holes encourages the flow of electrons in the semiconductor material, and the conductivity is increased. Semiconductor material that conducts by virtue of the free electrons is called **n-type** material; material that conducts by virtue of an electron deficiency is called **p-type.**

Electron and Hole Conduction

If a piece of p-type material is joined to a piece of n-type material as at A in Fig. 4-1 and a voltage is applied to the pair as at B, current will flow across the boundary or junction between the two (and also in the external circuit) when the battery has the polarity indicated. Electrons, indicated by the minus symbol, are attracted across the junction from the n material through the p material to the positive terminal of the battery, and holes, indicated by the plus symbol, are attracted in the opposite direction across the junction by the negative potential of the battery. Thus current flows through the circuit by means of electrons moving one way and holes the other.

If the battery polarity is reversed, as at C, the excess electrons in the n material are attracted away from the junction and the holes in the p material are attracted by the negative potential of the battery away from the junction. This leaves the junction region without any current carriers, consequently there is no conduction.

In other words, a junction of p- and n-type materials constitutes a rectifier. It differs from the tube diode rectifier in that there is a measurable, although comparatively very small, reverse current. The reverse current results from the presence of some carriers of the type opposite to those which principally characterize the material.

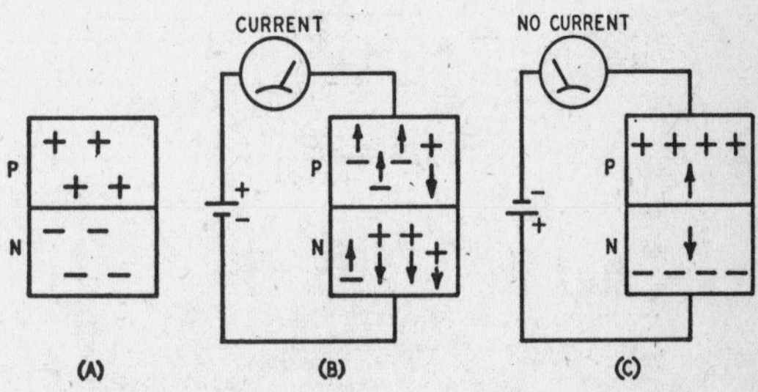

Fig. 4-1 — A p-n junction (A) and its behavior when conducting (B) and nonconducting (C).

With the two plates separated by practically zero spacing, the junction forms a capacitor of relatively high capacitance. This places a limit on the upper frequency at which semiconductor devices of this construction will operate, as compared with vacuum tubes. Also, the number of excess electrons and holes in the material depends upon temperature, and since the conductivity in turn depends on the number of excess holes and electrons, the device is more temperature sensitive than is a vacuum tube.

Capacitance may be reduced by making the contact area very small. This is done by means of a **point contact,** a tiny p-type region being formed under the contact point during manufacture when n-type material is used for the main body of the device.

SEMICONDUCTOR DIODES

Point-contact and junction-type diodes are used for many of the same purposes for which tube

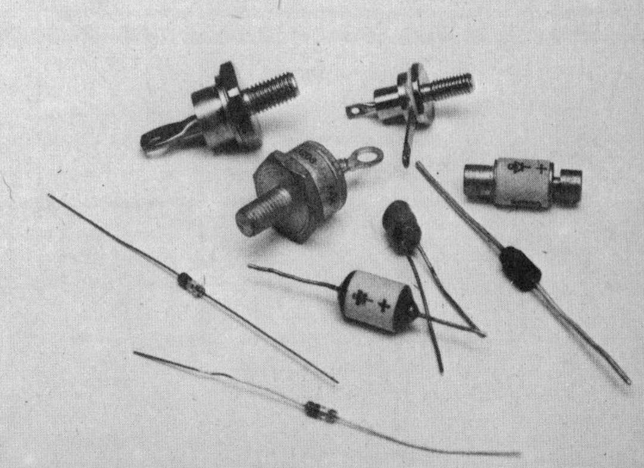

Typical silicon and germanium diodes of the present era. The larger units are designed to handle high current.

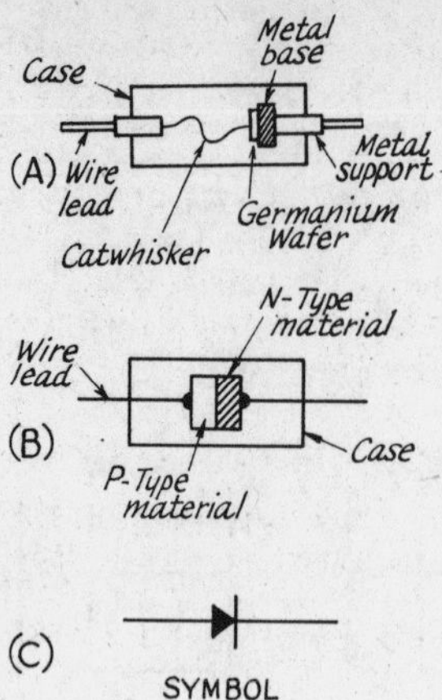

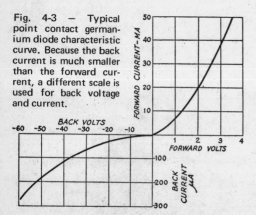

Fig. 4-2 – At A, a germanium point-contact diode. At B, construction of a silicon junction-type diode. The symbol at C is used for both diode types and indicates the direction of minimum resistance measured by conventional methods. At C, the arrow corresponds to the plate (anode) of a vacuum-tube diode. The bar represents the tube's cathode element.

diodes are used. The construction of such diodes is shown in Fig. 4-2. Germanium and silicon are the most widely used materials; silicon finds much application as a microwave mixer diode. As compared with the tube diode for rf applications, the semiconductor point-contact diode has the advantages of very low interelectrode capacitance (on the order of 1 pF or less) and not requiring any heater or filament power.

The germanium diode is characterized by relatively large current flow with small applied voltages in the "forward" direction, and small, although finite, current flow in the reverse or "back" direction for much larger applied voltages. A typical characteristic curve is shown in Fig. 4-3. The dynamic resistance in either the forward or back direction is determined by the change in current that occurs, at any given point on the curve, when the applied voltage is changed by a small amount. The forward resistance shows some variation in the region of very small applied voltages, but the curve is for the most part quite straight, indicating fairly constant dynamic resistance. For small applied voltages, the forward resistance is of the order of 200 ohms or less in most such diodes. The back resistance shows considerable variation, depending on the particular voltage chosen for the measurement. It may run from a few thousand ohms to well over a megohm. In applications such as meter rectifiers for rf indicating instruments (rf voltmeters, wavemeter indicators, and so on) where the load resistance may be small and the applied voltage of the order of several volts, the resistances vary with the value of the applied voltage and are considerably lower.

Fig. 4-3 – Typical point contact germanium diode characteristic curve. Because the back current is much smaller than the forward current, a different scale is used for back voltage and current.

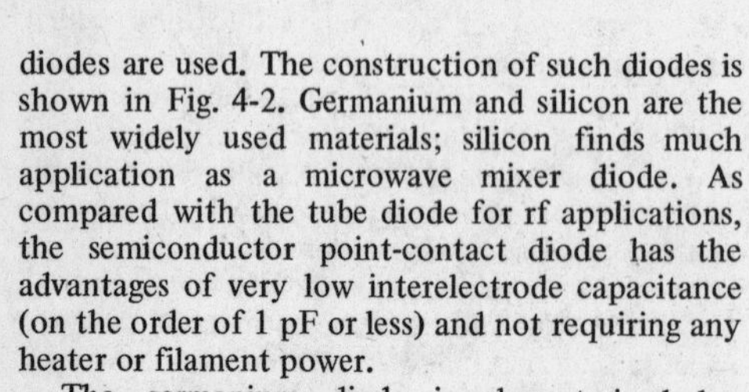

FORWARD CURRENT-MA: 50, 40, 30, 20, 10
BACK VOLTS: -60, -50, -40, -30, -20, -10
FORWARD VOLTS: 1, 2, 3, 4
BACK CURRENT μA: -100, -200, -300

Junction Diodes

Junction-type diodes made of silicon are employed widely as rectifiers. Depending upon the design of the diode, they are capable of rectifying currents up to 40 or 50 amperes, and up to reverse peak voltages of 2500. They can be connected in series or in parallel, with suitable circuitry, to provide higher capabilities than those given above. A big advantage over thermionic rectifiers is their large surge-to-average-current ratio, which makes them suitable for use with capacitor-only filter circuits. This in turn leads to improved no-load-to-full-load voltage characteristics. Some consideration must be given to the operating temperature of silicon diodes, although many carry ratings to 150 degrees C or so. A silicon junction diode requires a forward voltage of from 0.4 to 0.7 volts to overcome the junction potential barrier.

Ratings

Semiconductor diodes are rated primarily in terms of **maximum safe inverse voltage** (PIV or PRV) and **maximum average rectified current.** Inverse voltage is a voltage applied in the direction opposite to that which would be read by a dc meter connected in the current path.

It is also customary with some types to specify standards of performance with respect to forward and back current. A minimum value of forward current is usually specified for one volt applied. The voltage at which the maximum tolerable back current is specified varies with the type of diode.

Zener Diodes

The **Zener diode** is a special type of silicon junction diode that has a characteristic similar to that shown in Fig. 4-4. The sharp break from non-conductance to conductance is called the Zener knee; at applied voltages greater than this breakdown point, the voltage drop across the diode is essentially constant over a wide range of currents. The substantially constant voltage drop over a wide range of currents allows this semiconductor device to be used as a constant voltage reference or control element, in a manner somewhat similar to the gaseous voltage-regulator tube. Voltages for Zener-diode action range from a

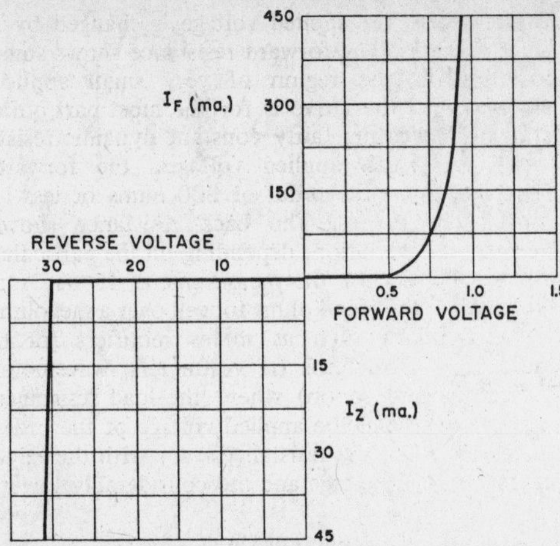

Fig. 4-4 – Typical characteristic of a Zener diode. In this example, the voltage drop is substantially constant at 30 volts in the (normally) reverse direction. Compare with Fig. 4-3. A diode with this characteristic would be called a "30-volt Zener diode."

few volts to several hundred and power ratings run from a fraction of a watt to 50 watts.

Zener diodes can be connected in series to advantage; the temperature coefficient is improved over that of a single diode of equivalent rating and the power-handling capability is increased.

Examples of Zener diode applications are given in Fig. 4-5. The illustrations represent some of the more common uses to which Zeners are put. Many other applications are possible, though not shown here.

Voltage-Variable Capacitor Diodes

Voltage-variable capacitors, **Varicaps** or **varactors**, are p-n junction diodes that behave as capacitors of reasonable Q when biased in the reverse direction. They are useful in many applications because the actual capacitance value is dependent upon the dc bias voltage that is applied. In a typical capacitor the capacitance can be varied over a 10-to-1 range with a bias change from 0 to -100 volts. The current demand on the bias supply is on the order of a few microamperes.

Typical applications include remote control of tuned circuits, automatic frequency control of receiver local oscillators, and simple frequency modulators for communications and for sweep-

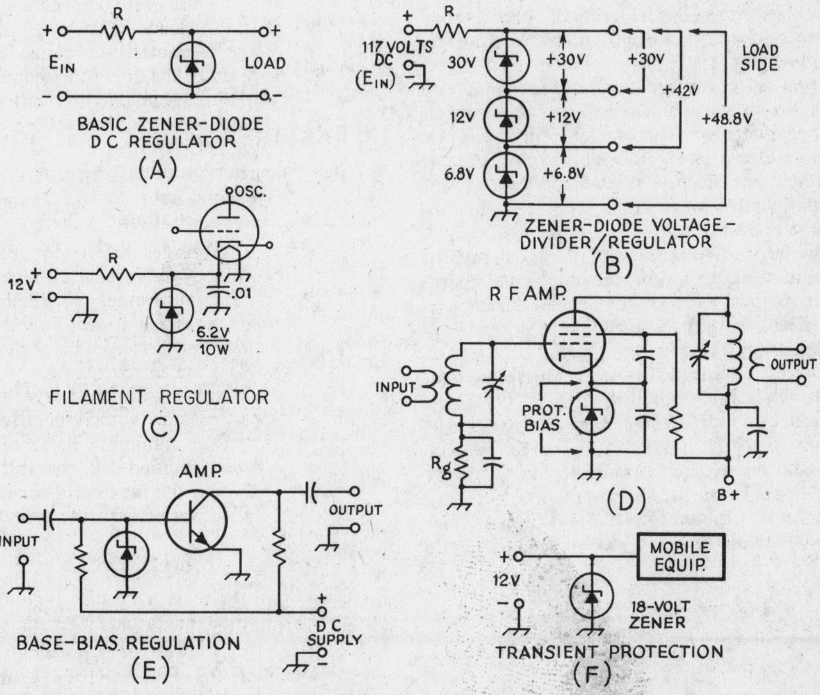

Fig. 4-5 – Zener diodes have many practical uses. Shown at A, is a simple dc voltage regulator which operates in the same manner as a gaseous regulator tube. Several Zener diodes can be connected in series (B) to provide various regulated voltages. At C, the filament line of a tube is supplied with regulated dc to enhance oscillator stability and reduce hum. In the circuit at D a Zener diode sets the bias level of an rf power amplifier. Bias regulation is afforded the bipolar transistor at E by connecting the Zener diode between base and ground. At F, the 18-volt Zener will clip peaks at and above 18 volts to protect 12-volt mobile equipment. (High peaks are frequently caused by transients in the automotive ignition system.)

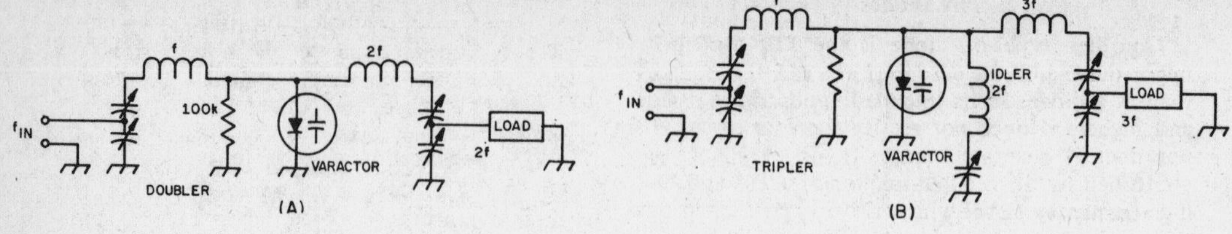

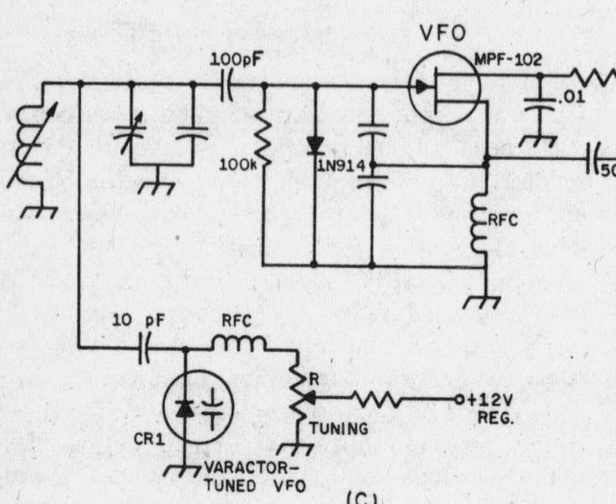

Fig. 4-6 — Varactor frequency multipliers are shown at A and B. In practice the tuned circuits and impedance-matching techniques are somewhat more complex than those shown in these representative circuits. At C, a varactor diode is used to vary the frequency of a typical JFET VFO. As the dc voltage is changed by control R, the junction capacitance of CR1 changes to shift the resonant frequency of the tuned circuit.

tuning applications. Diodes used in these applications are frequently referred to as "Varicap" or "Epicap" diodes.

An important transmitter application of the varactor is as a high-efficiency frequency multiplier. The basic circuits for varactor doublers and triplers are shown in Fig. 4-6, at A and B. In these circuits the fundamental frequency flows around the input loop. Harmonics generated by the varactor are passed to the load through a filter tuned to the desired harmonic. In the case of the tripler circuit at B, an **idler** circuit, tuned to the second harmonic, is required. Tripling efficiencies of 75 percent are not too difficult to come by, at power levels of 10 to 25 watts.

Fig. 4-6C illustrates how a voltage-variable capacitor diode can be used to tune a VFO. These diodes can be used to tune other rf circuits also, and are particularly useful for remote tuning such as might be encountered in vehicular installations. These diodes, because of their small size, permit tuned-circuit assemblies to be quite compact. Since the *Q* of the diode is a vital consideration in such applications, this factor must be taken into account when designing a circuit. Present-day manufacturing processes have produced units whose *Q*s are in excess of 200 at 50 MHz.

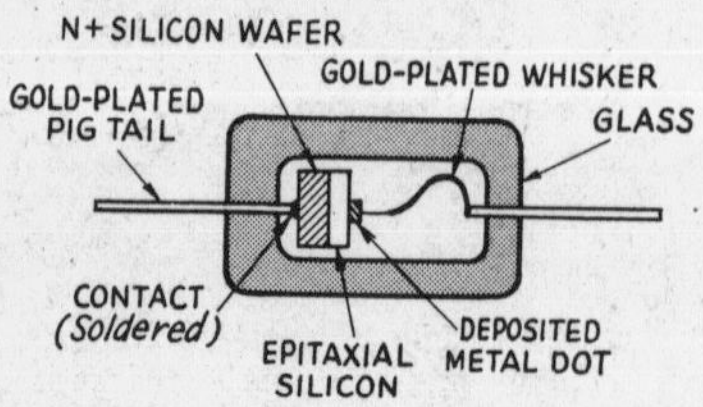

Fig. 4-7 — Cross-sectional view of a hot-carrier diode.

HOT-CARRIER DIODES

The hot-carrier diode is a high-frequency and microwave semiconductor whose characteristics fall somewhere between those of the point-contact diode and the junction diode. The former is comparable to the point-contact diode in high-frequency characteristics, and exceeds it in uniformity and reliability. The hot-carrier diode is useful in high-speed switching circuits and as a mixer, detector, and rectifier well into the microwave spectrum. In essence, the hot-carrier diode is a rectifying metal-semiconductor junction. Typical metals used in combination with silicon of either the n- or p-type are platinum, silver, gold or palladium.

The hot-carrier diode utilizes a true Schottky barrier, whereas the point-contact diode used a metal whisker to make contact with the semiconductor element. In a hot-carrier diode a planar area provides a uniform contact potential and uniform current distribution throughout the junction. This geometry results in lower series resistance, greater power capability, lower noise characteristics, and considerably greater immunity to burnout from transient pulses or spikes. A cross-sectional view of a hot-carrier diode is shown in Fig. 4-7 (courtesy of Hewlett Packard Associates). A comparison in characteristics between a point-contact diode and a hot-carrier diode is given in Fig. 4-8. Detailed information on the characteristics of hot-carrier diodes and their many applications is given in Hewlett Packard *Application Note 907*.

PIN Diodes

Another type of diode is the **PIN diode.** It might more aptly be described as a variable resistor than as a diode. In its intended application (at vhf and higher) it does not rectify the applied signal, nor does it generate harmonics. Its resistance is controlled by dc or a low-frequency signal, and the high-frequency signal which is being controlled by the diode sees a constant polarity-independent resistance. The dynamic resistance of the PIN diode is often larger than 10,000 ohms, and its junction capacitance is very low.

PIN diodes are used as variable shunt or series resistive elements in microwave transmission lines, and as agc diodes in the signal input lead to vhf and uhf fm receivers. The PIN diode offers many interesting possibilities.

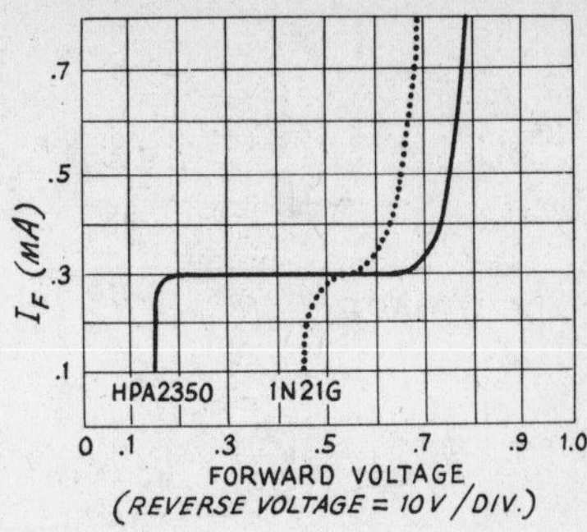

Fig. 4-8 — Curves showing the comparison in characteristics between a 1N21G point-contact diode and a Hewlett-Packard HPA2350 hot-carrier diode.

TRANSISTORS

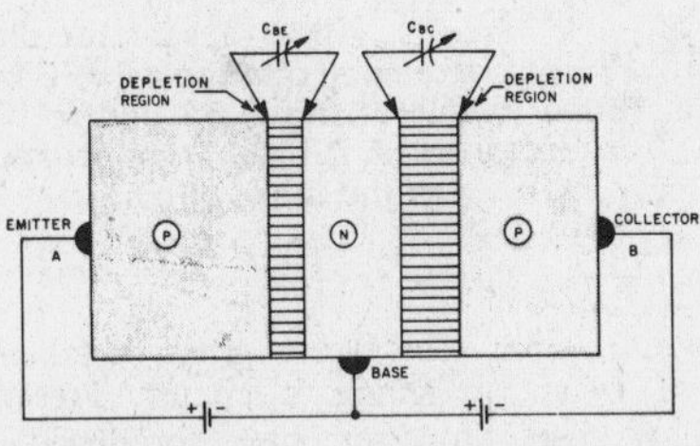

Fig. 4-9 — Illustration of a junction pnp transistor. Capacitances Cbe and Cbc are discussed in the text, and vary with changes in operating and signal voltage.

Fig. 4-9 shows a "sandwich" made from two layers of p-type semiconductor material with a thin layer of n-type between. There are in effect two pn junction diodes back to back. If a positive bias is applied to the p-type material at the left, current will flow though the left-hand junction, the holes moving to the right and the electrons from the n-type material moving to the left. Some of the holes moving into the n-type material will combine with the electrons there and be neutralized, but some of them also will travel to the region of the right-hand junction.

If the pn combination at the right is biased negatively, as shown, there would normally be no current flow in this circuit. However, there are now additional holes available at the junction to travel to point *B* and electrons can travel toward point *A*, so a current can flow even though this section of the sandwich is biased to prevent conduction. Most of the current is between *A* and *B* and does not flow out through the common connection to the n-type material in the sandwich.

A semiconductor combination of this type is called a **transistor**, and the three sections are known as the **emitter, base** and **collector**, respectively. The amplitude of the collector current depends principally upon the amplitude of the emitter current; that is, the collector current is controlled by the emitter current.

Between each p-n junction exists an area known as the **depletion**, or **transition region.** It is similar in characteristics to a dielectric layer, and its width varies in accordance with the operating voltage. The semiconductor materials either side of the depletion region consitute the plates of a capacitor. The capacitance from base to emitter is shown as C_{be} (Fig. 4-9), and the collector-base capacitance is represented as C_{bc}. Changes in signal and operating voltages cause a nonlinear change in these junction capacitances, which must be taken into account when designing some circuits. A base-emitter resistance, *rb'*, also exists. The junction capacitance, in combination with rb' determines the useful upper frequency limit (f_T or f_a) of a transistor by establishing an *RC* time constant.

Power Amplification

Because the collector is biased in the back direction the collector-to-base resistance is high.

This photo shows various modern-day bipolar and field-effect transistors. Various case styles and power classes are represented here.

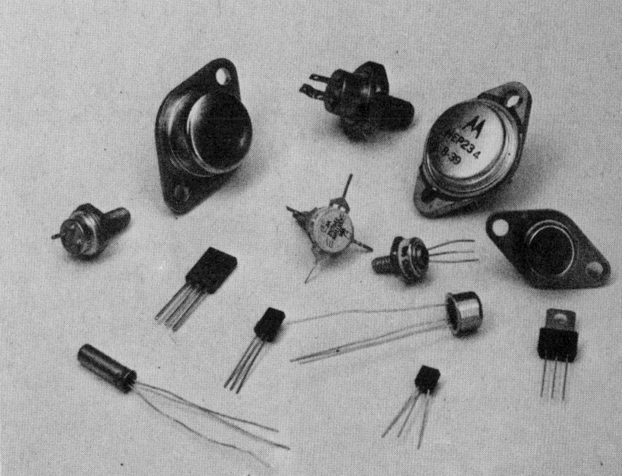

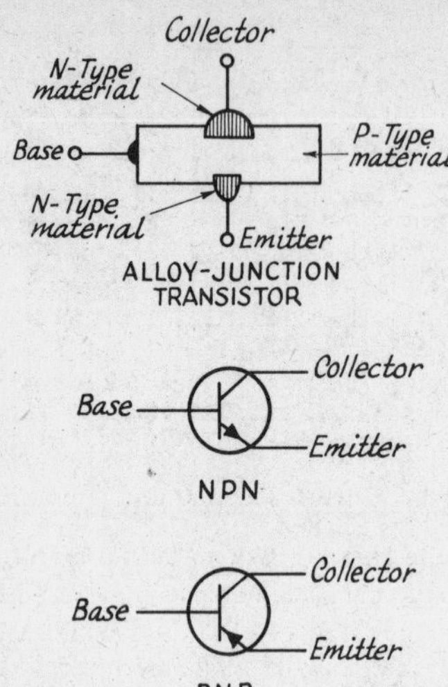

Fig. 4-10 – Schematic and pictorial representations of junction-type transistors. In analogous terms the base can be thought of as a tube's grid, the collector as a plate, and the emitter as a cathode. (See Fig. 4-12.)

On the other hand, the emitter and collector currents are substantially equal, so the power in the collector circuit is larger than the power in the emitter circuit ($P = I^2R$, so the powers are proportional to the respective resistances, if the currents are the same). In practical transistors emitter resistance is of the order of a few hundred ohms while the collector resistance is hundreds or thousands of times higher, so power gains of 20 to 40 dB or even more are possible.

Types

The transistor may be one of the types shown in Fig. 4-10. The assembly of p- and n-types materials may be reversed, so that pnp and npn transistors are both possible.

The first two letters of the npn and pnp designations indicate the respective polarities of the voltages applied to the emitter and collector in normal operation. In a pnp transistor, for example, the emitter is made positive with respect to both the collector and the base, and the collector is made negative with respect to both the emitter and the base.

Manufacturers are constantly working to improve the performance of their transistors – greater reliability, higher power and frequency ratings, and improved uniformity of characteristics for any given type number. Recent developments provided the **overlay transistor,** whose emitter structure is made up of several emitters which are joined together at a common case terminal. This process lowers the base-emitter resistance, *rb'*, and improves the transistor's input time constant, which is determined by *rb'* and the junction capacitance of the device. The overlay transistor is extremely useful in vhf and uhf applications, and is capable of high-power operation well above 1000 MHz. These transistors are quite useful as frequency doublers and triplers, and are able to provide an actual power gain in the process.

Another multi-emitter transistor has been developed for use from hf through uhf, and should be of particular interest to the radio amateur. It is called a **balanced-emitter transistor** (BET), or "ballasted" transistor. The transistor chip contains several triode semiconductors whose bases and collectors are connected in parallel. The various emitters, however, have built-in emitter resistors (typically about 1 ohm) which provide a current-limiting safety factor during overload periods, or under conditions of significant mismatch. Since the emitters are brought out to a single case terminal the resistances are effectively in parallel, thus reducing the combined emitter resistances to a fraction of an ohm. (If a significant amount of resistance were allowed to exist it would cause degeneration in the stage and would lower the gain of the circuit.)

Most modern transistors are of the junction variety. Various names have been given to the several types, some of which are junction alloy, mesa, and planar. Though their characteristics may differ slightly, they are basically of the same family and simply represent different physical properties and manufacturing techniques.

Transistor Characteristics

An important characteristic of a transistor is its **beta** (β), or **current-amplification factor**, which is sometimes expressed as h_{FE} (static forward-current

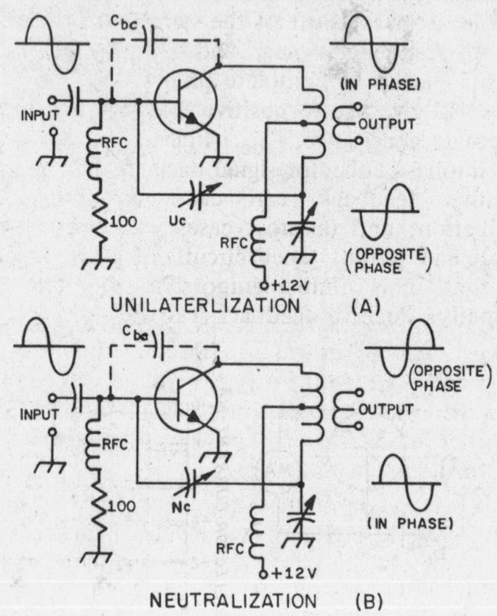

Fig. 4-11 – Transit-time effects (in combination with base-collector capacitance Cbc) can cause the positive-feedback condition shown at A. Normally, the phase of the collector signal of an amplifier is the inverse of the base signal. Positive feedback can be corrected by using unilateralization, feeding an equal amount of opposite-phase signal back to the base through Uc. Neutralization is shown at B, and deals with negative feedback, as can be seen by the phase relationships shown.

transfer ratio) or hfe (small-signal forward-current transfer ratio). Both symbols relate to the grounded-emitter configuration. Beta is the ratio of the base current to the collector current. Thus, if a base current of 1 mA causes the collector current to rise to 100 mA the beta is 100. Typical betas for junction transistors range from as low as 10 to as high as several hundred.

A transistor's **alpha** (α) is the ratio of the emitter and collector currents. Symbols h_{FB} (static forward-current transfer ratio) and hfb (small-signal forward-current transfer ratio), common-base hookup, are frequently used in connection with gain. The smaller the base current, the closer the collector current comes to being equal to that of the emitter, and the closer alpha comes to being 1. Alpha for a junction transistor is usually between 0.92 and 0.98.

Transistors have frequency characteristics which are of importance to circuit designers. Symbol f_T is the **gain bandwidth product** (common-emitter) of the transistor. This is the frequency at which the gain becomes unity, or 1. The expression "alpha cutoff" is frequently used to express the useful upper-frequency limit of a transistor, and this relates to the common-base hookup. Alpha cutoff is the point at which the gain is 0.707, its value at 1000 Hz.

Another factor which limits the upper frequency capability of a transistor is its **transit time.** This is the period of time required for the current to flow from emitter to collector, through the semiconductor base material. The thicker the base material, the greater the transit time. Hence, the thicker the base material the more likelihood there will be of phase shift of the signal passing through it. At frequencies near and above f_T or alpha cutoff partial or complete phase shift can occur. This will give rise to **positive feedback** because the internal capacitance, C_{bc}, (Fig. 4-11) feeds part of the in-phase collector signal back to the base. The positive feedback can cause instability and oscillation, and in most cases will interlock the input and output tuned circuits of an rf amplifier so that it is almost impossible to tune them properly. Positive feedback can be corrected by

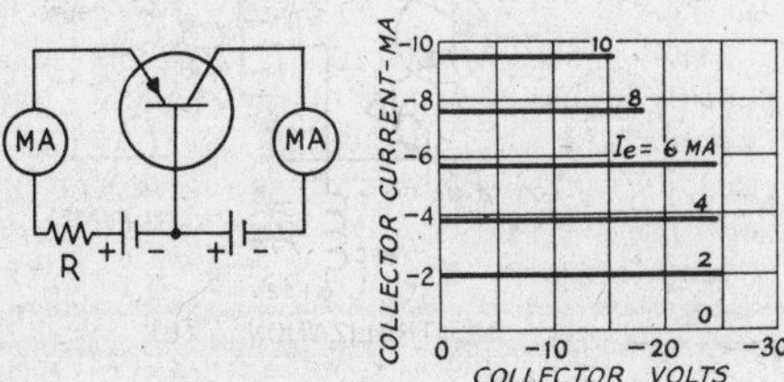

Fig. 4-12 – A typical collector-current vs. collector-voltage characteristic of a junction-type transistor, for various emitter-current values. The circuit shows the setup for taking such measurements. Since the emitter resistance is low, a current-limiting resistor, R, is connected in series with the source of current. The emitter current can be set at a desired value by adjustment of this resistance.

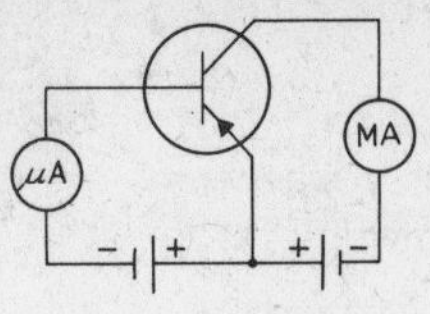

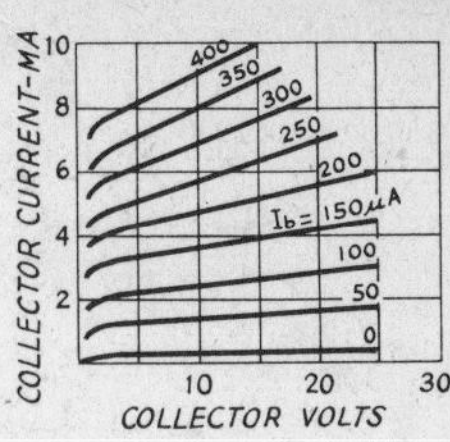

Fig. 4-13 – Collector current vs. collector voltage for various values of base current, for a junction-type transistor. The values are determined by means of the circuit shown.

using a form of neutralization called **unilateralization.** In this case the feedback conditions are balanced out. These conditions include a resistive as well as a capacitive component, thus changing a network from bilaterial to one which is unilateral. Negative feedback caused by C_{bc}, on the other hand, can be corrected by neutralization. Examples of both techniques are given in Fig. 4-11.

Characteristic Curves

The operating characteristics of transistors can be shown by a series of characteristic curves. One such set of curves is shown in Fig. 4-12. It shows the collector current *vs.* collector voltage for a number of fixed values of emitter current. Practically the collector current depends almost entirely on the emitter current and is independent of the collector voltage. The separation between curves representing equal steps of emitter current is quite uniform, indicating that almost distortionless output can be obtained over the useful operating range of the transistor.

Another type of curve is shown in Fig. 4-13, together with the circuit used for obtaining it. This also shows collector current *vs* collector voltage, but for a number of different values of base current. In this case the emitter element is used as the common point in the circuit. The collector current is not independent of collector voltage with this type of connection, indicating that the output resistance of the device is fairly low. The base current also is quite low, which means that the resistance of the base-emitter circuit is moderately high with this method of connection. This may be contrasted with the high values of emitter current shown in Fig. 4-12.

Ratings

The principal maximum ratings for transistors are collector dissipation, collector voltage, collector current, and emitter current. Variations in these basic ratings, such as maximum collector-to-base voltage, are covered in the symbols chart later in this chapter. The designer should study the maximum ratings of a given transistor before selecting it for use in a circuit.

The dissipation rating can be a troublesome matter for an inexperienced designer. Techniques must be employed to reduce the operating

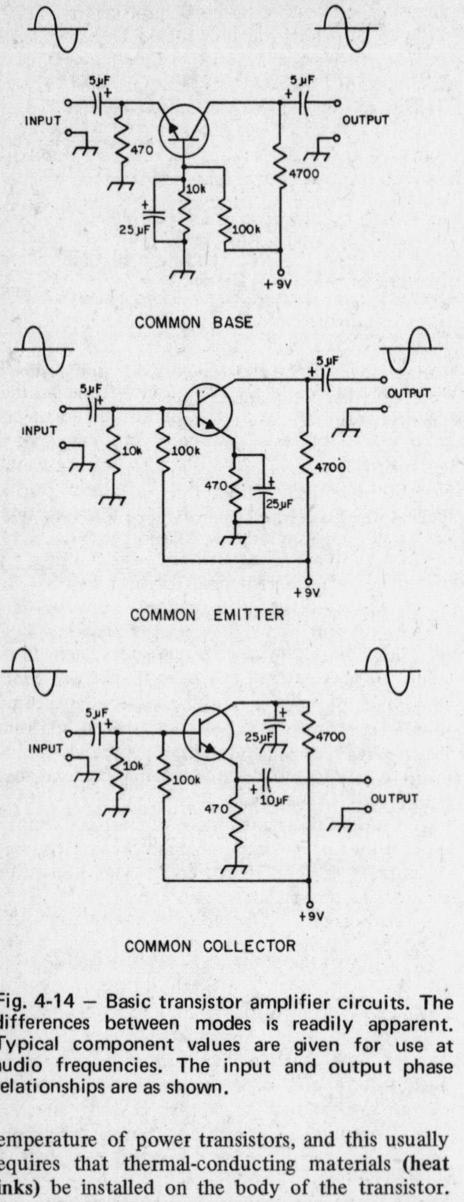

Fig. 4-14 – Basic transistor amplifier circuits. The differences between modes is readily apparent. Typical component values are given for use at audio frequencies. The input and output phase relationships are as shown.

temperature of power transistors, and this usually requires that thermal-conducting materials **(heat sinks)** be installed on the body of the transistor. The specification sheets list the maximum transistor dissipation in terms of case temperatures up to 25 degrees C. Symbol T_C is used for the case temperature and P_T represents the total dissipation. Silicone grease is often used to assure proper thermal transfer between the transistor and its heat sink. Additional information on the use of heat sinks is given in Chapter 18.

Excessive heat can lead to a condition known as **thermal runaway**. As the transistor gets hotter its internal resistance becomes lower, resulting in an increase of emitter-to-collector and emitter-to-base current. The increased current raises the dissipation and further lowers the internal resistance. The effects are cumulative, and eventually the transistor will be destroyed. It can be seen from this discussion that the use of heat sinks is important, where applicable.

TRANSISTOR AMPLIFIERS

Amplifier circuits used with transistors fall into one of three types, known as the **common-base, common-emitter,** and **common-collector** circuits. These are shown in Fig. 4-14 in elementary form. The three circuits correspond approximately to the grounded-grid, grounded-cathode and cathode-follower circuits, respectively, used with vacuum tubes.

The important transistor **parameters** in these circuits are the **short-circuit current transfer ratio,** the **cut-off frequency,** and the **input** and **output impedances.** The short-circuit current transfer ratio is the ratio of a small change in output current to the change in input current that causes it, the output circuit being short-circuited. The cutoff frequency was discussed earlier in this chapter. The input and output impedances are, respectively, the impedance which a signal source working into the transistor would see, and the internal output impedance of the transistor (corresponding to the plate resistance of a vacuum tube, for example).

Common-Base Circuit

The input circuit of a common-base amplifier must be designed for low impedance, since the emitter-to-base resistance is of the order of $25/I_e$ ohms, where I_e is the emitter current in milliamperes. The optimum output load impedance, R_L, may range from a few thousand ohms to 100,000, depending upon the requirements.

In this circuit the phase of the output (collector) current is the same as that of the input (emitter) current. The parts of these currents that flow through the base resistance are likewise in phase, so the circuit tends to be regenerative and will oscillate if the current amplification factor is greater than 1.

Common-Emitter Circuit

The common-emitter circuit shown in Fig. 4-14 corresponds to the ordinary grounded-cathode vacuum-tube amplifier. As indicated by the curves of Fig. 4-13, the base current is small and the input impedance is therefore fairly high – several thousand ohms in the average case. The collector resistance is some tens of thousands of ohms, depending on the signal source impedance. The common-emitter circuit has a lower cutoff frequency than does the common-base circuit, but it gives the highest power gain of the three configurations.

In this circuit the phase of the output (collector) current is opposite to that of the input (base) current so such feedback as occurs through the small emitter resistance is negative and the amplifier is stable.

Common-Collector Circuit

Like the vacuum-tube cathode follower, the common-collector transistor amplifier has high input impedance and low output impedance. The latter is approximately equal to the impedance of the signal input source multiplied by $(1 - \alpha)$. The input resistance depends on the load resistance, being approximately equal to the load resistance divided by $(1 - \alpha)$. The fact that input resistance is directly related to the load resistance is a disadvantage of this type of amplifier if the load is one whose resistance or impedance varies with frequency.

The current transfer ratio with this circuit is :

$$\frac{1}{1 - a}$$

and the cut-off frequency is the same as in the grounded-emitter circuit. The output and input currents are in phase.

PRACTICAL CIRCUIT DETAILS

The bipolar transistor is no longer restricted to use in low-voltage circuits. Many modern-day transistors have voltage ratings as high as 1400. Such transistors are useful in circuits that operate directly from the 117-volt ac line, following rectification. For this reason, battery power is no longer the primary means by which to operate transistorized equipment. Many low-voltage transistor types are capable of developing a considerable amount of af or rf power, hence draw amperes of current from the power supply. Dry batteries are seldom practical in circuits of this type. The usual approach in powering high-current, high-wattage transistorized equipment is to employ a wet-cell storage battery, or operate the equipment from a 117-volt ac line, stepping the primary voltage down to the desired level by means of a transformer, then rectifying the ac with silicon diodes.

Coupling and Impedance Matching

In contrast to vacuum tubes, bipolar transistors present low input and output impedances when used as amplifiers. Field-effect transistors are the exception, exhibiting terminal impedances similar to those of triode vacuum tubes. Therefore, the designer of bipolar transistor circuits must deal with specific matching techniques that assure efficient power transfer and acceptable stability of operation. Most of the *LC* networks used in tuned transistor amplifiers are of established standard configuration, but in practice call for much higher *C*-to-*L* ratios than are common to circuits using tubes. The low terminal impedances of bipolar transistors result from the fact that current is being amplified rather than voltage. High base or collector current (plus relatively low operating voltages) establishes what may at times seem to be unworkable terminal impedances – ten ohms or less. The greater the power input and output of an amplifier stage the more pronounced the matching problem becomes, requiring the employment of special matching techniques. Low-level amplifying stages are not so seriously affected, and the usual procedure is to use simple *RC*-coupling techniques for audio (and some rf) amplifiers. This being the case, the discussion will relate primarily to common-emitter stages that are called upon to deliver significant amounts of output power.

When designing matching network for efficient transfer of power from the collector to a given load impedance, the designer must first establish what the level of power output will be in watts. He must know also what the operating voltage for the collector (collector to emitter) will be. Once these quantities are determined the collector load impedance can be calculated by using the formula:

$$R_L = \frac{V_{cc}^2}{2P_o\,(\text{watts})}$$

where R_L = Collector load impedance at resonance

V_{cc} = Dc operating voltage, collector to emitter

P_o = Required power output in watts

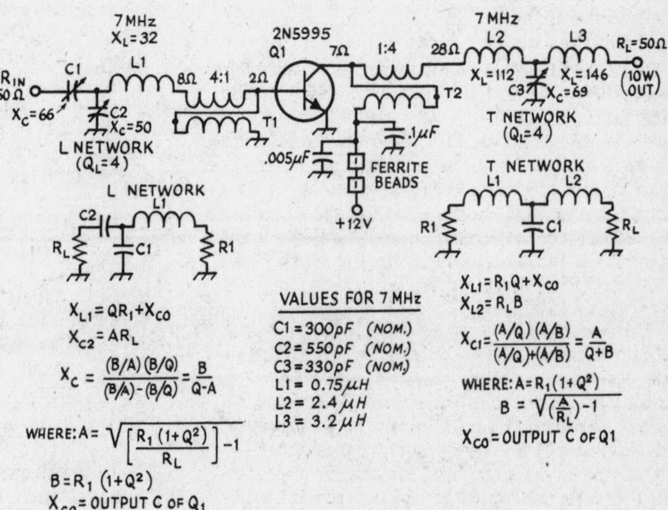

Fig. 4-15 – A practical example illustrating the problems encountered when designing networks for use with solid-state power amplifiers. Transformers T1 and T2 can be used to bring the base and collector impedences up to a practical value for matching with *L* and *T* networks. The transformers are broad-band, toroidal types.

Example: An amplifier stage must deliver 10 watts to a known resistive load. The dc voltage from collector to emitter is 13.6. R_L is

$$R_L = \frac{V_{cc}^2}{2P_o} = \frac{184.96}{20} = 9.248 \text{ ohms}$$

It is not difficult to determine from this that an amplifier delivering, say, 25 watts output at a collector supply of 12 volts would have an extremely low collector impedance (2.88 ohms). Few standard *LC* networks are suitable for transforming that value to the typical 50-ohm nonreactive antenna impedance. The situation becomes even more complex when matching a power driver to the base element of a power-amplifier stage. In such a case it would not be uncommon to match an 18-ohm collector impedance to a 3-ohm base impedance, or similar.

Two common networks are illustrated in Fig. 4-15. Additional information is contained in Chapter 6 of this book. An excellent design aid is Motorola's *Matching Network Designs with Computer Solutions*, Application Note AN-267. The bibliography at the end of this chapter lists other recommended texts for amateur and professional designers.

Broadband toroidal-wound transformers and baluns are frequently used to match difficult impedances. They can be used in combination with tuned circuits or networks to arrive at practical network values. Resonant networks are employed to provide needed selectivity for assurance of clean output waveforms from amplifiers. A practical upper limit for network Q_L (loaded Q) is 5, though some professional engineers design for values higher than 5. It should be understood that the higher the Q_L the greater the chance for electrical instability. It is recommended that the amateur adhere to the practice of designing his networks for Q_L values between 3 and 5. Values as low as 1 are suitable for some circuits, especially low-pass harmonic filters of the variety used in the 50-ohm output line from many amplifiers.

Bias and Bias Stabilization

Transistors must be forward biased in order to conduct significant current. In the npn design case the collector and base must be positive with respect to the emitter. The same is true when working with a pnp device, but the base and collector must be negative with respect to the emitter. The required bias is provided by the collector-to-emitter voltage, and by the emitter-to-base voltage. These bias voltages cause two currents to flow – emitter-to-collector current and emitter-to-base current. Either type of transistor, pnp or npn, can be used with a negative- or positive-ground power source by changing the circuit hookup as shown in Fig. 4-16. Forward bias is still properly applied in each instance. The lower the forward bias, the lower the collector current. As the forward bias is increased the collector current rises and the junction temperature increases. If the bias is continuously increased a point will be reached where the transistor becomes overloaded and burns out. This condition, called *thermal runaway* was discussed earlier in the chapter. To prevent damage to the transistor, some form of bias stabilization should be included in the design. Some practical bias-stabilization techniques are given in Fig. 4-17. At A and B, R1 in series with the emitter, is for the purpose of "swamping out" the resistance of the emitter-base diode; this swamping helps to stabilize the emitter current. The resistance of R1 should be large compared with that of the emitter-base diode, which is approximately equal to 25 divided by the emitter current in mA .

Since the current in R1 flows in such a direction as to bias the emitter negatively with respect to the base (a pnp transistor is assumed), a base-emitter bias slightly greater than the drop in R1 must be supplied. The proper operating point is achieved through adjustment of voltage divider R2R3, which is proportioned to give the desired value of no-signal collector current.

In the transformer-coupled circuit, input signal currents flow through R1 and R2, and there would be a loss of signal power at the base-emitter diode if these resistors were not bypassed by C1 and C2. The capacitors should have low reactance com-

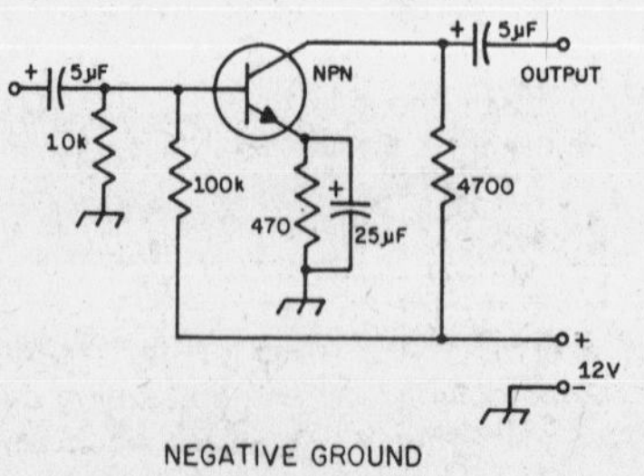

5µF
100k
10k
NPN
470
25µF
5µF
OUTPUT
4700
12V
POSITIVE GROUND

Fig. 4-16 – An example of how the circuit polarity can be changed to accommodate either a positive or negative power-supply ground. Npn transistors are shown here, but the same rules apply to pnp types.

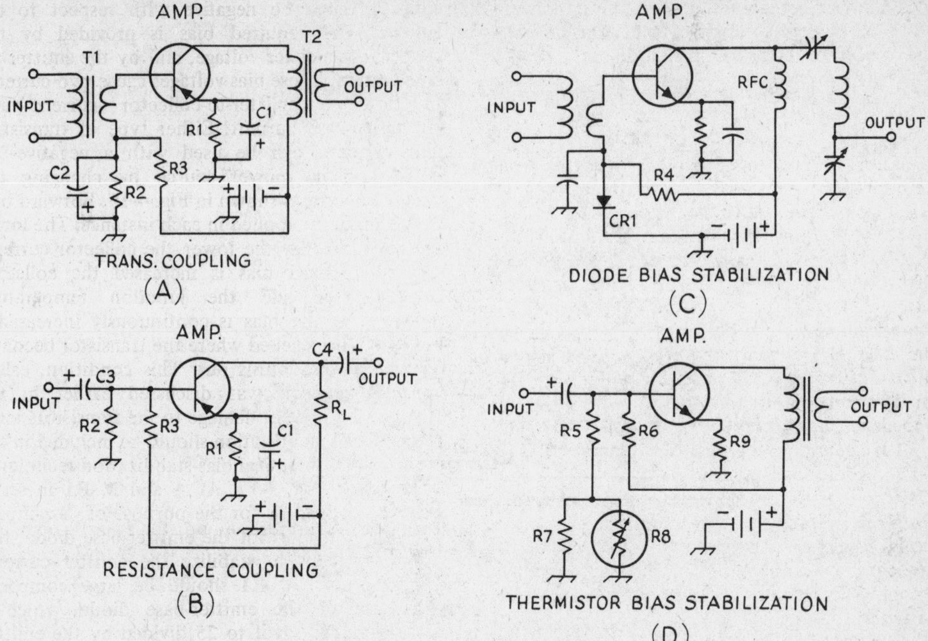

Fig. 4-17 – Examples of bias-stabilization techniques. A text discussion is given.

pared with the resistances across which they are connected. In the resistance-coupled circuit R2 serves as part of the bias voltage divider and also as part of the load for the signal-input source. As seen by the signal source, R3 is in parallel with R2 and thus becomes part of the input load resistance. C3 must have low reactance compared with the parallel combination of R2R3 and the base-to-emitter resistance of the transistor. The load impedance will determine the reactance of C4.

The output load resistance in the transformer-coupled case will be the actual load as reflected at the primary of the transformer, and its proper value will be determined by the transistor characteristics and the type of operation (Class A, B). The value of R_L in the resistance-coupled case is usually such as to permit the maximum ac voltage swing in the collector circuit without undue distortion, since Class-A operation is usual with this type of amplifier.

Transistor currents are sensitive to temperature variations, and so the operating point tends to shift as the transistor heats. The shift in operating point is in such a direction as to increase the heating, leading to thermal runaway. The heat developed depends on the amount of power dissipated in the transistor, so it is obviously advantageous in this respect to operate with as little internal dissipation as possible; i.e., the dc input should be kept to the lowest value that will permit the type of operation desired and should never exceed the rated value for the particular transistor used.

A contributing factor to the shift in operating point is the collector-to-base leakage current (usually designated I_{co}) – that is, the current that flows from the collector to base with the emitter connection open. This current, which is highly temperature sensitive, has the effect of increasing the emitter current by an amount much larger than I_{co} itself, thus shifting the operating point in such a way as to increase the collector current. This effect is reduced to the extent that I_{co} can be made to flow out of the base terminal rather than through the base-emitter diode. In the circuits of Fig. 4-17, bias stabilization is improved by making the resistance of R1 as large as possible and both R2 and R3 as small as possible, consistent with gain and power-supply economy.

It is common practice to employ certain devices in the bias networks of transistor stages to enhance bias stability. **Thermistors** or diodes can be used to advantage in such circuits. Examples of both techniques are given in Fig. 4-17 at C and D. Thermistors (temperature-sensitive resistors) can be used to compensate the rapid increase in collector current which is brought about by an increase in temperature. As the temperature in that part of the circuit increases, the thermistor's resistance decreases, reducing the emitter-to-base voltage (bias). As the bias is reduced in this manner, the collector current tends to remain the same, thus providing bias stabilization.

Resistors R5 and R7 of Fig. 4-17D are selected to give the most effective compensation over a particular temperature range.

A somewhat better bias-stabilization method is shown in Fig. 4-17C. In this instance, a diode is used between the base of the transistor and ground, replacing the resistor that is used in the circuits at A and B. The diode establishes a fixed value of forward bias and sets the no-signal collector current of the transistor. Also, the diode

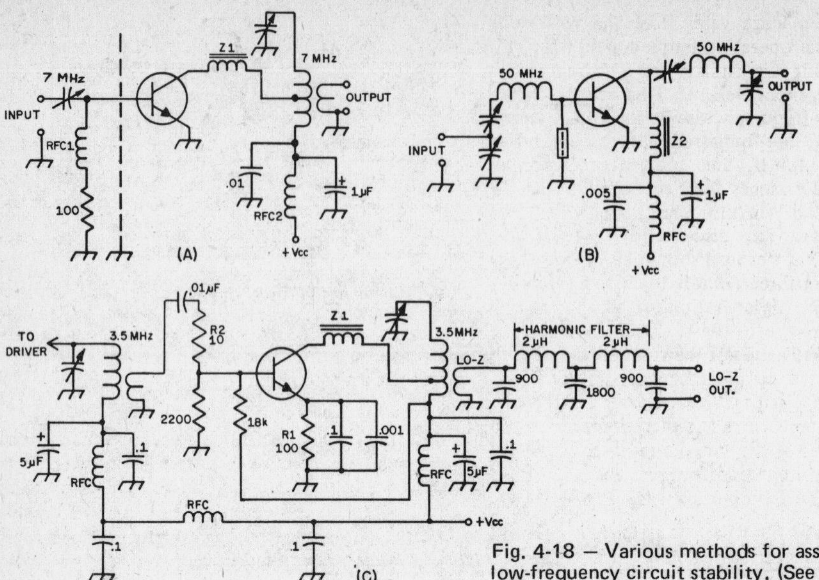

Fig. 4-18 – Various methods for assuring high- and low-frequency circuit stability. (See text.)

bias current varies in direct proportion with the supply voltage, tending to hold the no-signal collector current of the transistor at a steady value. If the diode is installed thermally close to the transistor with which it is used (clamped to the chassis near the transistor heat sink), it will provide protection against bias changes brought about by temperature excursions. As the diode temperature increases so will the diode bias current, thus lowering the bias voltage. Ordinarily, diode bias stabilization is applied to Class B stages. With germanium transistors, diode bias stabilization reduces collector-current variations to approximately one fifth of that obtainable with thermistor bias protection. With silicon transistors, the current variations are reduced to approximately one-fifteenth the thermistor-bias value.

Frequency Stability

Parasitic oscillations are a common source of trouble in transistor circuits. If severe enough in magnitude they can cause thermal runaway and destroy the transistor. Oscillation can take place at any frequency from just above dc to the f_T of the device, and these parasitics can often pass unnoticed if the waveforms are not examined with an oscilloscope. In addition to posing a potential danger to the device itself, the oscillations can cause distortion and unwanted radiation of spurious energy. In an amateur transmitter this condition can lead to violation notices from the FCC, interference to other services, and TVI. In the case of receivers, spurious energy can cause "birdies" and poor noise figures.

A transistor chosen for high-frequency operation (f_T at least five times greater than the proposed operating frequency) can easily oscillate *above* the operating frequency if feedback conditions are correct. Also, the device gain in the spectrum below the operating frequency will be very high, giving rise to low-frequency oscillation. At vhf and uhf phase shifts come into play, and this condition can encourage positive feedback, which leads to instability. At these higher frequencies it is wise to avoid the use of rf chokes and coupling capacitors whenever possible. The capacitors can cause shifts in phase (as can the base semiconductor material in the transistor), and the rf chokes, unless of very low Q, can cause a tuned-base tuned-collector condition. Some precautionary measures against instability are shown in Fig. 4-18. At A, RFC1 has its Q lowered by the addition of the 100-ohm series resistor. Alternatively, RFC1 could be shunted by a low-value resistor, but at some sacrifice in driving power. One or more ferrite beads can be slipped over the pigtail of an rf choke to lower the Q of the inductor. This method may be preferred in instances where the addition of a low-value resistor might establish an undesirable bias condition, as in the base return of a Class C stage. Parasitic choke Z1 consists of three ferrite beads slipped over a short piece of wire. The choke is installed as close to the collector terminal as possible. This low-Q choke will help prevent vhf or uhf instability. RFC2 is part of the decoupling network in the collector supply lead. It is bypassed for the operating frequency by means of the .01-µF capacitor, but is also bypassed for low frequencies by the addition of the 1-µF capacitor. In the vhf amplifier at B, Z1 and Z2 are ferrite-bead chokes. They present a high impedance to the base and collector elements, but because they are low-Q chokes there is little chance for them to permit a tuned-base tuned-collector oscillation. At C, the stage operates Class A, a typical arrangement in the low-level section of a transmitter, and the emitter is above ground by virtue of bias resistor R1. It must be bypassed to assure maximum stage gain. Here the emitter is bypassed for the operating frequency and for vhf. By not bypassing the emitter for low frequencies the stage is degenerative at lf. This will lessen the chance of low-frequency oscillation. The supply leads, however, are bypassed for the operating frequency and for lf, thus preventing unwanted feedback between stages along the supply leads. Z1 is a ferrite-bead vhf/uhf parasitic choke. The 10-ohm resistor, R2, also helps suppress vhf parasitics. The emitter lead should be kept as short as possible in all three circuits to enhance stability and to prevent degeneration at the operating frequency. It is wise to use rf shields between the input and output halves of the rf amplifier stage to prevent unwanted coupling between the base and collector tuned circuits. At operating frequencies where toroid cores are suitable, the shields can often be omitted if the tuned circuits use toroidal inductors. Toroidal transformers and inductors have self-shielding properties – an asset to the designer.

FIELD-EFFECT TRANSISTORS

Still another semiconductor device, the field-effect transistor, (FET) is superior to bipolar transistors in many applications because it has a high input impedance, its characteristics more nearly approach those of a vacuum tube.

The Junction FET

Field-effect transistors are divided into two main groups: junction FETs, and MOSFETs. The basic JFET is shown in Fig. 4-19.

The reason for the terminal names will become clear later. A dc operating condition is set up by starting a current flow between source and drain. This current flow is made up of free electrons since the semiconductor is n-type in the channel, so a positive voltage is applied at the drain. This positive voltage attracts the negatively charged free electrons and the current flows (Fig. 4-20). The next step is to apply a gate voltage of the polarity shown in Fig. 4-20. Note that this reverse-biases the gates with respect to the source, channel, and drain. This reverse-bias gate voltage causes a depletion layer to be formed which takes up part of the channel, and since the electrons now have less volume in which to move the resistance is greater and the current between source and drain is reduced. If a large gate voltage is applied the depletion regions meet, causing **pinch off,** and consequently the source-drain current is reduced

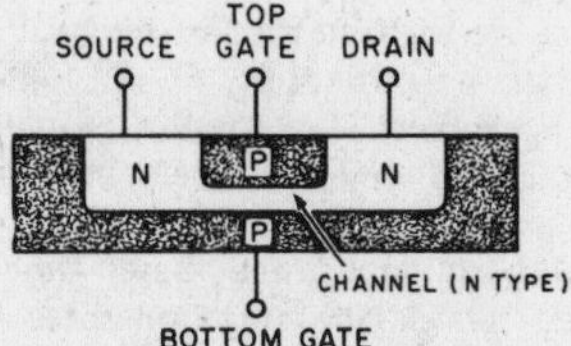

Fig. 4-19 – The junction field-effect transistor.

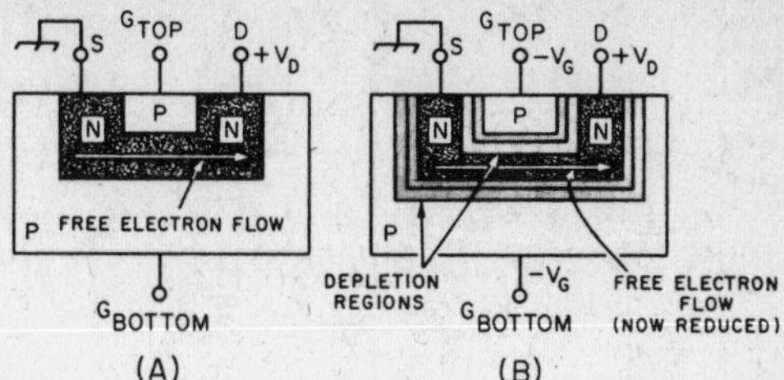

Fig. 4-20 – Operation of the JFET under applied bias. A depletion region (light shading) is formed, compressing the channel and increasing its resistance to current flow.

nearly to zero. Since the large source-drain current changed with a relatively small gate voltage, the device acts as an amplifier. In the operation of the JFET, the gate terminal is never foward biased, because if it were the source-drain current would all be diverted through the forward-biased gate junction diode.

The resistance between the gate terminal and the rest of the device is very high, since the gate terminal is always reverse biased, so the JFET has a very high input resistance. The source terminal is the *source* of current carriers, and they are *drained* out of the circuit at the drain. The gate *opens* and *closes* the amount of channel current which flows in the pinch-off region. Thus the operation of a FET closely resembles the operation of the vacuum tube with its high grid input impedance. Comparing the JFET to a vacuum tube, the source corresponds to the cathode, the gate to the grid, and the drain to the plate.

MOSFETs

The other large family which makes up field-effect transistors is the insulated-gate FET, or MOSFET, which is pictured schematically in Fig. 4-21. In order to set up a dc operating condition, a positive polarity is applied to the drain terminal. The substrate is connected to the source, and both are at ground potential, so the channel electrons are attracted to the positive drain. In order to regulate this source-drain current, voltage is applied to the gate contact. The gate is insulated from the rest of the device by a layer of very thin dielectric material, so this is not a p-n junction between the gate and the device – thus the name insulated gate. When a negative gate polarity is applied, positive-charged holes from the p-type substrate

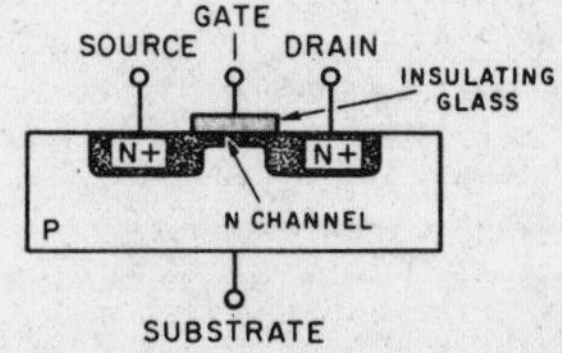

Fig. 4-21 – The insulated-gate field-effect transistor.

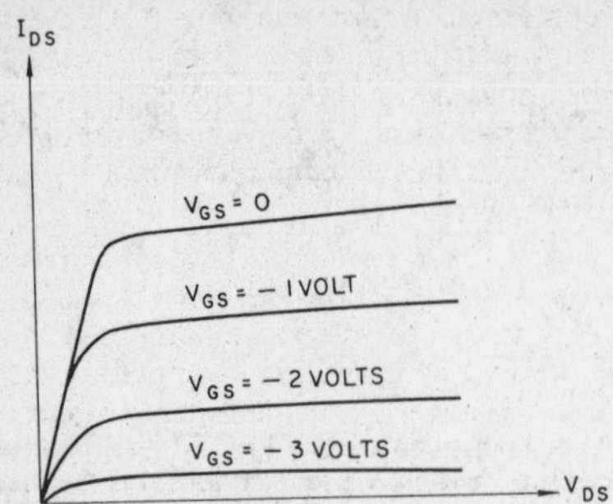

Fig. 4-21A–Typical JFET characteristic curves.

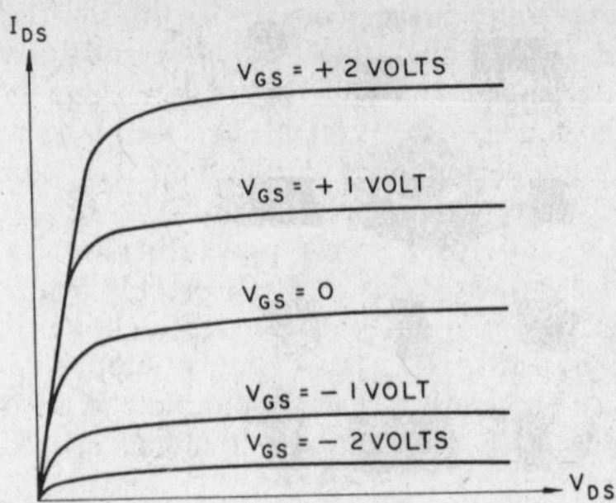

Fig. 4-21B–Typical MOSFET characteristic curves.

are attracted toward the gate and the conducting channel is made more narrow; thus the source-drain current is reduced. When a positive gate voltage is connected, the holes in the substrate are repelled away, the conducting channel is made larger, and the source-drain current is increased. The MOSFET is more flexible since either a positive or negative voltage can be applied to the gate. The resistance between the gate and the rest of the device is extremely high because they are separated by a layer of thin dielectric. Thus the MOSFET has an extremely high input impedance. In fact, since the leakage through the insulating material is generally much smaller than through the reverse-biased p-n gate junction in the JFET, the MOSFET has a much higher input impedance. Typical values of R_{in} for the MOSFET are over a million megohms, while R_{in} for the JFET ranges from megohms to over a thousand megohms. There are both single-gate and dual-gate MOSFETs available. The latter has a signal gate, Gate 1, and a control gate , Gate 2. The gates are effectively in series making it an easy matter to control the dynamic range of the device by varying the bias on Gate 2. Dual-gate MOSFETs are widely used as agc-controlled rf and i-f amplifiers, as mixers and product detectors, and as variable attenuators. The isolation between the gates is relatively high in mixer service. This helps lessen oscillator "pulling" and reduces oscillator radiation. The forward **trans-admittance** (transconductance, or g_m) of modern MOSFETs is as high as 18,000, and they are designed to operate efficiently well into the uhf spectrum.

Characteristic Curves

The characteristic curves for the FETs described above are shown in Figs. 4-21A and 4-21B, where drain-source current is plotted against drain-source voltage for given gate voltages.

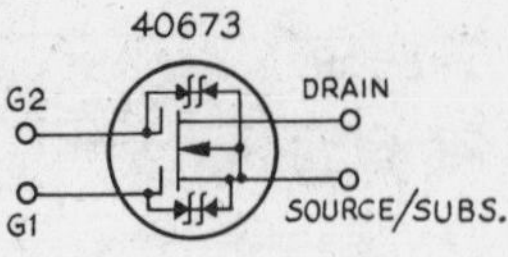

Fig. 4-22 – Schematic presentation of a gate-protected MOSFET. Back-to-back Zener diodes are bridged internally from gates 1 and 2 to the source/substrate element.

Classifications

Field-effect transistors are classed into two main groupings for application in circuits, ENHANCEMENT MODE and DEPLETION MODE. The enhancement-mode devices are those specifically constructed so that they have *no* channel. They become useful only when a gate voltage is applied that causes a channel to be formed. IGFETs can be used as enhancement-mode devices since both polarities can be applied to the gate without the gate becoming forward biased and conducting.

A depletion-mode unit corresponds to Figs. 4-19 and 4-21 shown earlier, where a channel exists with no gate voltage applied. For the JFET we can apply a gate voltage and deplete the channel, causing the current to decrease. With the MOSFET we can apply a gate voltage of either polarity so the device can be depleted (current decreased) or enhanced (current increased).

To sum up, a depletion-mode FET is one which has a channel constructed; thus it has a current flow for zero gate voltage. Enhancement-mode FETs are those which have no channel, so no current flows with zero gate voltage.

Gate-Protected FETs

Most JFETs are capable of withstanding up to 80 volts pk-pk from gate to source before junction damage occurs. Insulated-gate FETs, however, can be damaged by allowing the leads to come in contact with plastic materials, or by the simple act of handling the leads with one's fingers. Static charges account for the foregoing, and the damage takes the form of punctured dielectric between the gate or gates and the remainder of the internal elements. Devices of the MFE3006 and 3N140 series are among those which can be easily damaged.

Gate-protected MOSFETs are currently available, and their gates are able to withstand pk-pk voltages (gate to source) of up to 10. Internal Zener diodes are connected back to back from each gate to the source/substrate element. The 40673 and 3N200 FETs are among the types which have built-in Zener diodes. Dual-gate MOSFETs which are gate-protected can be used as single-gate protected FETs by connecting the two gate leads in parallel. A gate-protected MOSFET is shown schematically in Fig. 4-22.

A collection of modern ICs. Various case styles of metal and epoxy materials are illustrated.

INTEGRATED CIRCUITS

Just as the term implies, integrated circuits (ICs) contain numerous components which are manufactured in such a way as to be suitably interconnected for a particular application, and on one piece of semiconductor base material. The various elements of the IC are comprised of bi-polar transistors, MOSFETs, diodes, resistances, and capacitances. There are often as many as ten or more transistors on a single IC chip, and frequently their respective bias resistors are formed on the chip. Generally speaking, ICs fall into four basic categories – **differential amplifiers, operational amplifiers**, diode or transistor arrays, and logic ICs.

IC Structures

The basic IC is formed on a uniform chip of n-type or p-type silicon. Impurities are introduced into the chip, their depth into it being determined by the diffusion temperature and time. The geometry of the plane surface of the chip is determined by masking off certain areas, applying photochemical techniques, and applying a coating of insulating oxide. Certain areas of the oxide coating are then opened up to allow the formation of interconnecting leads between sections of the IC. When capacitors are formed on the chip, the oxide serves as the dielectric material. Fig. 4-23 shows a representative three-component IC in both pictorial and schematic form. Most integrated circuits are housed in TO-5 type cases, or in flat-pack epoxy blocks. ICs may have as many as 12 or more leads which connect to the various elements on the chip.

Types of IC Amplifiers

Some ICs are called differential amplifiers and others are known as operational amplifiers. The basic differential-amplifier IC consists of a pair of transistors that have similar input circuits. The inputs can be connected so as to enable the transistors to respond to the difference between two voltages or currents. During this function, the circuit effectively suppresses like voltages or currents. For the sake of simplicity we may think of the differential pair of transistors as a push-pull amplifier stage. Ordinarily, the differential pair of transistors are fed from a controlled, constant-current source (Q3 in Fig. 4-24A. Q1 and Q2 are the differential pair in this instance). Q3 is commonly called a **transistor current sink.** Excellent balance exists between the input terminals of differential amplifiers because the base-to-emitter voltages and current gains (beta) of

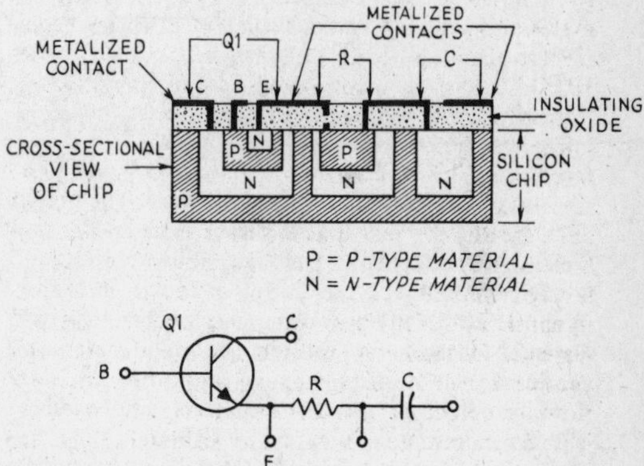

Fig. 4-23 – Pictorial and schematic illustrations of a simple IC device.

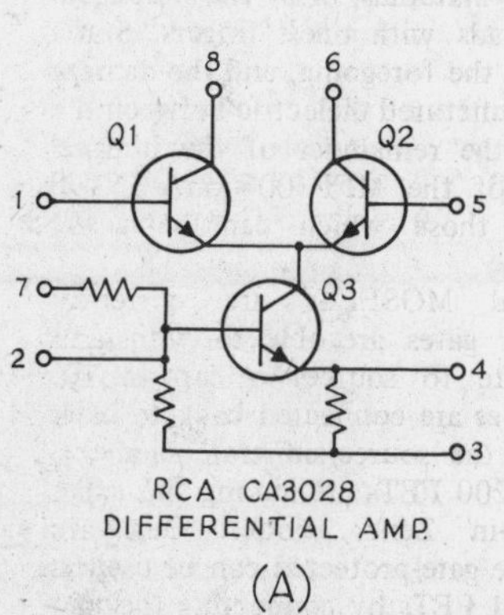

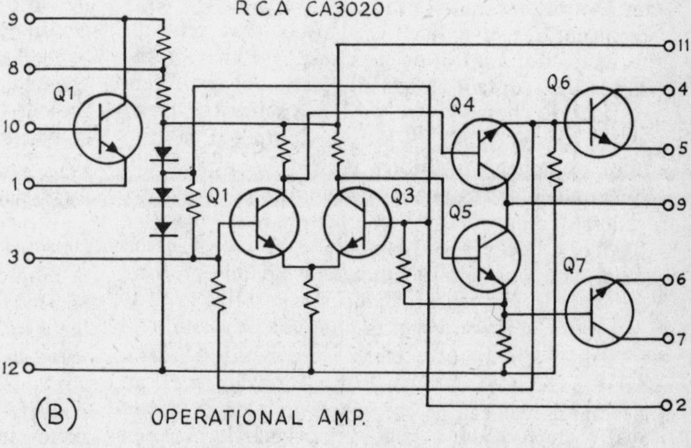

Fig. 4-24 – At A, a representative circuit for a typical differential IC. An Operational Amplifier IC is illustrated at B, also in representative form.

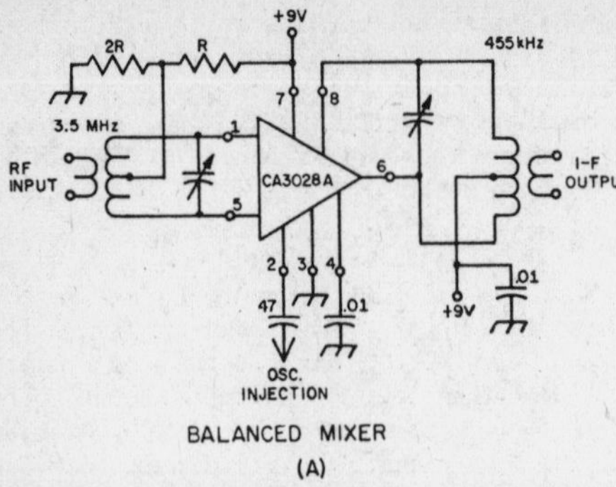

BALANCED MIXER

(A)

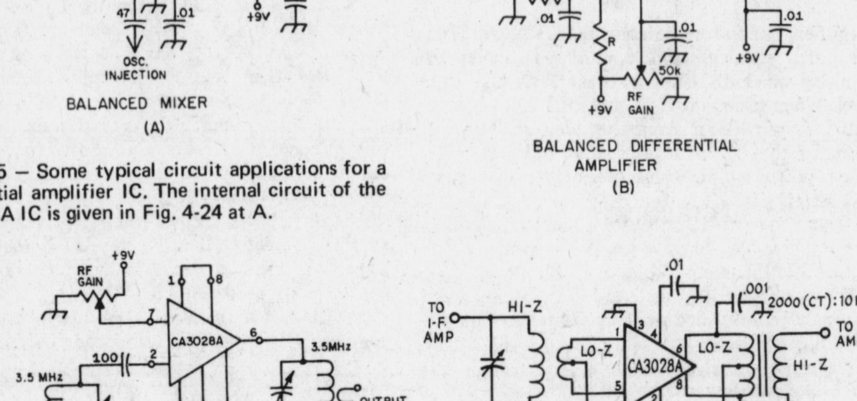

BALANCED DIFFERENTIAL AMPLIFIER

(B)

Fig. 4-25 – Some typical circuit applications for a differential amplifier IC. The internal circuit of the CA3028A IC is given in Fig. 4-24 at A.

CASCODE AMP.

(C)

PRODUCT DETECTOR

(D)

the two transistors are closely matched. The match results from the fact that the transistors are formed next to one another on the same silicon chip.

Differential ICs are useful as linear amplifiers from dc to the vhf spectrum, and can be employed in such circuits as limiters, product detectors, frequency multipliers, mixers, amplitude modulators, squelch, rf and i-f amplifiers, and even in signal-generating applications. Although they are designed to be used as differential amplifiers, they can be used in other types of circuits as well, treating the various IC components as discrete units.

Operational-amplifier ICs are basically very-high-gain direct-coupled amplifiers that rely on feedback for control of their response characteristics. They contain cascaded differential amplifiers of the type shown in Fig. 4-24A. A separate output stage, Q6–Q7, Fig. 4-24B, is contained on the chip. Although operational ICs can be successfully operated under open-loop conditions, they are generally controlled by externally applied negative feedback. Operational amplifiers are most often used for audio amplification, as frequency-shaping (peaking, notching, or bandpass) amplifiers, or as integrator, differentiator, or comparator amplifiers.

Diode-ICs are also being manufactured in the same manner as outlined in the foregoing section. Several diodes can be contained on a single silicon wafer to provide a near-perfect match between diode characteristics. The diode arrangement can take the form of a bridge circuit, series-connected groups, or as separate components. Diode ICs of this kind are useful in balanced-modulator circuits, or to any application requiring closely matched diodes.

Fig. 4-25 demonstrates the versatility of just one type of IC, an RCA CA3028A differential amplifier. Its internal workings are shown in Fig. 4-24A, permitting a comparison of the schematic diagram and the block representations of Fig. 4-25. The circuit at B in Fig. 4-25 is characterized by its high input and output impedances (several thousand ohms), its high gain, and its stability. This circuit can be adapted as an audio amplifier by using transformer or RC coupling. In the circuits of B and C terminal 7 is used to manually control the rf gain, but agc can be applied to that terminal instead. In the circuit at D the CA3028A provides low-noise operation and exhibits good conversion gain as a product detector. The CA3028A offers good performance from dc to 100 MHz.

PRACTICAL CONSIDERATIONS

Some modern-day ICs are designed to replace nearly all of the discrete components used in earlier composite equipment. One example can be seen in the RCA CA3089E flat-pack IC which contains nearly the entire circuit for an fm receiver. The IC contains 63 bipolar transistors, 16 diodes, and 32 resistors. The CA3089E is designed for an i-f of 10.7 MHz and requires but one outboard tuned circuit. The chip consists of an i-f

Fig. 4-26 — The circuit at A shows practical component values for use with the CA3089E fm subsystem IC. A COS/MOS array IC is illustrated at B in schematic-diagram form. It consists of three complementary-symmetry MOSFET pairs. The illustration at C shows how the CA3600E can be connected in cascade to provide at least 100 dB of audio amplification.

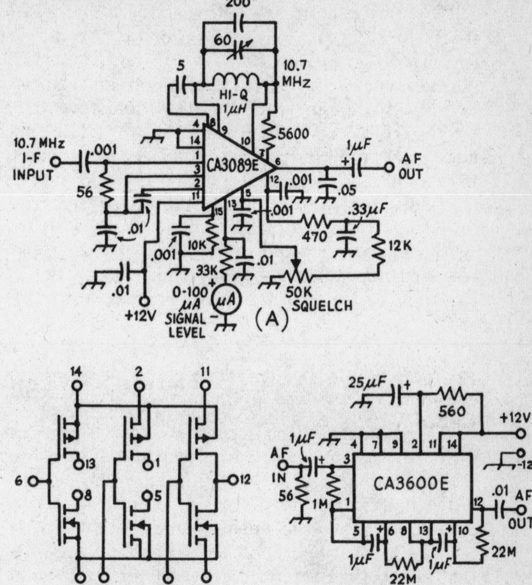

RCA 3600E COS/MOS ARRAY (GOOD TO 5 MHz)

CASCADE 100-dB AF AMPLIFIER

EXCEPT AS INDICATED, DECIMAL VALUES OF CAPACITANCE ARE IN MICROFARADS (μF) ; OTHERS ARE IN PICOFARADS (pF OR μμF); RESISTANCES ARE IN OHMS ; k = 1 000, M = 1 000 000.

amplifier, quadrature detector, audio preamplifier, agc, afc, squelch, and a tuning-meter circuit. Limiting of -3 dB takes place at the 12-μV input level. When using an IC of this kind it is necessary only to provide a front-end converter for the desired frequency of reception, an audio amplifier, and a power supply (plus speaker, level controls, and meter).

There are two IC subsystem units designed for a-m receiver use. Each is similar in complexity to the CA3089E illustrated in Fig: 4-26. These components are identified as CA3088E and CA3123E. The latter is described in RCA Data File No. 631. Both ICs are readily adaptable to communications receiver use and should become popular building blocks for amateurs who desire compact, portable receiving equipment.

TRANSISTOR ARRAYS

Amateur designers should not overlook the usefulness of transistor- and diode-array ICs. These devices contain numerous bipolar or MOSFET transistors on a common substrate. In most instances the transistors can be employed as one would treat discrete npn devices. An entire receiver can be made from one transistor-array IC if one wishes to construct a compact assembly. The CA3049 is a dual independent differential rf/i-f amplifier chip with an f_T of 1.3 GHz. It is especially well suited to applications which call for double-balanced mixers, detectors, and modulators. Another device of similar usefulness is the CA3018A. The CA3045 should also be of interest to the amateur. Matched electrical characteristics of the transistors in these ICs offer many advantages not available when using discrete transistors. Fig. 4-27 shows the internal workings of the CA3018A and CA3045 ICs.

COS/MOS (complementary-symmetry metal-oxide silicon) ICs are becoming increasingly popular, and one RCA part, the CA3600E, contains an array of complementary-symmetry MOSFET pairs (three) which can be used individually or in cascade, as shown in Fig. 4-26 at B. Detailed information is given in RCA File No. 619. The CA3600E is a high-input impedance, micropower component which is suitable for use as a preamplifier, differential amplifier, op amp, comparator, timer, mixer, chopper, or oscillator.

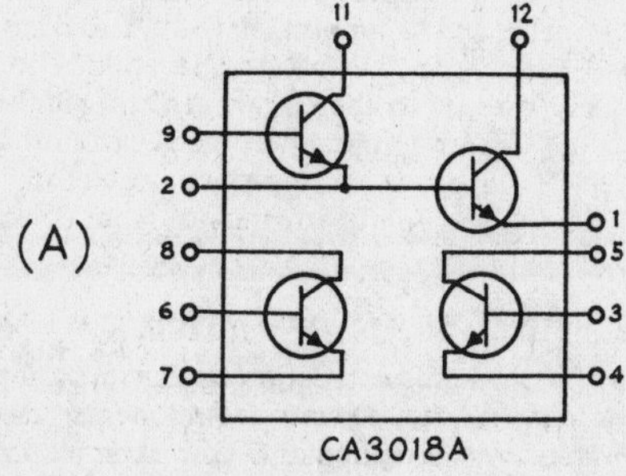

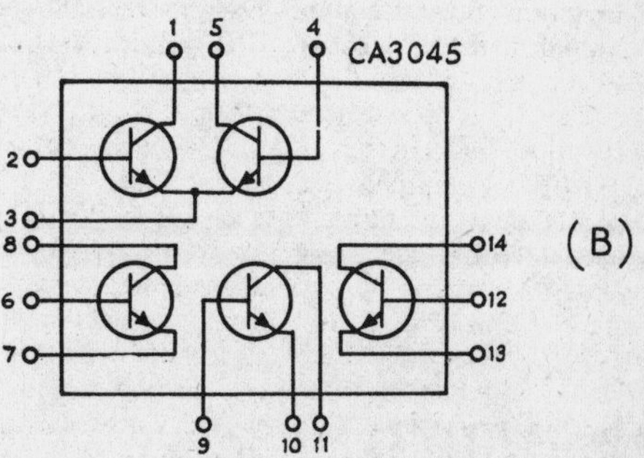

Fig. 4-27 — Transistor arrays offer unlimited application because several circuit combinations are possible. The CA3018A IC at A has a Darlington-connected pair plus two separate transistors. At B, two transistors are internally connected in a differential amplifier fashion. Three separate transistors are available for use in other functions. The arrays shown here are useful into the vhf spectrum.

One of the more interesting and useful array of ICs is the RCA CA3102E. It contains two differential pairs and two current-source transistors. The device is ideally suited for use in doubly balanced mixers, modulators, and product detectors. The CA3102E is excellent for use in the following additional applications: vhf amplifiers, vhf mixers, rf amp./mixer/oscillator combinations, i-f amplifiers (differential and/or cascode mode), synchronous detectors, and sense amplifiers. This IC is similar in configuration to the CA3049T array, but has an independent substrate connection which is common to an internal shield that separates the two differential amplifiers. The shield helps assure good isolation in applications where that feature is required.

F_T for CA3102E is in excess of 1000 MHz. Noise figure at 100 MHz single transistor is 1.5 dB, R_S = 500 ohms. Noise figure at 200 MHz cascode mode is 4.6 dB. Additional specifications can be found in *RCA Data File* No. 611. The CA3102E offers almost limitless possibilities for applications in amateur radio design work. The chip is manufactured in a 14-lead DIP package. The CA3049T comes encased in a standard TO-5 package.

DIGITAL-LOGIC INTEGRATED CIRCUITS

Digital logic is the term used to describe an overall design procedure for electronic systems in which "on" and "off" are the important words, not "amplification," "detection," and other terms commonly applied to most amateur equipment. It is "digital" because it deals with discrete events that can be characterized by digits or integers, in contrast with linear systems in which an infinite number of levels may be encountered. It is "logic" because it follows mathematical laws, in which "effect" predictably follows "cause."

Just like linear integrated circuits, digital ICs are manufactured in such a way that the internal components are interconnected for particular applications. Packaging of the digital ICs is the same for their linear counterparts, with the full package range pictured earlier being used. From outward appearances, it would be impossible to tell the difference between the two types of ICs except from the identification numbers.

Linear ICs are constructed to respond to continuously variable or analog signals, such as in an amplifier. Digital devices, on the other hand, generally have active components operating only in either of two conditions – cutoff or saturation. Digital ICs find much application in on-off switching circuits, as well as in counting, computation, memory-storage, and display circuits. Operation of these circuits is based on binary mathematics, so words such as "one" and "zero" have come into frequent use in digital-logic terminology. These terms refer to specific voltage levels, and vary between manufacturers and devices. Nearly always, a "0" means a voltage near ground, while "1" means whatever the manufacturer specifies. One must distinguish between "positive logic" and "negative logic." In positive logic, a 1 is more positive than a 0, though both may be negative voltages. In negative logic, the reverse is true. Often the terms "high" and "low" are used in reference to these voltage levels. The definitions of these terms are the same for both positive and negative logic. A "high" is the most positive or least negative potential, while a "low" is the least positive or most negative.

For practical use in some applications it is desirable to convert binary data into decimal equivalents, such as in electronic counting and display systems. In other applications, such as for the graphic recording or metering of summations or products of integers, it is convenient to convert the digital data into analog equivalents. Specialized integrated circuits designed to perform these functions are also considered to be included in the digital-IC category.

LOGIC SYMBOLS

With modern microcircuit technology, hundreds of components can be packaged in a single case. Rather than showing a forest of transistors, resistors, and diodes, logic diagrams show symbols based on the four distinctive shapes given in Fig. 4-28 at A through D. These shapes may be "modified" or altered slightly, according to

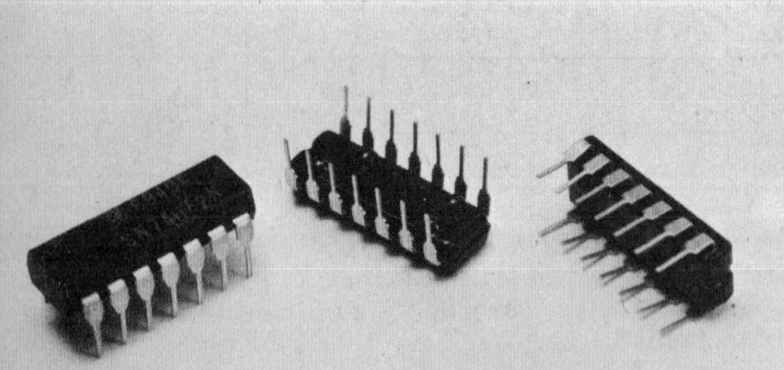

From outward appearances, these three ICs appear to be identical. Although each is a *J-K* flip-flop, there are differences in their characteristics. Pictured at the left is a Texas Instruments SN74H72N integrated circuit, called a *J–K* master-slave flip-flop. Shown in the center is a Motorola MC1927P IC, which is a 120-MHz ac-coupled *J-K* flip-flop. Both of these ICs might be considered "universal" flip-flops, for they may be used in a variety of ways. Shown at the right is a Motorola MC726P, a simple *J-K* flip-flop.

specific functions performed. Examples are shown at E through H of Fig. 4-28.

The square, Fig. 4-28D and H, may appear on logic diagrams as a rectangle. This symbol is a somewhat universal one, and thus must be identified with supplemental information to indicate the exact function. Internal labels are usually used. Common identification labels are:

FF – Flip-flop
FL – Flip-flop latch
SS – Single shot
ST – Schmitt trigger.

Other logic functions may also be represented by the square or rectangle, and the label should adequately identify the function performed. Unique identifying shapes are used for gates and inverters, so these need no labels to identify the *function*. Hardware- or package-identification information may appear inside any of the symbols on logic diagrams.

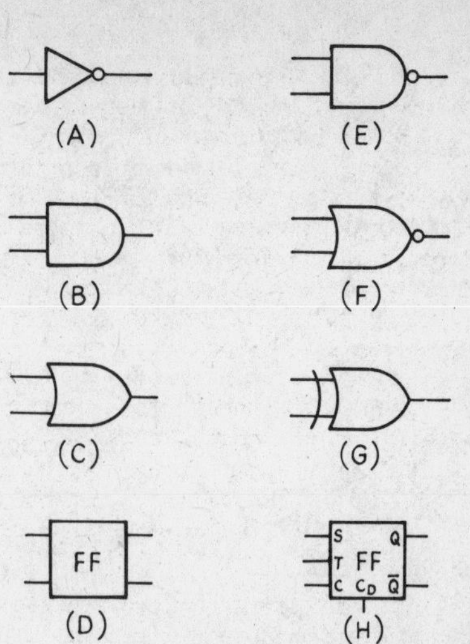

Fig. 4-28 – Distinctive symbols for digital logic diagrams. At A is shown an inverter, at B an AND gate, at C an OR gate, and at D a flip-flop. Additions to these basic symbols indicate specific functions performed. A small circle, for example, placed at the output point of the symbol, denotes that inversion occurs at the output of the device. Shown at E is an inverting AND or NAND gate, and at F is an inverting OR or NOR gate. At G is the symbol for an exclusive OR gate. The symbol at H represents a J-K flip-flop.

TYPES OF DIGITAL ICs

Digital integrated circuits perform a variety of functions, but these functions can generally be cataloged into just a few categories: gates, inverters, flip-flops, drivers and buffers, adders and subtractors, registers, and memories, plus the special-purpose ICs as mentioned earlier – decoders and converters. Some of these types, such as adders and subtractors, registers, and memories, find use primarily in computer systems. More universally used types of ICs are the inverters, gates and flip-flops.

Inverters

A single chip in one IC package may be designed to perform several functions, and these functions can be independent of each other. One example of an IC of this type is Motorola's MC789P, which bears the name, "hex inverter." This IC contains six identical inverter sections. The schematic diagram of one section is shown in Fig. 4-29A. In operation, 3.0 to 3.6 volts are applied between +Vcc and ground. For this device in positive-logic applications, a 0 is defined as any potential less than approximately 0.6 volt, and a 1 is any voltage greater than about 0.8. With a logic 0 applied at the input, the transistor will be at or near cutoff. Its output will be a potential near +Vcc, or a logic 1. If the 0 at the input is replaced by a 1, the transistor goes into saturation and its output drops nearly to ground potential; a 0 appears at the output. The output of this device is always the opposite or *complement* of the input logic level. This is sometimes called a NOT gate, because the input and output logic levels are *not* the same, under any conditions of operation.

Shown at the right in Fig. 4-29A is the logic symbol for the inverter. In all logic symbols, the connections for +Vcc and the ground return are omitted, although they are understood to be made. The proper connections are given in the manufacturer's data sheets, and, of course, must be made before the device will operate properly. In the case of all multiple-function ICs, such as the hex inverter, a single ground connection and a single +Vcc connection suffice for all sections contained in the package.

Gates

Another example of an IC containing several independent functions in one package is Motorola's MC724P, a quad 2-input gate. Four gates are contained in one chip. The schematic diagram and logic symbols for a gate section are shown at B in Fig. 4-29. As with the MC789P, a supply of 3.0 to 3.6 volts is used; for positive logic a 0 is a potential less than 0.6 volt, and a 1 is a potential greater than 0.8 volt. It may be seen from the schematic diagram that the two transistors have an independent input to each base, but they share a common collector resistor. Either transistor will be saturated with a logic 1 applied at its input, and a 0 output will result. A 0 at the input of either transistor will cause that transistor to be cut off, but a 1 at the opposite input will hold the output at 0. Thus, a 1 at either Input 1 *or* Input 2 will cause a 0 (or a NOT 1) to appear at the output. The NOT functions are usually written with a bar over them, so $\overline{1}$ means the same thing as NOT 1,

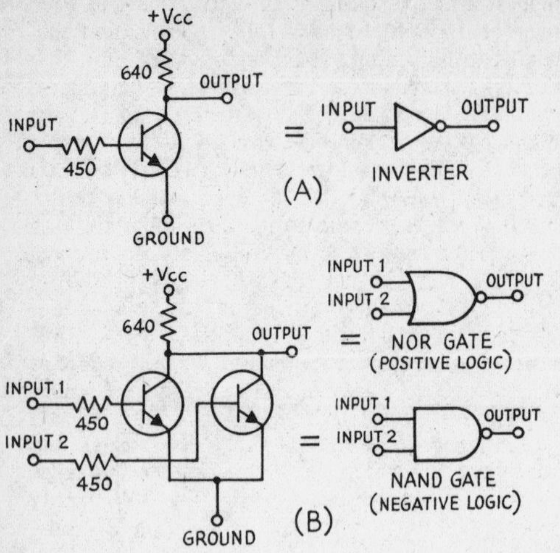

Fig. 4-29 – Digital circuits and their equivalent logic symbols. See text. Indicated resistor values are typical.

and is expressed as NOT 1 when reading the term. Logic-circuit operation can be expressed with equations. **Boolean algebra**, a form of binary mathematics, is used. These equations should not be confused with ordinary algebraic equations. The logic equation for the operation of the circuit in Fig. 4-28A is $1\ v\ 1 = \overline{1}$. The little v means OR. Sometimes "+" is used instead of "*v*." In plain words, the equation says that a 1 at Input 1 *or* Input 2 will yield a NOT 1 at the output. This is equivalent of saying the circuit is an inverting OR gate, or a NOT OR gate. This latter name is usually contracted to NOR gate, the name by which the circuit is known.

If the circuit of Fig. 4-29B is used with negative logic, circuit operation remains the same; only the definitions of terms are changed. A logic 1, now, is a voltage level less than 0.6, and a 0 is a level greater than 0.8 volt. If a logic 1 is applied at both inputs, 1 *and* 2, both transistors will be cut off. The output is near +Vcc, which is a logic 0 or NOT 1. The equation for this operation is $1 \cdot 1 = \overline{1}$, where the dot means AND. In this way, with negative logic, the circuit becomes an inverting AND gate, or a NOT AND gate or, more commonly, a NAND gate. Manufacturers' literature frequently refers to this type of device as a NAND/NOR gate, because it performs either function.

Flip-Flops

It is not necessary for the various functions on a single chip to be identical. Motorola's MC780P IC, a decade up-counter, contains four flip-flops, an inverter, and a 2-input gate. These functions are interconnected to provide divide-by-10 operation, with ten input pulses required for every output pulse which appears. Intermediate outputs are also provided (in binary-coded form) so that the number of pulses which have entered the input can be determined at all times. These **binary-coded decimal (BCD)** outputs, after decoding, may be used to operate decimal-readout indicators.

The term, **medium-scale integration (MSI)** is frequently applied to ICs such as this decade up-counter, which contains the equivalent of 15 or more gates on a single chip. **Large-scale integration (LSI)** describes ICs containing the equivalent of 100 or more gates on a single chip. These terms, when applied to a particular IC, convey an idea of the complexity of the circuitry.

A flip-flop is a device which has two outputs that can be placed in various 1 and 0 combinations by various input schemes. Basically, one output is a 1 when the other is a 0, although situations do occur (sometimes on purpose) where both outputs are alike. One output is called the Q output, or "set" output, while the other is the $\overline{Q}$ (NOT Q) or "reset" output. If $Q = 1$ and $\overline{Q} = 0$, the flip-flop is said to be "set" or in the "1 state," while for the reverse, the flip-flop is "reset," or "cleared," or in the "0 state." A variety of inputs exist, from which the flip-flops derive their names.

The *R-S* flip-flop is the simplest type. Its outputs change directly as a result of changes at its inputs. The type *T* flip-flop "toggles," "flips," or changes its state during the occurrence of a *T* pulse, called a clock pulse. The *T* flip-flop can be considered as a special case of the *J-K* flip-flop described later. The type *D* flip-flop acts as a storage element. When a clock pulse occurs, the complementary status of the *D* input is transferred to the *Q* output. The flip-flop remains in this state even though the input may change, as it can change states only when a clock pulse occurs.

Although there is some disagreement in the nomenclature, a *J-K* flip-flop is generally considered to be a toggled or clocked *R-S* flip-flop. It may also be used as a storage element. The *J* input is frequently called the "set" or *S* input; the *K* is called the "clear" or *C* input (not to be confused with the clock input). The clock input is called *T*, as in the type *T* flip-flop. A clear-direct or C_D input which overrides all other inputs to clear the flip-flop to 0 is provided in most *J-K* flip-flop packages. The logic symbol for the *J-K* flip-flop is shown in Fig. 4-28H. A simple *J-K* flip-flop circuit contains 13 or 14 transistors and 16 or 18 resistors.

There are essentially two types of flip-flop inputs, the dc or level-sensitive type, and the "ac" or transistion-sensitive type. It should not be concluded that an ac input is capacitively coupled. This was true for the discrete-component flip-flops, but capacitors just do not fit into microcircuit dimensions. The construction of an ac input uses the "master-slave" principle, where the actions of a master flip-flop driving a slave flip-flop are combined to produce a shift in the output level during a transit of the input.

DIGITAL-LOGIC IC FAMILIES

There are seven categories or families of which nearly all semiconductor digital ICs are members.

Each family has its own inherent advantages and disadvantages. Each is geared to its own particular market, meeting a specific set of needs.

Resistor-Transistor Logic – RTL

RTL is known primarily for its economy. It is well named, since it contains resistors and transistors exclusively. The circuits of Fig. 4-29 are RTL. Advantages of the RTL family are economy, ease of use in system designs, ease of interface with discrete components, and high speed–power product. There are a wide number of functions available in this family. Disadvantages are low immunity to voltage noise (transients, rf pickup, and the like), and relatively low **fanout** (the number of loads that may be connected to an output before performance is degraded). The RTL family requires a supply of 3.0 to 3.6 volts.

Diode-Transistor Logic – DTL

DTL ICs contain diodes, as well as resistors and transistors. Early DTL ICs used design criteria carried over from the use of discrete components, where diodes were inexpensive compared to transistors. These ICs required negative and positive voltage sources. Later DTL ICs are of a modified design which lends itself more easily to IC processing. Performance characteristics are also enhanced, with less input current being required, and only a single voltage source needed. Members of the DTL family are limited generally to gates. Advantages of this family are low power dissipation, compatibility with TTL (see later section), low cost, ease of use in system design, ease of interface with discrete circuits, and relatively high fanout. DTL disadvantages are low noise immunity, especially in the high state where the input impedance is relatively high, rapid change in voltage thresholds with temperature, speed slowdown with capacitive loading, and lower speed capabilities than some other families. The DTL family requires a supply voltage of 5.

High-Threshold Logic – HTL

HTL devices are designed for high noise immunity. The circuit form is the same as DTL except that breakdown (Zener) diodes are used at the inputs. Higher supply voltages and higher power dissipations accompany the HTL family. These ICs find applications in industrial environments and locations likely to have high electrical noise levels. Advantages are high noise immunity, stable operation over very large temperature ranges, interfaces easily with discrete components, electromechanical components, and linear functions (operational amplifiers and multipliers), and a constant threshold-versus-temperature characteristic. Disadvantages are higher cost than other families, and relatively high power dissipation. The HTL family requires a supply voltage of 15.

Transistor-Transistor Logic –TTL

TTL has characteristics that are similar to DTL, and is noted for many complex functions and the highest available speed of any saturated logic. TTL may be thought of as a DTL modification that results in higher speed and driving capability. It is noted for better noise immunity than that offered by DTL, and is more effective for driving high-capacitance loads because of its low output impedance in both logic states. TTL ICs fall into two major categories – medium speed and high speed. Various manufacturing techniques are used to increase the speed, including gold doping and incorporation of high-speed Schottky diodes on the chip. Another advantage of TTL is that it is compatible with various other families. Multiple sources and extensive competition have resulted in low prices for TTL devices. Disadvantages are that more care is required in the layout and mechanical design of systems because of its high speed, and additional capacitors are required for bypassing because of switching transients. The TTL family requires a supply of 5 volts.

Emitter-Coupled Logic – ECL

ECL has the highest speed of any of the logic forms. It is sometimes called current-mode logic. This family is different from standard saturating logic in that circuit operation is analogous to that of some linear devices. In this case, the transistors do not saturate and the logic swings are reduced in amplitude. Very high speeds can be attained because of the small voltage swings and the use of nonsaturating transistors. The input circuitry of ECL devices is of the nature of a differential amplifier, resulting in much higher input impedances than saturated-logic devices. Emitter-follower outputs are of low impedance with high fanout capabilities, and are suited for driving 50-ohm transmission lines directly. Disadvantages are higher power dissipation, less noise immunity than some saturated logic, translators are required for interfacing with saturated logic, and slowed-down operation with heavy capacitive loading. The ECL family requires a supply of -5.2 volts.

Metal-Oxide Semiconductor (MOS)

Digital MOS devices are gaining significance in industrial applications, with p-channel or P-MOS ICs being the most popular. Large, complex repetitive functions, such as long shift registers and high-capacity memories, have proved very practical. Gates and basic logic circuits have not become as popular, because they exhibit lower drive capability than other IC families. Input impedances to these devices are essentially capacitive (an open circuit for dc). This feature allows very high fanout where speed is not a consideration. Bidirectional devices give more flexibility to the circuit designer. P-MOS technology results in the lowest cost per bit for memories and long shift registers, because many more functions can be contained on a given chip size than in bipolar devices. Disadvantages are that devices must be handled more carefully than bipolar ICs because excessive static electricity can destroy the narrow gate oxide, even with internal breakdown-diode input protection. Drive capability is limited because of the high output impedances characteristic of these devices. Two power supplies are usually required. The P-MOS family requires supplies of -13 and -27 volts.

Complementary Metal-Oxide Semiconductor – CMOS

CMOS technology employs both p-channel and n-channel devices on the same silicon substrate. Both types are enhancement-mode devices; that is, gate voltage must be increased in the direction that inverts the surface in order for the device to conduct. Only one of the two complementary devices of a circuit section is turned on at a time, resulting in extremely low power dissipation. Dissipation is primarily from the switching of devices through the active region and the charging and discharging of capacitances. Advantages are low power dissipation, good noise immunity, very wide power supply voltage variations allowed, high fanout to other CMOS devices, and full temperature-range capabilities. Disadvantages are restricted interfacing capabilities because of high output impedance, and medium to high cost. The CMOS family requires a supply of 1.5 to 16 volts, 10 volts being nominal.

IC Family Groups

The popular digital-logic families have several groups where basic designs have been modified for medium speed, high speed, or low power consumption. The TTL family ICs have single-letter designators added to the part number to identify the group: S – Schottky high speed, H – medium speed, L – low power. ECL logic, as yet, has no such simple identification system. Manufacturers group their ECL products by propagation delay, an expression of the maximum speed at which the logic device will operate. Motorola, for example, calls the ECL group with 8-ns delay MECL. MECL II has a speed of 4 ns; MECL 10,000, 2 ns; and MECL III, 1.1 ns. With a propagation delay of 1 ns, operation at 300 MHz is possible.

Special Digital ICs

In addition to the logic families, many special-purpose digital ICs are available to accomplish specific tasks. A divide-by-10 circuit, such as the Fairchild U6B95H9059X, operates up to 320 MHz and is used as a **prescaler** to extend the range of a frequency counter. This IC has been designed to operate with low-level input signals, typically 100 mV at 150 MHz.

Large MOS arrays are being used for a number of applications which require the storage of logic instructions. These ICs are called memories. Instructions are stored in the memory by a process named programming. Some memories can be programmed only once; they are called **ROMs (Read-Only Memory).** ROMs must be read in sequence, but another group of devices called **RAMs (Random-Access Memory)** can be used a section at a time. Both ROMs and RAMs are also made in reprogrammable versions, where the information stored in the memory can be changed as desired. These models are named **PROMs** and **PRAMs**, respectively.

Large memory arrays are often used for the generation and conversion of information codes. One IC can be programmed to convert the 5-level RTTY code to the 8-level ASCII code popular in computer devices. National Semiconductor manufactures a single IC which generates the entire 56-character 8-level code. Several ICs are now available for character generation where letters and numerals are produced for display on an oscillograph screen.

OTHER DEVICES

THE UNIJUNCTION TRANSISTOR

Unijunction transistors (UJT) are being used by amateurs for such applications as side-tone oscillators, sawtooth generators, pulse generators, and timers.

Structurally, the UJT is built on an n-type silicon bar which has ohmic contacts – base one (B1) and base two (B2) – at opposite ends of the bar. A rectifying contact, the emitter, is attached between B1 and B2 on the bar. During normal operation B1 is grounded and a positive bias is supplied to B2. When the emitter is forward biased, emitter current will flow and the device will conduct. The symbol for a UJT is given in Fig. 4-30 at C. A circuit showing a typical application in which a UJT is employed is shown in Fig. 4-30.

SILICON CONTROLLED RECTIFIERS

The silicon controlled rectifier, also known as a Thyristor, is a four-layer (p-n-p-n or n-p-n-p) three-electrode semiconductor rectifier. The three terminals are called anode, cathode and gate, Fig. 4-28B.

The SCR differs from the silicon rectifier in that it will not conduct until the voltage exceeds the *forward breakover* voltage. The value of this voltage can be controlled by the gate current. As the gate current is increased, the value of the forward breakover voltage is decreased. Once the rectifier conducts in the forward direction, the gate current no longer has any control, and the rectifier behaves as a low-forward-resistance diode. The gate regains controls when the current through the rectifier is cut off, as during the other half cycle.

The SCR finds wide use in power-control applications and in time-delay circuits. SCRs are available in various voltage and wattage ratings.

TRIACS

The **triac**, similar to the SCR, has three electrodes – the main terminal (No. 1), another

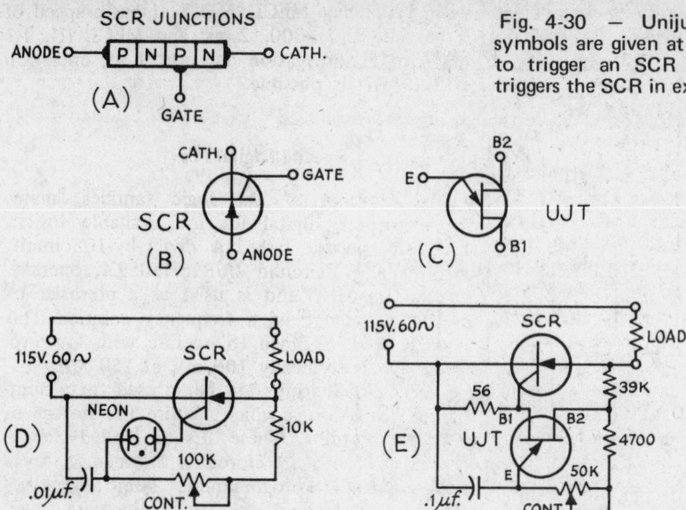

Fig. 4-30 – Unijunction transistor and SCR symbols are given at B and C. A neon lamp is used to trigger an SCR in the circuit at D. A UJT triggers the SCR in example E.

main terminal (No. 2), and a gate. The triac performs in the same manner as the SCR, but for either polarity of voltage applied to its main terminals. The SCR, as mentioned in the foregoing, conducts only during one half the sine-wave cycle. When an SCR is used in a motor-speed control, therefore, the motor cannot be brought up to full speed. The triac, however, does trigger on both halves of the cycle. Therefore, triacs are preferred to SCRs in many control circuits. The triac can be regarded as a device in which two SCRs are employed in parallel and oriented in opposite directions as shown in the drawing of Fig. 4-30. An example of a motor-speed control which uses a triac is given in the construction chapter of this book.

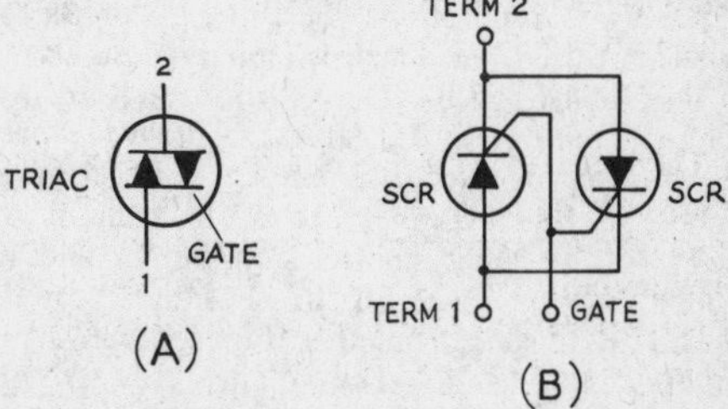

Fig. 4-31 – The symbol for a triac is given at A. The illustration at B shows how a triac compares to two SCRs connected for the same performance offered by a triac, thus permitting conduction during both halves of the cycle.

OPERATIONAL AMPLIFIERS

Early analog computers used amplifier blocks which became known as **operational amplifiers,** or simply **op amps.** Operational amplifiers can be constructed using tubes or transistors, and as hybrid or monolithic integrated circuits. The monolithic IC has become the most popular type of op amp. Today op-amp ICs cost approximately one dollar for the preferred types. They are used as building blocks in many circuit applications.

The op amp is a dc-coupled multistage linear amplifier which, in an ideal device, would have infinite input impedance and infinite gain. While the ideal op amp remains an unobtainable goal, voltage gains of 100,000 or more can be achieved. FET-input op amps have sufficiently high input impedance that the current required from the driving source is measured in pA (μμA).

Gain and Feedback

The internal circuit of a popular op-amp IC, the Fairchild μA741 (also produced by most other semiconductor manufacturers) is shown in Fig. 4-32. Two inputs are provided, one the complement or inverse of the other. An amplifier with two such inputs is known as a **differential amplifier.** If a small positive voltage is applied to the noninverting (+) terminal, it will produce a positive output. The same positive voltage applied to the inverting (–) terminal will result in a negative output. If the same voltage was applied to both terminals, the output would be zero. Both inputs can be used, called the differential connection, or one can be returned to ground for single-ended operation. In practical ICs, the output may not be exactly zero when both inputs are at zero potential. Any output under these conditions is called **offset** – some op amps have provision for connections to an external control which compensates for any offset voltage by applying bias current to the input transistors. The offset connections for the μA741 are shown in Fig. 4-32. Op amps are available in all of the popular IC packages; consult

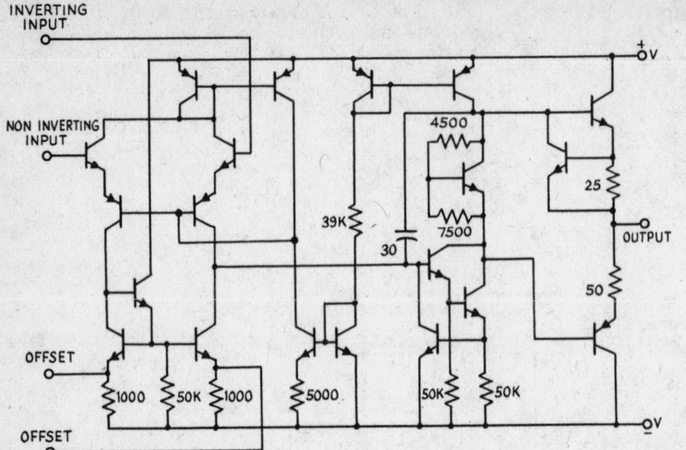

Fig. 4-32 – Internal circuit of a µA741 operational amplifier.

the manufacturer's literature for pin connections. Usually the pin connections are not the same for a particular device when it is made up in different package styles.

For most applications the full gain of the op amp is not used. Feedback is employed, as shown in Figs. 4-34A and B.. The addition of a resistive divider network, Ro-Ri, causes negative feedback by allowing part of the output voltage to be applied to the inverting input. The gain of the device will be equal to the sum of Ro and Ri, divided by the value of Ri. Feedback can be applied in a similar manner for a noninverting amplifier, Fig. 4-33B.. The voltage summer, Fig. 4-33C, provides an output voltage which is the sum of all input voltages multiplied by the gain of the operational amplifier. This circuit is often employed as an audio mixer. Fig. 4-33D shows the voltage-follower connections. The load at the output of this circuit can draw a large current while the input draws almost no current. The output voltage follows the level of the input potential almost exactly. The output of the differentiator (Fig. 4-33E) is proportional to the rate of change of the input voltage, while the integrator (Fig. 4-33F) averages the level of a voltage that varies over a short period of time. A differential connection of a single op amp is shown at G.

Stability

Because op amps are high-gain devices with frequency response from dc to several megahertz,

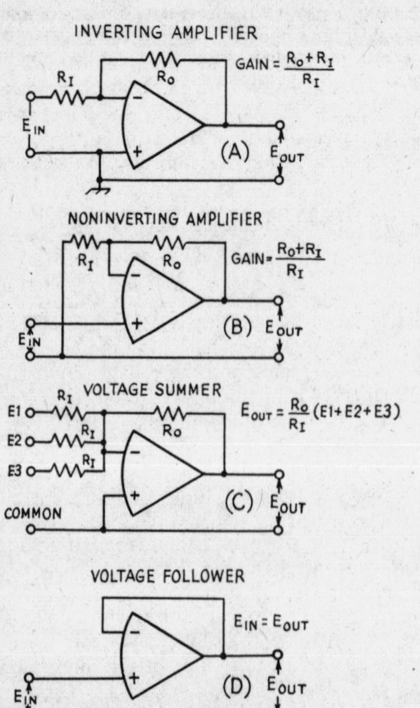

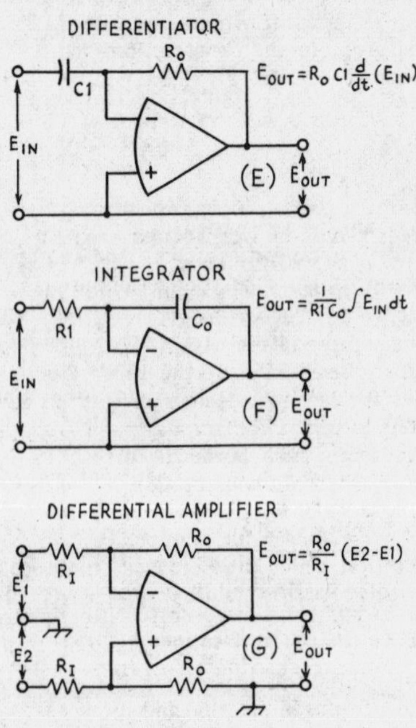

Fig. 4-33 – Basic op-amp circuits.

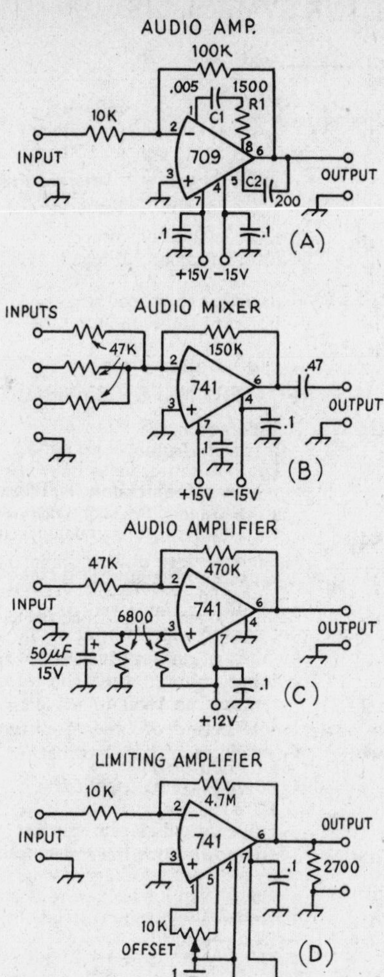

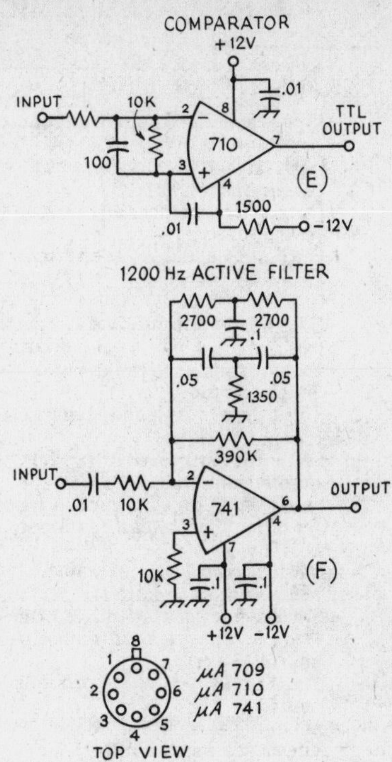

Fig. 4-34 – Some typical applications of operational amplifiers. The pin numbers shown are all for the metal can (TO-99) package.

oscillation can occur. In any op-amp circuit layout, the inputs should be well isolated from the output. Input leads should be kept as short as possible. Supply-voltage terminals should be bypassed with 0.1- or .01-μF capacitors. As the frequency is increased, the stages within an op amp will introduce phase shift. If the phase shift in the amplifier reaches 180 degrees before the gain has decreased to unity, the amplifier will be unstable. Some op amps, such as the μA709 of Fig. 4-34A. require an external compensation network, R1-C1, to reduce the gain of the device at hf. Others, the μA741 of Fig. 4-34B for example, contain internal compensation and, thus, require no additional components to assure stability.

Applications

Most monolithic op-amp ICs require supply voltages of plus 5 to 15 and minus 5 to 15. Practical examples of an audio amplifier and audio mixer are given in Fig. 4-33A and B,, respectively. In some amateur applications, the dual-polarity requirement can be eliminated by using a resistive divider to bias the noninverting input as indicated in Fig. 4-34C. If the amplifier is intended to be used as a limiting device (the input stage of an RTTY demodulator is an example) an offset control should be added to allow adjustment for equal clipping of the negative and positive peaks (Fig. 4-34D).

Another popular use for the op amp is as a **comparator** – see Fig. 4-34E. A comparator is used to indicate when a difference exists between a reference voltage and an input voltage. The output of the comparator will swing from its maximum positive voltage to maximum negative when the input exceeds the reference (zero voltage if the reference is zero). A number of op amps optimized for comparator service are available; they are often used as interface devices between linear and digital circuits. The operational amplifier is often employed in *active filters*, which use *RC* components to provide low-pass, high-pass, and bandpass characteristics. A simple illustration, an *RC* filter network tuned to 1200 Hz connected in parallel with the feedback resistor, is given in Fig. 4-34F. This design is for low *Q* giving a characteristic suitable for a cw receiver. The gain at resonance is approximately 40. Additional information about active filters and other op-amp circuits is available in the publications listed in the bibliography at the end of this chapter.

ABBREVIATED SEMICONDUCTOR SYMBOL LIST

BIPOLAR TRANSISTOR SYMBOLS

- C_{ibo} – Input capacitance, open circuit (common base)
- C_{ieo} – Input capacitance, open circuit (common emitter)
- C_{obo} – Output capacitance, open circuit (common base)
- C_{oeo} – Output capacitance, open circuit (common emitter)
- f_c – Cutoff frequency
- f_T – Gain-bandwidth product (frequency at which small-signal forward current-transfer ratio, common emitter, is unity, or 1)
- g_{me} – Small-signal transconductance (common emitter)
- h_{FB} – Static forward-current transfer ratio (common base)
- h_{fb} – Small-signal forward-current transfer ratio, short circuit (common base)
- h_{FE} – Static forward-current transfer ratio (common emitter)
- h_{fe} – Small-signal forward-current transfer ratio, short circuit (common emitter)
- h_{IE} – Static input resistance (common emitter)
- h_{ie} – Small-signal input impedance, short circuit (common emitter)
- I_b – Base current
- I_c – Collector current
- I_{CBO} – Collector-cutoff current, emitter open
- I_{CEO} – Collector-cutoff current, base open
- I_E – Emitter current
- MAG – Maximum available amplifier gain
- P_{CE} – Total dc or average power input to collector (common emitter)
- P_{OE} – Large-signal output power (common emitter)
- R_L – Load resistance
- R_s – Source resistance
- V_{BB} – Base-supply voltage
- V_{BC} – Base-to-collector voltage
- V_{BE} – Base-to-emitter voltage
- V_{CB} – Collector-to-base voltage
- V_{CBO} – Collector-to-base voltage (emitter open)
- V_{CC} – Collector-supply voltage
- V_{CE} – Collector-to-emitter voltage
- V_{CEO} – Collector-to-emitter voltage (base open)
- $V_{CE(sat)}$ – Collector-to-emitter saturation voltage
- V_{EB} – Emitter-to-base voltage
- V_{EBO} – Emitter-to-base voltage (collector open)
- V_{EE} – Emitter-supply voltage
- Y_{fe} – Forward transconductance
- Y_{ie} – Input Admittance
- Y_{oe} – Output Admittance

FIELD-EFFECT TRANSFER SYMBOLS

- A – Voltage amplification
- C_c – Intrinsic channel capacitance
- C_{ds} – Drain-to-source capacitance (includes approximately 1-pF drain-to-case and interlead capacitance)
- C_{gd} – Gate-to-drain capacitance (includes 0.1-pF interlead capacitance)
- C_{gs} – Gate-to-source interlead and case capacitance
- C_{iss} – Small-signal input capacitance, short circuit
- C_{rss} – Small-signal reverse transfer capacitance, short circuit
- g_{fs} – Forward transconductance
- g_{is} – Input conductance
- g_{os} – Output conductance
- I_D – Dc drain current
- $I_{DS(OFF)}$ – Drain-to-source OFF current
- I_{GSS} – Gate leakage current
- r_c – Effective gate series resistance
- $r_{DS(ON)}$ – Drain-to-source ON resistance
- r_{gd} – Gate-to-drain leakage resistance
- r_{gs} – Gate-to-source leakage resistance
- V_{DB} – Drain-to-substrate voltage
- V_{DS} – Drain-to-source voltage
- V_{GB} – Dc gate-to-substrate voltage
- V_{GB} – Peak gate-to-substrate voltage
- V_{GS} – Dc gate-to-source voltage
- V_{GS} – Peak gate-to-source voltage
- $V_{GS(OFF)}$ – Gate-to-source cutoff voltage
- Y_{fs} – Forward transadmittance $\approx g_{fs}$
- Y_{os} – Output admittance
- Y_L – Load admittance

Semiconductor Bibliography

Garrett, "Integrated-Circuit Digital Logic Families," in three parts, *IEEE Spectrum*, October, November, and December, 1970.

Heilweil, *Introduction to Boolean Algebra and Logic Design*, McGraw-Hill, 1964.

Maley, *Manual of Logic Circuits*, Prentice-Hall, 1970.

Pike, "The Operational Amplifier," Parts I and II, *QST*, August and September, 1970.

Pos, "Digital Logic Devices," *QST*, July, 1968.

Pos, "Integrated-Circuit Flip-Flops," *QST*, February, 1971.

RCA Transistor, Thyristor, and Diode Manual, Series SC-14, RCA, Harrison, NJ 07029.

RCA Power Circuits, DC to Microwaves, Series SP-51, RCA, Harrison, NJ 07029.

RCA Linear Integrated Circuits, Series IC-42, RCA, Harrison, NJ 07029.

RCA Hobby Circuits Manual, Series HM-91, RCA, Harrison, NJ 07029.

Solid-State Communications McGraw-Hill.

Transistor Circuit Design, McGraw-Hill.

Malmstadt and Enke, *Digital Electronics for Scientists*, W. A. Benjamin, Inc., New York, NY 10016.

Malmstadt and Enke, *A Laboratory Workbook* (computer logic). W. A. Benjamin, Inc., New York, NY 10016.

Chapter 5

AC-Operated Power Supplies

> *Power-line voltages have been "standardized" throughout the U.S. at 115 – 230 V in residential areas where a single voltage phase is supplied. These figures represent nominal voltages, however. "Normal" line voltage in a particular area may be between approximately 110 and 125 volts, but generally will be above 115 volts. In many states, the service is governed by the state's public utilities commission. The voltage average across the country is approximately 117 volts. Source of information: Edison Electric Company (an association of power companies), New York, NY.*

The electrical power required to operate amateur radio equipment is usually taken from the ac lines when the equipment is operated where this power is available; in mobile operation the prime source of power is usually the storage battery.

The high-voltage dc for the plates of vacuum tubes used in receivers and transmitters is derived from the commercial ac lines by the use of a transformer-rectifier-filter system. The transformer changes the voltage of the ac to a suitable value, and the rectifier converts it to pulsating dc. The filter reduces the pulsations to a suitably low level, and may have either a capacitor input or a choke input, depending on whether a shunt capacitor or a series inductor is the first filter element. Essentially pure direct current is required to prevent hum in the output of receivers, speech amplifiers, modulators and transmitters. In the case of transmitters, a pure dc plate supply is also dictated by government regulations. If a constant supply voltage is required under conditions of changing load or ac line voltage, a regulator is used following the filter.

When the prime power source is dc (a battery), the dc is first changed to ac, and is then followed by the transformer-rectifier-filter system. Additional information on this type of supply is contained in Chapter 10.

The cathode-heating power can be ac or dc in the case of indirectly heated cathode tubes, and ac or dc for filament-type tubes if the tubes are operated at a high power level (high-powered audio and rf applications). Low-level operation of filament-type tubes generally requires dc on the filaments if undue hum is to be avoided.

Occasionally **transformerless power supplies** are used in some applications (notably in the ac-dc type of broadcast receiver). Such supplies operate directly from the power line, and it is necessary to connect the chassis or common-return point of the circuit directly to one side of the ac line. This type of power supply represents an extreme shock hazard when the equipment is interconnected with other apparatus in the amateur station, or when the chassis is exposed. For safety reasons, an isolation transformer should be used with such equipment when it is present in an amateur station.

POWER-LINE CONSIDERATIONS

POWER LINE CONNECTIONS

In most residential systems, three wires are brought in from the outside to the distribution board, while in other systems there are only two wires. In the three-wire system, the third wire is the **neutral** which is grounded. The voltage between the other two wires normally is 230, while half of this voltage (115) appears between each of these wires and neutral, as indicated in Fig. 5-1A. In systems of this type, usually it will be found that the 115-volt household load is divided as evenly as possible between the two sides of the circuit, half of the load being connected between one wire and the neutral, while the other half of the load is connected between the other wire and neutral. Heavy appliances, such as electric stoves and heaters, normally are designed for 230-volt operation and therefore are connected across the two ungrounded wires. While both ungrounded wires should be fused, a fuse should never be used in the wire to the neutral, nor should a switch be used in this side of the line. The reason for this is that opening the neutral wire does not disconnect the equipment. It simply leaves the equipment on one side of the 230-volt circuit in series with whatever load may be across the other side of the

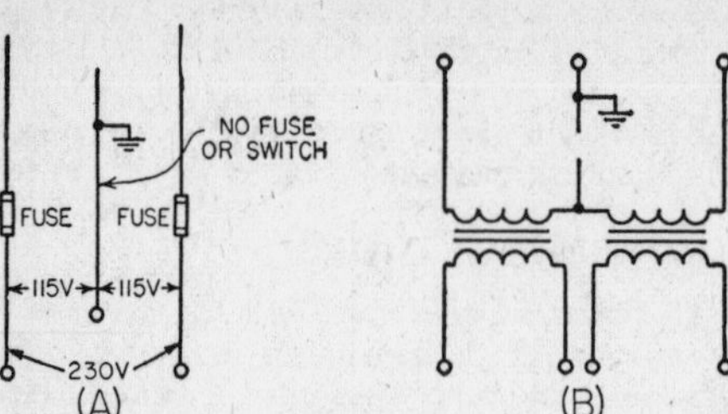

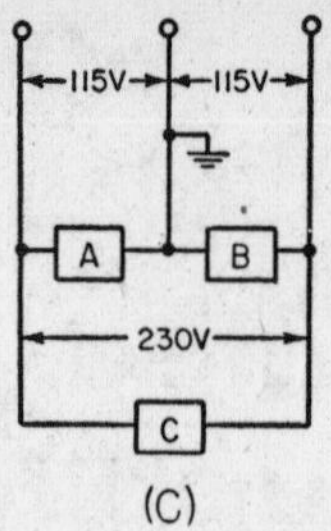

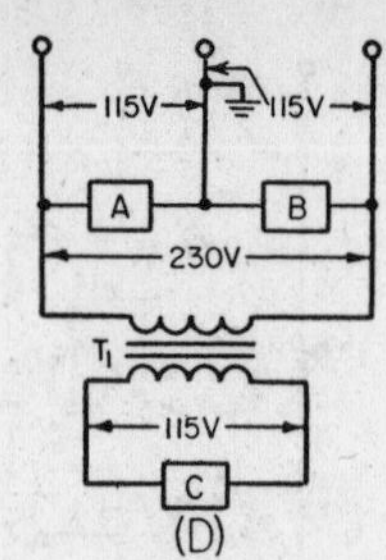

Fig. 5-1 – Three-wire power-line circuits. A – Normal 3-wire-line termination. No fuse should be used in the grounded (neutral) line. B – Showing that a switch in the neutral does not remove voltage from either side of the line. C – Connections for both 115- and 230-volt transformers. D – Operating a 115-volt plate transformer from the 230-volt line to avoid light blinking. T1 is a 2-to-1 step-down transformer.

circuit, as shown in Fig. 5-1B. Furthermore, with the neutral open, the voltage will then be divided between the two sides in inverse proportion to the load resistance, the voltage on one side dropping below normal, while it soars on the other side, unless the loads happen to be equal.

The usual line running to baseboard outlets is rated at 15 amperes. Considering the power consumed by filaments, lamps, transmitter, receiver and other auxiliary equipment, it is not unusual to find this 15-A rating exceeded by the requirements of a station of only moderate power. It must also be kept in mind that the same branch may be in use for other household purposes through another outlet. For this reason, and to minimize light blinking when keying or modulating the transmitter, a separate heavier line should be run from the distribution board to the station whenever possible. (A three-volt drop in line voltage will cause noticeable light blinking.)

If the system is of the three-wire 230-V type, the three wires should be brought into the station so that the load can be distributed to keep the line balanced. The voltage across a fixed load on one side of the circuit will increase as the load current on the other side is increased. The rate of increase will depend upon the resistance introduced by the neutral wire. If the resistance of the neutral is low, the increase will be correspondingly small. When the currents in the two circuits are balanced, no current flows in the neutral wire and the system is operating at maximum efficiency.

Light blinking can be minimized by using transformers with 230-volt primaries in the power supplies for the keyed or intermittent part of the load, connecting them across the two ungrounded wires with no connection to the neutral, as shown in Fig. 5-1C. The same can be accomplished by the insertion of a step-down transformer with its primary operating at 230 volts and secondary delivering 115 volts. Conventional 115-volt transformers may be operated from the secondary of the step-down transformer (see Fig. 5-1D).

When a special heavy-duty line is to be installed, the local power company should be consulted as to local requirements. In some localities it is necessary to have such a job done by a licensed electrician, and there may be special requirements to be met. Some amateurs terminate the special line to the station at a switch box, while others may use electric-stove receptacles as the termination. The power is then distributed around the station by means of conventional outlets at convenient points. All circuits should be properly fused.

Three-Wire 115-V Power Cords

To meet the requirements of state and national codes, electrical tools, appliances and many items of electronic equipment now being manufactured to operate from the 115-volt line must be equipped with a 3-conductor power cord. Two of the conductors carry power to the device in the usual fashion, while the third conductor is connected to the case or frame.

When plugged into a properly wired mating receptacle, the 3-contact polarized plug connects this third conductor to an earth ground, thereby grounding the chassis or frame of the appliance and preventing the possibility of electrical shock to the user. All commercially manufactured items of electronic test equipment and most ac-operated amateur equipments are being supplied with these 3-wire cords. Adapters are available for use where older electrical installations do not have mating receptacles. For proper grounding, the lug of the green wire protruding from the adapter must be attached underneath the screw securing the cover plate of the outlet box where connection is made, and the outlet box itself must be grounded.

Fusing

All transformer primary circuits should be properly fused. To determine the approximate current rating of the fuse to be used, multiply each current being drawn from the supply in amperes by the voltage at which the current is being drawn. Include the current taken by bleeder resistances and voltage dividers. In the case of series resistors, use the source voltage, not the voltage at the equipment end of the resistor. Include filament power if the transformer is supplying filaments. After multiplying the various voltages and currents, add the individual products. Then divide by the line voltage and add 10 or 20 percent. Use a fuse with the nearest larger current rating.

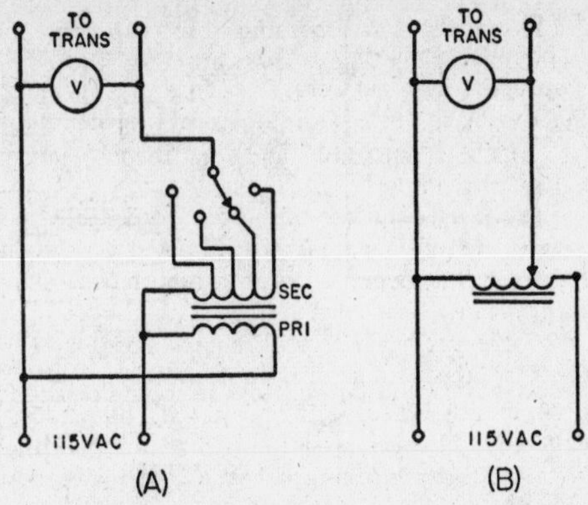

Fig. 5-2 – Two methods of transformer primary control. At A is a tapped toy transformer which may be connected so as to boost or buck the line voltage as required. At B is indicated a variable transformer or autotransformer (Variac) which feeds the transformer primaries.

LINE-VOLTAGE ADJUSTMENT

In certain communities trouble is sometimes experienced from fluctuations in line voltage. Usually these fluctuations are caused by a variation in the load on the line. Since most of the variation comes at certain fixed times of the day or night, such as the times when lights are turned on at evening, they may be taken care of by the use of a manually operated compensating device. A simple arrangement is shown in Fig. 5-2A. A toy transformer is used to boost or buck the line voltage as required. The transformer should have a tapped secondary varying between 6 and 20 volts in steps of 2 or 3 volts and its secondary should be capable of carrying the full load current.

The secondary is connected in series with the line voltage and, if the phasing of the windings is correct, the voltage applied to the primaries of the transmitter transformers can be brought up to the rated 115 volts by setting the toy-transformer tap switch on the right tap. If the phasing of the two windings of the toy transformer happens to be reversed, the voltage will be reduced instead of increased. This connection may be used in cases where the line voltage may be above 115 volts. This method is preferable to using a resistor in the primary of a power transformer since it does not affect the voltage regulation as seriously. The circuit of 5-2B illustrates the use of a variable autotransformer (Variac) for adjusting line voltage.

Constant-Voltage Transformers

Although comparatively expensive, special transformers called **constant-voltage transformers** are available for use in cases where it is necessary to hold line voltage and/or filament voltage constant with fluctuating supply-line voltage. These are static-magnetic voltage regulating transformers operating on principles of ferroresonance. They have no tubes or moving parts, and require no manual adjustments. These transformers are rated over a range of less than one VA at 5 volts output up to several thousand VA at 115 or 230 volts. On the average they will hold their output voltages within one percent under an input voltage variation of ±15 percent.

SAFETY PRECAUTIONS

All power supplies in an installation should be fed through a single main power-line switch so that all power may be cut off quickly, either before working on the equipment, or in case of an accident. Spring-operated switches or relays are not sufficiently reliable for this important service. Foolproof devices for cutting off all power to the transmitter and other equipment are shown in Fig. 5-3. The arrangements shown in Fig. 5-3A and B are similar circuits for two-wire (115-volt) and three-wire (230-volt) systems. S is an enclosed double-throw switch of the sort usually used as the entrance switch in house installations. J is a standard ac outlet and P a shorted plug to fit the outlet. The switch should be located prominently in plain sight, and members of the household should be instructed in its location and use. I is a red lamp located alongside the switch. Its purpose is not so much to serve as a warning that the power is on as it is to help in identifying and quickly

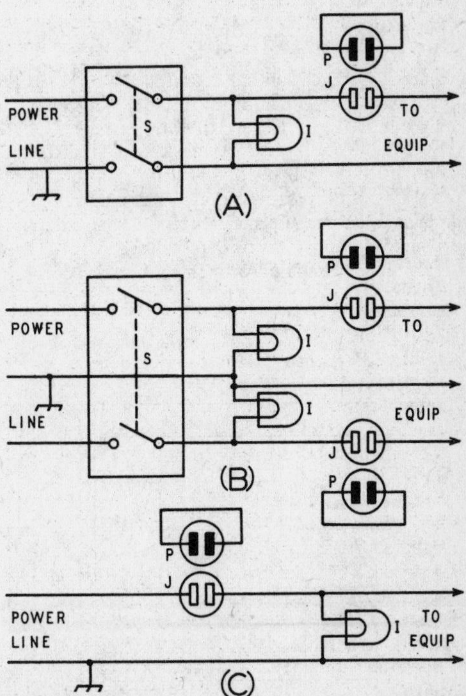

Fig. 5-3 – Reliable arrangements for cutting off all power to the transmitter. S is an enclosed double-pole power switch, J a standard ac outlet, P a shorted plug to fit the outlet and I a red lamp.

A is for a two-wire 115-volt line, B for a three-wire 230-volt system, and C a simplified arrangement for low-power stations.

locating the switch should it become necessary for someone else to cut the power off in an emergency.

The outlet J should be placed in some corner out of sight where it will not be a temptation for children or others to play with. The shorting plug can be removed to open the power circuit if there are others around who might inadvertently throw the switch while the operator is working on the rig. If the operator takes the plug with him, it will prevent someone from turning on the power in his absence and either hurting themselves or the equipment or perhaps starting a fire. Of utmost importance is the fact that the outlet J *must* be placed in the *ungrounded* side of the line.

Those who are operating low power and feel that the expense or complication of the switch isn't warranted can use the shorted-plug idea as the main power switch. In this case, the outlet should be located prominently and identified by a signal light, as shown in Fig. 5-3C.

The test bench should be fed through the main power switch, or a similar arrangement at the bench, if the bench is located remotely from the transmitter.

A bleeder resistor with a power rating which gives a considerable margin of safety should be used across the output of all transmitter power supplies, so that the filter capacitors will be discharged when the high-voltage is turned off.

PLATE AND FILAMENT TRANSFORMERS

Output Voltage

The output voltage which the plate transformer must deliver depends upon the required dc load voltage and the type of filter circuit.

With a choke-input filter (see Fig. 5-4), the required rms secondary voltage (each side of center-tap for a center-tap rectifier) can be calculated by the equation:

$$E_t = 1.1\ [E_o + I\,(R_1 + R_2 + R_s)]$$

where E_o is the required dc output voltage, I is the load current (including bleeder current) in amperes, R1 and R2 are the dc resistances of the chokes, and R_s is the series resistance (transformer and rectifier). E_t is the open-circuit rms voltage.

With a capacitive-input filter system, the approximate transformer output voltage required to give a desired dc output voltage with a given load can be calculated with the aid of Fig. 5-5.

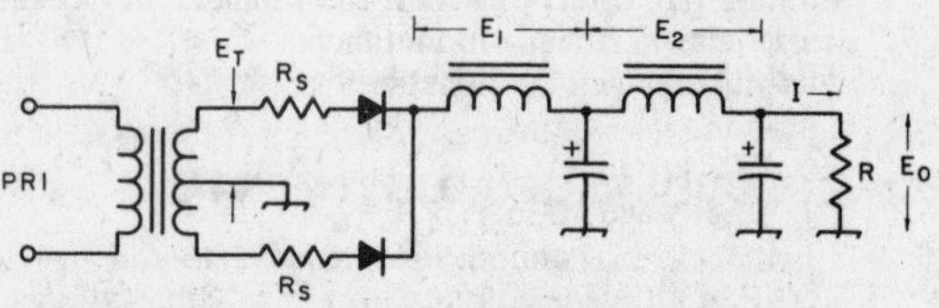

Fig. 5-4 – Diagram showing various voltage drops that must be taken into consideration in determining the required transformer voltage to deliver the desired output voltage.

Example:
Required dc output volts – 25
Load current to be drawn – 500 mA (0.5 ampere)
Input capacitor – 1000 μF

Series resistance – 5 ohms

Load resistance = $\frac{25}{0.5}$ = 50 ohms

$RC = 50 \times 1000 = 50{,}000$

$R_s/R = 5/50 = 0.1$

Fig. 5-5 shows that the ratio of dc volts to the required transformer rms voltage is 1.07.

The required transformer terminal voltage under load is

$$E_{AC} = \frac{E_{DC} + I \times R_s}{1.07}$$

where I is the load current in amperes.

$$E_{AC} = \frac{25 + 0.5 \times 5}{1.07}$$

$$= \frac{27.5}{1.07} = 25.7 \text{ volts}$$

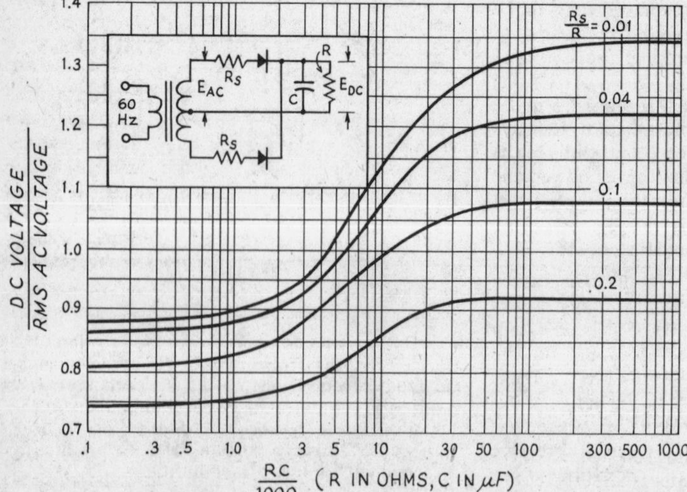

Fig. 5-5 – Dc output voltages from a full-wave rectifier circuit as a function of the filter capacitance and load resistance. R_s includes transformer winding resistance and rectifier forward resistance. For the ratio R_s/R, both resistances are in ohms; for the RC product, R is in ohms and C is in μF.

The required transformer is one having a 51.4-V center-tapped secondary. A 50- or 55-V secondary would be entirely satisfactory. Should the filter section contain one or more filter chokes connected between the input capacitor and the load, the dc-resistance values of the chokes are added to the value of R_s in the equation before multiplying by the load-current value.

Volt-Ampere Rating

The number of volt-amperes delivered by a transformer depends upon the type of filter (capacitor or choke input) used, and upon the type of rectifier used (full-wave center tap, or full-wave bridge). With a capacitive-input filter the heating effect in the secondary is higher because of the high ratio of peak-to-average current. The volt-amperes handled by the transformer may be several times the watts delivered to the load. With a choke-input filter, provided the input choke has at least the critical inductance, the secondary volt-amperes can be calculated quite closely by the equation:

$$\text{(Full-wave ct)}\ Sec.\ VA = \frac{.707\ EI}{1000}$$

$$\text{(Full-wave bridge)}\ Sec.\ VA = \frac{EI}{1000}$$

where E is the *total* rms voltage of the secondary (between the outside ends in the case of a center-tapped winding) and I is the dc output current in milliamperes (load current plus bleeder current). The primary volt-amperes will be somewhat higher because of transformer losses.

BROADCAST & TELEVISION REPLACEMENT TRANSFORMERS

Small power transformers of the type sold for replacement in broadcast and television receivers are usually designed for service in terms of use for several hours continuously with capacitor-input filters. In the usual type of amateur transmitter service, where most of the power is drawn intermittently for periods of several minutes with equivalent intervals in between, the published ratings can be exceeded without excessive transformer heating.

With a capacitor-input filter, it should be safe to draw 20 to 30 percent more current than the rated value. With a choke-input filter, an increase in current of about 50 percent is permissible. If a bridge rectifier is used, the output voltage will be approximately doubled. In this case, it should be possible in amateur transmitter service to draw the rated current, thus obtaining about twice the rated output power from the transformer.

This does not apply, of course, to amateur transmitter plate transformers, which usually are already rated for intermittent service.

REWINDING POWER TRANSFORMERS

Although the home winding of power transformers is a task that few amateurs undertake, the

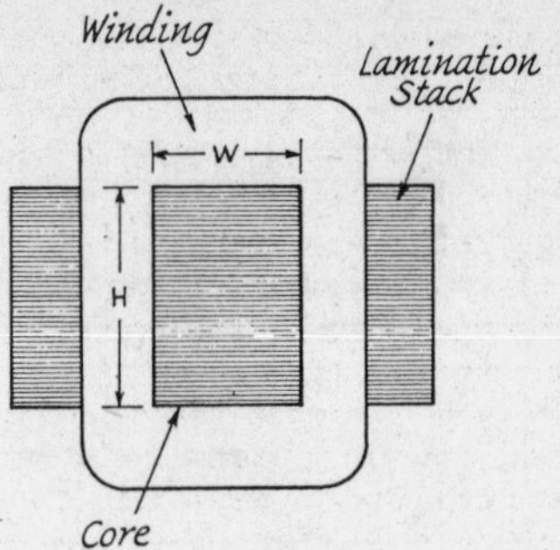

Fig. 5-6 — Cross-sectional drawing of a typical power transformer. Multiplying the height (or thickness of the laminations) times the width of the central core area in inches gives the value to be applied to Fig. 5-7.

rewinding of a transformer secondary to give some desired voltage for powering filaments or a solid-state device is not difficult. It involves a matter of only a small number of turns and the wire is large enough to be handled easily. Often a receiver power transformer with a burned-out high-voltage winding or the power transformer from a discarded TV set can be converted into an entirely satisfactory transformer without great effort and with little expense. The average TV power transformer for a 17-inch or larger set is capable of delivering from 350 to 450 watts, continuous duty. If an amateur transmitter is being powered, the service is not continuous, so the ratings can be increased by a factor of 40 or 50 percent without danger of overloading the transformer.

The primary volt-ampere rating of the transformer to be rewound, if known, can be used to determine its power-handling capability. The secondary volt-ampere rating will be ten to twenty percent less than the primary rating. The power rating may also be determined approximately from the cross-sectional area of the core which is *inside* the windings. Fig. 5-6 shows the method of determining the area, and Fig. 5-7 may be used to convert this information into a power rating.

Before disconnecting the winding leads from their terminals, each should be marked for identification. In removing the core laminations, care should be taken to note the manner in which the core is assembled, so that the reassembling will be done in the same manner. Most transformers have secondaries wound over the primary, while in some the order is reversed. In case the secondaries are on the inside, the turns can be pulled out from the center after slitting and removing the fiber core.

The turns removed from one of the original filament windings of known voltage should be carefully counted as the winding is removed. This will give the number of turns per volt and the same figure should be used in determining the number of turns for the new secondary. For instance, if the

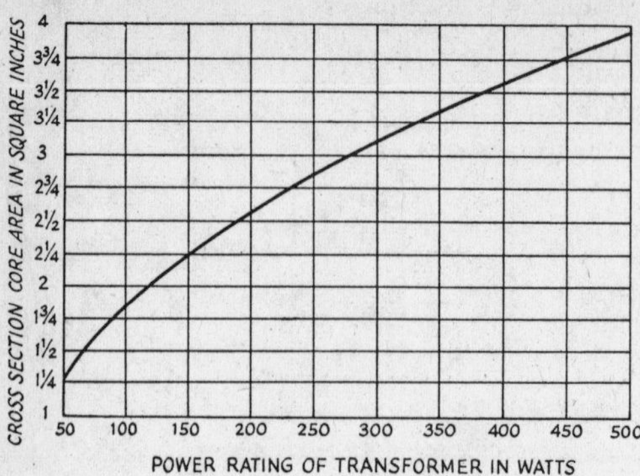

Fig. 5-7 – Power-handling capability of a transformer versus cross-sectional area of core.

old filament winding was rated at 5 volts and had 15 turns, this is 15/5 = 3 turns per volt. If the new secondary is to deliver 18 volts, the required number of turns on the new winding will be 18 X 3 = 54 turns.

In winding a transformer, the size of wire is an important factor in the heat developed in operation. A cross-sectional area of 1000 circular mils per ampere is conservative. A value commonly used in amateur-service transformers is 700 cmil/A. The larger the cmil/A figure, the cooler the transformer will run. The current rating in amperes of various wire sizes is shown in the copper-wire table in another chapter. If the transformer being rewound is a filament transformer, it may be necessary to choose the wire size carefully to fit the small available space. On the other hand, if the transformer is a power unit with the high-voltage winding removed, there should be plenty of room for a size of wire that will conservatively handle the required current.

After the first layer of turns is put on during rewinding, secure the ends with cellulose tape. Each layer should be insulated from the next; ordinary household waxed paper can be used for the purpose, a single layer being adequate. Sheets cut to size beforehand may be secured over each layer with tape. Be sure to bring all leads out the same side of the core so the covers will go in place when the unit is completed. When the last layer of the winding is put on, use two sheets of waxed paper, and then cover those with vinyl electrical tape, keeping the tape as taut as possible. This will add mechanical strength to the assembly.

The laminations and housing are assembled in just the opposite sequence to that followed in disassembly. Use a light coating of shellac between each lamination. During reassembly, the lamination stack may be compressed by clamping in a vise. If the last few lamination strips cannot be replaced, it is better to omit them than to force the unit together.

RECTIFIER CIRCUITS

Half-Wave Rectifier

Fig. 5-8 shows three rectifier circuits covering most of the common applications in amateur equipment. Fig. 5-8A is the circuit of a half-wave rectifier. The rectifier is a device that will conduct current in one direction but not in the other. During one half of the ac cycle the rectifier will conduct and current will flow through the rectifier to the load. During the other half of the cycle the rectifier does not conduct and no current flows to the load. The shape of the output wave is shown in (A) at the right. It shows that the current always flows in the same direction but that the flow of current is not continuous and is pulsating in amplitude.

The average output voltage – the voltage read by the usual dc voltmeter – with this circuit (no filter connected) is 0.45 times the rms value of the ac voltage delivered by the transformer secondary. Because the frequency of the pulses is relatively low (one pulsation per cycle), considerable filtering is required to provide adequately smooth dc output, and for this reason this circuit is usually limited to applications where the current involved is small, such as supplies for cathode-ray tubes and for protective bias in a transmitter.

The **peak reverse voltage (PRV)**, the voltage the rectifier must withstand when it isn't conducting, varies with the load. With a resistive load it is the peak ac voltage (1.4 E_{RMS}) but with a capacitor load drawing little or no current it can rise to 2.8 E_{RMS}.

Another disadvantage of the half-wave rectifier circuit is that the transformer must have a considerably higher primary volt-ampere rating (approximately 40 percent greater), for the same dc power output, than in other rectifier circuits.

Full-Wave Center-Tap Rectifier

A commonly used rectifier circuit is shown in Fig. 5-8B. Essentially an arrangement in which the outputs of two half-wave rectifiers are combined, it makes use of both halves of the ac cycle. A transformer with a center-tapped secondary is required with the circuit.

The average output voltage is 0.9 times the rms voltage of half the transformer secondary; this is the maximum voltage that can be obtained with a suitable choke-input filter. The peak output voltage is 1.4 times the rms voltage of half the transformer secondary; this is the maximum voltage that can be obtained from a capacitor-input filter (at little or no load).

The peak reverse voltage across a rectifier unit is 2.8 times the rms voltage of half the transformer secondary.

As can be seen from the sketches of the output wave form in (B) to the right, the frequency of the output pulses is twice that of the half-wave rectifier. Therefore much less filtering is required.

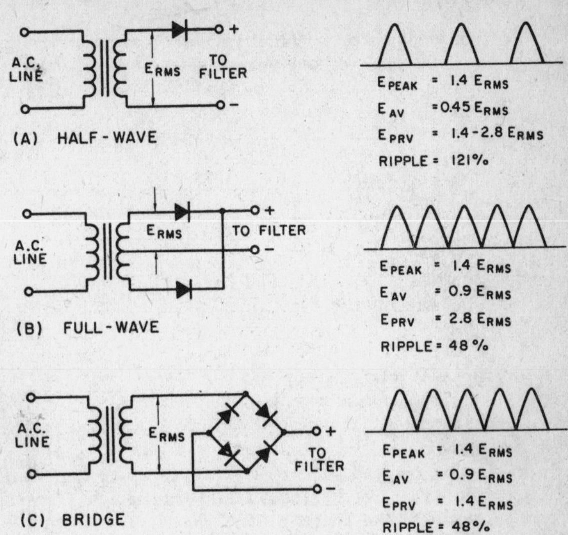

Fig. 5-8 — Fundamental rectifier circuits. A — Half-wave (E_{PRV} = 1.4 E_{RMS} with resistive load, = 2.8 E_{RMS} with capacitor-input filter). B — Full-wave. C — Full-wave bridge. Output voltage values do not include rectifier voltage drops.

Since the rectifiers work alternately, each handles half of the load current, and the load-current rating of each rectifier need be only half the total load current drawn from the supply.

Two separate transformers, with their primaries connected in parallel and secondaries connected in series (with the proper polarity) may be used in this circuit. However, if this substitution is made, the primary volt-ampere rating must be reduced to about 40 percent less than twice the rating of one transformer.

Full-Wave Bridge Rectifier

Another full-wave rectifier circuit is shown in Fig. 5-8C. In this arrangement, two rectifiers operate in series on each half of the cycle, one rectifier being in the lead to the load, the other being in the return lead. The current flows through two rectifiers during one half of the cycle and through the other two rectifiers during the other half of the cycle. The output wave shape (C), to the right, is the same as that from the simple center-tap rectifier circuit. The maximum output voltage into a resistive load or a properly designed choke-input filter is 0.9 times the rms voltage delivered by the transformer secondary; with a capacitor-input filter and a very light load the output voltage is 1.4 times the secondary rms voltage. The peak reverse voltage per rectifier is 1.4 times the secondary rms voltage. Each rectifier in a bridge circuit should have a minimum load-current rating of one-half the total load current to be drawn from the supply.

RECTIFIER RATINGS

All rectifiers are subject to limitations as to breakdown voltage and current-handling capability. Some tube types are rated in terms of the maximum rms voltage that should be applied to the rectifier plate. This is sometimes dependent on whether a choke- or capacitive-input filter is used. Others, particularly mercury-vapor and semiconductor types, are rated according to maximum peak reverse voltage.

Rectifiers are rated also as to maximum dc load current, and some may carry peak-current ratings in addition. To assure normal life, all ratings should be carefully observed.

HIGH-VACUUM RECTIFIERS

High-vacuum rectifiers depend entirely upon the thermionic emission from a heated filament and are characterized by a relatively high internal resistance. For this reason, their application usually is limited to low power, although there are a few types designed for medium and high power in cases where the relatively high internal voltage drop may be tolerated. This high internal resistance makes them less susceptible to damage from temporary overload and they are free from the bothersome electrical noise sometimes associated with other types of rectifiers.

Some rectifiers of the high-vacuum full-wave type in the so-called receiver-tube class will handle up to 275 mA at 400- to 500-volts dc output. Those in the higher power class can be used to handle up to 500 mA at 2000 volts dc in full-wave circuits. Most low-power high-vacuum rectifiers are produced in the full-wave type, while those for greater power are invariably of the half-wave type, two tubes being required for a full-wave rectifier circuit. A few of the lower voltage types have indirectly heated cathodes, but are limited in heater-to-cathode voltage rating.

SEMICONDUCTOR RECTIFIERS

Silicon rectifiers are being used almost exclusively in power supplies for amateur equipment. Types are available to replace high-vacuum and mercury-vapor rectifiers. The semiconductors have the advantages of compactness, low internal voltage drop, low operating temperature and high current-handling capability. Also, no filament transformers are required.

Silicon rectifiers are available in a wide range of voltage and current ratings. In peak reverse voltage ratings of 600 or less, silicon rectifiers carry current ratings as high as 400 amperes, and at 1000 PRV the current ratings may be 1.5 amperes or so. The extreme compactness of silicon types makes feasible the stacking of several units in series for higher voltages. Standard stacks are available that will handle up to 10,000 PRV at a dc load current of 500 mA, although the amateur can do much better, economically, by stacking the rectifiers himself.

PROTECTION OF SILICON POWER DIODES

The important specifications of a silicon diode are:

1) PRV (or PIV), the peak reverse (or peak inverse) voltage,

2) I_o, the average dc current rating.

3) I_{REP}, the peak repetitive forward current, and

4) I_{SURGE}, the peak one-cycle surge current. The first two specifications appear in most catalogs. The last two often do not, but they are very important.

Since the rectifier never allows current to flow more than half the time, when it does conduct it has to pass at least twice the average direct current. With a capacitor-input filter, the rectifier conducts much less than half the time, so that when it does conduct, it may pass as much as ten to twenty times the average dc current, under certain conditions. This peak current is I_{REP}, the peak repetitive forward current.

Also, when the supply is first turned on, the discharged input capacitor looks like a dead short, and the rectifier passes a very heavy current. This is I_{SURGE}. The maximum I_{SURGE} rating is usually for a duration of one cycle (at 60 Hz), or about 16.7 milliseconds.

If a manufacturer's data sheet is not available, an educated guess about a diode's capability can be made by using these rules of thumb for silicon diodes of the type commonly used in amateur power supplies:

Rule 1) The maximum I_{REP} rating can be assumed to be approximately four times the maximum I_o rating.

Rule 2) The maximum I_{SURGE} rating can be assumed to be approximately twelve times the maximum I_o rating. (This should provide a reasonable safety factor. Silicon rectifiers with 750-mA dc ratings, as an example, seldom have 1-cycle surge ratings of less than 15 amperes; some are rated up to 35 amperes or more.) From this then, it can be seen that the rectifier should be selected on the basis of I_{SURGE} and not on I_o ratings.

Thermal Protection

The junction of a diode is quite small, hence it must operate at a high current density. The heat-handling capability is, therefore, quite small. Normally, this is not a prime consideration in high-voltage, low-current supplies. When using high-current rectifiers at or near their maximum ratings (usually 2-ampere or larger stud-mount rectifiers), some form of heat sinking is necessary. Frequently, mounting the rectifier on the main chassis – directly, or by means of thin mica insulating washers – will suffice. If insulated from the chassis, a thin layer of silicone grease should be used between the diode and the insulator, and between the insulator and the chassis to assure good heat conduction. Large high-current rectifiers often require special heat sinks to maintain a safe operating temperature. Forced-air cooling is sometimes used as a further aid. Safe case temperatures are usually given in the manufacturer's data sheets and should be observed if the maximum capabilities of the diode are to be realized.

Surge Protection

Each time the power supply is activated, assuming the input filter capacitor has been discharged, the rectifiers must look into what represents a dead short. Some form of surge protection is usually necessary to protect the diodes until the input capacitor becomes nearly charged. Although the dc resistance of the transformer secondary can be relied upon in some instances to provide ample surge-current limiting, it is seldom enough on high-voltage power supplies to be suitable. Series resistors can be installed between the secondary and the rectifier strings as illustrated in Fig. 5-4, but are a deterrent to good

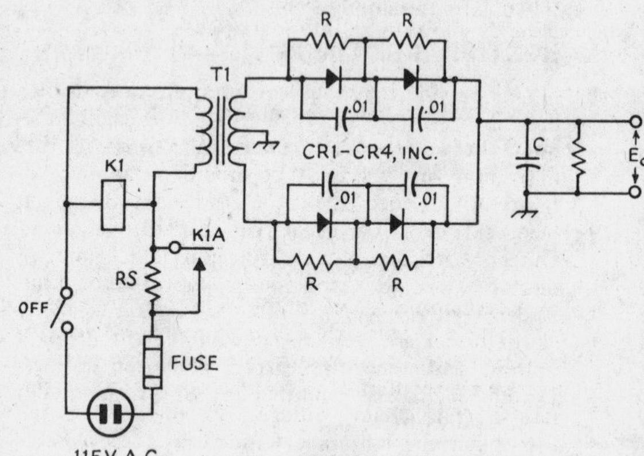

Fig. 5-9 – The primary circuit of T1 shows how a 115-volt ac relay and a series dropping resistor, R_S, can provide surge protection while C charges. When silicon rectifiers are connected in series for high-voltage operation, the inverse voltage does not divide equally. The reverse voltage drops can be equalized by using equalizing resistors, as shown in the secondary circuit. To protect against voltage "spikes" that may damage an individual rectifier, each rectifier should be bypassed by a .01-μF capacitor. Connected as shown, two 400-PRV silicon rectifiers can be used as an 800-PRV rectifier, although it is preferable to include a safety factor and call it a "750-PRV" rectifier. The rectifiers, CR1 through CR4, should be the same type (same type number and ratings).

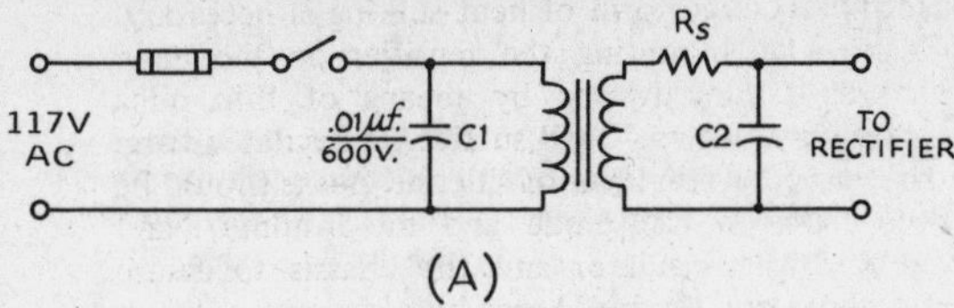

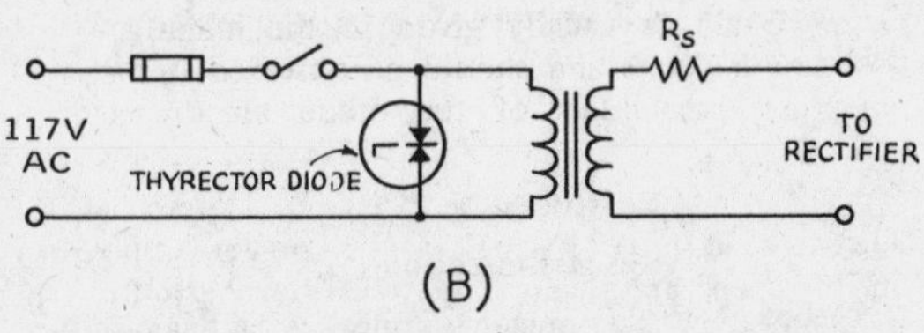

Fig. 5-10 – Methods of suppressing line transients. See text.

voltage regulation. By installing a surge-limiting device in the primary circuit of the plate transformer, the need for series resistors in the secondary circuit can be avoided. A practical method for primary-circuit surge control is shown in Fig. 5-9. The resistor, R_s introduces a voltage drop in the primary feed to T1 until C is nearly charged. Then, after C becomes partially charged, the voltage drop across R_s lessens and allows K1 to pull in, thus applying full primary power to T1 as K1A shorts out R_s.R_s is usually a 25-watt resistor whose resistance is somewhere between 15 and 50 ohms, depending upon the power supply characteristics.

Transient Problems

A common cause of trouble is transient voltages on the ac power line. These are short spikes, mostly, that can temporarily increase the voltage seen by the rectifier to values much higher than the normal transformer voltage. They come from distant lightning strokes, electric motors turning on and off, and so on. Transients cause unexpected, and often unexplained, loss of silicon rectifiers.

It's always wise to suppress line transients, and it can be easily done. Fig. 5-10A shows one way. C1 looks like 280,000 ohms at 60 Hz, but to a sharp transient (which has only high-frequency components), it is an effective bypass. C2 provides additional protection on the secondary side of the transformer. It should be .01μF for transformer voltages of 100 or less, and .001μF for high-voltage transformers.

Fig. 5-10B shows another transient-suppression method using selenium suppressor diodes. The diodes do not conduct unless the peak voltage becomes abnormally high. Then they clip the transient peaks. General Electric sells protective diodes under the trade name, "Thyrector." Sarkes-Tarzian uses the descriptive name, "Klip-volt."

Transient voltages can go as high as twice the normal line voltage before the suppressor diodes clip the peaks. Capacitors cannot give perfect suppression either. Thus, it is a good idea to use power-supply rectifiers rated at about twice the expected PRV.

Diodes in Series

Where the PRV rating of a single diode is not sufficient for the application, similar diodes may be used in series. (Two 500-PRV diodes in series will withstand 1000 PRV, and so on.) When this is done, a resistor and a capacitor should be placed across each diode in the string to equalize the PRV drops and to guard against transient voltage spikes, as shown in Fig. 5-9. Even though the diodes are of the same type and have the same PRV rating, they may have widely different back resistances when they are cut off. The reverse voltage divides according to Ohm's Law, and the diode with the higher back resistance will have the higher voltage developed across it. The diode may break down.

If we put a swamping resistor across each diode, R as shown in Fig. 5-9, the resultant resistance across each diode will be almost the same, and the back voltage will divide almost equally. A good rule of thumb for resistor size is this: Multiply the PRV rating of the diode by 500 ohms. For example, a 500-PRV diode should be shunted by 500 X 500, or 250,000 ohms.

The shift from forward conduction to high back resistance does not take place instantly in a silicon diode. Some diodes take longer than others to develop high back resistance. To protect the "fast" diodes in a series string until all the diodes are properly cut off, a .01-μF capacitor should be placed across each diode. Fig. 5-9 shows the complete series-diode circuit. The capacitors should be noninductive, ceramic disk, for example, and should be well matched. Use 10-percent-tolerance capacitors if possible.

Diodes in Parallel

Diodes can be placed in parallel to increase current-handling capability. Equalizing resistors should be added as shown in Fig. 5-11. Without the resistors, one diode may take most of the current. The resistors should be selected to have about a 1-volt drop at the expected peak current.

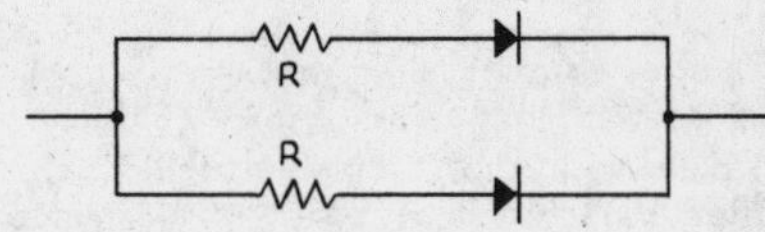

Fig. 5-11 – Diodes in parallel should have equalizing resistors. See text for appropriate value.

FILTERING

The pulsating dc waves from the rectifiers are not sufficiently constant in amplitude to prevent hum corresponding to the pulsations. Filters are required between the rectifier and the load to smooth out the pulsations into an essentially constant dc voltage. Also, upon the design of the filter depends to a large extent the dc voltage output, the voltage regulation of the power supply, and the maximum load current that can be drawn from the supply without exceeding the peak-current rating of the rectifier. Power supply filters are low-pass devices using series inductors and shunt capacitors.

Load Resistance

In discussing the performance of power-supply filters, it is sometimes convenient to express the load connected to the output terminals of the supply in terms of resistance. The load resistance is equal to the output voltage divided by the total current drawn, including the current drawn by the bleeder resistor.

Voltage Regulation

The output voltage of a power supply always decreases as more current is drawn, not only because of increased voltage drops on the transformer, filter chokes and the rectifier (if high-vacuum rectifiers are used) but also because the output voltage at light loads tends to soar to the peak value of the transformer voltage as a result of charging the first capacitor. By proper filter design the latter effect can be eliminated. The change in output voltage with load is called *voltage regulation* and is expressed as a percentage.

$$\text{Percent regulation} = \frac{100\,(E1 - E2)}{E2}$$

Example: No-load voltage = E1 = 1550 volts.
Full-load voltage = E2 = 1230 volts.

$$\text{Percentage regulation} = \frac{100\,(1550 - 1230)}{1230} = \frac{32{,}000}{1230} = 26 \text{ percent}$$

A steady load, such as that represented by a receiver, speech amplifier or unkeyed stages of a transmitter, does not require good (low) regulation as long as the proper voltage is obtained under load conditions. However, the filter capacitors must have a voltage rating safe for the highest value to which the voltage will soar when the external load is removed.

A power supply will show more (higher) regulation with long-term changes in load resistance than with short temporary changes. The regulation with long-term changes is often called the **static regulation**, to distinguish it from the **dynamic regulation** (short temporary load changes). A load that varies at a syllabic or keyed rated, as represented by some audio and rf amplifiers, usually requires good dynamic regulation (15 percent or less) if distortion products are to be held to a low level. The dynamic regulation of a power supply is improved by increasing the value of the output capacitor.

When essentially constant voltage regardless of current variation is required (for stabilizing an oscillator, for example), special voltage-regulating circuits described elsewhere in this chapter are used.

Bleeder

A bleeder resistor is a resistance connected across the output terminals of the power supply. Its functions are to discharge the filter capacitors as a safety measure when the power is turned off and to improve voltage regulation by providing a minimum load resistance. When voltage regulation is not of importance, the resistance may be as high as 100 ohms per volt. The resistance value to be used for voltage-regulating purposes is discussed in later sections. From the consideration of safety, the power rating of the resistor should be as conservative as possible, since a burned-out bleeder resistor is more dangerous than none at all!

Ripple Frequency and Voltage

The pulsations in the output of the rectifier can be considered to be the resultant of an alternating current superimposed upon a steady direct current. From this viewpoint, the filter may be considered to consist of shunting capacitors which short-circuit the ac component while not interfering with the flow of the dc component, and series chokes which pass dc readily but which impede the flow of the ac component.

The alternating component is called the ripple. The effectiveness of the filter can be expressed in terms of percent ripple, which is the ratio of the rms value of the ripple to the dc value in terms of percentage. Any multiplier or amplifier supply in a code transmitter should have less than 5 percent ripple. A linear amplifier can tolerate about 3 percent ripple on the plate voltage. Bias supplies for linear amplifiers, and modulator and modulated-amplifier plate supplies, should have less than 1 percent ripple. VFOs, speech amplifiers and receivers may require a ripple reduction to .01 percent.

Ripple frequency is the frequency of the pulsations in the rectifier output wave – the number of pulsations per second. The frequency of the ripple with half-wave rectifiers is the same as the frequency of the line supply – 60 Hz with 60-Hz supply. Since the output pulses are doubled with a full-wave rectifier, the ripple frequency is doubled – to 120 Hz with a 60-Hz supply.

The amount of filtering (values of inductance and capacitance) required to give adequate smoothing depends upon the ripple frequency, with more filtering being required as the ripple frequency is lowered.

Type of Filter

Power-supply filters fall into two classifications, capacitor input and choke input. Capacitor-input filters are characterized by relatively high output voltage in respect to the transformer voltage. Advantage of this can be taken when silicon rectifiers are used or with any rectifier when the load resistance is high. Silicon rectifiers have a higher allowable peak-to-dc ratio than do thermionic rectifiers. This permits the use of capacitor-input filters at ratios of input capacitor to load resistance that would seriously shorten the life of a thermionic rectifier system. When the series resistance through a rectifier and filter system is appreciable, as when high-vacuum rectifiers are used, the voltage regulation of a capacitor-input power supply is poor.

The output voltage of a properly designed choke-input power supply is less than would be obtained with a capacitor-input filter from the same transformer.

CAPACITIVE-INPUT FILTERS

Capacitive-input filter systems are shown in Fig. 5-12. Disregarding voltage drops in the chokes, all have the same characteristics except in respect to ripple. Better ripple reduction will be obtained when LC sections are added, as shown in Figs. 5-12B and C.

Output Voltage

To determine the approximate dc voltage output when a capacitive-input filter is used, reference should be made to the graph of Fig. 5-5.

Example:

Transformer rms voltage – 350
Load resistance – 2000 ohms

Series resistance – 200 ohms
200 ÷ 2000 = 0.1
Input capacitor $C = 20\ \mu F$

$$\frac{RC}{1000} = \frac{2000 \times 20}{1000} = 40$$

From curve 0.1 and $RC = 40$, dc voltage = 350 × 1.06 = 370.

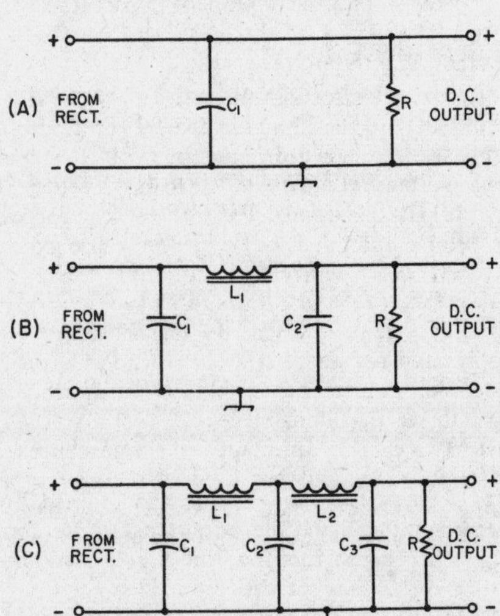

Fig. 5-12 – Capacitive-input filter circuits. A – Simple capacitive. B – Single-section. C – Double-section.

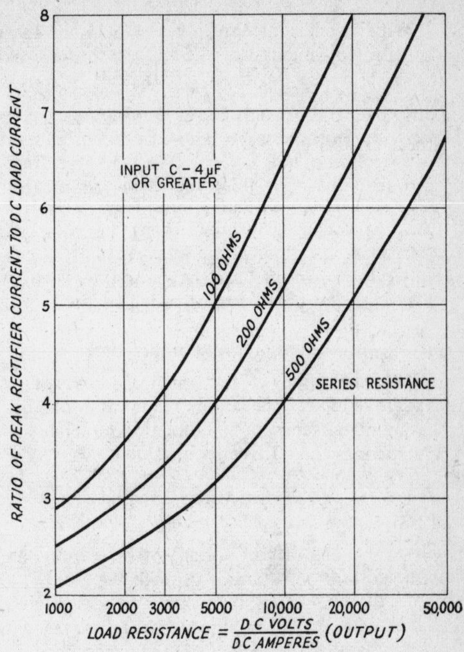

Fig. 5-13 – Graph showing the relationship between the dc load current and the rectifier peak current with capacitive input for various values of load and input resistance.

Regulation

If a bleeder resistance of 20,000 ohms is used in the example above, when the load is removed and R becomes 20,000, the dc voltage will rise to 470. For minimum regulation with a capacitor-input filter, the bleeder resistance should be as high as possible, or the series resistance should be low and the filter capacitance high, without exceeding the transformer or rectifier ratings.

Maximum Rectifier Current

The maximum current that can be drawn from a supply with a capacitive-input filter without exceeding the peak-current rating of the rectifier may be estimated from the graph of Fig. 5-13. Using values from the preceding example, the ratio of peak rectifier current to dc load current for 2000 ohms, as shown in Fig. 5-13, is 3. Therefore, the maximum load current that can be drawn without exceeding the rectifier rating is 1/3 the peak rating of the rectifier. For a load current of 185 mA, as above (370 V ÷ 2000 Ω), the rectifier peak current rating should be at least 3 X 185 = 555 mA.

With bleeder current only, Fig. 5-13 shows that the ratio will increase to 6.5. But since the bleeder draws 23.5 mA dc, the rectifier peak current will be only 153 mA.

CHOKE-INPUT FILTERS

With thermionic rectifiers better voltage regulations results when a choke-input filter, as shown in Fig. 5-4, is used. Choke input permits better utilization of the thermionic rectifier, since a higher load current usually can be drawn without exceeding the peak current rating of the rectifier.

Minimum Choke Inductance

A choke-input filter will tend to act as a capacitive-input filter unless the input choke has at least a certain minimum value of inductance called the **critical** value. This critical value is given by

$$L_{crit}\text{ (henrys)} = \frac{E\text{ (volts)}}{I\text{ (mA)}}$$

where E is the output voltage of the supply, and I is the current being drawn through the filter.

If the choke has at least the critical value, the output voltage will be limited to the average value of the rectified wave at the input to the choke (see Fig. 5-8) when the current drawn from the supply is small. This is in contrast to the capacitive-input filter in which the output voltage tends to soar toward the peak value of the rectified wave at light loads.

Minimum-Load – Bleeder Resistance

From the formula above for critical inductance, it is obvious that if no current is drawn from the supply, the critical inductance will be infinite. So that a practical value of inductance may be used, some current must be drawn from the supply at all times the supply is in use. From the formula we find that this minimum value of current is

$$I\text{ (mA)} = \frac{E\text{ (volts)}}{L_{crit}}$$

In the majority of cases it will be most convenient to adjust the bleeder resistance so that the bleeder will draw the required minimum current. From the formula, it may be seen that the value of critical inductance becomes smaller as the load current increases.

Swinging Chokes

Less costly chokes are available that will maintain at least the critical value of inductance over the range of current likely to be drawn from practical supplies. These chokes are called **swinging chokes.** As an example, a swinging choke may have an inductance rating of 5/25 H and a current rating of 200 mA. If the supply delivers 1000 volts, the minimum load current should be 1000/25 = 40 mA. When the full load current of 200 mA is drawn from the supply, the inductance will drop to 5 H. The critical inductance for 200 mA at 1000 volts is 1000/200 = 5 H. Therefore the 5/25 H choke maintains the critical inductance at the full current rating of 200 mA. At all load currents between 40 mA and 200 mA, the choke will adjust its inductance to the approximate critical value.

Output Voltage

Provided the input-choke inductance is at least the critical value, the output voltage may be calculated quite close by the following equation:

$$E_o = 0.9E_t - (I_B + I_L)\,(R1 + R2) - E_r$$

where E_o is the output voltage; E_t is the rms voltage applied to the rectifier (rms voltage between center-tap and one end of the secondary in the case of the center-tap rectifier); I_B and I_L are the bleeder and load currents, respectively, in amperes; R_1 and R_2 are the resistances of the first and second filter chokes; and E_r is the voltage drop across the rectifier. The various voltage drops are shown in Fig. 5-4. At no load I_L is zero; hence the no-load voltage may be calculated on the basis of bleeder current only. The voltage regulation may be determined from the no-load and full-load voltages using the formula previously given.

OUTPUT CAPACITOR

Whether the supply has a choke- or capacitor-input filter, if it is intended for use with a Class A af amplifier, the reactance of the output capacitor should be low for the lowest audio frequency; 16 μF or more is usually adequate. When the supply is used with a Class B amplifier (for modulation or for ssb amplification) or a cw transmitter, increasing the output capacitance will result in improved dynamic regulation of the supply. However, a region of diminishing returns can be reached, and 20 to 30 μF will usually suffice for any supply subjected to large changes at a syllabic (or keying) rate.

RESONANCE

Resonance effects in the series circuit across the output of the rectifier, formed by the first choke and first filter capacitor, must be avoided, since the ripple voltage would build up to large values. This not only is the opposite action to that for which the filter is intended, but may also cause excessive rectifier peak currents and abnormally high peak-reverse voltages. For full-wave rectification the ripple frequency will be 120 Hz for a 60-Hz supply, and resonance will occur when the product of choke inductance in henrys times capacitor capacitance in microfarads is equal to 1.77. At least twice this product of inductance and capacitance should be used to ensure against resonance effects. With a swinging choke, the minimum rated inductance of the choke should be used.

RATINGS OF FILTER COMPONENTS

In a power supply using a choke-input filter and properly designed choke and bleeder resistor, the no-load voltage across the filter capacitors will be about nine-tenths of the ac rms voltage. Nevertheless, it is advisable to use capacitors rated for the *peak* transformer voltage. This large safety factor is suggested because the voltage across the capacitors can reach this peak value if the bleeder should burn out and there is no load on the supply.

In a capacitive-input filter, the capacitors should have a working-voltage rating at least as high, and preferably somewhat higher, than the peak voltage from the transformer. Thus, in the case of a center-tap rectifier having a transformer delivering 550 volts each side of the center tap, the minimum safe capacitor voltage rating will be 550 X 1.41 or 775 volts. An 800-volt capacitor should be used, or preferably a 1000-volt unit.

Filter Capacitors in Series

Filter capacitors are made in several different types. Electrolytic capacitors, which are available for peak voltages up to about 800, combine high capacitance with small size, since the dielectric is an extremely thin film of oxide on aluminum foil. Capacitors of this type may be connected in series for higher voltages, although the filtering capacitance will be reduced to the resultant of the two capacitances in series. If this arrangement is used, it is important that *each* of the capacitors be shunted with a resistor of about 100 ohms per volt of supply voltage applied to the individual capacitors, with an adequate power rating. These resistors may serve as all or part of the bleeder resistance. Capacitors with higher voltage ratings usually are made with a dielectric of thin paper impregnated with oil. The working voltage of a capacitor is the voltage that it will withstand continuously.

Filter Chokes

Filter chokes or inductances are wound on iron cores, with a small gap in the core to prevent magnetic saturation of the iron at high currents. When the iron becomes saturated its permeability decreases, and consequently the inductance also decreases. Despite the air gap, the inductance of a choke usually varies to some extent with the direct current flowing in the winding; hence it is necessary to specify the inductance at the current which the choke is intended to carry. Its inductance with little or no direct current flowing in the winding will usually be considerably higher than the value when full load current is flowing.

NEGATIVE-LEAD FILTERING

For many years it has been almost universal practice to place filter chokes in the positive leads of plate power supplies. This means that the insulation between the choke winding and its core (which should be grounded to chassis as a safety measure) must be adequate to withstand the output voltage of the supply. This voltage requirement is removed if the chokes are placed in the negative lead as shown in Fig. 5-14. With this connection, the capacitance of the transformer secondary to ground appears in parallel with the filter chokes tending to bypass the chokes. However, this effect will be negligible in practical application except in cases where the output ripple must be reduced to a very low figure. Such applications are usually limited to low-voltage devices such as receivers, speech amplifiers and VFOs where insulation is no problem and the chokes may be placed in the positive side in the conventional manner. In higher voltage applications, there is no reason why the filter chokes should not be placed in the negative lead to reduce insulation requirements. Choke terminals, negative capacitor terminals and the transformer center-tap terminal should be well protected against accidental contact, since these will assume full supply voltage to chassis should a choke burn out or the chassis connection fail.

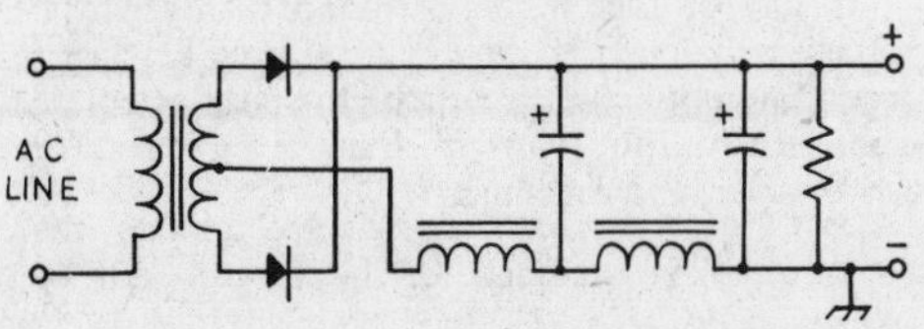

Fig. 5-14 — In most applications, the filter chokes may be placed in the negative instead of the positive side of the circuit. This reduces the danger of a voltage breakdown between the choke winding and core.

THE "ECONOMY" POWER SUPPLY

In many transmitters of the 100-watt class, an excellent method for obtaining plate and screen voltages without wasting power in resistors is by the use of the "economy" power-supply circuit. Shown in Fig. 5-15, it is a combination of the full-wave and bridge-rectifier circuits. The voltage at E1 is the normal voltage obtained with the full-wave circuit, and the voltage at E2 is that obtained with the bridge circuit (see Fig. 5-8). The *total* dc power obtained from the transformer is, of course, the same as when the transformer is used in its normal manner. In cw and ssb applications, additional power can usually be drawn without excessive heating, especially if the transformer has a rectifier filament winding that isn't being used.

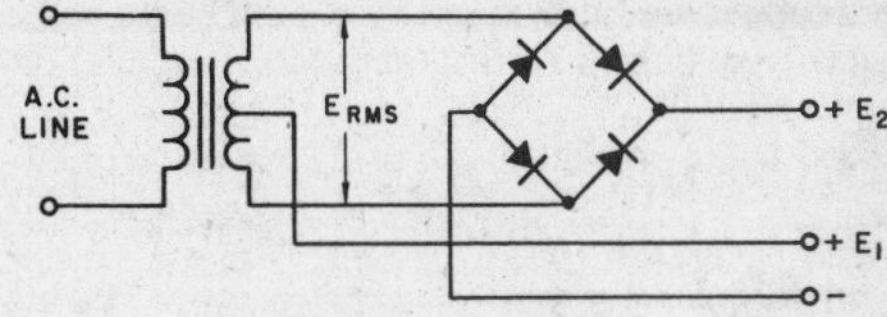

Fig. 5-15 — The "economy" power supply circuit is a combination of the full-wave and bridge-rectifier circuits.

VOLTAGE-MULTIPLYING CIRCUITS

Although vacuum-tube rectifiers can be used in voltage-multiplying circuits, semiconductor rectifiers are recommended.

A simple half-wave rectifier circuit is shown in Fig. 5-16. Strictly speaking this is not a voltage-multiplying circuit. However, if the current demand is low (a milliampere or less), the dc output voltage will be close to the peak voltage of the source, or $1.4E_{rms}$. A typical application of the circuit would be to obtain a low bias voltage from a heater winding; the + side of the output can be grounded by reversing the polarity of the rectifier and capacitor. As with all half-wave rectifiers, the output voltage drops quickly with increased current demand.

The resistor R1 in Fig. 5-16 is included to limit the current through the rectifier, in accordance with the manufacturer's rating for the diode. If the resistance of the transformer winding is sufficient, R1 can be omitted.

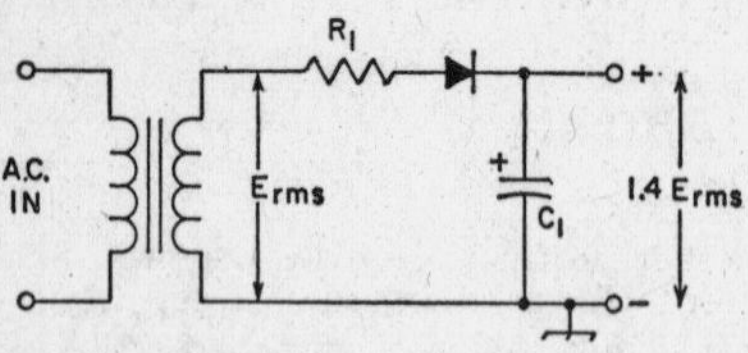

Fig. 5-16 – If the current demand is low, a simple half-wave rectifier will deliver a voltage increase. Typical values, for E_{RMS} = 117 and a load current of 1 mA:
C1 – 50-μF, 250-V electrolytic.
E_{output} – 160 volts.
R1 – 22 ohms.

VOLTAGE DOUBLERS

Several types of voltage-doubling circuits are in common use. Where it is not necessary that one side of the transformer secondary be at ground potential, the voltage-doubling circuit of Fig. 5-17 is used. This circuit has several advantages over the voltage-doubling circuit to be described later. For a given output voltage, compared to the full-wave rectifier circuit (Fig. 5-8B), this full-wave doubler circuit requires rectifiers having only half the PRV rating. Again for a given output voltage, compared to a full-wave bridge circuit (Fig. 5-8C) only half as many rectifiers (of the same PRV rating) are required.

Resistors R1 in Fig. 5-17 are used to limit the surge currents through the rectifiers. Their values are based on the transformer voltage and the rectifier surge-current rating, since at the instant the power supply is turned on the filter capacitors look like a short-circuited load. Provided the limiting resistors can withstand the surge current, their current-handling capacity is based on the maximum load current from the supply.

Output voltages approaching twice the peak voltage of the transformer can be obtained with the voltage-doubling circuit of Fig. 5-17. Fig. 5-18 shows how the voltage depends upon the ratio of the series resistance to the load resistance, and the product of the load resistance times the filter capacitance.

When one side of the transformer secondary must be at ground potential, as when the ac is derived from a heater winding, the voltage-multiplying circuits of Fig. 5-19 can be used. In the voltage-doubling circuit at A, C1 charges through the left-hand rectifier during one half of the ac cyle; the other rectifier is nonconductive during this time. During the other half of the cycle the right-hand rectifier conducts and C2 becomes charged; they see as the source the transformer plus the voltage in C1. By reversing the polarities of the capacitors and rectifiers, the + side of the output can be grounded.

VOLTAGE TRIPLING AND QUADRUPLING

A voltage-tripling circuit is shown in Fig. 5-19B. On one half of the ac cycle C1 is charged to the source voltage through the left-hand rectifier. On the opposite half of the cycle the middle rectifier conducts and C2 is charged to twice the source voltage, because it sees the transformer plus the charge in C1 as its source. (The left-hand rectifier is cut off on this half cycle.) At the same time the right-hand rectifier conducts and, with the transformer and the charge in C2 as the source, C3 is charged to three times the transformer voltage. The + side of the output can be grounded if the polarities of all of the capacitors and rectifiers are reversed.

The voltage-quadrupling circuit of Fig. 5-19C works in substantially similar fashion.

In any of the circuits of Fig. 5-19, the output voltage will approach an exact multiple (2, 3 or 4, depending upon the circuit) of the peak ac voltage when the output current drain is low and the capacitance values are high.

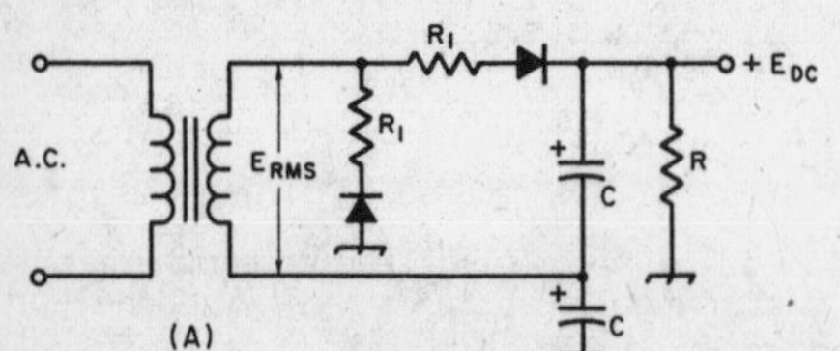

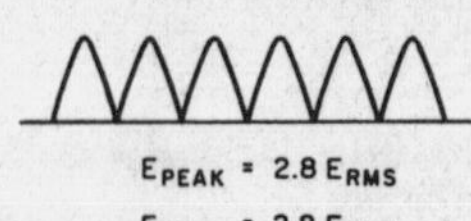

Fig. 5-17 – Full-wave voltage-doubling circuit. Values of limiting resistors, R1, depend upon allowable surge currents of rectifiers.

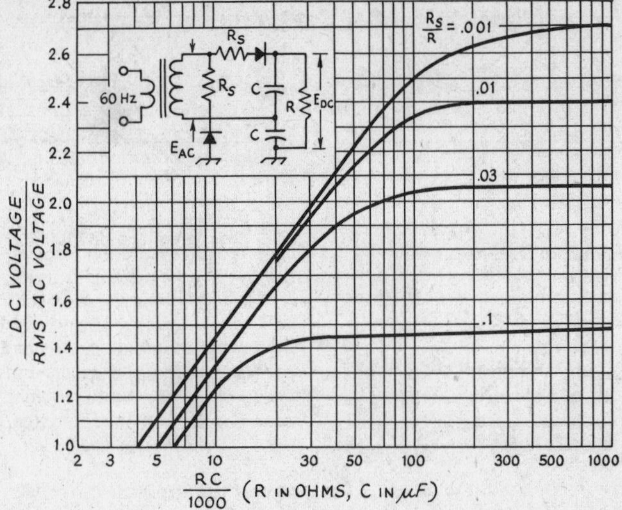

Fig. 5-18 – Dc output voltages from a full-wave voltage-doubling circuit as a function of the filter capacitances and load resistance. For the ratio R_s/R and for the RC product, resistances are in ohms and capacitance is in microfarads. Equal resistance values for R_s and equal capacitance values for C are assumed.

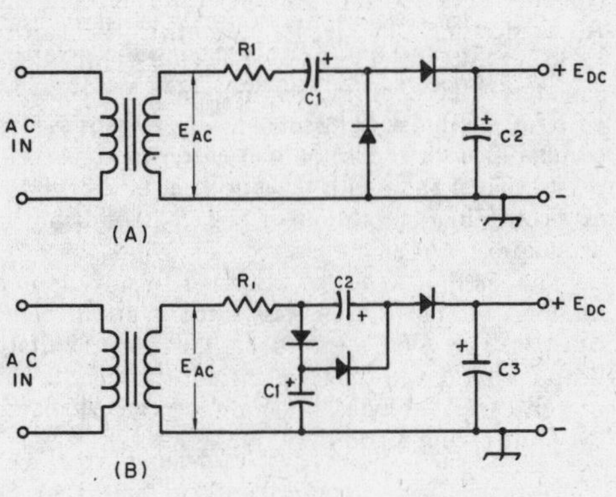

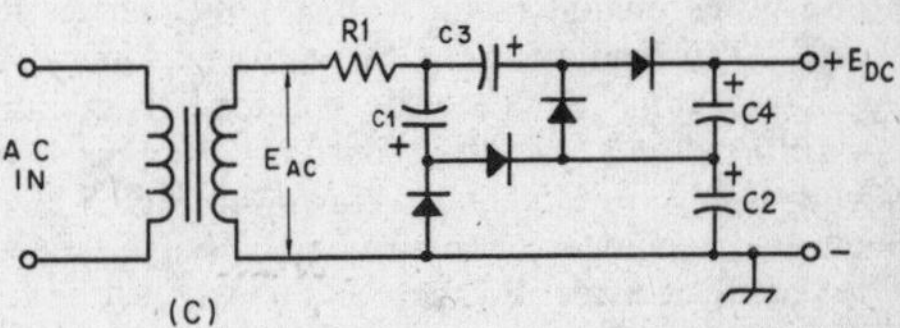

Fig. 5-19 – Voltage-multiplying circuits with one side of transformer secondary grounded. (A) Voltage doubler (B) Voltage tripler (C) Voltage quadrupler.

Capacitances are typically 20 to 50 µF depending upon output current demand. Dc ratings of capacitors are related to E_{peak} (1.4 E_{ac}):

C1 – Greater than E_{peak}
C2 – Greater than $2E_{peak}$
C3 – Greater than $3E_{peak}$
C4 – Greater than $4E_{peak}$

VOLTAGE DROPPING

Series Voltage-Dropping Resistor

Certain plates and screens of the various tubes in a transmitter or receiver often require a variety of operating voltages differing from the output voltage of an available power supply. In most cases, it is not economically feasible to provide a separate power supply for each of the required voltages. If the current drawn by an electrode (or combination of electrodes operating at the same voltage) is reasonably constant under normal operating conditions, the required voltage may be obtained from a supply of higher voltage by means of a voltage-dropping resistor in series, as shown in Fig. 5-20A. The value of the series, resistor, R1, may be obtained from Ohm's Law,

$$R = \frac{E_d}{I}$$

where E_d is the voltage *drop* required from the supply voltage to the desired voltage and I is the total rated current of the load.

Example: The plate of the tube in one stage and the screens of the tubes in two other stages require an operating voltage of 250. The nearest available supply voltage is 400 and the total of the rated plate and screen currents is 75 mA. The required resistance is

$$R = \frac{400 - 250}{.075} = \frac{150}{.075} = 2000 \text{ ohms}$$

The power rating of the resistor is obtained from P (watts) = I^2R = $(0.075)^2 \times (2000)$ = 11.2 watts. A 20-watt resistor is the nearest safe rating to be used.

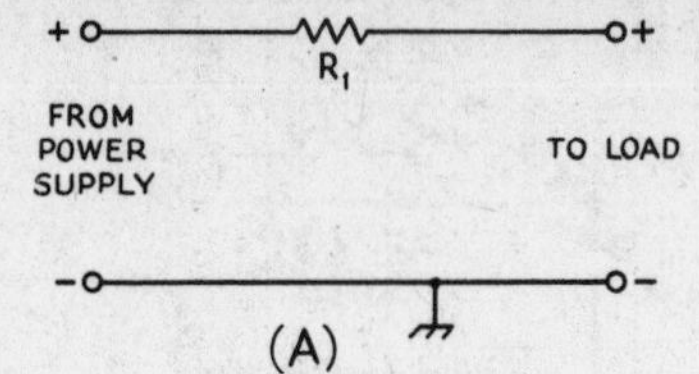

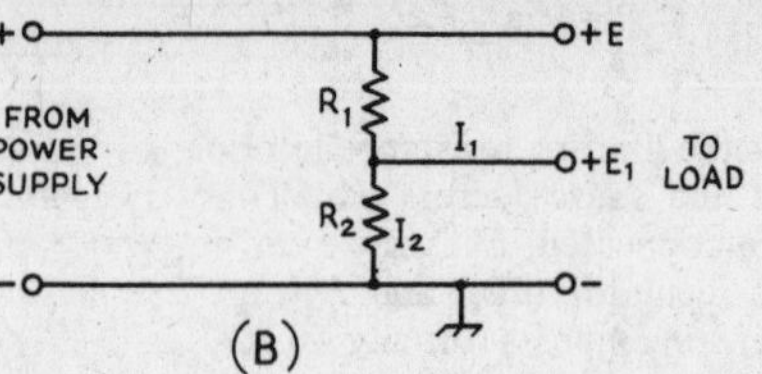

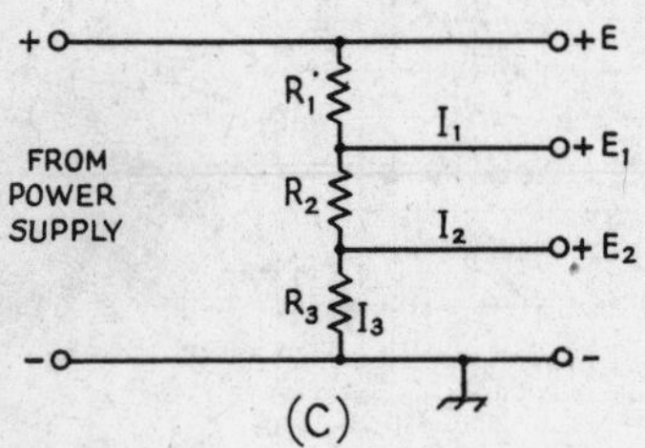

Fig. 5–20 — A – Series voltage-dropping resistor. B – Simple voltage divider.

$$R2 = \frac{E1}{I2}\ ;\ R1 = \frac{E - E1}{I1 + I2}$$

$I2$ must be assumed.

C – Multiple divider circuit.

$$R3 = \frac{E2}{I3};\ R2 = \frac{E1 - E2}{I2 + I3};\ R1 = \frac{E - E1}{I1 + I2 + I3}$$

$I3$ must be assumed.

Voltage Dividers

The regulation of the voltage obtained in this manner obviously is poor, since any change in current through the resistor will cause a directly proportional change in the voltage drop across the resistor. The regulation can be improved somewhat by connecting a second resistor from the low-voltage end of the first to the negative power-supply terminal, as shown in Fig. 5-20B. Such an arrangement constitutes a **voltage divider.** The second resistor, R2, acts as a constant load for the first, R1, so that any variation in current from the tap becomes a smaller percentage of the total current through R1. The heavier the current drawn by the resistors when they alone are connected across the supply, the better will be the voltage regulation at the tap.

Such a voltage divider may have more than a single tap for the purpose of obtaining more than one value of voltage. A typical arrangement is shown in Fig. 5-20C. The terminal voltage is E, and two taps are provided to give lower voltages, E1 and E2, at currents I1 and I2 respectively. The smaller the resistance between taps in proportion to the total resistance, the lower is the voltage between the taps. The voltage divider in the figure is made up of separate resistances, R1, R2 and R3. R3 carries only the bleeder current, I3; R2 carries I2 in addition to I3; R1 carries I1, I2 and I3. To calculate the resistances required, a bleeder current, I3, must be assumed; generally it is low compared with the total load current (10 percent or so). Then the required values can be calculated as shown in the caption of Fig. 5-20, I being in decimal parts of an ampere.

The method may be extended to any desired number of taps, each resistance section being calculated by Ohm's Law using the needed voltage drop across it and the total current through it. The power dissipated by each section may be calculated by multiplying I and E or I^2 and R.

VOLTAGE STABILIZATION

Gaseous Regulator Tubes

There is frequent need for maintaining the voltage applied to a low-voltage low-current circuit at a practically constant value, regardless of the voltage regulation of the power supply or variations in load current. In such applications, gaseous regulator tubes (0B2/VR105, 0A2/VR150, etc.) can be used to good advantage. The voltage drop across such tubes is constant over a moderately wide current range. Tubes are available for regulated voltages near 150, 105, 90 and 75 volts.

The fundamental circuit for a gaseous regulator is shown in Fig. 5-21. The tube is connected in series with a **limiting resistor**, R1, across a source of voltage that must be higher than the **starting** voltage. The starting voltage is about 30 to 40 percent higher than the operating voltage. The load is connected in parallel with the tube. For stable operation, a minimum tube current of 5 to 10 mA is required. The maximum permissible current with most types is 40 mA; consequently, the load current cannot exceed 30 to 35 mA if the voltage is to be stabilized over a range from zero to maximum load. A single VR tube may also be used to regulate the voltage to a load current of almost any value as long as the *variation* in the current does not exceed 30 to 35 mA. If, for example, the average load current is 100 mA, a VR tube may be used to hold the voltage constant provided the current does not fall below 85 mA or rise above 115 mA.

The value of the limiting resistor must lie between that which just permits minimum tube current to flow and that which just passes the maximum permissible tube current when there is no load current. The latter value is generally used. It is given by the equation:

$$R = \frac{(E_s - E_r)}{I}$$

where R is the limiting resistance in ohms, E_s is the voltage of the source across which the tube and resistor are connected, E_r is the rated voltage drop across the regulator tube, and I is the maximum tube current in amperes (usually 40 mA, or .04 A).

Two tubes may be used in series to give a higher regulated voltage than is obtainable with one, and also to give two values of regulated voltage. Regulation of the order of 1 percent can be obtained with these regulator tubes when they are operated within their proper current range. The capacitance in shunt with a VR tube should be limited to 0.1 μF or less. Larger values may cause the tube drop to oscillate between the operating and starting voltages.

ZENER DIODE REGULATION

A Zener diode (named after Dr. Carl Zener) can be used to stabilize a voltage source in much the same way as when the gaseous regulator tube is used. The typical circuit is shown in Fig. 5-22A. Note that the cathode side of the diode is connected to the positive side of the supply. The electrical characteristics of a Zener diode under conditions of forward and reverse voltage are given in Chapter 4.

Zener diodes are available in a wide variety of voltages and power ratings. The voltages range from less than 2 to a few hundred, while the power ratings (power the diode can dissipate) run from less than 0.25 watt to 50 watts. The ability of the Zener diode to stabilize a voltage is dependent upon the conducting impedance of the diode, which can be as low as one ohm or less in a low-voltage high-power diode to as high as a thousand ohms in a low-power high-voltage diode.

Diode Power Dissipation

Unlike gaseous regulator tubes, Zener diodes of a particular voltage rating have varied maximum current capabilities, depending upon the power ratings of each of the diodes. The power dissipated in a diode is the product of the voltage across it and the current through it. Conversely, the maximum current a particular diode may safely conduct equals its power rating divided by its voltage rating. Thus, a 10-V 50-W Zener diode, if

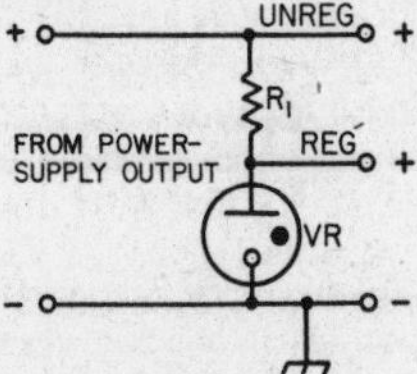

Fig. 5-21 — Voltage stabilization circuit using a VR tube. A negative-supply output may be regulated by reversing the polarity of the power-supply connections and the VR-tube connections from those shown here.

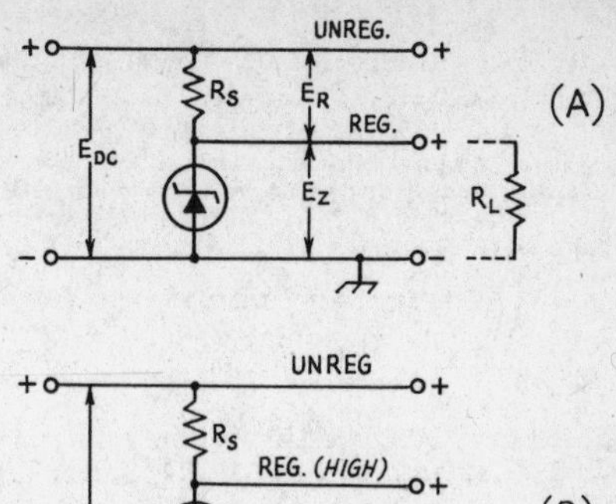

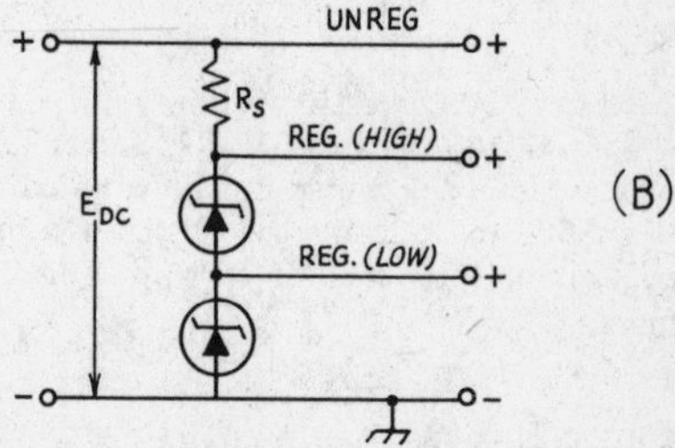

Fig. 5-22 — Zener-diode voltage regulation. The voltage from a negative supply may be regulated by reversing the power-supply connections and the diode polarities.

operated at its maximum dissipation rating, would conduct 5 amperes of current. A 10-V 1-W diode, on the other hand, could safely conduct no more than 0.1 A, or 100 mA. The conducting impedance of a diode is its voltage rating divided by the current flowing through it, and in the above examples would be 2 ohms for the 50-W diode, and 100 ohms for the 1-W diode. Disregarding small voltage changes which may occur, the conducting impedance of a given diode is a function of the current flowing through it, varying in inverse proportion.

The power-handling capability of most Zener diodes is rated at 25 degrees C, or approximately room temperature. If the diode is operated in a higher ambient temperature, its power capability must be derated. A typical 1-watt diode can safely dissipate only 1/2 watt at 100 degrees C.

Limiting Resistance

The value of R_s in Fig. 5-22 is determined by the load requirements. If R_s is too large the diode will be unable to regulate at large values of I_L, the current through R_L. If R_s is too small, the diode dissipation rating may be exceeded at low values of I_L. The optimum value for R_s can be calculated by:

$$R_S = \frac{E_{DC}\,(\text{min}) - E_Z}{1.1\, I_L\,(\text{max})}$$

When R_S is known, the maximum dissipation of the diode, P_D, may be determined by:

$$P_D = \left[\frac{E_{DC}\,(\text{max}) - E_Z}{R_S} - I_L\,(\text{min})\right] E_Z$$

In the first equation, conditions are set up for the Zener diode to draw 1/10 the maximum load current. This assures diode regulation under maximum load.

Example: A 12-volt source is to supply a circuit requiring 9 volts. The load current varies between 200 and 350 mA.

E_Z = 9.1 V (nearest available value).

$$R_S = \frac{12-9.1}{1.1 \times 0.35} = \frac{2.9}{0.385} = 7.5 \text{ ohms}$$

$$P_D = \left[\frac{12-9.1}{7.5} - 0.2\right] 9.1 = .185 \times 9.1 = 1.7 \text{ W}$$

The nearest available dissipation rating above 1.7 W is 5; therefore, a 9.1-V 5-W Zener diode should be used. Such a rating, it may be noted, will cause the diode to be in the safe dissipation range even though the load is completely disconnected [I_L (min) = 0].

Obtaining Other Voltages

Fig. 5-22B shows how two Zener diodes may be used in series to obtain regulated voltages not normally obtainable from a single Zener diode, and also to give two values of regulated voltage. The diodes need not have equal breakdown voltages, because the arrangement is self equalizing. However, the current-handling capability of each diode should be taken into account. The limiting resistor may be calculated as above, taking the sum of the diode voltages as E_Z, and the sum of the load currents as I_L.

ELECTRONIC VOLTAGE REGULATION

Several circuits have been developed for regulating the voltage output of a power supply electronically. While more complicated than the VR-tube and Zener-diode circuits, they will handle higher voltage and current variations, and the output voltage may be varied continuously over a wide range.

Voltage regulators fall into two basic types. In the type most commonly used by amateurs, the dc supply delivers a voltage higher than that which is available at the output of the regulator, and the regulated voltage is obtained by dropping the voltage down to a lower value through a dropping "resistor." Regulation is accomplished by varying either the current through a fixed dropping resistance as changes in input voltage or load currents occur (as in the VR-tube and Zener-diode regulator circuits), or by varying the equivalent resistive value of the dropping element with such changes. This latter technique is used in electronic regulators where the voltage-dropping element is a vacuum tube or a transistor, rather than an actual resistor. By varying the dc voltage at the grid or current at the base of these elements, the conductivity of the device may be varied as necessary to hold the output voltage constant. In solid-state regulators the series-dropping element is called a pass transistor. Power transistors are available which will handle several amperes of current at several hundred volts, but solid-state regulators of this type are usually operated at potentials below 100 volts.

The second type of regulator is a switching type, where the voltage from the dc source is rapidly switched on and off (electronically). The average dc voltage available from the regulator is proportional to the duty cycle of the switching wave form, or the ratio of the ON time to the total period of the switching cycle. Switching frequencies of several kilohertz are normally used to avoid the need for extensive filtering to smooth the switching frequency from the dc output.

The above information pertains essentially to voltage regulators. A circuit can also be constructed to provide current regulation. Such regulation is usually obtained in the form of current limitation – to a maximum value which is either preset or adjustable, depending on the circuit. Relatively simple circuits, such as described later,

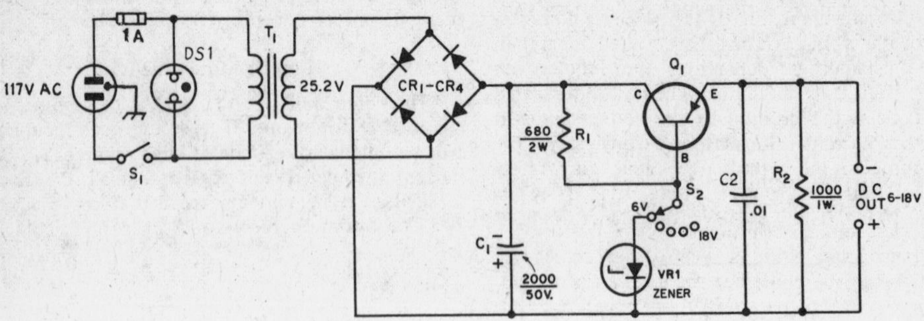

Fig. 5-23 — Schematic diagram of the power supply. Capacitances are in μF; capacitors marked with a polarity are electrolytic. Resistances are in ohms; R1 and R2 are composition.

C1 — 2000-μF 50 volts dc electrolytic (Mallory CG23U50C1).

C2 — .01-μF disk ceramic.

CR1-CR4, incl. — 50 PRV 3-A silicon diode (Motorola 1N4719).

DS1 — Neon lamp assembly with resistor (Leecraft 32-2111).

Q1 — 2N1970.

S1 — Spst toggle switch.

S2 — Phenolic rotary, 1 section, 2-pole (1 used), 6-position, shorting (Mallory 3126J).

T1 — Filament transformer, 25.2 V, 2 A (Knight 54 D 4140 or similar).

VR1 — Voltage regulator diode.

can be used to provide current limiting only. Current limiting circuitry may also be used in conjunction with voltage regulators.

Solid-State Regulators

One of the simplest forms of solid-state regulation is shown at Fig. 5-23. A bridge rectifier supplies 25 volts dc to a series regulator transistor, Q1, whose base bias is established by means of a Zener diode, VR1, providing a voltage reference of a fixed level. C1 is the input capacitor for the filter. R1 is chosen to establish a safe Zener-diode current, which is dependent upon the wattage rating of the diode. A 1-watt Zener diode is adequate for the circuit of Fig. 5-23. R2 is a bleeder resistor and C2 is an rf bypass. If several output voltages are desired, say from 6 to 18 volts, Zener diodes from 6 to 18 volts can be wired to S2 as shown. When a 2N1970 is used at Q1, the value of R1 will be 680 ohms. This value offers a compromise for the 5 reference diodes used (6,9,12,15, and 18 volts).

The output of the supply is equal to the Zener voltage minus the emitter-to-base bias voltage of Q1. Both the Zener voltage and bias voltage will be approximately zero with only R2 as a load, but will rise to roughly 0.3 volt with a 1-A load connected to the output. An increase in load current lowers the unregulated dc input voltage which appears across VR1 and R1. Zener current is reduced, decreasing the voltage at which the diode regulates. How much the voltage drops depends upon the characteristics of the particular Zener employed.

This power supply has very low output ripple. The main limitation of the circuit is the possibility of destroying Q1, the series-regulator transistor, when a dead short or heavy overload is connected across the output of the supply. To protect Q1 during normal operation, it should be mounted on a fairly large heat sink which is thermally coupled to the main chassis of the supply. The transistor should be insulated from the sink by means of a mica spacer and a thin layer of silicone grease. The sink can then be bolted directly to the chassis.

IC Regulators

The solid-state regulator described above provides only fixed voltages. Regulator circuits with the output voltage continuously variable over a wide range and with a very high degree of regulation can be built, but the number of circuit components is comparatively large when discrete components are used. Integrated-circuit devices can be used in a solid-state regulator circuit to replace many or all of the discrete components, depending on the output requirements. The voltage reference, control, shut-down (for current limiting) and pass-transistor driver elements are contained on a single silicon chip. The construction of a regulated power supply is simplified to a few interconnections if an IC regulator is used.

Fig. 5-24 is the diagram of a regulator using an IC and a single pass transistor. With a dc potential of 24 to 30 volts applied at E_{IN} the circuit as shown will provide an adjustable output voltage between 5 and 15. The circuit will handle up to 5 amperes of current, provided, of course, that the dc source will deliver this amount. If the load requires no more than 150 mA of current the pass transistor may be eliminated from the circuit altogether; in this case pins 2 and 10 of the IC should be interconnected.

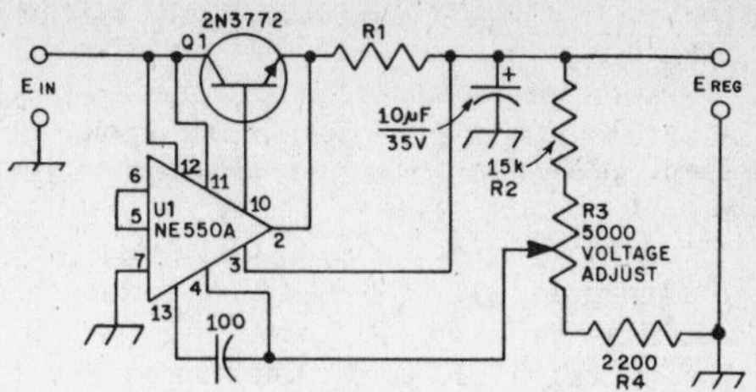

Fig. 5-24 — Schematic diagram of 15-V 5-A regulator (W1KLK, *QST* for November, 1971).

Q1 — Motorola power transistor; 30-cubic-inch heat sink required (Delco 7281366 radiator or equiv.).
R1 — 0.1-ohm resistor, made from 8 feet of No. 22 enam. copper wire.
R2, R4 — For text reference.
R3 — Linear taper.
U1 — Signetics IC.

The NE550 regulator will safely accept input voltages as high as 50, and output voltages may be adjusted by appropriate resistance values for R2, R3, and R4 from 2 to 40 volts. The value of R1 determines the shut-down current (maximum cur-

Table 5-1

Voltage Divider			*Current Limit*	
V_{OUT}	R_A	R_B	I_{MAX}	R_1
3.6	6135	2967	.05	12
5	4417	3654	0.1	6
9	11,043	2442	0.5	1.2
12	14,724	2314	1.0	0.6
13.6	16,687	2272	1.5	0.4
15	18,405	2243	2	0.3
20	24,540	2177	2.5	0.24
28	34,356	2122	3.0	0.20
			5	0.12
			10	.006

Table 5-1 — Resistance values for various voltage and current outputs from the regulator of Fig. 5-24. These values were determined by mathematical calculation and are not necessarily available from stock supplies. The figures given do indicate the practical values which may be used along with an appropriate-value control for R2 in the circuit of Fig. 5-24.

R_A — R2 plus top portion of R3.
R_B — R4 plus bottom portion of R3.

rent which the circuit will deliver into a short circuit) and is usually selected to protect either the pass transistor or the power supply transformer, whichever has the lower current rating. Table 5-1 gives resistance values for various levels of voltage and current from the regulator.

The use of a high-gain pass device improves the output regulation, and a Darlington-connected pair is frequently employed. Of course it is easy to purchase a ready-made Darlington transistor, but the enterprising amateur can make his own, as shown in Fig. 5-25A. However, some of the IC regulators which are available on the market have so much internal gain that it is difficult to avoid oscillation with a high-gain pass transistor.

High-Current-Output Regulators

When a single pass transistor is not available to handle the current which may be required from a regulator, the current-handling capability may be increased by connecting two or more pass transistors in parallel. The circuits at B and C of Fig. 5-25 show the method of connection. The resistances in the emitter leads of each transistor are necessary to equalize the currents.

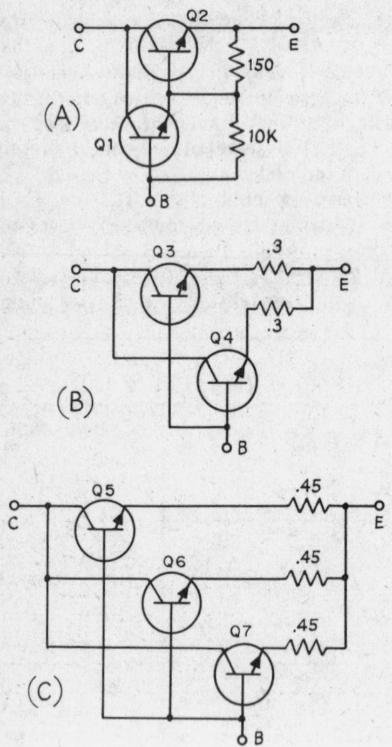

Fig. 5-25 – At A, a Darlington-connected pair for use as the pass element in a series-regulating circuit. At B and C, the method of connecting two or more transistors in parallel for high current output. Resistances are in ohms. The circuit at A may be used for load currents from 100 mA to 5 A, at B for currents from 6 to 10 A, and at C for currents from 9 to 15 A.

Q1 – Motorola MJE 340 or equivalent.
Q2-Q7, incl. – Power transistor such as 2N3055 or 2N3772.

Fixed-Voltage IC Regulators

IC regulators with all circuitry contained on a single silicon chip are becoming available for different values of fixed-voltage outputs. The LM309 five-volt regulator, manufactured by National Semiconductor and others, is one type of such ICs. These regulators are three-terminal devices, for making connections to the positive unregulated input, positive regulated output, and ground. They are designed for local regulation on digital-logic circuit-board cards to eliminate the distribution problems associated with single-point regulation. For this reason they are frequently called **on-card regulators.**

The LM309 is available in two common transistor packages. The LM309H in a TO-5 package can deliver output currents in excess of 200 mA if adequate heat sinking is provided, and the LM309K in the TO-3 power package can provide an output current greater than 1 A. The regulator is essentially blow-out proof, with current limiting included in the circuit. In addition, thermal shutdown is provided to keep the IC from overheating. If internal dissipation becomes too great, the regulator will shut down to prevent excessive heating.

It is not necessary to bypass the output of the LM309, although bypassing does improve immunity from transient responses. Input bypassing is needed, however, if the regulator is located very far from the filter capacitor of the power supply. Typical values of input bypass capacitance are 0.15 and 0.22 μF. Although designed primarily as a fixed-voltage regulator, the LM309 can be used to obtain a regulated output at voltages higher than five. This is done by returning the "ground" connection of the IC to a tap point on a voltage divider which is connected between the regulated output and a true circuit ground. An adjustable output regulator for voltages above five can be had if the "ground" pin is connected to the junction of a 300-ohm fixed resistor and one end of a 1000-ohm linear control. The opposite end of the 300-ohm resistor should be connected to the output pin, and the wiper contact and third lug of the control to a true circuit ground.

Switching Regulator

Switching regulators are used when it is necessary or desired to minimize power losses which would otherwise occur in the series pass transistor (or transistors) with large variations in input or output voltages. The basic operation of the switching regulator, known as the flyback type, may be understood by referring to Fig. 5-26A. Assume that the switch is closed and the circuit has been in operation long enough to stabilize. The voltage across the load, R_L, is zero, and the current through L is limited only by R_I, the internal resistance of the inductor. At the instant the switch is opened, the voltage across the load goes to a value higher than the source voltage, E, because of the series-aiding or "flyback" effect of the inductor. When the magnetic lines of flux about the inductor collapse completely, the voltage across R_L will be equal to that of the source (minus the small voltage drop across R_I). Each time the switch is closed and then opened, the process is repeater. By opening and closing the switch rapidly, voltage pulses may be applied across R_L which are higher than the dc input voltage. A capacitor may be connected across R_L to produce a dc output voltage. To keep the capacitor from discharging when the switch is closed, a diode can be connected in series with the load and its parallel-connected capacitor.

In a practical switching-regulator circuit the switching is performed by a transistor, as shown at B of Fig. 5-26. The transistor may be driven by any number of circuits. In the practical circuit shown later (Fig. 5-27) four sections make up the driving circuit, as shown in block diagram form in Fig. 5-26B. The oscillator triggers the monostable multivibrator and determines the frequency of operation. The sensor measures the output voltage and controls the pulse width of the multivibrator accordingly. The monostable multivibrator combines the signals from the oscillator and sensor to produce the correct pulse width. The driver receives the multivibrator output and drives the power transistor, Q1.

The voltage step-up capability of the inductor has been mentioned briefly. However, in choosing the value of the inductor, energy is an important consideration. During the time the transistor is turned on, the inductor stores energy. This energy is added to the supply and delivered to the load when the transistor turns off. The total energy must be enough to supply the load and maintain output voltage. As the load is increased, the transistor must remain on longer in order to store more energy in the inductor. The required value of inductance depends on frequency of operation, duty cycle, and load. A linear change in current through the inductor is a desirable condition and indicates operation is over a small segment of the inductor's charging and discharging curve. A powdered-iron-core inductor is normally used to

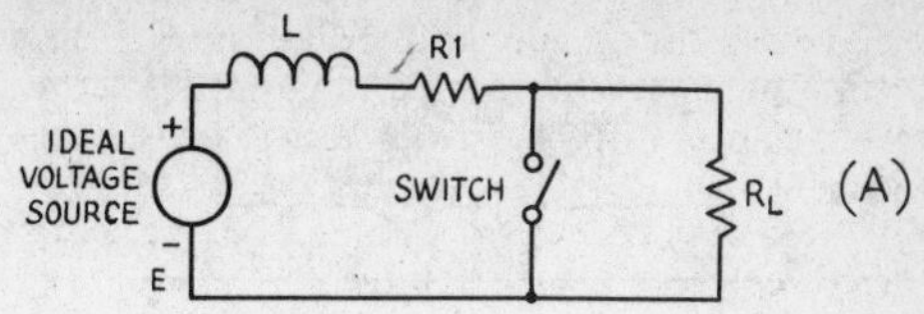

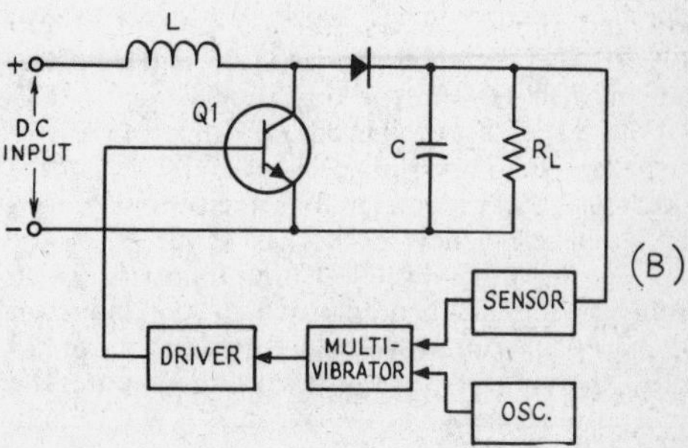

Fig. 5-26 – At A, the fundamental circuit of a flyback switching regulator, and at B, the elements of a practical circuit.

prevent a large inductance change with increased current.

Efficiency of the circuit depends mainly upon the switching and saturation losses of the power transistor. The peak current through the transistor is considerably greater than the input current. The flyback diode must have a fast reverse recovery time and low forward drop. There will be a large current spike through the transistor if the diode is slow.

The complete circuit of a switching regulator is given in Fig. 5-27. This regulator will handle 100 watts of power efficiently, at output voltages as much as 6 volts above the input voltage. The switching rate of the regulator is 9 kHz, and it operates with an input of 22 to 28 volts. Regula-

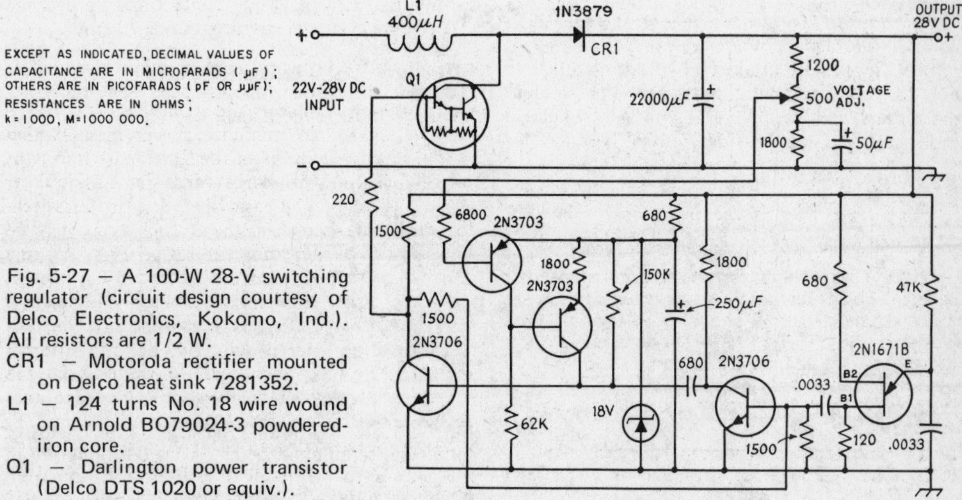

Fig. 5-27 – A 100-W 28-V switching regulator (circuit design courtesy of Delco Electronics, Kokomo, Ind.). All resistors are 1/2 W.

CR1 – Motorola rectifier mounted on Delco heat sink 7281352.

L1 – 124 turns No. 18 wire wound on Arnold BO79024-3 powdered-iron core.

Q1 – Darlington power transistor (Delco DTS 1020 or equiv.).

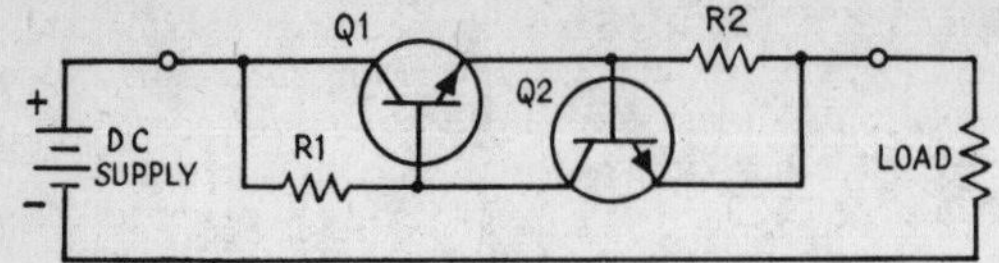

Fig. 5-28 – Two-terminal current limiter. See text for discussion of component values and types.

tion and ripple are less than 1 percent at full output. The switching device, Q1, is a commercially available Darlington transistor.

The efficiency of the circuit drops off at low power levels. This is because the losses of the circuit are not proportional to the output power. Maximum efficiency occurs at about 80 watts because the duty cycle of the transistor is an optimum for the chosen value of the inductor. Whenever the input voltage increases above 28 volts, the output voltage tracks the input. The difference between the two voltages is the drop in the flyback diode.

Output voltage variations resulting from changes in ambient temperature are caused by two major factors; positive temperature coefficient of the Zener diode, and the negative temperature coefficient of the emitter-base junctions of the transistors. One way to compensate partially for temperature is to connect diodes that have negative temperature coefficients in series with the Zener diode.

Two-Terminal Current Limiter

The simple circuit of Fig. 5-28 performs the current limiting function of fuses or circuit breakers with greater speed, accuracy, reliability and automatic resetting. Fuses and circuit breakers are commonly used for protection of dc power supplies or experimental solid state devices under test and development, but such protective devices are not fast enough to cope with instantaneous overcurrents. The circuit uses only two transistors and two resistors. The necessary supply voltage for operation is obtained from the power source being protected, with the load functioning as the return to the power source. Q1 is a series element which allows current, up to a desired maximum, to flow to the load. R1 provides a suitable bias for Q1 to permit such current to flow. R2 is a sensing resistor interposed between the series transistor and the load, and provides bias for Q2. Normally this bias is low enough to prevent Q2 from conducting. Q2 controls the bias applied to Q1. When excess current flows through R2 as a result of a circuit malfunction or a short across the load, the voltage drop across R2 rises, biasing Q2 into conduction. When Q2 turns on, it reduces the bias on Q1 and limits the amount of current flow. The maximum amount of current flow can be varied by changing the value of R2. If an adjustable limiting level is desired, R2 may be a variable resistor. The limiting level is an inverse function of the resistance value.

The current limiter works equally well with germanium or silicon, or npn or pnp types of semiconductors (so long as proper polarities are observed). The circuit values are not critical but one must not exceed the maximum voltage rating or the dissipation rating of the components used, as in any other circuit. The voltage and dissipation ratings are the only actual limiting factors in using this circuit; the device ratings may be scaled up or down depending on their utilization. For protecting micro-circuitry (low current protection), for example, Q1 and Q2 may be 2N4401 silicon npn 310-mW audio transistors. If R1 is 10,000 ohms and R2 is 350 ohms, the current will be limited to approximately 2 mA with a 9-V supply. If R1 is changed to 820 ohms and R2 changed to 24 ohms, the current will be limited to approximately 30 mA. With fixed resistance values and with a fixed voltage input, the limited current value will be somewhat dependent upon the beta of the transistors. If regulation is of concern, germanium transistors will exhibit less voltage drop, and R2 may be made only about 1/3 the value for equivalent limiting with silicon transistors.

BIAS SUPPLIES

Bias supplies are used to provide grid voltage to the PA and modulator stages of amateur transmitters, to supply grid voltage to linear amplifiers, and to provide control voltage for cutting off receiver and transmitter output. Negative bias voltage is also used for grid-block keying in most modern amateur exciters.

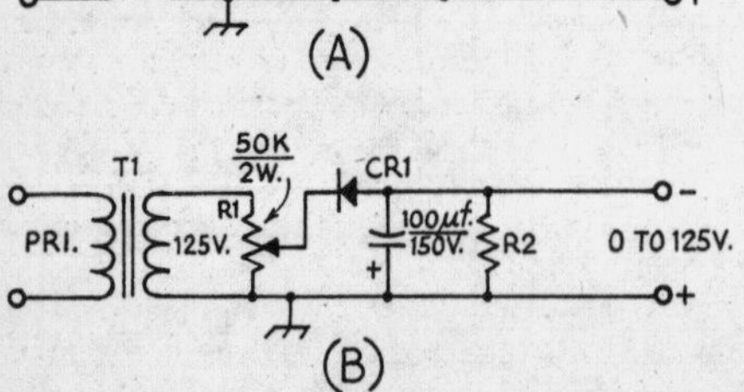

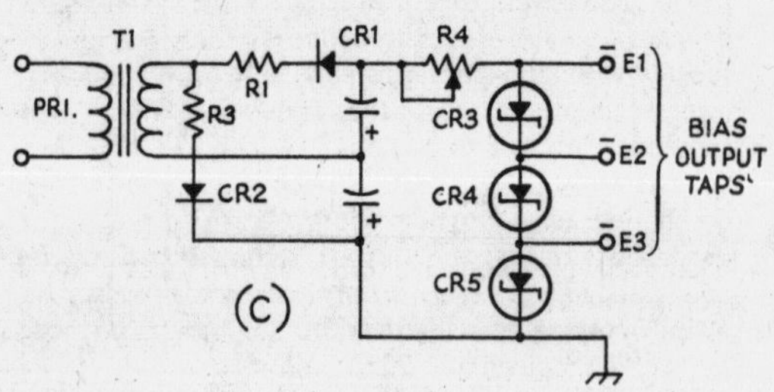

Fig. 5-29 – Circuits of typical bias supplies using solid-state rectifiers. The circuit at B is preferred if the bias is to be supplied to a Class C amplifier stage. Zener-diode regulation is shown at C.

Typical circuits for bias supplies are shown in Fig. 5-29. At A, a simple half-wave rectifier (CR1) provides dc voltage to R1, which is adjusted for the desired output. If the bias is being fed to a Class C amplifier, the circuit at B is preferred. R1 is used to set the bias voltage at the desired level and R2 is the value that would ordinarily be used as a grid-leak resistor for the Class C stage. No other grid resistor should be used.

A voltage-doubler bias supply is shown at C. T1 is chosen to provide the desired output voltage, when doubled, while allowing for the voltage drop across R4. Zener diodes are connected in series (CR3 through CR5, incl.) to offer regulation and to enable the user to obtain three different bias voltages. The Zener diodes are selected for the operating voltages required. Fewer, or more, Zener diodes can be connected in the string, or a single Zener diode can be used. R4 is adjusted to provide the proper Zener-diode current for the string, and its wattage must be sufficient to handle the current flowing through it. R2 and R3 are current-limiting resistors to protect CR1 and CR2.

Of course, full-wave center-tapped and full-wave bridge rectifiers can be used in place of the half-wave examples shown in Fig. 5-29. Similarly, voltage triplers can be used in bias supplies. The full-wave rectifiers are easier to filter and may be preferred for some applications.

CONSTRUCTION OF POWER SUPPLIES

The length of most leads in a power supply is unimportant, so the arrangement of components from this consideration is not a factor. More important are the points of good high-voltage insulation, adequate conductor size for filament wiring – and most important of all – safety to the operator. Exposed high-voltage terminals or wiring which might be bumped into accidentally should not be permitted to exist. They should be covered with adequate insulation or made inaccessible to contact during normal operation and adjustment of the transmitter. Power-supply units should be fused individually. All negative terminals of plate supplies and positive terminals of bias supplies should be securely grounded to the chassis, and the chassis connected to a waterpipe or radiator ground. All transformer, choke, and capacitor cases should also be grounded to the chassis. Ac power cords and chassis connectors should be arranged so that exposed contacts are never "live." Starting at the conventional ac wall outlet which is female, one end of the cord should be fitted with a male plug. The other end of the cord should have a female receptacle. The input connector of the power supply should have a male receptacle to fit the female receptacle of the cord. The power-output connector on the power supply should be a female socket, never a male type. A male plug to fit this socket should be connected to the cable going to the equipment. The opposite end of the cable should be fitted with a female connector, and the series should terminate with a male connector on the equipment. There should be no "live" exposed contacts at any point, regardless of where a disconnection may be made.

Rectifier filament leads should be kept short to assure proper voltage at the rectifier socket. Through a metal chassis, grommet-lined clearance holes will serve for voltages up to 500 or 750, but ceramic feedthrough insulators should be used for higher voltages. Bleeder and voltage-dropping resistors should be placed where they are open to air circulation. Placing them in a confined space reduces the rating. Other precautions are given earlier in this chapter, in the section on power-line considerations.

ADJUSTABLE REGULATED TRANSISTOR POWER SUPPLY

This power supply will develop from 3.5 to 21 volts at 1.5 amperes. These capabilities should prove adequate for powering most solid-state devices, or for general-purpose use as a bench supply for solid-state projects. An RCA CA3055 integrated-circuit regulator and a 2N3055 pass transistor are the only active components needed beyond those of a simple unregulated supply. The design includes short-circuit protection, so that a dead short across the output terminals will cause no damage to the supply, even though the output-voltage control may be set for maximum.

The Circuit

A potential of approximately 26 volts is delivered by the bridge rectifier and 3000-μF filter capacitor to the regulator section of the circuit. The conduction of Q1 is governed by the voltage applied to its base from the output of U1, thereby controlling the output voltage. U1 contains its own Zener reference diode. The regulated output voltage is adjusted with R2. R1, a 56-ohm fixed resistor, establishes the limiting value for the current delivered to the load. Increasing the value of this shutdown resistor will decrease the maximum available current, and vice versa. The function is approximately linear in inverse proportion – halving the resistance value doubles the value at which the output current is limited. The 56-ohm value of Fig. 2 was selected to maintain a current level within the maximum ratings of T1 and Q1 in the event a short circuit of extended duration was connected across the output. A variable control, such as a 1000-ohm value, could be placed in series with R1 to provide

Fig. 1 — The regulated power supply is housed in a homemade two-piece metal box. Binding posts are used for the dc output, neither side of which is grounded. The third jack is a ground connected to the case. On-off and meter switches flank the meter. The knob at the lower left is mounted on the voltage-control potentiometer.

for adjustable current limiting at the regulated output.

A 0- to 3-mA meter, M1, is used to monitor either the output voltage or the output current, with selection made at S2. R3 serves as the shunt element for current measurements, and R4 plus R5 serve as the multiplier resistors for voltage measurements. R3 is homemade from a 1 1/2-inch length of No. 30 copper wire, wound over a 1-megohm 1/2 watt resistor. This shunt causes M1 to indicate at full scale with a load current of 1.5 amperes. With meter movements other than that specified in the parts list, it may be necessary to alter the length of wire for the desired current range. In any event, the current readings should be checked against an ammeter having reliable calibration.

The meter is calibrated to read half scale at 15 volts with S2 in the VOLTAGE position. Calibration adjustment is made with R4 against a known standard.

Construction

The power supply is built into a two-piece cabinet assembly. The bottom piece serves as the main chassis, front panel, and rear panel. The top piece serves also as the sides. Figs. 1 and 3 show the arrangement of parts used in this model, although the layout is not critical. Neither the positive nor the negative side of the output connections is grounded to the chassis. Instead, three binding posts are used, the third being connected to the chassis. By appropriate jumpering at the front-panel binding posts, either a negative-ground or a positive-ground output may be used.

Most of the small circuit components are mounted on a piece of etched circuit board which

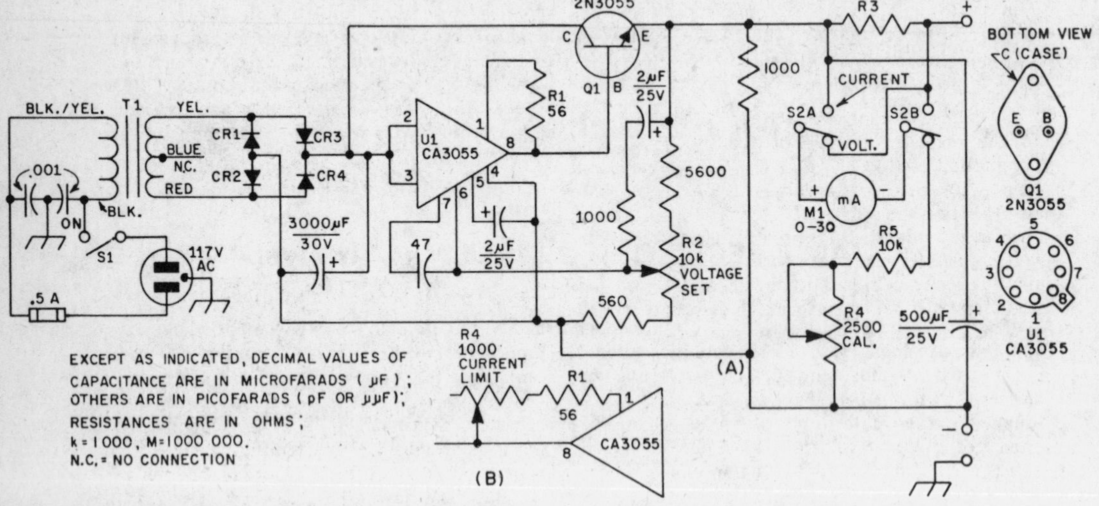

Fig. 2 — Circuit of the transistor power supply. Resistances are in ohms; resistors are 1/2 watt 10-percent tolerance unless otherwise noted. Capacitors with polarity indicated are electrolytic; others are ceramic.

CR1-CR4, incl. — 100 PRV 3 A (Motorola 1N4720 or equiv.)
M1 — 0-3 mA (Knight 701-0021 or equiv.)
Q1 — Silicon npn power transistor, 2N3055 (Radio Shack Archer 276-592 suitable).
R1, R5 — For text reference.
R2 — Linear taper, panel mount.
R3 — See text.
R4 — Linear taper, printed-circuit type.
S1 — Spst.
S2 — Dpdt.
T1 — Primary 117 V; 21-V, 1.5-A secondary (Stancor TP-4 or equiv.)
U1 — Integrated circuit voltage regulator, RCA CA3055.

Fig. 3 – View of the regulated transistor supply from the side. The transistor mounted in the U-shaped heat sink is Q1. The rectifiers, CR1 through CR4, are mounted beneath the meter on a tie point strip, and are partially hidden in this view. The large capacitor sitting atop the etched circuit board is the 3000-μF filter capacitor connected at the rectifier output.

is mounted vertically. This board is visible in Fig. 3 between the front panel and the homemade heat sink for Q1. Components in the metering circuit are mounted on tie-point strips located near the front panel.

The case of Q1 must be insulated from the chassis. A mica washer coated with silicone grease and insulating sleeves for the mounting screws should be used.

A HEAVY-DUTY REGULATED SUPPLY

This power supply is designed to be used with fm transceivers in the 25-watt class. It is a regulated supply with voltage adjustment from 0 to 15 volts and with current limiting to 5 amperes. It also makes an excellent general-purpose bench supply to power solid-state devices.

Circuit Details

A Motorola MC1466L integrated-circuit regulator is used in the supply. Two parallel-connected 2N3055s are used for the pass transistors to handle the current loads. The design of the supply includes short-circuit protection, so that a dead short across the output terminals will cause no damage to the supply, even at maximum output voltage.

A voltage of approximately 25 volts is delivered to the regulator section of the MC1466L. The conduction of Q1 and Q2, a Darlington-connected pair, is governed by the voltage applied to the base of Q1 from the output of U1, thereby controlling the output voltage. R4 is used to adjust the output voltage and R5 can be set to establish the current limiting value delivered to the load. M1 is a 0 – 15-volt meter for monitoring the output voltage and M2 is a 0 – 10-ampere meter for current monitoring.

Construction Information

The supply is housed in a cabinet, 11-1/2 × 7-1/2 × 4-3/4 inches. This is a commercial cabinet manufactured by Apollo Products, Box 245, Vaughnsville, OH 45893. However, any suitable enclosure will serve. The MC1466L, Q1, Q2, and

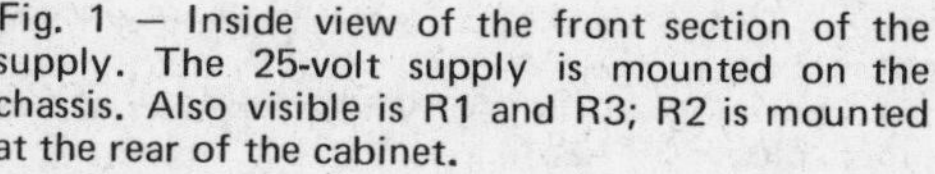

Fig. 1 – Inside view of the front section of the supply. The 25-volt supply is mounted on the chassis. Also visible is R1 and R3; R2 is mounted at the rear of the cabinet.

associated components are mounted in an etched circuit board. The 25-volt supply that provides the regulator voltage to pins 7, 13 and 14 of U2 is also mounted on an etched board. The pass transistors, Q3 and Q4, are installed on a heat sink which is mounted on the rear of the chassis.

Fig. 2 – Here is the back portion of the supply showing the etched board for U1 and associated components. Rectifiers CR1 and CR2 are mounted on a homemade bracket which is installed on the chassis.

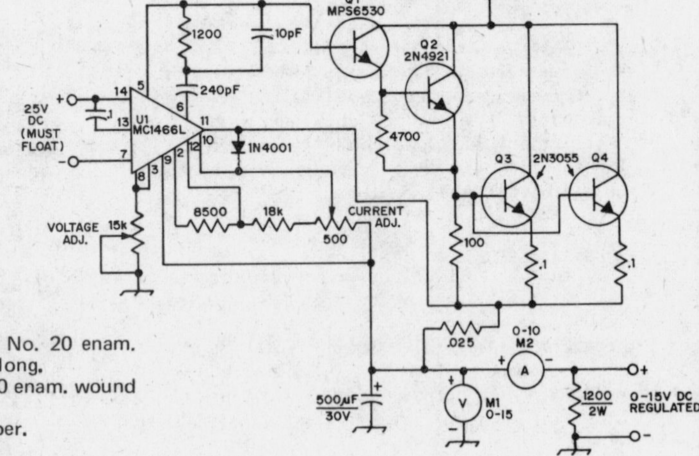

Fig. 3 – Schematic diagram of the regulated supply. Resistances are in ohms; resistors are 1/2 watt unless otherwise specified. Capacitors with polarity indicated are electrolytic, others are disk ceramic.

M1 – 0-15 V (Calectro D1-920 suitable).
M2 – 0-10 A (Calectro D1-917 suitable).
Q1 – Motorola MPS6530 or equiv.
Q2 – 2N4921.
Q3, Q4 – 2N3055.
R1, R2 – 0.1 ohm, 9.66 feet of No. 20 enam. wound on 1/4-inch form, 1-inch long.
R3 – .025 ohm; 2.42 feet of No. 20 enam. wound on 1/4-inch form, 1-inch long.
R4 – 15,000-ohm control, linear taper.
R5 – 500-ohm control, linear taper.

A UNIVERSAL POWER SUPPLY FOR THE AMATEUR STATION

Presented here is a general-purpose unit with provisions for 117-220-volt operation, and it is adapted easily for use with most commercially available gear by constructing appropriate power cords. The supply delivers 800 V at 300 mA dc, 300 V at 175 mA dc, and 0 to -130 V at 25 mA. In addition the supply provides ac filament potentials of 6.3 V at 11 A or 12.6 V at 5.5 A.

Often the station power supply is a heavy black box that is tucked away in a corner and just sits there. A large cable interconnects this device with the station transmitter or transceiver and the amateur never comes directly in contact with it; all of the supply functions are remotely controlled

Fig. 1 – The Universal Power Supply is constructed on a standard-size aluminum chassis. Back-to-back plugs with appropriate jumper wires make changing from 117-V to 220-V input operation or from 6.3-V to 12.6-V filament operation a simple matter of reversing a plug.

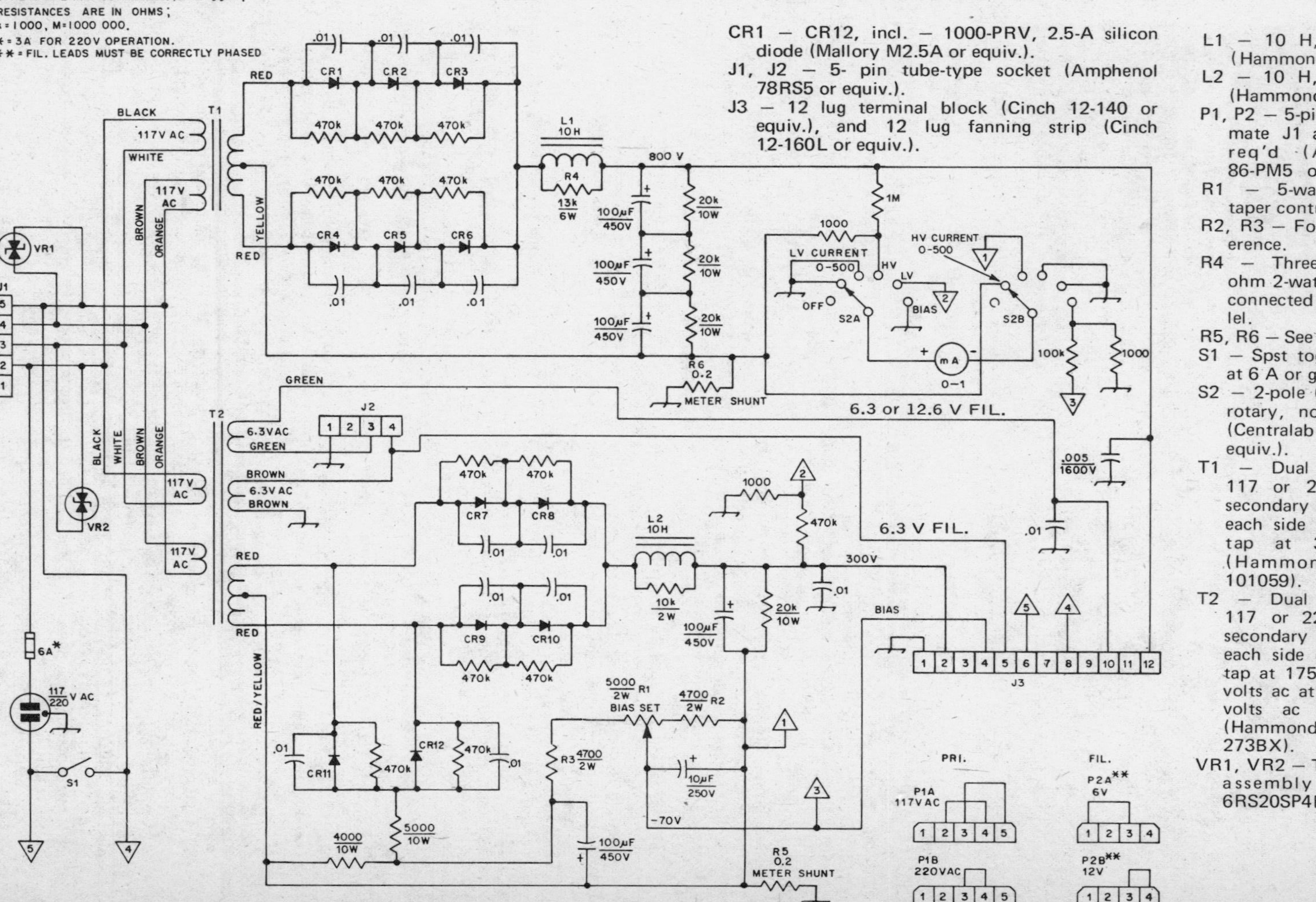

Fig. 2 — Circuit diagram for the Universal Power Supply. Component designations not listed below are for text reference.

CR1 — CR12, incl. — 1000-PRV, 2.5-A silicon diode (Mallory M2.5A or equiv.).
J1, J2 — 5- pin tube-type socket (Amphenol 78RS5 or equiv.).
J3 — 12 lug terminal block (Cinch 12-140 or equiv.), and 12 lug fanning strip (Cinch 12-160L or equiv.).
L1 — 10 H, 200 mA (Hammond 193J).
L2 — 10 H, 300 mA (Hammond 193M).
P1, P2 — 5-pin plugs to mate J1 and J2, 4 req'd (Amphenol 86-PM5 or equiv.).
R1 — 5-watt linear-taper control.
R2, R3 — For text reference.
R4 — Three 39,000-ohm 2-watt resistors connected in parallel.
R5, R6 — See text.
S1 — Spst toggle rated at 6 A or greater.
S2 — 2-pole 6-position rotary, nonshorting (Centralab 1411 or equiv.).
T1 — Dual primary, 117 or 220 V ac; secondary 890 volts each side of center tap at 300 mA (Hammond type 101059).
T2 — Dual primary, 117 or 220 V ac; secondary 350 volts each side of center tap at 175 mA, 6.3 volts ac at 6 A, 6.3 volts ac at 5 A (Hammond special 273BX).
VR1, VR2 — Thyrector assembly (G E 6RS20SP4B4).

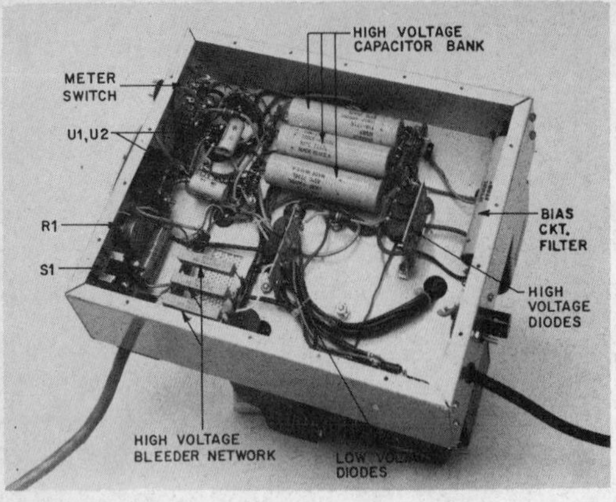

Fig. 3 — Bottom view of the Universal Power Supply.

from the panel of the station transmitting gear. But what happens if an instance arises where a particular voltage (or combination of voltages) is needed for an experimental project? Can that "black box" in the corner be pressed readily into service? And what about the amateur who buys two power supplies for his station because his mobile transceiver cannot be plugged directly into his home-station transmitter power supply? This supply is designed to fill all these needs.

Many of today's commercially available ac supplies are not equipped for 220-volt operation. If the station includes a two-kilowatt amplifier, a separate 220-volt line should be available in the shack. Blinking house lights are not always a result of running a high-powered amplifier. It could be caused by the intermittent 400- or 500-watt load presented by an exciter power supply to the 117-volt source. Connecting the exciter supply to a 220-volt outlet (providing a dual-primary transformer is used) can be helpful in this regard.

Circuit Details

The supply is shown in Figs. 1 through 3. Primary power may be applied to the supply in two ways. First, terminals 6 and 8 of J3 may be shorted together; this is normally the function of the station transmitting equipment on-off switch (see Fig. 2). On the other hand, S1 may be actuated when the supply is used independently. Transient voltages on the ac line are eliminated by Thyrector assemblies VR1 and VR2.

Full-wave rectification is employed in the secondary circuit of each power transformer to develop the three dc operating voltages. Choke-input filtering provides adequate regulation of both the 300- and 800-volt outputs. Both L1 and L2 are shunted with suitable resistors to reduce the possibility of diode damage when primary power to the supply is removed.

The bias voltage is adjustable and may be set to any value between −40 and −80. Should a range between −80 and −130 volts be required, R1 may be interchanged with R3. Likewise, if a range from 0 to −40 volts is needed, R1 may be swapped with R2.

Metering

A six-position switch and a 0-1-mA meter allows monitoring of high and low voltages, the current for each of these, and the bias voltage. The sixth position permits the meter to be disabled. The meter shunts for both current positions of S2 are homemade and provide a full-scale reading of 500 mA on each range. The proper resistance for the shunts is determined by dividing the meter internal resistance (approximately 100 ohms in this case) by 500, and is equal to 0.2 ohm. No. 30 enameled copper wire has a resistance of 105 ohms per 1000 feet, or 0.105 ohm per foot. Extending the division another step, one inch of wire has a resistance of .008 ohm. Approximately 23 inches of wire provided the correct value for the shunts. Each 23-inch length of wire is wound on a 100,000-ohm, two-watt composition resistor which serves as a form.

Construction

The supply is built on a 10 × 8 × 3-inch aluminum chassis. The spot welds at the four corners are reinforced with No. 6 hardware since the transformers are quite heavy. The total weight of the completed supply is slightly more than 40 pounds. Several one-inch-diameter holes are cut in the chassis bottom plate to allow adequate air circulation.

All of the power-supply output voltages are present on a 12-connection terminal block. The end of the cable used to interconnect the supply to the station transceiver is equipped with a 12-lug fanning strip, providing a convenient means to disconnect it.

One special wiring precaution is necessary; the bleeder resistors for both the high and low-voltage circuits should be mounted in the clear to allow plenty of air circulation around them. Perforated aluminum stock is placed over a 1 × 3-inch cut in the chassis which is directly above the mounting position for the 800-volt bleeder network.

Operation

Two jumper plugs are mounted "back-to-back", making the change from 117-volt operation to 220 volts a simple matter of reversing P1. P2 performs an identical function to select 6 or 12 volts for the filament line.

The cost for this project should be under $100, even if all of the parts are purchased new. The price of the two power transformers and two filter chokes comprises approximately 60 percent of the total cost.[1]

---

[1] A package including the two power transformers and the two filter chokes is available from Hammond Manufacturing Company, Inc., 1051 Clinton Street, Buffalo, NY 14240, for approximately $60. In Canada, the address is Hammond Mfg. Co., Ltd., 394 Edinburgh Rd., North Guelph, Ontario. Catalog available.

A 3000-VOLT POWER SUPPLY

This high-voltage power supply may be used with linear amplifiers that are capable of operating at maximum legal input power levels. It was designed for use with a one-kilowatt 3-500Z amplifier, but with minor modifications to the control circuitry to suit individual circumstances it can be used with amplifiers having a pair of 3-500Z tubes, a single 3-1000Z, 4-1000A, or any tube or tubes calling for 2500 to 3000 volts at up to 700 mA. Examples of such amplifiers may be found in Chapter 6.

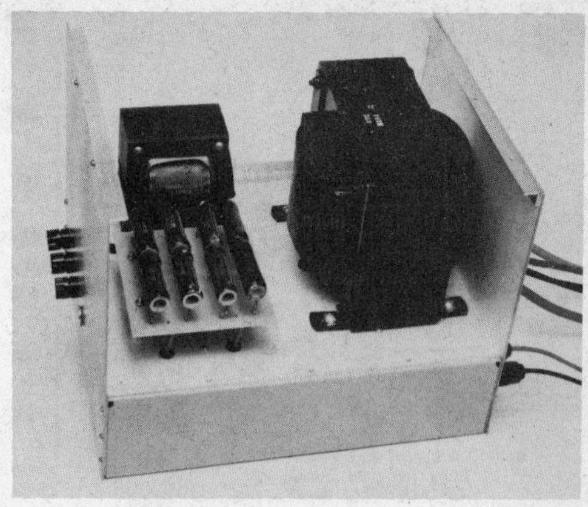

Fig. 1 – Top chassis view of the 3000-volt power supply as constructed by WA1JZC. The circuit board in the foreground holds the bleeder resistors, which are spaced apart and supported a short distance above the board for proper cooling. The large transformer is for the high-voltage supply, and the small transformer provides filament power for the amplifier.

The Circuit

A voltage-doubler circuit connected to the secondary of T1 provides approximately 3000 volts dc. See Fig. 3. The primary of T1 can be operated from either a 117-volt line or a 220-volt source; the latter voltage is preferred. VR1 and VR2 are suppressors included to prevent transients from damaging the high-voltage capacitor bank or the rectifier diodes. Since T1 has two 117-volt primary windings, a suppressor is connected across each. The windings and suppressors are connected in parallel for 117-volt operation, and they are series connected for a 220-volt line.

A relay (K1) is necessary to switch the high-current inrush when the supply is activated. Ordinary toggle switches cannot be used to activate the power supply directly. Surge protection is accomplished by placing R1 in series with one lead of the ac line. K2B shorts out this resistor a few seconds after the main power switch (S1, located on the amplifier front panel) is actuated. A separate line cord for the power supply allows this section to be operated on 220 volts while permitting other circuits in the amplifier to operate on 117 volts. The 120 volts needed to energize the coil of K2 are taken from a half-wave rectified dc supply located on the amplifier chassis. Note that the B-minus terminal is held a few volts above ground by the 15-ohm, 2-watt resistor, for metering purposes in the companion amplifier.

Construction

The power supply is built on a standard 10 × 12 × 3-inch aluminum chassis. Construction is straightforward, as can be seen from Figs. 1 and 2. The front and rear panels are made from 9 × 10-inch pieces of 1/16-inch thick aluminum, and the bottom plate and the U-shaped top cover are made out of perforated aluminum stock.

The primary and control-circuit components, as well as the rectifier board and capacitor bank, are mounted underneath the chassis. Reasonable care must be taken to prevent any part of the primary or control wiring from coming into contact with the high-voltage components. Each of the 100-μF capacitors in the capacitor bank is shunted by a 25,000-ohm, 20-watt wirewound resistor. These resistors equalize the voltage drops across the series-connected capacitors, and also serve as the bleeder resistance. Since these resistors get quite hot during normal operation, they are mounted away from the electrolytic capacitors on a separate circuit board above the chassis, to allow for adequate ventilation. The other large heat-generating components are the power and filament

Fig. 2 – The primary and control-circuit components are grouped at the bottom, with the high-voltage capacitor bank and rectifier board occupying the upper portion of this bottom chassis view of the power supply. R1 is visible in the lower right-hand corner.

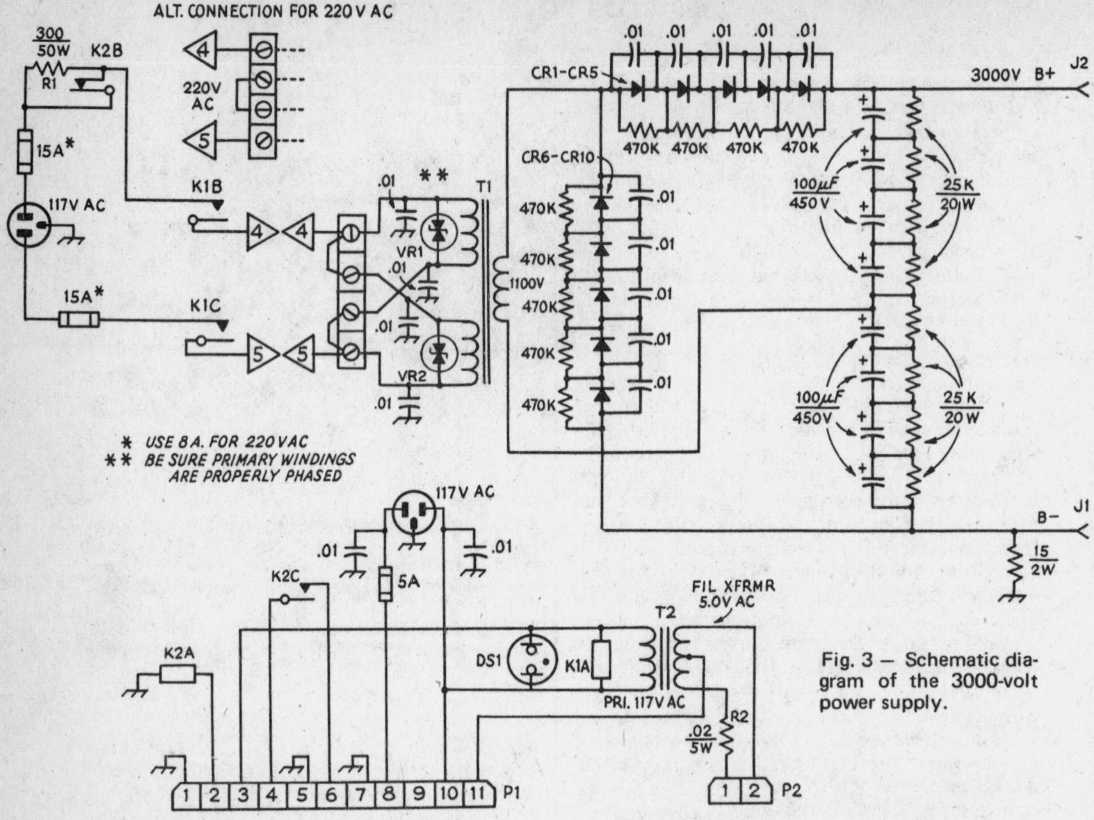

Fig. 3 — Schematic diagram of the 3000-volt power supply.

CR1 — CR10, inc. — 1000-PRV, 2.5-A (Mallory M2.5A or equiv.).
DS1 — 117-volt ac neon pilot lamp assembly.
J1, J2 — High-voltage chassis connector (Millen 37001). K1 — Power relay, dpdt, 117-volt coil (Potter and Brumfeld PR-11AY or equiv.).
K2 — Dpdt 10 A contacts, 120-V dc coil (Potter and Brumfeld KA11DG or equiv.).
P1 — Cable-mounted 11-pin power connector.
P2 — Cable-mounted 2-pin power connector.
R2 — 8 feet No. 14 enam. wire wound on 3-inch long, 3/4-inch dia Plexiglas rod.
T1 — Dual 117-volt primary, 1100-V secondary, 600 VA (Berkshire 6181 or equiv.).
T2 — 117-volt primary; secondary 5.0 volts at 15 A (Stancor P6433 or equiv.).
VR1, VR2 — Transient-voltage suppressor, 120-volt (General Electric 6RS20SP4B4 or equiv.).

transformers (T1 and T2), which are also mounted above chassis.

A small etched circuit board supports CR1 through CR10 and their associated equalizing resistors and transient-suppressing disk capacitors. In actual operation, the filament voltage measured at the amplifier tube socket exceeded the maximum voltage recommended by the tube manufacturer slightly, so R2 was included to reduce the voltage to a suitable value. To avoid excessive voltage drop in the cable connecting T2 with the amplifier, it is recommended that the cable be made of No. 10 wire or larger (in many cases, R2 will not be necessary).

NICKEL-CADMIUM BATTERY CHARGER

Any advantage that a NiCad (nickel-cadmium) battery may have over other types can be lost through improper charging. This information concerning NiCad charging techniques was contributed by WAØUZO. NiCads can even be ruined on the *first* recharging cycle. If connected to a constant-voltage source, initial current may be quite high. Normally, no damage would result unless the battery voltage is low (fully discharged). Using a constant current for battery charging is permissible at the start of the charging cycle, however, as the battery reaches full charge, the voltage may rise to an excessive value.

The correct solution is a combination of the two methods. Any circuit used for charging NiCads should limit both the current and voltage, such as the one described here.

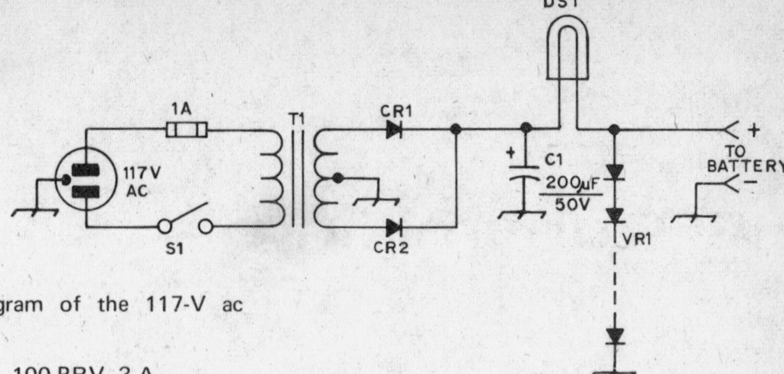

Fig. 1 — Schematic diagram of the 117-V ac charger.
C1 — Electrolytic.
CR1, CR2 — Silicon diodes, 100 PRV, 3 A.
DS1 — See text.
T1 — Primary 117 V ac, secondary 25.6 V at 500 mA. Calectro D1-752 (or equiv.).
VR1 — See text.

Some other precautions which should be observed while charging NiCads are:

1) Battery temperature should be between 40°and 80°F. It should never exceed 100°F.

2) Two or more batteries with the same voltage rating may be charged in parallel, but be sure that the charger has sufficient current capability.

3) Check the manufacturer's data sheet for the maximum allowable charging rate. A typical figure would be ten percent of the ampere-hour rating (a 10-ampere-hour battery would require a current of 1A).

4) Do not attempt to charge two batteries in series with a constant current unless the batteries are of the same type and capacity, and are in the same state of charge (voltage on one may be excessive).

5) To determine the approximate charging time, divide the ampere-hour rating by the charging current used, and multiply the resulting time by 1.25.

Suitable Charging Circuits

Figs. 1 and 2 show two versions of the same basic charging circuit. The circuit shown in Fig. 1 is used with 117 V ac, and the one in Fig. 2 can be used with the car battery. The latter circuit could be connected to the cigarette lighter, and is suitable for battery packs of up to 14 volts.

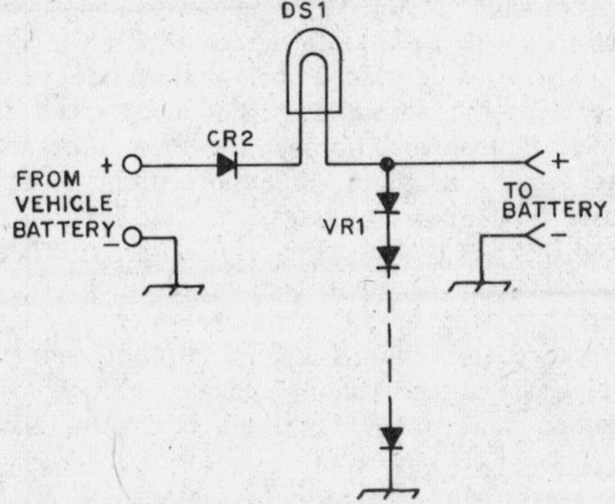

Fig. 2 — Schematic diagram of NiCad battery charger suitable for mobile use. See text for explanation of DS1 and VR1. CR2 protects the components in the event of accidental reversal of input leads. See Fig. 1 for CR2.

The dial lamp (DS1) is used to limit the current. One with a rating of 100 to 150 mA should work fine with most batteries. The voltage rating should be approximately that of the charging source (for example, two 12-V bulbs in series may be necessary if a 26-V supply is used).

The voltage regulator shown in Fig. 3 is based on the fact that a forward-biased diode will not conduct until approximately 0.75 V dc is applied. By adding a suitable number of diodes in series as shown, a voltage regulator for the maximum battery voltage can be built easily. The circuit shown in Fig. 3 can be used in either Fig. 1 or 2, for VR1. It will draw little current until the battery voltage reaches a permissible value during charge. Once the voltage reaches a preset level, the diodes start to conduct and limit any further increases.

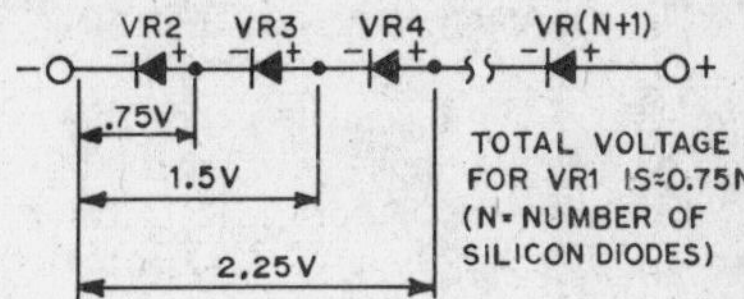

Fig. 3 — Schematic diagram of the voltage regulator (VR1, Figs. 1 and 2).

Initial Testing

After the circuit is wired and checked, apply power (without a battery connected for charging). The bulb should light to less than full brilliance. Measure the voltage across the regulator. It should be 3 to 8 percent above the rated voltage of the batteries to be charged. Adding or removing some diodes in VR1 may be necessary. Connect the discharged batteries and measure the charging current (either a built-in meter could be used, or a temporary one could be connected in series with the battery). The current should be typically 100 mA with partially discharged batteries. The current will decrease as the charging time increases, and a value of 5 mA indicates a fully charged condition. No damage will result if the batteries are left on charge continuously.

Chapter 6

HF Transmitting

Regardless of the transmission mode – code, a-m, fm, single sideband, radioteletype, amateur TV – vacuum tubes and semiconductors are common elements in all transmitters. They are used as oscillators, amplifiers, frequency multipliers and frequency converters. These four building blocks, plus suitable power supplies, are basically all that is required to make any of the popular transmission systems.

The simplest code transmitter is a keyed oscillator working directly into the antenna; a more elaborate (and practical) code transmitter, the type popular with many beginners, will include one or more frequency-multiplication stages and one or more power-amplifier stages. Any code transmitter will obviously require a means for keying it. The bare skeleton is shown in Figs. 6-2A and B. The rf generating and amplifying sections of a double-sideband phone transmitter (a-m or fm) are similar to those of a code transmitter.

The overall design depends primarily upon the bands in which operation is desired and the power output. A simple oscillator with satisfactory frequency stability may be used as a transmitter at the lower frequencies, but the power output obtainable is small. As a general rule, the output of the oscillator is fed into one or more amplifiers to bring the power fed to the antenna up to the desired level.

An amplifier whose output frequency is the same as the input frequency is called a **straight amplifier.** A **buffer amplifier** is the term sometimes applied to an amplifier stage to indicate that its primary purpose is one of isolation, rather than power gain.

Because it becomes increasingly difficult to maintain oscillator frequency stability as the frequency is increased, it is most usual practice in working at the higher frequencies to operate the oscillator at a low frequency and follow it with one or more **frequency multipliers** as required to arrive at the desired output frequency. A frequency multiplier is an amplifier that delivers output at a multiple of the exciting frequency. A **doubler** is a multiplier that gives output at twice the exciting frequency; a **tripler** multiplies the exciting frequency by three, etc. From the viewpoint of any particular stage in a transmitter, the preceding stage is its **driver.**

As a general rule, frequency multipliers should not be used to feed the antenna system directly, but should feed a straight amplifier which, in turn, feeds the antenna system.

Good frequency stability is most easily obtained through the use of a **crystal-controlled oscillator**, although a different crystal is needed for each frequency desired (or multiples of that frequency). A **self-controlled oscillator** or **VFO** (variable-frequency oscillator) may be tuned to any frequency with a dial in the manner of a receiver, but requires great care in design and construction if its stability is to compare with that of a crystal oscillator.

Many transmitters use tubes, but for low-power hf and channelized vhf fm transmitters, transistors are dominant. New solid-state devices are being developed which allow dc inputs of 100 watts or more with a low-level of IM distortion products. As the cost of these transistors is reduced it can be assumed that at some point in the future tubes will be used only for high-power amplification.

The best stage or stages to key in a code transmitter is a matter which is discussed in a later chapter. The oscillator/multiplier/amplifier type of transmitter (Fig. 6-2B) has long been popular. However, the excellent frequency stability and the advantages of grid-block keying (which are explained in the Code Transmission chapter) have

Fig. 6-1 – An amateur's transmitter is his on-the-air voice. He is judged by the quality of that "voice," whatever the mode that he chooses to operate.

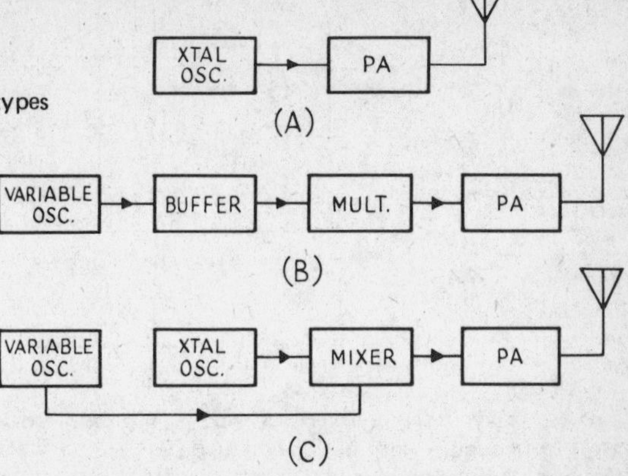

Fig. 6-2 – Block diagrams of the three basic types of transmitters.

made the heterodyne exciter of Fig. 6-2C increasingly popular, in spite of the slightly more complex circuitry required.

An fm transmitter can only be modulated in or following the oscillator stage. An a-m phone transmitter can only be modulated in the output stage, unless the modulated stage is followed by a linear amplifier. However, following an amplitude-modulated stage by a linear amplifier is an inefficient process, convenient as an expedient, but not recommended for best efficiency.

Following the generation of a single-sideband phone signal, its frequency can be changed only by frequency conversion (not multiplication), in exactly the same manner that signals in a receiver are heterodyned to a different frequency. Complete details of ssb transmitter design and construction are given in Chapter 13.

CRYSTAL OSCILLATORS

The frequency of a crystal-controlled oscillator is held constant to a high degree of accuracy by the use of a quartz crystal. The frequency depends almost entirely on the dimensions of the crystal (essentially its thickness); other circuit values have comparatively negligible effect. However, the power obtainable is limited by the heat the crystal will stand without fracturing. The amount of heating is dependent upon the rf cyrstal current which, in turn, is a function of the amount of feedback required to provide proper excitation. Crystal heating short of the danger point results in frequency drift to an extent depending upon the way the crystal is cut. Excitation should always be adjusted to the minimum necessary for proper operation.

The most stable type of crystal oscillator is that which provides only a small voltage output (lightly loaded), and which operates the crystal at a low drive level. Such oscillators are widely used in receivers and heterodyne transmitters. The oscillator/multiplier/amplifier type of transmitter usually requires some power from the oscillator stage. For either type of crystal oscillator, the active element may be a tube or a transistor.

Oscillator Circuits

The simplest crystal-oscillator circuit is shown in Fig. 6-3A. Feedback in this circuit is provided by the gate-source and drain-source capacitance. The circuit shown at B is the equivalent of the tuned-grid, tuned-plate circuit discussed in the chapter on vacuum-tube principles, using the crystal to replace the tuned grid circuit. Although JFETs are shown in the sample circuits at A and B, MOSFETs or triodes may also be employed, using the connections shown in 6-3C through F.

For applications where some power is required from the crystal oscillator, the circuits shown in

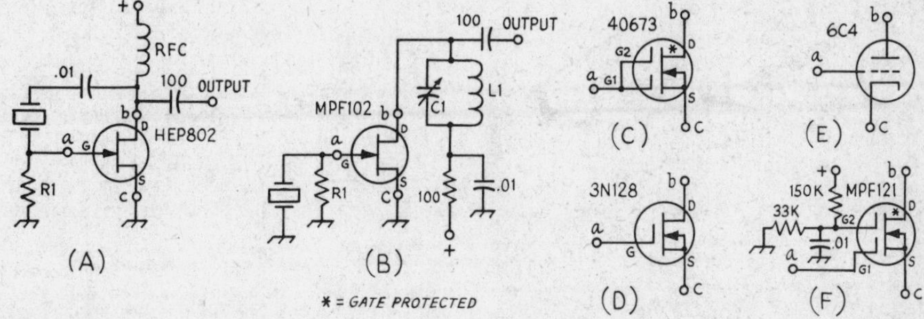

Fig. 6-3 – Simple crystal oscillator circuits. (A) Pierce, (B) FET, (C-F) other devices that can also be used in the circuits of A and B with appropriate changes in supply voltage.

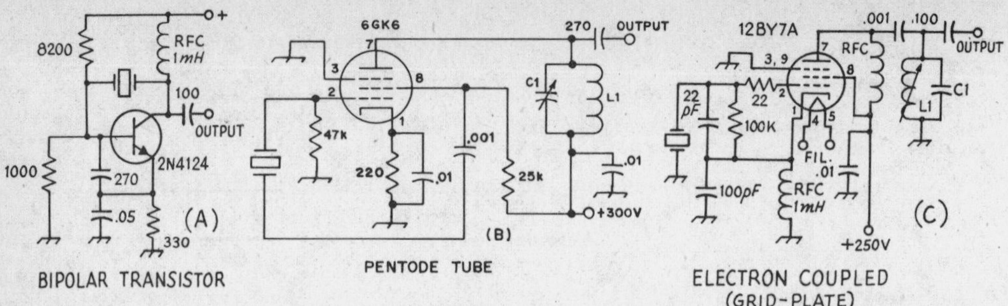

Fig. 6-4 – Crystal-oscillator circuits that are designed to deliver power. L1/C1 resonate at the crystal frequency, or a multiple thereof if the second, third, or fourth harmonic is the desired output frequency.

Fig. 6-4 may be employed. At A, a bipolar transistor is used, while the tube circuits (B, C) are somewhat more complicated. They combine the functions of oscillator and amplifier or frequency multiplier in a single tube. In these circuits, the screen of a tetrode or pentode is used as the plate in a triode oscillator. Power output is taken from a separate tuned tank circuit in the actual plate circuit. Although the oscillator itself is not entirely independent of adjustments made in the plate tank circuit when the latter is tuned near the fundamental frequency of the crystal, the effects can be satisfactorily minimized by proper choice of the oscillator tube.

The oscillators of Fig. 6-4B and 6-4C are a modification of the grid-plate circuit of Fig. 6-3B. In Fig. 6-4C the ground point has been moved from the cathode to the plate of the oscillator (in other words, to the screen of the tube). Excitation is adjusted by proper proportioning of 22- and 100-pF feedback capacitors.

When some types of tubes are used in the circuits of Fig. 6-4B, oscillation will stop when the output plate circuit is tuned to the crystal frequency, and it is necessary to operate with the plate tank circuit critically detuned for maximum output with stability. However, when the 6GK6, 12BY7A, 5763, or the lower-power 6AH6 is used with proper adjustment of excitation, it is possible to tune to the crystal frequency without stopping oscillation. These tubes also operate with less crystal current than most other types for a given power output, and less frequency change occurs when the plate circuit is tuned through the cyrstal frequency (less than 25 Hertz at 3.5 MHz).

Crystal current may be estimated by observing relative brilliance of a 60-mA dial lamp connected in series with the crystal. Current should be held to the minimum for satisfactory output by careful adjustment of excitation. With the operating voltages shown, satisfactory output should be obtained with crystal currents of 40 mA or less.

In these tube circuits, output may be obtained at multiples of the crystal frequency by tuning the plate tank circuit to the desired harmonic, the output dropping off, of course, at the higher harmonics. Especially for harmonic operation, a low-*C* plate tank circuit is desirable.

Practical Considerations

The operation of a crystal oscillator is often hampered because vhf parasitic oscillations also occur in the circuit. An effective way of killing parasitics is the use of a low-value composition resistor or ferrite bead, as shown in Fig. 6-5. The parasitic stopper can be located on the gate (grid or base) lead, and it should be placed as close as possible to the transistor. The circuit at A may be used for low-power applications. If a crystal above 1 MHz is to be used it may be advisable to include a trimmer capacitor across the crystal to allow the crystal frequency to be set exactly.

It is often desirable in fm and ssb gear to use several crystals, switch-selected in a single oscilla-

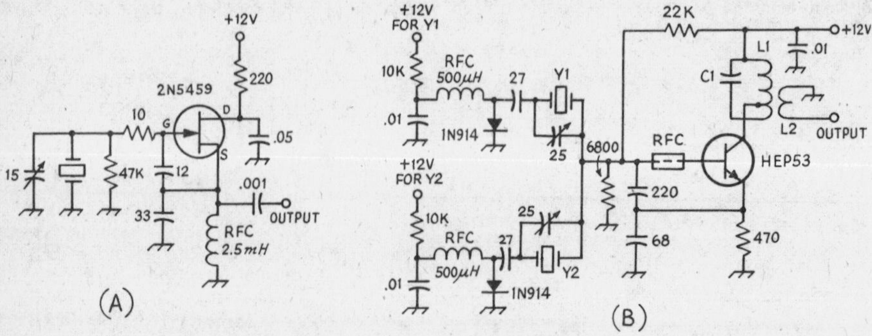

Fig. 6-5 – Two practical crystal-oscillator designs. (A) For low-power output applications such as a conversion oscillator or BFO, (B) an example of diode switching of crystals. The rf choke on the base lead of the transistor is a ferrite bead which prevents vhf parasitic oscillation.

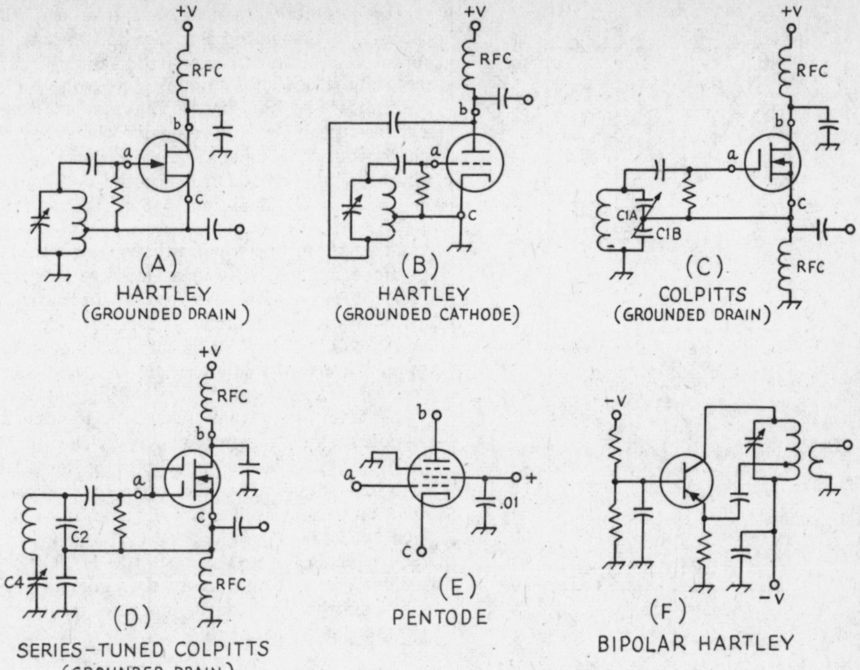

Fig. 6-6 – VFO circuits. The devices shown in Fig. 6-2C through F may also be employed as the active component.

tor. If manual switching is used, the leads to the switch may introduce sufficient additional capacitance to upset the operation of the circuit. Therefore, the use of **diode switching**, such as shown in Fig. 6-5B, is now popular. Any high-speed switching diode may be employed. The use of diode switching for low-level tank circuits, especially in receivers, has gained wide acceptance. A special diode known as the PIN has been developed for this purpose. In any diode-switching circuit it is important to insure that the switching bias is many times larger than the peak rf voltage present.

VARIABLE-FREQUENCY OSCILLATORS

The frequency of a VFO depends entirely on the values of inductance and capacitance in the circuit. Therefore, it is necessary to take careful steps to minimize changes in these values not under the control of the operator. As examples, even the minute changes of dimensions with temperature, particularly those of the coil, may result in a slow but noticeable change in frequency called **drift**. The effective input capacitance of the oscillator tube, which must be connected across the circuit, changes with variations in electrode voltages. This, in turn, causes a change in the frequency of the oscillator. To make use of the power from the oscillator, a load, usually in the form of an amplifier, must be coupled to the oscillator, and variations in the load may reflect on the frequency. Very slight mechanical movement of the components may result in a shift in frequency, and vibration can cause modulation.

In the past different techniques have been used to design the VFOs for transmitters and receivers. However, today the same circuits may be used for either application. In receivers the VFO is usually called an HFO.

VFO Circuits

Fig. 6-6 shows the most commonly used circuits. They are all designed to minimize the effects mentioned above. The oscillating circuits in Figs. 6-6A and B are the Hartley type; those in C and D are Colpitts circuits. (See chapter on vacuum-tube principles.) In the circuits of A, B and C, all of the above-mentioned effects, except changes in inductance, are minimized by the use of a high-*Q* tank circuit obtained through the use of large tank capacitances. Any uncontrolled changes in capacitance thus become a very small percentage of the total circuit capacitance.

In the series-tuned Colpitts circuit of Fig. 6-6D (sometimes called the Clapp circuit), a high-*Q* circuit is obtained in a different manner. The tube is tapped across only a small portion of the oscillating tank circuit, resulting in very loose coupling between tube and circuit. The taps are provided by a series of three capacitors across the coil. In addition, the tube capacitances are shunted by large capacitors, so the effects of the tube – changes in electrode voltages and loading – are still

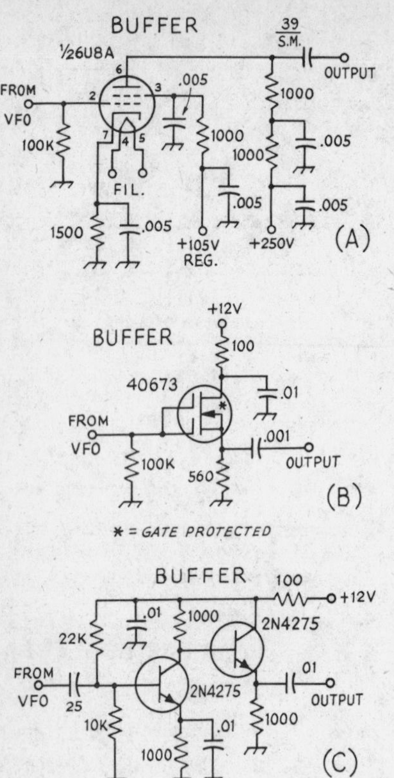

Fig. 6-7 – Isolating stages to be used between a VFO and the following amplifier or mixer stage.

further reduced. In contrast to the preceding circuits, the resulting tank circuit has a high L/C ratio and therefore the tank current is much lower than in the circuits using high-C tanks. As a result, it will usually be found that, other things being equal, drift will be less with the low-C circuit.

For best stability, the ratio of C2 to C4 should be as high as possible without stopping oscillation. The permissible ratio will be higher the higher the Q of the coil and the mutual conductance of the tube. If the circuit does not oscillate over the desired range, a coil of higher Q must be used or the capacitance of C2 and C3 reduced.

The pentode tube of 6-6E or any of the active devices shown in Fig. 6-3 may be used in either the Hartley or Colpitts circuits. Good results can be obtained with both tubes and transistors, so the choice of the active device is often a matter of personal preference.

Load Isolation

In spite of the precautions already discussed, the tuning of later stages in the transmitter may cause a noticeable change in frequency. This effect can be reduced considerably by designing a pentode oscillator for half the desired frequency and doubling frequency in the output circuit.

It is desirable, although not a strict necessity if detuning is recognized and taken into account, to approach as closely as possible the condition where the adjustment of tuning controls in the transmitter, beyond the VFO frequency control, will have negligible effect on the frequency. This can be done by adding isolating stage or stages whose tuning is fixed between the oscillator and the first tunable amplifier stage in the transmitter.

Fig. 6-7A shows such an arrangement that gives good isolation. A pentode tube is operated with a low-impedance resistive load, and regulated screen voltage. At B a simple follower circuit is used. The disadvantage of this circuit is that the level of the output will be quite low, usually less than one volt. Bipolar transistors are used in a direct-coupled follower arrangement in Fig. 6-7C, providing a higher level of output (above 3 V) than was possible with the design shown at B. The ability of a buffer stage to isolate the VFO from the load can be tested simply. Use a receiver to monitor the VFO, and listen as the buffer output is first left open and then shorted. A good buffer will hold the frequency change to less than 100 Hz. Often the frequency change may be in the order of several kHz when this test is made, an indication that the buffer is not doing its job.

Chirp, Pulling and Drift

Any oscillator will change frequency with an extreme change in plate screen voltages, and the use of stabilized sources for both is good practice. But steady source voltages cannot alter the fact of the extreme voltage changes that take place when an oscillator is keyed or heavily amplitude-modulated. Consequently some chirp or fm is the inescapable result of oscillator keying or heavy amplitude modulation.

A keyed or amplitude-modulated amplifier presents a variable load to the driving stage. If the driving stage is an oscillator, the keyed or modulated stage (the variable load) may "pull" the oscillator frequency during keying or modulation. This may cause a "chirp" on cw or incidental fm on a-m phone. In either case the cure is to provide one or more "buffer" or isolating stages between the oscillator stage and the varying load. If this is not done, the keying or modulation may be little better than when the oscillator itself is keyed or modulated.

Frequency **drift** is minimized by limiting the temperature excursions of the frequency-determining components to a minimum. This calls for good ventilation and a minimum of heat-generating components.

Variable capacitors should have ceramic insulation, good bearing contacts and should preferably be of the double bearing type. Fixed capacitors should have zero-temperature coefficients. The tube socket should have ceramic insulation.

Temperature Compensation

If, despite the observance of good oscillator construction practice, the warm-up drift of an oscillator is too high, it is caused by high-tempera-

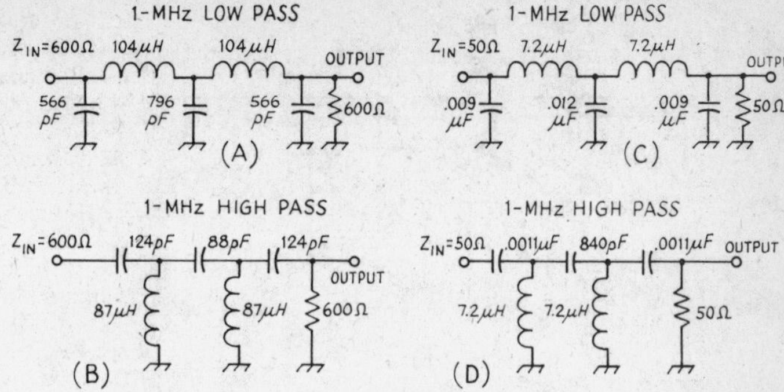

Fig. 6-8 – Universal high- and low-pass filter designs. The values given are for 1 MHz; they may be divided by the desired cutoff frequency (in MHz) to determine the value of the components needed. For example, if the 600-ohm high-pass design at A was to be used at 10 MHz, the values of C and L shown are divided by 10. The input and output impedance remains at 600 ohms.

ture operation of the oscillator. If the ventilation cannot be improved (to reduce the ultimate temperature), the frequency drift of the oscillator can be reduced by the addition of a "temperature-coefficient capacitor." These are available in negative and positive coefficients, in contrast to the zero-coefficient "NPO" types.

Most uncorrected oscillators will drift to a lower frequency as the temperature rises. Such an oscillator can be corrected (at a frequency f) by adding an N750-type capacitor (-750 parts per million per ^{0}C) of a value determined by making two sets of measurements. Measure the drift f_1 from cold to stability (e.g., 1 1/2 hours). To the cold (cooled-off) oscillator, add a *trial* N750 capacitor (e.g., 50 pF) and retune the cold oscillator to frequency f_1 (by retuning a padder capacitor or the tuning capacitor). Measure the new warm-up drift f_2 over the same period (e.g., 1 1/2 hours). The required corrective N750 capacitor is then

$$\text{Corrective } C = C_{\text{trial}} \frac{f_1}{f_1 - f_2}$$

If the trial capacitor results in a drift to a higher frequency, the denominator becomes $f_1 + f_2$.

Oscillator Coils

The Q of the tank coil used in the oscillating portion of any of the circuits under discussion should be as high as circumstances (usually space) permit, since the losses, and therefore the heating, will be less. With recommended care in regard to other factors mentioned previously, most of the drift will originate in the coil. The coil should be well spaced from shielding and other large metal surfaces, and be of a type that radiates heat well, such as a commercial air-wound type, or should be would tightly on a threaded ceramic form so that the dimensions will not change readily with temperature. The wire with which the coil is wound should be as large as practicable, especially in the high-C circuits.

Mechanical Vibration

To eliminate mechanical vibration, components should be mounted securely. The capacitor should preferably have small, thick plates and the coil braced, if necessary, to prevent the slightest mechanical movement. Wire connections between tank-circuit components should be as short as possible and flexible wire will have less tendency to vibrate than solid wire. It is advisable to cushion the entire oscillator unit by mounting on sponge rubber or other shock mounting.

Output Filtering

The output of an oscillator contains a good deal of harmonic energy in addition to the desired frequency. Often these harmonics can cause the generation of spurious products in heterodyne transmitters which result in signals being radiated outside the amateur bands. In receivers, the oscillator harmonics cause "birdies" and sprious responses in the tuning range. In general, transistor circuits generate a higher level of harmonic energy than do tube designs. Thus, the output of a tube VFO often can be used without filtering, while most solid-state VFOs require an output low-pass filter.

W7ZOI has provided general-purpose filter designs shown in Fig. 6-8. These designs have been developed using **computer-aided design (CAD)**, where a digital computer models or "synthesizes" the circuit. Not only filters, but models of tubes, transistors and complete circuits may be developed in this way, allowing a designer to optimize a circuit without taking days of cut and try. However, the CADs are just models, and often once a circuit is built additional refinement is still required.

The filter shown in Figs. 6-8A and B are designed for 600-ohm input and output impedances, while C and D are for use in 50-ohm lines. The values shown are for 1 MHz. A design for higher frequencies may be obtained by dividing the values shown by the desired frequency. For example, if a VFO were to be used in tuning 5 to 5.5 MHz, the output filter of Fig. 6-8A might be employed with a cut-off frequency of 6 MHz. The LC values shown would be divided by 6. The result will usually be an odd number, so the closest standard value may be used.

A PRACTICAL VFO CIRCUIT

The circuit shown in Fig. 6-9 is for a solid-state VFO covering 3.5 to 4 MHz. A number of measures have been taken to prevent harmonic and spurious outputs that so often plague transistor designs. Examination of Fig. 6-9 will show that a diode, CR2, is connected between the signal gate

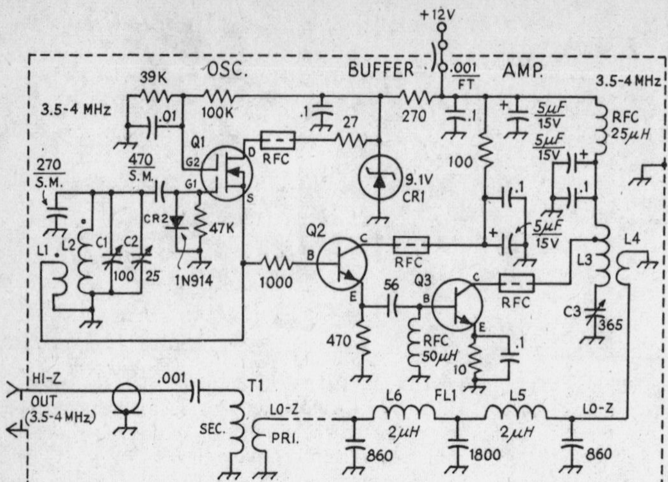

Fig. 6-9 – A typical VFO design showing extensive use of buffering and filtering to achieve a highly stable output with low spurious-frequency content.

of Q1 and ground. This diode should be designed for high-speed switching – a 1N914 is suitable – and should be connected with its anode toward gate 1. It clamps on the positive-going half of the cycle to prevent Q1 from reaching high peak transconductance, the time period when the output from the oscillator is rich in harmonic energy. This technique should be applied to any JFET or MOSFET oscillator, but does not work with bipolar-transistor oscillators. CR2 does not impair the performance of the VFO. Additional harmonics can be generated at Q2 and Q3, so attention must be given to that part of the circuit as well. Note that the collector of Q3 is tapped well down on L3. The tap provides an impedance match for the circuit, but still represents a high impedance at the harmonic frequencies, if not located too near the cold end of L3, thus contributing to a cleaner output signal. However, even though these precautions are taken, it is not uncommon to find that the second and third harmonics from a transistor output stage are only down some 10 to 15 decibels in level from the fundamental signal. By taking the VFO output at low impedance, L4, a low-pass, double-section filter can be used to diminish the harmonic to a level that is some 30 decibels or more below that of the desired output signal. FL1 is designed for 3.5 to 4-MHz use, and assures a clean output signal from the VFO.

VFO Output Level and Impedance

One of the things that perplexes many first-time users of transistorized VFOs is the matter of sufficient signal output to properly excite a transmitter input stage, or to supply adequate injection voltage to a receiver or transmitter mixer. The rms output of a solid-state VFO is limited by its low-impedance output port. In the circuits of Fig. 6-9 the output would usually be taken across the emitter resistor of Q2, the buffer. Typically, the rms output voltage at that point in the circuit will be on the order of 0.5 to 2 volts. Tube mixers can require up to several volts of oscillator signal in order to function properly. Most solid-state transmitters need from 3 to 10 volts of drive on the base of the first power stage, and a reasonable amount of driving power is needed to satisfy this requirement. Driving power is generally required by the grid of the first stage of a tube transmitter. The VFO should, therefore, be capable of supplying from 0.5 to 1 watt of power output. The Class-C amplifier, Q3, provides the needed power output. Should the driven stage present a low-impedance to the VFO, output can be taken directly from the side of FL1 opposite Q3. If, however, the driven stage of the transmitter or receiver has a high input impedance, some method must be used to provide the required impedance transformation, low to high. A broad-band toroidal step-up transformer, T1, is used for this purpose in Fig. 6-9. The secondary of the transformer is resonant somewhere in the operating range of the VFO, and takes advantage of the stray circuit capacitance, normally around 10 pF, to establish resonance. The impedance-transformation ratio is set by adjusting the number of turns on the primary winding. Alternatively, T1 can be replaced by a tuned circuit of conventional design. It can be equipped with a fixed-value capacitor and a slug-tuned inductor, or a fixed-value inductor can be used with a variable capacitor to permit peaking the output at the operating frequency. The use of a tuned circuit will assure somewhat better efficiency than will the broadband transformer, T1. Thus, it can be seen that the circuit must be tailored to the need.

Checking VFO Stability

A VFO should be checked thoroughly before it is placed in regular operation on the air. Since succeeding amplifier stages may affect the signal characteristics, final tests should be made with the complete transmitter in operation. Almost any VFO will show signals of good quality and stability when it is running free and not connected to a load. A well-isolated monitor is a necessity. Perhaps the most convenient, as well as one of the most satisfactory, well-shielded monitoring arrangements is a receiver combined with a harmonic from a frequency standard. (See the Measurements chapter for suitable circuits.) The receiver BFO is turned off and the VFO signal is tuned to beat with the signal from the crystal oscillator instead. In this way any receiver instability caused by overloading the input circuits, which may result in "pulling" of the hf oscillator in the receiver, or by a change in line voltage to the receiver when the transmitter is keyed, will not affect the reliability of the check. Most crystals have a sufficiently low temperature coefficient to give a check on drift as well as on chirp and signal quality if they are not overloaded.

Harmonics of the crystal may be used to beat with the transmitter signal when monitoring at the higher frequencies. Since any chirp at the lower frequencies will be magnified at the higher frequencies, accurate checking can best be done by monitoring at a harmonic.

The distance between the crystal oscillator and receiver should be adjusted to give a good beat between the crystal oscillator and the transmitter signal. When using harmonics of the crystal oscillator, it may be necessary to attach a piece of wire to the oscillator as an antenna to give sufficient signal in the receiver. Checks may show that the stability is sufficiently good to permit oscillator keying at the lower frequencies, where break-in operation is of greater value, but that chirp becomes objectionable at the higher frequencies. If further improvement does not seem possible, it would be logical in this case to use oscillator keying at the lower frequencies and amplifier keying at the higher frequencies.

Premixing

It is difficult to build a variable-frequency oscillator for operation above 10 MHz with drift of only a few Hz. A scheme called **premixing**, shown in Fig. 6-10A, may be used to obtain VFO output in the 10- to 50-MHz range. The output of a highly stable VFO is mixed with energy from a crystal-controlled oscillator. The frequencies of the two oscillators are chosen so that spurious outputs generated during the mixing process do not fall within the desired output range. A bandpass filter at the mixer output attenuates any out-of-band spurious energy. The charts given in Chapter 8 can be used to choose oscillator combinations which will have a minimum of spurious outputs. Also, Chapter 8 contains a discussion of mixer-circuit design.

PLL

Receivers and transmitters of advanced design are now using phase-locked loops (PLLs) to generate highly stable local oscillator energy up into the microwave region. The PLL has the advantage that no mixing stage is used in conjunction with the output oscillator, so the output energy is quite "clean." The Galaxy R-530, the Collins 651S-1, and the National HRO-600 currently use PLL high-frequency oscillator systems.

The basic diagram of a PLL is shown in Fig. 6-10B. Output from a **voltage-controlled oscillator (VCO)** and a frequency standard are fed to a phase detector which produces an output voltage equal to the difference in frequency between the two signals. The *error* voltage is amplified, filtered, and applied to the VCO. The error voltage changes the frequency of the VCO until it is locked to the standard. The bandwidth of the error-voltage filter determines the frequency range over which the system will remain in phase lock.

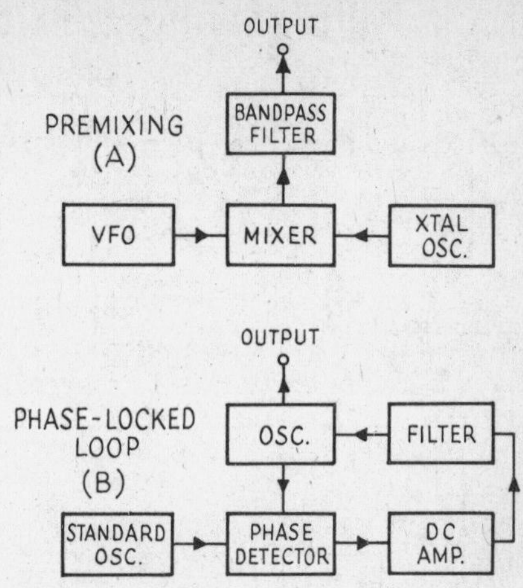

Fig. 6-10 — Block diagrams of the (A) premixing and (B) phase-lock-loop schemes.

Three types of phase-locked loops are now in use. The simplest type uses harmonics of a crystal standard to phase-lock an HFO, providing the injection for the first mixer in a double-conversion receiver. A typical circuit is given in Fig. 6-11. Complete construction details on this PLL were given in *QST* for January, 1972. A second type of phase-locked loop uses a stable mf VFO as the standard which stabilizes the frequency of an hf or vhf VCO. This approach is used in the receiver described by Fischer in *QST*, March, 1970.

The other PLL system also uses a crystal-controlled standard, but with programmable frequency dividers included so that the VCO output is always locked to a crystal reference. The frequency is changed by modifying the instructions to the dividers; steps of 100 Hz are usually employed for hf receivers while 10-kHz increments are popular in vhf gear. The use of a PLL for fm demodulation is covered separately in Chapter 14.

VFO DIALS

One of the tasks facing an amateur builder is the difficulty of finding a suitable dial and drive assembly for a VFO. A dial should provide a sufficiently slow rate of tuning – 10- to 25-kHz per knob revolution is considered optimum – without backlash. Planetary drives are popular because of their low cost; however, they often develop objectional backlash after a short period of use. Several types of two-speed drives are available. They are well suited to homemade amateur

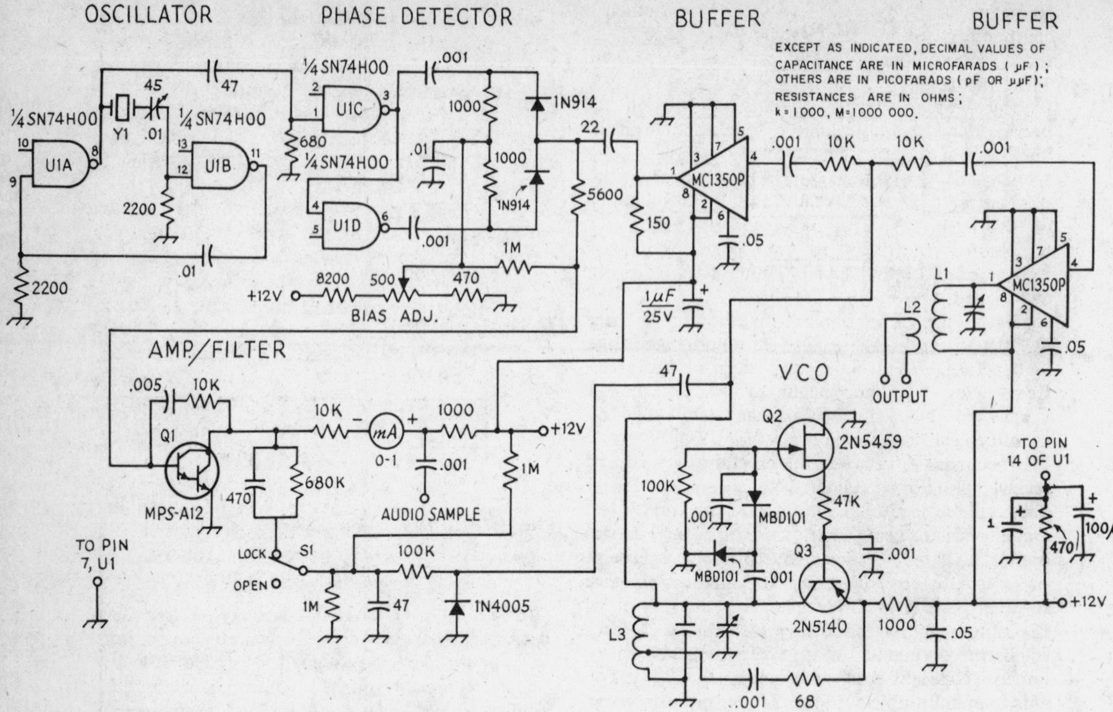

Fig. 6-11 – A practical phase-locked oscillator intended for application as the crystal-controlled HFO in a transmitter or receiver. The crystal frequency should be chosen so that the harmonic content of the standard is sufficient at the desired output frequency. A 200-kHz crystal is good to 40 MHz, 500-kHz crystal to 60 MHz, and 1-MHz crystal to 80 MHz. L1 and L3 are chosen to resonate at the desired output frequency.

equipment. Several of the construction projects described elsewhere in this book employ this type of dial. The Eddystone 898 precision dial has long been a favorite with amateurs, although the need to elevate the VFO far above the chassis introduces some mechanical-stability problems. If a permeability tuned oscillator (PTO) is used, one of the many types of turn counters made for vacuum variable capacitors or rotary inductors may be employed.

Linear Readout

If linear-frequency readout is desired on the dial, the variable capacitor must be only a small portion of the total capacitance in the oscillator tank. Capacitors tend to be very nonlinear near the ends of rotation. A gear drive providing a 1.5:1 reduction should be employed so that only the center of the capacitor range is used. Then, as a final adjustment, the plates of the capacitor must be filed until linear readout is achieved. In a PTO, the pitch of the oscillator coil winding may be varied so that linear frequency change results from the travel of the tuning slug. Such a VFO was described in *QST* for July, 1964. A different approach was employed by Lee (*QST*, November, 1970), using a variable-capacitance diode (Varicap) as the VFO tuning element. A meter which reads the voltage applied to the Varicap was calibrated to indicate the VFO frequency.

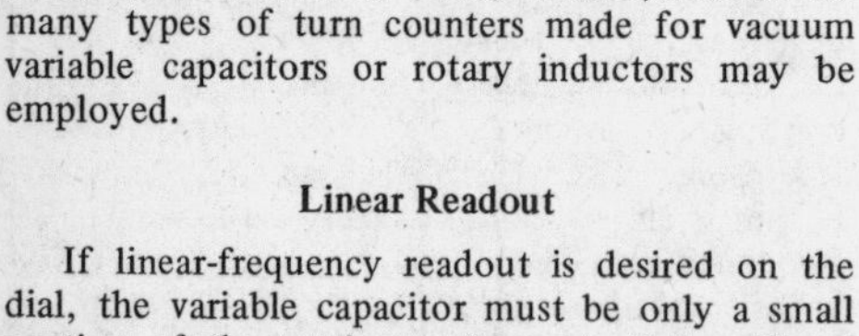

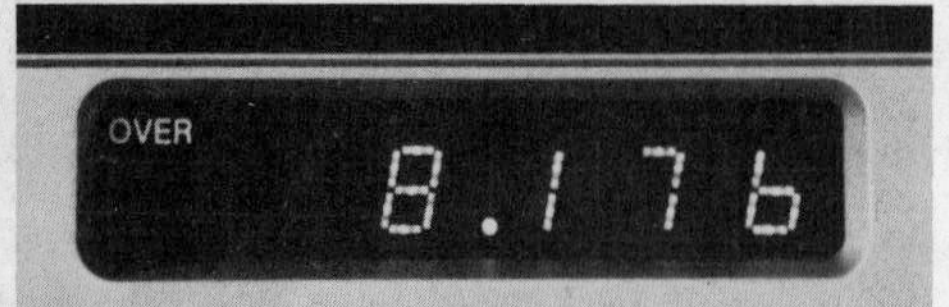

Fig. 6-12 – A 5-digit readout using light-emitting diodes.

Electronic Dials

An electronic dial consists of a simplified frequency counter which reads either the VFO or operating frequency of a transmitter or receiver. The advantage of an electronic dial is the excellent accuracy (to one Hertz, if desired) and the fact that VFO tuning does not have to be linear. The readout section of the dial may use neon-glow tubes called **Nixies** (a trade name of the Burroughs Corp.), or a seven-segment display using incandescent lamps, filament wires in a vacuum tube, or **LEDs (light-emitting diodes)**. A typical LED display is shown in Fig. 6-12. The use of MSI and LSI circuits, some containing as many as 200 transistors on a single chip, reduces the size required for an electronic dial to a few square inches of circuit-board space.

Fig. 6-13 – Block diagram of a frequency counter.

A typical counter circuit is given in Fig. 6-13. The accuracy of the counter is determined by a crystal standard which is often referred to as a **clock.** The output from a 100-kHz calibration oscillator, the type often used in receivers and transceivers, may be employed if accuracy of 100 Hz is sufficient. For readout down to 1 Hz, a 1- to 10-MHz AT-cut crystal should be chosen, because this type of high-accuracy crystal exhibits the best temperature stability. The clock output energy is divided in decade-counter ICs to provide the pulse which opens the input gate of the counter for a preset time. The number of rf cycles which pass through the gate while it is open are counted and stored. Storage is used so that the readout does not blink. At the end of each counting cycle the information that has been stored activates the display LEDs, which present the numbers counted until another count cycle is complete. A complete electronic dial arranged to be combined with an existing transmitter or receiver was described in *QST* for October 1970. Also, Macleish *et al* reported an adapter which allows a commercially made frequency counter to be mated with ham gear so that the counter performs as an electronic dial (*QST*, May, 1971).

FREQUENCY MULTIPLIERS

Single-Tube Multiplier

Output at a multiple of the frequency at which it is being driven may be obtained from an amplifier stage if the output circuit is tuned to a harmonic of the exciting frequency instead of to the fundamental. Thus, when the frequency at the grid is 3.5 MHz, output at 7 MHz, 10.5 MHz, 14 MHz, etc., may be obtained by tuning the plate tank circuit to one of these frequencies. The circuit otherwise remains the same as that for a straight amplifier, although some of the values and operating conditions may require change for maximum multiplier efficiency.

A practical limit to efficiency and output within normal tube ratings is reached when the multiplier is operated at maximum permissible plate voltage and maximum permissible grid current. The plate current should be reduced as necessary to limit the dissipation to the rated value by increasing the bias and decreasing the loading.

Multiplications of four or five sometimes are used to reach the bands above 28 MHz from a lower-frequency crystal, but in the majority of lower-frequency transmitters, multiplication in a single stage is limited to a factor of two or three. Screen-grid tubes make the best multipliers because their high power-sensitivity makes them easier to drive properly than triodes.

Since the input and output circuits are not tuned close to the same frequency, neutralization usually will not be required. Instances may be encountered with tubes of high transconductance, however, when a doubler will oscillate in t.g.t.p. fashion.

Frequency multipliers using tubes are operated Class C, with the bias and drive levels adjusted for plate-current conduction of less than 180 degrees.

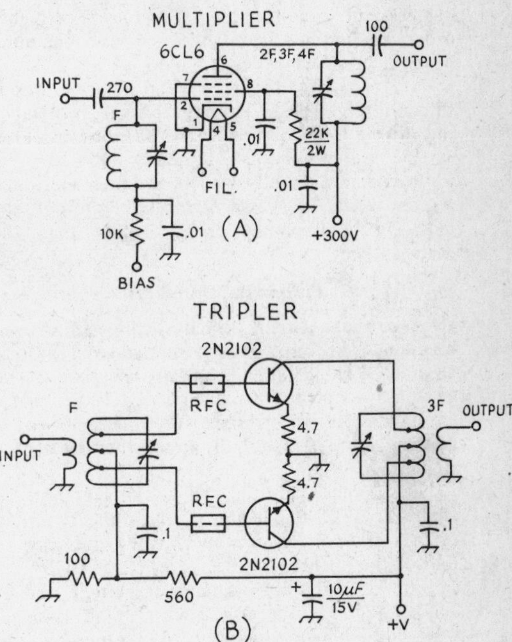

Fig. 6-14 – Frequency-multiplier circuits.

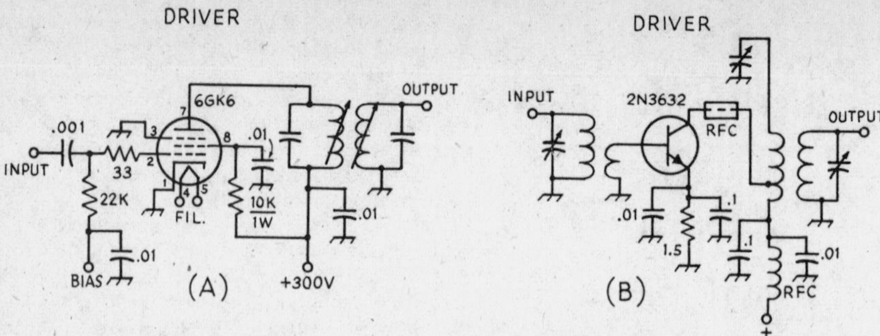

Fig. 6-15 – Driver stages using (A) a pentode tube and (B) a bipolar power transistor.

For maximum efficiency, a doubler requires a plate-conduction angle of about 110 degrees, while a tripler needs 100 degrees, a quadrupler 80 degrees, and a quintupler 65 degrees. For higher orders of multiplication increased bias and more drive are needed.

A typical circuit using a 6CL6 pentode tube is shown in Fig. 6-14A. The input circuit is tuned to the driving frequency while the output tank is set for the desired harmonic. If such a multiplier were to be operated directly into an antenna, additional selectivity would be necessary to prevent the radiation of harmonic energy (other than the desired frequency).

Push-Push Multipliers

A two-tube circuit which works well at even harmonics, but not at the fundamental or odd harmonics, is known as the **push-push** circuit. The grids are connected in push-pull while the plates are connected in parallel. The efficiency of a doubler using this circuit approaches that of a straight amplifier.

This arrangement has an advantage in some applications. If the heater of one tube is turned off, its grid-plate capacitance, being the same as that of the remaining tube, serves to neutralize the circuit. Thus provision is made for either straight amplification at the fundamental with a single tube, or doubling frequency with two tubes.

Push-Pull Multiplier

A single- or parallel-tube multiplier will deliver output at either even or odd multiples of the exciting frequency. A push-pull stage does not work as a doubler or quadrupler but it will work as a tripler.

Transistor Multipliers

A transistor develops harmonic energy with good efficiency, often causing harmonic-output problems in straight-through amplifiers. Two harmonic-generating modes are present, parametric multiplication and multiplication caused by the nonlinear characteristic presented by the base-collector junction. Transistors may be used in single-ended, push-pull, or push-push circuits. A typical push-pull tripler is shown in Fig. 6-14B. A small amount of forward bias has been added to the bases of the 2N2102s to reduce the amount of drive required. If a high level of drive is available, the bias circuit may be omitted.

A number of integrated circuits can be employed as frequency multipliers. The circuit at C uses a Motorola MC1496G (or the Signetics S5596, or Fairchild μA796) as a doubler. The input signal is balanced out in the IC, so only the desired second harmonic of the input frequency appears at the output. With suitable bypass capacitors this doubler can be used from audio to vhf.

DRIVERS

Pentode tubes are usually chosen for the driver stages of tube transmitters because they provide high amplification, often without requiring neutralization. Many of the receiving-type pentodes and smaller TV sweep tubes may be employed. The 6CL6, 6GK6, 12BY7A, 6BA6, 6AU6, and 6DC6 are often chosen. In cw and fm service the driver stage is operated Class C, while for ssb operation the Class-A mode is preferred to keep distortion to a minimum (third-order products at least 50 dB down). In ssb exciters alc voltage is often applied to a driver stage, in which case a semiremote-cutoff tube is desirable. Sharp-cutoff types are not acceptable because of a rapid increase in distortion as alc voltage drives the grid increasingly negative.

A typical tube driver stage is shown in Fig. 6-15 at A. The output load is a parallel-resonant circuit. Often a bandpass network is used so that the stage does not have to be tuned by a panel control. Also, coupling with a bandpass transformer provides a higher order of attenuation of harmonic and spurious signals. At Fig. 6-15B, a 2N3632 medium-power transistor serves as a Class-C driver. Note that this circuit is not suitable for ssb service.

Broadband Driver

Transistor circuits often require complex interstage coupling networks, because of the low input and output impedance characteristics of bipolar devices. Designing a solid-state multiband hf transmitter often requires some very complex band-switch arrangements. To eliminate this problem, the current trend is to use a broadband multistage driver that covers 3.5 to 30 MHz, for example, without switching or tuning adjustments. A typical circuit, similar to that used in Signal/One's CX-7 transceiver, is shown in Fig.

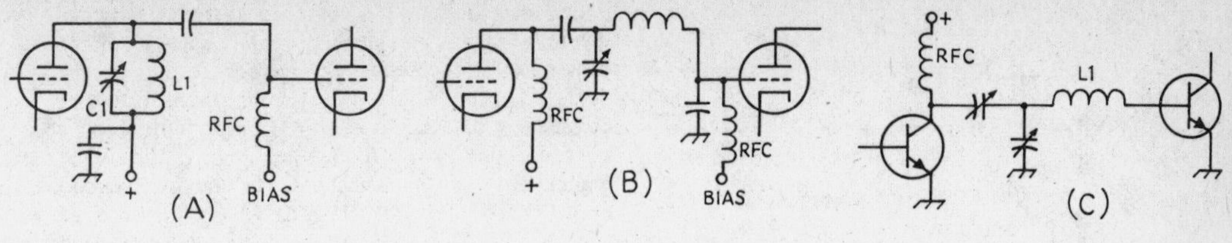

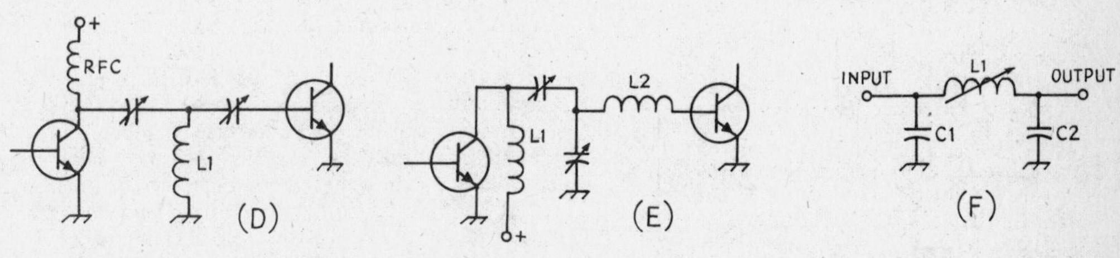

Fig. 6-16 — Interstage coupling networks for (A, B) tubes, (C-E) transistor stages, and (F) a grounded-grid amplifier.

6-17. Only a few millivolts of ssb or cw drive will provide sufficient output to drive a 4CX250B operating Class AB_1. Interstage coupling is accomplished with broadband toroidal transformers. Feedback is added from the collector to the emitter of each bipolar-transistor stage to improve linearity. Output impedance of the broadband driver is approximately 390 ohms.

Interstage Coupling

To achieve the maximum transfer of power between the driver and the succeeding amplifier stage, the output impedance of the driver must be matched to the input impedance of the following amplifier. Some form of rf coupling or impedance-matching network is needed. The capacitive system of Fig. 6-16A is the simplest of all coupling systems. In this circuit, the plate tank circuit of the driver, C1L1, serves also as the grid tank of the amplifier. Although it is used more frequently than any other system, it is less flexible and has certain limitations that must be taken into consideration.

The two stages cannot be separated physically any appreciable distance without involving loss in transferred power, radiation from the coupling lead and the danger of feedback from this lead. Since both the output capacitance of the driver tube and the input capacitance of the amplifier are across the single circuit, it is sometimes difficult to obtain a tank circuit with a sufficiently low Q to provide an efficient circuit at the higher frequencies. The coupling can be varied by altering the capacitance of the coupling capacitor, C2. The driver load impedance is the sum of the amplifier grid resistance and the reactance of the coupling capacitor in series, the coupling capacitor serving simply as a series reactor. The driver load resistance increases with a decrease in the capacitance of the coupling capacitor.

When the amplifier grid impedance is lower than the optimum load resistance for the driver, a transforming action is possible by tapping the grid down on the tank coil, but this is not recommended because it invariably causes an increase in vhf harmonics and sometimes sets up a parasitic circuit.

So far as coupling is concerned, the Q of the circuit is of little significance. However, the other considerations discussed earlier in connection with tank-circuit Q should be observed.

Pi-Network Interstage Coupling

A pi-section tank circuit, as shown in Fig. 6-16B, may be used as a coupling device between screen-grid amplifier stages. The circuit can also be considered a coupling arrangement with the grid of the amplifier tapped down on the circuit by means of a capacitive divider. In contrast to the tapped-coil method mentioned previously, this system will be very effective in reducing vhf harmonics, because the output capacitor provides a direct capacitive shunt for harmonics across the amplifier grid circuit.

To be most effective in reducing vhf harmonics, the output capacitor should be a mica capacitor connected directly across the tube-socket terminals. Tapping down on the circuit in this manner also helps to stabilize the amplifier. Since the coupling to the grid is comparatively loose under any condition, it may be found that it is impossible to utilize the full power capability of the driver stage. If sufficient excitation cannot be obtained, it may be necessary to raise the plate voltage of the

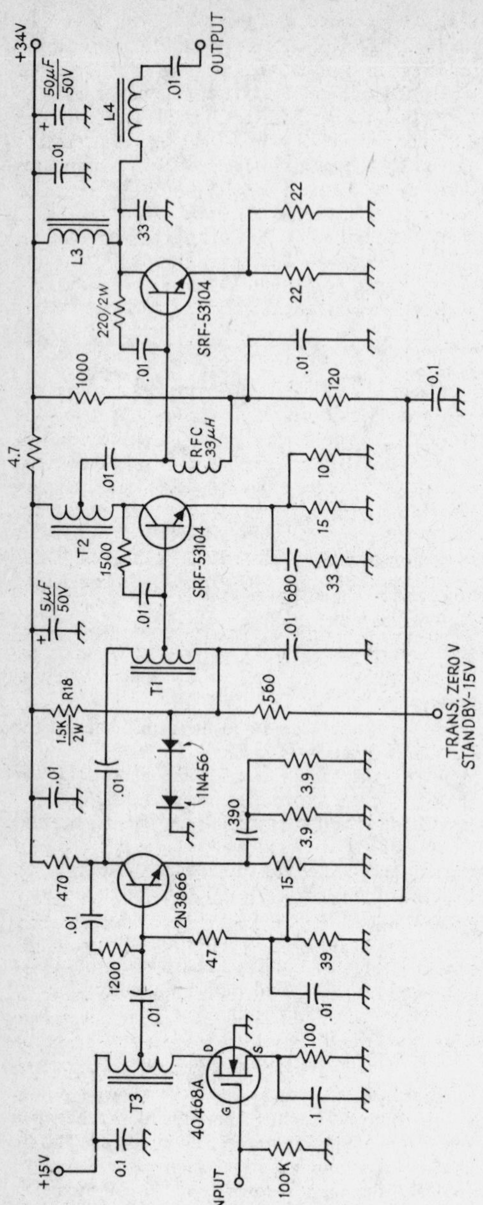

Fig. 6-17 – A solid-state broadband driver for 3 to 30 MHz. The design of transformers T1, T2 and T3 is covered later in the chapter.

driver, if this is permissible. Otherwise a larger driver tube may be required. As shown in Fig. 6-16B, parallel driver plate feed and amplifier grid feed are necessary.

Coupling Transistor Stages

In stages using bipolar power transistors, the input circuit must provide a match between the driver collector and the PA base. The latter exhibits a very low impedance. The input impedance of an rf power transistor is between several tenths of an ohm and several ohms. Generally, the higher the power rating of the device, the lower the input impedance. The base connection also has a reactive component which is capacitive at low frequencies and inductive at higher frequencies. At some frequency, usually between 50 and 150 MHz, the base lead will be self-resonant. The input impedance will vary with drive level, which makes a cut-and-try adjustment of the interstage network necessary.

An interstage network must provide the proper impedance transformation while tuning out reactance in the transistors. The reactive components of the base and collectors of power transistors are of such magnitude that they must be included in any network calculations. Fig. 6-16 shows several networks capable of interstage matching in a multistage transistor amplifier. At C, a T network is pictured. The value of the inductor is chosen so that its reactance is much greater than the capacitive reactance of the second transistor's base circuit. The capacitive divider provides the impedance match between the collector and the base.

The circuit of 6-16D is also basically a T network in which both the inductor and second capacitor are chosen to have reactance of a greater magnitude than the base-emitter capacitance of the second transistor. The circuits of C and D require that the collector of the driver transistor be shunt fed through a high-impedance rf choke. Fig. 6-16E shows a coupling network that eliminates the need for a choke. Here the collector of the driver transistor is parallel-tuned and the base-emitter junction of the following stage is series-tuned.

The remaining circuit, Fig. 6-16F, shows the pi-section network that is often used to match the 50-ohm output of an exciter to a grounded-grid power amplifier. A Q of 1 or 2 is chosen so that the circuit will be broad enough to operate across an amateur band without retuning. The network is designed for a 50-ohm input impedance and to match an output load of 30 to 150 ohms (the impedance range of the cathode of typical grounded-grid stages). Typical *LC* values are given in the construction projects presented later in this chapter.

RF POWER AMPLIFIER CIRCUITRY

Tube Operating Conditions

In addition to proper tank and output-coupling circuits, an rf amplifier must be provided with suitable operating voltages and an rf driving or excitation voltage. All rf amplifier tubes require a voltage to operate the filament or heater (ac is usually permissible), and a positive dc voltage between the plate and filament or cathode (plate voltage). Most tubes also require a negative dc voltage (biasing voltage) between control grid (grid No. 1) and filament or cathode. Screen-grid tubes require in addition a positive voltage (screen voltage or grid No. 2 voltage) between screen and filament or cathode.

Biasing and plate voltages may be fed to the

tube either in series with or in parallel with the associated rf tank circuit as discussed in the chapter on electrical laws and circuits.

It is important to remember that true plate, screen or biasing voltage is the voltage between the particular electrode and filament or cathode. Only when the cathode is directly grounded to the chassis may the electrode-to-chassis voltage be taken as the true voltage. The required rf driving voltage is applied between grid and cathode.

Power Input and Plate Dissipation

Plate power input is the dc power input to the plate circuit (dc plate voltage X dc plate current). Screen power input likewise is the dc screen voltage X the dc screen current.

Plate dissipation is the difference between the rf power delivered by the tube to its loaded plate tank circuit and the dc plate power input. The screen, on the other hand, does not deliver any output power, and therefore its dissipation is the same as the screen power input.

TRANSMITTING-TUBE RATINGS

Tube manufacturers specify the maximum values that should be applied to the tubes they produce. They also publish sets of typical operating values that should result in good efficiency and normal tube life.

Maximum values for all of the most popular transmitting tubes will be found in the tables of transmitting tubes in the last chapter. Also included are as many sets of typical operating values as space permits. However, it is recommended that the amateur secure a transmitting-tube manual from the manufacturer of the tube or tubes he plans to use.

CCS and ICAS Ratings

The same transmitting tube may have different ratings depending upon the manner in which the tube is to be operated, and the service in which it is to be used. These different ratings are based primarily upon the heat that the tube can safely dissipate. Some types of operation, such as with grid or screen modulation, are less efficient than others, meaning that the tube must dissipate more heat. Other types of operation, such as cw or single-sideband phone are intermittent in nature, resulting in less average heating than in other modes where there is a continuous power input to the tube during transmissions. There are also different ratings for tubes used in transmitters that are in almost constant use (CCS – Continuous Commercial Service), and for tubes that are to be used in transmitters that average only a few hours of daily operation (ICAS – Intermittent Commercial and Amateur Service). The latter are the ratings used by amateurs who wish to obtain maximum output with reasonable tube life.

Maximum Ratings

Maximum ratings, where they differ from the values given under typical operating values, are not normally of significance to the amateur except in special applications. No single maximum value should be used unless all other ratings can simultaneously be held within the maximum values. As an example, a tube may have a maximum plate-voltage rating of 2000, a maximum plate-current rating of 300 mA, and a maximum plate-power-input rating of 400 watts. Therefore, if the maximum plate voltage of 2000 is used, the plate current should be limited to 200 mA (instead of 300 mA) to stay within the maximum power-input rating of 400 watts.

SOURCES OF TUBE ELECTRODE VOLTAGES

Filament or Heater Voltage

The heater voltage for the indirectly heated cathode-type tubes found in low-power classifications may vary 10 percent above or below rating without seriously reducing the life of the tube. But the voltage of the higher-power filament-type tubes should be held closely between the rated voltage as a minimum and 5 percent above rating as a maximum. Make sure that the plate power drawn from the power line does not cause a drop in filament voltage below the proper value when plate power is applied.

Thoriated-type filaments lose emission when the tube is overloaded appreciably. If the overload

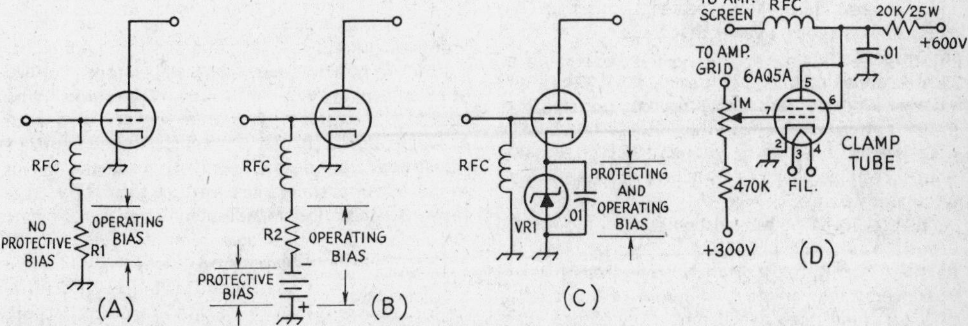

Fig. 6-18 – (A-C) Various systems for obtaining protective and operating bias. (D) Screen clamper circuit for protecting power tetrodes.

has not been too prolonged, emission sometimes may be restored by operating the filament at rated voltage with all other voltages removed for a period of 10 minutes, or at 20 percent above rated voltage for a few minutes.

Plate Voltage

Dc plate voltage for the operation of rf amplifiers is most often obtained from a transformer-rectifier-filter system (see power-supply chapter) designed to deliver the required plate voltage at the required current. However, batteries or other dc-generating devices are sometimes used in certain types of operation (see portable-mobile chapter).

Bias and Tube Protection

Several methods of obtaining bias are shown in Fig. 6-18. At A, bias is obtained by the voltage drop across a resistor in the grid dc return circuit when rectified grid current flows. The proper value of resistance may be determined by dividing the required biasing voltage by the dc grid current at which the tube will be operated. Then, so long as the rf driving voltage is adjusted so that the dc grid current is the recommended value, the biasing voltage will be the proper value. The tube is biased only when excitation is applied, since the voltage drop across the resistor depends upon grid-current flow. When excitation is removed, the bias falls to zero. At zero bias most tubes draw power far in excess of the plate-dissipation rating. So it is advisable to make provision for protecting the tube when excitation fails by accident, or by intent as it does when a preceding stage in a cw transmitter is keyed.

If the maximum cw ratings shown in the tube tables are to be used, the input should be cut to zero when the key is open. Aside from this, it is not necessary that plate current be cut off completely but only to the point where the rated dissipation is not exceeded. In this case plate-modulated phone ratings should be used for cw operation, however.

With triodes this protection can be supplied by obtaining all bias from a source of fixed voltage, as shown in Fig. 6-18B. It is preferable, however, to use only sufficient fixed bias to protect the tube and obtain the balance needed for operating bias from a grid leak. The grid-leak resistance is calculated as above, except that the fixed voltage is subtracted first.

Fixed bias may be obtained from dry batteries or from a power pack (see power-supply chapter). If dry batteries are used, they should be checked periodically, since even though they may show normal voltage, they eventually develop a high internal resistance.

In Fig. 16-8D, bias is obtained from the voltage drop across a Zener diode in the cathode (or filament center-tap) lead. Protective bias is obtained by the voltage drop across VR1 as a result of plate (and screen) current flow. Since plate current must flow to obtain a voltage drop across the resistor, it is obvious that cutoff protective bias cannot be obtained.

The voltage of the cathode biasing Zener diode VR1 should be chosen for the value which will give the correct operating bias voltage with rated grid, plate and screen currents flowing with the amplifier loaded to rated input. When excitation is removed, the input to most types of tubes will fall to a value that will prevent damage to the tube, at least for the period of time required to remove plate voltage. A disadvantage of this biasing system is that the cathode rf connection to ground depends upon a bypass capacitor.

Screen Voltage

For cw and fm operation, and under certain conditions of phone operation (see amplitude-modulation chapter), the screen may be operated from a power supply of the same type used for plate supply, except that voltage and current ratings should be appropriate for screen requirements. The screen may also be operated through a series resistor or voltage-divider from a source of higher voltage, such as the plate-voltage supply, thus making a separate supply for the screen unnecessary. Certain precautions are necessary, depending upon the method used.

It should be kept in mind that screen current varies widely with both excitation and loading. If the screen is operated from a fixed-voltage source, the tube should never be operated without plate voltage and load, otherwise the screen may be damaged within a short time. Supplying the screen through a series dropping resistor from a higher-voltage source, such as the plate supply, affords a measure of protection, since the resistor causes the screen voltage to drop as the current increases, thereby limiting the power drawn by the screen. However, with a resistor, the screen voltage may vary considerably with excitation, making it necessary to check the voltage at the screen terminal under actual operating conditions to make sure that the screen voltage is normal. Reducing excitation will cause the screen current to drop, increasing the voltage; increasing excitation will have the opposite effect. These changes are in addition to those caused by changes in bias and plate loading, so if a screen-grid tube is operated from a series resistor or a voltage divider, its voltage should be checked as one of the final adjustments after excitation and loading have been set.

An approximate value for the screen-voltage dropping resistor may be obtained by dividing the voltage *drop* required from the supply voltage (difference between the supply voltage and rated screen voltage) by the rated screen current in decimal parts of an ampere. Some further adjustment may be necessary, as mentioned above, so an adjustable resistor with a total resistance above that calculated should be provided.

Protecting Screen-Grid Tubes

Considerably less grid bias is required to cut off an amplifier that has a fixed-voltage screen supply than one that derives the screen voltage through a high value of dropping resistor. When a "stiff" screen voltage supply is used, the necessary grid cutoff voltage may be determined from an inspection of the tube curves or by experiment.

When the screen is supplied from a series dropping resistor, the tube can be protected by the use of a clamper tube, as shown in Fig. 6-18D. The grid-leak bias of the amplifier tube with excitation is supplied also to the grid of the clamper tube. This is usually sufficient to cut off the clamper tube. However, when excitation is removed, the clamper-tube bias falls to zero and it draws enough current through the screen dropping resistor usually to limit the input to the amplifier to a safe value. If complete screen-voltage cutoff is desired, a Zener diode may be inserted in the screen lead. The regulator diode voltage rating should be high enough so that it will cease conducting when excitation is removed.

Feeding Excitation to the Grid

The required rf driving voltage is supplied by an oscillator generating a voltage at the desired frequency, either directly or through intermediate amplifiers, mixers, or frequency multipliers.

As explained in the chapter on vacuum-tube fundamentals, the grid of an amplifier operating under Class C conditions must have an exciting voltage whose peak value exceeds the negative biasing voltage over a portion of the excitation cycle. During this portion of the cycle, current will flow in the grid-cathode circuit as it does in a diode circuit when the plate of the diode is positive in respect to the cathode. This requires that the rf driver supply power. The power required to develop the required peak driving voltage across the grid-cathode impedance of the amplifier is the rf driving power.

The tube tables give approximate figures for the grid driving power required for each tube under various operating conditions. These figures, however, do not include circuit losses. In general, the driver stage for any Class C amplifier should be capable of supplying at least three times the driving power shown for typical operating conditions at frequencies up to 30 MHz and from three to ten times at higher frequencies.

Since the dc grid current relative to the biasing voltage is related to the peak driving voltage, the dc grid current is commonly used as a convenient indicator of driving conditions. A driver adjustment that results in rated dc grid current when the dc bias is at its rated value, indicates proper excitation to the amplifier when it is fully loaded.

In coupling the grid input circuit of an amplifier to the output circuit of a driving stage the objective is to load the driver plate circuit so that the desired amplifier grid excitation is obtained without exceeding the plate-input ratings of the driver tube.

Driving Impedance

The grid-current flow that results when the grid is driven positive in respect to the cathode over a portion of the excitation cycle represents an average resistance across which the exciting voltage must be developed by the driver. In other words, this is the load resistance into which the driver plate circuit must be coupled. The approximate grid input resistance is given by:

$$\textit{Input impedance}\text{ (ohms)} = \frac{\textit{driving power (watts)}}{\textit{dc grid current}\text{ (mA)}^2} \times 620{,}000$$

For normal operation, the driving power and grid current may be taken from the tube tables. Since the grid input resistance is a matter of a few thousand ohms, an impedance step-up is necessary if the grid is to be fed from a low-impedance transmission line

TRANSISTOR RATINGS

Transistor ratings are similar in some respects to the maximum limits given for tubes. However, solid-state devices are generally not so forgiving of overload; they can quickly be ruined if a voltage or current parameter of the device is exceeded. All semiconductors undergo irreversible changes if their temperature is allowed to go above a critical limit.

Voltage Rating

In general, the higher the collector-emitter voltage rating of a transistor the less the chance of damage when used as an rf power amplifier. A mismatched load, or the loss of the load entirely, causes high voltages to appear between the collector and emitter of the transistor. If the maximum rating is exceeded, the transistor may break down and pass reverse current. Transistor manufacturers are now including a resistance in series with the emitter lead of each of the many junctions that make up the power transistor as break-down protection. This technique is called **ballasting** or **balanced emitters.** Another way to protect a power transistor is to include a Zener diode from collector to emitter. The break-down voltage rating of the diode should be above the peak rf voltage to be developed in the circuit, but below the maximum rating of the power device.

Current and Heat

The current that a power device can stand is related to its ability to dissipate heat. A transistor is physically small, so high-power models must use effective heat radiators, called heat sinks, to insure that the operating temperature is kept to a moderate value even when large currents are flowing through the device.

Cooling considerations for practical solid-state amplifiers are outlined below. Manufacturer's specification sheets describe a safe operating area for an individual power transistor. Also, transistors are rated in terms of power output, rather than input, so it should be remembered that a device specified to deliver 80 watts of output power will probably be running 160 watts or more input. Transistor amplifiers pass an appreciable amount of driver power to the output, as do grounded-grid tube stages, and this fact must also be taken into account by the circuit designer.

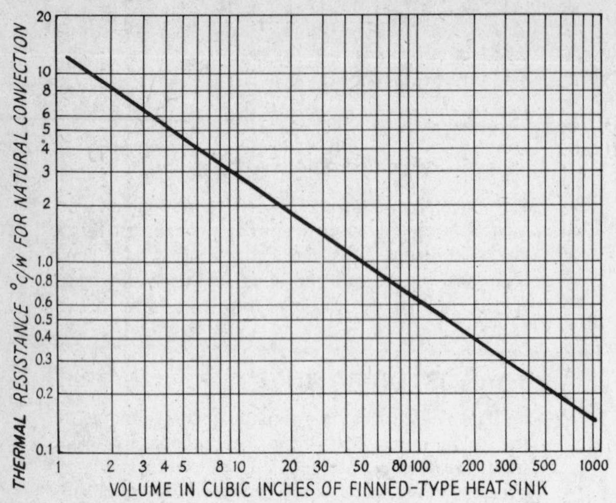

(A)

Device Case	*5W*	*10W*	*25W*	*50W*	*100W*
TO-5	17.2	7.2	1.2	.71	.35
TO-44	1.2	9.2	.44	n/a	n/a

(B)

Fig. 6-19 – (A) Graph to determine the thermal resistance of a heat sink of a given size. The heat sink volume may be computed by multiplying cross-sectional area by height. (B) Approximate thermal resistance needed for proper cooling of two types of transistor cases when operated at the proper levels given.

COOLING

Tubes

Vacuum tubes must be operated within the temperature range specified by the manufacturer if long tube life is to be achieved. Tubes with glass envelopes rated at up to 25 watts of plate dissipation may be run without forced-air cooling, if a moderate amount of cooling by convection can be arranged. If a cane-metal enclosure is used, and a ring of 1/4-inch diameter holes are placed around the tube socket, normal air flow can be relied upon to remove excess heat at room temperatures.

For tubes with greater plate dissipation, or those operated with plate currents in excess of the manufacturer's ratings (often the case with TV sweep tubes) forced air cooling with a fan or blower is needed. Fans, especially those designed for cooling hi-fi cabinets, are preferred because they operate quietly. However, all fans lose their ability to move air when excessive back pressure exists. For applications where a stream of air must be directed through a tube socket, a blower is usually required. Blowers vary in their ability to work against back pressure, so this specification should be checked when selecting a particular model. Some air will always leak around the socket and through other holes in a chassis, so the blower chosen should have a capacity which is 30 to 50 percent beyond that called for by the tube manufacturer.

An efficient blower is required when using the external-anode tubes, such as the 4X150A. Such tubes represent a trade-off which allows high-power operation with a physically small device at the expense of increased complexity in the cooling system. Other types of external-anode tubes are now being produced for conductive cooling. An electrical insulator which is also an excellent thermal conductor, such as AlSiMag, couples the tube to a heat sink. Requirements for the heat dissipator are calculated in the same way as for power transistors, as outlined below. Similar tubes are made with special anode structures for water or vapor cooling, allowing high-power operation without producing an objectionable noise level from the cooling system.

Transistor Cooling

Bipolar power transistors usually have the collector connected directly to the case of the device, as the collector must dissipate most of the heat generated when the transistor is in operation. However, even the larger case designs cannot conduct heat away fast enough to keep the operating temperature of the device functioning within the **safe area**, the maximum temperature that a device can stand without damage. Safe area is usually specified in a device data sheet, often in graphical form. Germanium power transistors may be operated at up to 100 degrees C while the silicon types may be run at up to 200 degrees C. Leakage currents in germanium devices can be very high at elevated temperatures; thus, for power applications silicon transistors are preferred.

A thermal sink, properly chosen, will remove heat at a rate which keeps the transistor junction temperature in the safe area. For low-power applications a simple clip-on heat sink will suffice, while for 100-watts of input power a massive cast-aluminum finned radiator will be necessary. In general, the case temperature of a power transistor must be kept below the point at which it will produce a burn when touched.

Heat-Sink Design

Simple heat sinks, made as described in the Construction Practices chapter, can be made more effective (by 25 percent or more) by applying a coat of flat-black paint. Finned radiators are most effective when placed where maximum air flow can be achieved – outside a case with the fins placed vertically. The size of a finned heat sink required to give a desired **thermal resistance**, a measure of the ability to dissipate heat, is shown in Fig. 6-19A. Fig. 6-19B is a simplified chart of the thermal resistance needed in a heat sink for transistors in TO-5 and TO-44 cases. These figures

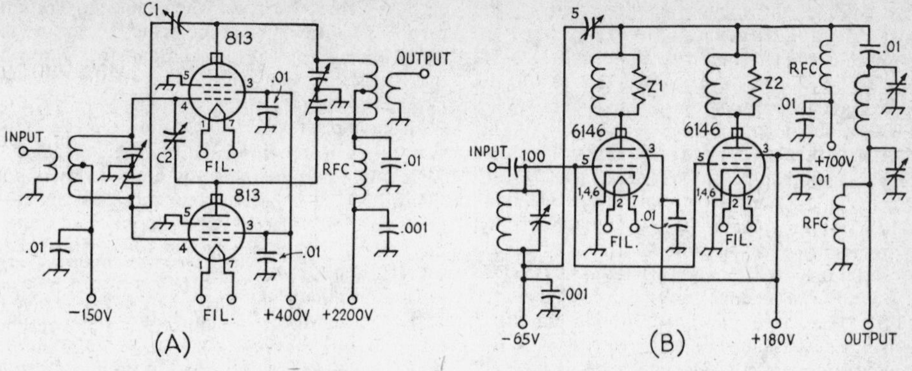

Fig. 6-20 – Typical (A) push-pull and (B) parallel amplifier circuits.

are based on several assumptions, so they can be considered a *worst-case* situation. Smaller heat sinks may be usable.

The thermal design of solid-state circuits has been covered in QST for April, 1972. The surface contact between the transistor case and the heat sink is extremely important. To keep the sink from being "hot" with dc, a mica insulator is usually employed between the transistor case and the heat dissipator. Newer types of transistors have a case mounting bolt insulated from the collector so that it may be connected directly to the heat sink. Whatever the arrangement, the use of a conductive compound such as silicone grease (Corning PC-4) is recommended between the transistor and the sink. For high-power designs, it may be desirable to add a small cooling fan, providing a stream of air across the heat sink, to keep the size of the heat dissipator within reasonable limits. Even a light air flow greatly increases the radiator's ability to dispose of excess heat.

OUTPUT POWER FROM TRANSMITTERS

CW or FM: In a cw or fm transmitter, any class of amplifier can be used as an output or intermediate amplifier. (For reasonable efficiency, a frequency multiplier *must* be operated Class C.) Class-C operation of the amplifier gives the highest efficiency (65 to 75 percent), but it is likely to be accompanied by appreciable harmonics and consequent TVI possibilities. If the excitation is keyed in a cw transmitter, Class-C operation of subsequent amplifiers will, under certain conditions, introduce key clicks not present on the keyed excitation (see chapter on Code Transmission). The **peak envelope power** (PEP) input or output of any cw (or fm) transmitter is the "key-down" input or output.

A-M: In an amplitude-modulated phone transmitter, plate modulation of a Class-C output amplifier results in the highest output for a given input to the output stage. The efficiency is the same as for cw or fm with the same amplifier, from 65 to 75 percent. (In most cases the manufacturer rates the *maximum allowable input* on plate-modulated phone at about 2/3 that of cw or fm.) A plate-modulated stage running 100 watts input will deliver a carrier output of from 65 to 75 watts, depending upon the tube, frequency and circuit factor. The PEP output of any a-m signal is four times the carrier output power, or 260 to 300 watts for the 100-watt input example.

Grid- (control or screen) modulated output amplifiers in a-m operation run at a carrier efficiency of 30 to 35 percent, and a grid-modulated stage with 100 watts input has a carrier output of 30 to 35 watts. (The PEP output, four times the carrier output, is 120 to 140 watts.)

Running the legal input limit in the United States, a plate-modulated output stage can deliver a carrier output of 650 to 750 watts, while a screen- or control-grid-modulated output amplifier can deliver only a carrier of 300 to 350 watts.

SSB: Only *linear* amplifiers can be used to amplify ssb signals without distortion, and this limits the choice of output amplifier operation to Classes A, AB_1, AB_2, and B. The efficiency of operation of these amplifiers runs from about 20 to 65 percent. In all but Class-A operation the indicated (by plate-current meter) input will vary with the signal, and it is not possible to talk about relative inputs and outputs as readily as it is with other modes. Therefore linear amplifiers are rated by PEP (input or output) at a given distortion level, which indicates not only how much ssb signal they will deliver but also how effective they will be in amplifying an a-m signal.

LINEAR AMPLIFIERS FOR A-M: In considering the practicality of adding a linear output amplifier to an existing a-m transmitter, it is necessary to know the carrier output of the a-m transmitter and the PEP output rating of the linear amplifier. Since the PEP output of an a-m signal is four times the carrier output, it is obvious that a linear with a PEP output rating of only four times the carrier output of the a-m transmitter is no amplifier at all. If the linear amplifier has a PEP output rating of 8 times the a-m transmitter carrier output, the output power will be doubled and a 3-dB improvement will be obtained. In most cases a 3-dB change is *just discernible* by the receiving operator.

By comparison, a linear amplifier with a PEP output rating of four times an existing ssb, cw or fm transmitter will *quadruple* the output, a 6-dB improvement, It should be noted that the linear amplifier must be rated for the mode (ssb, cw or fm) with which it is to be used.

GROUNDED-GRID AMPLIFIERS: The preceding discussion applies to vacuum-tube amplifiers connected in a grounded-cathode or grounded-grid circuit. However, there are a few points that apply only to grounded-grid amplifiers.

A tube operated in a given class (AB_1, B, C) will require more driving power as a grounded-grid amplifier than as a grounded-cathode amplifier. This is not because the grid losses run higher in the grounded-grid configuration but because some of the driving power is coupled directly through the tube and appears in the plate load circuit. Provided enough driving power is available, this increased requirement is of no concern in cw or linear operation. In a-m operation, however, the fed-through power prevents the grounded-grid amplifier from being fully modulated (100 percent).

AMPLIFIER CIRCUITS

Parallel and Push-Pull Amplifiers

The circuits for parallel-tube amplifiers are the same as for a single tube, similar terminals of the tubes being connected together. The grid impedance of two tubes in parallel is half that of a single tube. This means that twice the grid tank capacitance shown in Fig. 6-20B should be used for the same *Q*.

The plate load resistance is halved so that the plate-tank capacitance for a single tube (Fig. 6-24) also should be doubled. The total grid current will be doubled, so to maintain the same grid bias, the grid-leak resistance should be half that used for a single tube. The required driving power is doubled. The capacitance of a neutralizing capacitor should be doubled and the value of the screen dropping resistor should be cut in half.

In treating parasitic oscillation, it is often necessary to use a choke in each plate lead, rather than one in the common lead to avoid building in a push-pull type of vhf circuit, a factor in obtaining efficient operation at higher frequencies.

Two or more transistors are often operated in parallel to achieve high output power, because several medium-power devices often cost less than a single high-power type. When parallel operation is used, precautions must be taken to insure that equal drive is applied to each transistor. Otherwise, one transistor may "hog" most of the drive and exceed its safe ratings.

A basic push-pull circuit is shown in Fig. 6-20A. Amplifiers using this circuit are cumbersome to bandswitch and consequently are not very popular below 30 MHz. However, since the push-pull configuration places tube input and output capacitances in series, the circuit is often used at 50 MHz and higher.

In the circuit shown at A two 813s are used. Cross neutralization is employed, with C1 connected from the plate of one tube to the grid of the second, while C2 is attached in the reverse order.

GROUNDED-GRID AMPLIFIERS

Fig. 6-21A shows the input circuit of a grounded-grid triode amplifier. In configuration it is similar to the conventional grounded-cathode circuit except that the grid, instead of the cathode, is at ground potential. An amplifier of this type is characterized by a comparatively low input impedance and a relatively high driver power requirement. The additional driver power is not consumed in the amplifier but is "fed through" to the plate circuit where it combines with the normal plate output power. The total rf power output is the sum of the driver and amplifier output powers less the power normally required to drive the tube in a grounded-cathode circuit.

Positive feedback is from plate to cathode through the plate-cathode capacitance of the tube. Since the grounded-grid is interposed between the plate and cathode, this capacitance is small, and neutralization usually is not necessary.

In the grounded-grid circuit the cathode must be isolated for rf from ground. This presents a practical difficulty especially in the case of a filament-type tube whose filament current is large. In plate-modulated phone operation the driver power fed through to the output is not modulated.

The chief application for grounded-grid amplifiers in amateur work below 30 MHz is in the case where the available driving power far exceeds the power that can be used in driving a conventional grounded-cathode amplifier.

Screen-grid tubes are also used sometimes in grounded-grid amplifiers. In some cases, the screen

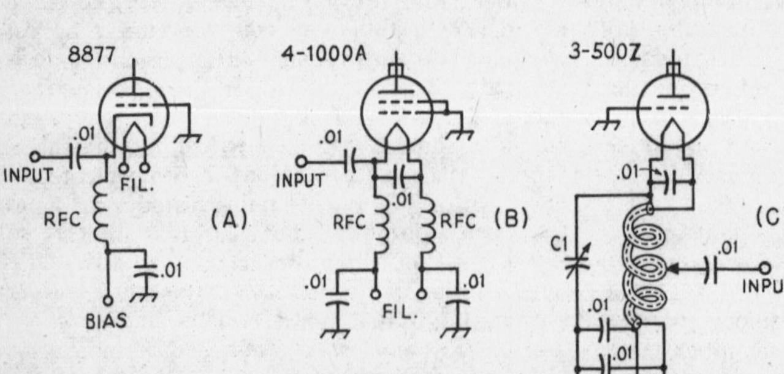

Fig. 6-21 — Input circuits for triode or triode-connected power tubes operated grounded grid.

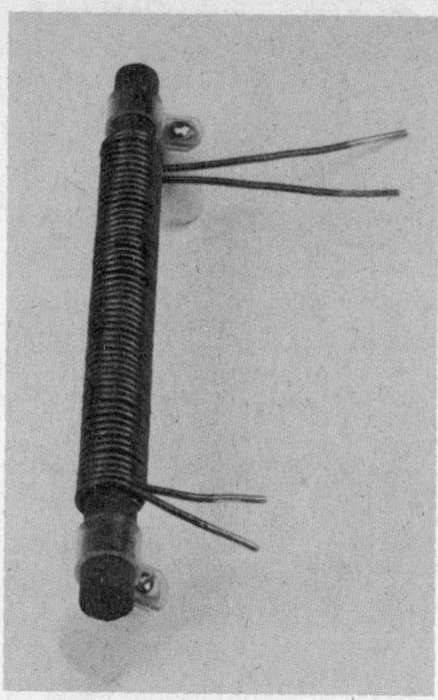

Fig. 6-22 – A 30-A filament choke for a grounded-grid power amplifier consisting of 28 turns of No. 10 enam. wire on a 1/2-inch diameter ferrite rod 7 inches long.

is simply connected in parallel with the grid, as in Fig. 6-21B and the tube operates as a high-μ triode. In other cases, the screen is bypassed to ground and operated at the usual dc potential, as shown at C. Since the screen is still in parallel with the grid for rf, operation is very much like that of a triode except that the positive voltage on the screen reduces driver-power requirements.

In indirectly-heated cathode tubes, the low heater-to-cathode capacitance will often provide enough isolation to keep rf out of the heater transformer and the ac lines. If not, the heater voltage must be applied through rf chokes.

In a directly-heated cathode tube, the filament must be maintained above rf ground. This can be done by using a pair of filament chokes or by using the input tank circuit, as shown in Fig. 6-21C. In the former method, a double solenoid (often wound on a ferrite core) is generally used, although separate chokes can be used. When the tank circuit is used, the tank inductor is wound from two (insulated) conductors in parallel or from an insulated conductor inside a tubing outer conductor. A typical filament choke is shown in Fig. 6-22.

The input impedance of a grounded-grid power stage is usually between 30 and 150 ohms. For circuits similar to those shown in Figs. 6-21A and B some form of input tuning network is needed. A high-*C*, low-*Q* parallel-resonant or pi-section network will suffice. The input network provides benefit other than impedance matching – a reduction in the IM distortion produced by the stage when amplifying an ssb signal. A typical input circuit is shown in Fig. 6-16F. When an amplifier is built for single-band operation, a tank circuit similar to that shown in Fig. 6-21C may be employed. Proper input matching is achieved by tapping the input down on the coil.

TRANSISTOR CIRCUITS

A transistor amplifier requires some means for impedance matching at the input and output of the stage. For conventional narrow-band amplifier designs, impedance matching is achieved with tuned networks (pi, L or T sections or combinations thereof). To simplify band-switching requirements, broadband amplifiers with four octaves or more of bandwidth are desirable. Wide bandwidths are achieved by using a special form of transmission-line transformer for interstage and output coupling that is described later in this chapter.

Most solid-state Class-C amplifiers are operated with both the base and emitter leads connected to dc ground. Thus, the transistor is practically off when no driving signal is present. The distortion of the drive signal by such an amplifier is appreciable. However, with cw, fm, or collector-modulated a-m, the harmonics produced are removed from the desired frequency by at least a factor of 2. Thus, harmonic energy can be reduced or eliminated by using appropriate filters.

Fig. 6-23A shows a basic Class-C transistor amplifier. The base input is held at dc ground through a radio-frequency choke. A second choke, consisting of two ferrite beads (collector lead), eliminates a tendency to vhf parasitic oscillation. At B, parallel-connected transistors are operated Class C. Adjustment of L1 and L2 provide equal levels of drive. The devices chosen for this circuit are designed for 30- to 50-MHz operation. Below 14 MHz some form of degenerative feedback will be needed to prevent self oscillation, as the gain of the transistors is quite high at lower frequencies.

For ssb operation transistors must be forward biased at the base. The lowest distortion results with Class-A operation, but, efficiency is poor. The best trade off between low distortion and high efficiency is Class-B operation, even though operation in this region introduces some severe requirements for the bias circuit. Whenever a transistor is forward biased, thermal runaway can be a problem. Also, ssb drive varies in amplitude causing large variations in the transistor base current. For best linearity, the dc base-bias voltage should remain constant as the rf drive level is varied. This situation is in conflict with the conditions needed to prevent thermal runaway. Exotic schemes have been designed to provide the proper base bias for Class-B ssb amplification. However, a simple diode circuit such as shown in Figs. 6-23C and D can provide the required dc stability with protection against thermal damage. The ballasted type of transistors are preferred for these circuits. Typical choices for Class-B ssb service are the 2N5941, 2N2942, 2N3375, 2N5070, 2N5071, and the 2N5093. The design of suitable broadband transformers for the circuits of Fig. 6-29 is covered later in this chapter.

The circuits at 6-23C and D are similar except for the choice of the active device. Both designs were developed by K7QWR. The base-bias circuit maintains a steady voltage while supplying current that varies by a factor of 100 to 1 with drive. The gain versus frequency of both circuits follows the

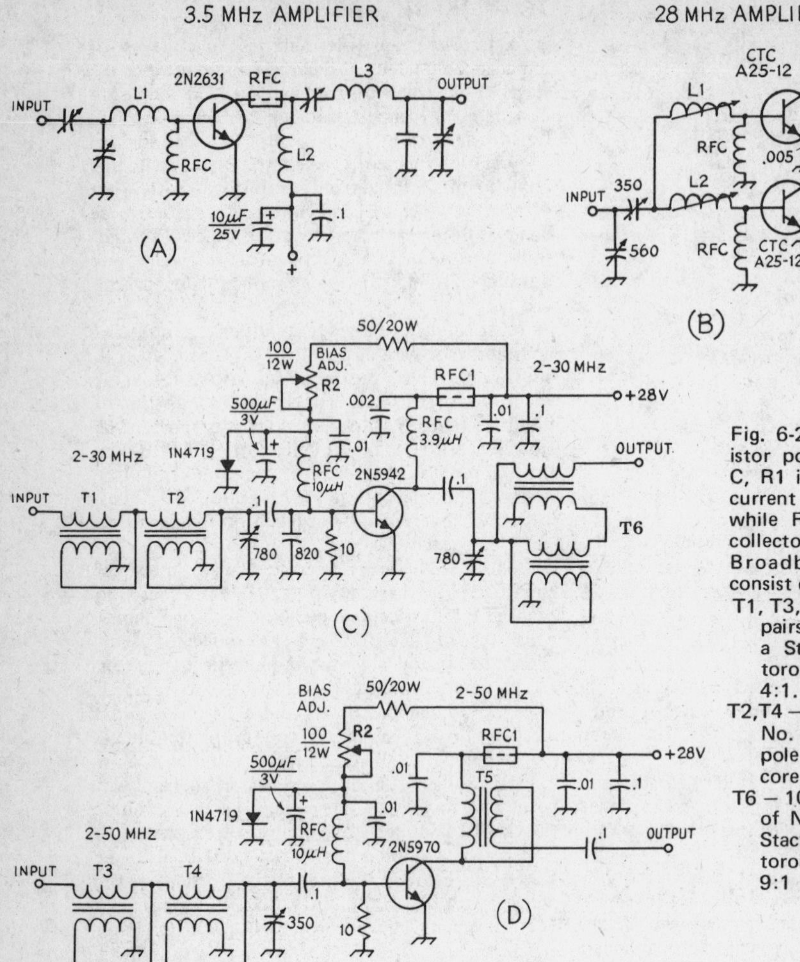

Fig. 6-23 – Some typical transistor power-amplifier circuits. At C, R1 is adjusted for a collector current of 40 mA with no drive, while R2 at D is set for 20 mA collector current with no input. Broadband transformers used consist of the following:

T1, T3, T5 – 6 turns of 2 twisted pairs of No. 26 enam. wire on a Stackpole 57-9322 No. 11 toroid core, connected for 4:1. (See table 6-A.)

T2,T4 – 4 turns of 4 twisted pairs of No. 26 enam. wire on a Stackpole 57-9322 No. 11 toroid core, connected for 4:1.

T6 – 10 turns of 3 twisted pairs of No. 28 enam. wire on two Stackpole 57-9074 No. 11 toroid cores, connected for 9:1

power-output curves of the transistors used, changing from 25 dB at 2 MHz to 13 dB at 30 MHz. IMD is typically 30 dB or more down with either circuit.

RF POWER-AMPLIFIER TANKS AND COUPLING

TANK *Q*

Rf power amplifiers used in amateur transmitters are operated under Class-C or -AB conditions (see chapter on tube fundamentals). The main objective, of course, is to deliver as much fundamental power as possible into a load, *R* without exceeding the tube ratings. The load resistance *R* may be in the form of a transmission line to an antenna, or the input circuit of another amplifier. A further objective is to minimize the harmonic energy (always generated by an amplifier) fed into the load circuit. In attaining these objectives, the *Q* of the tank circuit is of importance. When a load is coupled inductively, the *Q* of the tank circuit will have an effect on the coefficient of coupling necessary for proper loading of the amplifier. In respect to all of these factors, a tank *Q* of 10 to 20 is usually considered optimum. A much lower *Q* will result in less efficient operation of the amplifier tube, greater harmonic output, and greater difficulty in coupling inductively to a load. A much higher *Q* will result in higher tank current with increased loss in the tank coil. Efficiency of a tank circuit is determined by the ratio of loaded *Q* to unloaded *Q* by the relationship:

$$Eff. = 100\left(1 - \frac{Q_L}{Q_U}\right)$$

where Q_L is the loaded *Q* and Q_U is the unloaded *Q*.

The *Q* is determined (see chapter on electrical laws and circuits) by the *L*/*C* ratio and the load resistance at which the tube is operated. The tube load resistance is related, in approximation, to the ratio of the dc plate voltage to dc plate current at which the tube is operated and can be computed from:

Class-A Tube:

$$R_L = \frac{\text{Plate Volts}}{1.3 \times \text{Plate Current}}$$

Class-B Tube:

$$R_L = \frac{\text{Plate Volts}}{1.57 \times \text{Plate Current}}$$

Class-C Tube:

$$R_L = \frac{\text{Plate Volts}}{2 \times \text{Plate Current}}$$

Transistor:

$$R_L = \frac{(\text{Collector Volts})^2}{2 \times \text{Power Output (Watts)}}$$

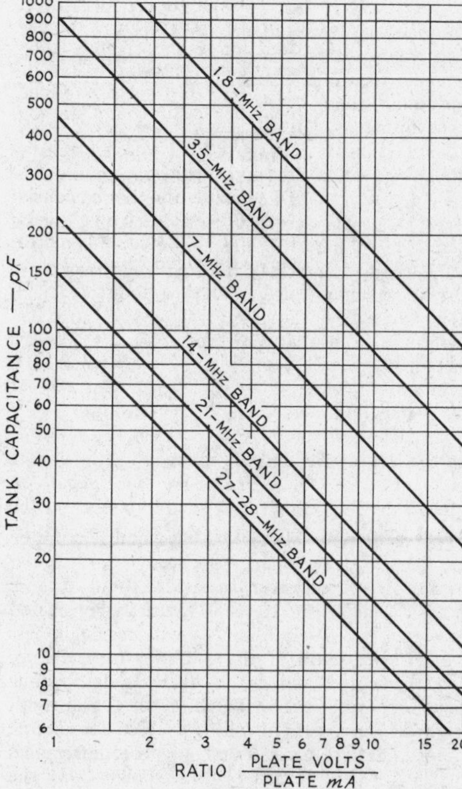

Fig. 6-24 — Chart showing plate tank capacitance required for a Q of 10. Divide the tube plate voltage by the plate current in milliamperes. Select the vertical line corresponding to the answer obtained. Follow this vertical line to the diagonal line for the band in question, and thence horizontally to the left to read the capacitance. For a given ratio of plate voltage/plate current, doubling the capacitance shown doubles the Q. When a split-stator capacitor is used in a balanced circuit, the capacitance of each section may be one half the value given by the chart.

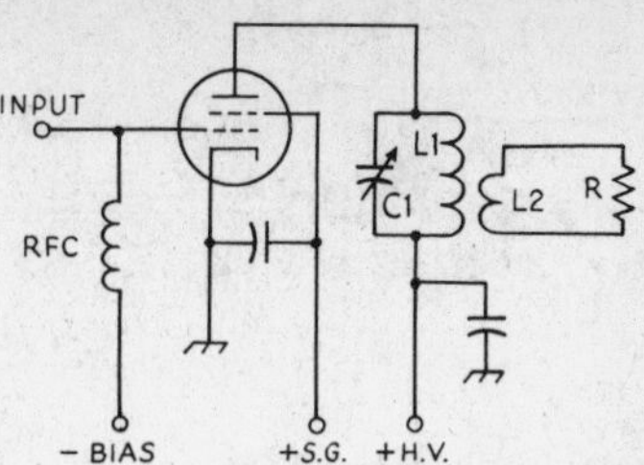

Fig. 6-25 — Inductive-link output coupling circuits.
C1 — Plate tank capacitor — see text and Fig. 6-24 for capacitance.
L1 — To resonate at operating frequency with C1. See *LC* chart and inductance formula in electrical-laws chapter, or use ARRL *Lightning Calculator.*
L2 — Reactance equal to line impedance. See reactance chart and inductance formula in electrical-laws chapter, or use ARRL *Lightning Calculator.*
R — Representing load.

Parallel-Resonant Tank

The amount of C that will give a Q of 10 for various ratios is shown in Fig. 6-24. For a given plate-voltage/plate-current ratio, the Q will vary directly as the tank capacitance, twice the capacitance doubles the Q, etc. For the same Q, the capacitance of *each section* of a split-stator capacitor in a balanced circuit should be half the value shown.

These values of capacitance include the output capacitance of the amplifier tube, the input capacitance of a following amplifier tube if it is coupled capacitively, and all other stray capacitances. At the higher plate-voltage/plate-current ratios, the chart may show values of capacitance, for the higher frequencies, smaller than those attainable in practice. In such a case, a tank Q higher than 10 is unavoidable.

INDUCTIVE-LINK COUPLING

Coupling to Flat Coaxial Lines

When the load R in Fig. 6-25 is located for convenience at some distance from the amplifier, or when maximum harmonic reduction is desired, it is advisable to feed the power to the load through a low-impedance coaxial cable. The shielded construction of the cable prevents radiation and makes it possible to install the line in any convenient manner without danger of unwanted coupling to other circuits.

If the line is more than a small fraction of a wavelength long, the load resistance at its output end should be adjusted, by a matching circuit if necessary, to match the impedance of the cable. This reduces losses in the cable and makes the coupling adjustments at the transmitter independent of the cable length. Matching circuits for use between the cable and another transmission line are discussed in the chapter on transmission lines, while the matching adjustments when the load is the grid circuit of a following amplifier are described elsewhere in this chapter.

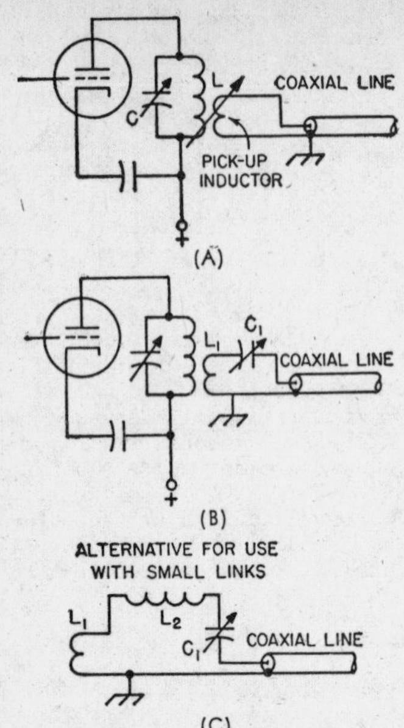

Fig. 6-26 – With flat transmission lines, power transfer is obtained with looser coupling if the line input is tuned to resonance. C1 and L1 should resonate at the operating frequency. See table for maximum usable value of C1. If circuit does not resonate with maximum C1 or less, inductance of L1 must be increased or added in series at L2.

Table 6-A

Capacitance in pF Required for Coupling to Flat Coaxial Lines with Tuned Coupling Circuit[1]

Frequency Band MHz	*Characteristic Impedance of Line* 52 *ohms*	75 *ohms*
3.5	450	300
7	230	150
14	115	75
21	80	50
28	60	40

[1] Capacitance values are maximum usable.
Note: Inductance in circuit must be adjusted to resonate at operating frequency.

Assuming that the cable is properly terminated, proper loading of the amplifier will be assured, using the circuit of Fig. 6-26A, if

1) The plate tank circuit has reasonably higher value of Q. A value of 10 is usually sufficient.

2) The inductance of the pickup or link coil is close to the optimum value for the frequency and type of line used. The optimum coil is one whose self-inductance is such that its reactance at the operating frequency is equal to the characteristic impedance, Z_0, of the line.

3) It is possible to make the coupling between the tank and pickup coils very tight.

The second in this list is often hard to meet. Few manufactured link coils have adequate inductance even for coupling to a 50-ohm line at low frequencies.

If the line is operating with a low SWR, the system shown in Fig. 6-26A will require tight coupling between the two coils. Since the secondary (pickup coil) circuit is not resonant, the leakage reactance of the pickup coil will cause some detuning of the amplifier tank circuit. This detuning effect increases with increasing coupling, but is usually not serious. However, the amplifier tuning must be adjusted to resonance, as indicated by the plate-current dip, each time the coupling is changed.

Tuned Coupling

The design difficulties of using "untuned" pickup coils, mentioned above, can be avoided by using a coupling circuit tuned to the operating frequency. This contributes additional selectivity as well, and hence aids in the suppression of spurious radiations.

If the line is flat the input impedance will be essentially resistive and equal to the Z_0 of the line. With coaxial cable, a circuit of reasonable Q can be obtained with practicable values of inductance and capacitance connected in series with the line's input terminals. Suitable circuits are given in Fig. 6-26 at B and C. The Q of the coupling circuit often may be as low as 2, without running into difficulty in getting adequate coupling to a tank circuit of proper design. Larger values of Q can be used and will result in increased ease of coupling, but as the Q is increased the frequency range over which the circuit will operate without readjustment becomes smaller. It is usually good practice, therefore, to use a coupling-circuit Q just low enough to permit operation, over as much of a band as is normally used for a particular type of communication, without requiring retuning.

Capacitance values for a Q of 2 and line impedances of 52 and 75 ohms are given in the accompanying table. These are the *maximum* values that should be used. The inductance in the circuit should be adjusted to give resonance at the

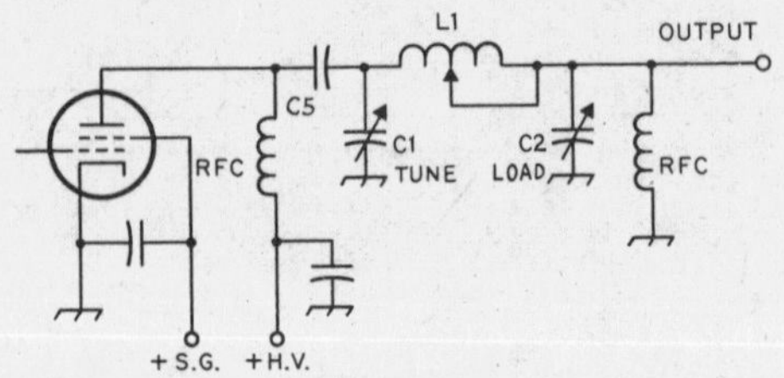

Fig. 6-27 – Pi and pi-L output-coupling networks.

operating frequency. If the link coil used for a particular band does not have enough inductance to resonate, the additional inductance may be connected in series as shown in Fig. 6-26C.

Characteristics

In practice, the amount of inductance in the circuit should be chosen so that, with somewhat loose coupling between L1 and the amplifier tank coil, the amplifier plate current will increase when the variable capacitor, C1, is tuned through the value of capacitance given by the table. The coupling between the two coils should then be increased until the amplifier loads normally, without changing the setting of C1. If the transmission line is flat over the entire frequency band under consideration, it should not be necessary to readjust C1 when changing frequency, if the values given in the table are used. However, it is unlikely that the line actually will be flat over such a range, so some readjustment of C1 may be needed to compensate for changes in the input impedance of the line. If the input impedance variations are not large, C1 may be used as a loading control, no changes in the coupling between L1 and the tank coil being necessary.

The degree of coupling between L1 and the amplifier tank coil will depend on the coupling-circuit Q. With a Q of 2, the coupling should be tight – comparable with the coupling that is typical of "fixed-link" manufactured coils. With a swinging link it may be necessary to increase the Q of the coupling circuit in order to get sufficient power transfer. This can be done by increasing the L/C ratio.

PI AND PI-L OUTPUT TANKS

A pi-section and pi-L tank circuit may also be used in coupling to an antenna or transmission line, as shown in Fig. 6-27. The optimum values of capacitance and inductance are dependent upon values of amplifier power input and output load resistance.

Values for L and C may be taken directly from the charts of Fig. 6-28 if the output load resistance is the usual 52 ohms. It should be borne in mind that these values apply only where the output load is resistive, i.e., where the antenna and line have been matched. Fig. 6-28 and 6-28A were provided by W6FFC.

Output-Capacitor Ratings

The voltage rating of the output capacitor will depend upon the SWR. If the load is resistive, receiving-type air capacitors should be adequate for amplifier input powers up to 2 kW PEP when

	TUBE LOAD IMPEDANCE (OPERATING Q)									
	MHz	*1500(12)*	*2000(12)*	*2500(12)*	*3000(12)*	*3500(12)*	*4000(12)*	*5000(13)*	*6000(14)*	*8000(16)*
C1	3.5	420	315	252	210	180	157	126	114	99
	7	190	143	114	95	82	71	57	52	45
	14	93	70	56	47	40	35	28	25	22
	21	62	47	37	31	27	23	19	17	15
	28	43	32	26	21	18	16	13	12	10
C2	3.5	2117	1776	1536	1352	1203	1079	875	862	862
	7	942	783	670	583	512	451	348	341	341
	14	460	382	326	283	247	217	165	162	162
	21	305	253	216	187	164	144	109	107	107
	28	210	174	148	128	111	97	72	70	70
L1	3.5	5.73	7.46	9.17	10.86	12.53	14.19	17.48	19.18	21.98
	7	3.14	4.09	5.03	5.95	6.86	7.77	9.55	10.48	12.02
	14	1.60	2.08	2.56	3.03	3.49	3.95	4.85	5.33	6.11
	21	1.07	1.39	1.71	2.02	2.34	2.64	3.25	3.56	4.09
	28	0.77	1.01	1.24	1.46	1.69	1.91	2.34	2.57	2.95

	TUBE LOAD IMPEDANCE (OPERATING Q)									
	MHz	*1500(12)*	*2000(12)*	*2500(12)*	*3000(12)*	*3500(12)*	*4000(12)*	*5000(12)*	*6000(12*	*8000(12)*
C3	3.5	406	305	244	203	174	152	122	102	76
	7	188	141	113	94	81	71	56	47	35
	14	92	69	55	46	40	35	28	23	17
	21	62	46	37	31	26	23	18	15	12
	28	43	32	26	21	18	16	13	11	8
C4	3.5	998	859	764	693	638	593	523	472	397
	7	430	370	329	298	274	255	225	203	171
	14	208	179	159	144	133	123	109	98	83
	21	139	119	106	96	89	82	73	65	55
	28	95	81	72	66	60	56	50	45	38
L2	3.5	7.06	9.05	10.99	12.90	14.79	16.67	20.37	24.03	31.25
	7	3.89	4.97	6.03	7.07	8.10	9.12	11.13	13.11	17.02
	14	1.99	2.54	3.08	3.61	4.13	4.65	5.68	6.69	8.68
	21	1.33	1.69	2.05	2.41	2.76	3.10	3.78	4.46	5.78
	28	0.96	1.22	1.48	1.74	1.99	2.24	2.73	3.22	4.17
L3	3.5	4.45	4.45	4.45	4.45	4.45	4.45	4.45	4.45	4.45
	7	2.44	2.44	2.44	2.44	2.44	2.44	2.44	2.44	2.44
	14	1.24	1.24	1.24	1.24	1.24	1.24	1.24	1.24	1.24
	21	0.83	0.83	0.83	0.83	0.83	0.83	0.83	0.83	0.83
	28	0.60	0.60	0.60	0.60	0.60	0.60	0.60	0.60	0.60

Fig. 6-28 – Chart to determine the values of L and C needed for a pi (A) and pi-L (B) network to match a range of input impedances to a 50-ohm load.

R1 Ohms	F MHz	C1 pF	L1 μH	C2 pF	R2 Ohms	Q Qual.
50	3.5	2600	0.94	4153	10	2.9
50	7.0	1179	0.49	1678	10	2.6
50	14.0	579	0.25	801	10	2.5
50	21.0	384	0.16	528	10	2.5
50	29.7	266	0.12	351	10	2.5
50	3.5	2098	1.27	2811	20	2.3
50	7.0	952	0.67	1220	20	2.1
50	14.0	467	0.34	593	20	2.1
50	21.0	310	0.23	393	20	2.0
50	29.7	214	0.16	268	20	2.0
50	3.5	2098	1.43	2533	30	2.3
50	7.0	952	0.76	1131	30	2.1
50	14.0	467	0.38	553	30	2.1
50	21.0	310	0.26	367	30	2.0
50	29.7	214	0.18	253	30	2.0
50	3.5	2098	1.55	2290	40	2.3
50	7.0	952	0.83	1033	40	2.1
50	14.0	467	0.42	506	40	2.1
50	21.0	310	0.28	336	40	2.0
50	29.7	214	0.20	232	40	2.0
50	3.5	2098	1.66	2098	50	2.3
50	7.0	952	0.88	952	50	2.1
50	14.0	467	0.45	467	50	2.1
50	21.0	310	0.30	310	50	2.0
50	29.7	214	0.21	214	50	2.0
50	3.5	2098	1.66	2098	50	2.3
50	7.0	952	0.88	952	50	2.1
50	14.0	467	0.45	467	50	2.1
50	21.0	310	0.30	310	50	2.0
50	29.7	214	0.21	214	50	2.0
75	3.5	1399	2.21	1630	50	2.3
75	7.0	634	1.17	731	50	2.1
75	14.0	311	0.59	358	50	2.1
75	21.0	207	0.40	238	50	2.0
75	29.7	143	0.28	164	50	2.0
100	3.5	1049	2.72	1337	50	2.3
100	7.0	476	1.43	591	50	2.1
100	14.0	234	0.72	288	50	2.1
100	21.0	155	0.48	191	50	2.0
100	29.7	107	0.35	131	50	2.0

R1 Ohms	F MHz	C1 pF	L1 μH	C2 pF	R2 Ohms	Q Qual.
125	3.5	839	3.19	1124	50	2.3
125	7.0	381	1.67	488	50	2.1
125	14.0	187	0.84	237	50	2.1
125	21.0	124	0.56	157	50	2.0
125	29.7	86	0.40	107	50	2.0
150	3.5	699	3.62	957	50	2.3
150	7.0	317	1.89	405	50	2.1
150	14.0	156	0.95	196	50	2.1
150	21.0	103	0.64	129	50	2.0
150	29.7	71	0.45	88	50	2.0
175	3.5	599	4.03	816	50	2.3
175	7.0	272	2.09	333	50	2.1
175	14.0	133	1.05	159	50	2.1
175	21.0	89	0.70	105	50	2.0
175	29.7	61	0.50	70	50	2.0
200	3.5	569	4.26	822	50	2.5
200	7.0	258	2.22	334	50	2.3
200	14.0	127	1.12	160	50	2.2
200	21.0	84	0.74	105	50	2.2
200	29.7	58	0.53	70	50	2.2
225	3.5	543	4.48	827	50	2.7
225	7.0	246	2.34	335	50	2.4
225	14.0	121	1.18	160	50	2.4
225	21.0	80	0.79	106	50	2.4
225	29.7	55	0.56	70	50	2.3
250	3.5	520	4.68	831	50	2.9
250	7.0	236	2.45	336	50	2.6
250	14.0	116	1.23	160	50	2.5
250	21.0	77	0.82	106	50	2.5
250	29.7	53	0.59	70	50	2.5
275	3.5	499	4.86	834	50	3.0
275	7.0	227	2.56	336	50	2.7
275	14.0	111	1.29	160	50	2.7
275	21.0	74	0.86	106	50	2.7
275	29.7	51	0.61	70	50	2.6
300	3.5	481	5.04	836	50	3.2
300	7.0	218	2.66	337	50	2.9
300	14.0	107	1.34	160	50	2.8
300	21.0	71	0.89	106	50	2.8
300	29.7	49	0.64	70	50	2.8

Fig. 6-28A – The following data is for a pi network with a Q of 2 at the top of each band. The Q shown is that for the same inductor at the bottom of the band. The capacitors are shown for the bottom of the band to indicate the maximum capacitance needed. If the transformation ratio exceeds 70 percent of maximum, the Q has been automatically recalculated in order to retain the characteristics of a pi network and that new value shown. Do not forget which end of the network represents 50 ohms!

feeding 52- 75-ohm loads. In obtaining the larger capacitances required for the lower frequencies, it is common practice to switch one or more fixed capacitors in parallel with the variable air capacitor. While the voltage rating of a mica or ceramic capacitor may not be exceeded in a particluar case, capacitors of these types are limited in current-carrying capacity. Postage-stamp silver-mica capacitors should be adequate for amplifier inputs over the range from about 70 watts at 28 MHz to 400 watts at 14 MHz and lower. The larger mica capacitors (CM-45 case) having voltage ratings of 1200 and 2500 volts are usually satisfactory for inputs varying from about 350 watts at 28 MHz to 1 kW at 14 MHz and lower. Because of these current limitations, particularly at the higher frequencies, it is advisable to use as large an air capacitor as practicable, using the micas only at the lower frequencies. Broadcast-receiver replacement-type capacitors can be obtained reasonably. Their voltage insulation should be adequate. for inputs of 1000 watts or more.

TRANSISTOR OUTPUT CIRCUITS

Since rf power transistors have a low output impedance (on the order of 5 ohms or less), the problem of coupling the transistor to the usual 50-ohm load is the reverse of the problem with a vacuum-tube amplifier. The 50-ohm load must be transformed to a low resistance.

Figs 6-29A and B show two types of parallel-tuned circuits used to couple the load to the collector circuit. The collector is tapped down on the inductor in both cases. C1 provides tuning

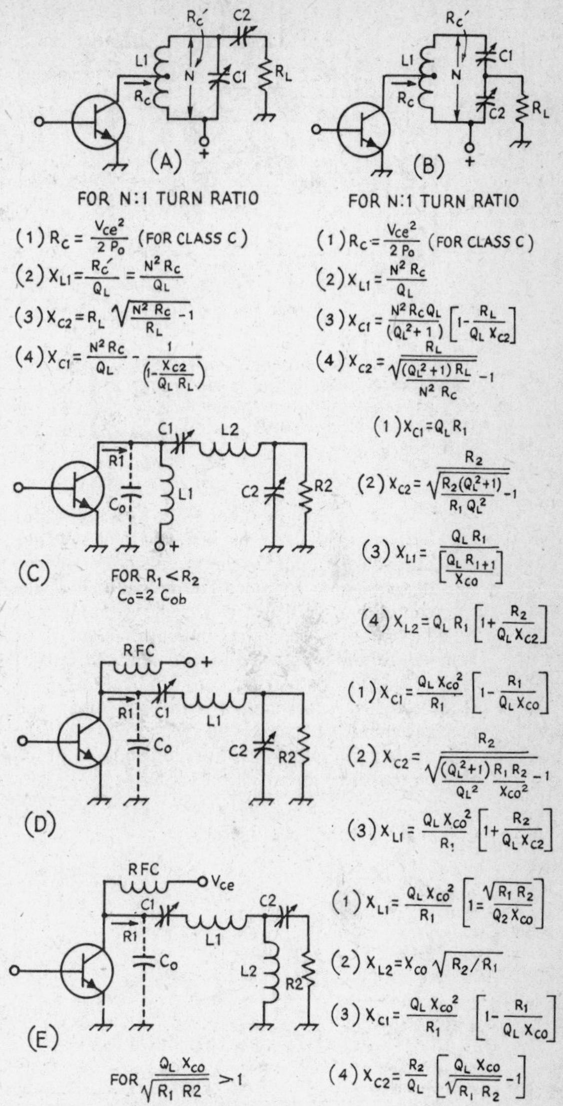

Fig. 6-29 — Typical transistor output-matching networks.

for the collector and C2 adjusts the coupling to the load to achieve the proper impedance transformation. The use of the tapped connection to the inductor helps to maintain the loaded Q of the circuit while minimizing variations in tuning with changes in the junction capacitance of the transistor.

Circuits of Figs. 6-29C through E are not dependent upon coupling coefficient of a tapped coil for load-impedance transformation, making them more suitable for use at hf than either A or B. The collector-emitter capacitance (C_o) of the transistor is a major factor in the calculations used to design these circuits. Unfortunately C_o is not constant, so cut-and-try adjustments are usually necessary to optimize a particular circuit.

Early tests of transistor rf power amplifiers should be made with low voltage, a dummy load and no drive. Some form of output indicator should be included. When it has been established that no instability exists, the drive can be applied in increments and adjustment made for maximum output. The amplifier should never be operated at high voltage and no load.

BROADBAND COUPLING

The techniques of broadband-transformer construction use transmission-line elements. A transformer consists of a short transmission line (one-eighth wavelength or less) made from a twisted-wire pair, coaxial or strip line, wound on a high-permeability toroid core to improve the low-frequency characteristics. At vhf the core may be omitted. Only discrete impedance transformations are possible; typical ratios are 9/4:1, 4:1, 9:1, 16:1, and 25:1. The higher ratios are difficult to achieve in practice, so several 4:1 transformers are employed for a large transformation ratio as shown in Fig. 6-23. Hybrid transformers, providing the 180-degree phase shift for input and output matching to push-pull stages, may also be made using broadband techniques.

Large toroid cores are not required for moderate power levels. A one-half inch diameter core is sufficient for operation at 100 watts at the low impedance levels found in transistor circuits. Because the current is high it is important to keep the resistance of the conductors low. Multiconductor leads (3 or 4 strands of No. 26 enam., twisted) or the flat enam. strip used for transformer windings) are suitable. Some typical designs are shown in Table 6-II.

STABILIZING AMPLIFIERS

A straight amplifier operates with its input and output circuits tuned to the same frequency. Therefore, unless the coupling between these two circuits is brought to the necessary minimum, the amplifier will oscillate as a tuned-plate tuned-grid circuit. Care should be used in arranging components and wiring of the two circuits so that there will be negligible opportunity for coupling external to the tube or transistor itself. Complete shielding between input and output circuits usually is required. All rf leads should be kept as short as possible and particular attention should be paid to the rf return paths from input and output tank circuits to emitter or cathode. In general, the best arrangement using a tube is one in which the cathode connection to ground, and the plate tank circuit are on the same side of the chassis or other shielding. The "hot" lead from the input tank (or driver plate tank) should be brought to the socket through a hole in the shielding. Then when the grid tank capacitor or bypass is grounded, a return path through the hole to cathode will be encouraged, since transmission-line characteristics are simulated.

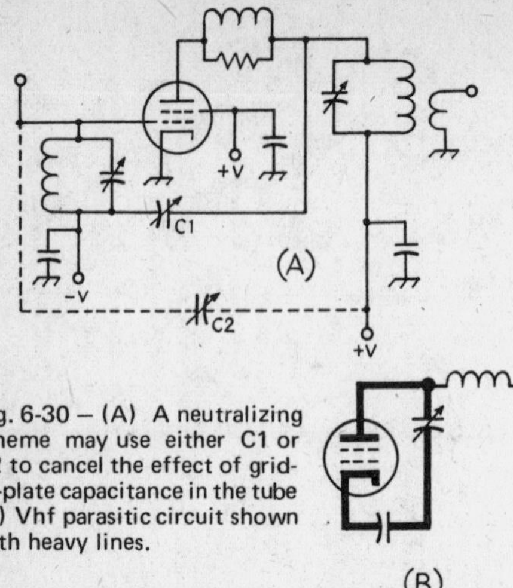

Fig. 6-30 – (A) A neutralizing scheme may use either C1 or C2 to cancel the effect of grid-to-plate capacitance in the tube (B) Vhf parasitic circuit shown with heavy lines.

A check on external coupling between input and output circuits can be made with a sensitive indicating device, such as the wavemeter shown in the Measurements chapter. The amplifying device is removed. With the driver stage running and tuned to resonance, the indicator should be coupled to the output tank coil and the output tank capacitor tuned for any indication of rf feedthrough. Experiment with shielding and rearrangement of parts will show whether the isolation can be improved. For additional information on transistor circuits see Chapter 4.

Screen-Grid Tube Neutralizing Circuits

The plate-grid capacitance of screen-grid tubes is reduced to a fraction of a picofarad by the interposed grounded screen. Nevertheless, the power sensitivity of these tubes is so great that only a very small amount of feedback is necessary to start oscillation. To assure a stable amplifier, it is usually necessary to load the grid circuit, or to use a neutralizing circuit.

The capacitive neutralizing system for screen-grid tubes is shown in Fig. 6-30A. C1 is the neutralizing capacitor. The capacitance should be chosen so that at some adjustment of C1,

$$\frac{C1}{C3} = \frac{\text{Tube grid-plate capacitance (or } C_{gp})}{\text{Tube input capacitance (or } C_{IN})}$$

The grid-cathode capacitance must include all strays directly across the tube capacitance, including the capacitance of the tuning-capacitor stator to ground. This may amount to 5 to 20 pF. In the case of capacitance coupling, the output capacitance of the driver tube must be added to the grid-cathode capacitance of the amplifier in arriving at the value of C1.

Neutralizing a Screen-Grid Amplifier Stage

There are two general procedures available for indicating neutralization in a screen-grid amplifier stage. If the screen-grid tube is operated with or without grid current, a sensitive output indicator

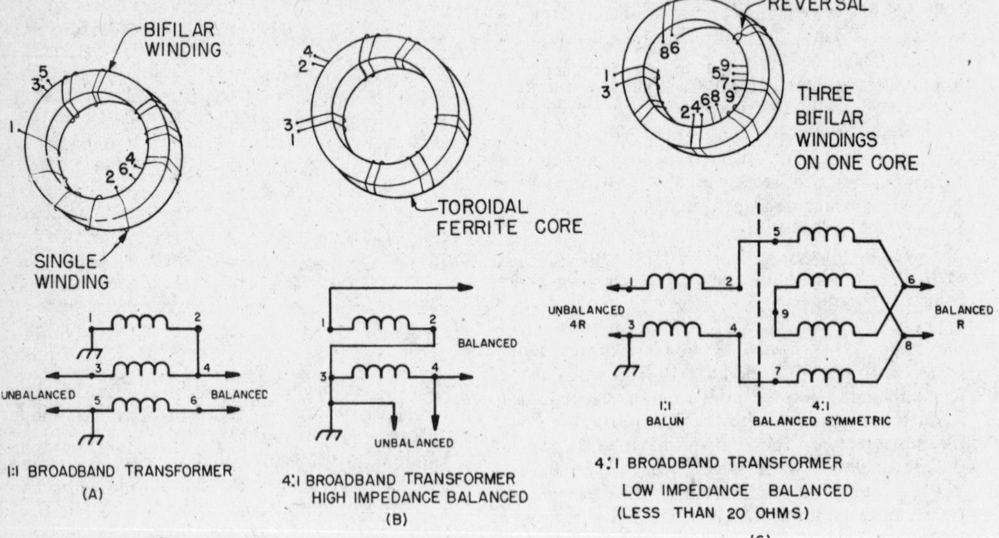

UNBALANCED 4R
UNBALANCED R
UNBALANCED AUTO-TRANSFORMER
(E)
UNBALANCED
UNBALANCED
1:1 PHASE REVERSING TRANSFORMER
(G)

Table 6-II – Basic broadband balun transformers. Bifilar windings are six to ten turns, depending on the ferrite-core permeability. A suitable ferrite material is Q1 with a permeability of 125. Very small size cores (1/4-to 3/4-inch OD) may be used for receiving and low-power applications. For full-power applications a 2-1/2-inch OD Q1 core with 1/2-inch cross section wound with No. 14 Formex copper wire, seven turns per winding, is recommended.

can be used. If the screen-grid tube is operated with grid current, the grid-current reading can be used as an indication of neutralization. When the output indicator is used, both screen and plate voltages must be removed from the tubes, but the dc circuits from the plate and screen to cathode must be completed. If the grid-current reading is used, the plate voltage may remain on but the screen voltage must be zero, with the dc circuit completed between screen and cathode.

The immediate objective of the neutralizing process is reducing to a minimum the rf driver voltage fed from the input of the amplifier to its output circuit through the grid-plate capacitance of the tube. This is done by adjusting carefully, bit by bit, the neutralizing capacitor or link coils until an rf indicator in the output circuit reads minimum, or the reaction of the unloaded plate-circuit tuning on the grid-current value is minimized.

The wavementer shown in the Measurements chapter makes a sensitive neutralizing indicator. The wavemeter coil should be coupled to the output tank coil at the low-potential or "ground" point. Care should be taken to make sure that the coupling is loose enough at all times to prevent buring out the meter or the rectifier. The plate tank capacitor should be readjusted for maximum reading after each change in neutralizing.

When the grid-current meter is used as a neutralizing indicator, the screen should be grounded for rf and dc, as mentioned above. There will be a change in grid current as the unloaded plate tank circuit is tuned through resonance. The neutralizing capacitor (or inductor) should be adjusted until this deflection is brought to a minimum. As a final adjustment, screen voltage should be returned and the neutralizing adjustment continued to the point where minimum plate current, maximum grid current and maximum screen current occur simultaneously. An increase in grid current when the plate tank circuit is tuned slightly on the high-frequency side of resonance indicates that the neutralizing capacitance is too small. If the increase is on the low-frequency side, the neutralizing capacitance is too large. When neutralization is complete, there should be a slight decrease in grid current on either side of resonance.

Grid Loading

The use of a neutralizing circuit may often be avoided by loading the grid circuit if the driving stage has some power capability to spare. Loading by tapping the grid down on the grid tank coil (or the plate tank coil of the driver in the case of capacitive coupling), or by a resistor from grid to cathode is effective in stabilizing an amplifier.

VHF Parasitic Oscillation

Parasitic oscillation in the vhf range will take place in almost every rf power amplifier. To test for vhf parasitic oscillation, the grid tank coil (or driver tank coil in the case of capacitive coupling) should be short-circuited with a clip lead. This is to prevent any possible t.g.t.p. oscillation at the operating frequency which might lead to confusion in identifying the parasitic. Any fixed bias should be replaced with a grid leak of 10,000 to 20,000 ohms. All load on the output of the amplifier should be disconnected. Plate and screen voltages should be reduced to the point where the rated dissipation is not exceeded. If a Variac is not available, voltage may be reduced by a 117-volt lamp in series with the primary of the plate transformer.

With power applied only to the amplifier under test, a search should be made by adjusting the input capacitor to several settings, including minimum and maximum, and turning the plate capacitor through its range for each of the grid-capacitor settings. Any grid current, or any dip or flicker in plate current at any point, indicates oscillation. This can be confirmed by an indicating absorption wavemeter tuned to the frequency of the parasitic and held close to the plate lead of the tube.

The heavy lines of Fig. 6-30B show the usual parasitic tank circuit, which resonates, in most cases, between 100 and 200 MHz. For each type of tetrode, there is a region, usually below the parasitic frequency, in which the tube will be self-neutralized. By adding the right amount of inductance to the parasitic circuit, its resonant frequency can be brought down to the frequency at which the tube is self-neutralized. However, the resonant frequency should not be brought down so low that it falls close to TV Channel 6 (88 MHz). From the consideration of TVI, the circuit may be loaded down to a frequency not lower than 100 MHz. If the self-neutralizing frequency is below 100 MHz, the circuit should be loaded down to somewhere between 100 and 120 MHz with inductance. Then the parasitic can be suppressed by loading with resistance. A coil of 4 or 5 turns, 1/4 inch in diameter, is a good starting size. With the tank capacitor turned to maximum capacitance, the circuit should be checked with a GDO to make sure the resonance is above 100 MHz. Then, with the shortest possible leads, a noninductive 100-ohm 1-watt resistor should be connected across the entire coil. The amplifier should be tuned up to its highest-frequency band and operated at low voltage. The tap should be moved a little at a time to find the minimum number of turns required to suppress the parasitic. Then voltage should be increased until the resistor begins to feel warm after several minutes of operation, and the power input noted. This input should be compared with the normal input and the *power* rating of the resistor increased by this proportion; i.e., if the power is half normal, the wattage rating should be doubled. This increase is best made by connecting 1-watt *carbon* resistors in parallel to give a resultant of about 100 ohms. Or, one of the Globar surge-protection resistors may be used. As power input is increased, the parasitic may start up again, so power should be applied only momentarily until it is made certain that the parasitic is still suppressed. If the parasitic starts up again when voltage is raised, the tap must be moved to include more turns. So long as the parasitic is suppressed, the resistors will heat up only from the operating-frequency current. In grounded-grid

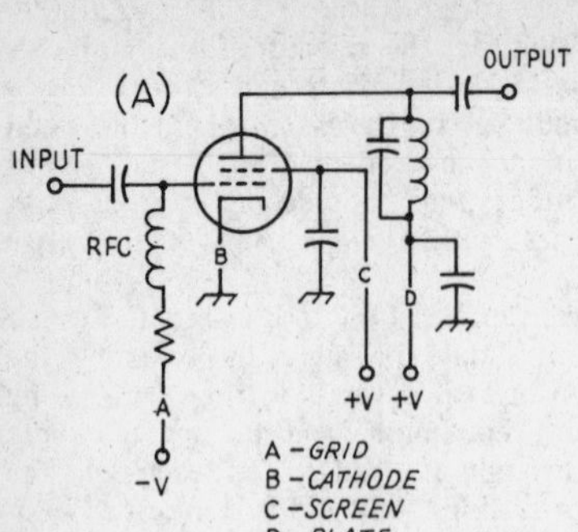

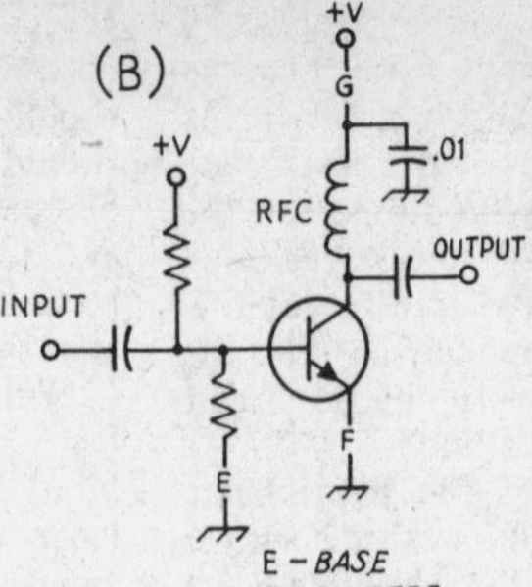

Fig. 6-31 – Metering circuits for (A) tubes and (B) transistors. To measure current, connect a meter at the point shown *in series with the lead.* For voltage measurements, connect the meter from the point indicated *to the common or ground connection.*

circuits it is useful to locate the parasitic suppressor in the cathode lead, as the rf power level is less than at the plate terminal.

Since the resistor can be placed across only that portion of the parasitic circuit represented by L_p, the latter should form as large a portion of the circuit as possible. Therefore, the tank and bypass capacitors should have the lowest possible inductance and the leads shown in heavy lines should be as short as possible and of the heaviest pratical conductor. This will permit L_p to be of maximum size without tuning the circuit below the 100-MHz limit.

Another arrangement that has been used successfully in transistor and low-level tube stages is to place one or more ferrite beads over the input or output leads, as close as possible to the amplifying device. The beads have sufficient low-Q inductance at vhf to discourage any tendency toward parasitic oscillation.

Low-Frequency Parasitic Oscillation

The screening of most transmitting screen-grid tubes is sufficient to prevent low-frequency parasitic oscillation caused by resonant circuits set up by rf chokes in grid and plate circuits. When rf chokes are used in both grid and plate circuits of a triode amplifier, the split-stator tank capacitors combine with the rf chokes to form a low-frequency parasitic circuit, unless the amplifier circuit is arranged to prevent it. Often, a resistor is substituted for the grid rf choke, which will produce the desired result. This resistance should be at least 100 ohms. If any grid-leak resistance is used for biasing, it should be substituted for the 100-ohm resistor.

Transistor LF Parasitics

Using transistors with shunt feed often means low-frequency parasitic trouble. A word about this problem is in order as it usually doesn't occur in vacuum-tube circuits and is often a rough problem for the newcomer to solid state. These parasitics manifest themselves as a wide spectrum of white noise (hash) around and below the operating frequency. They can often be heard on a broadcast receiver several feet away from a transmitter under test. The desired signal may sound clean, so it is necessary to check far below the operating frequency. Two transistor characteristics combine to cause this trouble. First, transistors have higher gain at lower frequencies than they do at hf. Second, interelement capacitances vary over a wide range of changes in voltage, the result being varactor action that causes spurious outputs. The best way to avoid the problem is to use a minimum of inductance in the collector circuit. Large chokes are unsatisfactory. Series feed is a good answer as no choke is needed. Bypass capacitors should be the minimum value required. Decoupling on power leads between stages should have at least two capacitors, one effective at the operating frequency and a second large capacitor that is good at low frequencies.

METERING

Fig. 6-31 shows how a voltmeter and milliammeter should be connected to read various voltages and currents. Voltmeters are seldom installed permanently, since their principal use is in preliminary checking. Also, milliammeters are not normally installed permanently in all of the positions shown. Those most often used are the ones reading grid current and plate current, or grid current and cathode current, or collector current.

Milliammeters come in various current ranges. Current values to be expected can be taken from the tube tables and the meter ranges selected accordingly. To take care of normal overloads and pointer swing, a meter having a current range of about twice the normal current to be expected should be selected.

Grid-current meters connected as shown in Fig. 6-31 and meters connected in the cathode circuit need no special precautions in mounting on the transmitter panel so far as safety is concerned. However, milliammeters having metal zero-adjusting screws on the face of the meter should be recessed behind the panel so that accidental contact with the adjusting screw is not possible, if the meter is connected in any of the other positions shown in Fig. 6-31. The meter can be mounted on a small subpanel attached to the front panel with long screws and spacers. The meter opening should be covered with glass or celluloid. Illuminated meters make reading easier. Reference should also be made to the TVI chapter of this *Handbook* in regard to wiring and shielding of meters to suppress TVI.

COMPONENT RATINGS

Output Tank Capacitor Voltage

In selecting a tank capacitor with a spacing between plates sufficient to prevent voltage breakdown, the peak rf voltage across a tank circuit under load, but without modulation, may be taken conservatively as equal to the dc plate or collector voltage. If the dc supply voltage also appears across the tank capacitor, this must be added to the peak rf voltage, making the total peak voltage twice the dc supply voltage. If the amplifier is to be plate-modulated, this last value must be doubled to make it four times the dc plate voltage, because both dc and rf voltages double with 100-percent amplitude modulation. At the higher voltages, it is desirable to choose a tank circuit in which the dc and modulation voltages do not appear across the tank capacitor, to permit the use of a smaller capacitor with less plate spacing.

Capacitor manufacturers usually rate their products in terms of the peak voltage between plates. Typical plate spacings are shown in the following table, 6-III.

Output tank capacitors should be mounted as close to the tube as temperature considerations will permit, to make possible the shortest capacitive path from plate to cathode. Especially at the higher frequencies where minimum circuit capacitance becomes important, the capacitor should be mounted with its stator plates well spaced from the chassis or other shielding. In circuits where the rotor must be insulated from ground, the capacitor should be mounted on ceramic insulators of size commensurate with the plate voltage involved and – most important of all, from the viewpoint of safety to the operator – a well-insulated coupling should be used between the capacitor shaft and the dial. *The section of the shaft attached to the dial should be well grounded.* This can be done conveniently through the use of panel shaft-bearing units.

Table 6-III

Typical Tank-Capacitor Plate Spacings

Spacing (In.)	*Peak Voltage*	*Spacing (In.)*	*Peak Voltage*	*Spacing (In.)*	*Peak Voltage*
0.015	1000	0.07	3000	0.175	7000
0.02	1200	0.08	3500	0.25	9000
0.03	1500	0.125	4500	0.35	11000
0.05	2000	0.15	6000	0.5	13000

Tank Coils

Tank coils should be mounted at least their diameter away from shielding to prevent a marked loss in Q. Except perhaps at 28 MHz it is not important that the coil be mounted quite close to the tank capacitor. Leads up to 6 or 8 inches are permissible. It is more important to keep the tank capacitor as well as other components out of the immediate field of the coil. For this reason, it is preferable to mount the coil so that its axis is parallel to the capacitor shaft, either alongside the capacitor or above it.

Wire Sizes for Transmitting Coils for Tube Transmitters

Power Input (Watts)	*Band (MHz)*	*Wire Size*
1000	28–21	6
	14–7	8
	3.5–1.8	10
500	28–21	8
	14–7	12
	3.5–1.8	14
150	28–21	12
	14–7	14
	3.5–1.8	18
75	28–21	14
	14–7	18
	3.5–1.8	22
25 or less*	28–21	18
	14–7	24
	3.5–1.8	28

* Wire size limited principally by consideration of Q.

There are many factors that must be taken into consideration in determining the size of wire that should be used in winding a tank coil. The considerations of form factor and wire size that will produce a coil of minimum loss are often of less importance in practice than the coil size that will fit into available space or that will handle the required power without excessive heating. This is particularly true in the case of screen-grid tubes where the relatively small driving power required can be easily obtained even if the losses in the driver are quite high. It may be considered preferable to take the power loss if the physical size of the exciter can be kept down by making the coils small.

Transistor output circuits operate at relatively low impedances because the current is quite high. Coils should be made of heavy wire or strap, with connections made for the lowest possible resistance. At vhf stripline techniques are often employed, as the small inductance values required for a lumped inductance become difficult to fabricate.

RF Chokes

The characteristics of any rf choke will vary with frequency, from characteristics resembling those of a parallel-resonant circuit, of high impedance, to those of a series-resonant circuit, where the impedance is lowest. In between these extremes, the choke will show varying amounts of inductive or capacitive reactance.

In series-feed circuits, these characteristics are of relatively small importance because the rf voltage across the choke is negligible. In a parallel-feed circuit, however, the choke is shunted across the tank circuit, and is subject to the full tank rf voltage. If the choke does not present a sufficiently high impedance, enough power will be abosrbed by the choke to cause it to burn out.

To avoid this, the choke must have a sufficiently high reactance to be effective at the lowest frequency, and yet have no series resonances near the higher-frequency bands.

A TWO-BAND VFO-CONTROLLED TRANSMITTER

The degree of circuit sophistication used in homemade amateur gear is usually decided on the basis of operating convenience, academic interest in circuit design, and the amount of money available for a project. Certainly, the foregoing is a self-evident piece of philosophy, but is worth stating here to establish the reasons behind what may appear to be extreme complexity in the design of a 10-watt transmitter. The basic purpose here is to expose a variety of circuit conveniences, many of which can be applied to transmitters which the reader may already have at hand. Bits and pieces of this composite may be of interest to those who are presently embarking upon a design venture for an original circuit to fill a specific need. Those wishing to duplicate the basic portion of this package should have no reservations about deleting all parts of the circuit which do not relate directly to the VFO and main transmitter sections. The keyer, SWR inductor, break-in delay circuit, and sidetone oscillator need not be included in the project in order to effect good performance. Similarly, the circuit can be built for single-band operation (40 or 20 meters), thus negating the need for a band switch.

When used separately, this transmitter will provide plenty of operating pleasure, even for the DX-minded amateur. If it is used in combination with a tube-type or solid-state "pair of shoes" one should be able to elevate the output power of the station. As a low-power (QRP) transmitter, this unit qualifies nicely for portable work at camp sites, for Field Day operation, or for emergency use. It can be connected to a 12-volt car or NiCad battery, or it can be powered from an ac-operated dc supply (preferably of the regulated variety). Total current consumption is on the order of 1 ampere.

Exterior view of the two-band 10-watt transmitter. A homemade aluminum box is used to house the circuit. The cover has been sprayed with black paint. The panel is gray. White press-on decals are used to identify the controls. A small LED is used as a panel lamp. It is located just above the on-off switch.

The IC VFO

An RCA CA3046 transistor-array IC was selected for use in the VFO portion of the rig (Fig. 1). The chip contains five npn bipolar transistors, two of which are connected as a differential pair (emitters in parallel). It seemed like a good idea to use the IC so that the differential pair could be employed as a push-push doubler to multiply the fundamental 7-MHz VFO energy to 14 MHz. Since the devices on the substrate of U1 have uniform characteristics the doubler should work very well, and indeed it does. Very little 7-MHz energy appears in the output of the doubler. A parallel-tuned trap was added to the 14-MHz output line to remove the residual 7-MHz component at the output port.

One of the separate bipolar transistors on the chip is used as a Colpitts VFO. Another is used between the oscillator and the doubler as a phase splitter, thus providing push-pull drive to the doubler. During operation on 40 meters the doubler B-plus voltage is removed and routed by means of S1 to an *R-C*-coupled 7-MHz buffer transistor, Q1. Drive to Q1 is taken from the emitter of the phase splitter. A 7-MHz buffer/amplifier was necessary to establish similar rms output levels from the VFO on each band of operation. The remaining transistor of U1 is unused. The CA3046 works very well at 7 and 14 MHz because the device has a rated f_T of 550 MHz. Three 10-ohm resistors are used (terminals 1, 5 and 9) to discourage vhf parasitic oscillations. CR1 is outboard from the VFO box, and is saturated during receive periods to shift the VFO frequency some 50 kHz away from the operating frequency, thereby preventing the VFO from interfering with reception of the incoming signal.

An RCA CA3045 will work equally well at U1. The terminal connections are the same. The only difference in the IC types is that one is packaged in a ceramic case, while the other is in a plastic housing. Two of these ICs were obtained as surplus for $1.

Stability of the VFO is excellent. Total drift at 7 MHz from a cold start to stabilization (3 minutes) was measured as 80 Hz. VR1 keeps the VFO operating voltage stabilized at 8.2 volts.

Buffer, Driver and PA

An untuned buffer is used at Q4, Fig. 3, to assure reasonable isolation between the VFO and the driver stage (Q5) of the transmitter strip. A low-cost 2N2222 transistor is used at Q3 because they were available from Poly Paks at five for $1. Transistors with similar electrical characteristics should work equally well at Q3. A 2N4427 boosts the signal from Q3 to a level suitable for driving PA transistor Q6. The tuned circuit in the collector of Q5 is resonant at 14 MHz until S2 is switched to the 40-meter position. At that time an additional trimmer capacitor is placed in parallel with the 20-meter trimmer, thus lowering the resonant frequency of the tank to 7 MHz. The collector of Q5 is tapped down on L4 to effect an impedance match and to maintain the *Q* of the tuned circuit through reduced loading effects from Q5.

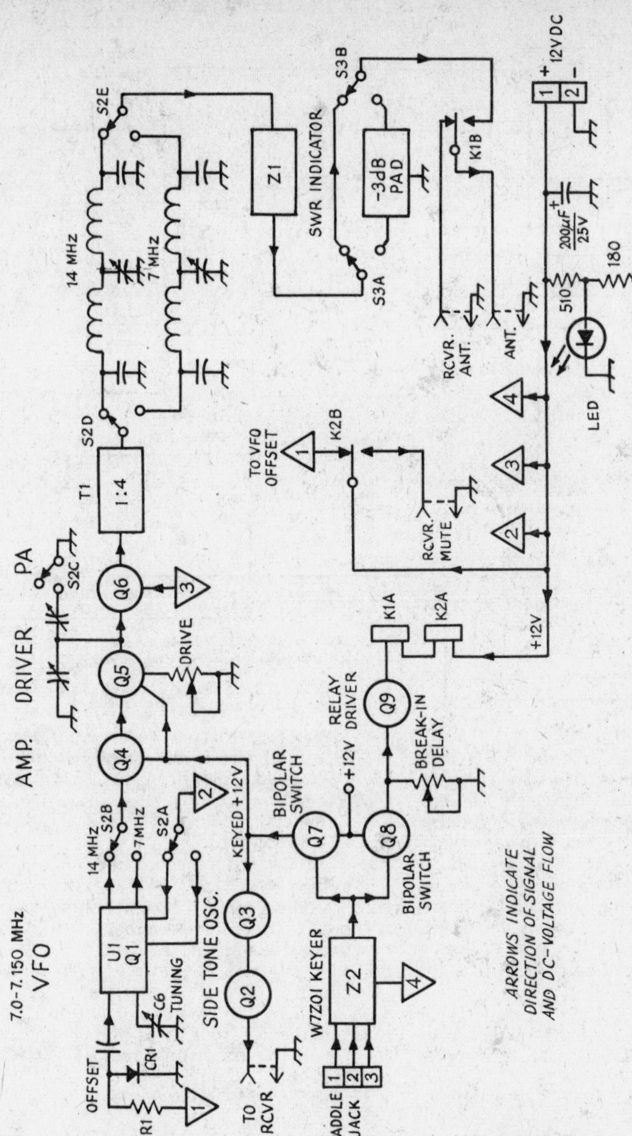

Fig. 1 — Block diagram which illustrates how the sections of the transmitter are connected. Z1 is the SWR indicator discussed in the text. Z1, Z2 and the −3 dB pad can be deleted if the builder so desires.

An RCA 2N5995 was chosen for the PA stage, Q6, because it is a vhf transistor capable of 10 watts output. When used for hf-band applications, it exhibits higher gain than at vhf. The increased beta permits the device to deliver comparable power output at drive levels considerably below those needed at vhf. The 2N5995 is "mismatch tested" by the manufacturer, and is unlikely to burn out during temporary periods (30 seconds) of no load, dead short, or somewhere between at the output of the collector tank.

The collector impedance of Q6 (7 watts output) is approximately 11 ohms, as determined from the formula, Z (collector) = $V\text{ce}^2 \div 2P\text{o}\ (W)$. This condition called for use of a 4:1 broadband toroidal transformer to raise the impedance to a 50-ohm value (44 ohms in reality). The 50-ohm impedance level is much less difficult to work with when doing network design with practical values of L and C. The PA tank network consists of two pi sections in cascade. Each is designed for a Q_L of 4, and each network is built to match 50 to 300 ohms. The 300-ohm ports are joined at the center of the network, where a trimmer capacitor is used to tune the tank circuit to resonance. Because pi networks are low-pass filters, harmonic output from the transmitter is down 50 dB or more (measured). In fact, no evidence of harmonic currents could be observed on the output wave form when checking for purity with a Tektronix 453 scope (50-MHz bandwidth). The loaded Q of the tank is sufficiently low to permit operation

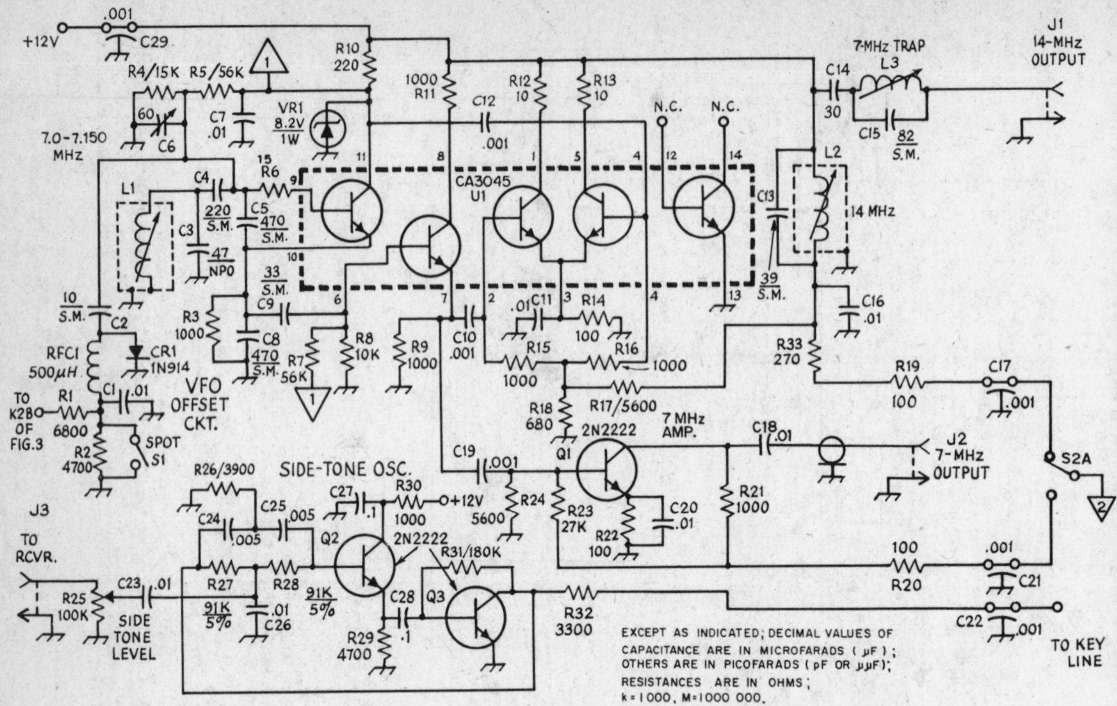

Fig. 2 — Schematic diagram of the VFO and sidetone circuits. Fixed-value resistors are 1/2 watt composition unless specified differently. Fixed-value capacitors are disk ceramic unless otherwise indicated. C17, 21, 22 and 29 are feedthrough types. The internal circuit of U1 is illustrated to aid the reader in understanding how the circuit operates. Triangles containing numbers indicate points within the circuit of Fig. 2 which are joined. Numbered components not appearing in the parts list are so numbered for pc-board identification purposes only.

C6 — 60-pF miniature air variable, double-bearing type recommended (J. W. Miller No. 1460 with all sections in parallel).

CR1 — Silicon switching diode. 1N914 or equiv.

J1 - J3, incl. — Phono jack, single-hole mount.

L1 — Shielded inductor, 3 to 7 µH (J. W. Miller 905 or equiv.).

L2 — Shielded inductor, 1.5 to 3 µH (J. W. Miller 9050 or equiv.).

L3 — Variable inductor, 5.5 to 8.6 µH (J. W. Miller 4505 or equiv.).

R25 — Linear-taper 100,000-ohm composition control (mounted external to VFO on rear apron of the main chassis).

RFC1 — 500-µH rf choke (Millen J300-500 or equiv.).

S1 — Spst momentary pushbutton switch (mounted on front panel of main chassis).

U1 — RCA transistor-array IC (CA3045 or CA3046).

VR1 — 8.2-V, 1-W Zener diode.

across the 7- and 14-MHz cw bands without need to retune the tank.

A drive control is connected in the emitter circuit of the driver stage, Q5, to enable the QRP "purist" to reduce power to practically zero output. This feature is beneficial also when adjusting power output to the necessary level for driving an outboard amplifier. One can operate the equipment from batteries by lowering the driving power. At, say, the 2-watt rf output level, the current drawn by the transmitter will be on the order of 250 mA. At reduced power the PA tank network will no longer be optimum in terms of impedance matching, but no ill effects will result.

Break-In Delay

Those not wanting to include the break-in delay circuit can "float" the key jack and make and break the operating voltage to the driver stage and side-tone board by means of the external key. Elimination of the break-in circuit would require the addition of an external antenna changeover relay or switch.

The delay circuit (Fig. 3) consists of two pnp bipolar switches, Q7 and Q8, which are saturated simultaneously when the keying line is grounded. Q7, when saturated, permits the flow of +12 volts to buffer Q4, driver Q5, and the side-tone circuit. The remaining solid-state switch, Q8, supplies a charging voltage to the *RC* timing circuit between the base of relay driver Q9 and ground. CR2 acts as a voltage gate, and CR3 in series with CR4 bias Q7 to cutoff under key-up conditions to enable K1 and K2 to drop out when the charging voltage of the timing network decays. CR5 is used across the relay field coils to prevent transients from reaching the 12-volt bus as the relay field coils are de-energized. The hold-in time of the delay circuit is

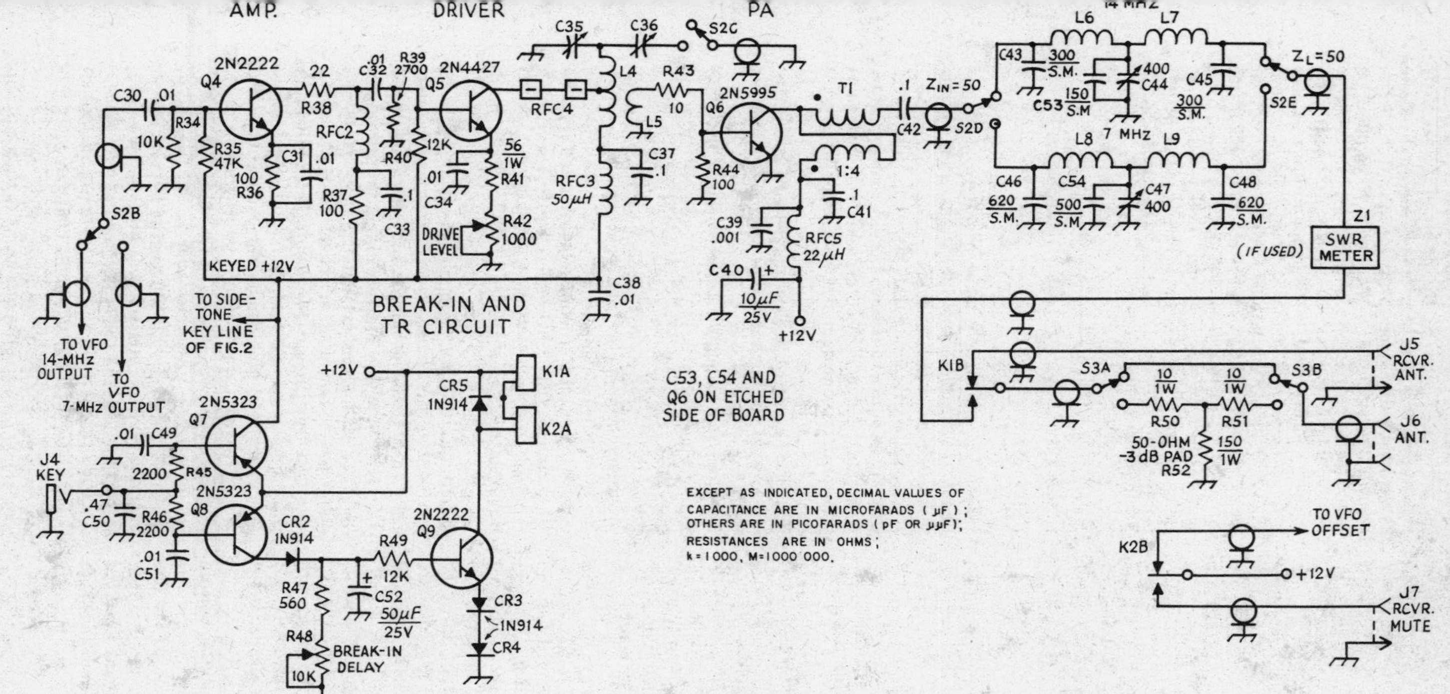

Fig. 3 — Schematic diagram of the transmitter and break-in delay circuits. Fixed-value resistors are 1/2 watt composition unless specified differently. Fixed-value capacitors are disk ceramic unless otherwise indicated. Numbered components not appearing in the parts list are so numbered for pc-board identification purposes only.

C35, C36 — 37 to 250-pF mica compression trimmer (Elmenco 426 or equiv.).
C44, C47 — 90 to 400-pF mica compression trimmer (Elmenco 429 or equiv.).
J4 — Two-circuit phone jack (used only if built-in W7ZOI keyer not used).
J5, J7 — Phono jack, single-hole mount.
J6 — SO-239 type coax connector.
K1, K2 — Spdt 500-ohm relay. Relay fields connected in series for 12-V use (Radio Shack/Archer No. 275-004 or equiv.).
L4 — 22 turns No. 24 enam. wire on Amidon T-50-6 toroid core (2.4 µH), tapped at 11 turns.
L5 — 4 turns No. 24 enam. wound over L4 winding.
L6, L7 — 12 turns No. 20 enam. wire on Amidon T-68-6 toroid core (1.1 µH).
L8, L9 — 18 turns No. 20 enam. wire on Amidon T-68-2 toroid core (2.2 µH).
Q5-Q8, incl. — RCA transistor. Use heat sinks on Q5 and Q6 transistors.
R42 — 1000-ohm linear-taper carbon control (mount on front panel).
R48 — 10,000-ohm linear-taper carbon control (mount on rear panel).
RFC2 — 1-mH rf choke (Millen J300-1000 or equiv.).
RFC3 — 50-µH rf choke (Millen J300-50 or equiv.).
RFC5 — 22-µH rf choke (Millen 34300-22 or equiv.).
S2 — 5-pole, 2-position rotary switch (phenolic or ceramic types suitable). Surplus Grayhill type used in this transmitter.
S3 — Dpdt toggle or wafer switch.
T1 — 4:1 broadband toroidal transformer. 16 turns No. 22 enam. wire, bifilar wound on Amidon T-68-2 toroid core. Connect windings as shown, observing correct phasing as indicated by dots.
Z1 — SWR indicator. See text if module is used in transmitter being built.

Inside view of the transmitter. The VFO and side-tone circuits are contained in the box at the upper center. The VFO tuning capacitor is visible at the right center of the photograph. A metal shield surrounds it to help keep rf energy (from the driver and PA stages) out of the VFO. The transmitter strip is in the lower foreground. A homemade heat sink is used on Q6 and is prominent at the center of the pc board. The break-in delay and SWR-indicator boards are located between the main transmitter board and the VFO box. Attached to the rear outer wall of the VFO box is the W7ZOI keyer. The VFO offset circuitry is assembled at the upper right of the picture, just below the meter. L-shaped brackets are used on the inner edges of the chassis to permit attachment of the cover by means of No. 6 sheet-metal screws.

adjustable by means of a 10,000-ohm control on the rear apron of the chassis.

Side-Tone Oscillator

Fig. 2 shows the two-transistor sidetone circuit. A simple twin-T audio oscillator is used to generate a 700-Hz note which follows the keying rate without clicks or chirp. Output is taken from the junction of two resistors in the frequency-determining *R-C* network. Output can be obtained at three points in the circuit, but the best wave form available is found at the terminal used here. A sidetone level control is located on the rear panel of the transmitter, and can be adjusted to provide comfortable listening with the receiver being used.

SWR Indicator

The SWR indicator was included as an operating convenience for use afield when it might be necessary to prune the length of a coax-fed antenna for lowest SWR. It is useful also in tuning the transmitter for maximum output into the antenna being used. Complete circuit and pc-board information for the module is given in *QST* for June, 1973, and will not be repeated here. A 3-dB T pad has been included in the line to the antenna jack. It can be switched into the line for use while adjusting an external Transmatch. The pad provides a nearly constant load for the PA until a 50-ohm match is obtained. This part of the circuit can also be eliminated.

One circuit appendage remains . . . the built-in keyer. This module can be left out of the package if the builder does not care to include it. The circuit for the keyer was described by Hayward in *QST* for November, 1971. Circuit boards for the keyer, plus layout information, are available from W7ZOI for $3.

Assembly Information

A homemade aluminum chassis/cabinet was formed from 1/16-inch stock. The dimensions (HWD) are 3 × 10 × 8-1/2 inches. Those wishing to use a commercially made enclosure of almost identical appearance and dimensions can order one by mail from Apollo Products.[1]

Sections of double-clad pc-board stock were used to form the VFO box. The sides are joined by soldering them at each corner (full length of seam) while using a medium-heat iron. The VFO compartment measures (HWD) 2 × 3-3/8 × 4-1/2 inches. This box, and all edge-mounted pc boards, are secured to the chassis by means of No. 6 spade bolts.[2]

Aluminum shielding is used around the VFO tuning capacitor to help prevent stray rf (from the high-level stages of the transmitter) from getting into the VFO. Feedthrough capacitors are mounted on the walls of the VFO box and are used to filter the dc-voltage leads which enter the compartment (also to eliminate unwanted rf in the VFO circuit). The VFO offset circuit is built on a terminal strip, and is located in front of the VFO box near the tuning capacitor.

All signal leads are made from RG-174/U miniature coax cable. The shield braid should be grounded to the chassis at each end of each cable. Unshielded wiring should be kept short and direct. The latter should be dressed close to the chassis.

A 2-inch-diameter vernier mechanism is employed to operate the VFO tuning capacitor. The part used here is a Micronta No. 274-615. It was purchased from Radio Shack. Earlier Radio Shack units of this product had dull-finish dial plates, and contained a three-wheel friction drive. The preferred new model has a shiny dial plate, and uses a ball drive which appears to be a copy of that used by Jackson Brothers. The latter is free of backlash and has considerably more torque capability than did the earlier version.

The original knob and dial plate were discarded and a 2-1/2 inch diameter homemade dial plate was

[1] Apollo Products, Model-G Dosy Box. Box 245, Vaughnsville, OH 45893. Send for catalog.

[2] Scale templates and parts layout for the VFO and main transmitter boards are available by writing to ARRL Hq. Send 50 cents and a large s.a.s.e. with order.

added (see photo). A piece of scrap plastic (white) was used to make the new plate, but one could use a disk of pc board and spray it with white paint. Calibration marks were made with india ink. The vernier mechanism is mounted on the *inner* surface of the panel.

An LED is used as a panel lamp (just above the on-off switch). A clearance hole was drilled in the panel, the lamp inserted, then epoxy cement was applied at the rear of the lamp to secure it to the panel.

Final Details

Checkout of the VFO should be undertaken prior to installing it in the main cabinet. Output from the VFO can be monitored on a communications receiver tuned to 7 MHz. With the VFO tuning capacitor fully meshed, adjust the oscillator-coil slug until output is heard at 7.0 MHz. When the tuning capacitor is completely unmeshed, output should appear at approximately 7.150 MHz. Thus, during 14-MHz operation the range of the VFO will be twice that amount . . . 14.0 to 14.3 MHz. An rf probe and VTVM can be used to measure the rms output voltage from the 7- and 14-MHz VFO ports. The level should be approximately 1 volt on each band when a 560-ohm terminating resistor is used. If a scope is available it can be used as a monitor while peaking the 14-MHz tuned circuit. The scope can be used while tuning the 7-MHz trap for best purity of the 14-MHz wave form. Alternatively, the 560-ohm test termination can be replaced by a coil consisting of six turns of hookup wire, then a wavemeter can be coupled to the coil (wavemeter tuned to 7 MHz) for use as an indicator while adjusting the 7-MHz trap. Similarly, the wavemeter can be used to observe the 14-MHz output when peaking the doubler tuned circuit.

Final checkout can begin after the VFO is installed in the main cabinet. Connect a 50-ohm dummy load to the transmitter output jack. Apply operating voltage (12 to 13.5 V dc). Select the 7-MHz band. Set the drive control in the emitter circuit of Q5 for maximum resistance (minimum power). Couple a wavemeter to the PA tank and close the key. Next, adjust the tuned-circuit trimmers of the driver and PA for maximum indication on the wavemeter. Increase the drive to maximum and repeak the tuned circuits. If the circuit is performing correctly there should be 6 or 7 watts of rf output from the transmitter (18 V rms across the 50-ohm load). Next, switch to 20 meters and repeat the foregoing procedure. Output power on both bands should be the same.

If the SWR indicator is included in the circuit, it should be adjusted before installing it in the box. Details on checking it out were given in the *QST* article.

After determining that all circuits are working properly, monitor the cw signal from the transmitter to make certain there is no chirp or hum present. Final calibration of the VFO should take place upon completion of the project.

Depending upon the characteristics of the transistors used, and to some extent the physical layout of the transmitter, there may be some "pulling" of the VFO frequency when the driver and PA tanks are tuned. If this happens, tweak them slightly (at full power output) so that the monitored cw signal has the same pitch during operation as when the spot switch is actuated. There will be no deterioration in transmitter performance if this is done. The adjustment should be made on both bands.

Adjustment of the break-in delay and side-tone level controls can be done in accordance with the operator's personal tastes. Once this is done the transmitter will be ready for use.

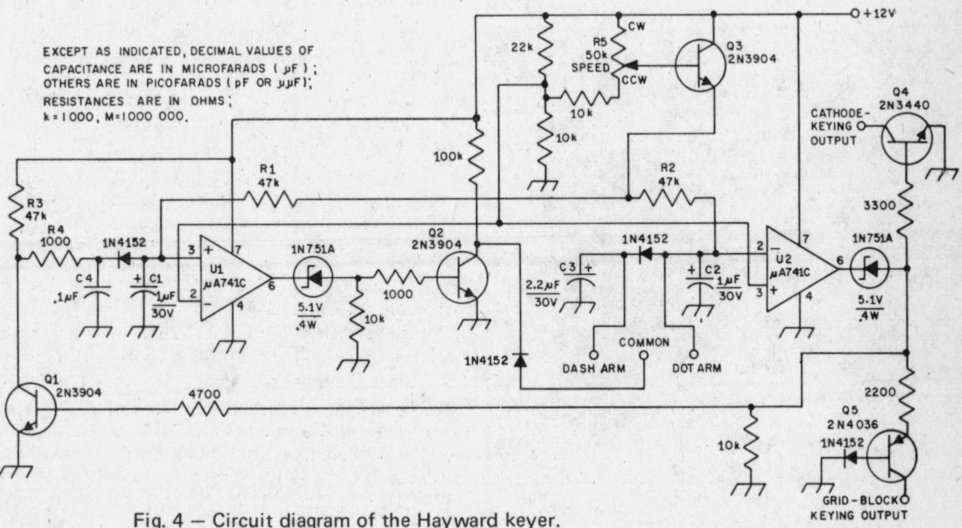

Fig. 4 — Circuit diagram of the Hayward keyer.

A 75-TO 120-WATT CW TRANSMITTER

The transmitter shown in Fig. 1 is designed to satisfy the cw requirements of either a Novice or higher-class licensee. The PA stage will operate at 75-watts dc input for the Novice. The rig provides station control and other operating features. Holders of General Class or higher licenses can run up to 120-watts dc input. A SPOT position is provided on the FUNCTION switch which permits identifying the operating frequency in a band. The transmitter has been designed for ease of assembly, with the beginner in mind.

The circuit diagram of the transmitter (Fig. 2) shows the oscillator tube, V1, to be a 6GK6. This pentode works "straight through" on some bands while multiplying in its plate circuit on others. An 80-meter crystal will develop either 80- or 40-meter energy in the subsequent stage (6146B) grid circuit, depending on the setting of S2 and C1. Similarly, a 40-meter crystal will permit the oscillator to drive the final tube on 40, 20, 15 and 10 meters. The final amplifier is always operated straight through for maximum power output. Since the amount of excitation will vary with the degree of frequency multiplication, a screen-voltage-adjustment control, R1, is included.

To insure stability, the 6146B amplifier is neutralized. This is done by feeding back a small amount of the output voltage, (out of phase) to the 6146B grid through C2. The adjustment of this circuit is described later. Provision is included to measure the grid and cathode current of the amplifier stage. With the 6146B it is important to insure that the grid current is kept below 3 mA at all times; *high grid currents will ruin the tube in short order.* The meter, which has a basic 0-1-mA movement, uses appropriate multiplier and shunt resistors to give a 0-10-mA scale for reading grid current, and 0-250 mA for monitoring plate current.

Fig. 1 — This 120-watt cw transmitter can be operated at 75-watts dc input for Novice-band use. The slide switch puts the meter in the grid or cathode circuit of the 6146B amplifier. Directly to the right of the slide switch is the FUNCTION switch and crystal socket. Continuing at this level, farther to the right is the GRID TUNING, grid BAND SWITCH, and the DRIVE level control. The controls to the upper right are the final BAND SWITCH, FINAL TUNING, and FINAL LOADING.

The plate tank for the final amplifier uses the pi-section configuration for simple band switching. This network is tuned by C3, and C4 provides adjustment of the antenna coupling. The pi-network also assures excellent suppression of harmonics when properly terminated, typically 35 to 45 dB. All connection points to the transmitter are filtered to "bottle up" harmonic energy, which, if radiated, could cause television interference.

Silicon rectifiers are used in the "economy" power supply. A center-tapped transformer with a bridge rectifier provides all of the operating voltages for the transmitter. Depending upon the line voltage, the high-voltage supply will deliver about 750 volts, key up, dropping to about 700 volts under load. If the line voltage is above 120, these figures will be increased by about 50 volts. The screen supply to the 6146B is regulated by two OB2 VR tubes.

The FUNCTION switch turns the transmitter on and selects the spot, tune or operate modes. Leads from this switch are brought out to the rear deck of the transmitter to mute the station receiver and key the antenna relay. Thus, S1 provides one-switch transmit-receive operation. In the OPERATE position, the oscillator and amplifier are keyed simultaneously by grounding the common cathode circuit. A *RC* network across the cathode line is included to shape the keying, thus preventing key clicks.

Construction

An 11 X 7 X 2-inch aluminum chassis (Bud AC-407) is used as the base for the transmitter. A homemade aluminum U shield encloses the final amplifier. The chassis is fitted with an 11 X 7-inch front panel which is cut from sheet aluminum. The panel is held to the chassis by the switches and panel bushings common to both units. Correct placement of the various parts can be determined by viewing the photographs. Only an experienced builder should try to relocate the major components. The rf compartment has 3/4-inch mounting lips bent along the back side and the ends to give a finished size of 5 X 8 3/4 inches. This rear housing is held to the chassis and front panel with 6-32 hardware, and a perforated metal cover is fastened to it with No. 6 sheet-metal screws.

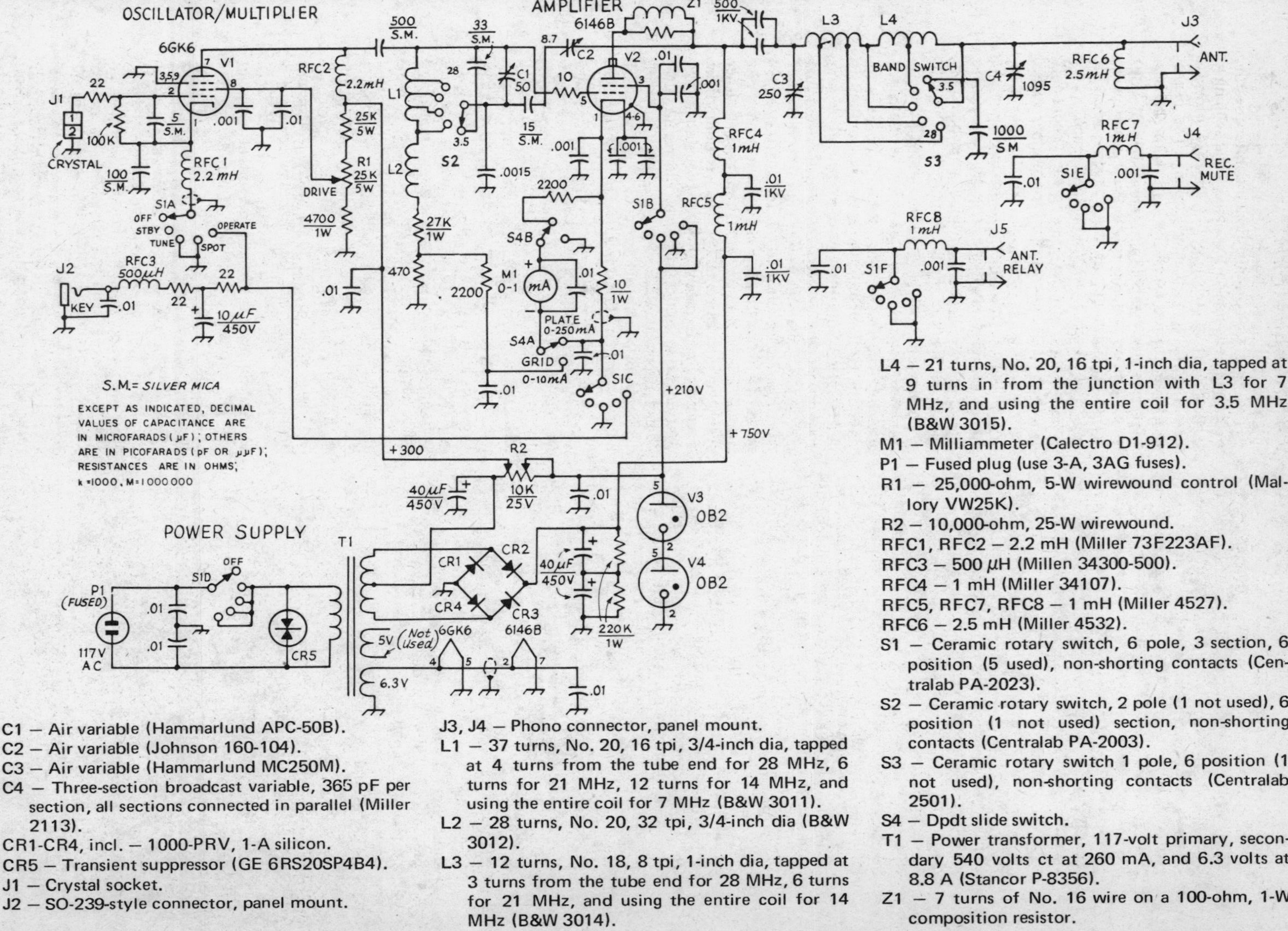

C1 — Air variable (Hammarlund APC-50B).
C2 — Air variable (Johnson 160-104).
C3 — Air variable (Hammarlund MC250M).
C4 — Three-section broadcast variable, 365 pF per section, all sections connected in parallel (Miller 2113).
CR1-CR4, incl. — 1000-PRV, 1-A silicon.
CR5 — Transient suppressor (GE 6RS20SP4B4).
J1 — Crystal socket.
J2 — SO-239-style connector, panel mount.
J3, J4 — Phono connector, panel mount.
L1 — 37 turns, No. 20, 16 tpi, 3/4-inch dia, tapped at 4 turns from the tube end for 28 MHz, 6 turns for 21 MHz, 12 turns for 14 MHz, and using the entire coil for 7 MHz (B&W 3011).
L2 — 28 turns, No. 20, 32 tpi, 3/4-inch dia (B&W 3012).
L3 — 12 turns, No. 18, 8 tpi, 1-inch dia, tapped at 3 turns from the tube end for 28 MHz, 6 turns for 21 MHz, and using the entire coil for 14 MHz (B&W 3014).
L4 — 21 turns, No. 20, 16 tpi, 1-inch dia, tapped at 9 turns in from the junction with L3 for 7 MHz, and using the entire coil for 3.5 MHz (B&W 3015).
M1 — Milliammeter (Calectro D1-912).
P1 — Fused plug (use 3-A, 3AG fuses).
R1 — 25,000-ohm, 5-W wirewound control (Mallory VW25K).
R2 — 10,000-ohm, 25-W wirewound.
RFC1, RFC2 — 2.2 mH (Miller 73F223AF).
RFC3 — 500 μH (Millen 34300-500).
RFC4 — 1 mH (Miller 34107).
RFC5, RFC7, RFC8 — 1 mH (Miller 4527).
RFC6 — 2.5 mH (Miller 4532).
S1 — Ceramic rotary switch, 6 pole, 3 section, 6 position (5 used), non-shorting contacts (Centralab PA-2023).
S2 — Ceramic rotary switch, 2 pole (1 not used), 6 position (1 not used) section, non-shorting contacts (Centralab PA-2003).
S3 — Ceramic rotary switch 1 pole, 6 position (1 not used), non-shorting contacts (Centralab 2501).
S4 — Dpdt slide switch.
T1 — Power transformer, 117-volt primary, secondary 540 volts ct at 260 mA, and 6.3 volts at 8.8 A (Stancor P-8356).
Z1 — 7 turns of No. 16 wire on a 100-ohm, 1-W composition resistor.

Fig. 2 — Circuit diagram of the 6146B transmitter. Capacitors with polarity marked are electrolytic, others are disk ceramic. Resistors are 1/2-watt composition.

Fig. 3 — Top view with the perforated metal cover removed. The small capacitor beside the 6146B provides the neutralizing adjustment. L3 and L4 are mounted one above the other. The smaller tube inside the rf compartment is the 6GK6 oscillator.

The lead to RFC4 is routed through an insulated bushing. A small bracket supports a piece of Lucite which insulates C2, the neutralizing capacitor, from ground. Another bracket supports C1 and S2. C1 is above ground for rf and dc, so an insulated coupling (Millen 39016) is to be used on its shaft. Tie strips are used to support the small capacitors, resistors, and rectifier diodes.

The 5-volt winding of T1 is not used. Therefore, these leads should be cut and taped to avoid accidental contact with the chassis. The filter capacitors and bleeder resistors are mounted on tie strips. Care should be used in making all high-voltage connections to prevent accidental shorts from occurring. Also, don't omit the "spike prevention" Thyrector diode, CR5, as this unit protects the supply from transient voltage surges.

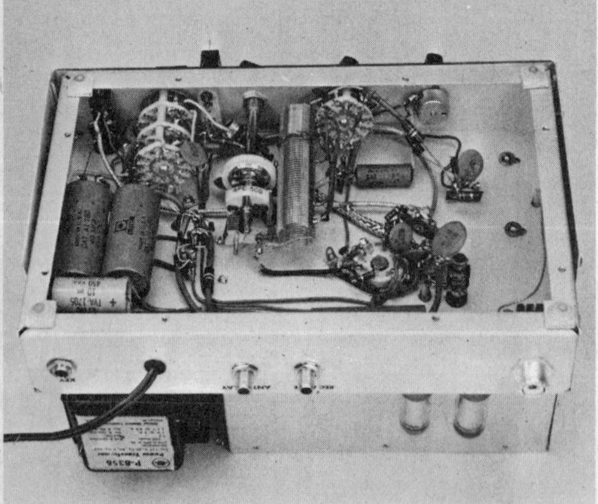

Adjustment

After the transmitter has been wired, check it a second time for possible wiring errors. Next, the two voltage-regulator tubes should be plugged in their sockets. With S1 at off, plug the line cord into a 117-volt outlet. When S1 is moved to STANDBY, the VR tubes should glow. The high voltage at RFC4 should measure about 750 volts. The oscillator voltage, checked at pin 7 of the 6GK6, should be close to 300 volts. If it is not, move the tap on R2 accordingly. *Make all measurements with care as these voltages are dangerous.* Then turn S1 to off and make certain the voltage drops to zero at RFC4, and at the 6GK6 socket. Normally, it will take at least a minute for the high voltage to drop to near zero (A fact which should be remembered during subsequent tests.).

Remove the line cord from the outlet – *never work on a transmitter unless the ac power is disconnected.* Install the tubes and connect the plate cap to the 6146B. Insert an 80-meter crystal in J1 and set both band switches to the 80-meter position. Set the FUNCTION switch to the tune position, and plug the power cord into the mains. After the tubes warm up, swing C1 through its range. If the oscillator stage is working, grid current will be read on M1. C1 should be used to peak the grid current. The total current drawn should be kept below 3 mA. Use the DRIVE control, R1, to set the drive level. Change S2 to the 40-meter position and confirm that the second harmonic of the crystal frequency can be tuned. With a 40-meter crystal in J1, it should be possible to obtain grid current with S2 set for 7, 14, 21 and 28 MHz. The maximum grid current obtainable on the higher-frequency bands will be somewhat less than on 80 and 40 meters (about 2.5 mA on 21 MHz, and 1.5 mA on 28 MHz). The latter value is not enough for full drive on the 10-meter band. The dc input power to the 6146B should be limited to 90 watts on 10 meters, and this operating condition will provide approximately 50 watts output. On the other bands 60 to 70 watts output will be possible. If an absorption wavemeter is available it is a good idea to check the setting of C1 for each band to insure that the tuned circuits are operating on the proper harmonic frequency. It may be possible to tune to an incorrect harmonic frequency, *which can lead to out-of-band operation.* Once the proper setting of C1 has been determined, mark the front panel so that this point can be returned to quickly when tuning up. Lacking a wavemeter, a receiver (with the antenna disconnected) can be used to check output on the various bands.

Fig. 4 — Looking inside the bottom of the transmitter, L1 and L2 are located at the center, next to the grid-tuning capacitor. All of the output jacks are spaced along the rear wall of the chassis. The bottom cover has been removed in this photograph. It should be kept in place during operation.

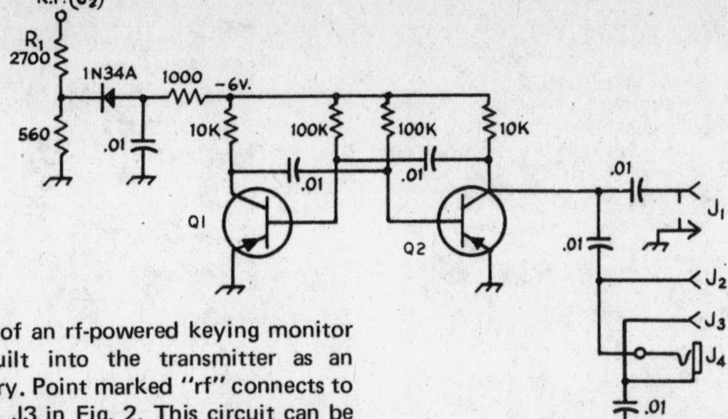

Fig. 5 – Circuit of an rf-powered keying monitor that may be built into the transmitter as an operating accessory. Point marked "rf" connects to the antenna jack, J3 in Fig. 2. This circuit can be used with any transmitter simply by selecting an input resistor, R1, that gives about –6 volts at the point shown. Only the desired output jacks need to be included.

J1 – Phono jack for audio output from the receiver.
J2, J3 – Tip jacks for headphones or receiver.
J4 – Phone jack for headphone connection.
Q1, Q2 – 2N406 or equivalent (pnp).

With S2 and S3 set for 15 meters, tune C1 for maximum grid current. Then, set the indicated value to about 2 mA with the DRIVE control. Set C4 at half scale, and slowly tune C3 while watching the grid-current meter. At the point which C3 tunes the tank through resonance, a dip in grid current will be seen, unless by chance the amplifier is already neutralized. A slow rate of tuning is required, as the indication will be quite sharp. When the dip has been found, adjust C2 until no dip can be noted, or, at least, the dip is less than 0.1 mA. All preliminary tests should be made as quickly as possible, as the transmitter is operating without a load, and extended operation can damage the final-amplifier tube.

When neutralization has been completed, and all circuits appear to be operating normally, connect a load to the transmitter. Preferably, this should be a 50-ohm dummy load, but a 100-watt light bulb will do. If an output indicator or SWR bridge is available, it should be connected between the transmitter and the load. The lamp is a fair output indicator on its own. Adjust the transmitter as outlined above for 2 mA of grid current on the desired band. With a key plugged in at J2, set C4 at full mesh, and switch S4 to read plate current. Watching the meter, close the key and adjust C3 for a plate-current dip. The dip indicates resonance. If the plate current dips below 150 mA, decrease the capacitance setting of C4, and again tune C3 for a dip. This dip-and-load procedure should be repeated until a plate current of 170 mA is reached at resonance. If the Novice 75-watt input limit is to be observed, the plate current at resonance must be held to 100 mA. This can be accomplished by using additional capacitance at C4.

If extended operation is planned at 75 watts or less input, it is advisable to reduce the screen voltage on the 6146B to insure that the rated screen dissipation rating of this tube is not exceeded. This can be done by using an OA2 in place of one OB2, jumpering the other VR-tube socket, and readjusting R2 so that the single VR tube draws about 25 mA. The OA2 will deliver 150 volts, regulated.

A HIGH-OUTPUT TRANSISTOR VFO

If a solid-state VFO is to be used with tube-type transmitters, it must have sufficient output to drive a crystal-oscillator stage as a doubler or tripler. Most of the Novice-class transmitters require 10-25 volts of rf to produce sufficient drive to succeeding stages. The VFO shown in Fig. 1 serves as a "crystal replacement" for the type of transmitter that uses a 6GK6, 6AG7, 12BY7 or similar tube in the oscillator. To provide sufficient output level, a two-watt amplifier is added to the basic transistor VFO. To reduce harmonic output and eliminate tuning of the amplifier stage, a fixed-value half-wave tank is used as the output circuit, followed by broadband rf step-up transformers. The VFO will develop 20 volts or more across a 5000- to 50,000-ohm load.

The basic VFO design was originally described in *QST*, June, 1970.

Circuit Data

In the circuit of Fig. 2 are two completely separate tuned circuits – one for 3.5 to 4.0 MHz, and one for 7 to 7.35 MHz. A split-stator broadcast-type variable, C3, is employed so that there is no need to switch a single tuning capacitor from one tuned circuit to the other. Also, the arrangement shown places the tuning-capacitor sections in different parts of the circuit for the two bands. The 7-MHz tuned circuit uses C3A from the junction of the feedback capacitor (C1 and C2) to ground. This gives the desired amount of

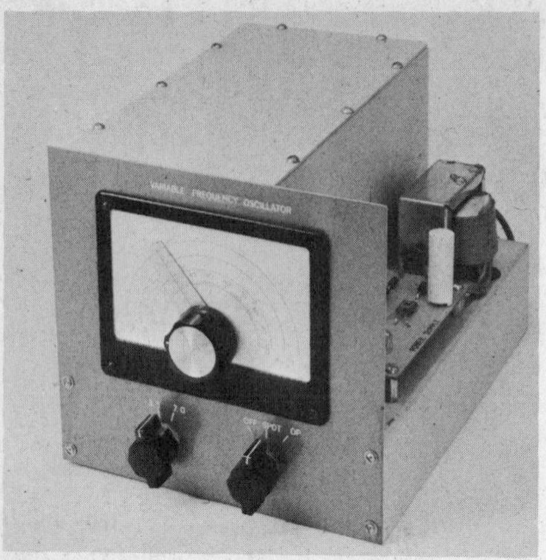

Fig. 1 – The two-band VFO. This unit operates on 3.5 to 4 and 7 to 7.3 MHz. Included is a 2-watt amplifier and broad-band rf transformers so that the VFO can drive tube-type transmitters directly.

The bottom view of the VFO shows only the two switches and the output transformers – other components are mounted on the etched circuit boards "topside."

bandspread for 40-meter operation, but, when hooking the 80-meter tuned circuit up the same way, only 200 kHz could be covered with C3B. So, for 3.5 to 3.8-MHz operation, C3B is connected from the high-impedance point on L2 to ground.

It will be noted that a rather high value of *C* is used in parallel with each of the inductors, L1 and L2. This measure was taken to enhance the frequency stability of the VFO. By using a high *CL* ratio, small changes in the junction capacitance of Q1 have a less pronounced effect on the tuned circuit than would be experienced when using smaller values of capacitance. Silver-mica capacitors are used in the interest of good stability. So that the oscillator will start readily, despite the high *C* to *L* ratio, Q1 was chosen to have high beta and f_T. However, the high gain and frequency ratings caused the stage to be unstable at vhf – approximately 150 MHz. As C3 was tuned, vhf oscillations could be seen on the output waveform. The vhf energy was tunable, and it was found that the lead from Q1's base-blocking capacitor, C6, to the arm of S1A, was long enough to act as a vhf inductance, which was being tuned by C3. The addition of a 3-ferrite-bead choke, RFC1, mounted right at the circuit-board terminal for C6, cured the problem. Ideally, RFC1 would be mounted on the base lead of Q1, with the beads up against the transistor body. However, this is not always a practical method of mounting, so one should attempt to get the beads as close to the base connection as possible, thus minimizing the possibility of a vhf inductance being set up in that part of the circuit. To further discourage parasitic oscillations a collector resistor, R2, was included. It would be connected as close to the collector terminal of Q1 as possible, for the same reasons given when discussing RFC1.

Output from Q1 is taken across R4. Direct coupling is used between the low-impedance takeoff point of Q1 and the base of emitter-follower, Q2. Resistor R1 sets the forward bias of Q2 by picking some dc voltage off the emitter of Q1. Sufficient rf passes through R5 to drive Q2.

The collector of Q2 is bypassed for high and low frequencies to assure stability. A 100-ohm collector resistor, R6, decouples the stages at rf.

The drive signal for Q3 is taken from the emitter of Q2 through a small-value capacitor, C7. The larger the capacitance, the greater will be the available output voltage across a given load, but the smaller the capacitance value used, the better will be the VFO isolation from the succeeding circuit. One should use only the amount of capacitance that will provide adequate peak output voltage.

An RCA 2N2102 is used in the output amplifier. This transistor has a power rating of 5 watts, so it can be safely operated at two-watts dc input without a large heat sink. This stage operates Class C, using no fixed forward bias. A Zener diode, CR1, is used to prevent destruction of the transistor if the load is inadvertently removed. The PA tank is fixed tuned. The output is essentially flat over the 80- and 40-meter bands. The constants have been chosen for a 50-ohm output, so it is necessary to transform this impedance up to the high *Z* found at the transmitter tube grid. Separate tuned circuits, L10 and L12, are used for this purpose. The length of the connecting cable will affect the tuning of the output stage; with the values shown, a 36-inch length of RG-58/U should be used.

Construction Information

The VFO is built on a 9 X 7 X 2-inch chassis which is fitted with a 9 X 4 1/2 X 4 1/4-inch box

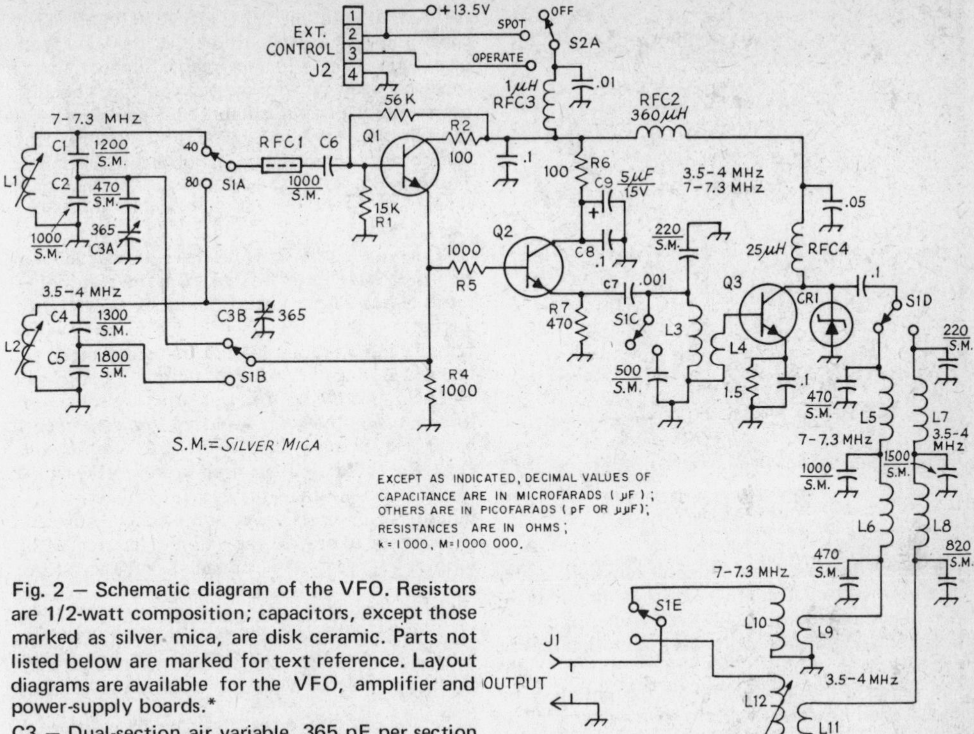

Fig. 2 — Schematic diagram of the VFO. Resistors are 1/2-watt composition; capacitors, except those marked as silver mica, are disk ceramic. Parts not listed below are marked for text reference. Layout diagrams are available for the VFO, amplifier and power-supply boards.*

C3 — Dual-section air variable, 365 pF per section (Miller 2112).
CR1 — Zener, 36 V, 1 W.
J1 — Phono connector, panel mount.
J2 — 4-terminal ceramic strip (Millen E-304).
L1 — 0.68-1.25 µH, slug tuned (Miller 42A106CBI).
L2 — 2.2-4.1 µH, slug tuned (Miller 42A336CBI).
L3 — 2 µH, 25 turns of No. 24 enam. wire on Amidon T-50-2 toroid core (Amidon Associates, 12033 Otsego Street, North Hollywood, CA 91607).
L4 — 12 turns No. 22 hook-up wire over L3.
L5, L6 — 13 turns of No. 20 enam. wire on Amidon T-68-2 core.
L7, L8 — 18 turns of No. 20 enam. wire on Amidon T-68-2 core.
L9 — 7 turns of No. 26 enam. wire over L10.
L10 — Approx. 3 µH, Miller 4405 with slug and 4 turns removed.
L11 — 7 turns No 26 enam. wire over L12.
L12 — 23 µH (Miller 4407).
Q1 — HEP-55.
Q2 — HEP-728.
Q3 — 2N2102.
RFC1 — Three Amidon ferrite beads on a 1/2-inch length of No. 22 wire. A 15-ohm resistor may serve as a substitute.
RFC2 — Miniature choke (Miller J300-360).
RFC3 — Miniature choke (Millen 34300).
RFC4 — 2.5 µH rf choke (Millen J300-25).
S1 — Home-assembled switch made from a Centralab PA272 kit and 3 Centralab RRD sections. (See Fig. 6-5).
S2 — Ceramic rotary switch, 2 pole, 3 position, one section, non-shorting contacts (Mallory 3223J).

* See *QST* for December, 1970.

to house the rf assemblies. The VFO circuit board is mounted on two brackets (Fig. 3). The amplifier etched-circuit board is mounted over a hole cut in the chassis. All components for the power supply (except the transformer) are mounted on a third circuit board, which is mounted on short stand-off pillars above the chassis. The power transformer is positioned on the right-rear side of the chassis.

S1 is a homemade assembly built from Centralab switch sections and parts. The mounting bushing supports the front end of the switch, and an aluminum L bracket supports the rear. The ceramic spacers supplied with the PA272 kit are used to separate the various wafers so that they are as close as possible to the circuits that they switch. A second switch, S2, turns the power supply on, as well as activating the VFO alone for zero-beating purposes. In operation, external connections are required from the station transmitter to J2 so that the VFO will come on simultaneously with the transmitter.

Adjustment

The power supply section should be tested before it is connected to the VFO. After the unit has been checked against the schematic diagram to

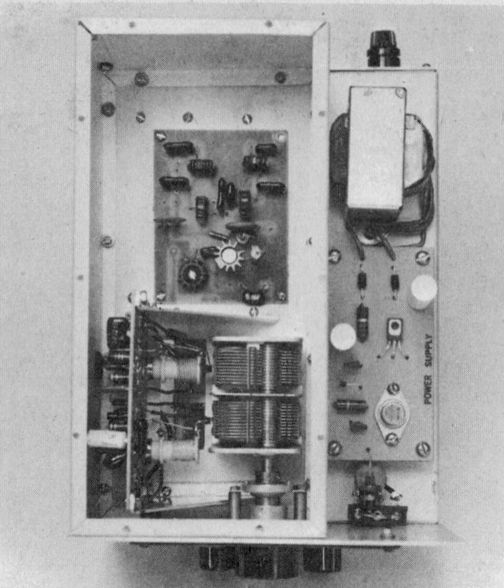

Fig. 3 – Top view, with the cover removed, of the rf compartment. The VFO board is mounted on two aluminum brackets. All leads from this circuit board should be made with heavy wire to minimize mechanical instability from vibration. The amplifier board is flush-mounted on the chassis. The dual-section broadcast variable is driven by a Miller MD-4 dial. L1 and L2 are adjusted through holes cut in the left side of the shielded compartment.

spot and correct any wiring errors, attach a voltmeter (VOM or VTVM) to the power-supply output. Plug P1 into a 117-volt outlet, and switch S2 to SPOT. The voltmeter should read approximately 13.5 volts. Then connect a 47-ohm, 2-watt resistor across the power supply output – the meter should continue to read the same voltage, even with the heavy load. If the power supply checks out correctly, remove the 47-ohm resistor and connect the supply to the VFO. With S1 set for 80-meter operation, tune a receiver across 3.5 to 4 MHz until the VFO signal is found. Then, check the 7-MHz range to see that the VFO is also operating in the 40-meter range. Connect a patch cable between the transmitter and the VFO. If a cable length other than the 36 inches is used, it may be necessary to add or subtract turns from L10 to achieve maximum drive to the transmitter. The slug in L12 should be set for maximum 80-meter drive to the following transmitter oscillator stage.

Once the entire VFO has been tested, the next step is calibration of the dial. With the plates of C3 set at about 95 percent of full mesh, adjust L1 for 7.0 MHz and L2 for 3.5 MHz. A receiver with a crystal calibrator, or a BC-221 frequency meter can be used during the dial calibration. *When using a VFO close to the band edge, always use some form of secondary frequency standard to insure in-band operation, in accordance with FCC regulations.* Once the calibration has been set, the VFO should again be connected to the transmitter, and a monitor receiver set up. In normal circumstances it is necessary to ground the antenna terminal of the receiver to prevent overload from the nearby transmitter. Even so, the signal heard from the receiver will be quite strong, so turn the rf gain control back until a moderately-strong signal is obtained. Then, key the transmitter and monitor the output signal with the receiver. The signal should be clean (free from hum, chirp and clicks). The VFO-transmitter combination should be checked on 80 through 10 meters in this manner.

It is also useful to zero beat the VFO against the crystal calibrator in the receiver. The VFO should be left on for 15 minutes or more, and the drift, as evidenced by a change in the beat note, should be less than 50 Hz on either fundamental range. Drift will be most noticeable on the 10-meter band, as any drift at 7-MHz will be multiplied by a factor of four in the transmitter. If excessive drift is found, it can usually be traced to a defective component. The process of finding such a troublesome part is time consuming; more often than not, a defective capacitor will be the cause.

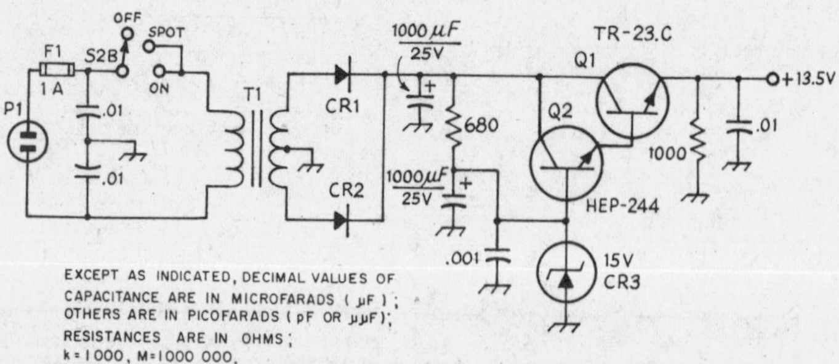

Fig. 4 – Power supply for the solid-state VFO. Capacitors with polarity marked are electrolytic, others are disk ceramic. Resistors are 1/2-watt composition.

CR1, CR2 – 100-PRV, 1-A silicon.

CR3 – Zener, 15 V, 1 W.

P1 – Fused plug (use 1-A, 3AG fuses).

Q1 – 40-watt npn power transistor (International Rectifier TR-23C).

Q2 – Motorola HEP-24.

S2 – See Fig. 2.

T1 – Filament transformer, 24 V ct at 1 A.

A 6-BAND TRANSMITTER FOR THE CW OPERATOR (T-9er)

Operating a transmitter and amplifier designed with cw as an afterthought can make cw very dull. Presented here is the T-9er, a hybrid circuit built with cw as the prime mode of service. Included are such features as full break-in, shaped keying, linear VFO calibration, T-R switch, built-in power supply, and a solid-state heterodyne conversion scheme. The PA stage uses a pair of 6146Bs and is capable of producing up to 240-watts input on 160 through 10 meters.

The Circuit

The VFO and buffer, Q1 and Q2 in Fig. 2, are an adaptation of a unit previously described in *QST*.[1] Q3, a second buffer, provides additional gain to assure adequate current to drive the base of the mixer, Q5. The VFO range is 5.0 to 5.2 MHz.

The heterodyne-frequency oscillator, Q4, operates at one of six crystal-controlled frequencies selected by the band switch. All of the crystals chosen oscillate at a frequency *above* the operating band. For this reason, the VFO dial tunes in the same direction on each band. CR13 is included to limit the oscillator voltage appearing at the mixer to 0.6.

Voltage from the VFO and HFO are coupled to the mixer, Q5, via C9 and C5, respectively. A tuned collector circuit operates at the *difference* frequency and provides a low-level signal to the driver stage, V1. The VFO actually tunes backwards with respect to the mixer output signal. The bottom edge of each amateur band corresponds to a VFO setting of 5.2 MHz.

A conventional grid-block system provides clickless, chirpless operation because neither oscillator is keyed. Q6 activates the mixer only when the key is depressed. The waveform transmitted is determined by R2 and C11 in the grid circuit of V1. Since the 6GK6 keys at a slightly slower rate than the mixer, any clicks generated in the earlier stages are not heard.

Voltage from the mixer is sufficient to power the driver to nearly full output on all bands. The plate circuit uses separate slug-tuned inductors for 160 through 20 meters. The 15- and 10-meter bands are covered with one coil. Neutralization of the 6GK6 is not required.

Output Circuit

A pi-network output circuit is employed with a pair of parallel-connected 6146Bs. Six 10-ohm resistors are connected between the cathodes and ground. Voltage developed across these resistors is used to indicate cathode current on the meter.

The amount of screen voltage is determined by the position of S3. When this switch is closed, the screen voltage is 150. Releasing S3 places R13 in series with the screen bus, lowering the voltage to 50. This lower voltage limits the transmitter input to approximately 60 watts. A neon lamp, DS2, has been included to indicate the position of S3. R15 and R16 form a voltage divider which allows ignition of DS2 during high screen-voltage conditions only.

Fig. 1 – Front view of the cw transmitter. All metal work is done with sheet and cane-metal sections.

A T-R switch, V4, permits using the same antenna for transmitting and receiving. The theory and operation of this unit was described in an earlier *QST*.[2] An antenna relay is not required.

The operating conditions of the final-amplifier stage may be checked with the panel meter, M1. A 6-position switch allows monitoring of grid current, relative output, screen, plate and bias voltages, and cathode current.

The Power Supply

A silicon-diode full-wave bridge rectifier is used in the secondary of T1 to produce slightly over 1000 V dc during no-load conditions. Although this is somewhat high for 6146Bs, it has not shortened tube life. A choke-input filter is connected in the transformer center-tap lead to obtain 300 volts for powering the driver tube and the T-R switch. Sixteen volts of dc for operating the solid-state circuitry are obtained by rectifying and filtering the combined output of the two filament windings, which are connected in series. If the windings buck each other, producing no voltage, one set of leads should be reversed.

Final-amplifier screen and bias voltages are developed by T2. This part of the supply uses one half-wave rectifier for each voltage.

Construction

The transmitter is completely self-contained. It is built on a 10 X 17 X 3-inch chassis with an 8 1/2-inch-high front panel. Shielding is used between each stage and between each band-switch wafer as shown in the photograph. The final-amplifier section on top of the chassis is completely enclosed in a perforated aluminum shield. Small pieces of circuit board are soldered

---

[1] DeMaw, "Building a Simple Two-Band VFO," QST, June, 1970.

[2] Myers, "Stepping Up T-R Switch Performance," QST, December, 1967.

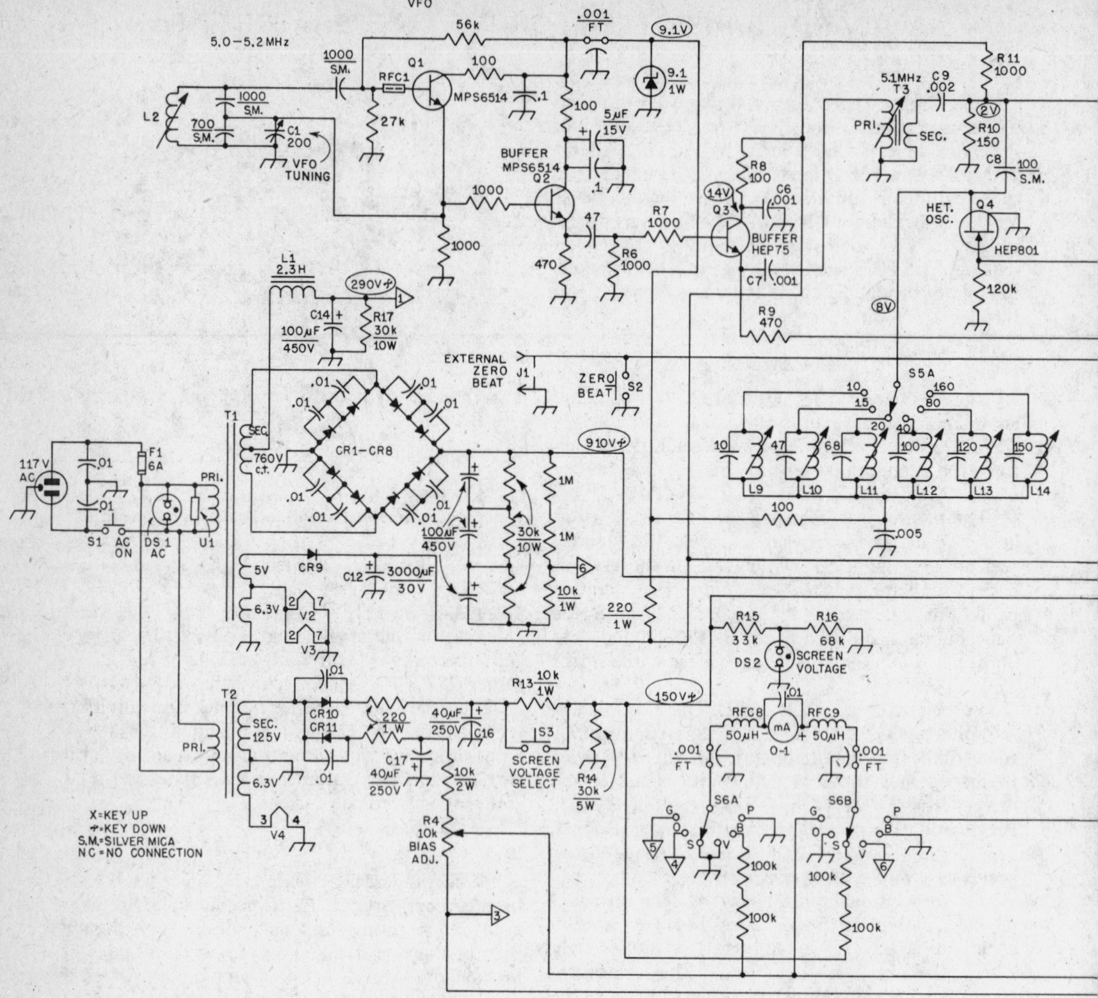

Fig. 2 — Circuit diagram for the T-9er. Component designations not listed below are for text reference.

C1 — 200-pF air variable (Hammarlund HFA-200A).

C2 — 100-pF air variable (Hammarlund MAPC-100B).

C3 — 300-pF air variable (Hammarlund RMC-325-S).

C4 — 1200-pF air variable (J. W. Miller 2113).

CR1-CR12, incl. — 1000-PRV, 2.5-A (Mallory M2.5A or equiv.).

CR13 — Silicon small-signal switching diode (1N914 or equiv.).

DS1, DS2 — Neon indicator lamp, 117-V (Leecraft 32-211).

J1, J2 — Phono jack, single hole mount.

J3 — Coax chassis connector, type SO-239.

J4 — Open-circuit key jack.

L1 — 2.3-H filter choke (Stancor C-2304 or equiv.).

L2 — 2.2- or 4.1-μH slug-tuned inductor (J. W. Miller 42A336CBI).

L3, L16 — 1.0- to 4.1-μH slug-tuned inductor (J. W. Miller 42A156CBI). Both coils are rewound with the wire supplied: 3 turns spaced over a 3/4-inch length.

L4, L9, L10, L11, L15 — 1.0-μH slug-tuned inductor (J. W. Miller 21A106RBI).

L5 — 2.2- to 4.1-μH slug-tuned inductor (J. W. Miller 42A336BCI).

L6 — 1.6- to 2.7-μH slug-tuned inductor (J. W. Miller 21A226RBI).

L7, L8, L13, L14, L18, L19 — 6.8- to 8.5-μH slug-tuned inductor (J. W. Miller 21A686RBI).

L12, L17 — 1.5- to 1.8-μH slug-tuned inductor (Miller 21A156RBI).

L20 — 9 1/2 turns, 8 tpi, 1 1/2-inch dia tapped from tube end at 2 1/2 turns for 10 meters and at 4 3/4 turns for 15 meters (B&W 3018).

L21 — 38 turns, 10 tpi, 2-inch dia tapped from J3 end at 18 turns for 80 meters, 28 turns for 40 meters (B&W 3027).

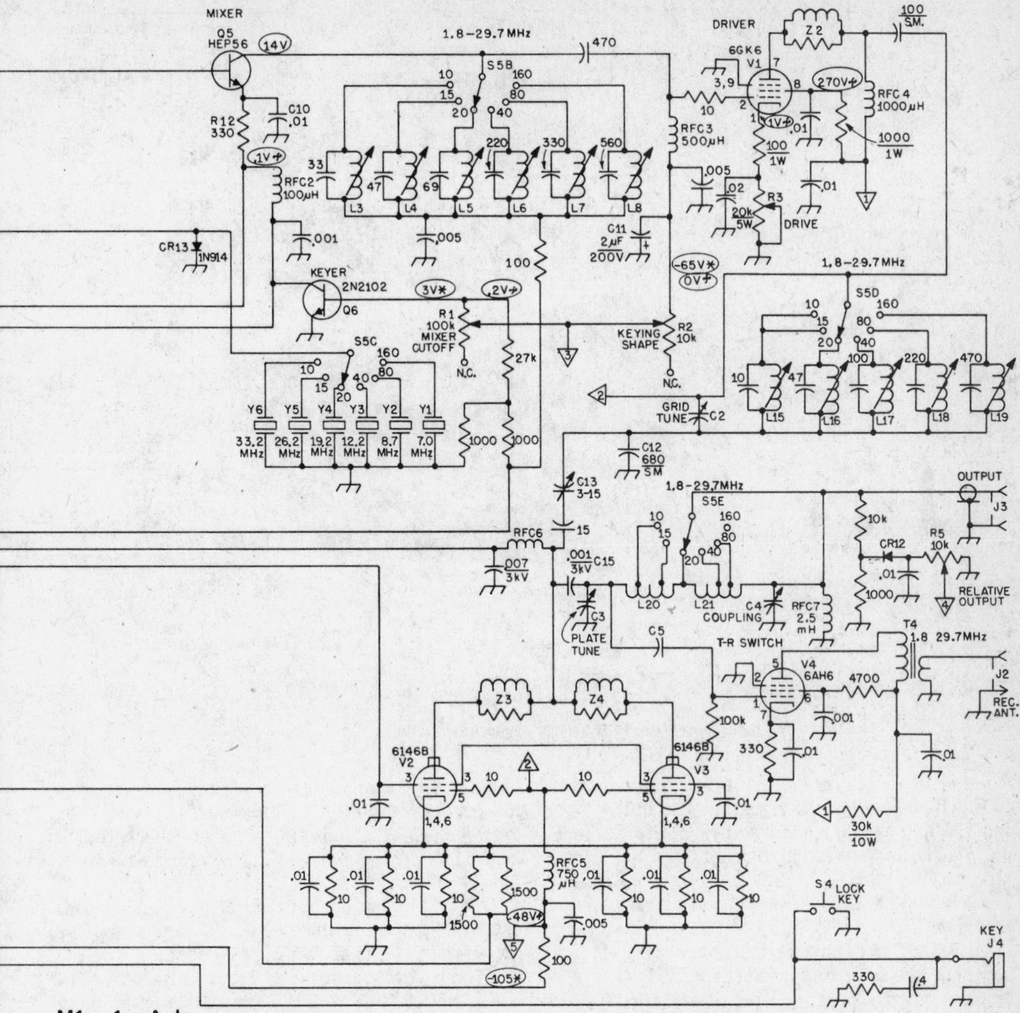

M1 – 1-mA dc.

R1 – 100,000-ohm, linear-taper, 2-watt carbon control (Allen Bradley).

R2, R4, R5 – 10,000-ohm, linear-taper, 2-watt carbon control (Allen Bradley).

R3 – 20,000-ohm, linear-taper, 4-watt, wire-wound control (Mallory M20MPK).

RFC1 – Three Amidon ferrite beads threaded on a 1/2-inch length of No. 22 wire. A 15-ohm 1/2-watt resistor may serve as a substitute. (Amidon Assoc., 12033 Otsego St., N. Hollywood, CA 91607).

RFC2 – 100-μH rf choke (Millen 34300-100).

RFC3 – 500-μH rf choke (Millen J300-500).

RFC4 – 1000-μH rf choke (Millen 34300-1000).

RFC5 – 750-μH rf choke (Millen 34300-752).

RFC6 – 1-mH rf choke (E. F. Johnson 102-752).

RFC7 – 2.5-H rf choke (Millen 34300-2500).

RFC8, RFC9 – 50-μH rf choke (Millen 34300-50).

S1-S4, incl. – Spst push button (Calectro E2-144).

S5 – Ceramic rotary switch, 5 poles, 6 positions, 5 sections (Centralab PA-272 index with 5 type XD wafers).

S6 – 2-pole, 6-position, single-section rotary (Centralab PA-2003).

T1 – 117-volt primary; secondary 760 volts at 220-mA, center tapped; 5-V at 3-A; 6.3-V at 5-A (Stancor P-8170 or equiv.).

T2 – 117-volt primary; secondary 125 volts at 50 mA; 6.3-V at 2-A (Stancor PA-8421 or equiv.).

T3 – Primary: 8.2- to 8.9-μH slug-tuned inductor (J. W. Miller 46A826CPC). Secondary: 2 turns No. 22 enameled wire wound on the cold end of the primary.

T4 – 20 turns No. 24 enameled wire wound on a 1-inch long, 1/2-inch dia iron core from a slug-tuned coil form. The secondary is 3 turns No. 24 enameled wire wound over the cold end of the primary.

U1 – Transient voltage suppressor, 120-volt (General Electric 6RS20SP4B4).

Z1 – 3 turns No. 22 wire space-wound on a 100-ohm, 1-watt composition resistor.

Z2, Z3 – 5 turns No. 18 wire space-wound on a 100-ohm, 2- watt composition resistor.

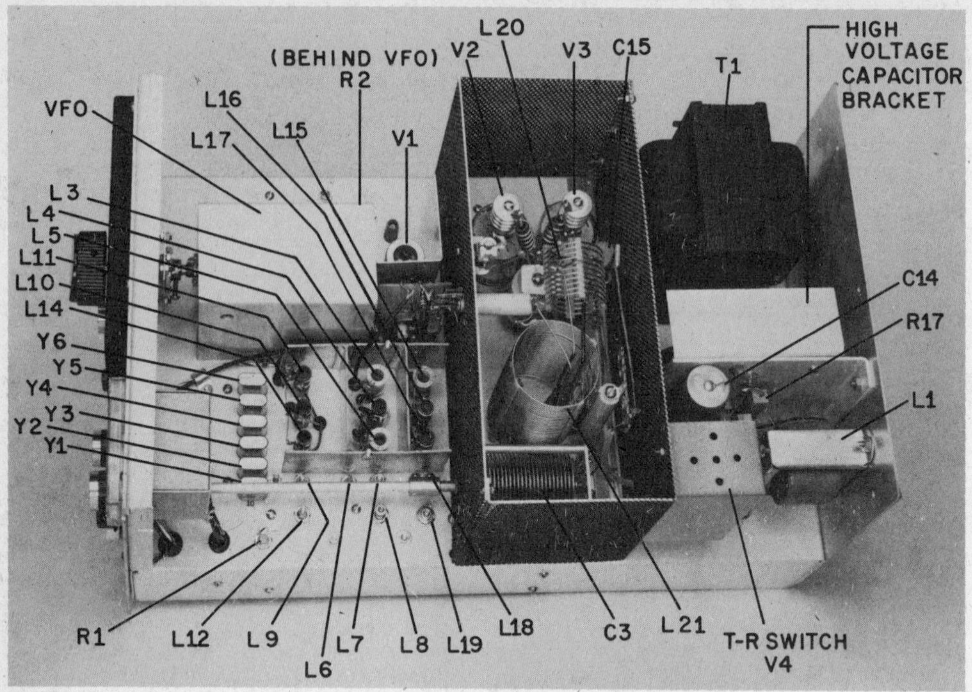

Fig. 3 – Top view of the cw transmitter.

together to form a compartment for the slug-tuned coils. The etched circuit board for the buffer, Q3, and the mixer, Q5, is mounted vertically between the slug-tuned coil compartment and the driver tube, V1. An aluminum box measuring 2 1/2 X 2 1/4 X 1 3/4 inches is used as a meter enclosure.

Most of the power-supply components are mounted on the rear quarter of the chassis. The bracket located next to the power transformer supports the three filter capacitors for the high-voltage supply. Accidental contact with the 1000-volt line is prevented by the top lip.

The T-R switch, V4, is mounted inside a Minibox attached to the rear of the amplifier shield compartment. The signal-input connection to V4 is made through the shield. Five holes in the top of the Minibox cover provide ventilation for the 6AH6.

The VFO is built on an etched circuit board and is completely enclosed in the shield cover behind the tuning dial. In order to enhance mechanical stability, the cover is made of 3/16-inch-thick aluminum. A small hole is drilled in the side of the cover to allow for adjustment of L1.

All of the wiring between stages is done with shielded cable. Additionally, all leads to the meter-switch compartment are shielded.

A capacitor constructed from a short piece of RG-59A/U is used for C5 (Fig. 2). The shield and inner conductor overlap approximately 1 inch. If a ceramic capacitor is used at this point it should have a capacitance of roughly 3 pF, and a voltage rating of 3 kV.

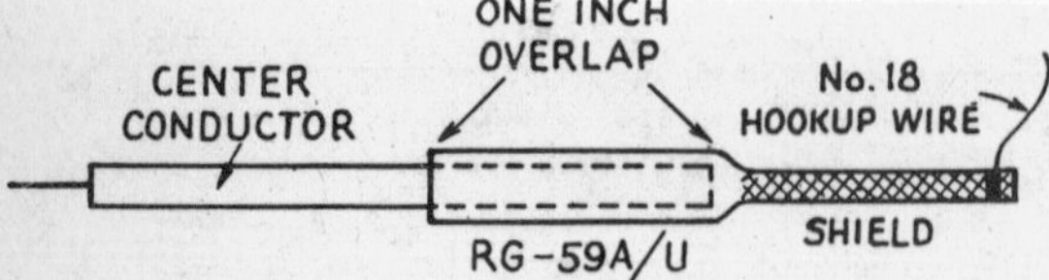

Fig. 4 – A high-voltage capacitor is constructed from a 3-inch piece of RG-59A/U. A 1-inch overlap between the braid and center conductor provides the correct amount of coupling for the T-R switch.

Adjustments

Before power is applied to the T-9er, resistance measurements should be made at several points to assure there are no wiring errors which could cause damage to the power supply.

A general-coverage receiver is used to check the operation of the heterodyne oscillator on each crystal frequency. Then, the receiver antenna is coupled to pin 2 of V1 through a 100-pF capacitor. By setting the bandswitch at 160 meters and adjusting the VFO signal to 5.2 MHz, a signal should appear at 1.8 MHz when the spotting switch is depressed. Adjust L3 for maximum S-meter reading. Tune L4 (80 meters) through L8 (10 meters) in a similar manner. All of the tubes should be removed for these tests.

The biggest pitfall in aligning the mixer is

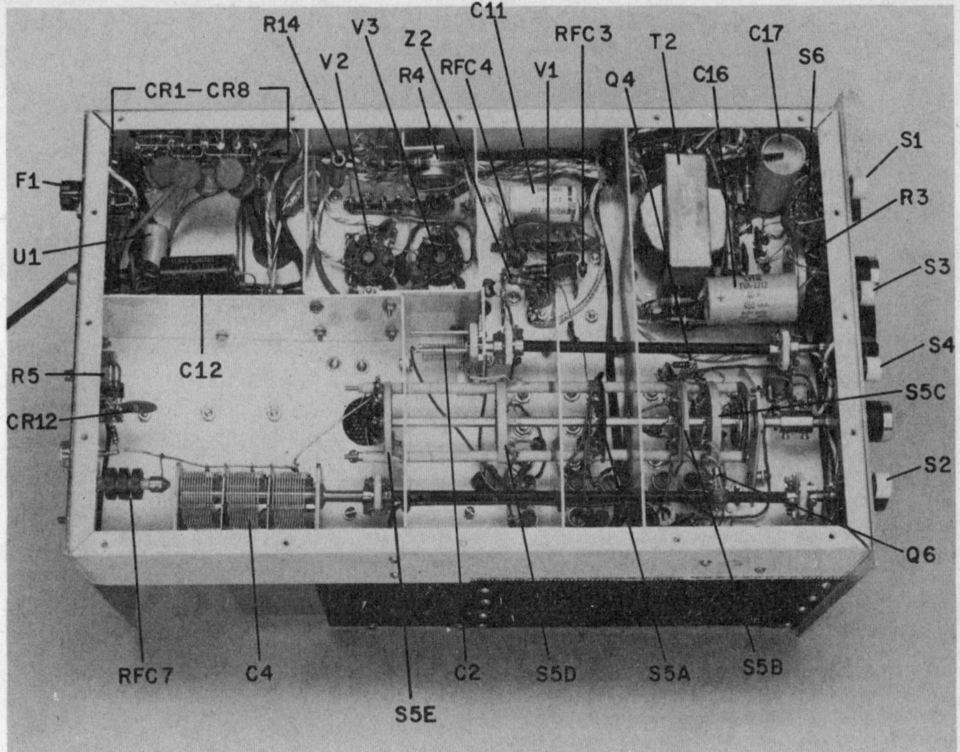

Fig. 5 – Chassis bottom view. The opening next to S5E is needed to make connections to L20 and L21.

tuning the output circuit to something other than the desired frequency. For instance, on 20 meters, the mixer can be tuned to the third harmonic of the VFO, producing output at 15.6 MHz! There are a few similar combinations which might be encountered.

After determining that the solid-state circuitry is functioning correctly on each band, the tubes are installed and the driver coils are adjusted. To set the final-amplifier bias, set the drive control at minimum (ccw), depress the key, and adjust R4 for a PA cathode current of 5 mA.

The entire alignment must be "touched up" under full-power output conditions. The heterodyne oscillator coils should be detuned to a point where the power output drops approximately 2 percent. This procedure assures proper oscillator injection at the mixer. When the rf alignment is completed, a receiver should be connected to J2. If any backwave is heard under key-up conditions, adjustment of R1 should eliminate it.

In a transmitter of this type, leads to the bandswitch lugs contribute stray inductance and capacitance. For this reason, the builder is advised to "tack" the mica capacitors across the inductors until it is determined that the various circuits will resonate at the proper frequencies. Only then should the capacitor leads be soldered permanently in place.

Performance

Power output from the T-9er is roughly 150 watts on 160 through 20 meters. On 15 meters the output drops to 125 watts, and on 10 meters it is slightly over 100 watts. The reduced output on the higher bands is caused by marginal drive to the 6GK6. It is not considered important enough to add another buffer stage with its associated bandswitch wafer coils.

The screen voltage (SV) switch is included to provide a low-power tune-up function. It is best not to operate (on the air) in the low-voltage position. If low power operation is desired, the drive can be reduced during normal screen-voltage conditions.

Every effort has been made to produce a TVI-free transmitter. The addition of a low-pass filter should make harmonic radiation almost immeasurable.

Keying Wave-Form Adjustment

A wide range of keying characteristics is available. R2 should be adjusted while observing the transmitted signal on an oscilloscope. Typical patterns are shown in the Code Transmission chapter. If an oscilloscope is not available, keying adjustment could be made on the air with the help of a local amateur. These tests should be made on a dead band, however, thus preventing needless QRM.

A 160-METER AMPLIFIER

Fig. 1 – Front view of the 160-meter amplifier. Note the use of perforated aluminum stock to permit ventilation of both the rf and power supply compartments. The large front-panel knob on the right controls C3, while the adjacent knob to the left controls C2. The power switch, S1, is controlled by the smaller knob located beneath C3. Both S1 and S2, the meter switch, are mounted below the chassis, and DS1 is mounted between the two switches.

Anyone who has operated in the 160-meter band lately can attest to the fact that interest in the "top band" is on the upswing. With only a handful of manufacturers producing gear for 160, this band is somewhat of a "homebrewers' haven." Most operation takes place during the evening hours, because the high level of daytime ionospheric absorption makes communication (other than strictly local) all but impossible for low powered stations. Summertime static makes things even more difficult. At present, amateurs occupy this band on a shared basis with various radionavigation services, with maximum input power limitations imposed to prevent harmful interference from occuring. These restrictions are greatest between sundown and sunrise, when the potential for interference is at maximum. However, during the daylight hours, amateurs in 29 states are permitted to use up to 1000 watts power input, while in the other 21, the maximum is 500 watts, in selected segments of the band.[1] The amplifier described below is for use with 160-meter exciters in the 50- to 100-watt output class, for ssb and cw operation.

Circuit Data

A pair of 572B/T160L triodes are used in a cathode-driven, grounded-grid configuration (see Fig. 3). A small amount of operating bias is provided by the 3.9-volt, 10-watt Zener diode in series with the cathode return lead, and the tubes are completely cut off during nontransmitting periods by opening that lead with K1A to reduce unnecessary power consumption and heat generation. The other contacts on K1 perform all necessary antenna switching functions for transceive or separate transmitter/receiver operation. Drive power from the exciter is fed to the directly heated cathodes through a parallel combination of three .01 μF disk capacitors, and a resonant cathode tank circuit helps minimize the amount of drive required. The filament choke, RFC2, isolates the driving signal from the filament transformer. A B&W FC-15A choke was used here. A single power switch, S1, applies 117 V ac to the primaries of both the power and filament transformers simultaneously, as the 572B's require no significant warmup time. S1 also activates the cooling fan, B1, and the front-panel pilot light assembly, DS1. The self-contained high-voltage power supply uses a straightforward voltage doubler circuit. No-load voltage is approximately 3100 V dc, dropping to 2600 V dc under one kilowatt key-down conditions. R2 limits the initial surge current to the filter capacitor bank to prevent exceeding the current handling capability of the rectifier string when the supply is first turned on.

A single 0-1 mA meter is used to monitor either plate voltage or cathode current. To measure plate voltage, a multiplier consisting of five series-connected 1-megohm 1-watt resistors with one end tied to the B plus line is switched in series with the meter to provide a full-scale reading of 5000 volts. A 1000-ohm one-watt resistor between the bottom of the meter multiplier and ground prevents the full B plus voltage from appearing across the meter switch, S2, when it is in the other position. To measure cathode current, the meter is placed in

Fig. 2 – Top view of the amplifier. The rf components occupy the foreground, while the heat-generating power-supply components are visible behind the compartment shield at the rear.

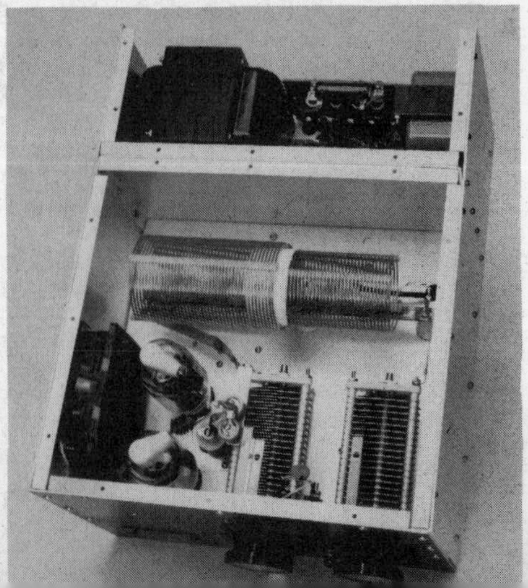

[1] A chart of U.S. and Canadian 160-meter sub-allocations is available from ARRL Headquarters; send a stamped, self-addressed envelope and request form S-15A.

Fig. 3 — Circuit diagram for the 160-meter amplifier. Fixed-value capacitors are ceramic disk unless otherwise indicated. Polarized capacitors are electrolytic. All resistors are 1/2-watt composition unless noted otherwise.

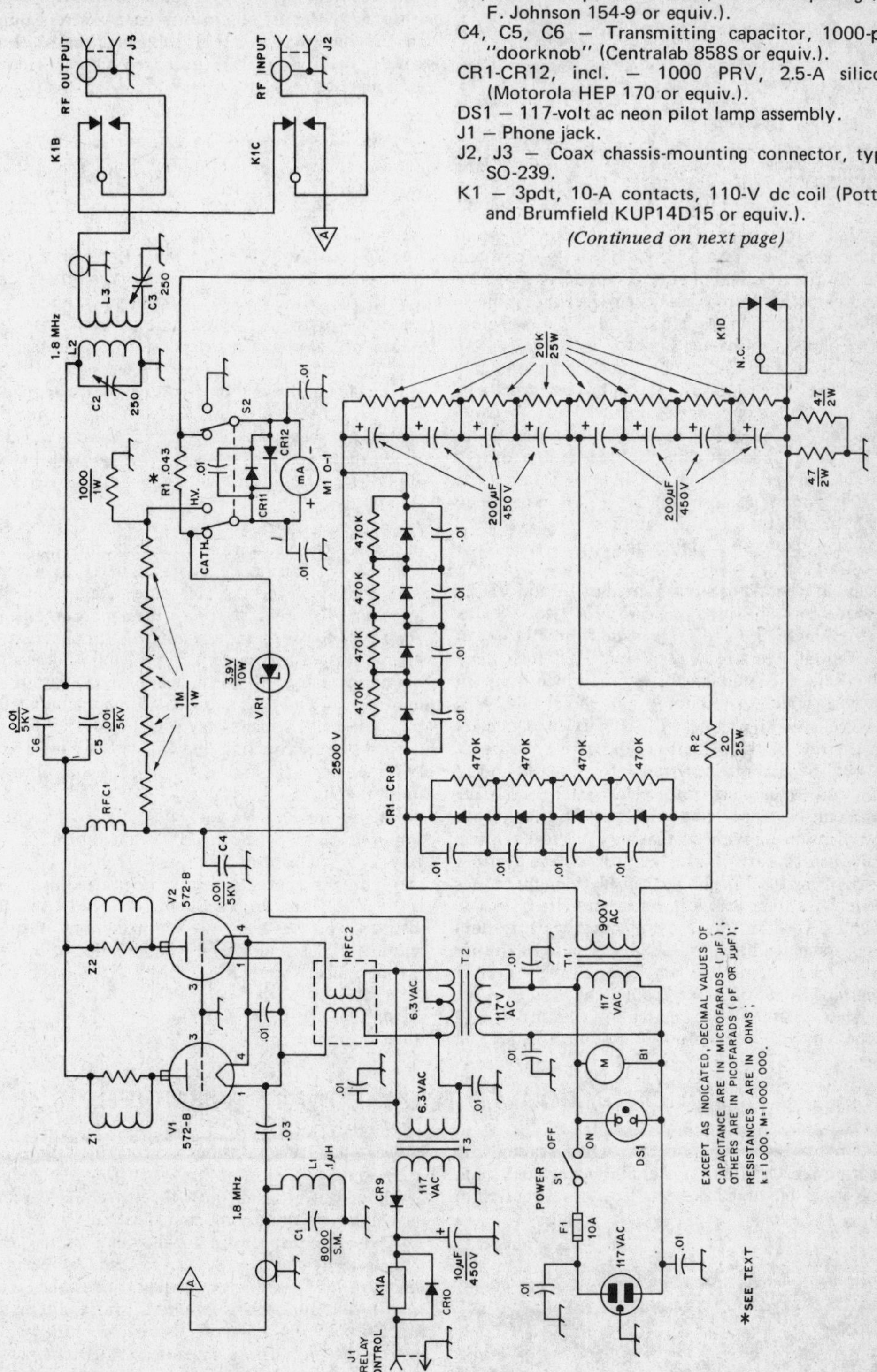

B1 — 117-volt axial fan (Rotron Whisper Fan or equiv.).

C1 — Parallel combination of one 5000, 2000, and 1000-pF silver-mica capacitors.

C2, C3 — 250-pF air variable, .075-inch spacing (E. F. Johnson 154-9 or equiv.).

C4, C5, C6 — Transmitting capacitor, 1000-pF "doorknob" (Centralab 858S or equiv.).

CR1-CR12, incl. — 1000 PRV, 2.5-A silicon (Motorola HEP 170 or equiv.).

DS1 — 117-volt ac neon pilot lamp assembly.

J1 — Phone jack.

J2, J3 — Coax chassis-mounting connector, type SO-239.

K1 — 3pdt, 10-A contacts, 110-V dc coil (Potter and Brumfield KUP14D15 or equiv.).

(Continued on next page)

L1 – 1.0 μH
L2, L3 – See text.
M1 – 1-mA dc (Simpson model 2121 or equiv.).
RFC1 – 1.0 mH, 500 mA (E. F. Johnson 102-752 or equiv.).
S1 – Spst rotary switch.
S2 – Dpdt rotary switch.
T1 – 117-volt primary; secondary 625-0-625 volts ac (ct not used) at 450 mA (Hammond No. 720).
T2 – 117-volt primary; secondary 6.3 V ct at 10 A (Stancor P-6464 or equiv.).
T3 – 117-volt primary; secondary 6.3 V ac.
VR1 – Zener, 3.9-V, 10-watt (Motorola HEP Z3500 or equiv.).

parallel with shunt R1, which remains in series with the cathode return lead at all times. To obtain a full-scale reading of one ampere, a shunt resistance of .043 ohms was used with the Simpson model 2121 meter, as it has an internal resistance of 43 ohms (see Chapter 17).

As this amplifier is designed for monoband operation, the mechanical and electrical complexities and compromises involved in the bandswitching of an output network are not a factor here. Tuned-link coupling is used in the output circuit. The grid of each 572B is tied directly to chassis ground, using short leads, to avoid problems with instability. Parasitic suppressors Z1 and Z2 also contribute to stability. Neutralization is not necessary.

B&W Miniductor stock is used at L2 and L3. L2 is made from 43 turns of B&W 3034 (No. 14 wire, 8 tpi, 3-inch dia.) and L3 is made from 39 turns of B&W 3030 (No. 14 wire, 8 tpi, 2-1/2-inch dia.). The coils are supported on a 10-inch strip of bakelite which is mounted on three 1-1/2-inch steatite insulating cones. L2 is epoxied into place on the side of the bakelite strip nearest the tubes. L3 will be partially inserted into the cold end of L2, and is epoxied into place after initial adjustments have been made. L3 must be able to slide freely inside L2 without making electrical contact. The first 10 turns of L3 may be covered with a layer of Scotch No. 27 glass insulating tape. Leads from L3 are made with teflon-insulated flexible stranded wire to allow the coil a degree of freedom of movement during initial adjustment. Rf output from L3 is connected to K1B through a short length of RG-58/U coaxial cable.

Meter shunt R1 is made by winding 12-1/2 inches of No. 26 enam. wire around a 1-megohm 2-watt resistor. If the meter used has an internal resistance other than 43 ohms, the appropriate shunt resistance value may be wound by referring to the copper wire resistance table in Chapter 18.

Parasitic suppressors Z1 and Z2 are each made with 3-1/2 turns of No. 14 enam. wire wound around the parallel combination of three 82-ohm, 1-watt composition resistors, mounted right at each plate cap.

Operation

The power supply should be tested before rf drive is applied to the amplifier. For initial tests, it is desirable to control the power transformer primary voltage with a Powerstat, while leaving the filament transformer primary and fan connected directly to the 117 V ac line. *Remember at all times that lethal voltages exist both above and below chassis.* Do not make any internal adjustments with the power on, or even with the power off until the bleeders have fully discharged the filter capacitors (at least 40 seconds with this particular amplifier). It is good practice to clip a lead from the B-plus terminal to ground after the capacitors have discharged, whenever working inside the amplifier (remember to remove it before applying power!). The tuned-input circuit (L1-C1), should be checked with a grid-dip meter for resonance at the frequency segment of interest. K1 must be closed during transmit; this may be effected by shorting the wire from J1 to ground with a relay inside the 160-meter exciter, or with an external switch. Starting with a plate voltage of about 1500 volts, drive is applied through J2 and C2 is adjusted for maximum rf output as indicated on an external rf wattmeter or relative output indicator. C3 is then adjusted for maximum output. The plate voltage may now be advanced to its normal level. The link may be moved in or out (with power off) and C2 and C3 again adjusted until the highest efficiency is obtained. At that point the link, L3, may be epoxied in place. In the amplifier described here, the optimum position for L3 was when eight of its turns were inside L2. This may be used as a starting point for the adjustment. Normal tune-up procedure involves only the adjustment of C2 and C3 for maximum output, within the maximum legal power limits, of course. During normal operation the 572B anodes may glow with a dull red color. The tubes draw about 50 mA resting current, when K1 is closed and no drive is applied.

A CONDUCTION-COOLED TWO-KILOWATT AMPLIFIER

One of the major concerns when dealing with high power amplifiers is heat and how to reduce it. The usual method has been to use a large fan or blower, but this solution is generally noisy. By using the principles of heat transfer, a noiseless amplifier can be made with the use of an adequate heat sink and conduction-cooled tubes.

The amplifier shown in the photographs and schematically in Fig. 1 uses a pair of recently designed 8873 conduction-cooled triode tubes. The circuit configuration is grounded grid and uses no tuned-input tank components. When properly adjusted, the amplifier is capable of IMD characteristics which are better than can be achieved by a

A 2-kW Amplifier

Top view of the 80-through 10-meter conduction-cooled amplifier. The chassis is 17 × 12 × 3 inches (43.2 × 30.5 × 7.6 cm) and is totally enclosed in a shield. A separate partition was fabricated to prevent rf leakage through the meter holes in the front panel. An old National Radio Company vernier dial is used in conjunction with the plate tuning capacitor to provide ease of adjustment (especially on 10 meters). The position of the dial for each band is marked on the dial skirt with a black pen and india ink.

typical exciter, therefore the added complexity of band switching a tuned-input circuit was deemed unnecessary.

Construction

Building an amplifier such as this is often an exercise in adapting readily available components to a published circuit. For this reason, a blow-by-blow description of this phase of the project will not be given. An effort was made, however, to use parts which are available generally, and should the builder desire, this model could be copied verbatim.

The most difficult constructional problem is that of aligning the tube sockets correctly. It is imperative that the sockets be aligned so that when the tubes are mounted in place, the flat surfaces of the anodes fit smoothly and snugly against the thermal-link heat-transfer material. Any misalignment here could destroy the tubes (or tube) the first time full power is applied. The mounting holes for the tube sockets are enlarged to allow final positioning after the tubes are "socked" in place with the clamping hardware. Pressure must be applied to the anodes so that they are always snug against the thermal link. The hardware used to perform this function must be nonconducting material capable of withstanding as much as 250°C. The pressure bracket used here was fabricated from several Millen jack-bar strips (metal clips removed) mounted in back-to-back fashion. The entire assembly is held in place by means of a long piece of No. 10 threaded brass rod which passes through a small hole in the center of the heat sink. An attempt to give meaningful comments about how tight the tubes should be pressured to the copper and aluminum sink will not be given. Suffice it to say that the tubes should fit flat and snugly against the thermal hardware. The heat sink was purchased from Thermaloy and is connected to a 1/4-inch thick piece of ordinary copper plate. The total cost for the copper and the aluminum sink is somewhat more than the price of a good centrifugal blower ($30) but the savings offered by not having to purchase special tube sockets and glass chimneys overcomes the cost differential.

The power supply is built on a separate chassis because the plate transformer is bulky and cumbersome. A special transformer was designed for this amplifier by Hammond Transformer Co. Ltd., of Guelph, Ont. Canada. The transformer contains two windings, one is for the plate supply to be used in a voltage-doubler circuit and the other is for the tube filaments. The power supply produces 2200 volts under a load of 500mA, and is rated for 2000 watts. The Hammond part number is given in Fig. 1. All of the interconnections for power-supply control and the operating voltages needed by the amplifier are carried by a seven-conductor cable. This excludes the B plus, however, which is connected between the units by means of a piece of test-probe wire (5-kV rating) with Millen high-voltage connectors mounted at both ends. The seven-conductor cable is made from several pieces of two-conductor household wire (No. 10) available at most hardware stores. Since the main power switch is mounted on the front panel of the amplifier, the power supply may be placed in some remote position, out of the way from the operator (not a bad idea!). A high-voltage meter was included with the power supply so that it could be used with other amplifiers. It serves no purpose with this system. The main amplifier deck has provisions for monitoring the plate voltage.

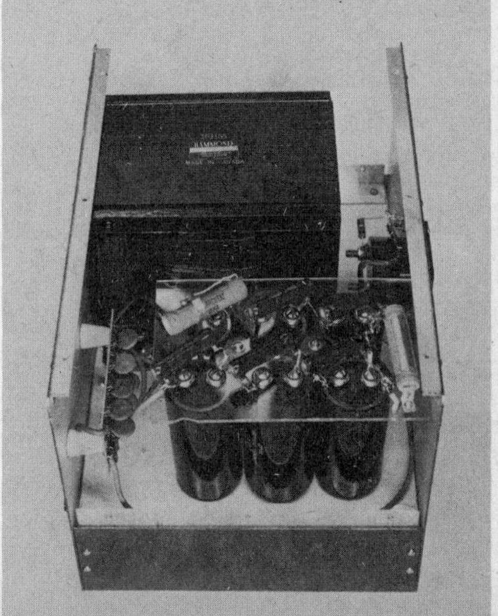

Top view of the power supply built by WA1JZC showing the technique for mounting the filter-capacitor bank. The diodes are mounted on a printed-circuit board which is fastened to the rear of the cabinet with cone insulators and suitable hardware.

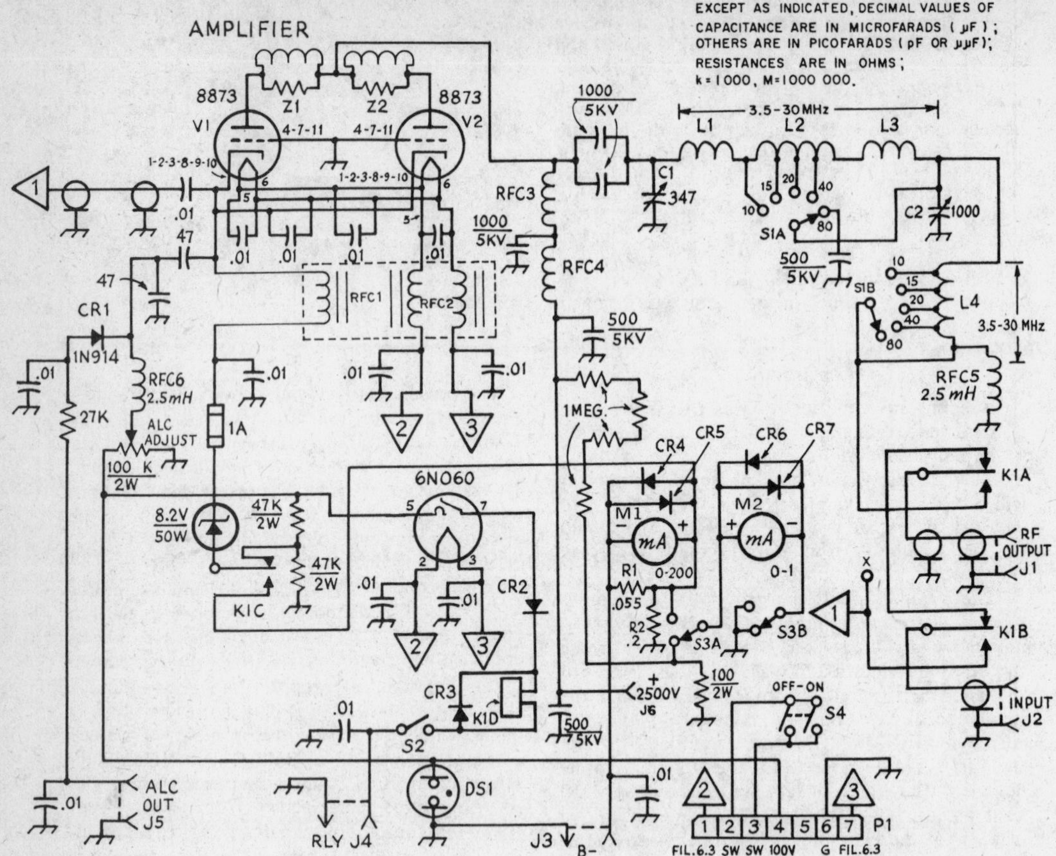

Fig. 1 – Circuit diagram for the 8873 conduction-cooled amplifier. Component designations not listed below are for text reference. RFC1 and RFC2 are wound on the same ferrite rod in the same direction; three wires are wound together (Amidon MU-125 kit). Tube sockets for V1 and V2 are E.F. Johnson 124-0311-100. The thermal links are available from Eimac with the tubes. The heat sink is part number 2559-080-A000 from Astrodyne Inc., 353 Middlesex Ave., Wilmington, MA 01887, and costs approximately $20.

C1 – Transmitting air variable, 347 pF (E.F. Johnson 154-0010-001).

C2 – Transmitting air variable, 1000 pF (E.F. Johnson 154-30).

CR2-CR7, incl. – 1000 PRV, 2.5 A (Motorola HEP170).

J1 – SO-239 chassis mounted coaxial connector.

J3, J4, J5 – Phono jack, panel mount.

J6 – High-voltage connection (Millen 37001).

K1 – Enclosed, three-pole relay, 110-volt dc coil (Potter and Brumfield KUP14D15).

L1 – 4-3/4 turns of 1/4-inch copper tubing, 1-3/4-inch inside diameter, 2-1/4 inches long.

L2 – 12-1/2 turns, 1/4-inch copper tubing, 2-3/4-inch inside diameter, tap at one turn from connection point with L1, 2-1/2 inches for 20 meters, 7-3/4 turns for 40 meters.

L3 – 11-1/2 turns, 2-inch diameter, 6 tpi (Barker and Williamson 3025).

L4 – 10 turns, 2-inch diameter, 6 tpi, with taps at 3 turns for 10 meters, 3-1/2 turns for 15 meters, 4-3/4 turns for 20 meters, 6-3/4 turns for 40 meters; all taps made from junction of L3 (Barker and Williamson 3025).

M1 – 200 mA full scale, 0.5-ohm internal resistance (Simpson Electric Designer Series Model 523).

M2 – 1 mA full scale, 43 ohms internal resistance (Simpson Electric, same series as M1).

R1 – Meter shunt, .05555 ohms constructed from 3.375 feet of No. 22 enam. wire wound over the body of any 2-watt resistor higher than 100 ohms in value.

R2 – Meter shunt, 0.2 ohms made from five 1-ohm, 1-watt resistors connected in parallel.

RFC1, RFC5, RFC6 – 2.5 mH (Millen 34300-2500).

RFC3 – Rf choke (Barker and Williamson Model 800 with 10 turns removed from the bottom end).

RFC4 – 22 μH (Millen 34300).

S1 – High-voltage band-selector style, double pole, six position (James Millen 51001 style).

Z1, Z2 – 2 turns 3/8-inch-wide copper strap wound over three 100-ohm, 2-watt resistors connected in parallel.

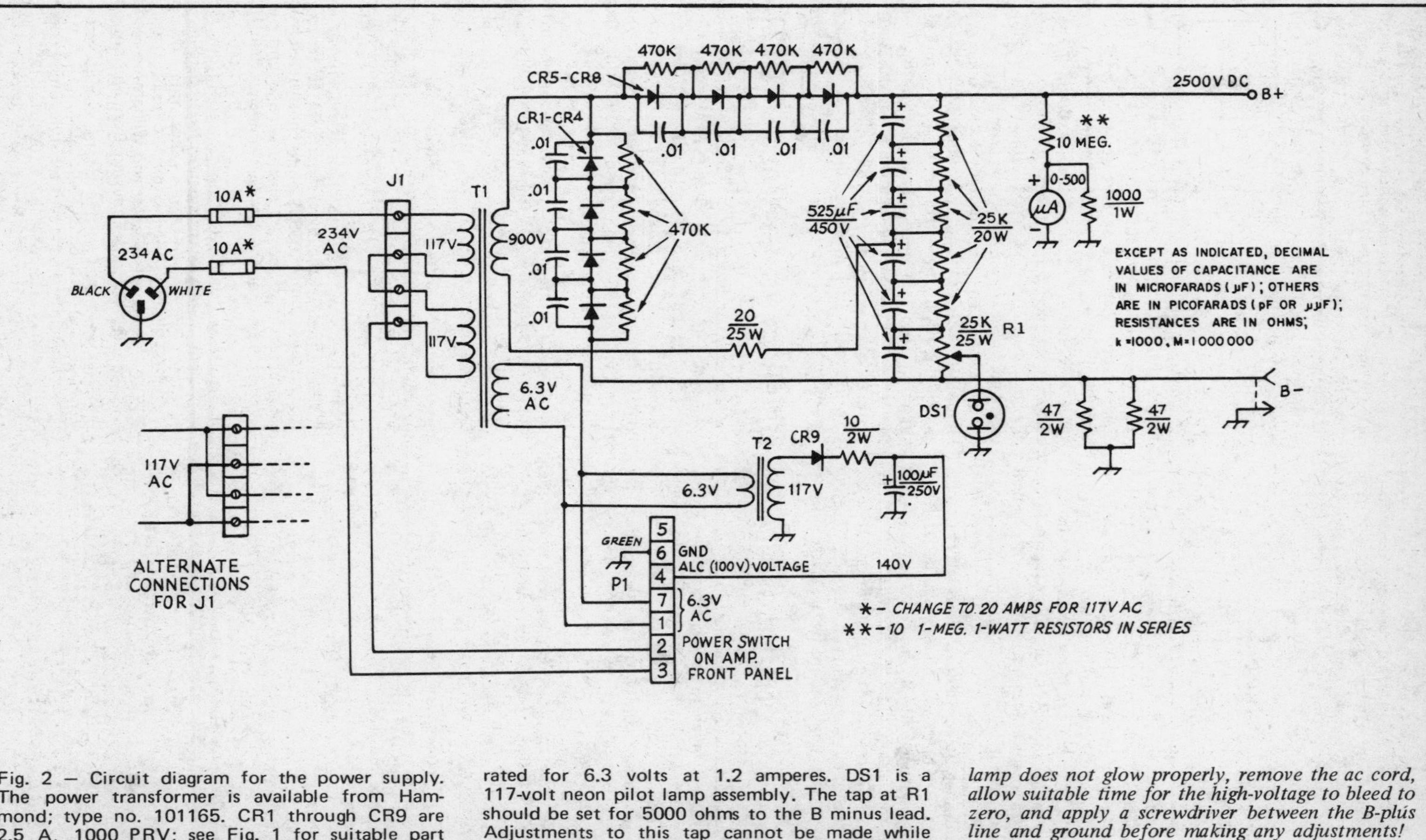

Fig. 2 – Circuit diagram for the power supply. The power transformer is available from Hammond; type no. 101165. CR1 through CR9 are 2.5 A, 1000 PRV; see Fig. 1 for suitable part number. T2 is Stancor part number P-8190 and is rated for 6.3 volts at 1.2 amperes. DS1 is a 117-volt neon pilot lamp assembly. The tap at R1 should be set for 5000 ohms to the B minus lead. Adjustments to this tap cannot be made while voltage is applied to the power supply. *If the pilot lamp does not glow properly, remove the ac cord, allow suitable time for the high-voltage to bleed to zero, and apply a screwdriver between the B-plus line and ground before making any adjustments!*

A conventional household light switch may be used for S4. If the switch is to be mounted horizontally, be sure to use a contactor device and not a mercury type (which operates in a vertical position only). A double-pole switch was used with both poles connected in parallel. The rating is 220 V at 10 A per section.

The RF Deck

The two sections of the pi-L network are isolated from each other by placing one of them under the chassis. Although not shown in the photograph, a shield was added to prevent rf energy from entering the control section underneath the chassis. The shield divides the chassis between the tube sockets and the inductors. The loading capacitor is mounted directly beneath the plate-tuning capacitor. This scheme provides an excellent mechanical arrangement as well as a neat front-panel layout.

The 8873s require a 60-second warmup time, and accordingly, a one-minute time-delay circuit is included in the design. The amplifier IN/OUT switch is independent of the main power switch and the time delay. Once the delay circuit "times out," the amplifier may be placed in or out of the line to the antenna, whenever desired. A safety problem exists here: there is no large blower running, and there are no brightly illuminated tubes to warn the operator that the amplifier is turned on. Except for the pilot lamp on the front panel, one might be fooled into believing the amplifier is turned off! And if the pilot lamp should burn out, there is *absolutely* no way to tell if the power is turned on (with the resultant high voltage at the anodes of the 8873s). *Beware!*

Operation

Tuning a pi-L-output circuit is somewhat different than tuning a conventional pi-network because the grid current should be monitored closely. Grid current depends on two items, drive power and amplifier loading. The procedure found to be most effective is to tune for maximum power output with the loading sufficiently heavy to keep the grid current below the maximum level while adjusting the drive power for the proper amount of plate current. The plate current for cw operation should be 450 mA and approximately 900 mA under single-tone tuning conditions for ssb. This presents a problem since it is not legal to operate under single-tone tuning conditions for ssb. Sixty watts of drive power will provide full input levels. For use with high-power exciters, see *QST* for October, 1973.

A ONE-KILOWATT AMPLIFIER USING A 3-500Z

Circuit design for high-power linear amplifiers hasn't changed much in recent years. The differences between various types of grounded-grid units are usually more mechanical than electrical. The degree of circuit complexity is determined primarily by the number of features desired and whether or not the power supply and control circuits are included on the same chassis as the amplifier. Described below is a power amplifier designed to operate cw as the primary mode. A suitable exciter is described earlier in the chapter.

The Amplifier Circuit

A single 3-500Z triode tube develops 1-kW input on cw and 1-kW PEP on ssb. The output circuit is a conventional pi network which tunes the hf amateur bands from 3.5 to 30 MHz. The *L/C* ratio of the tank circuit is designed for operation at 2500 to 2800 volts. The T-R switch is coupled to the tank circuit via C1. This capacitor is constructed of RG-8A/U. A 2-inch overlap between the braid and center conductor provides the correct amount of coupling for the T-R switch (see top view photograph).

Filament voltage is applied to the 3-500Z through a bifilar-wound rf choke. Drive power is coupled to the filament circuit via C2, a combination of three .01-μF disc ceramic capacitors in parallel. A 7.5-volt Zener diode in the cathode-return lead is used to develop grid bias. K1D opens the cathode-return lead during standby, completely cutting off plate current.

S1, located on the front panel, switches on the fan motor, the pilot light, and activates the control circuits. Input jacks for high voltage, as well as filament and control voltages, are located on the rear panel.

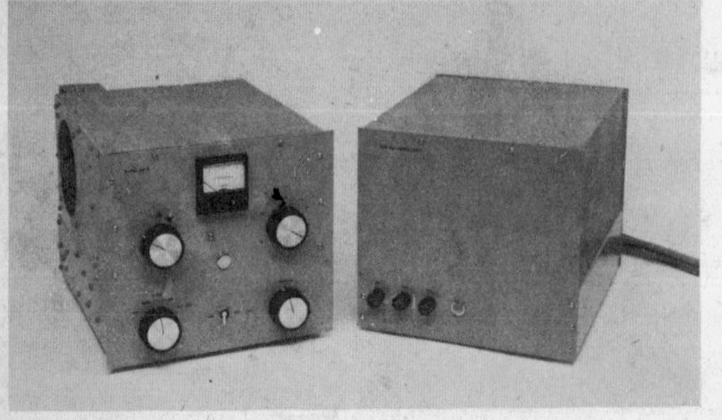

The Multimeter

A 1-mA meter is used to measure grid current, cathode current, plate voltage, and power output. R4, mounted on the rear chassis apron, allows adjustment of the relative-output circuit sensitivity. A voltage-dropping resistor network, R3, provides a full-scale reading of 5 kV. R5 maintains a load at the meter end of R3 preventing full B+ from appearing across S2 when it is in one of the three other positions. R3 consists of five 1-

Inside view of the amplifier built by WA1JZC. The unusual plate cap is described in the text. A T-R switch is included for break-in cw operation and is mounted in a Minibox attached to the rear compartment panel.

megohm, 1-watt composition resistors connected in series thereby reducing the voltage across any one resistor to less than 600.

Grid current is measured by placing the meter in series with the grid (ground) and the cathode. The grid meter shunt, R2, provides a full-scale reading of 200 mA. R2 is equal to the internal resistance of the meter divided by 200. The resistance of M1 is 43 ohms; therefore R2 is 0.21 ohm. It is made by winding 24-1/4 inches of No. 30 wire on a 1-megohm, 2-watt composition resistor. Cathode current is measured by placing the meter in series with the cathode-return lead. Meter shunt R1 was chosen to provide a full-scale reading of 1 Ampere. It is made by winding 12-1/2 inches of No. 26 wire on a 1-megohm, 2-watt composition resistor, for a shunt resistance of .043 ohms. R2 is the primary path for the high-voltage negative lead to chassis ground. R6 provides protection in the event this meter shunt opens.

Construction

The amplifier is built on a 10 × 12 × 3-inch aluminum chassis. The high-voltage power-supply components and the 5-volt filament transformer are mounted on a separate chassis (see chapter 5). The complete amplifier occupies slightly less than 3/4 of a cubic foot, making a compact package that will fit on almost any operating desk. Location of the various components is shown in the photographs. All of the circuits carrying rf are completely shielded to reduce any instability or TVI. The amplifier exhibits no tendency to "take off" when operated without a parasitic suppressor. However, if problems with instability are encountered, a suitable suppressor made of 3 turns, No. 12, copper wire, 1-1/4-inch dia. wound over three 150-ohm, 2-watt composition resistors can be inserted between the plate cap and the top of RFC1.

The rf-output circuit is completely shielded in a compartment constructed of cane metal and sheet aluminum. Perforated material is needed to allow adequate air flow past the tube. The socket (E.F. Johnson Co. type 122-275 or equiv.) is mounted 1/2 inch above the chassis, allowing air to circulate

Bottom view of the amplifier.

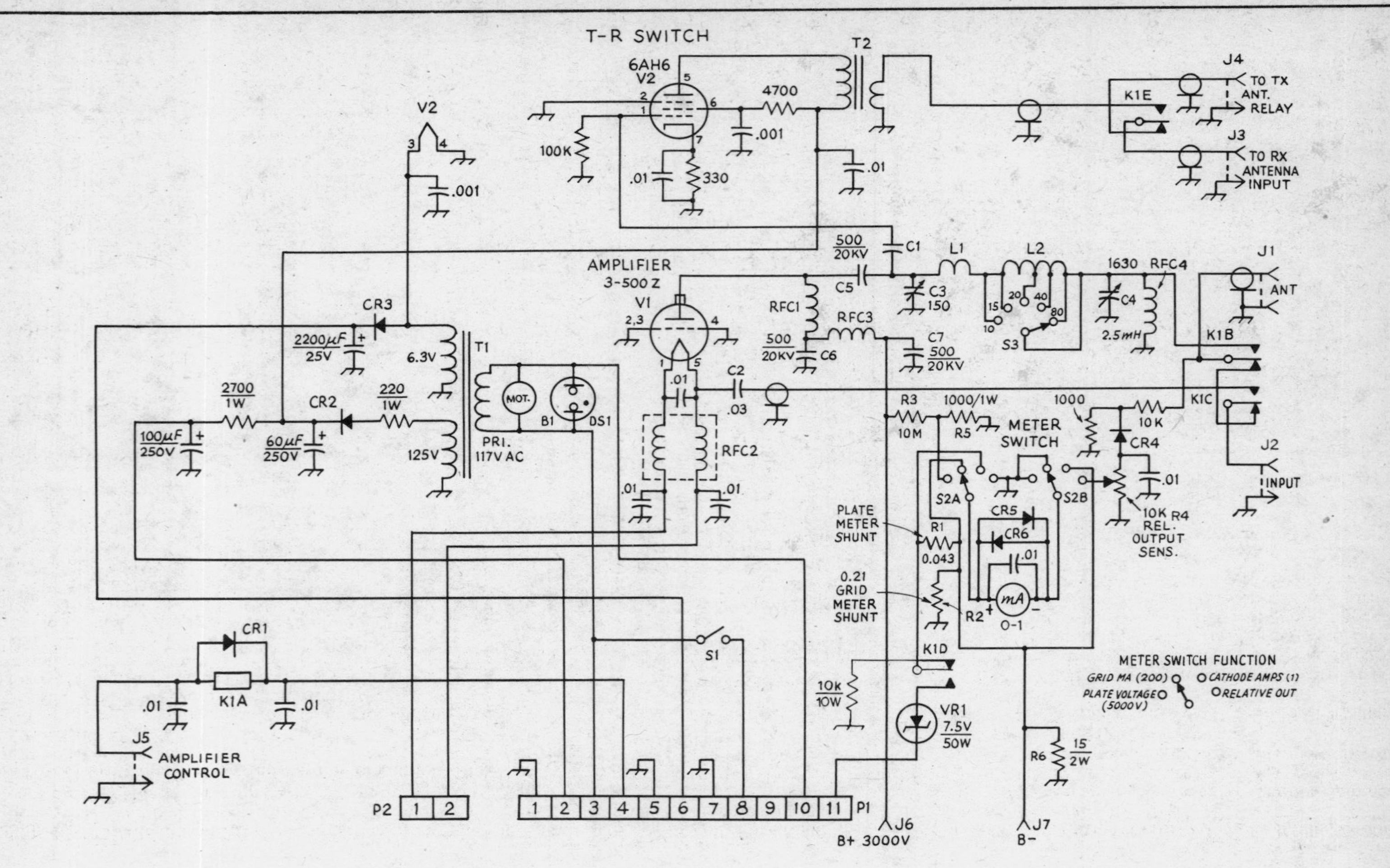
T-R SWITCH
6AH6
V2
4700
.001
100K
.01
330
.01
T2
K1E
J4
TO TX
ANT.
RELAY
J3
TO RX
ANTENNA
INPUT
V2
.001
AMPLIFIER
3-500 Z
V1
2,3
500
20KV
C1
C5
L1
L2
1630
RFC4
J1
ANT
C3
150
C4
2.5mH
S3
K1B
RFC1
RFC3
500
20KV
C6
C7
500
20KV
.01
C2
.03
K1C
J2
INPUT
R3
10M
1000/1W
R5
METER
SWITCH
1000
10K
CR4
.01
10K R4
REL.
OUTPUT
SENS.
S2A
S2B
CR5
CR6
.01
mA
0-1
PLATE
METER
SHUNT
R1
0.043
0.21
GRID
METER
SHUNT
R2
RFC2
.01
.01
CR3
2200µF
25V
6.3V
T1
MOT.
B1
DS1
PRI.
117V AC
2700
1W
CR2
220
1W
100µF
250V
60µF
250V
125V
K1D
10k
10W
VR1
7.5V
50W
METER SWITCH FUNCTION
GRID MA (200)
CATHODE AMPS (1)
PLATE VOLTAGE (5000V)
RELATIVE OUT
R6
15
2W
CR1
K1A
.01
.01
J5
AMPLIFIER
CONTROL
S1
P2
P1
J6
B+ 3000V
J7
B-

Fig. 1 — Circuit diagram for the amplifier. Component designations not listed are for text reference only. Polarized capacitors are electrolytic.

B1 — 117-volt fan (Rotron Whisper Fan or equiv.).
C1 — See text.
C2 — See text.
C3 — 180-pF air variable, .077-inch air gap (Millen 16250 with 4 stator plates removed).
C4 — 1630-pF maximum, receiving-type air variable.
C5, C6, C7 — Transmitting capacitor, 500-pF "doorknob" (Sprague 20DK-T5 or equiv.).
CR1-CR5, incl. — 1000 PRV, 2.5 A (Mallory M2.5A or equiv.).
DS1 — 117-volt ac neon pilot lamp assembly.
J1 — Coax chassis-mount connector, type SO-239.
J2-J5, incl. — Phone jack, single-hole mount.
J6, J7 — High-voltage chassis connector (Millen 37001).
K1 — 4-pdt, 5-A, 6-V dc coil (Potter and Brumfield GPD coil and GP-17 contact arrangement or equiv.).
L1 — 4-1/2 turns, No. 14, 1-3/4-inch dia., tapped at 1-1/2 turns, as measured from S3 end. (Coil stock: Barker and Williamson 3022).
L2 — 23 turns, No. 12, 2-1/2-inch dia., tapped at 10-3/4 turns for 40 meters, 19-1/2 turns for 20 meters, as measured from the C4 end. (Coil stock: Barkerpand Williamson 3029.)
M1 — 1-mA dc (Simpson model 2122-17430 or equiv.).
P1 — Chassis-mounted 11 pin power connector.
P2 — Chassis-mounted 2 pin power connector.
RFC1 — Transmitting rf choke (Barker and Williamson model 800 or equiv.).
RFC2 — Bifilar-wound filament choke (Amidon 10-A choke kit).
RFC3 — 2.7 µH, 1700 mA, rf choke (Millen 34300 -2.7 or equiv.).
S1 — Spst toggle switch (Cutler-Hammer 8381K21C or equiv.).
S2 — Double-pole, 6-position rotary (4 used), nonshorting (Mallory type 3226J or equiv.).
S3 — Rf switch, single-pole, 6-position (Millen 51001).
T1 — 117-volt primary; secondary 125 volts at 50 mA; 6.3-V at 2-A (Stancor PA-8421 or equiv.).
T2 — 20 turns, No. 24 enam. wire wound on a 1-inch long, 1/2-inch dia iron core from a slug-tuned coil form. The secondary is 3 turns, No. 24 enam. wire wound over the cold end of the primary.
VR1 — Zener, 7.5-V, 50 watt.

around the base connections and seal. The grid pins of the socket are soldered to lugs mounted on the chassis. When a standard Eimac plate cap is used with the 3-500Z, the cap extends above the edge of the cabinet. Therefore, a 1/4-inch thick aluminum plate, 1-3/4 inches square, is used in place of the Eimac unit.

The plate-tuning capacitor, C3, has too high a minimum capacitance for proper operation on 10 and 15 meters. Removing 4 of its stator plates reduces its minimum capacitance sufficiently. C4 has a shaft diameter of 3/8 inch, requiring special attention. A standard 1/4-inch coupling with one end drilled out slightly over 3/8 inch is used as an adapter. Fine-mesh screen is placed between the cabinet wall and the fan to maintain an rf-tight enclosure. The screen does not appear to reduce the air flow appreciably.

Finishing touches are added by selecting front-panel knobs, painting the amplifier cabinet with light avocado green paint, and applying appropriate decals.

Hookup and Switch Functions

The Amplifier is designed to permit true cw break-in operation when used with a separate transmitter and receiver. In most commercially made ssb/cw transmitter-receiver combinations, all transmit-receive changeover functions on both modes are handled by a VOX circuit, and relay contacts inside the transmitter perform the receiver antenna switching and muting duties. When using a combination with this amplifier, the receiver antenna terminal is connected directly to J3 on the rear chassis apron, and a cable connects J4 and the receiver antenna terminal of the transmitter. The amplifier control relay contacts of the transmitter are connected to J5, and the rf output of the transmitter is connected to input jack J2. In this configuration, the receiver is connected directly to the antenna during standby, and during transmit, the T-R switch takes over.

If the transmitter (such as the T-9er described earlier in this chapter) does not incorporate a relay-switching arrangement, then antenna changeover is handled entirely by the T-R switch. The receiver antenna is connected to J3, the transmitter rf output connects to J2, and a shorted phono plug is inserted in J5.

For use with a transceiver, the transceiver output is connected to J2, and the amplifier control relay contacts of the transceiver are connected to J5. The transceiver operates "straight through" when the amplifier is off, and K1 provides the required antenna switching functions when the amplifier is in use.

Operation

After the position of each tank-coil tap has been determined, the relative-output sensitivity control, R4, can be adjusted for 3/4 scale meter reading at full power input. The amplifier should be tuned for maximum power output into a 50-ohm nonreactive load, which should coincide approximately with the point of minimum plate current.

TWO-KILOWATT AMPLIFIER USING A SINGLE 8877 TRIODE

The 8877 is a big brother to the new 8873 series of ceramic/metal power tubes. It is a zero-biased high-mu triode having an oxide-coated cathode. The plate dissipation is 1500 watts. Heater-to-cathode capacitance is low eliminating the need for filament chokes when operated below 30 MHz. An inexpensive 7-pin socket may be used reducing the overall cost. The grid connection is near the chassis level and permits low-inductance grounding. Average IMD products for the 8877 in linear service run 38 dB below one tone of a two-tone test signal for 3rd order products, and 44.5 dB for 5th order products.

The cathode impedance of an 8877/3CX1500A7 is about 54 ohms. Direct coupling from the exciter to the cathode without the use of a cathode-tuned circuit *will* work, but performance will be degraded. The reduced-drive requirements and improved distortion products make the small effort of putting a "flywheel" in the input circuit worthwhile.

The opening in a shield surface where blower air enters the chassis may be a source of rf leakage. In this amplifier, brass-wire screen is mounted in the air stream to minimize this leakage. Tiny globs of solder at several crossover points assure positive connection on the screen. The disadvantage of this method is the eventual collection of dust, restricting air flow. It requires periodic cleaning.

INPUT CIRCUIT						OUTPUT CIRCUIT		
BAND MHz	*NO. TURNS*	*WIRE SIZE*	*INDUCTANCE RANGE IN μH*	*F* MHz*	*C1 AND C2*	*C10*	*IND.*	*C11*
3/8-inch Diameter Forms								
3.5	14	24	1.64 - 4.58	5.05	(820)	273	8.54	1473
4.0	14	24	1.64 - 4.58	5.8	(750)	239	7.47	1289
7.0	10	24	0.96 - 2.32	10.1	(430)	136	4.27	737
14.0	7	16	0.44 - .74	19.5	(220)	68	2.14	368
21.0	5	16	0.28 - 0.52	29.2	(150)	45	1.42	246
28.0	4	16	0.17 - 0.34	40	(100)	34	1.07	184

* A grid dip meter should be used to assure that the inductor resonates at the indicated frequency. These adjustments should be made with capacitors C1 and C2 out of the circuit.

Laboratory tests at Eimac indicate best performance to be at an anode potential of 2700 to 3000 volts. The efficiency runs between 60 and 65 percent.

Plate impedance figures are based on a 2 kW PEP input using 2700 volts at 740 milliamperes. The grid current for the 8877 runs about 15 percent of the plate current. At full power input, the grid current should be about 110 mA.

When plate voltage is applied, the zero-signal plate current should be about 95 mA. Drive should be applied through a directional coupler. On each band, after fully loading the amplifier to the above conditions, tune the input coil for minimum reflected power. No further adjustment is required and the directional coupler can be removed. For additional construction details, see September, 1971, *QST*.

Top view of the 8877 Amplifier built by K6DC.

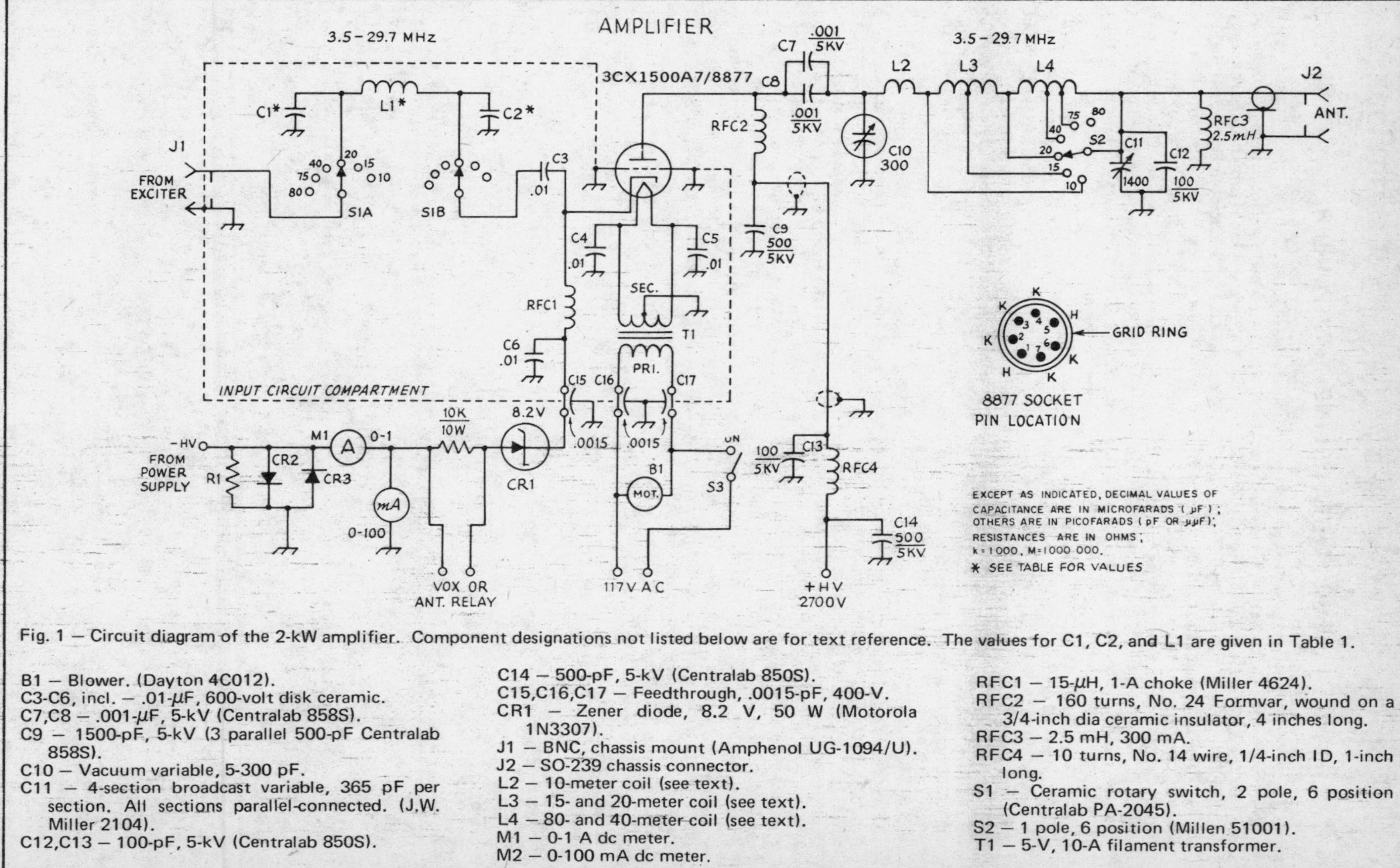

Fig. 1 — Circuit diagram of the 2-kW amplifier. Component designations not listed below are for text reference. The values for C1, C2, and L1 are given in Table 1.

B1 — Blower. (Dayton 4C012).
C3-C6, incl. — .01-µF, 600-volt disk ceramic.
C7,C8 — .001-µF, 5-kV (Centralab 858S).
C9 — 1500-pF, 5-kV (3 parallel 500-pF Centralab 858S).
C10 — Vacuum variable, 5-300 pF.
C11 — 4-section broadcast variable, 365 pF per section. All sections parallel-connected. (J.W. Miller 2104).
C12,C13 — 100-pF, 5-kV (Centralab 850S).
C14 — 500-pF, 5-kV (Centralab 850S).
C15,C16,C17 — Feedthrough, .0015-pF, 400-V.
CR1 — Zener diode, 8.2 V, 50 W (Motorola 1N3307).
J1 — BNC, chassis mount (Amphenol UG-1094/U).
J2 — SO-239 chassis connector.
L2 — 10-meter coil (see text).
L3 — 15- and 20-meter coil (see text).
L4 — 80- and 40-meter coil (see text).
M1 — 0-1 A dc meter.
M2 — 0-100 mA dc meter.
RFC1 — 15-µH, 1-A choke (Miller 4624).
RFC2 — 160 turns, No. 24 Formvar, wound on a 3/4-inch dia ceramic insulator, 4 inches long.
RFC3 — 2.5 mH, 300 mA.
RFC4 — 10 turns, No. 14 wire, 1/4-inch ID, 1-inch long.
S1 — Ceramic rotary switch, 2 pole, 6 position (Centralab PA-2045).
S2 — 1 pole, 6 position (Millen 51001).
T1 — 5-V, 10-A filament transformer.

A SOLID-STATE LINEAR AMPLIFIER

In this section a 15-watt solid-state linear amplifier for 3.5 to 30 MHz is described. A filter at the amplifier output attenuates the harmonic energy. With the proper filter in place, no tuning is necessary for complete coverage of each band. The circuit utilizes two transistors that are available surplus for $2.99 each.[1] The amplifier delivers 15-watts peak power for ssb operation, or 15 watts on cw. The collector efficiency from 3.5 to 30 MHz is no lower than 50 percent, but is approximately 57 percent on 80 meters. Intermodulation distortion products for a two-tone test signal are down 30 dB from pep at all frequencies of operation. The amplifier showed a minimum gain of 16 dB. A maximum power of 375 mW is required to drive the amplifier to 15-watts output. This excitation power is easily obtainable with a Class A driver.

A push-pull amplifier circuit is employed with suitable forward base bias to eliminate cross-over distortion (see Fig. 1). The input and output transformers are designed to match the base impedance to a 50-ohm input impedance, and the collector load impedance to the 50-ohm output impedance. Since the gain of the transistors decreases as the frequency of operation increases, a compensating network is placed at the amplifier input to attenuate the drive to the transistors as the operating frequency is lowered. The maximum SWR looking into the compensating circuit is 1.2:1, providing a constant 50-ohm load for the exciter.

1 Poly Paks, P.O. Box 942M, Lynnfield, MA 01940.

In a push-pull circuit there is inherent cancelation of the even harmonics. Laboratory measurements for the circuit in Fig. 1 show that all harmonics are in excess of 20 dB below the fundamental signal. This figure is not acceptable for harmonic rejection, so a low-pass filter design (Fig. 6-IV) is shown that does provide sufficient attenuation of the harmonics. As long as the filter output is terminated by a 50-ohm load, the filter input looks like 50-ohms below the filter cutoff frequency. No tuning is necessary when changing frequency within any given band. A bank of four filters can be constructed to cover the 80- through 10-meter ham bands. (Only one filter is needed for both the 10- and 15-meter bands.) Band changing is accomplished simply by switching in the appropriate filter for the band of operation. If the builder is interested in only one band the remaining filters need not be constructed.

Construction of the input and output transformers is somewhat unconventional although not too difficult. The transformers are built by placing two cylinders of 3E2A ferrite material side by side and running the wires for the windings through the two holes in the cylinders as shown in Fig. 2. The wire running from A to A′ would be one turn on the primary with the wire from B to B′ being one turn on the secondary. Since the ferrite cylinders aren't available at a reasonable price, they can be constructed by stacking two toroids together for each cylinder of the output transformer and four toroids together for the input transformer. The Ferroxcube series 266 toroids are used for the

Topside view of the linear amplifier with the compensating network attached by means of BNC hardware.

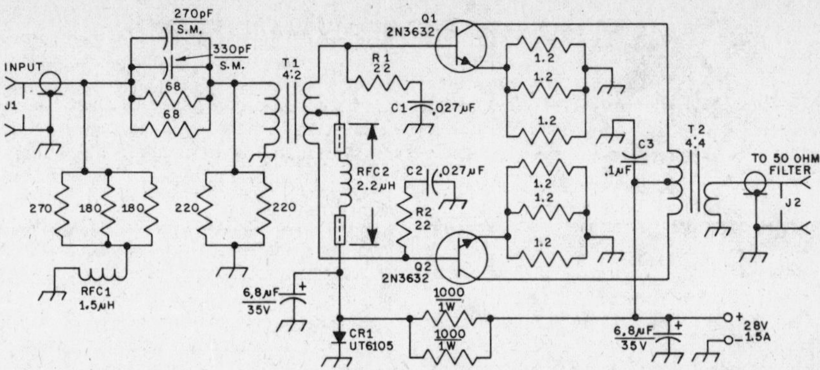

Fig. 1 – Schematic diagram of the amplifier. Resistance is in ohms, resistors are 1/2 watt unless otherwise indicated, except for R1 and R2 which are 1/4 watt. SM = silver mica. Polarized capacitors are electrolytic. C1, C2, and C3 are Aerovox Hi-*Q* units, type CK05 (available from Newark Electronics, Chicago, IL, catalog No. 101). RFC1 and RFC2 are small encapsulated chokes. See text for discussion of other components shown here.

output transformer, and the series 1041 toroids are used for the input transformer.[2] In order to reduce flux leakage the center winding of the primary of the output transformer (and the secondary of the input transformer) should be made of braid similar to the shield-diameter of small coaxial cable. A broadband match to a low-impedance termination is readily achieved with these transformers.

Following is a step-by-step procedure for fabricating the output transformer. First, slip a 1-inch-long piece of braid over a 2-inch-long 10-32 screw, preferably one that does not take solder easily. Next, place two of the cores over the braid, pushing the cores tightly against each other. Now, flare out the ends of the braid on each end of the cores and flow solder in the flared portions of the braid as shown in Fig. 3. After this step is completed the excess braid can be clipped close to the edge of the cylinders at one end. When both cylinders are constructed they can be individually wrapped with tape and then taped together side by side. On the end where the braid was left extending over the edge of the core, a solder connection is made to join the two cylinders electrically. Of course, some pruning is necessary in order to get the two cylinders mechanically close to each other. When this step is completed, the point where the braid from the two cylinders is joined is the center tap of the transformer primary. If a total of 2 turns is required on each side of the center tap, the braid from the center tap to one end of one of the cylinders is a half a turn. Therefore, 1 1/2 more turns of No. 22 enameled wire must be added by tacking the wire with solder to the end of the braid and running the wire through the holes left in the cylinders after removing the 10-32 screws. Similarly, 1 1/2 turns are added from the other cylinder end. Fig. 4 shows the transformer. The secondary is wound by running 4 turns of wire through the same two holes in the cylinders but with the leads extending out the opposite side of the transformer.

The transformer at the input of the amplifier is constructed in a similar manner with a 4:2 turns ratio. In this case the smaller Ferroxcube toroid core, series 1041, can be used. These cylinders are made by stacking 4 cores on top of each other. With a total of two turns required on the secondary, only 1/2 turn of enameled wire is needed to complete the winding once the braid is through the cylinders. No. 28 wire is used on the input transformer. Four more turns of wire (with the leads extending out the other end of the transformer) make up the primary winding of the input transformer.

The amplifier is constructed on a 1/8-inch-thick aluminum plate, 4 inches long by 3 inches wide. This plate should provide an adequate heat sink for the duty cycle incurred with ssb or cw operation. The transistors are mounted 2 inches from the end

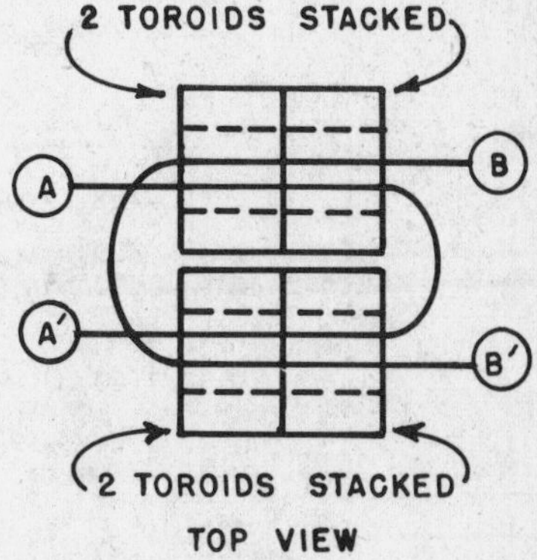

Fig. 2 – Illustration of how the broadband transformers are assembled.

[2] Elna Ferrite Laboratories, Inc., 9 Pine Grove St., Woodstock, NY 12498.

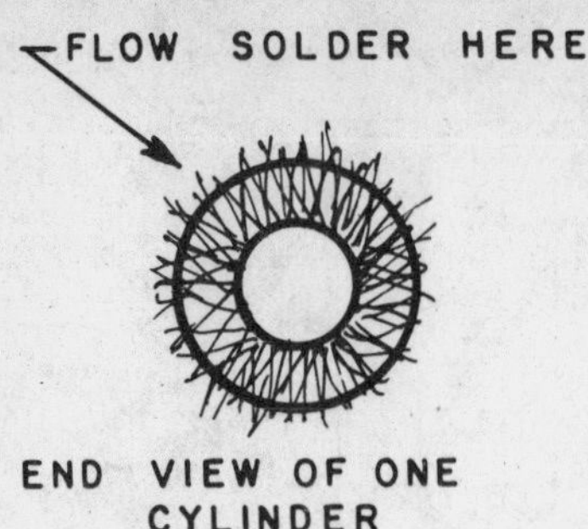

Fig. 3 – Drawing of end view of one cylinder of the broadband transformers.

of the plate and 3/8 inch off the center line running the length of the plate. Very short leads are maintained for the emitter resistors to minimize lead inductance. The two 1000-ohm biasing resistors, the biasing diode, and the 6.8-μF capacitor are located on the bottom side of the plate. The biasing diode used in the original circuit is a Unitrode UT6105 rectifier diode. This diode is fairly expensive, but any silicon rectifier diode rated at 3 A and 50 volts PRV should work.

A circuit diagram of the filters is shown in Fig. 5, and component values are given in Table 6-IV. L1 and C2 should be resonated at the proper frequency before being placed in the rest of the circuit. L1, L2, and L3 can be wound on toroid cores available from Amidon[3] when the inductance values are too large for convenient air coils.

Before applying voltage to the amplifier, a check should be made with an ohmmeter to insure there are no shorts between the primary and secondary of the transformer. If all looks well at that step, connect a 50-ohm load and apply dc voltage. Always terminate the amplifier output with a 50-ohm load before applying voltage; otherwise instability may result. The amplifier idling current, with no drive applied, should be approximately 100 mA. If this value is not obtained, there is probably a short in one of the transformers. If the correct idling current is present, apply drive (375 mW cw or peak ssb), and 15 watts of rf power should appear at the output. If a two-tone signal is used for ssb tests, the output level will indicate only 7.5 watts on an averaging-type wattmeter. Now, the amplifier is ready to connect to the antenna (one with an SWR below 1.5:1). Operation in any part of any band is acceptable, as long as the filter for that band is used and the SWR is low.

3 Amidon Associates, 12033 Otsego Street, North Hollywood, CA 91607.

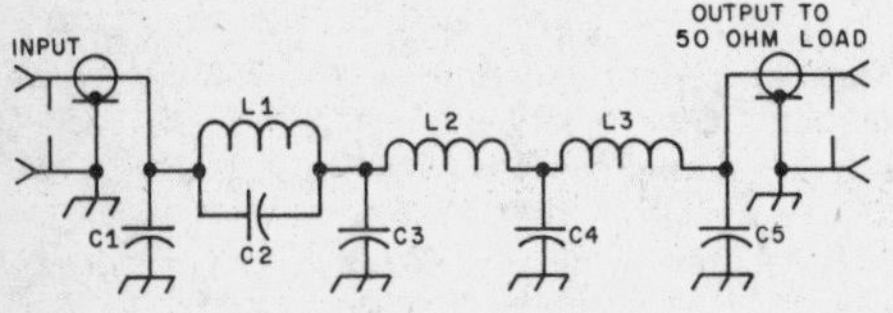

Fig. 5 – Circuit diagram for a low-pass filter.

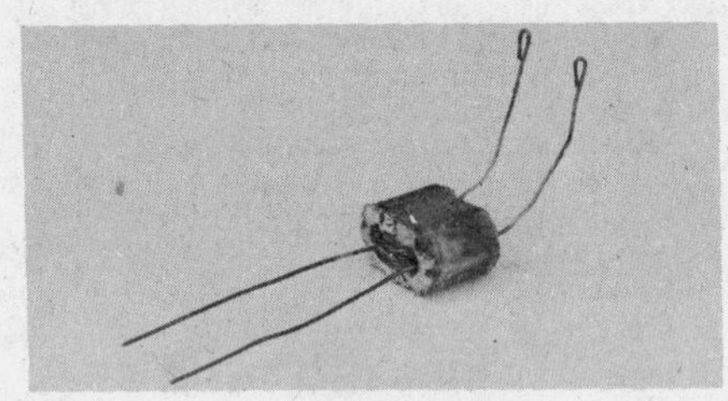

Fig. 4 – Close-up view of the input transformer used in the circuit of Fig. 1.

Bibliography

Gray and Graham, *Radio Transmitters*, McGraw-Hill Publishing Company, 1961.

Hejhall, *Solid-State Linear Amplifier Design*, Motorola Semiconductor Products Application Note AN-546, 1971.

Orr, *Radio Handbook*, Editors and Engineers, 1970.

Pitzalis *et al*, "Broadband 60-W HF Linear Amplifier," *IEEE Journal of Solid-State Circuits*, June, 1971.

RCA Power Circuits, RCA Electronics Components, Division of RCA, 1969.

Single Sideband for the Radio Amateur, American Radio Relay League, 5th Edition, 1970.

Southerland, *Care and Feeding of Power Grid Tubes*, Eimac Division of Varian, 1967.

TABLE 6-IV

Impedance at f_u	*80M f_u = 4 MHz*	*40M f_u = 8 MHz*	*20M f_u = 15 MHz*	*15M & 10M f_u = 30 MHz*
C1 –j50	800 pF	400 pF	210 pF	105 pF
C2 –j60	680 pF	340 pF	180 pF	90 pF
C3 –j18	2200 pF	1100 pF	590 pF	300 pF
C4 –j14	2800 pF	1400 pF	750 pF	380 pF
C5 –j35	1150 pF	575 pF	300 pF	150 pF
L1 +j30	1.2 μH	0.59 μH	0.32 μH	0.16 μH
L2 +j42	1.6 μH	0.80 μH	0.45 μH	0.23 μH
L3 +j50	2.0 μH	1.0 μH	0.52 μH	0.26 μH
Resonant Frequency for L1 & C2	5.55 MHz	11.1 MHz	20.8 MHz	41.6 MHz

Table of values for the filter shown schematically in Fig. 1.

CHAPTER 7

VHF and UHF Transmitting

Before planning operation on the frequencies above 50 MHz, we should understand the FCC rules, as they apply to the bands we are interested in. The necessary information is included in the allocations table in the first chapter of this *Handbook* and in *The Radio Amateur's License Manual*, but some points will bear emphasis here.

Standards governing signal quality in the 50-MHz band are the same as for all lower amateur frequencies. Frequency stability, modulation, keying characteristics, and freedom from spurious products must be consistent with good engineering practice. Simultaneous amplitude and frequency modulation is prohibited. These standards are not *imposed by law* on amateur frequencies from 144 MHz up. This is not to say that we should not strive for excellence on the higher bands, as well as on 50 MHz, but it is important to remember that we may be cited by FCC for failing to meet the required standards in 50-MHz work.

A sideband signal having excessive bandwidth, an a-m signal whose frequency jumps when modulation is applied, an fm signal that is also amplitude-modulated, a cw signal with excessive keying chirp or objectionable key clicks – any of these is undesirable on any band, but they are all *illegal* on 50 MHz. Any of them could earn the operator an FCC citation in 50-MHz work. And misinterpretation of these points in an FCC examination could cost the would-be amateur his first ticket.

The frequencies above 50 MHz were once a world apart from the rest of amateur radio, in equipment required, in modes of operation and in results obtained. Today these worlds blend increasingly. Thus, if the reader does not find what he needs in these pages to solve a transmitter problem, it will be covered in the hf transmitting chapter. This chapter deals mainly with aspects of transmitter design and operation that call for different techniques in equipment for 50 MHz and up.

DESIGNING FOR SSB AND CW

Almost universal use of ssb for voice work in the hf range has had a major impact on equipment design for the vhf and even uhf bands. Many amateurs have a considerable investment in hf sideband gear. This equipment provides accurate frequency calibration and good mechanical and electrical stability. It is effective in cw as well as ssb communication. These qualities being attractive to the vhf operator, it is natural for him to look for ways to use his hf gear on frequencies above 50 MHz.

Thus increasing use is being made of vhf accessory devices, both ready made and home-built. This started years ago with the vhf converter, for receiving. Rather similar conversion equipment for transmitting has been widely used since ssb began taking over the hf bands. Today the hf trend is to one-package stations, called transceivers. The obvious move for many vhf men is a companion box to perform both transmitting and receiving conversion functions. Known as **transverters**, these are offered by several transceiver manufacturers. They are also relatively simple to build, and are thus likely projects for the home-builder of vhf gear.

Transverter vs. Separate Units

It does not necessarily follow that what is popular in hf work is ideal for vhf use. Our bands are wide, and piling-up in a narrow segment of a band, which the transceiver encourages, is less than ideal use of a major asset of the vhf bands – spectrum space. Separate ssb exciters and receivers, with separate vhf conversion units for transmitting and receiving, tend to suit our purposes better than the transceiver-transverter combination, at least in home-station service.

Future of Other Modes

It should not be assumed that ssb will monopolize voice work in the world above 50 MHz in the way that it has the amateur voice frequencies below 29 MHz. Sideband is unquestionably far superior to other voice modes for weak-signal DX work, but where there is plenty of room, as there is in all vhf and higher bands, both amplitude and frequency modulation have merit. A low-powered a-m transmitter is a fine construction project for a vhf beginner, and fm has been gaining in popularity rapidly in recent years. A reprint of a very popular 4-part *QST* series describing a complete two-band vhf station for the beginner is available from ARRL for 50 cents.

The decline in use of amplitude modulation has been mainly in high-powered stations. The heavy-iron modulator seems destined to become a thing of the past, but this should not rule out use of a-m. Many ssb transceivers are capable of producing high-quality a-m, and one linear amplifier stage can build as little as 2 watts a-m output up to 200 watts or so, with excellent voice quality, if the equipment is adjusted with care. It should be remembered that the transmitting converter (or heterodyne unit as it is often called) is not a sideband device only. It will serve equally well with a-m, fm or cw drive.

THE OSCILLATOR-MULTIPLIER APPROACH

Where modes other than ssb are used, most vhf transmitters have an oscillator, usually in the hf range, one or more frequency multiplier stages, and at least one amplifier stage. The basics of this type of transmitter are well covered in the preceding chapter, so only those aspects of design that are of special concern in vhf applications will be discussed here.

Oscillators

Because any instability in the oscillator is multiplied along with the frequency itself, special attention must be paid to both mechanical and electrical factors in the oscillator of a vhf transmitter. The power source must be pure dc, of unvarying voltage. The oscillator should run at low input, to avoid drift due to heating. Except where fm is wanted, care should be taken to isolate the oscillator from the modulated stage or stages.

Crystal oscillators in vhf transmitters may use either *fundamental* or *overtone* crystals. The fundamental type is normally supplied for frequencies up to 18 MHz. For higher frequencies the overtone type is preferred in most applications, though fundamental crystals for up to about 30 MHz can be obtained on order. The fundamental crystal oscillates on the frequency marked on its holder. The marked frequency of the overtone type is approximately an odd multiple of its fundamental frequency, usually the third multiple for frequencies between 12 and 54 MHz, the fifth for roughly 54 to 75 MHz, and the seventh or ninth for frequencies up to about 150 MHz. Crystals are seldom used for direct frequency control above about 75 MHz in amateur work, though crystals for 144-MHz oscillation can be made.

Most fundamental crystals can be made to oscillate on at least the third overtone, and often higher, with suitable circuits to provide feedback at the desired overtone frequency. Conversely, an overtone crystal is likely to oscillate on its fundamental frequency, unless the tuned circuit is properly designed. An overtone crystal circuit should be adjusted so that there is no oscillation at or near one-third of the frequency marked on the holder, nor should there be energy detectable on the *even* multiples of the fundamental frequency.

It should be noted that the overtone is not necessarily an exact multiple of the fundamental. An 8000-kHz fundamental frequency does not guarantee overtone oscillation on 24.000 MHz, though it may work out that way in some circuits, with some crystals. Overtone crystals can also be made to oscillate on other overtones than the intended one. A third-overtone 24-MHz crystal can be used for its fifth overtone, about 40 MHz, or its seventh, about 56 MHz, by use of a suitable tuned circuit and careful adjustment of the feedback.

Variable-frequency oscillators are in great demand for vhf-transmitter frequency control, but except where heterodyning to a higher frequency is used, as opposed to frequency multiplication, the VFO is generally unsatisfactory. Small instabilities, hardly noticeable in hf work, are multiplied to unacceptable proportions in the oscillator-multiplier type of transmitter. The fact that many such unstable VFO rigs are on the air, particularly on 6 meters, does not make them desirable, or even *legal.* Only careful attention to all the fine points of VFO design and use can result in satisfactory stability in vhf transmitters.

Frequency Multipliers

Frequency multiplication is treated in Chapter 6. The principal factor to keep in mind in multipliers for the vhf bands is the probability that frequencies other than the desired harmonics will be present in the output. These can be sources of TVI in vhf transmitters. Examples are the 9th harmonic of 6 MHz and the 7th harmonic of 8 MHz, both falling in TV Channel 2. The 10th harmonic of 8-MHz oscillators falling in Channel 6 is a similar problem. These unwanted multiples can be held down by the use of the highest practical degree of selectivity in interstage coupling circuits in the vhf transmitter, and by proper shielding and interstage impedance matching. This last is particularly important in transistor frequency multipliers and amplifiers. More on avoiding TVI will be found later in this chapter, and in the chapter on interference problems.

The **varactor multiplier** (see Chapter 4) is much used for developing power in the 420-MHz band. Requiring no power supply, it uses only driving power from a previous stage, yet quite high orders of efficiency are possible. Two examples are shown later in this chapter. A 220-MHz exciter tuned down to 216 MHz makes a good driver for a 432-MHz varactor doubler. More commonly used is a tripler such as the one described in this chapter, using 144-MHz drive. The output of a varactor multiplier tends to have appreciable amounts of power at other frequencies than the desired, so use of a strip-line or coaxial filter is recommended, whether the multiplier drives an amplifier or works into the antenna directly.

AMPLIFIER DESIGN AND OPERATION

Amplifiers in vhf transmitters all once ran Class C, or as near thereto as available drive levels would permit. This was mainly for high-efficiency cw, and quality high-level amplitude modulation. Class C is now used mostly for cw or fm, and in either of these modes the drive level is completely uncritical, except as it affects the operating efficiency. The influence of ssb techniques is seen clearly in current amplifier trends. Today Class AB_1 is popular and most amplifiers are set up for linear amplification, for ssb and – to a lesser extent – a-m. The latter is often used in connection with small amplitude-modulated vhf transmitters, having their own built-in audio equipment. Where a-m output is available from the ssb exciter, it is also useful with the Class AB_1 linear amplifier, for only a watt or two of driver output is required.

There is no essential circuit difference between the AB_1 linear amplifier and the Class-C amplifier;

only the operating conditions are changed for different classes of service. Though the plate efficiency of the AB_1 linear amplifier is low in a-m service, this type of operation makes switching modes a very simple matter. Moving toward the high efficiency of Class C from AB_1, for cw or fm service, is accomplished by merely raising the drive from the low AB_1 level. In AB_1 service the efficiency is typically 30 to 35 percent. No grid current is ever drawn. As the grid drive is increased, and grid current starts to flow, the efficiency rises rapidly. In a well-designed amplifier it may reach 60 percent, with only a small amount of grid current flowing. Unless the drive is run well into the Class C region, the operating conditions in the amplifier can be left unchanged, other than the small increasing of the drive, to improve the efficiency available for cw or fm. No switching or major adjustments of any kind are required for near-optimum operation on ssb, a-m, fm or cw, if the amplifier is designed primarily for AB_1 service. If high-level a-m were to be used, there would have to be major operating-conditions changes, and very much higher available driving power.

Tank-Circuit Design

Except in compact low-powered transmitters, conventional coil-and-capacitor circuitry is seldom used in transmitter amplifiers for 144 MHz and higher frequencies. U-shaped loops of sheet metal or copper tubing, or even copper-laminated circuit board, generally give higher *Q* and circuit efficiency at 144 and 220 MHz. At 420 MHz and higher, coaxial tank circuits are effective. Resonant cavities are used in some applications above 1000 MHz. Examples of all types of circuits are seen later in this chapter. Coil and capacitor circuits are common in 50-MHz amplifiers, and in low-powered, mobile and portable equipment for 144 and even 220 MHz.

Stabilization

Most vhf amplifiers, other than the grounded-grid variety, require neutralization if they are to be satisfactorily stable. This is particularly true of AB_1 amplifiers, which are characterized by very high power sensitivity. Conventional neutralization is discussed in Chapter 6. An example is shown in Fig. 7-1A.

A tetrode tube has some frequency where it is inherently neutralized. This is likely to be in the lower part of the vhf region, for tubes designed for hf service. Neutralization of the opposite sense may be required in such amplifiers, as in the example shown in Fig. 7-1B.

Conventional screen bypassing methods may be ineffective in the vhf range. Series-tuning the screen to ground, as in 7-1C, may be useful in this situation. A critical combination of fixed capacitance and lead length may accomplish the same result. Neutralization of transistorized amplifiers is not generally practical, at least where bipolar transistors are used.

Parasitic oscillation can occur in vhf amplifiers, and, as with hf circuits, the oscillation is usually at a frequency considerably higher than the operating

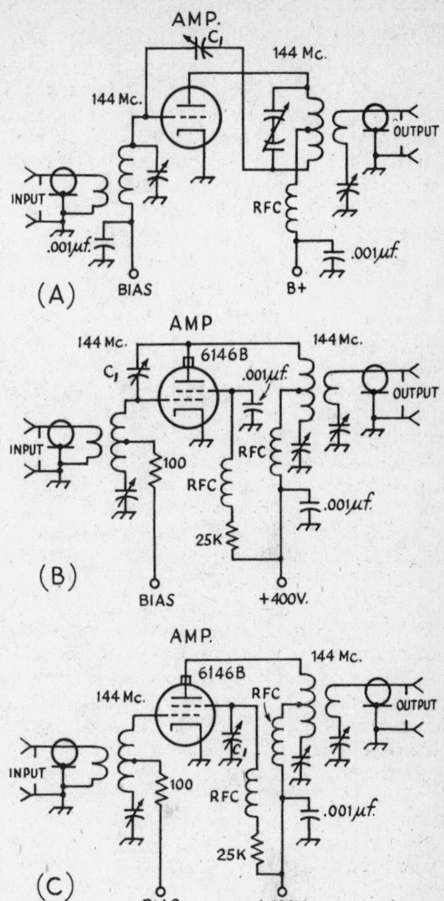

Fig. 7-1 – Representative circuits for neutralizing vhf single-ended amplifiers. The same techniques are applicable to stages that operate in push-pull. At A, C1 is connected in the manner that is common to most vhf or uhf amplifiers. The circuits at B and C are required when the tube is operated above its natural self-neutralizing frequency. At B, C1 is connected between the grid and plate of the amplifier. Ordinarily, a short length of stiff wire can be soldered to the grid pin of the tube socket, then routed through the chassis and placed adjacent to the tube envelope, and parallel to the anode element. Neutralization is effected by varying the placement of the wire with respect to the anode of the tube, thus providing variable capacitance at C1. The circuit at C is a variation of the one shown at B. It too is useful when a tube is operated above its self-neutralizing frequency. In this instance, C1 provides a low-*Z* screen-to-ground path at the operating frequency. RFC in all circuits shown are vhf types and should be selected for the operating frequency of the amplifier.

frequency, and it cannot be neutralized out. Usually it is damped out by methods illustrated in Fig. 7-2. Circuits A and B are commonly used in 6-meter transmitters. Circuit A may absorb sufficient fundamental energy to burn up in all but low-power transmitters. A better approach is to use

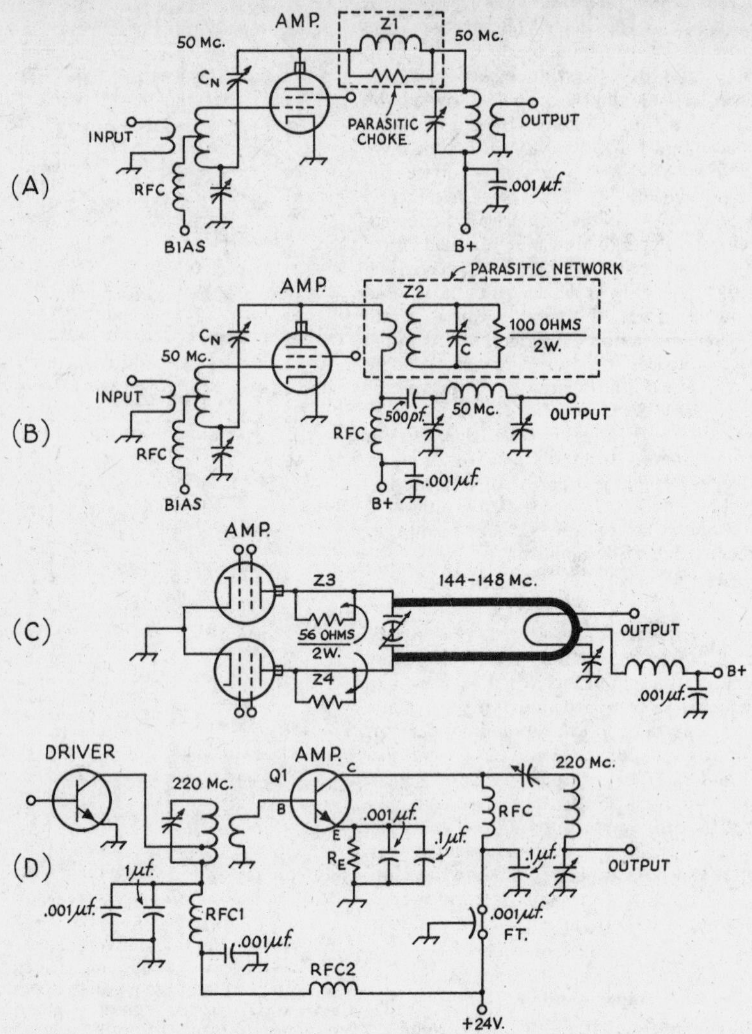

Fig. 7-2 – Representative circuits for vhf parasitic suppression are shown at A, B, and C. At A, Z1 (for 6-meter operation) would typically consist of 3 or 4 turns of No. 14 wire wound on a 100-ohm 2-watt non-inductive resistor. Z1 overheats in all but very low power circuits. The circuit at B, also for 6-meter use, is more practical where heating is concerned. Z2 is tuned to resonance at the parasitic frequency by C. Each winding of Z2 consists of two or more turns of No. 14 wire – determined experimentally – wound over the body of a 100-ohm 2-watt (or larger) noninductive resistor. At C, an illustration of uhf parasitic suppression as applied to a 2-meter amplifier. Noninductive 56-ohm 2-watt resistors are bridged across a short length of the connecting lead between the tube anode and the main element of the tank inductor, thus forming Z3 and Z4.

The circuit at D illustrates how bypassing for both the operating frequency and lower frequencies is accomplished. Low-frequency oscillation is discouraged by the addition of the 0.1-µF disk ceramic capacitors. RFC1 and RFC2 are part of the decoupling network used to isolate the two stages. This technique is not required in vacuum-tube circuits.

the selective circuit illustrated at B. The circuit is coupled to the plate tank circuit and tuned to the parasitic frequency. Since a minimum amount of the fundamental energy will be absorbed by the trap, heating should no longer be a problem.

At 144 MHz and higher, it is difficult to construct a parasitic choke that will not be resonant at or near the operating frequency. Should uhf parasitics occur, an effective cure can often be realized by shunting a 56-ohm 2-watt resistor across a small section of the plate end of the tuned circuit as shown in Fig. 7-2, at C. The resistor should be attached as near the plate connector as practical. Such a trap can often be constructed by bridging the resistor across a portion of the flexible strap-connector that is used in some transmitters to join the anode fitting to the plate-tank inductor.

Instability in solid-state vhf and uhf amplifiers can often be traced to oscillations in the lf and hf regions. Because the gain of the transistors is very high at the lower frequencies, instability is almost certain to occur unless proper bypassing and decoupling of stages is carried out. Low-frequency oscillation can usually be cured by selecting a bypass-capacitor value that is effective at the frequency of oscillation and connecting it in parallel with the vhf bypass capacitor in the same part of the circuit. It is not unusual, for example, to employ a 0.1-μF disk ceramic in parallel with a .001-μF disk capacitor in such circuits as the emitter, base, or collector return. The actual values used will depend upon the frequencies involved. This technique is shown in Fig. 7-2D. For more on transmitter stabilization, see Chapter 6.

TIPS ON AB_1 LINEAR AMPLIFIERS

As its name implies, the function of a linear is to amplify an amplitude-modulated signal in a manner so that the result is an exact reproduction of the driving signal. (Remember, ssb is a form of amplitude modulation.) The nature of the a-m signal with carrier is such that linear amplification of it is inherently an inefficient process, in terms of power input to power output, which is the conventional way of looking at amplifier efficiency. But when all factors are considered, particularly the very small exciter power required and elimination of the cumbersome and expensive high-level plate-modulation equipment, "efficiency" takes on a different meaning. Viewed in this way, the Class-AB_1 a-m linear has only two disadvantages: it is incapable of providing as much power output (within the amateur power limit of 1 kW) as the high-level-modulated amplifier, and it requires considerable skill and care in adjustment.

The maximum plate efficiency possible with an AB_1 a-m linear is about 35 percent. The power output in watts that is possible with a given amplifier tube is roughly half its rated plate dissipation. If the first factor is exceeded the result is poor quality and splatter. If the second is ignored, the tube life is shortened markedly.

There being no carrier to worry about in ssb operation, the linear amplifier can run considerably higher efficiency in amplifying ssb signals, and the popularity of ssb has brought the advantages of the linear amplifier for all classes of service into focus. The difference between a-m with carrier and ssb without carrier, in the adjustment of a linear, is mainly a matter of the drive level. Drive can never be run up to the point where the stage begins to draw grid current, but it can run close with ssb, whereas it must be held well below the grid-current level when the carrier is present.

With a-m drive the plate and screen currents must remain steady during modulation. (The screen current may be negative in some amplifiers, so observation of it is simpler if the screen-current meter is the zero-center type.) The plate, screen and grid meters are the best simple indicator of safe AB_1 operation, but they do not show whether or not you are getting all you can out of the amplifier. The signal can be monitored in the station receiver, if the signal in the receiver can be held below the point at which the receiver is overloaded. Cutting the voltage from a converter amplifier stage is a good way to do this. But the only way to know for sure is to use an oscilloscope.

One that can be used conveniently is the Heath Monitor Scope, any version. Some modification of the connections to this instrument may be needed, to prevent excessive rf pickup and resultant pattern distortion, when using it for vhf work. Normally a coupling loop within the scope, connected between two coaxial fittings on the rear of the instrument, is used. The line from the transmitter to the antenna or dummy load runs through these two fittings. For vhf service, a coaxial T fitting is connected to one of these terminals, and the line is run through it, only. With full power it may even be necessary to remove the center pin from the T fitting, to reduce the input to the scope still further, particularly in 144-MHz service.

Really effective adjustment of the linear amplifier, whether with ssb or a-m drive, involves many factors. The amplifier must be loaded as heavily as possible. Its plate and grid circuits must be tuned carefully for maximum amplifier output. (Detuning the grid circuit is *not* the way to cut down drive.) If the power level is changed, all operating conditions must be checked carefully again. Constant metering of the grid, screen and plate currents is very helpful. One meter, switched to the various circuits, is definitely not recommended. A relative-power indicator in the antenna line is a necessity.

All this makes it appear that adjustment of a linear is a very complex and difficult process, but with experience it becomes almost second nature, even with all the points that must be kept in mind. It boils down to keeping the amplifier adjusted for maximum power output, and the drive level low enough so that there is no distortion, but high enough so that maximum efficiency is obtained. Practice doing this with the amplifier running into a dummy load, and the process will soon become almost automatic. Your amateur neighbors (and perhaps TV viewers nearby, as well) will appreciate your cooperation!

About Driver Stages

If the amplifier is capable of reproducing the driving signal exactly, it follows that the driver quality must be above reproach. This is quite readily assured, in view of the low driving power required with the AB_1 linear. Only about two watts exciter power is needed to drive a grounded-cathode AB_1 linear of good design, so it is possible to build excellent quality and modulation charac-

Fig. 7-3 – The 6-meter transverter, with shield cover in place. Large knobs are for amplifier tuning and loading. Small knob, lower right is for a meter sensitivity control. The meter switch is just above it.

teristics into the a-m driver or ssb exciter. If this is done, and the amplifier is operated properly, the result can be a signal that will bring appreciative and complimentary reports from stations worked, on both a-m and ssb.

VHF TVI CAUSES AND CURES

The principal causes of TVI from vhf transmitters are as follows:

1) Adjacent-channel interference in Channels 2 and 3 from 50 MHz.

2) Fourth harmonic of 50 MHz in Channels 11, 12 or 13, depending on the operating frequency.

3) Radiation of unused harmonics of the oscillator or multiplier stages. Examples are 9th harmonic of 6 MHz, and 7th harmonic of 8 MHz in Channel 2; 10th harmonic of 8 MHz in Channel 6; 7th harmonic of 25-MHz stages in Channel 7; 4th harmonic of 48-MHz stages in Channel 9 or 10; and many other combinations. This may include i-f pickup, as in the cases of 24-MHz interference in receivers having 21-MHz i-f systems, and 48-MHz trouble in 45-MHz i-fs.

4) Fundamental blocking effects, including modulation bars, usually found only in the lower channels, from 50-MHz equipment.

5) Image interference in Channel 2 from 144 MHz, in receivers having a 45-MHz i-f.

6) Sound interference (picture clear in some cases) resulting from rf pickup by the audio circuits of the TV receiver.

There are other possibilities, but nearly all can be corrected completely, and the rest can be substantially reduced.

Items 1, 4 and 5 are receiver faults, and nothing can be done at the transmitter to reduce them, except to lower the power or increase separation between the transmitting and TV antenna systems. Item 6 is also a receiver fault, but it can be alleviated at the transmitter by using fm or cw instead of a-m phone.

Treatment of the various harmonic troubles, Items 2 and 3, follows the standard methods detailed elsewhere in this *Handbook*. It is suggested that the prospective builder of new vhf equipment familiarize himself with TVI prevention techniques, and incorporate them in new construction projects.

Use as high a starting frequency as possible, to reduce the number of harmonics that might cause trouble. Select crystal frequencies that do not have harmonics in TV channels in use locally. Example: The 10th harmonic of 8-MHz crystals used for operation in the low part of the 50-MHz band falls in Channel 6, but 6-MHz crystals for the same band have no harmonic in that channel.

If TVI is a serious problem, use the lowest transmitter power that will do the job at hand. Keep the power in the multiplier and driver stages at the lowest practical level, and use link coupling in preference to capacitive coupling. Plan for complete shielding and filtering of the rf sections of the transmitter, should these steps become necessary.

Use coaxial line to feed the antenna system, and locate the radiating portion of the antenna as far as possible from TV receivers and their antenna systems.

50-MHZ TRANSVERTER

With the increase in use of ssb on the vhf bands, there is much interest in adapting hf ssb gear to use on higher frequencies. The transverter of Fig. 7-3 will provide transceiver-style operation on 50 MHz, when used with a low-powered 28-MHz transceiver. The output of the transmitter portion is about 40 watts, adequate for much interesting work. It can be used to drive an amplifier such as the grounded-grid 3-500Z unit described later in this chapter. The receiving converter combines simplicity, adequate gain and noise figure, and freedom from overloading problems.

Circuit Details

The receiving front end uses a grounded-gate JFET rf amplifier, Q1 in Fig. 7-5, followed by a dual-gate MOSFET mixer, Q2. Its 22-MHz injection voltage is taken from the oscillator and buffer stages that also supply injection for transmitter mixing. The difference frequency is 28 MHz, so the transceiver dial reading bears a direct 28-50 relationship to the 50-MHz signal being received. For more detail on the converter construction and adjustment, see Fig. 9-9 and associated text. The transverter uses the grounded-gate rf amplifier circuit, while the converter referred to above has a grounded source, but they are quite similar otherwise.

The triode portion of a 6LN8, V1A, is a

22-MHz crystal oscillator. The pentode, V1B, is a buffer, for isolation of the oscillator, and increased stability. Injection voltage for the receiving mixer is taken from the buffer output circuit, L8, through a two-turn link, L9, and small-diameter coax, to gate 2 of the mixer, through a 10-pF blocking capacitor.

The grid circuit of the 6EJ7 transmitting mixer, V2, is tuned to 22 MHz and is inductively coupled to the buffer plate circuit. The 28-MHz input is applied to the grid circuit through a link around L11, and small-diameter coax. The mixer output, L12, is tuned to the sum frequency, 50 MHz, and coupled to a 6GK6 amplifier, V3, by a bandpass circuit, L12 and L13. The 6GK6 is bandpass-coupled to the grid of a 6146 output stage, V4. This amplifier employs a pi-network output stage.

The 6146 plate dissipation is held down during the receiving periods by fixed bias that is switched in by relay K1. The mixer and driver tubes have their screen voltage removed during receiving, by the same relay, which also switches the antenna and 28-MHz input circuits for transmitting and receiving. The relay is energized by grounding pin 7 of P1 through an external switch, or by the VOX relay in the transceiver.

Fig. 7-4 – Top view of the transverter. The receiving converter is inside the shield at the left. The 22-MHz crystal oscillator and buffer are in the left rear portion of the chassis. In the right corner is the transmitting mixer. Above it is the first amplifier. The 6146 output amplifier is in the shielded compartment at the left front.

Construction

A 7 X 9 X 2-inch aluminum chassis is used for the transverter, with a front panel 6 inches high, made of sheet aluminum. The top and sides are enclosed by a one-piece cover of perforated aluminum. The output-stage tuning control, C5, is on the upper left of the panel, 2 inches above the chassis. The loading control, C6, is immediately below, under the chassis. The meter, upper right, monitors either 6146 plate current or relative output, as selected by the switch, S1, immediately below it. A sensitivity control for calibrating the output-metering circuit completes the front-panel controls.

The output connector, J2, is centered on the rear apron of the chassis, which also has the input jack, J1, the 8-pin connector, P1, and the bias-adjusting control mounted on it.

The meter is a 1-mA movement, with multiplier resistors to give a full-scale reading on a current of 200 mA. The front cover snaps off easily, to allow calibration marks to be put on as desired.

An enclosure of perforated aluminum, 3 1/4 inches high, 4 inches wide and 4 3/4 inches long shields the 6146 and its plate circuit. There is also an L-shaped shield around the 6146 socket, under the chassis.

The receiving converter is built on a 2 1/2 X 4 1/4-inch etched board, and mounted vertically in a three-sided shield of sheet aluminum. Before mounting the converter shield, be sure to check for clearance with the terminals on the meter. Remember, the meter has full plate voltage on it when the switch is set to read plate current, even when the transverter is in the receiving mode.

Testing of the transverter was done with the General-Purpose Supply for Transceivers, described in the power supply chapter. Separate provision must be made for 12 volts dc for the receiving converter.

Injection voltage, signal input and i-f output connections to the converter are made with small-diameter coax. These and the 12-volt wiring are brought up through small holes in the chassis, under the converter. As seen in Fig. 9-11, the input JFET, Q1, is on the left. The mixer is near the center. The 28-MHz output coils, L5 and L6, are just to the right of Q2.

Note that there are two sets of relay contacts, K1D and K1F, in series in the receiver line. This guarantees high isolation of the receiver input, to protect the rf amplifier transistor. Another protective device is the diode, CR1, across the coil of the relay. If there are other relays external to this unit that use the same 12-volt supply, it is advisable to put diodes across their coils also. Spikes of several volts can be induced with making and breaking of the coil circuits.

Adjustment

A dip meter is very useful in the preliminary tuning. Be sure that L7 and L8 are tuned to 22 MHz and L12 and L13 are tuned to 50 MHz. The driver and output circuits should also be tuned to 50 MHz. Check to be sure that slug-tuned coils really tune *through* the desired frequency. Quite

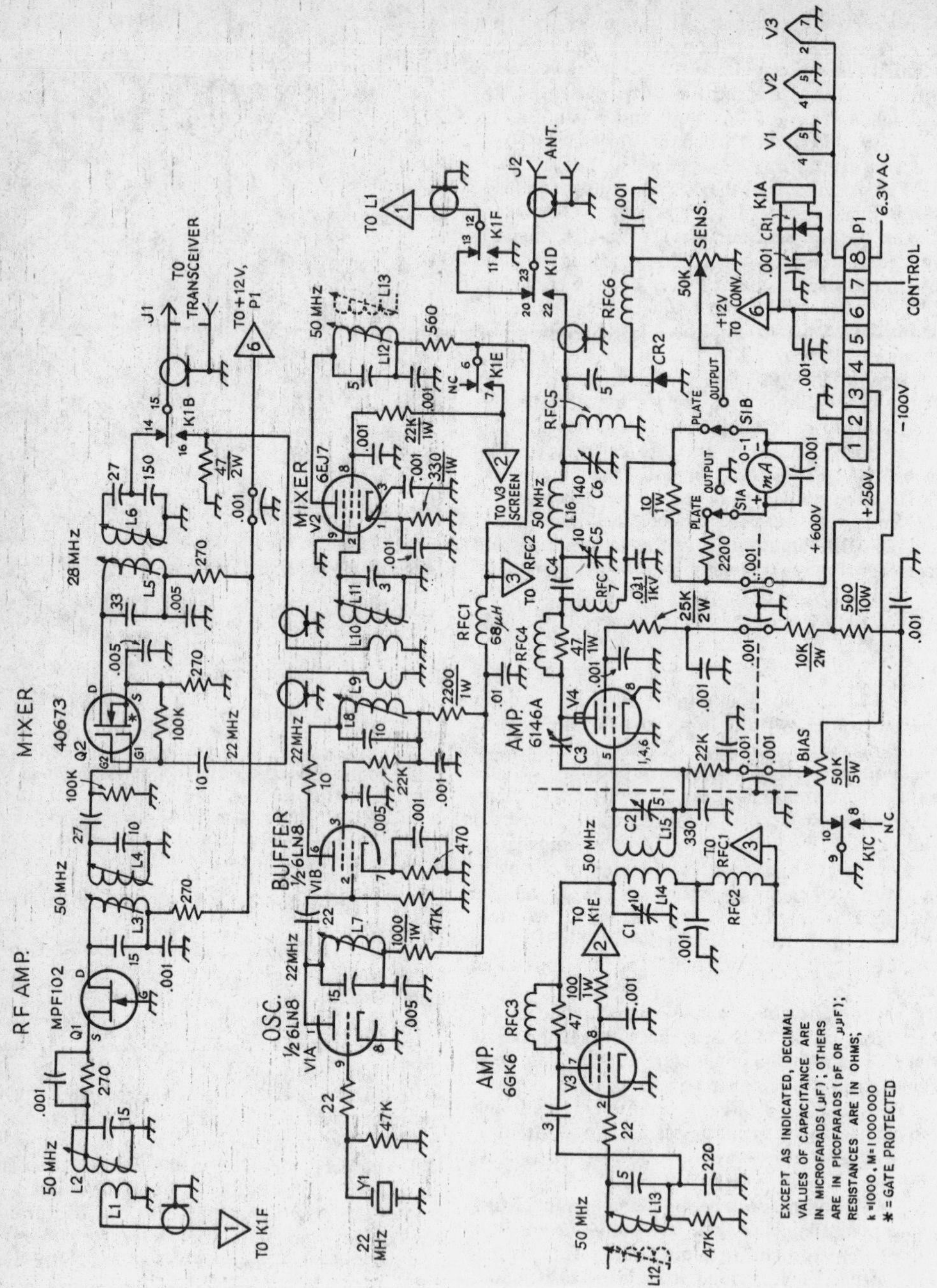

often troubles are eventually traced to coils where the circuit is only approaching resonance as the core centers in the winding. Such a circuit will appear to work, but drive will be low, and spurious outputs will tend to be high. This is a common trouble in overtone oscillators, with slug-tuned coils.

Once the circuits have been set approximately, apply heater and plate voltage to the oscillator, and tune L7 for best oscillation, as checked with a wavemeter or a receiver tuned to 22 MHz. Connect a 28-MHz receiver to the input, J1, and apply dc to the converter. It should be possible to hear a strong local station or test signal immediately. Peak all coils for best reception, then stagger-tune L5 and L6 for good response across the first 500 kHz of the band.

Before applying plate voltage to the 6146, it is advisable to protect the tube during tuneup by inserting a 1500- or 2000-ohm 25-watt resistor in series with the plate supply. Connect a 50-ohm load to the output jack, and energize K1. Adjust

Fig. 7-5 – Schematic diagram and part information for the 50-MHz transverter.
C1 – 10-pF subminiature variable (Hammarlund MAC-10).
C2 – 5-pF subminiature variable (Hammarlund MAC-5).
C3 – 2 1/2-inch length No. 14 wire, parallel to and 1/4 inch away from tube envelope. Cover with insulating sleeve.
C4 – 500-pF 3000-volt disk ceramic.
C5 – 10-pF variable (Johnson 149-3, with one stator and one rotor plate removed).
C6 – 140-pF variable (Millen 22140).
CR1 – 1N128 diode.
CR2 – 1N83A diode.
J1 – Phono jack.
J2 – Coaxial jack, SO-239.
K1 – 6-pole double-throw relay, 12-volt dc coil.
L1 – 2 turns small insulated wire over ground end of L2.
L2, L3, L4 – 10 turns No. 24 enamel closewound on J. W. Miller 4500-4 iron-slug form.
L5, L6 – 12 turns No. 24 enamel on J. W. Miller 4500-2 iron-slug form.
L7, L8, L11 – Iron-slug coils adjusted for 4.1, 5.5 and 5.5 μH, respectively (Miller 4405).
L9, L10 – 2 turns small insulated wire over ground ends of L8 and L11.
L12, L13 – 1-μH iron-slug coil J. W. Miller 4403, 3 turns removed.
L14 – 7 turns No. 20, 1/2-inch dia, 1/2 inch long (B & W 3003).
L15 – Like L14, but 6 turns.
L16 – 6 turns No. 20, 5/8-inch dia, 3/4 inch long (B & W 3006).
P1 – 8-pin power connector.
RFC1 – 68-μH rf choke (Millen 34300).
RFC2 – 8.2-μH rf choke (Millen J-300).
RFC3 – 5 turns No. 22 on 47-ohm 1/2-watt resistor.
RFC4 – 4 turns No. 15 on 47-ohm 1-watt resistor.
RFC5, RFC6, RFC7 – 8.2-μH rf choke (Millen 34300).
S1 – Dpdt toggle.
Y1 – 22-MHz overtone crystal (International Crystal Co., Type EX).

Fig. 7-6 – Bottom of the transverter, with the 6146 socket inside the shield compartment at the right. Three sets of inductively-coupled circuits are visible in the upper-right corner. The first two, near the top of the picture, are on 22 MHz. Next to the right and down, are the mixer plate and first-amplifier grid circuits. The self-supporting 6GK6 plate and 6146 grid coils are just outside the amplifier shield compartment. The large variable capacitor is the loading control.

the bias control for 25 to 30 mA plate current. Apply a small amount of 28-MHz drive. A fraction of a watt, enough to produce a dim glow in a No. 47 pilot lamp load, will do. Some output should be indicated on the meter, with the sensitivity control fully clockwise. Adjust the amplifier tuning and loading for maximum output, and readjust all of the 50-MHz circuits likewise.

After the circuits have been peaked up, adjust the bandpass circuits by applying first a 28.1-MHz input and then a 28.4-MHz input, and peaking alternate coils until good operation is obtained over the range of 50.0 to 50.5 MHz. Most ssb operation currently is close to 50.1 MHz, so uniform response across a 500-kHz range is not too important, if only this mode is used. If the 10-meter transceiver is capable of a-m operation, and you want to use this mode, coverage up to 50.5 with uniform output may be more desirable. Adjust the position of the neutralizing wire, C3, for minimum rf in L16, with drive on, but no screen or plate voltage on the 6146.

Now apply full plate voltage. With no drive, set the bias adjustment for a 6146 plate current of 25 to 30 mA. With the dummy load connected, experiment with the amount of drive needed to reach maximum plate current. Preferably, use a scope to check for flat-topping as the drive is increased. An output of 40 watts, cw, should be obtainable. The quality of the ssb signal is determined first by the equipment generating it, but it can be ruined by improper operation. Over driving the mixer or the 6146, and improper loading of the amplifier will cause distortion and splatter. Continuous monitoring with a scope is the best preventive measure.

Because of the frequencies mixed, and the bandpass coupling between stages, the output of the transverter is reasonably clean. Still, use of an antenna coupler or filter between the transverter and antenna is good insurance. The same treatment of the transverter output is desirable when driving a linear amplifier.

Fig. 7-7 — Panel view of the 2-meter transverter. This version is patterned after a transmitting converter design by K9UIF. The on-off switches for ac and dc sections of the power supply are mounted on the front panel of the unit as are the pilot lamps and plate meter for the PA stage. The tuning controls for the various stages are accessible from the top of the chassis.

B1 — Small 15-volt battery.
C1 — 20-pF miniature variable (E. F. Johnson 160-110 suitable).
C2, C3, C5 — 10-pF per section miniature butterfly (E. J. Johnson 167-21 suitable).
C4 — 5-pF per section miniature butterfly (E. F. Johnson 160-205 suitable).
C6 — 20-pF miniature variable (same as C1).
I1, I2 — 117-Vac neon panel lamp assembly.
J1-J3, incl. — SO-239-style coax connector.
J3 — Closed-circuit phone jack.
L1 — 15 turns No. 28 enam. wire, close-wound, on 1/4-inch dia slug-tuned form (Millen 69058 form suitable).
L2 — 12 turns No. 28 enam. wire, close-wound, on same type form as L1.
L3 — 5 turns No. 18 wire space-wound to 7/8-inch length, 1/2-inch dia, center-tapped.
L4 — 3 turns No. 18 wire, 1/2-inch dia, 3/8-inch long, center-tapped.
L5 — 5 turns No. 18 wire, 1/2-inch dia, 5/8-inch long, center-tapped.
L6 — 3 turns No. 18 wire, 1/2-inch dia, 5/8-inch long, center-tapped.
L7 — 4 turns No. 18 wire, 1/2-inch dia, 1/2-inch long, center-tapped.
L8 — 1-turn link of insulated hookup wire, 1/2-inch dia, inserted in center of L7.
L9 — 2 turns of insulated hookup wire over L3.
M1 — 0 to 200-mA dc meter.
P1 — 11-pin chassis-mount male plug (Amphenol 86PM11).
R1 — 50,000-ohm linear-taper, 5-watt control.
RFC1-RFC3, incl. — 2.7-μH rf choke (Millen 34300-2.7).
S1, S2 — Spst rocker-type switch (Carling TIGK60).
Y1 — 43.333-MHz third-overtone crystal for 14-MHz input. If a 28-MHz transceiver will be used, a 38.667-MHz crystal is required.

A 2-METER TRANSVERTER

This transverter is designed to be used with any 14- or 28-MHz ssb exciter capable of delivering approximately 20 watts peak output. It is stable both in terms of frequency and general operating conditions. It can provide up to 20 watts PEP output at 144 MHz – sufficient, say, for driving a pair of 4CX250 tubes in Class C for cw operation, or the same pair of tubes can be operated AB_1 to provide 1200 watts PEP input with this unit as a driver. The output signal is clean and TVI should not be experienced except where receiver faults are involved.

It is not recommended that beginners attempt this project since vhf ssb circuits require special care in their construction and operation, sometimes a requirement that is a bit beyond the inexperienced builder.

How It Operates

Starting with V1A, the oscillator, Fig. 7-8, a 43.333-MHz or overtone crystal is used at Y1 to provide the local-oscillator signal for the exciter. Output from V1A is amplified by V1B to a suitable level for driving the tripler, V2. 130-MHz or 116-MHz energy is fed to the grids of V3, a 6360 mixer, by means of a bandpass tuned circuit, L3,C1, and L4,C2. The selectivity of this circuit is high, thus reducing unwanted spurious energy at the mixer grids.

Output from the exciter is supplied through an attenuator pad at J1 and is injected to the mixer, V3, at its cathode circuit, across a 270-ohm resistor. The attenuator pad can be eliminated if a very low-power exciter is to be used. The values shown in Fig. 7-8 were chosen for operation with a Central Electronics 20A exciter operating at full input, or nearly so. The amount of driving power needed at the cathode of V3 is approximately 4 or 5 watts PEP.

After the 130-MHz and 14-MHz signals are mixed at V3, the *sum* frequency of 144-MHz is coupled to the grids of V4, the PA stage, by means of another bandpass tuned circuit – further reducing spurious output from the exciter. PA stage V4 operates in the AB_1 mode. Its idling plate current is approximately 25 mA. The plate current rises to approximately 100 mA at full input.

If cw operation is desired, the grid-block keying circuit in the mixer stage (J3) can be included. If ssb operation is all that is contemplated, the minus 100-volt bias line can be eliminated along with J3, R1, and the shaping network at J3. In that case the 15,000-ohm grid resistor from the center tap of L4 would be grounded to the chassis.

The receiving section uses a low-noise uhf MOSFET as the rf amplifier and a second dual-gate MOSFET as the mixer. See Fig. 7-10. The gate-1 and drain connections of the rf amplifier are tapped down on the tuned circuits so that unconditional stability is achieved without neutralization. Oscillator energy is sampled with a two-turn link wound over L3. A short length of RG-58A/U carries the injection energy to Q2. The converter is built in a 5 X 2 1/4 X 2 1/4-inch box constructed from four pieces of double-sided circuit board that have been soldered on all abutting edges. The unit is mounted on the transverter front panel.

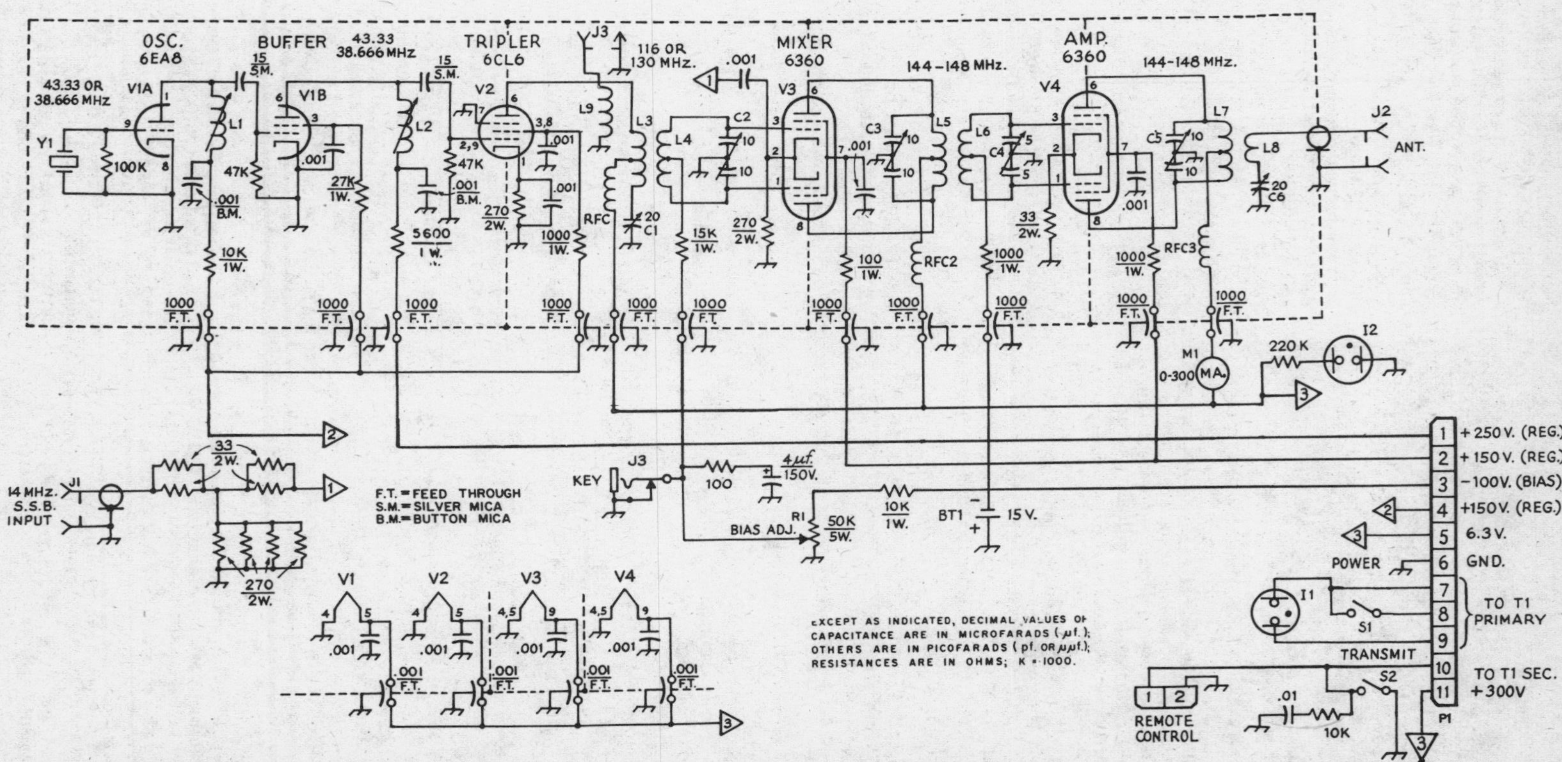

Fig. 7-8 — Schematic diagram of the transmitting converter portion of the transverter. Fixed-value capacitors are disk ceramic unless noted differently. The polarized capacitor is electrolytic. Fixed-value resistors are 1/2-watt carbon unless otherwise noted.

Fig. 7-9 – Inside view of the converter. Shields are used between the rf amplifier input and output circuits, and between the latter and the mixer input circuit. The cable entering the bottom side of the enclosure carries the oscillator injection energy. Output to the associated receiver or transceiver is taken through the jack to the left.

Construction Notes

The photographs show the construction techniques that should be followed for duplicating this equipment. The more seasoned builder should have no difficulty changing the prescribed layout to fit his particular needs, but the shielding and bypassing methods used here should be adhered to even if changes are made.

An 8 X 12 X 3-inch aluminum chassis is used for this equipment. An internal chassis, 5 inches wide, 3 inches deep, and 12 inches long, is made from flashing copper and installed along one edge of the main chassis. This method makes it possible to solder directly to the chassis for making positive ground connections rather than rely on mechanical joints. Shield partitions are made of copper and are soldered in place as indicated on the schematic diagram and in the photo. An aluminum bottom plate is used to enclose the underside of the chassis for confining the rf.

Feedthrough capacitors are used to bring power leads into the copper compartment. Though this adds somewhat to the overall cost of the project, it provides excellent bypassing and decoupling, thus reducing unwanted interstage coupling. It also contributes to TVI reduction. Most surplus houses stock feedthrough capacitors, and offer them at reasonable cost.

Tune-Up

An antenna-changeover relay and a set of normally-open relay contacts, both operated by the exciter, must be provided. The remote control leads, from P2, should be connected to the relay contacts. With power applied to the converter, L12 should be set for maximum noise input to the transceiver. Then, using a signal generator or off-the-air weak signal, peak L9, L10 and L11 for best signal-to-noise ratio.

The transmitter section can be powered by the circuit of Fig. 7-12, or the builder can design a supply of his own choice. Regulated voltages are

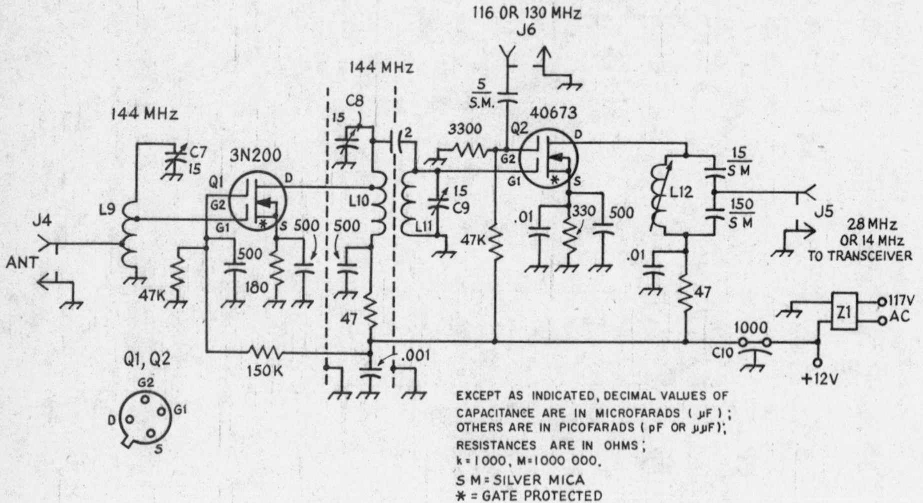

Fig. 7-10 – Diagram of the converter section. Resistors are 1/4-watt composition and capacitors are disk ceramic, except as noted otherwise.

C7-C9, incl. – Air variable, pc mount (Johnson 189-505-5).

C10 – Feedthrough type.

L9 – 4 1/2 turns, No. 18 tinned wire, 1/4-inch ID. Tap at 1 1/2 turns up from the ground end for the antenna connection, and at 3 turns for the Q1 gate.

L10 – 4 1/2 turns, No. 18 tinned wire, 1/4-inch ID. Tap at 3 turns up from the cold end for the Q1 drain connection.

L11 – 5 turns No. 18 tinned wire, 1/4-inch ID.

L12 – 1.99-2.42-μH slug-tuned coil, pc mount, for 28-MHz output (J. W. Miller 46A226CPC); or, for 14-MHz output, 7.3-8.9-μH (J. W. Miller 46A826CPC).

J4-J6, incl. – Phono type.

Q1, Q2 – RCA dual-gate MOSFET.

Z1 – 12-V miniature power supply, transistor radio type.

Fig. 7-11 — Looking into the bottom of the chassis, the rf section is enclosed in a shield compartment made from flashing copper. Additional divider sections isolate the input and output tuned circuits of the last three stages of the exciter. Feedthrough capacitors are mounted on one wall of the copper compartment to provide decoupling of the power leads.

recommended for best operation.

With a dummy load connected to J2, apply operating voltage. Couple a wavemeter to L1 and tune the oscillator plate for maximum output. Then, detune the slug of L1 slightly (toward minimum inductance) to assure reliable oscillator starting. Couple the wavemeter to L2 and tune for peak output. With the wavemeter applied to L4, adjust C1 and C2 for maximum indicated output.

The next step is to connect the transceiver to J1 and supply just enough drive to cause a rise in PA plate current of a few milliamperes. Tune C3 and C4 for maximum indicated plate current at M1, then adjust C5 and C6 for maximum power output to the dummy load. C1, C2, C3 and C4 should be readjusted at this point for maximum plate current of the PA stage. Use only enough drive to bring the PA plate current up to 100 mA at maximum dc input power.

A closed-circuit keying jack is used at J3 so that the mixer stage is not biased to cutoff during voice operation. Inserting the key permits full bias to be applied, thus cutting off V3. R1 should be adjusted for complete cutoff of V3 when the key is open.

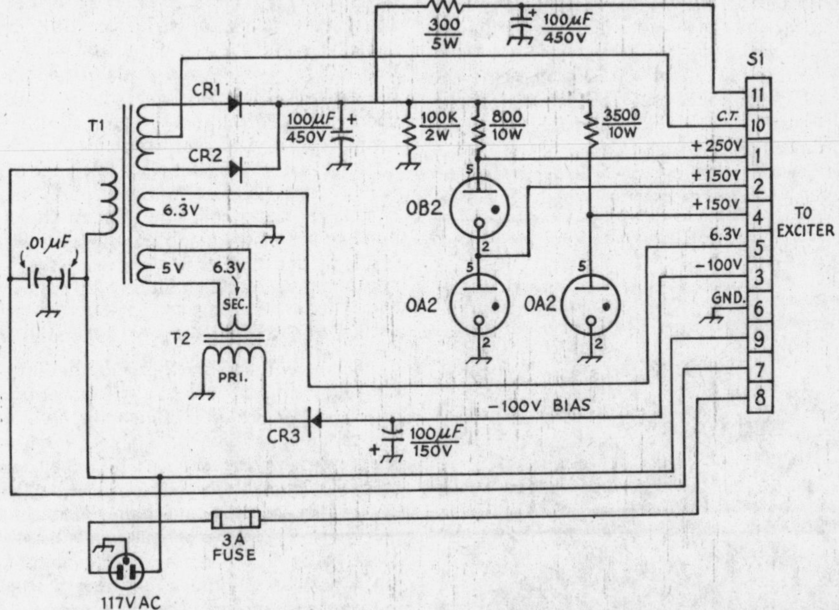

Fig. 7-12 — Schematic of the power supply section. On-off switches for the ac and dc circuits are mounted in the rf deck along with the pilot lamps. Polarized capacitors are electrolytic, others are disk ceramic. CR1 and CR2 are 1000-volt, 1-ampere silicon diodes. CR3 is a 200-PRV 600-mA silicon diode. T1 is a power transformer with a 540-volt ct secondary at 120 mA. Filament windings are 5 volts at 3 A, and 6.3 volts at 3.5 A. T2 is a 6.3-volt, 1-ampere filament transformer connected back to back with the 5-volt winding of T1. S1 is an 11-pin socket (female). A 10,000-ohm resistor and a .01-µF disk capacitor are connected in series between the center tap of T1's secondary and ground for transient suppression when S2 is switched to on. The suppressor is mounted at S2, in the rf deck.

A 500-WATT FM AND CW TRANSMITTER FOR 220 MHZ

This 220-MHz transmitter was designed and built by R. B. Stevens, W1QWJ, and was first described in May 1969 *QST*. It is capable of 300 watts output, cw or fm, or the exciter portion can be used alone to deliver approximately 8 watts output.

The RF Circuits

Looking at the schematic diagram, Fig. 7-15, it will be seen that the first three stages of the transmitter look very much like any vhf transmitter using vacuum tubes. A conventional 6CL6 crystal oscillator, V1, uses 6-, 8- or 12-MHz crystals, multiplying in its plate circuit to 24 MHz (12 MHz crystals should be the fundamental type.) A 6BQ5, V2, triples to 73 MHz, and drives a 2E26 amplifier, V3, straight-through on this frequency. A variable capacitor, C6, across the crystal, permits a small adjustment of the frequency.

A varactor tripler, driven by the 2E26, is used to get up to 220. Requiring no power supply of its own, it is capable of more than enough power output at 220 to drive our 500-watt amplifier.

The output of a varactor multiplier contains harmonics other than the desired one, so a strip-line filter is connected between the varactor output and the final amplifier grid circuit. The filter is a separate assembly mounted on the end of the chassis, visible in two of the photographs. Full details of the filter may be found in any edition of the *VHF Manual*, and in this *Handbook.*

The final amplifier is a 4CX250 series external-anode tube, with a coaxial tank circuit. The B version is used here, but the R and F types have the same mechanical design.

The coaxial plate circuit follows a standard design. Such a tank has extremely high *Q*, and the heavy copper (or brass) construction offers considerable heat sinking. Probably its only disadvantage is the necessity for feeding the high voltage in through some kind of rf bypassing device. This and the other mechanical features of a good coaxial tank are not readily made with the simpler tools. Details of the assembly are given in Fig. 7-19.

The final grid circuit, visible in the end view along with the varactor multiplier and the strip-line filter, is a half-wave strip-line. The fan blows cooling air into the grid compartment, up through the 4CX250 socket, and out through the end of the tank assembly, by way of the hollow inner conductor, L10. The coaxial output fitting, J6, the coupling loop, L11, and its series capacitor, C21, are mounted on a small detachable plate bent to fit the curvature of the coaxial assembly, and mounted near the outer end. The varactor tripler is built into the top of the amplifier grid assembly, and is visible in the end view along with the final grid circuit and the strip-line filter.

[1] Brayley, "Coaxial-Tank Amplifier for 220 and 420 MHz," *QST*, May 1951. Also, *VHF Manual*, Chapter 10.

Fig. 7-13 – The 220-MHz transmitter is set up for rack mounting on 8 3/4-inch panel. Meters at the left can be switched to read driver plate, amplifier screen and amplifier plate currents, and amplifier plate voltage.

Generating the Frequency Modulation

Where only a small swing at the control frequency is needed, as in a vhf or uhf transmitter having a high order of frequency multiplication, the modulation can be applied very easily. A voltage-variable capacitor, CR1, changes capacitance in relation to the audio voltage applied across it, and this changing capacitance is used to "pull" the frequency of the crystal oscillator slightly. A good 8-MHz crystal can be pulled about 600 Hz in this way. With 27-times frequency multiplication this gives a maximum deviation in excess of 16 kHz

Fig. 7-14 – Rear view of the 220-MHz transmitter. The exciter stages are on a circuit board in the foreground. Chassis at the right side houses the varactor tripler and the amplifier grid circuit. Air blows into this compartment and out through the center conductor of the coaxial plate-circuit assembly.

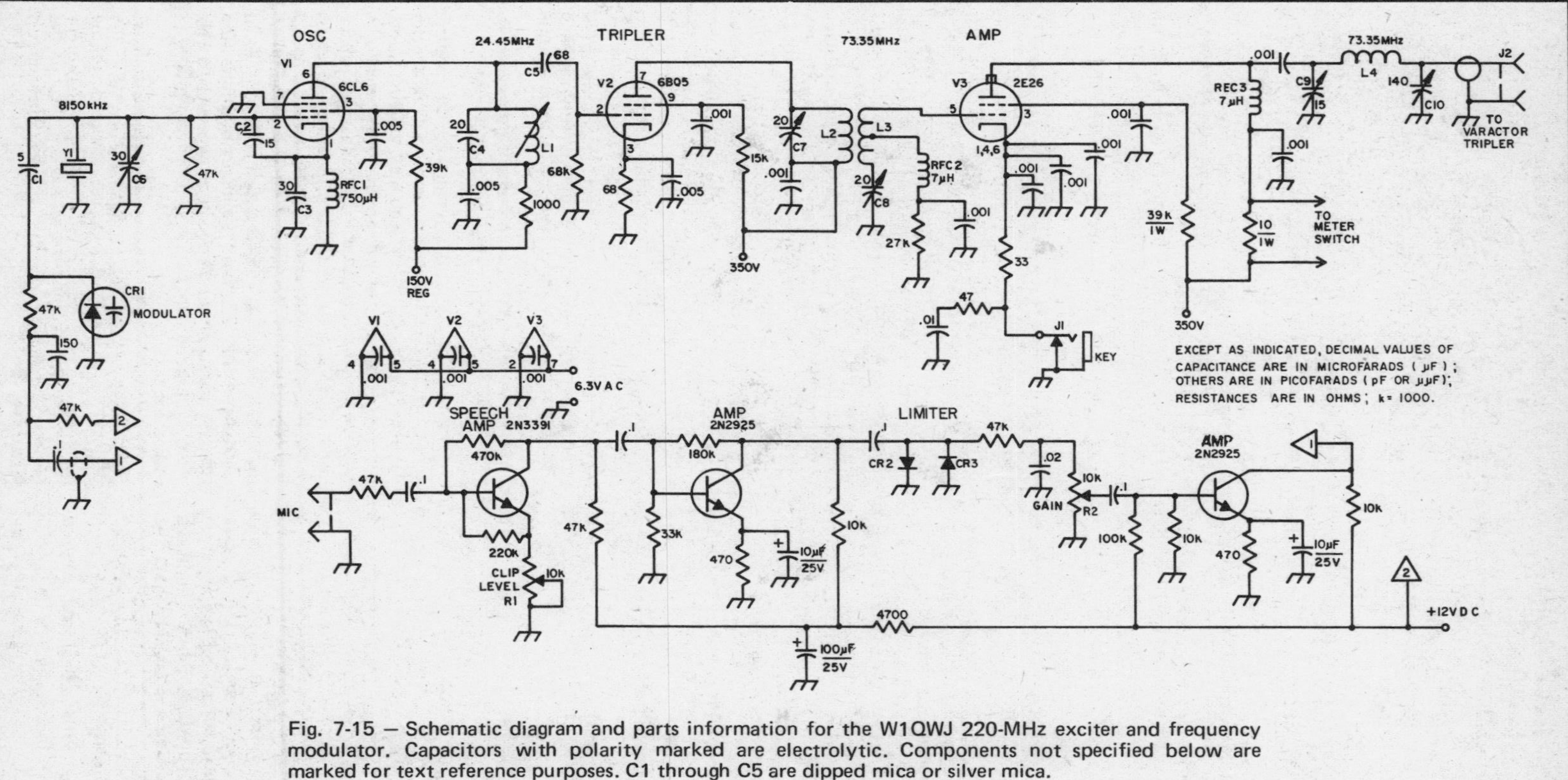

Fig. 7-15 — Schematic diagram and parts information for the W1QWJ 220-MHz exciter and frequency modulator. Capacitors with polarity marked are electrolytic. Components not specified below are marked for text reference purposes. C1 through C5 are dipped mica or silver mica.

C6 — 30-pF miniature trimmer (Johnson 160-130).
C7, C8 — 20-pF miniature trimmer (Johnson 160-110).
C9 — 15-pF variable, double-spaced (Hammarlund HF-15-X).
C10 — 140-pF variable (Hammarlund HF-140).
CR1 — Varicap diode.
CR2, CR3 — Any silicon diode (Motorola 2105 or similar).
J1 — Closed-circuit jack.
J2 — BNC chassis fitting.
L1 — 10 turns No. 22 enamel, closewound on 1/4-inch slug-tuned form.
L2 — 4 turns No. 22, 1/2-inch dia, 7/16 inch long.
L3 — 7 turns No. 22, 1/2-inch dia, 3/8 inch long. Tap 4 turns from grid end.
L4 — 5 turns No. 16, 1/2-inch dia, 1 inch long.
Y1 — 8150-kHz crystal, HC-6/U holder preferred. 6112 kHz or 12223-kHz fundamental crystal also usable. Frequencies given are for low-frequency end of the band. Use C6 for slight frequency adjustment.

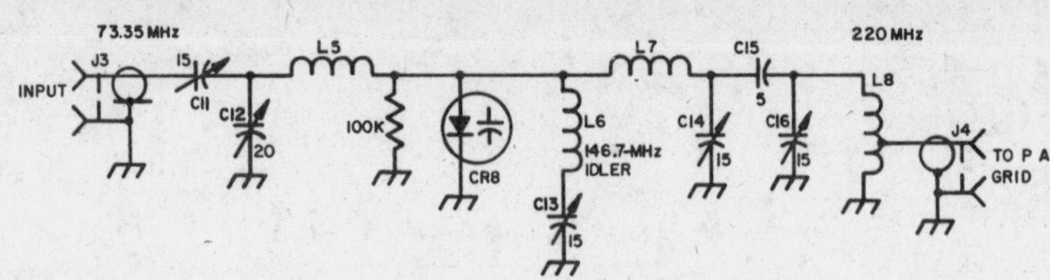

Fig. 7-16 – Circuit of the varactor multiplier, 73 to 220 MHz.

C11, C13, C14, C16 – 15-pF miniature variable (Johnson 160-107). Rotor of C11 must be insulated from chassis.
C12 – 20-pF miniature variable (Johnson 160-110).
C15 – 5-pF ceramic.
L5 – 8 turns No. 16, 1/2-inch dia, 7/8 inch long.
L6 – 4 turns No. 16, 1/2-inch dia, 1/2 inch long.
L7 – 3 turns No. 16, 3/8-inch dia, 3/8 inch long.
L8 – 3 turns No. 16, 3/8-inch dia, 3/8 inch long, tapped at 1 turn from grounded end.
CR8 – Varactor diode (Amperex H4A/1N4885).
J3, J4 – BNC fitting.

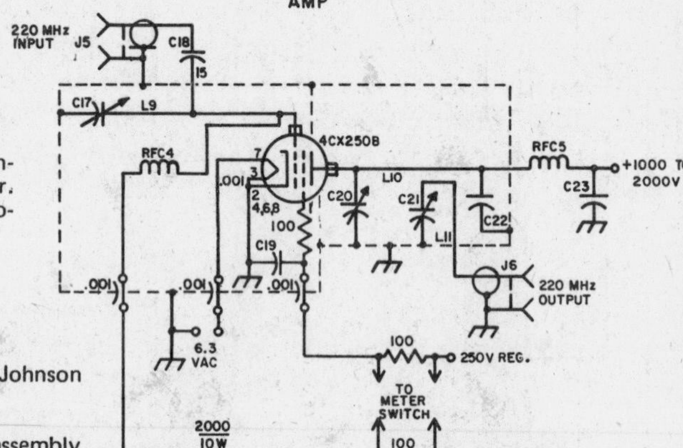

Fig. 7-17 – Schematic diagram and parts information for the 220-MHz final amplifier. Decimal values of capacitance are in microfarads (μF); others in pF.

C17 – 20-pF miniature variable (Johnson 160-110). Stator supports end of L9.
C18 – 15-pF silver mica.
C19 – Capacitor built into socket assembly (Johnson 124-109-1 socket, with 124-113-1 bypass ring and 124-111-1 chimney).
C20 – Disk-type tuning capacitor; see Fig. 7-19.
C21 – 15-pF miniature variable (Johnson 160-110).
C22 – Built-in bypass capacitor; see Fig. 7-19.
C23 – 500-pF, 5-kV or more.
J6 – N-type fitting.
L9 – Brass strip, 1/16 by 3/8 by 6 1/2 inches. Bolts to grid terminal on socket. Tap C18 7/8 inch from grid.
L10 – Coaxial line inner conductor; see Fig. 7-19.
L11 – Output coupling loop made from 3 1/4 inches No. 16. Cover with insulating sleeving and bend to 3/4 inch high and 1 3/4 inch long. See Fig. 7-1.
RFC4, RFC5 – 0.84 μH rf choke (Ohmite Z-235).
J5 – BNC fitting.

at the operating frequency, close to the optimum for most of the fm receivers currently in use in fixed-frequency service on 6 and 2. Lesser deviation, for working into communications receivers, most of them having about a 3-kHz bandwidth today, is merely a matter of applying less audio.

Adjustment and Operation

This is not intended to be a beginner's project, so detailed discussion of the mechanical layout will be omitted. The mechanical arrangement of the components could be altered to suit one's own requirements, since the complete transmitter is made up of many subassemblies. Adjustment for best results may be somewhat strange to anyone who has not had experience with varactor multipliers.

The first step is to get a good 52-ohm load. For the present, it will have to handle a maximum of about 10 watts. A good SWR bridge is also needed for the tests. The first step is to adjust the exciter. Procedure here is like that for any similar lineup of tubes, but the 2E26 must be adjusted for optimum

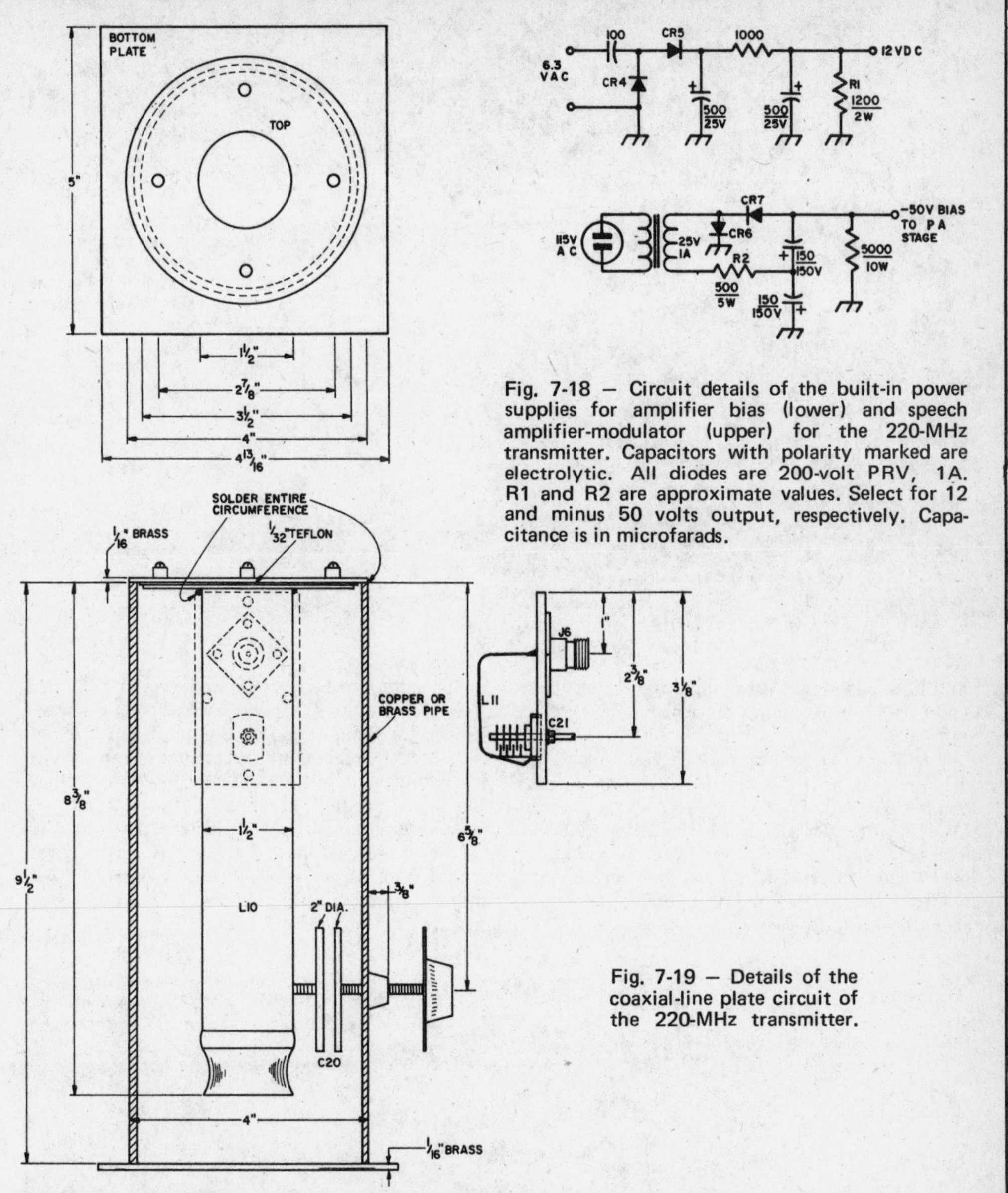

Fig. 7-18 – Circuit details of the built-in power supplies for amplifier bias (lower) and speech amplifier-modulator (upper) for the 220-MHz transmitter. Capacitors with polarity marked are electrolytic. All diodes are 200-volt PRV, 1A. R1 and R2 are approximate values. Select for 12 and minus 50 volts output, respectively. Capacitance is in microfarads.

Fig. 7-19 – Details of the coaxial-line plate circuit of the 220-MHz transmitter.

results when working into a 52-ohm load. Once an output of 10 to 12 watts is obtained in this way, leave the tuning of the 2E26 and preceding stages alone thereafter.

Now connect the SWR bridge output to J3 of the varactor multiplier, and tune C11 and C12 for lowest SWR indication. Leave the 2E26 adjustments alone.

Now connect a coaxial cable from J2 to J3, and connect the bridge or wattmeter in a line from J4 to the dummy load. Adjust C13, C14 and C16 for maximum output at 220 MHz. Adjustments in the multiplier interlock, and several passes through all adjustments may be needed for best output. But remember that the 2E26 is set for a 52-ohm load. Leave it alone, and make the multiplier adjustments do the job. An indication of some 8 watts or so of output should be obtained. Part of this will be harmonic energy, however, so the SWR bridge should now be connected between the strip-line filter and the amplifier grid circuit, and the filter adjusted for maximum forward power and the

Fig. 7-20 – Looking underneath the chassis of the 220-MHz transmitter, we see the speech amplifier-clipper at the lower left, the exciter circuits across the top, power supply components at the upper left, and meter switching, lower right.

amplifier input circuit for minimum reflected. This should result in maximum grid current in the final amplifier.

It is likely that getting enough grid current for the 4CX250B will not be difficult, as the lineup described gives more than ample drive. Up to 20 mA grid current has been obtained, but not this much is needed. In fact, with fm or cw operation, only a slight increase in efficiency is noted after the drive is raised beyond the point where grid current begins to flow.

Adjustment of the coupling loop, L11, and the loading capacitor, C21, will be fairly critical when striving for the absolute maximum output. Following the manufacturer's recommendations as to maximum plate voltage and current, 2000 volts at 250 mA, resulted in about 320 watts output. Raising the plate current to 300 mA, by increasing the screen voltage, netted 400 watts output. Even at this input the tube seemed to be operating well and the tank circuit did not indicate excessive heating.

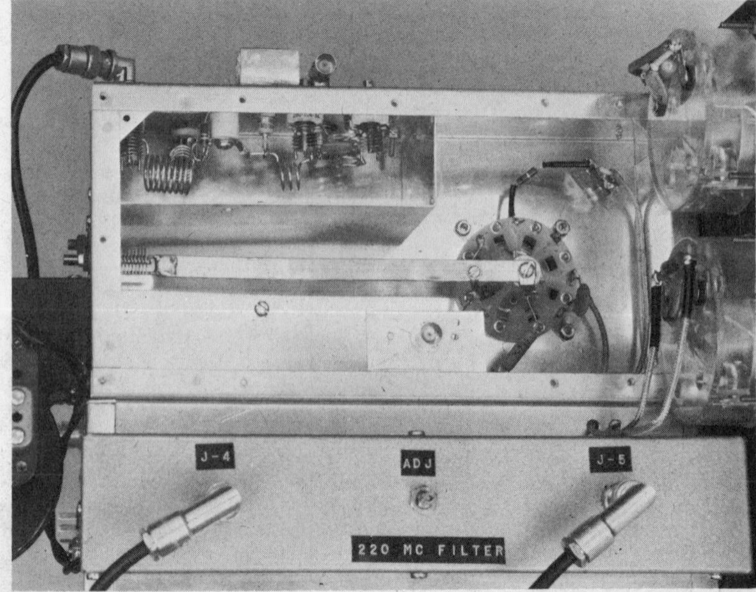

Fig. 7-21 – Looking into the amplifier grid compartment. The varactor tripler is in the upper left portion. Below the compartment is the 220-MHz strip-line filter.

A VARACTOR TRIPLER FOR 420 MHz

It is indeed fortunate that the 420-MHz band is related harmonically to the 144-MHz band, since a simple exciter or transmitter for the lower frequency can be pressed into service as an exciter for the higher band as well. Discussions and designs using varactor diodes as frequency multipliers have been seen in printed form many times, and all have pointed out the ease of obtaining output at the second, third, fourth or higher order of multiplication.

Many of the designs had some drawbacks that prevented their acceptance to other than the avid experimenter; the simple circuits had too many unwanted frequencies in the rf output and the "clean" designs were large physically. The tripler presented in Fig. 1 is a step toward overcoming some of these deficiencies.

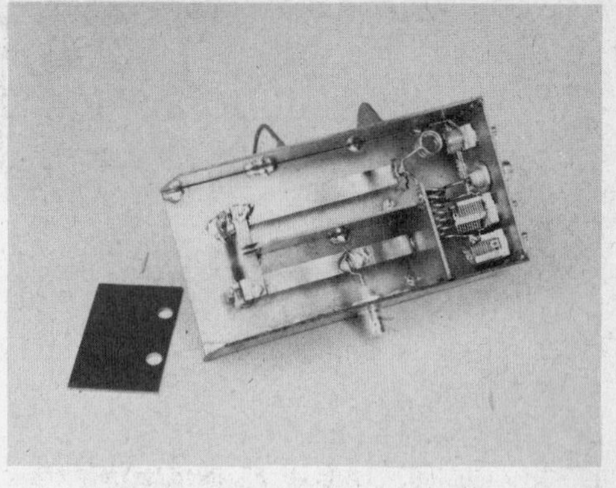

Fig. 2 – The varactor tripler is assembled in a box made from double-sided pc board. Input is at the right. The idler coil, L3, is mounted at right angles to L1 and L2 to prevent undesired coupling. The copper strips tune to the output frequency. Two tabs of copper provide coupling between the strips. Output is taken from J2, at the bottom center. A piece of pc board with holes for access to C4 and C6 should be soldered to the end of the enclosure. Other pieces can be soldered to the top to provide complete shielding, if desired. The box is 3-in. wide × 5-1/4-in. long and 1-1/2-in. high.

The Circuit

The input circuit for this varactor multiplier was chosen because it does its job well, and of no less importance, it is not as confusing in schematic form. L1 is the input-coupling link and its reactance is tuned out by C1. L2-C2 form a conventional series-resonant circuit tuned to the input frequency. The combination of these circuits, then, becomes the familiar tuned circuit with link-coupled input. The link is coupled to the cold end of L2 and the amount of coupling is adjustable by changing the position of L1. It is easier to visualize the end of L2 as being "cold" by remembering that the varactor diode is a low impedance device.

L3-C3 is the series-tuned idler circuit that is necessary for efficient harmonic generation, and L4-C4 is a series-tuned circuit for the output frequency. L5 and C6 are resonant at the output frequency also, with a small capacitor, C5, to provide coupling to the diode output circuitry.

Construction

Double-sided pc-board material was used as a housing for the tripler, shown in Fig. 2. J1, C1, C2 and C3 are all mounted on one end of the box. The diode is mounted on the bottom of the enclosure, fastened in place by means of a nut on the outside. A small piece of aluminum sheet, used as a heat sink, is placed over the diode mounting stud before

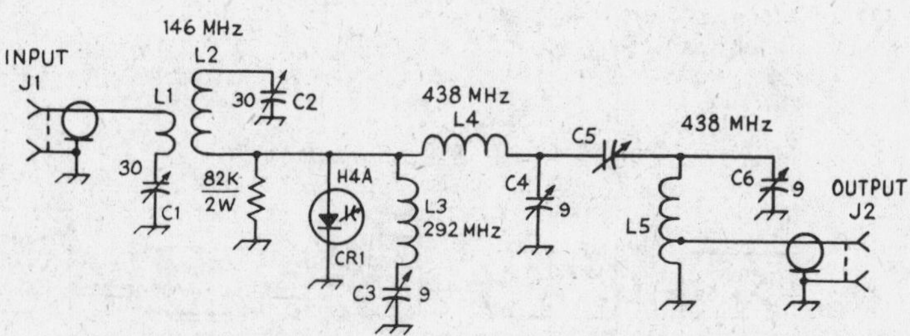

Fig. 1 – Schematic for the varactor tripler.

C1, C2 – 2.2- to 34-pF miniature variable (E.F. Johnson 190-0010-001).

C3, C4, C6 – 1.4- to 9.2-pF miniature variable (E.F. Johnson 189-563-001).

C5 – Copper strip 1-in. long × 1/4-in. wide. Bend one end up to form a tab 3/8-in. long. Spacing between tabs approx. 1/8 inch.

CR1 – Varactor diode (Amperex H4A or equiv.).

J1, J2 – Coaxial connector. Type BNC suitable.

L1 – 3 turns No. 16 enam., 3/8-in. ID × 3/8-in. long.

L2 – 6-1/2 turns No. 16 tinned bus wire, 3/8-in. ID × 7/8-in. long.

L3 – 3-1/2 turns No. 16 tinned bus wire, 3/8-in. ID × 1/2-in. long.

L4 – Copper strip, 3-1/4-in. long × 3/8-in. wide. Space 1/2-in. above ground.

L5 – Copper strip, 3-3/8-in. long × 3/8-in. wide. Space 1/2-in. above ground. Tap 1-3/8 in. from ground end.

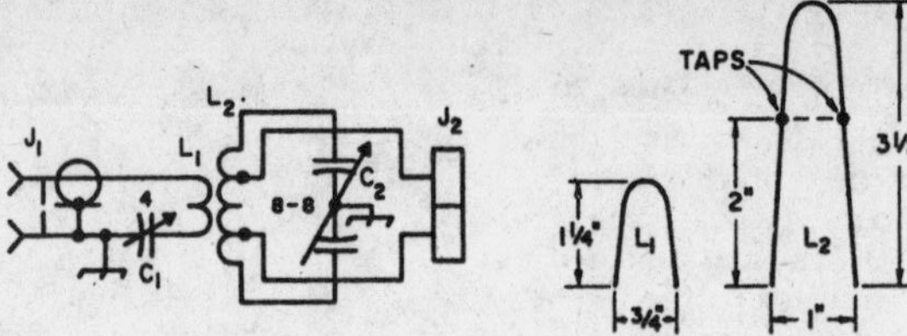

Fig. 3 – 432-MHz transmatch diagram.

C1 – 15-pF variable (Johnson 160-107).
C2 – 8-8-pF dual-section variable (Johnson 160-208).

J1 – BNC coaxial receptacle, chassis mounting.
J2 – Crystal socket.
L1 – Hairpin loop No. 14 wire; see above.
L2 – Hairpin loop No. 10 wire; see above; tap as shown.

the nut is secured. The heat sink need be only two or three inches square for drive levels up to five or six watts. For higher input power, the heat sink should be larger; three or four inches on a side of finned aluminum will be needed if the diode is pushed to its rated limit. L4 is a copper strip with one end connected directly to the diode. C4 is mounted at the end of L4 opposite the varactor. L5 is likewise a strip of copper, and is tuned by C6. The ground end of L5 connects to a shield that isolates the input circuitry from the rest of the compartment. Another shield is placed lengthwise in the box to separate L4 and L5. The coupling capacitor, C5, is made from two small tabs of copper strip bent into an L shape. Coupling is adjusted by bending the tabs slightly. Output is taken from a tap connection near the ground end of L5.

Adjustment

Tune-up of the tripler is not difficult if a few pieces of test gear are available. An SWR indicator will be needed for the input, and an output-power indicator should be connected to J2. A grid-dip meter is also of great help. The first step should be to tune the input, L1-C1 and L2-C2, to resonance as indicated by the dip meter. Likewise, the idler circuit should be tuned to the second harmonic of the intended input frequency, 292 MHz, if the input is 146 MHz. Not many of the currently available dip meters will tune to 440 MHz, but a pilot-lamp dummy load should provide an indication of output when L4-C4 is tuned while low driving power is applied to J1.

The input circuits should be tuned for minimum reflected power at J1, and then the output circuits adjusted for maximum output as shown by a lamp load or power meter. The copper tabs of C5 can be bent toward or away from each other by means of an insulated tuning tool. Overcoupling is indicated by the tuning of C4 and C6 becoming quite broad or even out of range of their adjustments.

Efficiency of the tripler can be as high as 70 percent, but it is recommended that the tuning be set to a condition where the most stable output results. If there is a sudden step, either up or down, in power output as the circuits are adjusted, the input coupling, or the capacitance of C5, should be increased slightly to alleviate this critical condition. With all circuits adjusted properly, the efficiency will be in the vicinity of 60 percent. Moderate temperature changes will have little effect on the output. Spurious signals should be 45 dB below the desired output.

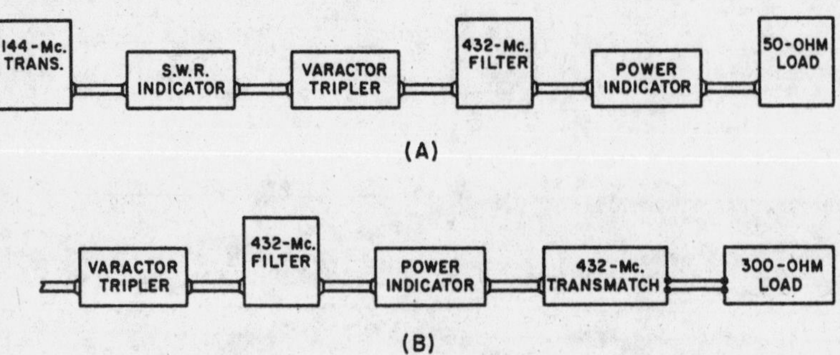

Fig. 4 – Test setups for checking varactor multipliers.

GROUNDED-GRID 50-MHZ AMPLIFIER

Increasing use of 50-MHz transceivers and transmitters having outputs of 25 watts or more has created a demand for amplifiers to be used with such equipment as the driver. The grounded-grid amplifier of Fig. 7-27 is designed for this use. With 30 watts or more of driving power it will deliver 600 watts cw output. As a Class-B linear, single-tone conditions, its rated PEP output is 750 watts.

Circuit

The Eimac 3-500Z triode is designed for grounded-grid service. As may be seen from Fig. 7-30, driving power is applied to the filament circuit, which must be kept above rf ground by means of high-current bifilar rf chokes, RFC1 and RFC2. These are a central feature of the bottom view, Fig. 7-29. The input impedance is low, so the input circuit, L1,C1, tunes broadly, and the 50-ohm line from the exciter is tapped well up on L1. The plate circuit is merely a coil of copper tubing, L2, inductively tuned by means of a "shorted turn" of copper strip, rotated inside its cold end. See Fig. 7-28. Tuning is smooth and the rotating loop avoids many problems commonly encountered in tuning high-powered amplifiers by conventional methods. Plate voltage is shunt fed to the tube, to prevent the high dc voltage from accidentally appearing on the output coupling loop or on the antenna line.

Most of the lower part of the schematic diagram has to do with control and metering, and is largely self-explanatory. The exciter voice-control relay shorts out R1, allowing grid current to flow, and making the amplifier operative, if the filament and primary-control switches, S1 and S2, have been closed. Feeding ac voltage to the plate-supply relay through J4, J5 and P1 makes application of plate voltage without the filament and blower being on impossible.

Construction

The amplifier chassis is aluminum, 10 X 12 X 3 inches in size, with the tube socket centered 3 1/8 inches from the front edge. The sheet-aluminum panel is 10 inches high. The decorative edging is "cove molding," used by cabinet makers for counter tops. Sides and back are also sheet aluminum. Where they need not be removable, parts are fastened together by pop-riveting. Tools and rivets for this work can be found in most hardware stores. Perforated aluminum (cane metal) is used for the top, and for covering the panel viewing hole.

Stretch the wire for the bifilar rf chokes, before winding. Then, with the wires side by side, under tension, wind them on a form of wood or metal. This is left in until the choke ends are soldered in position. Then remove the form and coat the windings with coil cement, to help maintain turn alignment.

Fig. 7-27 — Table-top 50-MHz amplifier of grounded-grid design, only 10 X 12 inches in size. Grid and plate current are monitored simultaneously. Knobs at the right are for input tuning, bottom, amplifier loading, center, and plate tuning, top.

Connections to the grid terminals (on opposite sides of the socket) are made with short 1/4-inch copper straps soldered to the pins and bolted to the chassis with No. 6 screws, nuts and lock-washers. Be sure that a clean, tight rf ground results.

In Fig. 7-28 it will be seen that the hot end of L2 is supported on the top of the two blocking capacitors, C3 and C4, which in turn, are mounted on the Teflon rod that serves as the form for RFC3. The ground end of L2 is supported on a vertical post made of 3/8-inch copper tubing, 1 3/8 inches high. The end of the coil can be fitted with a heavy copper lug, or pounded flat. A hole is drilled in the flat portion and a 2-inch brass bolt runs through it and the post and chassis. Be sure that there is a permanent solid rf ground at this point.

The shunt-feed rf choke is effectively across the tuned circuit, so it must be a good one. Hand-winding as described below is strongly recommended, as no ready-made choke is likely to be as good. Teflon is slippery, so a light thread cut in the form will help keep the winding in place. If this cannot be done, prepare and wind two wires, as for the filament chokes. Feed the wire ends through one hole in the form, and wind a bifilar coil. Pull the other ends through the finish hole, bending one

Fig. 7-28 – Interior view of the 50-MHz amplifier shows the shorted-turn tuning system, plate coil and output coupling, upper right. The tuning and loading controls are mounted on a bracket to the right of the 3-500Z tube and chimney. Meter shielding is partially visible in the left front corner.

back tightly at the hole edge. Remove the other winding, which should leave a tight evenly-spaced coil that makes an excellent vhf choke.

The blocking capacitors, C3 and C4, are mounted between brass plates, one of which is fastened to the top of the rf choke form with a sheet-metal screw. The other plate is connected to the hot end of L2 by means of a wrap-around clip of flashing copper. The lead to the tube plate cap is made with braid removed from a scrap of coax. A strip of flashing copper about 1/4 inch wide is also good for this. Use a good heat-dissipating connector such as the Eimac HR6.

The shorted-turn tuning ring is centered between the first two turns of L2. The ring is attached to a ceramic pillar, and that to a 1/4-inch shaft, the end of which is tapped for 8-32 thread. This shaft runs through a bearing mounted in a bracket 4 inches high and 2 3/4 inches wide, fastened to the chassis and the side of the enclosure. The output loading capacitor, C6, is also mounted on this bracket. It is one inch above the chassis, and the tuning-ring shaft is 3 1/4 inches above the chassis. The input tuning capacitor, C1, is mounted under the chassis, with equal spacing between the three, for symmetrical appearance.

The output coupling loop, L3, is just inside the cold end of L2. It can be adjusted for optimum coupling by "leaning" it slightly into or out of L2. Be sure that it clears the shorted turn throughout movement of the latter.

The coaxial output jack, J3, is on the rear wall of the enclosure. A small bracket of aluminum grounds it to the chassis, independent of the bonding between the chassis and the enclosure. Plate voltage enters through a Millen 37001 high-voltage connector, J2, on the rear wall, and is bypassed immediately inside the compartment with a TV "doorknob" high-voltage capacitor, C5.

The blower assembly in the left rear corner of the chassis draws air in through a hole in the back of the compartment, and forces it down into the enclosed chassis. The only air path is then back up through the socket and chimney (Eimac parts SK-410 and SK-406 recommended) and out through the top of the enclosure. The data sheet for the 3-500Z specifies an air flow of at least 13 cubic feet per minute, when the tube is operated at 500 watts plate dissipation. The ac leads for the blower motor come into the enclosure on feed-through capacitors.

The meters are enclosed in a shield fastened to the front and side panels. Meter terminals are bypassed for rf inside the shield, and leads come through the chassis on feedthrough capacitors. The rocker-type switches just below the meters have built-in illumination. The high-voltage switch is not meant to control the plate supply directly, but rather through a relay, as in the 3000-volt supply shown in Chapter 5. The plate meter is in the negative lead, so be sure that your supply is compatible with this arrangement. Do not use this system where a potential difference exists between the amplifier and power supply chassis. All power leads are made with shielded wire (Belden 8862) and all exposed points are bypassed to ground.

Adjustment and Use

Do not apply drive to the 3-500Z without the plate voltage being on. Also, it is recommended that initial testing be done with low drive, and with a plate voltage of 1500 or less. With a 50-ohm load

Fig. 7-29 – With the bottom cover removed, a look into the chassis from the rear shows the input circuit, L1,C1, right, the bifilar filament chokes, foreground, filament transformer and control switches. Opening in the rear wall is for air intake.

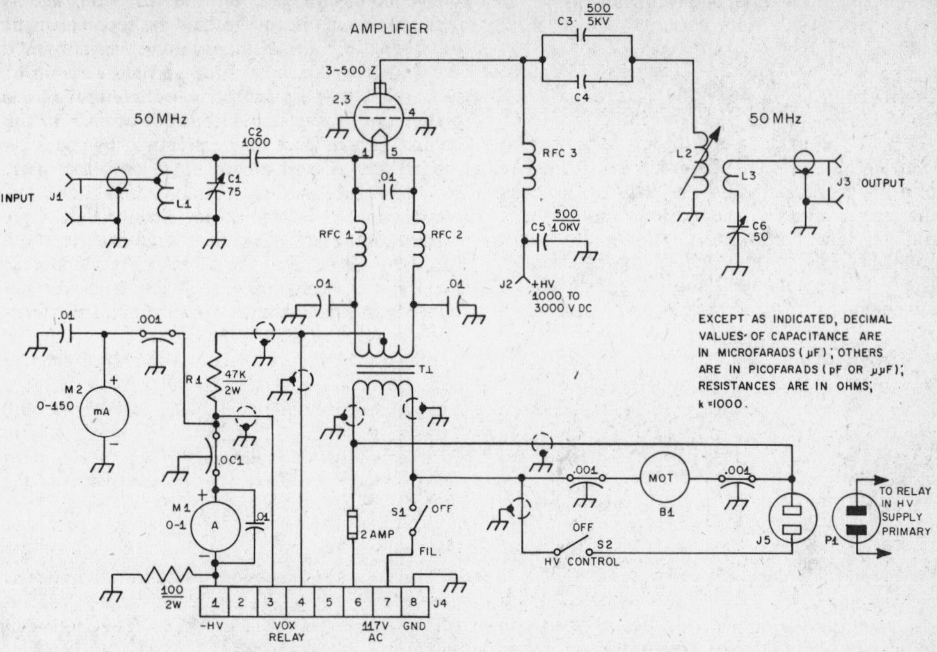

Fig. 7-30 — Schematic diagram and parts information for the 50-MHz grounded-grid amplifier.

B1 – Blower, 15 ft^3/min or more.
C1 – 75-pF variable (Johnson 167-4).
C2 – 1000-pF dipped mica.
C3, C4 – 500-pF 5-kV transmitting ceramic (Centralab 858S-500).
C5 – 500-pF, 10-kV or more, TV "Doorknob."
C6 – 50-pF variable (Johnson 167-3).
J1 – BNC coaxial receptacle.
J2 – High-voltage connector (Millen 37001).
J3 – Type N coaxial receptacle.
J4 – 8-pin male power connector, chassis-mounting.
J5 – AC receptacle, chassis-mounting.
L1 – 4 turns No. 12 enam, 1 inch long, 1inch dia. Tap 2 1/2 turns from ground end.
L2 – 3 1/2 turns 1/4-inch copper tubing, 3 1/2-inch dia, 5 1/4 inches long. Diameter is finished dimension, not that of form used for winding. See text and photo for turn spacing. Tuning ring is closed loop of 1/2-inch copper strip, 2 5/8-inch dia.
L3 – 1 turn, 3-inch dia, and leads, made from one piece of 1/8-inch copper tubing or No. 8 wire.
M1 – DC meter, 0-1 ampere (Simpson Wide-Vue, Model 1327).
M2 – 0-300 mA, like M1.
P1 – AC plug, on cable to power supply.
R1 – 47,000-ohm 2-watt resistor.
RFC1, RFC2 – 21 turns each, No. 12 enam, 1/2-inch dia, bifilar.
RFC3 – 30 turns No. 20 enam, spaced wire dia, on 3/4-inch Teflon rod, 3 3/4 inches long. Drill end holes 1/2 and 2 3/4 inches from top.
S1, S2 – Spst, rocker-type, neon-lighted (Carling LT1L, with snap-in bracket).
T1 – Filament transformer, 5 V, 15 A (Stancor P6433; check any electrical equivalent for fit under 3-inch chassis).

connected to J3, apply 1000 to 1500 volts through J2, and turn on the driver. Adjust the tuning ring inside L2 for a dip in plate current. Tune C1 for maximum grid current. Tune C6 and adjust the position of L3 with respect to L2 for maximum output. If the amplifier seems to be running properly, connect an SWR bridge between the driver and J1, and check reflected power. It should be close to zero. If otherwise, adjust the tap position on L1.

Tuning range of the plate circuit can be checked with a grid-dip meter, with the power off the amplifier. The range is affected by turn spacing overall, and at the cold end. The closer the first two turns are together the greater the effect of the tuning ring. No other tuning device is used, so some experimentation with diameter and length of L2 may be needed if you want other than the 49.8 to 52.7 MHz obtained with the graduated turn spacing visible in the interior view. The highest frequency is reached with the ring in a vertical plane. Dimensions that affect tuning range are as follows: Grounded support for L2 – 1 1/8 inches from right side of chassis, and 3 1/4 inches from rear. RFC3 mounting position – 4 inches from rear and 5 1/2 inches from left. Shorted turn approximately centered between turns 1 and 2 of L2. The start of L3 bends from the stator of C6 to near the start of L2. The end toward J2 passes between the first two turns of L2, clearing the tuning ring in any position of the latter.

Once the amplifier seems to work normally at

moderate plate voltages, apply higher, up to the maximum of 3000. Plate current, with no drive, should be about 160 mA. It can be lowered by inserting 0.1 to 0.4 ohm in series with R1 and the filament center-tap. A Zener diode, 2 to 9 volts, 10 watts, could do this job, as well.

Keep the amplifier tuned for maximum output. Do not decouple to reduce output; cut down drive and/or plate voltage instead. Adjustment for linear operation requires a scope. Maximum output, minimum plate current and maximum grid current should all occur at the same setting of the plate tuning. If they do not, the output loading is over coupled, or there is regeneration in the amplifier. The plate-current dip at resonance is noticeable and smooth, but not of great magnitude.

Typical operating conditions given by the manufacturer, and in the tube-data section of the *Handbook*, are guides to good practice. The amplifier works well with as little as 1000 volts on the tube plate, so varying the ac voltage to the plate-supply transformer is a convenient way to control power level. It is seldom necessary to run the maximum legal power in vhf communication, so some provision for this voltage control is recommended. With just one high-voltage supply needed and no critical tuning adjustments, power variations from 100 to 600 watts output are quickly and easily made. This amplifier was built by Tom McMullen, W1SL, and first described in *QST* for November, 1970.

KILOWATT AMPLIFIER FOR 144 MHZ

The vast difference in design problems for the two bands is highlighted in the nature of the 50- and 144-MHz amplifiers described herewith. They could hardly be more dissimilar, yet each is a logical way to increase power. The 50-MHz amplifier is a grounded-grid device, but a push-pull amplifier of the grounded-cathode type is preferred for 144-MHz service. External-anode tetrodes for this application include the 4X150A, 4X250B, 4CX250B and R, and others having the same basing. The 8122, 4CX300A, 4CX250K and others have various basing arrangements. Except for heater voltage and base design these types are much alike. Early glass-insulated tubes of the 150-250 series (no C in the prefix) may have to run at slightly lower maximum input than their ceramic-insulated (CX) replacements.

Our 144-MHz amplifier, Fig. 7-31, can be run in Class AB_1, for a-m or ssb linear service; or Class C, for high-efficiency a-m, cw or fm. Driver power output should be 2 or 3 watts for AB_1, and 10 watts or more for Class C. For more on operating conditions, see information on linear amplifiers earlier in this chapter, the tube manufacturer's data sheets, or the tube data section of this *Handbook*.

Fig. 7-31 – The 144-MHz amplifier is built in conventional rack-and-panel style, with the entire top of cane metal, to provide free air flow. Controls are grid-circuit tuning, C2, lower left; output loading capacitor, C5, center; and plate-circuit tuning, C4, with vernier dial, right. The slotted end of the Teflon shaft on C1 is visible as a white spot just below the loading control.

Construction

The principal difference between this amplifier and its many predecessors using similar tubes lies in the plate-circuit design. The inductor is cut from flat sheet brass, in the form of a U. The circuit is tuned by a simple handmade variable capacitor that avoids problems commonly encountered in this part of a high-powered vhf amplifier. The circuit is practically identical to several previously described in *QST*, the *VHF Manual* and recent editions of this *Handbook*.

The amplifier is built on a 17 X 8 X 3-inch aluminum chassis, fitted with a bottom cover which completes the shielding and directs the flow of cooling air. The top portion of the enclosure is of similar size, except that it is 3 3/4 inches high, and it has a cane-metal top. It was made by bending up the necessary sheet aluminum, but angle stock and flat sheets could be used equally well. Angle stock along the back of the front panel completes the enclosure. The gray-wrinkle aluminum panel is 7 inches high.

The tube sockets are mounted 2 inches in from the right side, as seen in the photographs, and 2 5/8 inches apart, center to center. The Eimac SK620A sockets, with their integral screen-ring shielding, are recommended. Other sockets may require slightly greater spacing, and some modification of the plate-circuit dimensions. The raised screen-ring shield is also a great aid in neutralizing the amplifier. Some form of shield should be added if early flat sockets are used. This need is particularly acute if the amplifier is to be operated in the Class AB_1 mode, which is characterized by very-high-power sensitivity.

The half-wave-line grid circuit, L2, is tuned at the end away from the tubes by the split-stator variable, C2, and balanced to ground by means of C3, a differential capacitor. This is supported on its stator tabs, which are soldered directly to L2, immediately adjacent to C2. A strap of 1/4-inch copper connects the rotor of C3 to the chassis, in the shortest practical manner. The slotted shaft of C3 is reached through a hole in the bottom cover of the chassis. This hole is sealed with black plastic tape after the adjustment is completed, in order to avoid air leakage.

Leads to the neutralizing tabs, C9 and C10, are tapped on the grid lines at a point 1 3/4 inches from the grid end. Feedthrough bushings (not visible in the photographs) are under the lines. The crossover is made by copper strips from the lines to the bushings. Variable capacitance to the plate line is provided by copper tabs 1/4 X 5/8 inch in size, soldered to the top ends of the bushings, just below the plate line, L3. Adjusting their position with respect to L3 provides the required neutralizing capacitance.

Connections to the grid ends of L2 are wrap-around copper clips slipped over the tubing ends and fastened to the grid posts of the tube sockets with screws. They are soldered to the line ends, for permanence. The connections to C2 are made in somewhat the same way, except that the tabs are soldered to the stator lugs. Note that the rotor of C2 is not grounded. It is supported on ceramic standoffs 5/8 inch high.

The grid-circuit isolating resistors, R1 and R2, are connected to L2 by means of spring clips which are slid over the line before assembly. These can be tube grid clips, if available. They are moved along the line to the point of minimum rf voltage, using the familiar lead-pencil test.

The shaft of C2 is rotated through an insulating shaft, fitted with an insulating flexible coupling, to minimize any tendency to unbalance the grid circuit. The shaft from C1 is also insulating material, and it has a flexible coupling. The capacitor is not adjusted often, so the shaft end is slotted, and is allowed to protrude through the front panel. It is just visible in the front view, below the output-loading control.

All power leads are made with shielded wire, bonded together by frequent spot-soldering, and to the chassis by means of grounding lugs. Exposed terminals are bypassed wherever necessary, to prevent rf pickup.

Each cathode pin on the socket is grounded through a separate lug, and nothing else uses these lugs for a ground path. Minimum cathode-lead inductance is important. Even the shortest lead shared with another circuit can cause unwanted coupling in a vhf amplifier.

The plate inductor, L3, is made of sheet brass, in the form of a U. Principal dimensions are given in Fig. 7-35. The stator plates of the tuning capacitor, C4, part A, are soldered to the plate line with their right edges 5/8 inch from the tube anodes. Connection to the latter is made with two brass tabs, part B, at the tube ends of the line. These were omitted from the drawing of the assembly in the interest of clarity, but their position is clearly visible in the photographs. These tabs are curved slightly after bending, to provide more contact surface to the anode. Clamping rings made of flashing copper wrap around the anode structure and hold the tabs tightly to it. This is a point of low rf current, so a large contact area is not vital.

Fig. 7-32 – Interior of the 2-meter amplifier, showing the brass plate-inductor and vane-tuning system. Note the position of RFC1, at the far left, out of the main rf field. The output coupling loop, L4, just below the plate line and barely visible here, is connected to the output jack, J4, on the rear wall with a short section of coax, and to the loading capacitor, C5, on the front panel by means of copper strip.

The plate line was made flat originally, but when the amplifier was tested it was found that this did not allow room to adjust the output coupling loop, L4, to the optimum position. The half-inch offset shown in Fig. 7-35 (but not in the photographs) netted a marked improvment in efficiency. The entire plate circuit was silver-plated after the photography. Careful checks on performance indicated no difference, before and after plating. Plating may be desirable on a long-term basis, as silver oxide is a good conductor, and other oxides are not.

The "stators" and the tabs for the anode connection were silver-soldered to L3. Ordinary soldering will be adequate, but it might be well to use screws to hold the tabs onto L3, as a precautionary measure. The stator plates have flat-head screws running through them and L3, into the insulating supports for the latter. These are 1-inch ceramic pillars. The closed end of the loop is supported on a 1 1/2-inch pillar.

The holes for these supports can be made slightly oval, to position the assembly so that no strain on tubes or sockets is caused when the anode rings are tightened. The mounting hole in the closed end of L3 is also elongated. The screw that holds the line on its support has Teflon washers above and below L3, to permit the line to move on its support, if expansion and contraction with heating and cooling of the line should be appreciable.

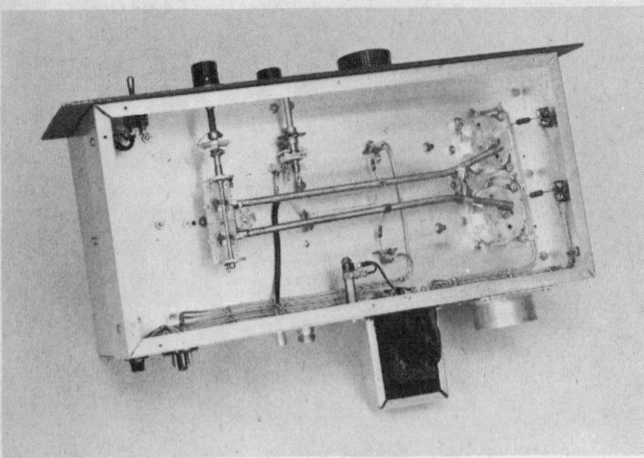

Fig. 7-33 – The principal feature of the bottom view is the half-wave grid circuit. Its split-stator capacitor, C2, is at the left end of the line, L2. The differential balancing capacitor, C3, is also across the line, just to the right of C2. Isolating resistors in the grid circuit, R1, and R2, are near the middle of the picture. The screen isolating resistors, R3 and R4, run to tie points on the right wall of the chassis.

The rotor of C4 is in the form of a shallow box made of flashing copper. It is shown in flat form in Fig. 7-36, along with other copper parts of the plate circuit. Its ends, 1 inch high, provide the variable capacitance to the stator plates on L3. After the box is bent to the desired form, its adjoining surfaces are soldered for additional strength and rigidity. The edge away from the tube anodes is supported on a fiber glass rod with 4-40 screws, the rod surface having been filed flat in this area previously. Reducing couplers at each end of the rod permit use of a 1/4-inch shaft bearing at the rear, and a National Velvet-Vernier dial mechanism at the front. Do not use heat-sensitive rod such as Lucite or Plexiglas. Nylon and some types of Bakelite are unstable in strong rf fields, and are also unsatisfactory. Teflon is probably good, but the fiber glass rod is stronger and easy to work. It is 6 3/8 inches long, and may be 1/2 or 3/8 inch in diameter.

Mechanical stops for the rotor are provided at both ends of its normal travel. A 3/8-inch Teflon rod 1 3/8 inches high, fastened to the chassis between the neutralizing feedthrough bushings, stops the rotor in the horizontal position. The rotor is prevented from "going through the roof" by a 1-inch setscrew in the vernier-drive hub, and a longer-than-normal screw for the lower left mounting screw for the driver assembly.

The rotor in its horizontal position is approximately 1/4 inch above L3, and the spacing at the end of the rotor is also 1/4 inch. The tubes are fitted with Eimac SK626 chimneys. The under surface of L3 should just clear these. If it does not, raise it by putting washers on the screws that run into the 1-inch pillars.

The output loop, L4, is supported under L3 by two 1/2-inch ceramic insulators. If the threaded holes go the whole length, be sure that the mounting screws do not ground the loop, or come close enough to allow arcing to ground. Connection to the coaxial output jack, J2, is made with a short piece of RG-8/U coax, using a shielding cone at the J2 end. The coax shield is grounded to chassis with a copper strap at the L4 end also, to make the rf path to ground independent of the chassis bonding. The rotor of C5 is also grounded independently. A copper strap connects the stator of C5 to the end of L4. After the final form and size of L4 have been determined, the connection to the strap should be soldered, to maintain a good rf bond. These circuits carry high rf currents, and permanent low resistance connections are important. The performance of many amplifiers falls off with aging, because factors like this were overlooked.

An adequate supply of cooling air must be provided. The manufacturer stipulates 4.6 cubic feet per minute, per tube, minimum, but much more should be available. The blower used here has a 3-inch diameter wheel, turning at 3300 rpm. It is connected to the rear of the chassis by way of an automotive defroster hose 2 1/8 inches in diameter.

Adjustment

Heater voltage (at the socket) should be 6.0 volts. This is adjusted by means of the slider on R5. Set the sliding clips on L2 at the approximate midpoint. Now apply 1 to 2 watts drive to the grid circuit, adjusting the position of L1 and the tuning of C1 and C2 for minimum reflected power, indicated on an SWR bridge connected between the exciter and J1.

With enough drive so that grid current will be measurable, meter each grid separately, and adjust the balancing capacitor, C3, for as near to the same value for each grid as possible. Readjust C2 for each change. When the currents are approximately equal, the neutralization should be adjusted. With a 50-ohm load connected to J2, and with the screen and plate circuits having some dc path to ground, such as through power supply bleeders, couple a sensitive rf indicator to L3. Still with no plate or screen voltage applied, tune C2 and C4 for maximum indication, then adjust the positions of the neutralizing tabs, C9 and C10, carefully for *minimum* rf feedthrough. Recheck the grid circuit balance and tuning each time a tab setting is changed.

The points of connection of the resistors R1 and R2 on the lines comprising L2 are not critical, unless the exciter is low on output, but they should be near the points of lowest rf voltage on the line. Check by running a pencil lead along the line and watching the current. The point at which there is no change in the meter indication is where the clip should be. Recheck all adjustments.

The approximate tuning range of the plate circuit can be checked with a grid-dip meter, with no power on the amplifier. It should tune more than the width of the 2-meter band. Now, with an output indicator and a good 50-ohm load connected to J2, the amplifier is ready for power.

EXCEPT AS INDICATED, DECIMAL VALUES OF CAPACITANCE ARE IN MICROFARADS (μF); OTHERS ARE IN PICOFARADS (pF OR μμF); RESISTANCES ARE IN OHMS; k=1000, M=1 000 000

Fig. 7-34 – Schematic diagram and parts information for the 144-MHz amplifier. Capacitors not described are disk ceramic.

C1 – 25-pF miniature variable (Hammarlund MAPC-25B).
C2 – 25-pF per section split-stator (Hammarlund HFD-25).
C3 – 1.5- to 5-pF differential (Hammarlund MAC-5-5).
C4 – Vane-type tuning capacitor; see text and photos.
C5 – 35-pF variable (Hammarlund HF-35).
C6 – 500-pF 10-kV TV "doorknob."
C7, C8 – Screen bypass; part of Eimac SK-620A socket.
C9, C10 – Neutralizing tabs 1/4 X 5/8-inch sheet copper, soldered to top of National FTB bushing.
I1 – 117-volt neon pilot lamp.
J1 – BNC coaxial jack.
J2 – Type N coaxial jack.
J3 – 8-pin power connector, male.
J4 – High voltage power connector (Millen 37501).
L1 – Copper strip 1/4 X 4 inches. See Fig. 7-36.
L2 – 1/4-inch copper tubing 10 1/2 inches long, 15/16 inch center to center. Bend to Y shape 2 inches from tube end.
L3 – .065-inch sheet brass; see text and Fig. 7-35.
L4 – Copper strip 15/16 X 7 1/2 inches, bent to roughly elliptical shape. See text and Fig. 7-36.
R1, R2 – 150-ohm composition, 1/2 watt.
R3, R4 – 150-ohm composition, 1 watt.
R5 – 20-ohm 10-watt, slider type.
RFC1 – 32 turns No. 24 enamel, closewound on 1/4-inch Teflon rod. See mounting position in interior photo.
S1 – Spst toggle switch.
T1 – 6.3-V 6-A filament transformer (Merit P-2947).

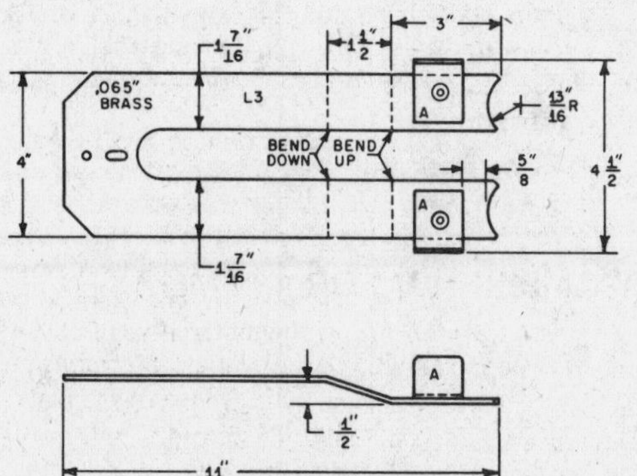

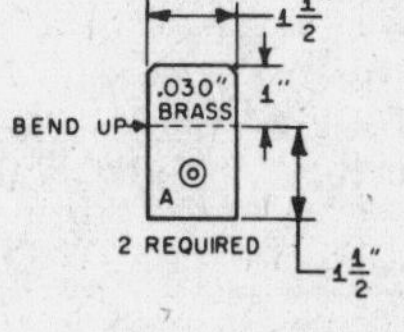

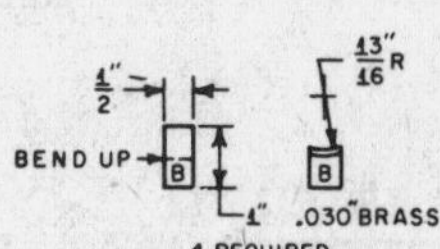

Fig. 7-35 – Principal dimensions of the brass parts of the amplifier plate circuit. The U-shaped inductor is shown in both top and side views, with the stator plates of C4 in place. These plates (A) are shown before bending, at the upper right. The small brackets (B) make contact with the tube anodes. Slight curvature, to fit tube anode, can be imparted by tapping with a small hammer, against a 1 1/2-inch pipe or rod, used as an anvil.

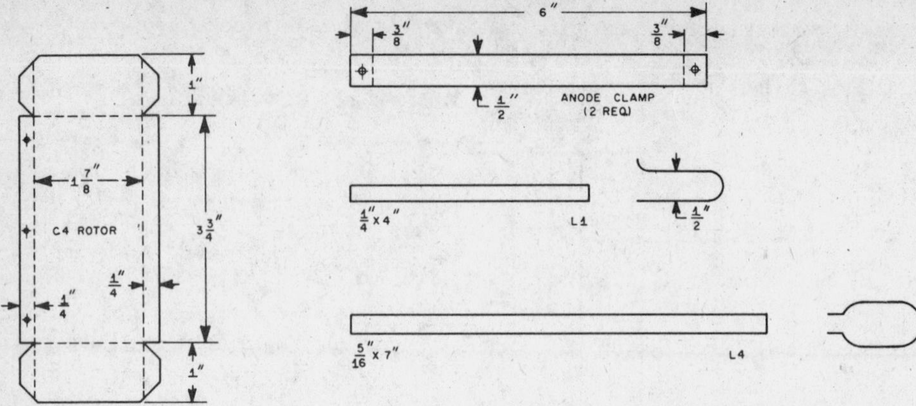

Fig. 7-36 – Flashing-copper parts used in the 2-meter amplifier. Broken lines indicate 90-degree bending required. The surfaces of the C4 rotor are soldered together after bending, for rigidity. The anode clamps, upper right, wrap around the tube cooling ring, and hold the brass tabs (Fig. 7-35) firmly in place. L1 and L4 are shown in the approximate shape, after bending, at the right.

For initial tests, the plate voltage should be 800 to 1000 volts. Screen voltage should be no more than 250, preferably regulated. There will be little difference in tuning or output with the cover on or off, so, with due regard for safety, leave it off, at first. Never reach inside the plate compartment when high voltage is applied. To be sure that it is off, short the plate inductor to ground with an insulated screwdriver or other safe shorting device. Do this every time before touching anything inside the compartment in any other way. Play it *safe*!

Apply plate and screen voltage, in that order. Adjust bias so that the plate current is about 150 mA. Apply drive, and tune C4 and C5 for maximum power output. With enough drive for about 5 mA grid current per tube, the plate efficiency should approach 70 percent, after the position of L4 with respect to L3 is adjusted with some care. Loop position and all tuning adjustments change with plate voltage and drive level, so in linear service all adjustments should be made under the conditions for which you want best linearity.

The shape and position of L4 are quite critical. Best efficiency was obtained with the loop roughly elliptical in shape, and about 3/8 inch below L3. Best results show at plate voltages between 1200 and 1800. The tube maker's typical operating conditions are the best guide to efficient operation, but they are only *typical.* If safe levels of grid, screen and plate dissipation are not exceeded, many variations are possible. See "Tips on Linears" earlier in this chapter.

This amplifier was built by W1SL, and described in February, 1971, *QST*.

References

The 50- and 144-MHz amplifiers described incorporate features from many previous *QST*, *Handbook* and *VHF Manual* projects.

Maer, "Perseids Powerhouse," *QST*, Oct., 1959 (dual-band amplifier for 50 and 144 MHz).

"High-Efficiency 2-Meter Kilowatt," *QST*, Feb., 1960 (PP 4CX300As).

Breyfogle, "Top Efficiency at 144 Mc. with 4X250Bs," *QST*, Dec., 1961.

"Kilowatt Amplifiers for 50 and 144 Mc.," *QST*, Feb., 1964. Basic information also in the *VHF Manual*, all editions, and in this *Handbook*, 1966 through 1970. Metering and control information applies to the 144-MHz amplifier described here.

A RESONANT-CAVITY AMPLIFIER FOR 432 MHZ

This highly-efficient 4CX250 amplifier operates at approximately 63-percent efficiency when used with a plate supply of 1750 volts and a screen supply of 255 volts. It can be operated with higher voltage on its plate, but at reduced efficiency. It provides power levels up to 500 watts input on cw and fm.

The grid circuit of the amplifier is as shown in Fig. 7-39 and is pretty much a duplication of the one shown in the 2nd Edition of *The Radio Amateur's VHF Manual* (ARRL), page 257. The plate side of the circuit is a resonant cavity and is shown in representative form in Fig. 7-39. Detailed information on how the plate circuit is built is given in Fig. 7-40.

Fig. 7-37 — View of the top of the assembled amplifier. Teflon bushings hold the square capacitor plate in place on the wall of the cavity. One bushing is not shown. The high voltage and rf choke connect to that bushing's screw when it is in place. Plate-tuning adjustments are made from the bottom of the cavity. The shaft for C3 is accessible on the bottom wall of the cavity. This amplifier was designed and built by H. E. Holshouser, Jr., K4QIF.

Construction

Much of the information concerning the way the amplifier is built can be taken from the photos. The dimensions of the plate cavity are given in Fig. 7-40. The cavity is constructed, cylindrical fashion, from 1/8-inch thick copper or brass stock and has an inside diameter of 6 1/4-inches. The wall height of the cylinder is 1 1/2 inches. Both end plates are fashioned from 1/8-inch thick copper or brass stock. A firm bond is essential between the end plates and the cylinder to assure maximum efficiency. It would be wise to have the cylinder milled flat on each end to assure a good fit, then use a liberal number of machine screws to hold the end plates in place. Mechanical rigidity is imperative with this type of structure, thus

Fig. 7-38 — Inside view of the amplifier. The grid circuit and filament transformer are inside the chassis. Plate and output-tuning adjustments are made from the bottom of the cavity (far right).

assuring good continuity at the high-current points of the cavity, and to enhance the tuning stability of the plate circuit.

The tube and socket are mounted 5/8 inch off center from the center of the cavity. The hole in the top plate of the cavity should be large enough in diameter to assure a 3/16-inch clearance all around the anode of the tube. Care should be taken to smooth the edges of the hole lest arcing occur during operation. The home-built capacitor, C6, is formed by making a 3 7/8-inch square copper or brass plate of 1/8-inch thick stock and placing a sheet of 10-mil teflon insulation between it and the cavity top plate. The plate has a clearance hole for the anode of the 4CX250 and is ringed with finger stock so that it contacts the tube's anode. Insulating bushings of teflon are used at each corner of the capacitor plate to secure it to the wall of the cavity, Fig. 7-37.

An Eimac SK-600 tube socket is used, and no chimney is needed. The socket has built-in bypass capacitors on the screen and filament terminals. These are not shown on the schematic diagram. The bottom of the tube socket projects into the main chassis where the grid circuit is located. The output link, L3, is a straight piece of 1/16-inch

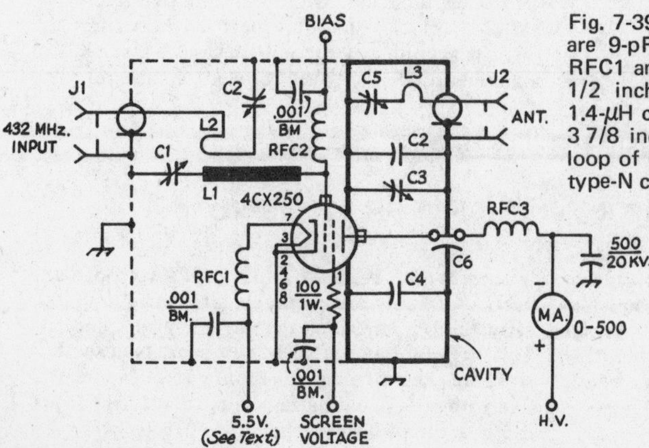

Fig. 7-39 — Schematic of the amplifier. C1 and C2 are 9-pF miniature variables (Johnson 160-104). RFC1 and RFC2 are each 8 turns of No. 16, enam, 1/2 inch diameter and 1 inch long. RFC3 is a 1.4-μH choke. L1 is a brass strip, 1/16 inch thick, 3 7/8 inches long, and 1 1/4 inches wide. L2 is a loop of No. 12 wire, 6 inches overall. J1 and J2 are type-N chassis connectors. B.M. = button mica.

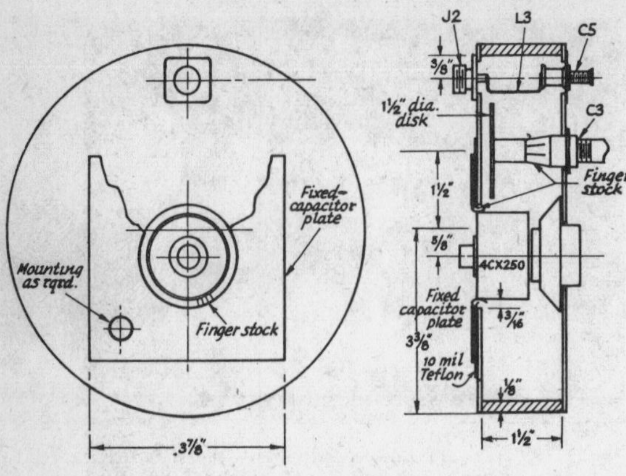

Fig. 7-40 – Mechanical layout of the plate cavity and its dimensions.

Fig. 7-41 – Inside view of the K4QIF amplifier cavity. The stationary capacitors, C2 and C4, are located on either side of the 4CX250 socket.

thick brass or copper, 1/8 inch wide, shaped as shown in Fig. 7-40.

Two fixed capacitors are shown in the schematic diagram, C2 and C4. These capacitors are not indicated on the mechanical drawing of Fig. 7-40 as they were added as a modification when some models of this amplifier showed a tendency toward arcing between the disk of C3 and the cavity wall. C2 and C4 are disks of copper which are 1 1/4 inches in diameter. They are spaced approximately 1/8 inch from the top wall of the cavity. They are supported from the bottom wall of the cavity by means of 3/8-inch diameter brass posts and are positioned generally as shown in Fig. 7-41. *A word of caution:* The tuning shaft of C3 should not pass through the grid compartment of the amplifier. The cavity assembly is offset on the main chassis so that the shaft is accessible outside the grid compartment.

The output tuning capacitor, C5, is a glass piston trimmer with a maximum capacitance of 10 pF. Do not try to use a plastic piston trimmer here as it will be destroyed because of its poor dielectric properties. Neutralization of this amplifier was not found to be necessary as no tendency toward instability was noted.

Operation

It is suggested that a 0.5-ampere fuse be used in series with the high-voltage lead to protect the plate meter should an arc or short circuit occur. The screen current should be metered so that at no time an excessive amount of current will be permitted to flow. Heed the manufacturer's ratings at all times.

The amplifier must always look into a nonreactive load if damage is not to occur. It is designed to work into a 50-ohm load, but a 75-ohm load will be acceptable if the SWR is kept low. *Warning:* The anode of the 4CX250 should be covered with a perforated box of some type to prevent accidental contact with the high voltage. It should allow the free passage of air from the forced-air cooling system, which is piped into the grid compartment. The grid compartment should be made as air-tight as possible to assure a heavy flow of air through the socket and the anode fins of the tube.

The heater voltage for this type of tube is 6.0 and not 6.3. It is satisfactory to use the 6-volt figure at the low frequencies, but at 432-MHz, the voltage should be reduced to 5.5 to compensate for the back-bombardment that the cathode is subjected to. The latter causes overheating, which in turn causes drifting of operating conditions and shortened tube life. Other operating voltages and currents for this amplifier must be chosen for the class of operation desired. It is best to consult the manufacturer's published ratings for this information.

GROUNDED-GRID AMPLIFIER FOR 1296 MHZ

There are few tubes available that will provide the radio amateur with low-cost construction while at the same time delivering moderate power output in the 1215-MHz region. One popular low-cost tube is the 2C39. Also available are its newer brothers the 2C39A, 2C39B, 3CX100A5, and 7289. All look pretty much alike, but only the early versions have appeared on the surplus market. This amplifier uses 2C39As in a cavity assembly and is capable of delivering 100 watts or more as a linear amplifier, with a gain of 6 to 10 decibels.[1] It can be built with simple hand tools.

[1] Described in January 1968 *QST*.

Amplifier Details

Uhf circuits, particularly those involving cavities, do not lend themselves well to conventional schematic presentation, but the circuit diagram, Fig. 7-43, may aid the reader in identifying the components and understanding their functions. The structural features of the amplifier are not all apparent from the photographs, so are described in some detail, using component designations of Fig. 7-45 in referring to the various parts.

This is a grounded-grid amplifier. The large square box visible in the pictures houses the cathode input circuit. The whole assembly is shown from the top in Fig. 7-42, and from the bottom in Fig. 7-44. Details of the principal metal parts are given in Fig. 7-45. It will be seen that the bottom cover of the cathode compartment (part D in Fig. 7-45) is cut diagonally to permit access to the cathode circuit for adjustment purposes. The tuned circuit, L1-C2, is effectively a half-wave line, tuned at the end opposite to the tubes. The inductance, part E in Fig. 7-45, is tuned by means of a beryllium copper spring finger, visible in the lower left corner of Fig. 7-44. It is actuated by an adjustment screw running through a shoulder nut mounted in the removable cover plate. Input coupling is capacitive, through C1, a small glass trimmer at the center of the line, between the tubes. An approximate input match is established by adjustment of this capacitor.

The plate circuit, L2-C3, is a square tuned cavity not visible in the pictures. It is made by bending part G into a square, and soldering it to the top of part C and to the bottom of part B, with all lined up on a common center. The *outside* of the cavity is at rf ground potential. The tubes are mounted on a diagonal, at equal distances from the center. The plate tuning capacitor, C3, is coaxial. Its movable element is a 6-32 screw, running through a shoulder nut in the top plate of the bypass capacitor, C4, soon to be described. The fixed portion is a metal sleeve 5/16 inch inside diameter and 5/8 inch high, soldered to the top side of part C. It is centered on a 6-32 binder-head screw, threaded into the center hole in part C. This screw also holds a 3/8-inch insulating spacer that supports the cathode inductor, part E. Output coupling is by means of a fixed loop, L3, on a BNC or TNC coaxial fitting mounted in the 3/8-inch hole in part G, the cavity wall.

The bypass capacitor, C4, consists of the top cover of the plate cavity, part B, a layer of 0.02-inch Teflon sheet, and the top plate, part A. This combination does not act as a pure capacitance, because of the large size of the plates in terms of wavelength at 1296 MHz. It is important not to make substitutions here, as variations in size of the plates or thickness of the insulation may cause the capacitor to become resonant. The plates are held together with nylon screws. Metal screws with insulating sleeving, and insulating shoulder washers, may also be used. Nylon screws and other insulation, other than Teflon, may melt if the bypass capacitor becomes resonant. Nylon is very lossy at 1296 MHz.

Fig. 7-42 – The 2-tube 1296-MHz amplifier. Two 2C39As are used in this grounded-grid setup. The large square base unit houses the cathode input circuit. The plate cavity is not visible, as it is obscured by the plate-bypass assembly seen here. *(Built by W6IOM)*

Construction

Major sheet-metal parts are cut from 0.04- or 0.05-inch sheet-brass. The cutting, bending and soldering can be done with hand tools. The soldering is done readily over a kitchen stove, or with a 300-watt or larger soldering iron. Silver plating is recommended, to assure good rf contact throughout. Several methods usable in the home are outlined in *The Radio Amateur's VHF Manual.* All sheet-brass parts are shown in Fig. 7-45, with dimensions and hole locations. Note that the bottom plate of the cathode assembly, part D, is cut diagonally, and fitted with spring finger stock to assure good electrical continuity when the assembly is closed.

On the smaller part of D is a 6-32 screw that runs through a shoulder nut soldered into the sheet, with the head of the screw on the outside when the cover is in place. The end of the screw bears on the beryllium copper spring finger, 5/8 inch wide, bent so that its position with respect to the cathode circuit varies with the position of the screw. Its position and approximate size should be evident from Fig. 7-44. The bottom end is soldered to the inside of part C. The free end should be wrapped with smooth insulating tape, so that the cathode bias will not be shorted out if the capacitor is closed down too far.

Spring finger stock is used to provide flexible low-inductance contact with the plate, grid and cathode elements of the tubes. Finger stock numbers are given for stock obtained from Instrument Specialty Co., Little Falls, N.J. The material used for tube contact purposes is No. 97-380. That on the triangular cover plate is 97-134. If tubes with recessed grid rings are used (example: the 7289) it is necessary to solder a small piece of brass against the bottom of the grid finger stock, to prevent the tube from being pushed in too far. Otherwise it is impossible to remove the tube without damage to either the finger stock or the tube. The finger stock used in the grid, plate and cathode holes should be preformed to fit, and then soldered in with a 200-watt or larger iron. That on part D is soldered to the outside of the plate. It may be necessary to strengthen the cover plate with a strip of brass soldered to the inside, opposite to the finger stock to prevent bulging. This should protrude about 1/16 inch from the edge of the cover plate. Any intermittent contact here will detune the input circuit severely.

The finger stock in the plate bypass should be flush with the sheet metal on the side facing the cavity. With the grid and cathode connections the stock may protrude somewhat. The soldering of the cavity parts should be done first. The parts should be lined up carefully, clamped together, and then soldered in place over a gas flame for preheating, doing the actual soldering with a small iron. Check alignment prior to final cool-down. The output BNC fitting can be soldered in at this time, adding the coupling loop later. It is merely a strip of copper or brass, 3/8 inch wide, soldered between the center pin of J2 and the cavity bottom. The strip should rest against the Teflon shoulder of the fitting, and extend 1/4 inch beyond the center pin before being bent 90 degrees down to the cavity bottom. Solder solidly to part A, and to the full length of the pin on J2. Now put in the finger stock. If a small iron is used, preheating with the gas flame, the heavy brass parts will not come loose. The top cover of the plate cavity, part B, is then soldered in place, using a clamp as before.

In cutting the Teflon insulation for the plate bypass, make tube holes only just large enough to clear the tube. There should also be some area of insulation around the outer edges of the top plate. These precautions are helpful in preventing arc-over.

Connection to the tube heaters is made by bending a U-shaped piece of beryllium copper or spring bronze to make a snug fit in the heater cup at the end of the tube. The air-wound rf choke is connected directly to this, with the other end running to the feedthrough bypasses. The heaters being brought out separately permits a check on condition of tubes, by turning off the heaters one at a time. Leaving the tube in place, but cold, does not detune the system, and a comparison of the tubes may be made in this way. Note that neither side of the heater circuit can be grounded.

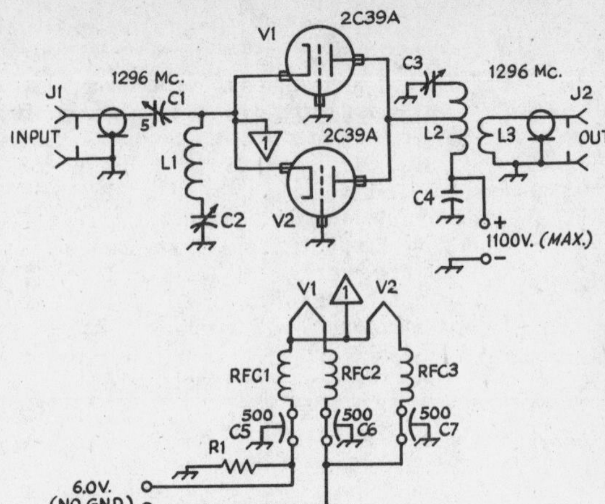

Fig. 7-43 – Representative circuit of the 1296-MHz cavity amplifier. The plate cavity and tuning device are indicated by L2,C3, the cathode inductance and tuning capacitor by L1,C2. Note that the heater supply must not be grounded.

C1 – 5-pF glass trimmer.
C2 – Beryllium-copper spring finger; see text and Fig. 7-44.
C3 – Coaxial plate capacitor (see text)
C4 – Plate bypass capacitor, composed of parts A and B, Fig. 7-45 separated by 0.02-inch Teflon sheet. See text.
C5, C6, C7 – Feedthrough bypass, 500 pF.
J1, J2 – Coaxial jack, BNC or TNC type.
L1 – Cathode inductor, part E, Fig. 7-45. See text and Fig. 7-44.
L2 – Plate cavity, composed of parts C, B and G of Fig. 7-45. See text.
L3 – Copper strap 3/8 inch wide, from pin of J2 to top side of part C.
RFC1, RFC2, RFC3 – 10 turns No. 22 enamel, 1/8-inch dia, 1 inch long.
R1 – 50 to 100 ohms, 2 watts (see text).

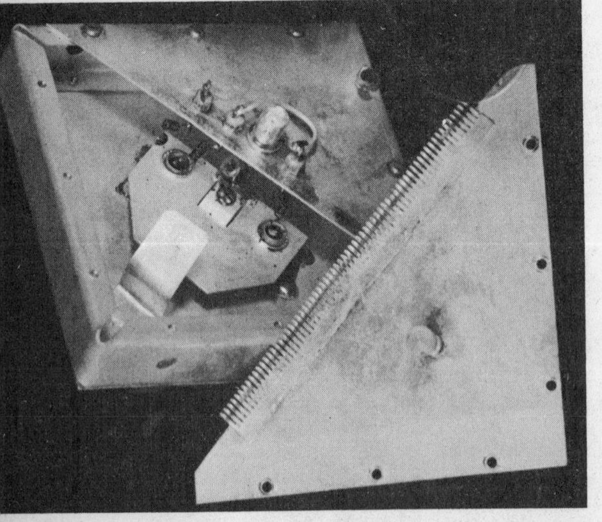

Fig. 7-44 – Bottom (or back) view of the cathode circuit and housing showing the divided cover plate, part D in Fig. 7-45. Inside are the cathode inductance, part E, and the spring-finger tuning capacitor plate, C2. The heater and cathode feedthrough bypasses and the input coaxial fitting are on the cover plate, near the center. The outside surface of the removable cover plate is shown.

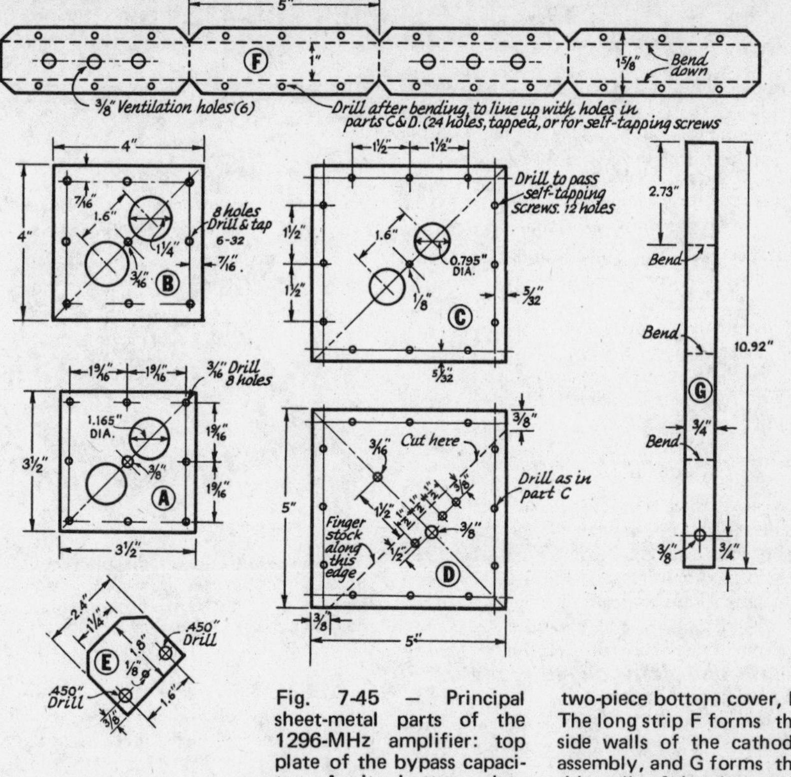

Fig. 7-45 — Principal sheet-metal parts of the 1296-MHz amplifier: top plate of the bypass capacitor, A; its bottom plate and top cover of the plate cavity, B; top plate of the cathode assembly, C; and two-piece bottom cover, D. The long strip F forms the side walls of the cathode assembly, and G forms the side walls of the plate cavity, both before bending into their square shape.

Tuning and Operation

When construction is completed and checked out, apply heater power to the tubes. Connect a milliammeter in series with the cathode resistor. Set the input glass trimmer at the middle of its range, and place the cover plate in position, but without putting in the screws as yet. Keep some pressure on it by hand to insure uniform contact. Apply 10 to 20 watts of driving power, tune C2, and observe the cathode current. Open the cathode compartment, move the input trimmer, replace the cover, and observe the current again. Repeat until highest current is achieved, but do not go over 120 mA. Reduce driving power, if necessary, to keep below this level. Fasten the cover plate in place, and recheck cathode current.

Supply cooling air, if this has not already been done. Be sure that adequate air flow is provided, especially if the plate input is to be near maximum ratings. If there is to be no cowling around the tube fins an air stream of some 150 ft^3/min from a low-pressure blower across the area of the tube fins is required. With an enclosure confining the air flow to a path through the fins a 30 ft^3/min high-pressure blower should suffice. In either case it does no harm to have more. If you have a quiet blower it probably is not enough!

Connect a 50-ohm termination to J2 and apply plate power, preferably at a lower voltage than the maximum that will be used eventually. Apply drive, and tune the input circuit for maximum plate current, and the output circuit for maximum output. A suitable indicator is an incandescent lamp connected at the end of a 50-foot length of RG-58 cable. This will be so lossy that it will look like 50 ohms, regardless of the termination, and the lamp will show relative output. Maximum output may not coincide with minimum plate current.

Once the amplifier appears to be working normally, plate voltage may be increased. Recheck the tuning adjustments for each change in plate voltage. Use a value of cathode resistance that will result in about 50 mA plate current with no drive. With 1000 volts on the plates do not operate the amplifier for more than a few seconds at a time under key-down conditions. With a normal cw keying duty cycle you can run up to 400 mA plate current. With ssb you may run up to 600 mA peak current, or a 300-mA indicated meter reading during normal voice operation. With the expected 100 watts output, with 300 to 400 in, the RG-58 cable should melt in a few minutes. This is not a very satisfactory method of measuring output, and some reliable power-indicating meter should be used for at least an intermittent check, if at all possible.

500-WATT AMPLIFIER FOR 432 MHz

One of the best tuned circuits, other than a resonant cavity, for an amplifier in the 420-MHz band is a coaxial line. To build a good one requires some metal work, but the assembly described here should not be difficult for the advanced worker. Amplifiers of this type have been built and used by W1QWJ and W1RVW, with excellent results. They run up to 500 watts input on fm and cw, and the amplifiers operate very much as they would on much lower frequencies.

Input circuit details are given for both 144 and 432 MHz, permitting the stage to be set up for tripling or straight-through operation. An inexpensive 4X150A running as a tripler will drive any of the 250-series tubes with ease.

Construction

The basic design should be clear from the photographs, Figs. 7-46, 47 and 49. Structural details may be obtained from Fig. 7-50. The straight-through amplifier and the 144-MHz grid circuit are shown schematically in Fig. 7-48. In the amplifier photographed, W1RVW used two separate 8 by 12-inch chassis, with their 8-inch surfaces fastened to a standard rack panel, 1 inch apart. They are held in firm alignment by an aluminum plate fastened at the back. One chassis carries the amplifier, the other a regulated screen supply.

Fig. 7-46 – Looking down at the coaxial plate circuit of the 500-watt uhf amplifier. Air fed into the screened intake, lower edge of the picture, flows through the enclosed chassis below, up through the tube socket and out through the hole at the end of the plate line.

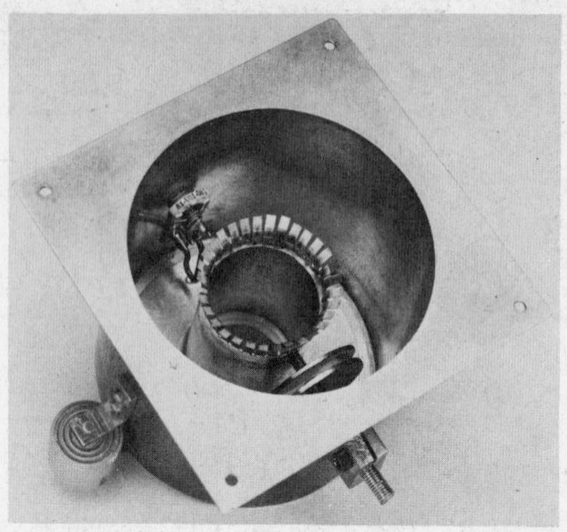

Fig. 7-47 – Interior of the plate circuit assembly, showing the center conductor with its ring of finger stock, the output-coupling loop, left, and the disk-type tuning capacitor, right.

The amplifier plate circuit is built in a 3 3/4-inch section of 4-inch copper tubing. This is mounted on a 5-inch square brass base plate. The top is a copper disk with a 1 3/8-inch air hole at the center. Inside the cover is a teflon-insulated capacitor plate, soldered to the inner conductor of the plate circuit, L3 in Fig. 7-48. The latter is 1 1/2-inch copper tubing, 2 3/16 inch long. A ring of finger stock extends 5/8 inch below the end of L3, for making contact to the 7203/4CX250B anode. Eimac CF-300 Finger Stock, 31/32 inch wide, is used.

The line is tuned by means of a brass-disk capacitor, C3, details of which are shown in Fig. 7-50. The method of keeping tension on the lead-screw may be of interest, since this is often a problem with this type of tuning device. Two methods have been used by the builders. The amplifier shown has a piece of brass 1/2 inch square and 3/4 inch long fastened to the outer wall. The screw passes through this, and the lower part of the block is slotted, up to the 1/4-inch hole. A tension screw threaded into the block makes it possible to pull the sides together slightly, as required. The other tension system is shown in Fig. 7-50. Here a springy piece of metal is threaded onto the lead-screw, and then put under tension slightly by screws at either end.

The capacitor plate, C5, at the top of the line is insulated from the cover with teflon sheet, the thickness of which is determined by the type of operation intended. If the amplifier is to be plate-modulated this sheet should be 1/32 inch. For cw or fm 0.01 inch is satisfactory. Four ceramic buttons insulate the screws that hold the capacitor together. Dimensions are not given for the holes required, as they will depend on the insulators available.

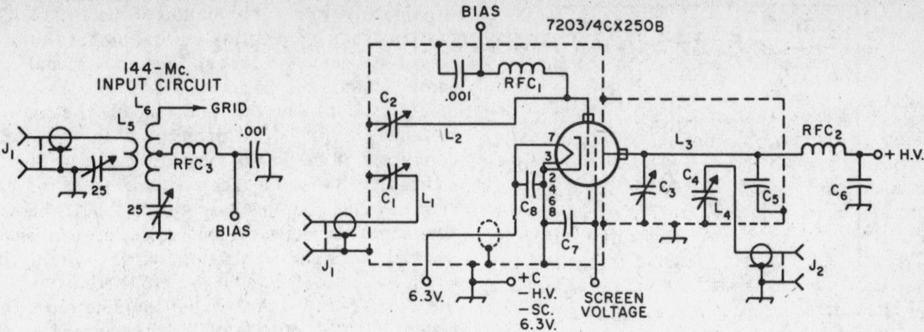

Fig. 7-48 – Schematic diagram of the 432-MHz amplifier, as set up for straight-through operation. An alternate 144-MHz input circuit for tripling is shown at the left.

C1, C2, C4 – 9-pF miniature trimmer (Johnson 160-104 or 9M11).
C3 – Disk-type tuning capacitor, 1 1/2-inch dia brass.
C5 – Teflon-insulated high-voltage bypass. See text.
C6 – 500-pF 20-kV TV-type capacitor.
C7, C8 – Built into socket.
J1, J2 – Coaxial fitting.
L1 – No. 12 wire loop, 6 inches overall. See Fig. 7-49-7-50.
L2 – 1/16-inch brass, 1 1/4 by 3 7/8 inches. See Fig. 7-49.
L3 – 1 1/2-inch copper tubing, with finger stock. See Fig. 7-50.
L4 – No. 16 wire loop, 1/4 inch wide. Top is 1/4 inch from C5.
L5 – 2 turns No. 16 enam., 1/2-inch dia, coupled to L6.
L6 – 4 turns No. 14 enam., 1/2-inch dia, 1 inch long, ct.
RFC1 – 8 turns No. 16 enam., 1/4-inch ID, 7/8 inch long.
RFC2 – 8 turns No. 20 enam., on 1-watt 1-meg-ohm resistor.
RFC3 – 1.4-μH rf choke.

Note that the high voltage is on these screws when the amplifier is in operation. It is fed into one of them through a small rf choke, RFC2, the outer end of which is supported on a TV-type 500-pF high-voltage capacitor, C6. The lower end of C6 is supported on a brass angle bracket fastened to the side of the line assembly.

Output coupling from the line is by means of a small loop of wire, L4, mounted in a vertical position near the top of the line. It is series-tuned by C4, directly below it.

Details of the 432-MHz grid circuit and its input coupling are given in Fig. 7-50. The input capacitance of these tubes is high, so a half-wave line must be used. Even with this type of grid circuit, the inductance must be very low to tune to 432 MHz. Note that L1 is less than 4 inches long, despite its 1 1/4-inch width.

Operation

Because of the high-efficiency coaxial plate circuit, the amplifier operates almost as it would on lower frequencies. The manufacturer's ratings may be followed, using the maximum figures if desired. It is usually desirable to make provision for lowering the plate voltage in some way, however, as the difference between the maximum rating and something perhaps 25 to 50 percent lower will make only a trifling difference in results, except where contact is being maintained under marginal conditions.

About the only variation from lower-frequency practice is the need for keeping the heater voltage low. The rated voltage for these tubes is 6.0, not 6.3, and at frequencies above 300 MHz it should be reduced. At 432 MHz the voltage should be 5.5. With higher voltages the back-bombardment that the cathode is subjected to raises the overall tube temperature and shortened tube life results. The drifting of operating conditions often observed in vhf and uhf amplifiers is likely to be traceable to excessive heater voltage.

Be sure to use plenty of air flow through the socket and tube anode. In the amplifier shown, air

Fig. 7-49 – Bottom view of the amplifier, showing the strip of brass used for the grid circuit inductance, L2.

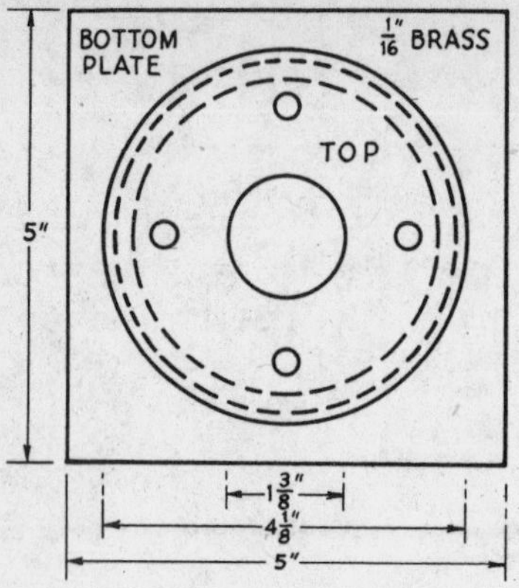

is fed into an opening in the top of the chassis. The bottom has a tight-fitting cover, so that the only air route open is through the socket and out through anode and L3.

Adjustment of the position of the output coupling loop, L4, with respect to the inner conductor of the line is fairly critical, if maximum efficiency is to be achieved. In one of the amplifiers the coupling loop, the coaxial fitting and the series capacitor were made into a single assembly on a curved plate of copper or brass. This could be removed at will, to permit adjustment of the shape and position of the coupling loop. It is fastened to the outside of the main cylinder with small brass screws, covering a rectangular hole in the cylinder cut for this purpose.

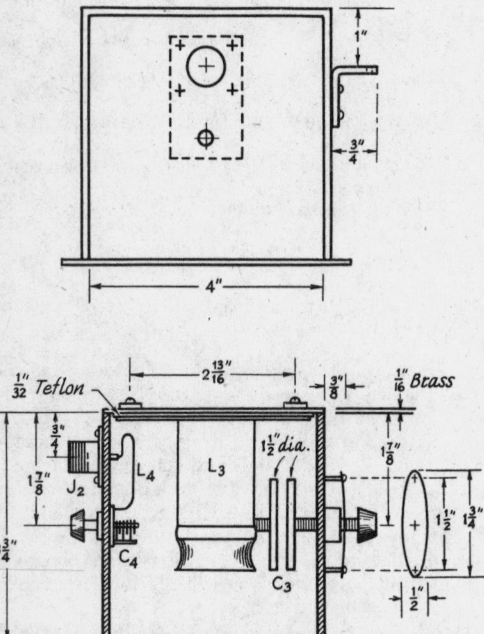

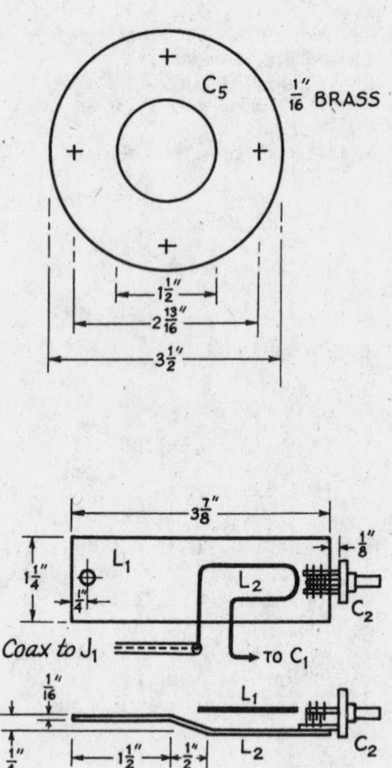

Fig. 7-50 – Principal mechanical details of the 432-MHz amplifier. The coaxial tank circuit is shown in cut-away form at the lower left, and in outline, center. The top view of the assembly and the capacitor plate for C5 are the other views. Details of the strip-line grid circuit are at the lower right.

Receiving Systems

The performance of a communications **receiver** can be measured by its ability to pick up weak signals and separate them from the noise and interference while at the same time holding them steady at the same dial settings. The difference between a good receiver and a poor one can be the difference between copying a weak signal well, or perhaps not copying it at all.

Whether the receiver is of home-made or commercial origin, its performance can range from excellent to extremely poor, and high cost or circuit complexity cannot assure proper results. Some of the simplest of receivers can provide excellent results if careful attention is given to their design and proper use. Conversely, the most expensive of receivers can provide poor results if not operated in a competent manner. Therefore, the operator's success at sorting the weak signals out of the noise and interference is dependent upon the correct use of a properly designed, correctly operated receiver.

Communications receivers are rated by their **sensitivity** (ability to pick up weak signals), their **selectivity** (the ability to distinguish between signals that are extremely close together in terms of frequency), and by their **stability**. The latter trait assures that once a stable signal is tuned in it will remain tuned without periodic retuning of the receiver controls (especially the main tuning and BFO controls).

A well-designed modern receiver must be able to receive all of the popular modes of emission if it is to be truly versatile. It should be capable of handling cw, ssb, a-m, fm, and RTTY signals.

The type of **detection** to be used will depend on the job the receiver is called upon to do. Simple receivers consisting of a single stage of detection (regenerative detector) followed by a one- or two-stage audio amplifier are often adequate for portable and emergency use over short distances. This type of receiver can be quite compact and light weight and can provide many hours of operation from a dry-battery pack if transistorized circuitry is used. Similarly, superregenerative detectors can be used in the same way, but are suitable for copying only a-m and wide-band fm signals. Superheterodyne receivers are the most popular and are capable of better performance than the foregoing types. *Heterodyne* detectors are used for ssb and cw reception in the latter. If a regenerative detector is made to oscillate and provide a steady signal, it is known as an **autodyne** detector. A **beat-frequency oscillator**, or BFO, is used to generate a steady signal in the superheterodyne receiver. This signal is applied to the detector stage to permit the reception of ssb and cw signals.

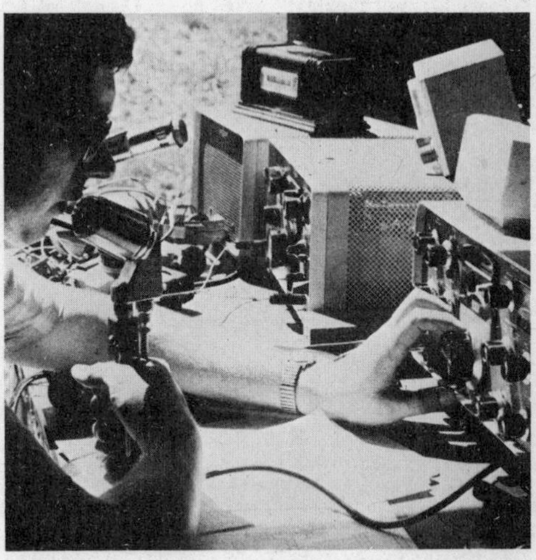

Fig. 8-1 – The success of amateur on-the-air operation is, in a large part, determined by a receiver. A good receiver, mated with a good pair of ears, is an unbeatable combination.

Communications receivers should have a slow tuning rate and a smooth-operating tuning-dial mechanism if any reasonable degree of selectivity is used. Without these features cw and ssb signals are extremely hard to tune in. In fact, one might easily tune past a weak signal without knowing it was there if a fast tuning rate were used.

RECEIVER CHARACTERISTICS

Sensitivity

In commercial circles "sensitivity" is defined as the signal at the input of the receiver required to give a signal-plus-noise output some stated ratio (generally 10 dB) above the noise output of the receiver. This is a useful sensitivity measure for the amateur, since it indicates how well a weak signal will be heard. However, it is not an absolute method, because the bandwidth of the receiver plays a large part in the result.

The random motion of the molecules in the antenna and receiver circuits generates small

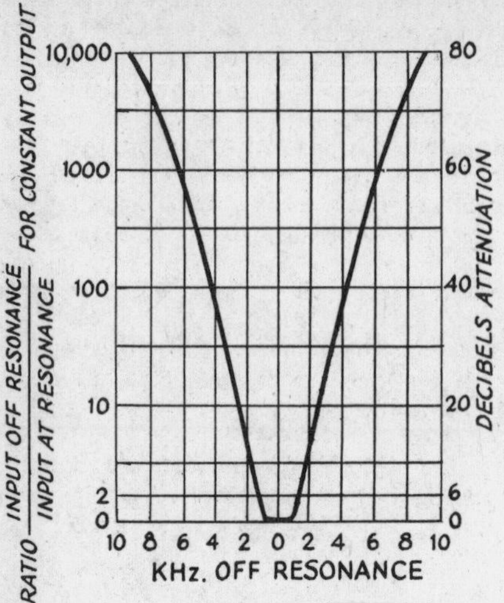

Fig. 8-2 – Typical selectivity curve of a modern superheterodyne receiver. Relative response is plotted against deviations above and below the resonance frequency. The scale at the left is in terms of voltage ratios, the corresponding decibel steps are shown at the right.

voltages called **thermal-agitation noise.** Thermal-agitation noise is independent of frequency and is proportional to the (absolute) temperature, the resistive component of the impedance across which the thermal agitation is produced, and the bandwidth. Noise is generated in vacuum tubes and semiconductors by random irregularities in the current flow within them; it is convenient to express this **shot-effect noise** as an equivalent resistance in the grid circuit of a noise-free tube. This **equivalent noise resistance** is the resistance (at room temperature) that placed in the grid circuit of a noise-free tube will produce plate-circuit noise equal to that of the actual tube. The equivalent noise resistance of a vacuum tube increases with frequency.

An ideal receiver would generate no noise in its tubes or semiconductors and circuits, and the minimum detectable signal would be limited only by the thermal noise in the antenna. In a practical receiver, the limit is determined by how well the amplified antenna noise overrides the other noise of the input stage. (It is assumed that the first stage of any good receiver will be the determining factor; the noise contributions of subsequent stages should be insignificant by comparison.) At frequencies below 20 or 30 MHz the site noise (atmospheric and man-made noise) is generally the limiting factor.

The degree to which a practical receiver approaches the quiet ideal receiver of the same bandwidth is given by the **noise figure** of the receiver. Noise figure is defined as the ratio of the signal to noise power ratio of the ideal receiver to the signal-to-noise power ratio of the actual receiver output. Since the noise figure is a ratio, it is usually given in decibels; it runs around 5 to 10 dB for a good communications receiver below 30 MHz. Although noise figures of 2 to 4 dB can be obtained, they are of little or no use below 30 MHz except in extremely quiet locations or when a very small antenna is used. The noise figure of a receiver is not modified by changes in bandwidth.

Selectivity

Selectivity is the ability of a receiver to discriminate against signals of frequencies differing from that of the desired signal. The overall selectivity will depend upon the selectivity and the number of the individual tuned circuits.

The selectivity of a receiver is shown graphically by drawing a curve that gives the ratio of signal strength required at various frequencies off resonance to the signal strength at resonance, to give constant output. A **resonance curve** of this type is shown in Fig. 8-2. The **bandwidth** is the width of the resonance curve (in Hz or kHz) of a receiver at a specified ratio; in the typical curve of Fig. 8-2 the bandwidths for response ratios of 2 and 1000 (described as "-6 dB" and "-60 dB") are 2.4 and 12.2 kHz respectively.

The bandwidth at 6 dB down must be sufficient to pass the signal and its sidebands if faithful reproduction of the signal is desired. However, in the crowded amateur bands, it is generally advisable to sacrifice fidelity for intelligibility. The ability to reject adjacent-channel signals depends upon the **skirt selectivity** of the receiver, which is determined by the bandwidth at high attenuation. In a receiver with excellent skirt selectivity, the ratio of the 6-dB bandwidth to the 60-dB bandwidth will be about 0.2 for code and 0.3 for phone. The minimum usable bandwidth at 6 dB down is approximately 150 Hz for code reception and approximately 2000 Hz for phone.

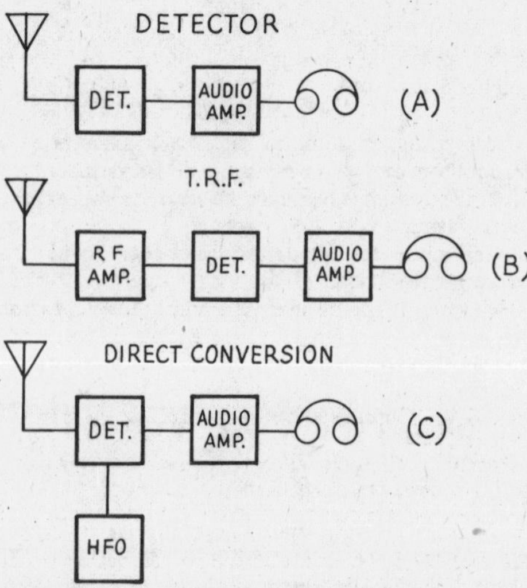

Fig. 8-3 – Block diagrams of three simple receivers.

Stability

The stability of a receiver is its ability to "stay put" on a signal under varying conditions of gain-control setting, temperature, supply-voltage changes and mechanical shock. The term "unstable" is also applied to a receiver that breaks into oscillation or a regenerative condition with some settings of its controls that are not specifically intended to control such a condition.

SIMPLE RECEIVERS

The simplest receiver design consists of a detector followed by an audio amplifier, as shown in Fig. 8-3A. Obviously, the sensitivity of the detector determines how well this receiver will work. Various schemes have been developed to increase detector sensitivity, including the regenerative and superregenerative detectors described later in this chapter. Another way to increase receiver sensitivity is to add one or more rf-amplifier stages before the detector. This approach is called the **tuned-radio-frequency**, or **TRF** receiver, Fig. 8-3B.

Another design which has become popular for use in battery-powered equipment is the **direct-conversion** receiver, Fig. 8-3C. Here, a detector is employed along with a variable-frequency oscillator which is tuned just slightly off the frequency of the incoming signal to produce a beat note. A narrow-bandwidth audio filter located between the detector and the aduio amplifier provides selectivity. However, the lack of automatic gain control limits the range over which the receiver can handle strong signals unless a manual rf-gain control is employed. FETs and ICs can be used as detectors to provide up to 90 dB of dynamic range – typically 3 μV to 100 mV of input signal.

DETECTION AND DETECTORS

Detection (demodulation) is the process of extracting the signal information from a modulated carrier wave. When dealing with an a-m signal, detection involves only the rectification of the rf signal. During fm reception, the incoming signal must be converted to an a-m signal for detection. See Chapter 14.

Detector sensitivity is the ratio of desired detector output to the input. Detector linearity is a measure of the ability of the detector to reproduce the exact form of the modulation on the incoming signal. The resistance or impedance of the detector is the resistance or impedance it presents to the circuits it is connected to. The input resistance is important in receiver design, since if it is relatively low it means that the detector will consume power, and this power must be furnished by the preceding stage. The signal-handling capability means the ability to accept signals of a specified amplitude without overloading or distortion.

Diode Detectors

The simplest detector for a-m is the diode. A germanium or silicon **crystal** is an imperfect form of diode (a small current can usually pass in the reverse direction), but the principle of detection in a semiconductor diode is similar to that in a vacuum-tube diode.

Circuits for both half-wave and full-wave diodes are given in Fig. 8-4. The simplified half-wave circuit at Fig. 8-4A includes the rf tuned circuit, L2C1, a coupling coil, L1, from which the rf energy is fed to L2C1, and the diode, CR1, with its load resistance, R1, and bypass capacitor, C2.

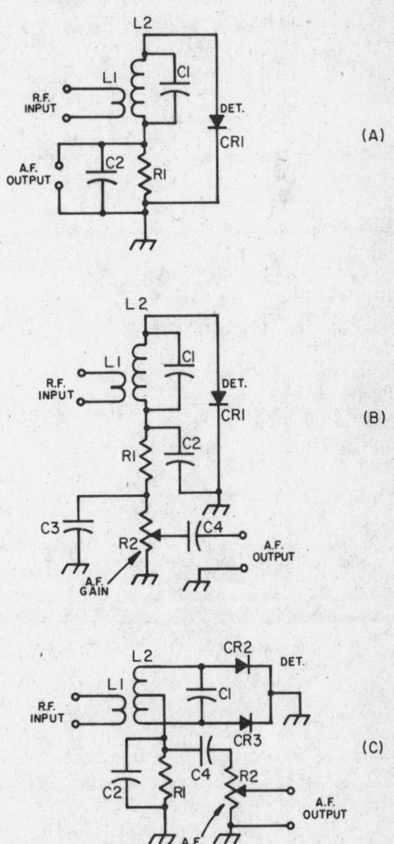

Fig. 8-4 – Simplified and practical diode detector circuits. A, the elementary half-wave diode detector; B, a practical circuit, with rf filtering and audio output coupling; C, full-wave diode detector, with output coupling indicated. The circuit, L2C1, is tuned to the signal frequency; typical values for C2 and R1 in A and C are 250 pF and 250,000 ohms, respectively; in B, C2 and C3 are 100 pF each; R1, 50,000 ohms; and R2, 250,000 ohms. C4 is 0.1 μF and R3 may be 0.5 to 1 megohm.

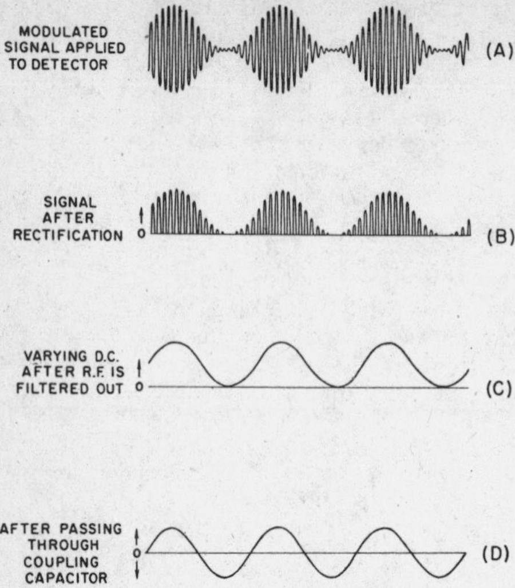

Fig. 8-5 – Diagrams showing the detection process.

The progress of the signal through the detector or rectifier is shown in Fig. 8-5. A typical modulated signal as it exists in the tuned circuit is shown at A. When this signal is applied to the rectifier, current will flow only during the part of the rf cycle when the anode is positive with respect to cathode, so that the output of the rectifier consists of half-cycles of rf. These current pulses flow in the load circuit comprised of R1 and C2, the resistance of R1 and the capacitance of C2 being so proportioned that C2 charges to the peak value of the rectified voltage on each pulse and retains enough charge between pulses so that the voltage across R1 is smoothed out, as shown in C. C2 thus acts as a filter for the radio-frequency component of the output of the rectifier, leaving a dc component that varies in the same way as the modulation on the original signal. When this varying dc voltage is applied to a following amplifier through a coupling capacitor (C4 in Fig. 8-4), only the *variations* in voltage are transferred, so that the final output signal is ac, as shown in D.

In the circuit at 8-4B, R1 and C2 have been divided for the purpose of providing a more effective filter for rf. It is important to prevent the appearance of any rf voltage in the output of the detector, because it may cause overloading of a succeeding amplifier stage. The audio-frequency variations can be transferred to another circuit through a coupling capacitor, C4. R2 is usually a "potentiometer" so that the audio volume can be adjusted to a desired level.

Coupling from the potentiometer (volume control) through a capacitor also avoids any flow of dc through the moving contact of control. The flow of dc through a high-resistance volume control often tends to make the control noisy (scratchy) after a short while.

The full-wave diode circuit at 8-4C differs in operation from the half-wave circuit only in that both halves of the rf cycle are utilized. The full-wave circuit has the advantage that rf filtering is easier than in the half-wave circuit. As a result, less attenuation of the higher audio frequencies will be obtained for any given degree of rf filtering.

The reactance of C2 must be small compared to the resistance of R1 at the radio frequency being rectified, but at audio frequencies must be relatively large compared to R1. If the capacitance of C2 is too large, response at the higher audio frequencies will be lowered.

Compared with most other detectors, the gain of the diode is low, normally running around 0.8 in audio work. Since the diode consumes power, the Q of the tuned circuit is reduced, bringing about a reduction in selectivity. The loading effect of the diode is close to one half the load resistance. The detector linearity is good, and the signal-handling capability is high.

Plate Detectors

The plate detector is arranged so that rectification of the rf signal takes place in the plate circuit of the tube or the collector of an FET. Sufficient negative bias is applied to the grid to bring the plate current nearly to the cutoff point, so that application of a signal to the grid circuit causes an increase in average plate current. The average plate current follows the changes in the signal in a fashion similar to the rectified current in a diode detector.

In general, transformer coupling from the plate circuit of a plate detector is not satisfactory, because the plate impedance of any tube is very high when the bias is near the plate-current cutoff point. The same is true of a JFET or MOSFET. Impedance coupling may be used in place of the

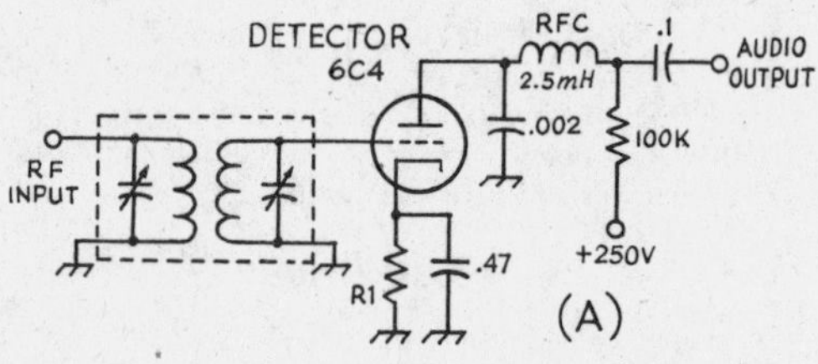

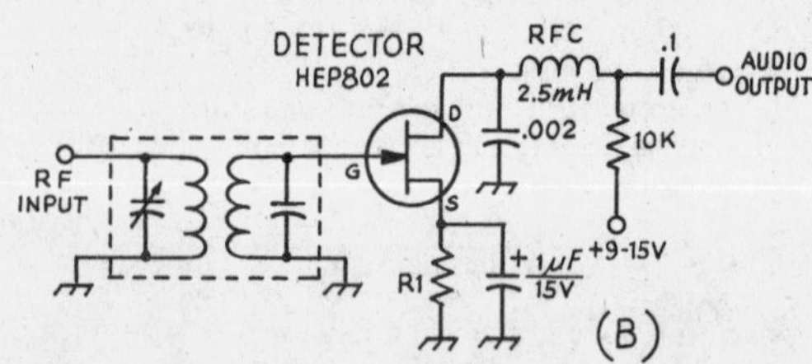

Fig. 8-6 – Circuits for plate detection. A, triode; B, FET. The input circuit, L2C1, is tuned to the signal frequency. Typical values for R1 are 22,000 to 150,000 ohms for the circuit at A, and 4700 to 22,000 ohms for B.

resistance coupling shown in Fig. 8-6. Usually 100 henrys or more of inductance are required.

The plate detector is more sensitive than the diode because there is some amplifying action in the tube or transistor. It will handle large signals, but is not so tolerant in this respect as the diode. Linearity, with the self-biased circuits shown, is good. Up to the overload point the detector takes no power from the tuned circuit, and so does not affect its Q and selectivity.

Infinite-Impedance Detector

The circuit of Fig. 8-7 combines the high signal-handling capabilities of the diode detector with low distortion and, like the plate detector, does not load the tuned circuit it connects to. The circuit resembles that of the plate detector, except that the load resistance, 27kΩ, is connected between source and ground and thus is common to both gate and drain circuits, giving negative feedback for the audio frequencies. The source resistor is bypassed for rf but not for audio, while the drain circuit is bypassed to ground for both audio and radio frequencies. An rf filter can be connected between the cathode and the output coupling capacitor to eliminate any rf that might otherwise appear in the output.

The drain current is very low at no signal, increasing with signal as in the case of the plate detector. The voltage drop across the source resistor consequently increases with signal. Because of this and the large initial drop across this resistor, the gate usually cannot be driven positive by the signal.

HETERODYNE AND PRODUCT DETECTORS

Any of the foregoing a-m detectors becomes a heterodyne detector when a local-oscillator (BFO) is added to it. The BFO signal amplitude should be 5 to 20 times greater than that of the strongest incoming cw or ssb signal if distortion is to be minimized. These heterodyne detectors are frequently used in receivers that are intended for a-m as well as cw and ssb reception. A single detector can thus be used for all three modes, and elaborate switching techniques are not required. To receive a-m it is merely necessary to disable the BFO circuit.

The name **product detector** has been given to heterodyne detectors in which special attention has been paid to minimizing distortion and intermodulation (IM) products. Product detectors have been thought of by some as a type of detector whose output signal vanishes when the BFO signal is removed. Although some product detectors function that way, such operation is not a criterion. A *product* is something that results from the combination of two or more things, hence any heterodyne detector can rightfully be regarded as a product detector. The two input signals (i-f and BFO) are fed into what is essentially a mixer stage. The difference in frequency (after filtering out and removing the i-f and BFO signals from the mixer output) is fed to the audio amplifier stages and increased to speaker or headphone level. Although product detectors are intended primarily for use with cw and ssb signals, a-m signals can be copied satisfactorily on receivers which have good i-f selectivity. The a-m signal is tuned in as though it were an ssb signal. When properly tuned, the heterodyne from the a-m carrier is not audible.

A triode product-detector circuit is given in Fig. 8-8A. The i-f signal is fed to the grid of the tube, while the BFO energy is supplied to the cathode. The two signals mix to produce audio-frequency output from the plate circuit of the tube. The BFO voltage should be about 2 V rms and the signal should not exceed 0.3 V rms for linear detection. The degree of plate filtering required will depend on the frequency of operation. The values shown in Fig. 8-8A are sufficient for 450-kHz operation. At low frequencies more elaborate filtering is needed. A similar circuit using a JFET is shown at B.

In the circuit of Fig. 8-8C, two germanium diodes are used, though a 6AL5 tube could be substituted. The high back resistance of the diodes is used as a dc return; if a 6AL5 is used the diodes must be shunted by 1-megohm resistors. The BFO signal should be at least 10 or 20 times the amplitude of the incoming signal.

At Fig. 8-8D a two-diode circuit, plus one transistor, provides both a-m and product detection. This circuit is used in the Drake SPR-4 receiver. Balanced output is required from the BFO. The a-m detector is forward biased to prevent the self-squelching effect common to single-diode detectors (caused by signals of low level not exceeding the forward voltage drop of the diode). The IC detector given in Fig. 8-8E has several advantages. First, the BFO injection only needs to be equal to the input signal, because of the additional amplification of the BFO energy which takes place within the IC. Also, output filtering is quite simple, as the double-balanced design reduces the level of i-f signal and BFO voltage appearing in the output circuit. Motorola's MC1496G has a dynamic range of 90 dB and a conversion gain of about 12 dB, making it a good choice for use in a direct-conversion receiver.

A multipurpose IC i-f amplifier/detector/agc system, the National Semiconductor LM373, is shown in Fig. 8-8F. A choice of a-m, ssb, cw, and fm detection is available, as well as a 60-dB-range agc system and i-f amplification of 70 dB. Recovered audio is typically 120 mV. L1Cl tune to the i-f frequency.

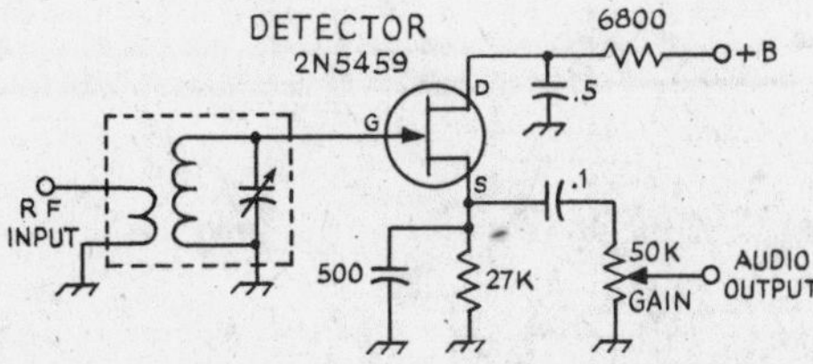

Fig. 8-7 — The infinite-impedance detector. The input circuit, L2C1, is tuned to the signal frequency.

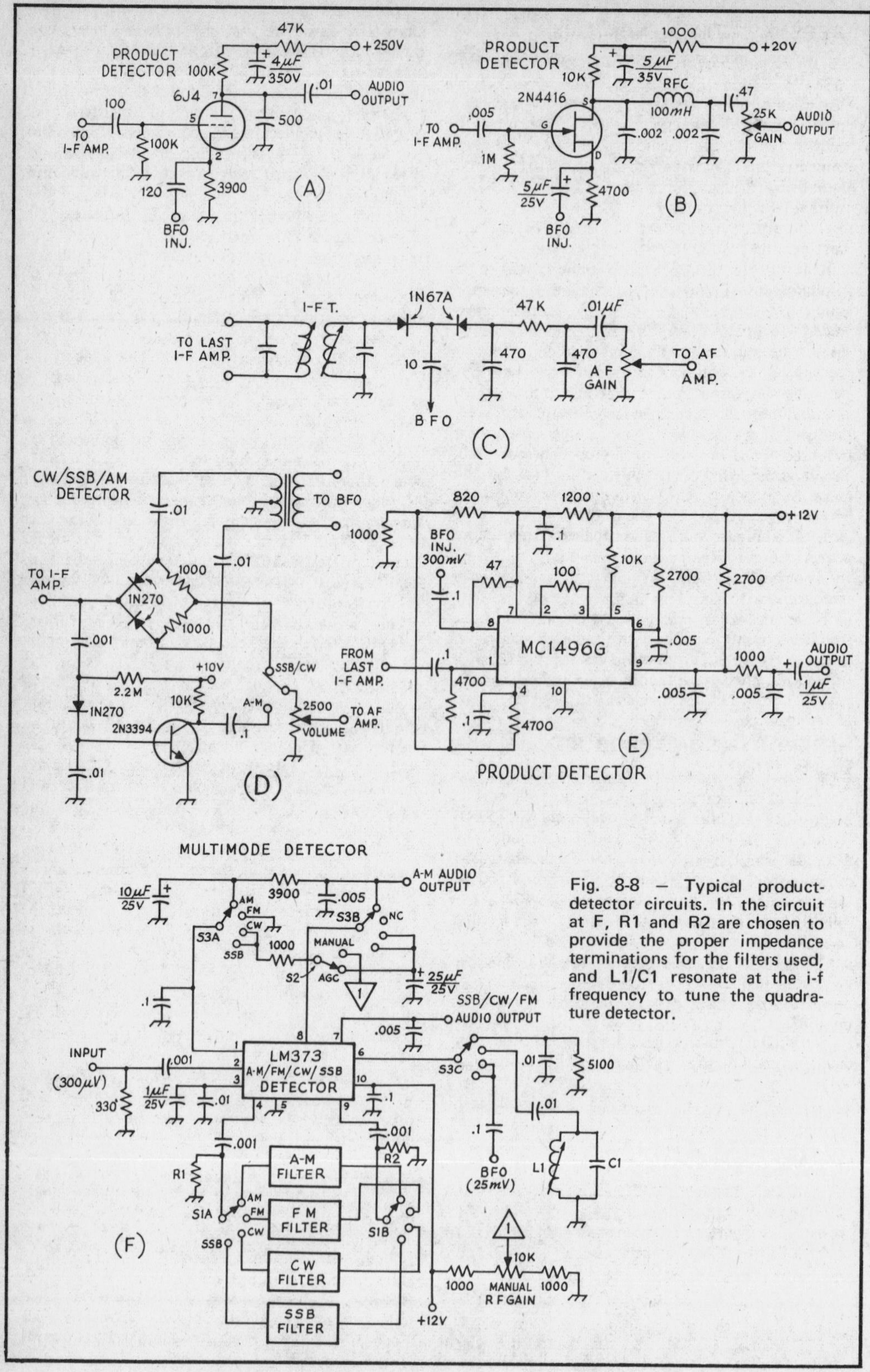

Fig. 8-8 — Typical product-detector circuits. In the circuit at F, R1 and R2 are chosen to provide the proper impedance terminations for the filters used, and L1/C1 resonate at the i-f frequency to tune the quadrature detector.

REGENERATIVE DETECTORS

By providing controllable rf feedback (regeneration) in a triode, pentode, or transistorized-detector circuit, the incoming signal can be amplified many times, thereby greatly increasing the sensitivity of the detector. Regeneration also increases the effective *Q* of the circuit and thus the selectivity. The grid-leak type of detector is most suitable for the purpose.

The grid-leak detector is a combination diode rectifier and audio-frequency amplifier. In the circuit of Fig. 8-9A, the grid corresponds to the diode plate and the rectifying action is exactly the same as in a diode. The dc voltage from rectified-current flow through the grid leak, R1, biases the grid negatively, and the audio-frequency variations in voltage across R1 are amplified through the tube as in a normal af amplifier. In the plate circuit, R2 is the plate-load resistance and C3 and RFC a filter to eliminate rf in the output circuit.

A grid-leak detector has considerably greater sensitivity than a diode. The sensitivity is further increased by using a screen-grid tube instead of a triode. The operation is equivalent to that of the triode circuit. The screen bypass capacitor should have low reactance for both radio and audio frequencies.

The circuit in Fig. 8-9B is regenerative, the feedback being obtained by feeding some signal from the drain circuit back to the gate by inductive coupling. The amount of regeneration must be controllable, because maximum regenerative amplification is secured at the critical point where the circuit is just about to oscillate. The ciritical point in turn depends upon circuit conditions, which may vary with the frequency to which the detector is tuned. An oscillating detector can be detuned slightly from an incoming cw signal to give *autodyne* reception. The circuit of Fig. 8-9B uses a control which varies the supply voltage to control regeneration. If L2 and L3 are wound end to end in the same direction, the drain connection is to the outside of the "tickler" coil, L3, when the gate connection is to the outside end of L2.

Although the regenerative detector is more sensitive than any other type, its many disadvantages commend it for use only in the simplest receivers. The linearity is rather poor, and the signal-handling capability is limited. The signal-handling capability can be improved by reducing R1 to 0.1 megohm, but the sensitivity will be decreased. The degree of antenna coupling is often critical.

A bipolar transistor is used in a regenerative detector hookup at C. The emitter is returned to dc ground through a 1000-ohm resistor and a 50,000-ohm regeneration control. The 1000-ohm resistor keeps the emitter above ground at rf to permit feedback between the emitter and collector. A 5-pF capacitor (more capacitance might be required) provides the feedback path. C1 and L2 comprise the tuned circuit, and the detected signal is taken from the collector return through T1. A transistor with medium or high beta works best in circuits of this type and should have a frequency rating which is well above the desired operating frequency. The same is true of the frequency rating of any FET used in the circuit at B.

Superregenerative detectors are somewhat more sensitive than straight regenerative detectors and can employ either tubes or transistors. An in-depth discussion of superregenerative detectors is given in Chapter 9.

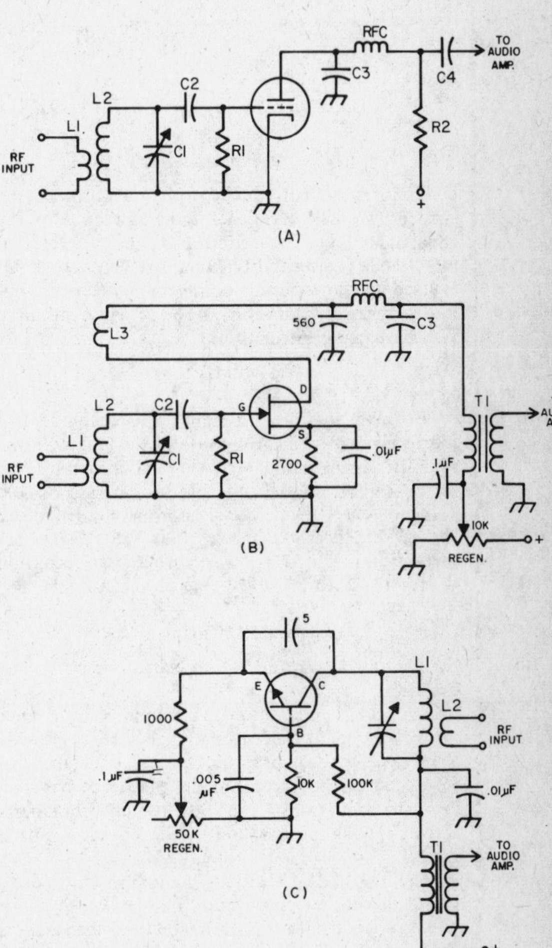

Fig. 8-9 – (A) Triode grid-leak detector combines diode detection with triode amplification. Although shown here with resistive plate load, R2, an audio choke coil or transformer could be used.

(B) Feeding some signal from the drain circuit back to the gate makes the circuit regenerative. When feedback is sufficient, the circuit will oscillate. The regeneration is adjusted by a 10,000-ohm control which varies the drain voltage.

(C) An npn bipolar transistor can be used as a regenerative detector too. Feedback occurs between collector and emitter through the 5-pF capacitor. A 50,000-ohm control in the emitter return sets the regeneration. Pnp transistors can also be used in this circuit, but the battery polarity must be reversed.

Tuning

For cw reception, the regeneration control is advanced until the detector breaks into a "hiss" which indicates that the detector is oscillating. Further advancing of the regeneration control will result in a slight decrease in the hiss.

Code signals can be tuned in and will give a tone with each signal depending on the setting of the tuning control. A low-pitched beat note cannot be obtained from a strong signal because the detector "pulls in" or "blocks."

The point just after the detector starts oscillating is the most sensitive condition for code reception. Further advancing the regeneration control makes the receiver less prone to blocking, but also less sensitive to weak signals.

If the detector is in the oscillating condition and an a-m phone signal is tuned in, a steady audible beat-note will result. While it is possible to listen to phone if the receiver can be tuned to exact zero beat, it is more satisfactory to reduce the regeneration to the point just before the receiver goes into oscillation. This is also the most sensitive operating point.

TUNING METHODS

Tuning

The resonant frequency of a circuit can be shifted by changing either the inductance or the capacitance in the circuit. Panel control of inductance (permeability-tuned oscillator, or **PTO**) is used to tune a few commercial receivers, but most receivers depend upon panel-mounted variable capacitors for tuning.

Tuning Rate

For ease in tuning a signal, it is desirable that the receiver have a tuning rate in keeping with the type of signal being received and also with the selectivity of the receiver. A tuning rate of 500 kHz per knob revolution is normally satisfactory for a broadcast receiver, but 100 kHz per revolution is almost too fast for easy ssb reception – around 25 to 50 kHz being more desirable.

Band Changing

The same coil and tuning capacitor cannot be used for, say, 3.5 to 14 MHz because of the impracticable maximum-to-minimum capcitance ratio required. It is necessary, therefore, to provide a means for changing the circuit constants for various frequency bands. As a matter of convenience the same tuning capacitor usually is retained, but new coils are inserted in the circuit for each band.

One method of changing inductances is to use a switch having an appropriate number of contacts, which connects the desired coil and disconnects the others. The unused coils are sometimes short-circuited by the switch, to avoid undesirable self-resonances.

Another method is to use coils wound on forms that can be plugged into suitable sockets. These plug-in coils are advantageous when space is at a premium, and they are also very useful when considerable experimental work is involved.

Bandspreading

The tuning range of a given coil and variable capacitor will depend upon the inductance of the coil and the change in tuning capacitance. To cover a wide frequency range and still retain a suitable tuning rate over a relatively narrow frequency range requires the use of **bandspreading. Mechanical bandspreading** utilizes some mechanical means to reduce the tuning rate; a typical example is the two-speed planetary drive to be found in some receivers. **Electrical bandspreading** is obtained by using a suitable circuit configuration. Several of these methods are shown in Fig. 8-10.

In A, a small **bandspread capacitor**, C1 (15- to 25-pF maximum), is used in parallel with capacitor C2, which is usually large enough (100 to 140 pF) to cover a 2-to-1 frequency range. The setting of C2 will determine the minimum capacitance of the circuit, and the maximum capacitance for bandspread tuning will be the maximum capacitance of C1 plus the setting of C2. The inductance of the coil can be adjusted so that the maximum-minimum ratio will give adequate bandspread. It is almost impossible, because of the nonharmonic relation of the various band limits, to get full bandspread on all bands with the same pair of capacitors. C2 is variously called the **bandsetting** or **main-tuning** capacitor. It must be reset each time the band is changed.

If the capacitance change of a tuning capacitor is known, the total fixed shunt capacitance (Fig. 8-10A) for covering a band of frequencies can be found from Fig. 8-11.

Example: What fixed shunt capacitance will allow a capacitor with a range of 5 to 30 pF to tune 3.45 to 4.05 MHz?

$$(4.05 - 3.45) \div 4.05 = 0.148$$

From Fig. 8-11, the capacitance ratio is 0.38, and hence the minimum capacitance is $(30 - 5) \div 0.38 = 66$ pF. The 5-pF minimum of the tuning capacitor, the tube capacitance and any stray capacitance must be included in the 66 pF.

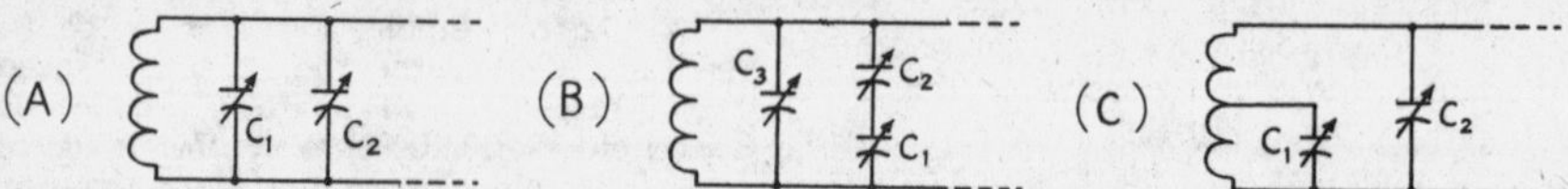

Fig. 8-10 – Essentials of the three basic bandspread tuning systems.

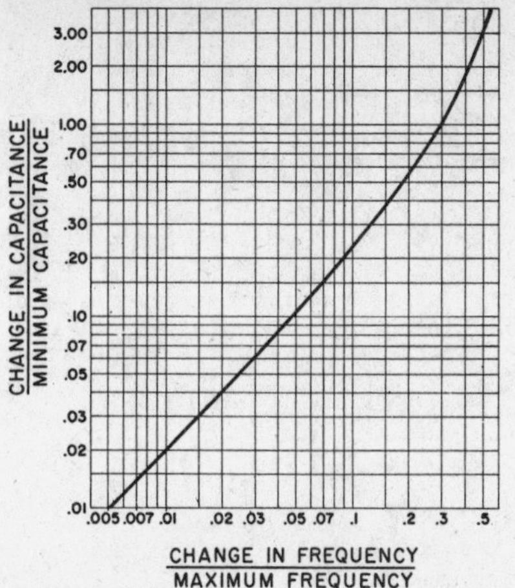

Fig. 8-11 – Minimum circuit capacitance required in the circuit of Fig. 8-10A as a function of the capacitance change and the frequency change. Note that *maximum* frequency and *minimum* capacitance are used.

The method shown at Fig. 8-10B makes use of capacitors in series. The tuning capacitor, C1, may have a maximum capacitance of 100 pF or more. The minimum capacitance is determined principally by the setting of C3, which usually has low capacitance, and the maximum capacitance by the setting of C2, which is in the order of 25 to 50 pF. This method is capable of close adjustment to practically any desired degree of bandspread. Either C2 or C3 must be adjusted for each band or separate preadjusted capacitors must be switched in.

The circuit at Fig. 8-10C also gives complete spread on each band. C1, the bandspread capacitor, may have any convenient value; 50 pF is satisfactory. C2 may be used for continuous frequency coverage ("general coverage") and as a bandsetting capacitor. The effective maximum-minimum capacitance ratio depends on C2 and the point at which C1 is tapped on the coil. The nearer the tap to the bottom of the coil, the greater the bandspread, and vice versa. For a given coil and tap, the bandspread will be greater if C2 is set at higher capacitance. C2 may be connected permanently across the individual inductor and preset, if desired. This requires a separate capacitor for each band, but eliminates the necessity for resetting C2 each time.

Ganged Tuning

The tuning capacitors of the several rf circuits may be coupled together mechanically and operated by a single control. However, this operating convenience involves more complicated construction, both electrically and mechanically. It becomes necessary to make the various circuits **track** – that is, tune to the same frequency for a given setting of the tuning control.

True tracking can be obtained only when the inductance, tuning capacitors, and circuit inductances and minimum and maximum capacitances are identical in all "ganged" stages. A small **trimmer** or **padding** capacitor may be connected across the coil, so that various minimum capacitances can be compensated. The use of the trimmer necessarily increases the minimum circuit capacitance but is a necessity for satisfactory tracking. Midget capacitors having maximum capacitances of 15 to 30 pF are commonly used.

The same methods are applied to bandspread circuits that must be tracked. The inductance can be trimmed by using a coil form with an adjustable brass (or copper) core. This core material will reduce the inductance of the coil, raising the resonant frequency of the circuit. Powdered-iron or ferrite core material can also be used, but will lower the resonant frequency of the tuned circuit because it increases the inductance of the coil. Ferrite and powdered-iron cores will raise the Q of the coil provided the core material is suitable for the frequency being used. Core material is now available for frequencies well into the vhf region.

The Superheterodyne

In a superheterodyne receiver, the frequency of the incoming signal is heterodyned to a new radio frequency, the **intermediate frequency** (abbreviated "i-f"), then amplified, and finally detected. The frequency is changed by modulating the output of a tunable oscillator (the high-frequency, or local oscillator) by the incoming signal in a **mixer** or **converter** stage to produce a side frequency equal to the intermediate frequency. The other side frequency is rejected by selective circuits. The audio-frequency signal is obtained at the detector. Code signals are made audible by heterodyne reception at the detector stage; this oscillator is called the "beat-frequency oscillator" or **BFO**. Block diagrams of typical single- and double-conversion receivers are shown in Fig. 8-12.

As a numerical example, assume that an intermediate frequency of 455 kHz is chosen and that the incoming signal is at 7000 kHz. Then the high-frequency oscillator frequency may be set to 7455 kHz in order that one side frequency (7455 minus 7000) will be at 455 kHz. The high-frequency oscillator could also be set to 6545 kHz and give the same difference frequency. To produce an audible code signal at the detector of, say, 1000 Hz, the heterodyning oscillator would be set to either 454 or 456 kHz.

The frequency-conversion process permits rf amplification at a relatively low frequency, the i-f. High selectivity and gain can be obtained at this frequency, and this selectivity and gain are constant. The separate oscillators can be designed for good stability and, since they are working at frequencies considerably removed from the signal frequencies, they are not normally "pulled" by the incoming signal.

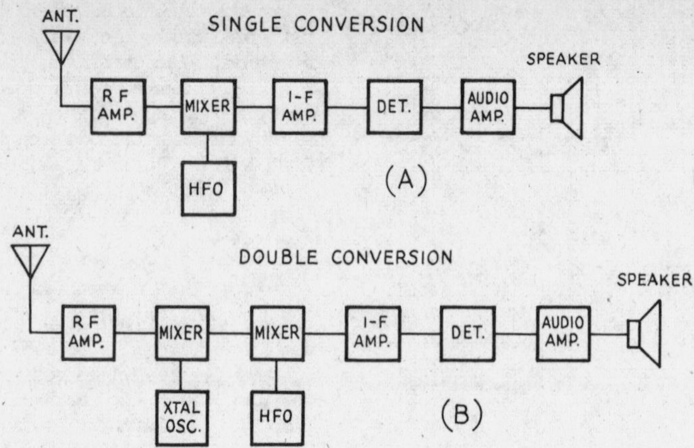

Fig. 8-12 – Block diagrams of a (A) single- and (B) double-conversion superheterodyne receiver.

Images

Each hf oscillator frequency will cause i-f response at two signal frequencies, one higher and one lower than the oscillator frequency. If the oscillator is set to 7455 kHz to tune to a 7000-kHz signal, for example, the receiver can respond also to a signal on 7910 kHz, which likewise gives a 455-kHz beat. The undesired signal is called the **image.** It can cause unnecessary interference if it isn't eliminated.

The radio-frequency circuits of the receiver (those used before the signal is heterodyned to the i-f) normally are tuned to the desired signal, so that the selectivity of the circuits reduces or eliminates the response to the image signal. The ratio of the receiver voltage output from the desired signal to that from the image is called the **signal-to-image ratio,** or **image ratio.**

The image ratio depends upon the selectivity of the rf tuned circuits preceding the mixer tube. Also, the higher the intermediate frequency, the higher the image ratio, since raising the i-f increases the frequency separation between the signal and the image and places the latter further away from the resonance peak of the signal-frequency input circuits.

The Double-Conversion Superheterodyne

At high and very-high frequencies it is difficult to secure an adequate image ratio when the intermediate frequency is of the order of 455 kHz. To reduce image response the signal frequently is converted first to a rather high (1500, 5000, or even 10,000 kHz) intermediate frequency, and then – sometimes after further amplification – converted to a lower i-f where higher adjacent-channel selectivity can be obtained. Such a receiver is called a **double-conversion superheterodyne** (Fig. 8-12B).

Other Spurious Responses

In addition to images, other signals to which the receiver is not tuned may be heard. Harmonics of the high-frequency oscillator may beat with signals far removed from the desired frequency to produce output at the intermediate frequency; such spurious responses can be reduced by adequate selectivity *before* the mixer stage, and by using sufficient shielding to prevent signal pickup by any means other than the antenna. When a strong signal is received, the harmonics generated by rectification in the detector may, by stray coupling, be introduced into the rf or mixer circuit and converted to the intermediate frequency, to go through the receiver in the same way as an ordinary signal. These "birdies" appear as a heterodyne beat on the desired signal, and are principally bothersome when the frequency of the incoming signal is not greatly different from the intermediate frequency. The cure is proper circuit isolation and shielding.

Harmonics of the beat oscillator also may be converted in similar fashion and amplified through the receiver; these responses can be reduced by shielding the beat oscillator and by careful mechanical design.

MIXER PRODUCTS

Additional spurious products are generated during the mixing process, and these products are the most troublesome of all, as it is difficult indeed to eliminate them unless the frequencies chosen for the mixing scheme are changed. The tables and chart given in Fig. 8-13 will aid in the choice of spurious-free frequency combinations, and they can be used to determine how receiver "birdies" are being generated. Only mixer products that fall close to the desired frequency are considered, as they are the ones that normally cause trouble. The horizontal axis of the chart is marked off in steps from 3 to 20, and the vertical axes from 0 to 14. These numbers can be taken to mean either kilohertz or megahertz, depending on the frequency range used. Both axes must use the same reference; one cannot be in kHz and the other in MHz.

Spurious Response Chart

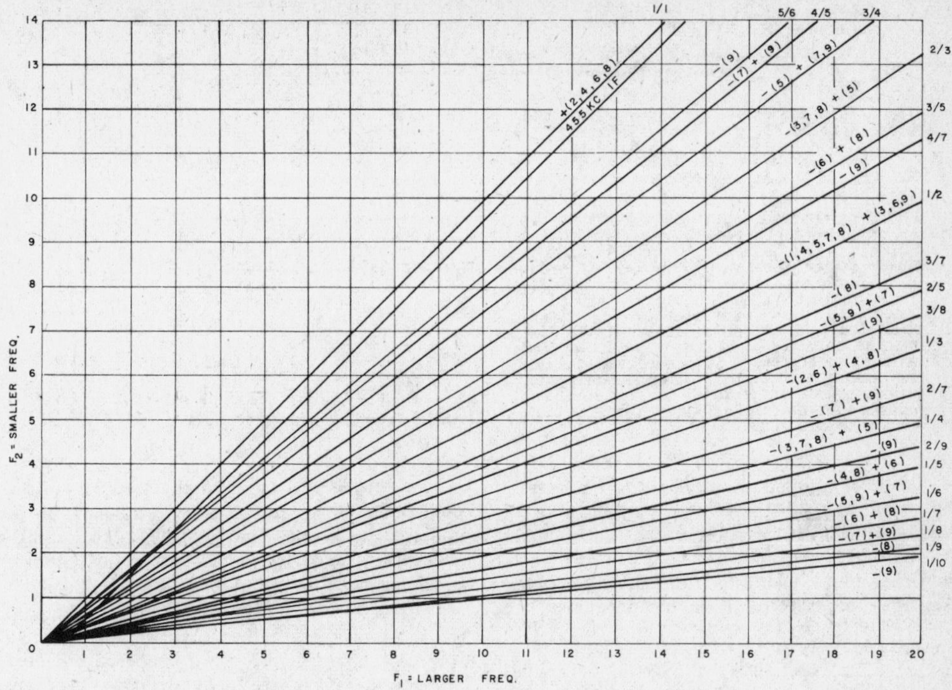

TABLE 1

$F_2 \sim F_1$

ORDER	1	2	3	4	5	6	7	8	9
1/1		•20 •02		•13 •31		•24 •42		•35 •53	
1/2	10		•12 •30	31	32	•33 •51	52	53	•54 •72
1/3		20		•22 •40		42 51		•53 •71	
1/4			30		•32 •50		52	71	
1/5				40		•42 •60		62	
1/6					50		•52 •70		72
1/7						60		•62 •80	
1/8							70		•72 •90
1/9								80	
1/10									90
2/3			21		•23 •41		43	53	

TABLE 2

$F_2 \sim F_1$

ORDER	1	2	3	4	5	6	7	8	9
2/5				41			•43 •61		63
2/7							61		•63 •81
2/9									81
3/4					32		•34 •52		54
3/5						42		•44 •62	
3/7								62	
3/8									72
4/5							43		•45 •63
4/7									63
5/6									54

• INDICATES SUM MIXING
OTHER – DIFF MIXING

Reprinted with permission of Collins Radio

Fig. 8-13 – Chart to aid in the calculation of spurious frequencies generated during the mixing process.

To demonstrate the use of the chart, suppose an amateur wanted to mix a 6- to 6.5-MHz VFO output with a 10-MHz ssb signal to obtain output in the 80-meter band (the same problem as with a receiver that tunes 3.5 to 4 MHz, using a 6- to 6.5-MHz VFO to heterodyne to a 10-MHz i-f). Thus, F1 is 10 MHz and F2 is 6 to 6.5 MHz. Examination of the chart shows the intersection of these frequencies to be near the lines marked 2/3 and 3/5. In the case of the transmitter, difference (subtractive) mixing is to be used. The order of the products that will be close to the desired mixer output frequency is given on each line in parentheses. A plus sign in front of the parentheses indicates the product order in a sum (additive) mix, and a minus sign the order of a difference mix. For this example, the chart indicates the 3rd-, 7th-, and 8th-order products in a 2/3 relationship are going to be near the 80-meter band, plus the 6th-order product of the 3/5 relationship.

The exact frequencies of these products can be found with the help of the two small tables in Fig. 8-13. The product orders from 1 to 9 are given for all the product lines on the chart. The first digit of each group in a box is the harmonic of the lower frequency, F2, and the second digit is the harmonic of the larger frequency, F1. The dot indicates sum mixing and no dot indicates products in a difference mix. In the example, the chart shows that the 2/3 relationship will yield a 3rd-order product 2F2-F1, a 7th-order product 4F2-3F1, and an 8th-order product 5F2-3F1.

(Continued on next page)

(2 X 6) – 10 = 2
(2 X 6.5) – 10 = 3 (3rd order)

(4 X 6) – (3 X 10) = -6
(4 X 6.5) – (3 X 10) = -4 (7th order)

(5 X 6) – (3 X 10) = 0
(5 X 6.5) – (3 X 10) = 2.5 (8th order)

The 3/4 relationship produces a 6th-order product 4F2-2F1.

(4 X 6) – (2 X 10) = 4
(4 X 6.5) – (2 X 10) = 6

Thus, the ranges of spurious signals near the desired output band are 2 to 3 MHz, 6 to 4 MHz, 0 to 2.5 MHz, and 4 to 6 MHz. The negative sign indicates that the 7th-order product moves in the opposite direction to the normal output frequency, as the VFO is tuned. In this example proper mixer operation and sufficient selectivity following the mixer should keep the unwanted products sufficiently down in level without the use of filters or traps. Even-order products can be reduced by employing a balanced or doubly balanced mixer circuit, such as shown in Fig. 8-16.

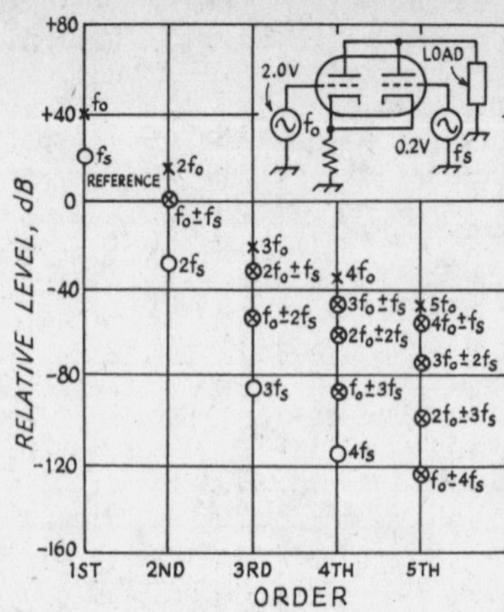

Fig. 8-14 — Chart showing the relative levels of spurious signals generated by a 12AU7A mixer.

The level of spurious products to be found in the output of a 12AU7 have been calculated by V. W. Bolie, using the assumption that the oscillator injection voltage will be 10 times (20 dB) greater than the input signal. This information is given in Fig. 8-14 for 1st- to 5th-order products. It is evident from the chart that multiples of the oscillator voltage produce the strongest of the undesired products. Thus, it follows that using a balanced-mixer design which reduces the level of oscillator signal in the output circuit will decrease the strength of the unwanted products.

MIXERS

A circuit tuned to the output frequency is placed in the plate circuit of the mixer, to offer a high impedance load for the output current that is developed. The signal- and oscillator-frequency voltages appearing in the plate circuit are rejected by the selectivity of this circuit. The output tuned circuit should have low impedance for these frequencies, a condition easily met if neither is close to the output frequency.

The **conversion efficiency** of the mixer is the ratio of output voltage from the plate circuit to rf signal voltage applied to the grid. High conversion efficiency is desirable. The device used as a mixer also should be low noise if a good signal-to-noise ratio is wanted, particularly if the mixer is the first active device in the receiver.

A change in oscillator frequency caused by tuning of the mixer grid circuit is called **pulling**. Pulling should be minimized, because the stability of the whole receiver or transmitter depends critically upon the stability of the hf oscillator. Pulling decreases with separation of the signal and hf-oscillator frequencies, being less with higher output frequencies. Another type of pulling is caused by lack of regulation in the power supply. Strong signals cause the voltage to change, which in turn shifts the oscillator frequency.

Circuits

If the mixer and high-frequency oscillator are separate tubes or transistors, the converter portion is called a "mixer." If the two are combined in one tube envelope (as is often done for reasons of economy or efficiency), the stage is called a "converter." In either case the function is the same.

Typical mixer circuits are shown in Figs. 8-15 and 8-16. The variations are chiefly in the way in which the oscillator voltage is introduced. In 8-15A, a pentode functions as a plate detector at the output frequency; the oscillator voltage is capacitance-coupled to the grid of the tube through C2. Inductive coupling may be used instead. The conversion gain and input selectivity generally are good, so long as the sum of the two voltages (signal and oscillator) impressed on the mixer grid does not exceed the grid bias. It is desirable to make the oscillator voltage as high as possible without exceeding this limitation. The oscillator power required is negligible. The circuit is a sensitive one and makes a good mixer, particularly with high-transconductance tubes like the 6CY5, 6EJ7 or 6U8A (pentode section). Triode tubes can be used as mixers in grid-injection circuits, but they are commonly used at 50 MHz and higher, where mixer noise may become a significant factor. The triode mixer has the lowest inherent noise, the pentode is next, and the multigrid converter tubes are the noisiest.

In the circuit of Fig. 8-15A the oscillator voltage could be introduced at the cathode rather than at the control grid. If this were done, C3 would have to be removed, and output from the oscillator would be coupled to the cathode of the mixer through a .001-μF capacitor. C2 would also be discarded. Generally, the same rules apply as when the tube uses grid injection.

It is difficult to avoid "pulling" in a triode or pentode mixer, and a pentagrid mixer tube provides much better isolation. A typical circuit is shown in Fig. 8-15B, and tubes like the 6BA7 or 6BE6 are commonly used. The oscillator voltage is introduced through an "injection" grid. Measurement of the rectified current flowing in R2 is used as a check for proper oscillator-voltage amplitude. Tuning of the signal-grid circuit can have little effect on the oscillator frequency because the injection grid is isolated from the signal grid by a screen grid that is at rf ground potential. The pentagrid mixer is much noisier than a triode or pentode mixer, but its isolating characteristics make it a very useful device.

Penagrid tubes like the 6BE6 or 6BA7 are somtimes used as "converters" performing the dual function of mixer and oscillator. The usual circuit resembles Fig. 8-15B except that the No. 1 grid connects to the top of a grounded parallel-tuned circuit by means of a larger grid-blocking capacitor, and the cathode (without R1 and C3) connects to a tap near the grounded end of the coil. This forms a Hartley oscillator circuit. Correct location of the cathode tap is indicated by the grid current; raising the tap increases the grid current because the strength of oscillation is increased.

The effectiveness of converter tubes of the type just described becomes less as the signal frequency is increased. Some oscillator voltage will be coupled to the signal grid through "space-charge" coupling, an effect that increases with frequency. If there is relatively little frequency difference between oscillator and signal, as for example a 14- or 28-MHz signal and an i-f of 455 kHz, this voltage can become considerable because the selectivity of the signal circuit will be unable to reject it. If the signal grid is not returned directly to ground, but instead is returned through a resistor or part of an agc system, considerable bias can be developed which will cut down the gain. For this reason, and to reduce image response, the i-f following the first converter of a receiver should be not less than 5 or 10 percent of the signal frequency.

Diodes, FETs, ICs, and bipolar transistors can be used as mixers. Examples are given in Figs. 8-15 and 8-16. A single-diode mixer is not shown here since its application is usually limited to circuits operating in the uhf region and higher. A discussion of diode mixers, plus a typical circuit, is given in Chapter 9.

Oscillator injection can be fed to the base or emitter elements of bipolar-transistor mixers, Fig. 8-15C. If emitter injection is used, the usual emitter bypass capacitor must be removed. Because the dynamic characteristics of bipolar transistors prevent them from handling high signal levels, FETs are usually preferred in mixer circuits, although they do not provide the high conversion gain available with bipolar mixers. FETs (Fig. 8-15D and E) have greater immunity to cross-modulation and overload than bipolar transistors, and offer nearly square-law performance. The circuit at D uses a junction FET, N-channel type, with oscillator injection being supplied to the source. The value of the source resistor should be adjusted to provide a bias of approximately 0.8 volts. This value offers a good compromise between conversion gain and good intermodulation-distortion characteristics. At this bias level a local-oscillator injection of approximately 1.5 volts is desirable for good conversion gain. The lower the oscillator-injection level, the lower the gain. High injection levels improve the mixers immunity to cross-modulation.

A dual-gate MOSFET is used as a mixer at E. Gate 2 is used for injecting the local-oscillator signal while gate 1 is supplied with signal voltage.

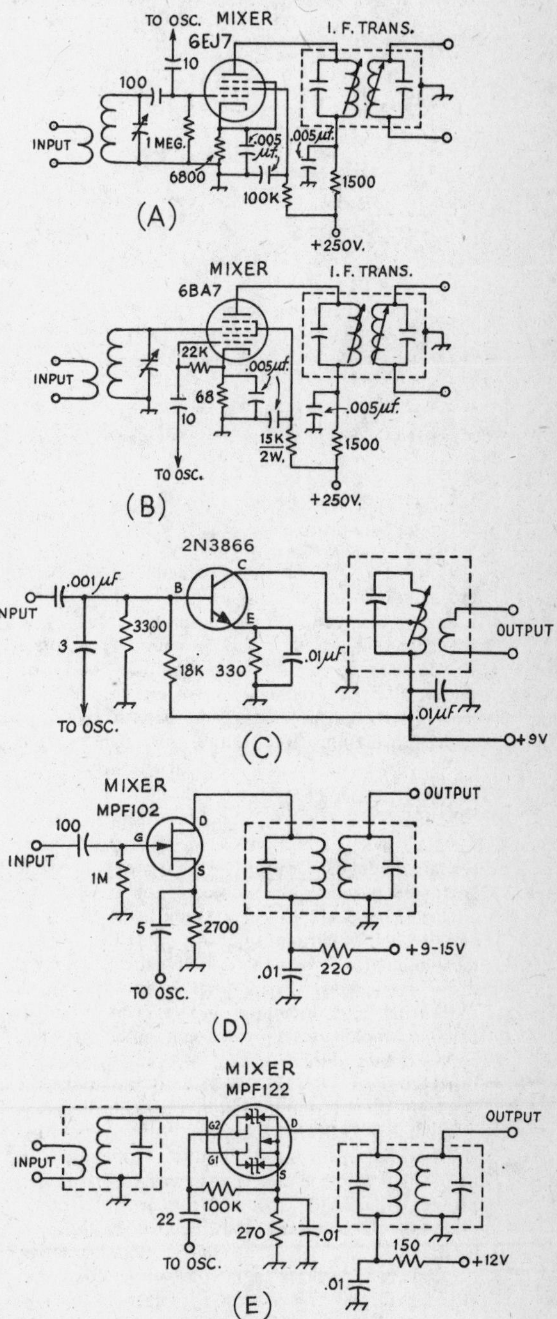

Fig. 8-15 — Typical single-ended mixer circuits.

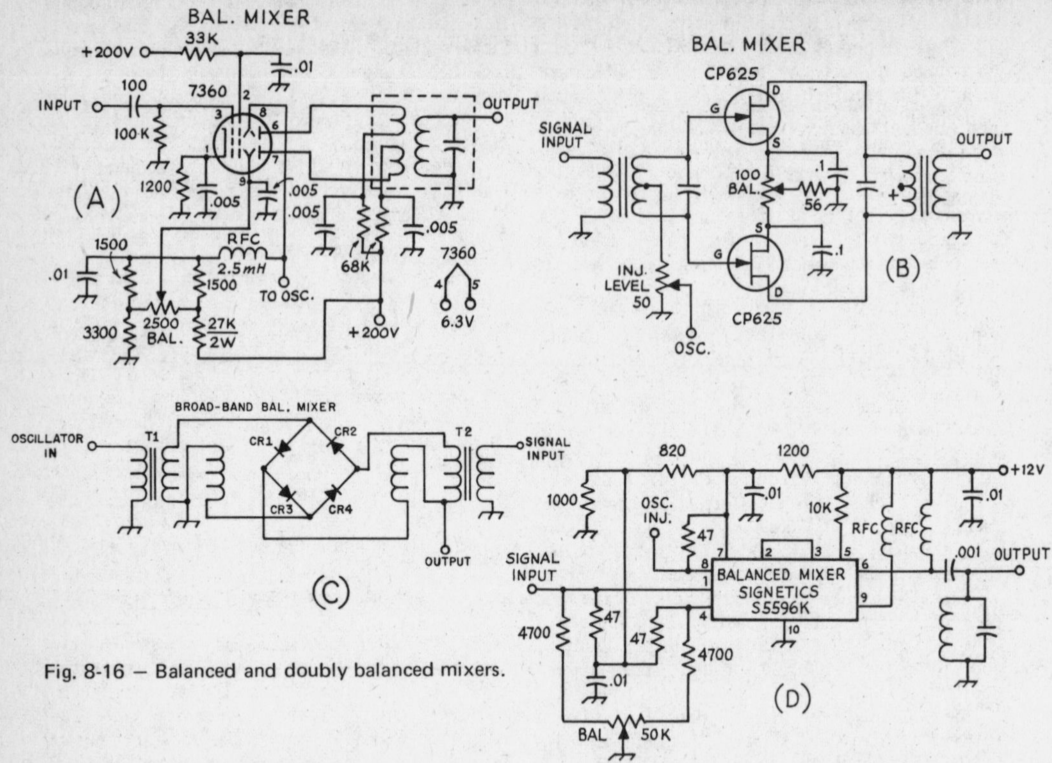

Fig. 8-16 — Balanced and doubly balanced mixers.

This type of mixer has excellent immunity to cross-modulation and overload. It offers better isolation between the oscillator and input stages than is possible with a JFET mixer. The mixers at D and E have high-Z input terminals, while the circuit at C has a relatively low-Z input impedance. The latter requires tapping the base down on the input tuned circuit for a suitable impedance match.

BALANCED MIXERS

The level of input and spurious signals contained in the output of a mixer may be decreased by using a balanced or doubly balanced circuit. The balanced mixer reduces leakthrough and even-order harmonics of one input (usually the local oscillator) while the doubly balanced designs lower the level of spurious signals caused by both the signal and oscillator inputs. One type of balanced mixer uses a 7360 beam-deflection tube, connected as shown in Fig. 8-16A. The signal is introduced at the No. 1 grid, to modulate the electron stream running from cathode to plates. The beam is deflected from one plate to the other and back again by the BFO voltage applied to one of the deflection plates. (If oscillator radiation is a problem, push-pull deflection by both deflection plates should be used.) At B, two CP625 FETs are used; these devices have a large dynamic range, about 130 dB, making them an excellent choice for either a transmitting or receiving mixer. Dc balance is set with a control in the source leads. The oscillator energy is introduced at the center tap of the input transformer.

In the circuit of Fig. 8-16C, hot-carrier diodes are employed as a broad-band balanced mixer. With careful winding of the toroid-core input and output transformers, the inherent balance of the mixer will provide 40- to 50-dB attenuation of the oscillator signal. The transformers, T1 and T2, having trifilar windings – using No. 32 enamel wire, 12 turns on a 1/2-inch core will provide operation on any frequency between 500 kHz and 100 MHz. Using Q3 cores the upper-frequency range can be extended to 300 MHz. CR1 to CR4, inc, comprise a matched quad of Hewlett-Packard HPA 5082-2805 diodes. Conversion loss in the mixer will be 6 to 8 dB.

Special doubly balanced mixer ICs are now available which can simplify circuit construction, as special balanced transformers are not required. Also, the ICs produce high conversion gain. A typical circuit using the Signetics S5596K is shown in Fig. 8-16D. The upper frequency limit of this device is approximately 130 MHz.

THE HIGH-FREQUENCY OSCILLATOR

Stability of the receiver is dependent chiefly upon the stability of the tunable hf oscillator, and particular care should be given this part of the receiver. The frequency of oscillation should be insensitive to mechanical shock and changes in voltage and loading. Thermal effects (slow change in frequency because of tube, transistor, or circuit heating) should be minimized. See Chapter 6 for sample circuits and construction details.

THE INTERMEDIATE-FREQUENCY AMPLIFIER

One major advantage of the superhet is that high gain and selectivity can be obtained by using a good i-f amplifier. This can be a one-stage affair in simple receivers, or two or three stages in the more elaborate sets.

Choice of Frequency

The selection of an intermediate frequency is a compromise between conflicting factors. The lower the i-f, the higher the selectivity and gain, but a low i-f brings the image nearer the desired signal and hence decreases the image ratio. A low i-f also increases pulling of the oscillator frequency. On the other hand, a high i-f is beneficial to both image ratio and pulling, but the gain is lowered and selectivity is harder to obtain by simple means.

An i-f of the order of 455 kHz gives good selectivity and is satisfactory from the standpoint of image ratio and oscillator pulling at frequencies up to 7 MHz. The image ratio is poor at 14 MHz when the mixer is connected to the antenna, but adequate when there is a tuned rf amplifier between antenna and mixer. At 28 MHz and on the very high frequencies, the image ratio is very poor unless several rf stages are used. Above 14 MHz, pulling is likely to be bad without very loose coupling between mixer and oscillator. Tuned-circuit shielding also helps.

With an i-f of about 1600 kHz, satisfactory image ratios can be secured on 14, 21 and 28 MHz with one rf stage of good design. For frequencies of 28 MHz and higher, a common solution is to use double conversion, choosing one high i-f for image reduction (5 and 10 MHz are frequently used) and a lower one for gain and selectivity.

In choosing an i-f it is wise to avoid frequencies on which there is considerable activity by the various radio services, since such signals may be picked up directly by the i-f wiring. Shifting the i-f or better shielding are the solutions to this interference problem.

Fidelity; Sideband Cutting

Amplitude modulation of a carrier generates sideband frequencies numerically equal to the carrier frequency plus and minus the modulation frequencies present. If the receiver is to give a faithful reproduction of modulation that contains, for instance, audio frequencies up to 5000 Hz, it must at least be capable of amplifying equally all frequencies contained in a band extending from 5000 Hz above or below the carrier frequency. In a superheterodyne, where all carrier frequencies are changed to the fixed intermediate frequency, the i-f amplification must be uniform over a band 5-kHz wide, when the carrier is set at one edge. If the carrier is set in the center, at 10-kHz band is required. The signal-frequency circuits usually do not have enough overall selectivity to affect materially the "adjacent-channel" selectivity, so that only the i-f-amplifier selectivity need be considered.

If the selectivity is too great to permit uniform amplification over the band of frequencies occupied by the modulated signal, some of the sidebands are "cut." While sideband cutting reduces fidelity, it is frequently preferable to sacrifice naturalness of reproduction in favor of communications effectiveness.

The selectivity of an i-f-amplifier, and hence the tendency to cut sidebands increases with the number of tuned circuits and also is greater the lower the intermediate frequency. From the standpoint of communication, sideband cutting is never serious with two-stage amplifiers at frequencies as low as 455 kHz. A two-stage i-f-amplifier at 85 or 100 kHz will be sharp enough to cut some of the higher frequency sidebands, if good transformers are used. However, the cutting is not at all serious, and the gain in selectivity is worthwhile in crowded amateur bands as an aid to QRM reduction.

Circuits

I-f amplifiers usually consist of one or more stages. The more stages employed, the greater the selectivity and overall gain of the system. In double-conversion receivers there is usually one stage at the first i-f, and sometimes as many as three or four stages at the second, or last, i-f. Most single-conversion receivers use no more than three stages of i-f amplification.

A typical vacuum-tube i-f stage is shown in Fig. 8-17 at A. The second or third stages would simply be duplicates of the stage shown. Remote cutoff pentodes are almost always used for i-f amplifiers, and such tubes are operated as Class-A amplifiers. For maximum selectivity, double-tuned transformers are used for interstage coupling, though single-tuned inductors and capacitive coupling can be used, but at a marked reduction in selectivity.

Agc voltage can be used to reduce the gain of the stage, or stages, by applying it to the terminal marked AGC. The agc voltage should be negative. Manual control of the gain can be effected by lifting the 100-ohm cathode resistor from ground and inserting a potentiometer between it and ground. A 10,000-ohm control can be used for this purpose. A small amount of B-plus voltage can be fed through a dropping resistor (about 56,000 ohms from a 250-volt bus) to the junction of the gain control and the 100-ohm cathode resistor to provide an increase in tube bias in turn reducing the mutual conduction of the tube for gain reduction.

An integrated-circuit i-f amplifier is shown at B. A positive-polarity agc voltage is required for this circuit to control the stage gain. If manual gain control provisions are desired, a potentiometer can be used to vary the plus voltage to the agc terminal of the IC. The control would be connected between the 9-volt bus and ground, its movable contact wired to the agc terminal of the IC.

A dual-gate MOSFET i-f amplifier is shown at B. Application of negative voltage to gate 2 of the

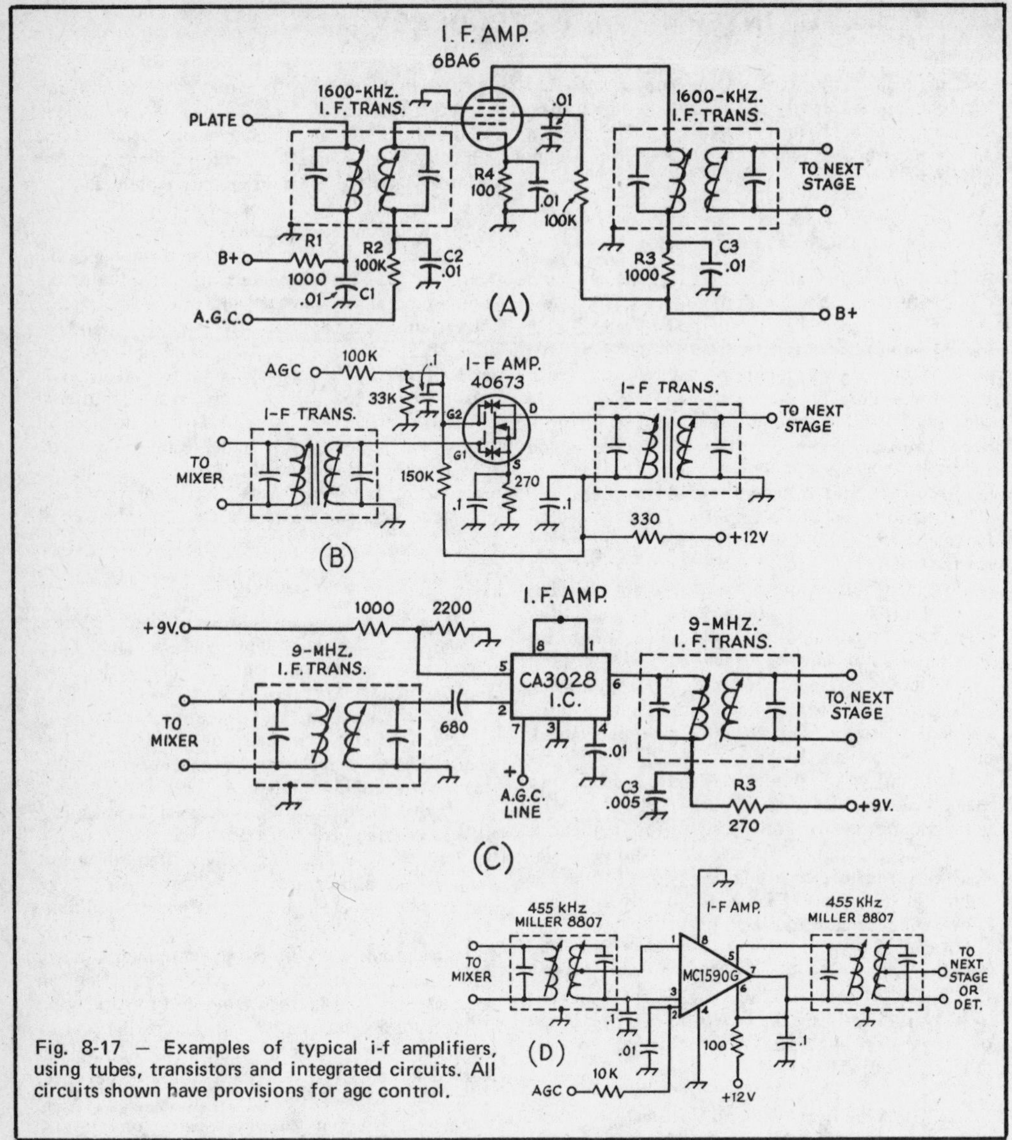

Fig. 8-17 – Examples of typical i-f amplifiers, using tubes, transistors and integrated circuits. All circuits shown have provisions for agc control.

device reduces the gain of the stage. To realize maximum gain when no agc voltage is present, it is necessary to apply approximately 3 volts of positive dc to gate 2. Neutralization is usually not required with a MOSFET in i-f amplifiers operating up to 20 MHz. Should instability occur, however, gate 1 and the drain may be tapped down on the i-f transformer windings.

High-gain linear ICs have been developed specifically for use as receiver i-f amplifiers. A typical circuit which uses the Motorola MC1590G is shown at D; 70 dB of gain may be achieved using this device. Agc characteristics of the IC are excellent. A 4-volt change at the agc terminal produces 60-dB change in the gain of the stage. Agc action starts at 5 volts, so a positive agc system with a fixed dc level must be employed.

Tubes for I-f Amplifiers

Variable-μ (remote cutoff) pentodes are almost invariably used in i-f amplifier stages, since grid-bias gain control is practically always applied to the i-f amplifier. Tubes with high plate resistance will have least effect on the selectivity of the amplifier, and those with high mutual conductance will give greatest gain. The choice of i-f tubes normally has no effect on the signal-to-noise ratio, since this is determined by the preceding mixer and rf amplifier.

The 6BA6, 6BJ6 and 6BZ6 are recommended for i-f work because they have desirable remote cutoff characteristics.

When two or more stages are used the high gain may tend to cause troublesome instability and oscillation, so that good shielding, bypassing, and careful circuit arrangement to prevent stray coupling between input and output circuits are necessary.

When vacuum tubes are used, the plate and grid leads should be well separated. When transistors are used, the base and collector circuits should be well isolated. With tubes it is advisable to mount the screen-bypass capacitor directly on the bottom of the socket, crosswise between the plate and grid pins, to provide additional shielding. As a further precaution against capacitive coupling, the grid and plate leads should be "dressed" close to the chassis.

I-f Transformers

The tuned circuits of i-f amplifiers are built up as transformer units consisting of a metal shield container in which the coils and tuning capacitors are mounted. Both air-core and powered-iron-core universal-wound coils are used, the latter having somewhat higher *Q*s and hence greater selectivity and gain. In universal windings the coil is wound in layers with each turn traversing the length of the coil, back and forth, rather than being wound perpendicular to the axis as in ordinary single-layer coils. In a straight multilayer winding, a fairly large capacitance can exist between layers. Universal winding, with its "criss-crossed" turns, tends to reduce distributed-capacitance effects.

For tuning, air-dielectric tuning capacitors are preferable to mica compression types because their capacitance is practically unaffected by changes in temperature and humidity. Iron-core transformers may be tuned by varying the inductance (permeability tuning), in which case stability comparable to that of variable air-capacitor tuning can be obtained by use of high-stability fixed mica or ceramic capacitors. Such stability is of great importance, since a circuit whose frequency "drifts" with time eventually will be tuned to a different frequency than the other circuits, thereby reducing the gain and selectivity of the amplifier.

The normal **interstage** i-f transformer is loosely coupled, to give good selectivity consistent with adequate gain. A so-called **diode transformer** is similar, but the coupling is tighter, to give sufficient transfer when working into the finite load presented by a diode detector. Using a diode transformer in place of an interstage transformer would result in loss of selectivity; using an interstage transformer to couple to the diode would result in loss of gain.

Besides the conventional i-f transformers just mentioned, special units to give desired selectivity characteristics have been used. For higher-than-ordinary adjacent-channel selectivity, **triple-tuned** transformers, with a third tuned circuit inserted between the input and output windings, have been made. The energy is transferred from the input to the output windings via this **tertiary winding**, thus adding its selectivity to the over-all selectivity of the transformer.

Selectivity

The overall selectivity of the i-f amplifier will depend on the frequency and the number of stages. The following figures are indicative of the bandwidths to be expected with good-quality circuits in amplifiers so constructed as to keep regeneration at a minimum:

Tuned Ckts.	*Freq.*	*Circuit Q*	*Bandwidth, kHz* −6 dB	−20 dB	−60 dB
4	50 kHz	60	0.5	0.95	2.16
4	455 kHz	75	3.6	6.9	16
6	1600 kHz	90	8.2	15	34

THE BEAT OSCILLATOR AND DETECTOR

The detector in a superheterodyne receiver functions the same way as do the simple detectors described earlier in this chapter (Fig. 8-4), but usually operates at a higher input level because of the amplification ahead of it. The detectors of Fig. 8-4 are satisfactory for the reception of a-m signals. When copying cw and ssb signals it becomes necessary to supply a beat-oscillator (BFO) signal to the detector stage as described in the earlier section on product detectors. Suitable circuits for variable-frequency and crystal-controlled BFOs are given in Chapter 6.

AUTOMATIC GAIN CONTROL

Automatic regulation of the gain of the receiver in inverse proportion to the signal strength is an operating convenience in phone reception, since it tends to keep the output level of the receiver constant regardless of input-signal strength. The average rectified dc voltage, developed by the received signal across a resistance in a detector circuit, is used to vary the bias on the rf and i-f amplifier stages. Since this voltage is proportional to the average amplitude of the signal, the gain is reduced as the signal strength becomes greater. The control will be more complete and the output more constant as the number of stages to which the agc bias is applied is increased. Control of at least two stages is advisable.

Carrier-Derived Circuits

A basic diode-detector/agc-rectifier circuit is given at Fig. 8-18A. Here a single germanium diode serves both as a detector and an agc rectifier, producing a negative-polarity agc voltage. Audio is taken from the return end of the i-f transformer secondary and is filtered by means of a 47,000-ohm resistor and two 470-pF capacitors.

At B, CR1 (also a germanium diode) functions as a detector while CR2 (germanium) operates as an agc rectifier. CR2 furnishes a negative agc voltage to the controlled stages of the receiver. Though solid-stage rectifiers are shown at A and B, vacuum-tube diodes can be used in these circuits. A 6AL5 tube is commonly used in circuits calling for two diodes (B), but a 1-megohm resistor should be shunted across the right-hand diode if a tube is used.

The circuit at C shows a typical hookup for agc feed to the controlled stages. S1 can be used to disable the agc when this is desired. For tube and FET circuits the value of R1 and R2 can be 100,000 ohms, and R3 can be 470,000 ohms. If bipolar transistors are used for the rf and i-f stages being controlled, R1 and R2 will usually be

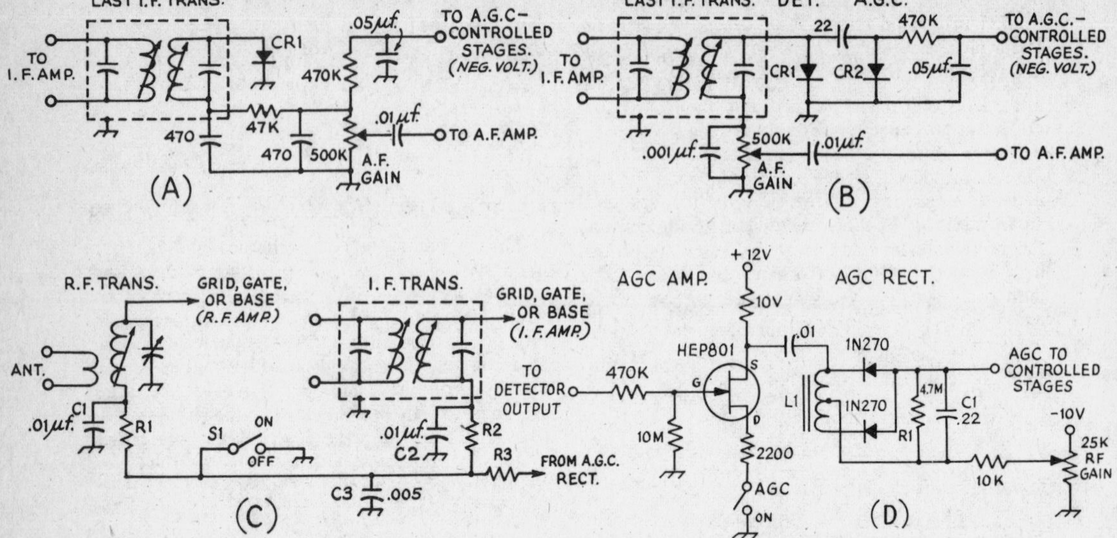

Fig. 8-18 – Methods for obtaining rectified voltage. At A the detector furnishes agc voltage. B shows separate diodes being used for the detector and agc circuits. C illustrates how negative agc voltage is fed to the rf and i-f stages of a typical receiver. D shows an audio-derived agc scheme. S1 is used to disable the agc when desired. R1, R2 and R3 in combination with C1, C2, and C3, are used for rf decoupling. Their values are dependent upon the device being used – tube or transistor. CR1 and CR2 at A and B are germanium diodes.

between 1000 and 10,000 ohms, depending upon the bias network required for the transistors used. R3 will also be determined by the bias value required in the circuit.

Agc Time Constant

The time constant of the resistor-capacitor combinations in the agc circuit is an important part of the system. It must be long enough so that the modulation on the signal is completely filtered from the dc output, leaving only an average dc component which follows the relatively slow carrier variations with fading. Audio-frequency variations in the agc voltage applied to the amplifier grids would reduce the percentage of modulation on the incoming signal. But the time constant must not be too long or the agc will be unable to follow rapid fading. The capacitance and resistance values indicated in 8-18A will give a time constant that is satisfactory for average reception.

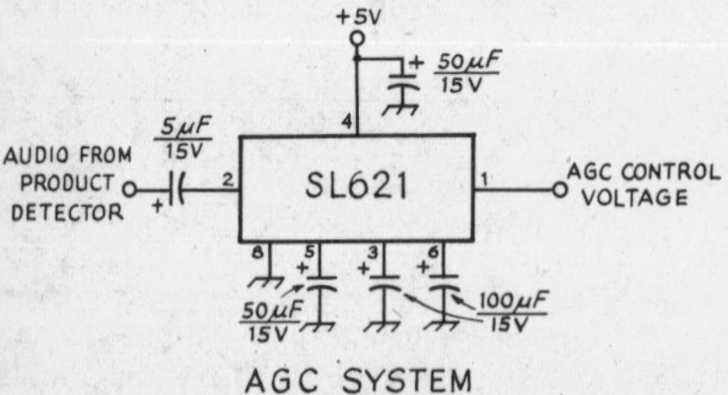

Fig. 8-19 – An IC agc system.

Cw and Ssb

Agc can be used for cw and ssb reception but the circuit is usually more complicated. The agc voltage must be derived from a rectifier that is isolated from the beat-frequency oscillator (otherwise the rectified BFO voltage will reduce the receiver gain even with no signal coming through). This is done by using a separate agc channel connected to an i-f amplifier stage ahead of the second detector (and BFO) or by rectifying the audio output of the detector. If the selectivity ahead of the agc rectifier isn't good, strong adjacent-channel signals may develop agc voltages that will reduce the receiver gain. When clear channels are available, however, cw and ssb agc will hold the receiver output constant over a wide range of signal inputs. Agc systems designed to work on these signals should have fast-attack and slow-decay characteristics to work satisfactorily, and often a selection of time constants is made available.

Audio-Derived Agc

Agc potential for use in a cw/ssb receiver may also be obtained by sampling the audio output of the detector and rectifying this signal. A typical circuit is shown in Fig. 8-18D. The JFET stage amplifies the audio signal; the output of the HEP801 is coupled to the secondary of an audio transformer, L1. The time constant of the agc line is established by R1C1. Manual gain control can be accomplished by adding a variable negative voltage to the common lead of the audio rectifier.

An improved audio-derived agc circuit is shown in Fig. 8-19, using the Plessey Microelectronics SL-621 integrated circuit. This design provides the fast-attack, slow-decay time constant required for ssb reception. High-level pulse signals that might "hang up" the agc system are sampled by the IC input circuit, activating a trigger which provides a fast-discharge path for the time-constant capacitor. Thus, noise bursts will not produce a change in the level of agc output voltage.

NOISE REDUCTION

Types of Noise

In addition to tube and circuit noise, much of the noise interference experienced in reception of high-frequency signals is caused by domestic or industrial electrical equipment and by automobile ignition systems. The interference is of two types in its effects. The first is the "hiss" type, consisting of overlapping pulses similar in nature to the receiver noise. It is largely reduced by high selectivity in the receiver, especially for code reception. The second is the "pistol-shot" or "machine-gun" type, consisting of separated impulses of high amplitude. The "hiss" type of interference usually is caused by commutator sparking in dc and series-wound ac motors, while the "shot" type results from separated spark discharges (ac power leaks, switch and key clicks, ignition sparks, and the like).

The only known approach to reducing tube and circuit noise is through the choice of low-noise front-end active components and through more overall selectivity.

Impulse Noise

Impulse noise, because of the short duration of the pulses compared with the time between them, must have high amplitude to contain much average energy. Hence, noise of this type strong enough to cause much interference generally has an instantaneous amplitude much higher than that of the signal being received. The general principle of devices intended to reduce such noise is to allow the desired signal to pass through the receiver unaffected, but to make the receiver inoperative for amplitudes greater than that of the signal. The greater the amplitude of the pulse compared with its time of duration, the more successful the noise reduction.

Another approach is to "silence" (render inoperative) the receiver during the short duration time of any individual pulse. The listener will not hear the "hole" because of its short duration, and very effective noise reduction is obtained. Such devices are called **"blankers"** rather than "limiters."

In passing through selective receiver circuits, the time duration of the impulses is increased, because of the Q of the circuits. Thus, the more selectivity ahead of the noise-reducing device, the more difficult it becomes to secure good pulse-type noise suppression. See Fig. 8-22.

Audio Limiting

A considerable degree of noise reduction in code reception can be accomplished by amplitude-limiting arrangements applied to the audio-output circuit of a receiver. Such limiters also maintain the signal output nearly constant during fading. These output-limiter systems are simple, and they are readily adaptable to most receivers without any modification of the receiver itself. However, they cannot prevent noise peaks from overloading previous stages.

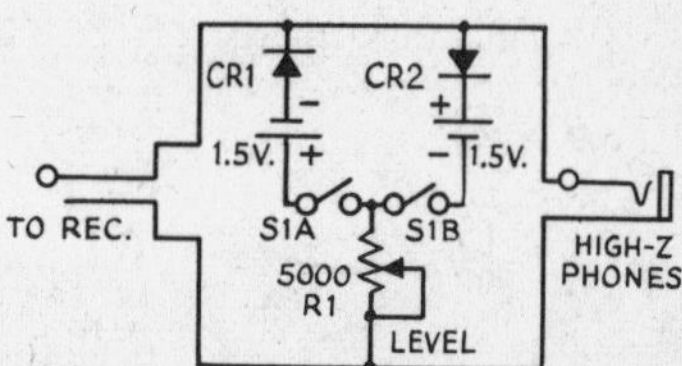

Fig. 8-20 — Circuit of a simple audio limiter/clipper. It can be plugged into the headphone jack of the receiver. R1 sets the bias on the diodes, CR1 and CR2, for the desired limiting level. S1 opens the battery leads when the circuit is not being used. The diodes can be 1N34As or similar.

NOISE-LIMITER CIRCUITS

Pulse-type noise can be eliminated to an extent which makes the reception of even the weakest of signals possible. The noise pulses can be clipped, or limited in amplitude, at either an rf or af point in the receiver circuit. Both methods are used by receiver manufacturers; both are effective.

A simple audio noise limiter is shown at Fig. 8-20. It can be plugged into the headphone jack of the receiver and a pair of headphones connected to the output of the limiter. CR1 and CR2 are wired to clip both the positive and negative peaks of the audio signal, thus removing the high spikes of pulse noise. The diodes are back-biased by 1.5-volt batteries to permit R1 to serve as a clipping-level control. This circuit also limits the amount of audio reaching the headphones. When tuning across the band, strong signals will not be ear-shattering and will appear to be the same strength as the weaker ones. S1 is open when the circuit is not in use to prevent battery drain. CR1 and CR2 can be germanium or silicon diodes, but 1N34As are generally used. This circuit is usable only with high-impedance headphones.

The usual practice in communications receivers is to use low-level limiting, Fig. 8-21. The limiting can be carried out at rf or af points in the receiver, as shown. Limiting at rf does not cause poor audio quality as is sometimes experienced when using series or shunt af limiters. The latter limits the normal af signal peaks as well as the noise pulses,

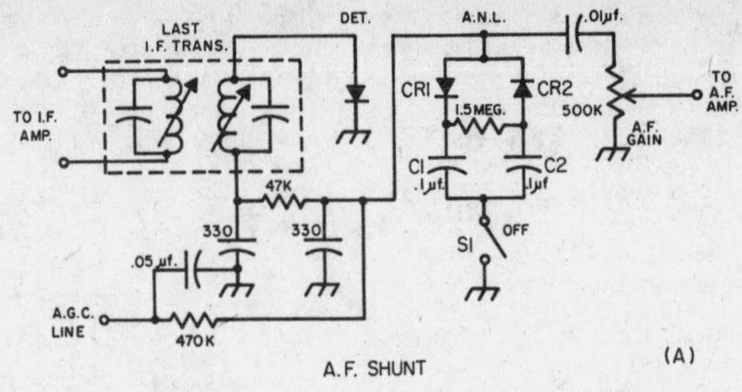

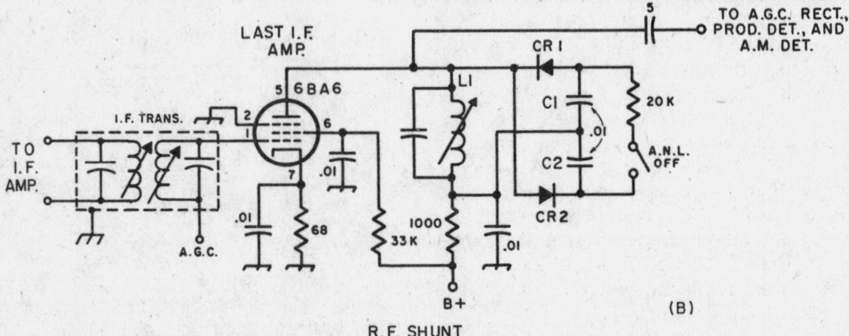

Fig. 8-21 – Typical rf and af anl circuits. A shows the circuit of a self-adjusting af noise limiter. CR1 and CR2 are self-biased silicon diodes which limit both the positive and negative audio and noise-pulse peaks. S1 turns the limiter on or off; B shows an rf limiter of the same type as A, but this circuit clips the positive and negative rf peaks and is connected to the last i-f stage. This circuit does not degrade the audio quality of the signal as does the circuit of A.

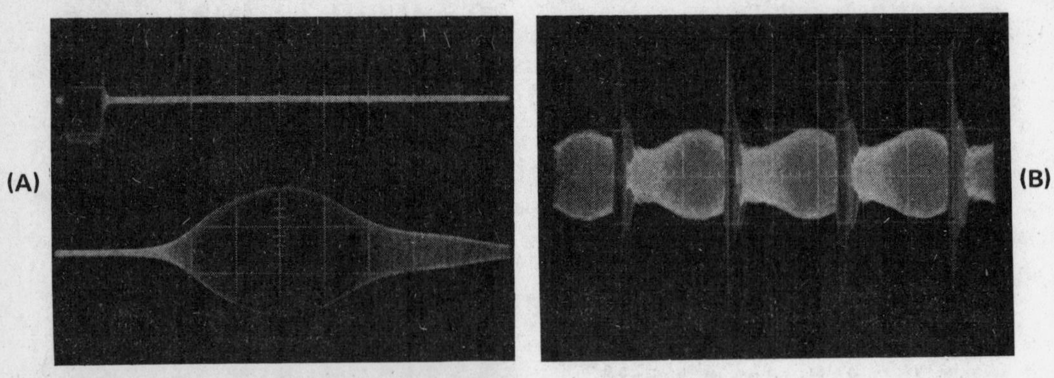

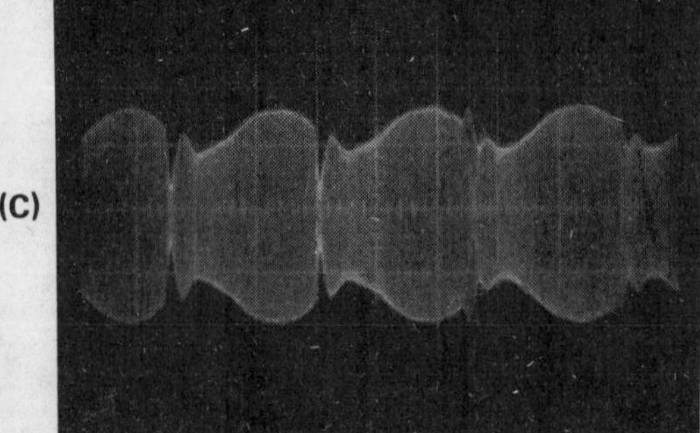

Fig. 8-22 – The delay and lengthening of a noise pulse when passed through a 2-kHz wide amplifier with good skirt selectivity (4 kHz at –60 dB). (B) a 3.75-MHz carrier modulated 30 percent, interfered with by noise pulses. The noise pulses were originally 1000 times the amplitude of the signal; they have been reduced (and lengthened) by overload in the i-f. The i-f bandwidth is 5 kHz. Sweep speed = 1 millisecond/cm. (C) Same as B but with a noise blanker on.

giving an unpleasant audio quality to strong signals.

In a series-limiting circuit, a normally conducting element (or elements) is connected in the circuit in series and operated in such a manner that it becomes nonconductive above a given signal level. In a shunt limiting circuit, a nonconducting element is connected in shunt across the circuit and operated so that it becomes conductive above a given signal level, thus short-circuiting the signal and preventing its being transmitted to the remainder of the amplifier. The usual conducting element will be a forward-biased diode, and the usual nonconducting element will be a back-biased diode. In many applications the value of bias is set manually by the operator; usually the clipping level will be set at about 1 to 10 volts.

The af shunt limiter at A, and the rf shunt limiter at B operate in the same manner. A pair of self-biased diodes are connected across the af line at A, and across an rf inductor at B. When a steady cw signal is present the diodes barely conduct, but when a noise pulse rides in on the incoming signal, it is heavily clipped because capacitors C1 and C2 tend to hold the diode bias constant for the duration of the noise pulse. For this reason the diodes conduct heavily in the presence of noise and maintain a fairly constant signal output level. Considerable clipping of cw signal peaks occurs with this type of limiter, but no apparent deterioration of the signal quality results. L1 at C is tuned to the i-f of the receiver. An i-f transformer with a conventional secondary winding could be used in place of L1, the clipper circuit being connected to the secondary winding; the plate of the 6BA6 would connect to the primary winding in the usual fashion.

I-F NOISE SILENCER

The i-f noise silencer circuit shown in Fig. 8-23 is designed to be used ahead of the high-selectivity section of the receiver. Noise pulses are amplified and rectified, and the resulting negative-going dc pulses are used to cut off an amplifier stage during the pulse. A manual "threshold" control is set by the operator to a level that only permits rectification of the noise pulses that rise above the peak amplitude of the desired signal. The clamp transistor, Q3, short circuits the positive-going pulse "overshoots." Running the 40673 controlled i-f amplifier at zero gate 2 voltage allows the direct application of agc voltage. See July 1971 *QST* for additional details.

SIGNAL-STRENGTH AND TUNING INDICATORS

It is convenient to have some means by which to obtain *relative* readings of signal strength on a communications receiver. The actual meter readings in terms of S units, or decibels above S9, are of little consequence as far as a meaningful report to a distant station is concerned. Few signal-strength meters are accurate in terms of decibels, especially across their entire indicating range. Some manufacturers once established a standard in which a certain number of microvolts were equal to S9 on the meter face. Such calibration is difficult to maintain when a number of different receiver circuits are to be used. At best, a meter can be calibrated for one receiver – the one in which it will be used. Therefore, most S meters are good only as relative indicating instruments for comparing the strength of signals at a given time, on a given amateur band. They are also useful for "on-the-nose-tuning" adjustments with selective receivers. If available, a signal generator with an accurate output attenuator can be used to calibrate an S meter in terms of microvolts, but a different calibration chart will probably be required for each band because of probable differences in receiver sensitivity from band to band. It is helpful to establish a 50-μV reading at midscale on the meter so that the very strong signals will crowd the high end of the meter scale. The weaker signals will then be spread over the lower half of the scale and will not be compressed at the low end. Midscale on the meter can be called S9. If S units are desired across the scale, below S9, a marker can be established at every 6 dB point.

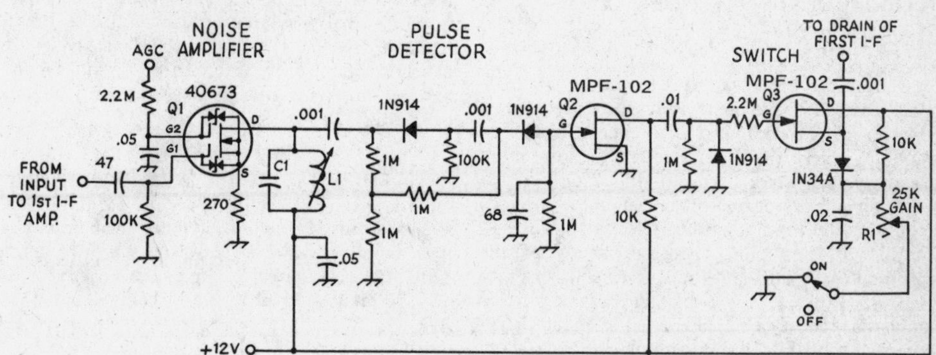

Fig. 8-23 – Diagram of the noise blanker. L1 and C1 are chosen to resonate at the desired i-f.

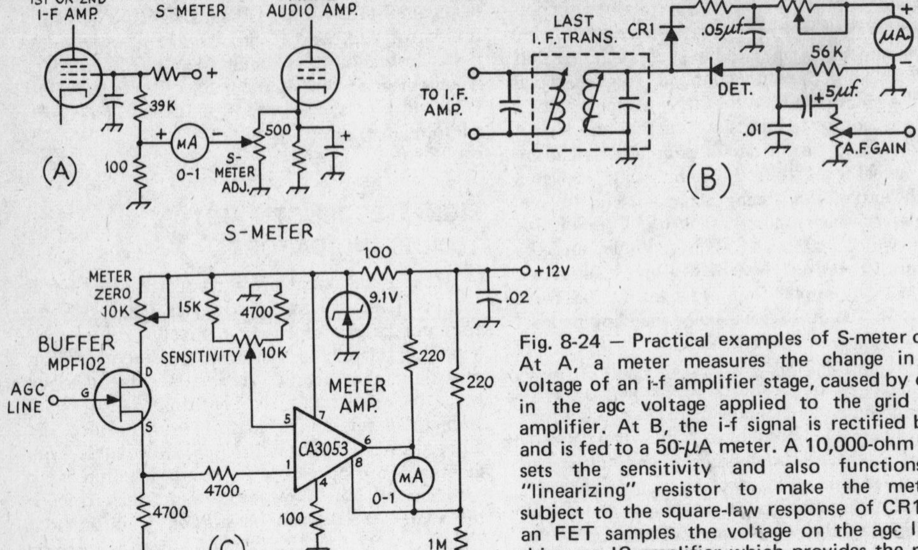

Fig. 8-24 – Practical examples of S-meter circuits. At A, a meter measures the change in screen voltage of an i-f amplifier stage, caused by changes in the agc voltage applied to the grid of the amplifier. At B, the i-f signal is rectified by CR1 and is fed to a 50-µA meter. A 10,000-ohm control sets the sensitivity and also functions as a "linearizing" resistor to make the meter less subject to the square-law response of CR1. At C, an FET samples the voltage on the agc line and drives an IC amplifier which provides the required current swing to operate a 1-mA meter.

S-METER CIRCUITS

A very simple meter indicator is shown at Fig. 8-24B. Rectified i-f is obtained by connecting CR1 to the take-off point for the detector. The dc is filtered by means of a 560-ohm resistor and a .05-µF capacitor. A 10,000-ohm control sets the meter at zero reading in the absence of a signal and also serves as a "linearizing" resistor to help compensate for the nonlinear output from CR1. The meter is a 50-µA unit, therefore consuming but a small amount of current from the output of the i-f.

Another simple approach is to meter the change in screen voltage of an i-f amplifier stage. The swing in screen potential is caused by changes in the agc voltage applied to the stage. A reference voltage is obtained from the cathode of the audio-output stage. A 1-mA meter is suitable for the circuit shown in Fig. 8-24A. At C, a more complex design is employed which can operate directly from the agc line of a transistorized receiver. The sensitivity of the metering circuit is adjusted by changing the gain of the IC meter amplifier. An FET buffer is employed to insure that loading of the agc line will be negligible.

IMPROVING RECEIVER SELECTIVITY

INTERMEDIATE-FREQUENCY AMPLIFIERS

One of the big advantages of the superheterodyne receiver is the improved selectivity that is possible. This selectivity is obtained in the i-f amplifier, where the lower frequency allows more selectivity per stage than at the higher signal frequency. For normal a-m (double-sideband) reception, the limit to useful selectivity in the i-f amplifier is the point where too many of the high-frequency sidebands are lost. The limit to selectivity for a single-sideband signal, or a double-sideband a-m signal treated as an ssb signal, is about 2000 Hz, but reception is much more normal if the bandwidth is opened up to 2300 or 2500 Hz. The correct bandwidth for fm or pm reception is determined by the deviation of the received signal; sideband cutting of these signals results in distortion. The limit to useful selectivity in code work is around 150 or 200 Hz for hand-key speeds, but this much selectivity requires excellent stability in both transmitter and receiver, and a slow receiver tuning rate for ease of operation.

Single-Signal Effect

In heterodyne cw (or ssb) reception with a superheterodyne receiver, the beat oscillator is set to give a suitable audio-frequency beat note when the incoming signal is converted to the intermediate frequency. For example, the beat oscillator may be set to 454 kHz (the i-f being 455 kHz) to give a 1000-Hz beat note. Now, if an interfering signal appears at 453 kHz or if the receiver is tuned to heterodyne the incoming signal to 453 kHz, it will also be heterodyned by the beat oscillator to produce a 1000-Hz beat. Hence every signal can be tuned in at two places that will give a 1000-Hz beat (or any other low audio frequency). The **audio-frequency image** effect can be reduced if the i-f selectivity is such that the incoming signal, when heterodyned to 453 kHz, is attenuated to a very low level.

When this is done, tuning through a given signal will show a strong response at the desired beat note on one side of zero beat only, instead of the two beat notes on either side of zero beat characteristic of less-selective reception, hence the name: **single-signal reception.**

The necessary selectivity is not obtained with nonregenerative amplifiers using ordinary tuned circuits unless a low i-f, or a large number of circuits, is used.

Regeneration

Regeneration can be used to give a single-signal effect, particularly when the i-f is 455 kHz or lower. The resonance curve of an i-f stage at critical regeneration (just below the oscillating point) is extremely sharp, a bandwidth of 1 kHz at 10 times down and 5 kHz at 100 times down being obtainable in one stage. The audio-frequency image of a given signal thus can be reduced by a factor of nearly 100 for a 1000-Hz beat note (image 2000 Hz from resonance).

Regeneration is easily introduced into an i-f amplifier by providing a small amount of capacity coupling between grid and plate. Bringing a short length of wire, connected to the grid, into the vicinity of the plate lead usually will suffice. The feedback may be controlled by a cathode-resistor gain control. When the i-f is regenerative, it is preferable to operate the tube at reduced gain (high bias) and depend on regeneration to bring up the signal strength. This prevents overloading and increases selectivity.

The higher selectivity with regeneration reduces the over-all response to noise generated in the earlier stages of the receiver, just as does high selectivity produced by other means, and therefore improves the signal-to-noise ratio. However, the regenerative gain varies with signal strength, being less on strong signals.

Crystal Filters; Phasing

A simple means for obtaining high selectivity is by the use of a piezoelectric quartz crystal as a selective filter in the i-f amplifier. Compared to a good tuned circuit, the *Q* of such a crystal is extremely high. The crystal is ground resonant at the i-f and used as a selective coupler between i-f stages. For single-signal reception, the audio-frequency image can be reduced by 50 dB or more. Besides practically eliminating the af image, the high selectivity of the crystal filter provides good discrimination against adjacent signals and also reduces the broadband noise.

BAND-PASS FILTERS

A single high-*Q* circuit (e.g., a quartz crystal or regenerative stage) will give adequate single-signal cw reception under most circumstances. For phone reception, however, either single-sideband or a-m, a **band-pass** characteristic is more desirable. A band-pass filter is one that passes without unusual attenuation a desired *band* of frequencies and rejects signals outside this band. A good band-pass filter for single-sideband reception might have a bandwidth of 2500 Hz at -6 dB and 4 kHz at -60 dB; a filter for a-m would require twice these bandwidths if both sidebands were to be accommodated, thus assuring suitable fidelity.

The simplest band-pass crystal filter is one using two crystals, as in Fig. 8-25A. The two crystals are separated slightly in frequency. If the frequencies are only a few hundred Hz apart the characteristic is a good one for cw reception. With crystals about 2 kHz apart, a reasonable phone characteristic is obtained. Fig. 8-2 shows a selectivity characteristic of an amplifier with a bandpass (at -6 dB) of 2.4 kHz, which is typical of what can be expected from a two-crystal bandpass filter.

More elaborate crystal filters, using four and six crystals, will give reduced bandwidth at -60 dB without decreasing the bandwidth at -6 dB. The resulting increased "skirt selectivity" gives better rejection of adjacent-channel signals. "Crystal-lattice" filters of this type are available commercially for frequencies up to 40 MHz or so, and they have also been built by amateurs from inexpensive transmitting-type crystals. (See Vester, "Surplus-Crystal High-Frequency Filters," *QST*, January, 1959; Healey, "High-Frequency Crystal Filters for SSB," *QST*, October, 1960.)

Two half-lattice filters of the type shown at Fig. 8-25A can be connected back to back as shown at B. The channel spacing of Y1 and Y2 will depend upon the receiving requirements as discussed in the foregoing text. Ordinarily, for ssb reception (and nonstringent cw reception) a frequency separation of approximately 1.5 kHz is suitable. The overall i-f strip of the receiver is tuned to a frequency which is midway between Y1 and Y2. C1 is tuned to help give the desired shape to the passband. L1 is a bifilar-wound toroidal inductor which tunes to the i-f frequency by means of C1. The values of R1 and R2 are identical and are determined by the filter response desired. Ordinarily the ohmic value is on the order of 600 ohms, but values as high as 5000 ohms are sometimes used. The lower the value of resistance, the broader and flatter will be the response of the filter. Though the circuit at B is shown in a transistorized circuit, it can be used with vacuum tubes or integrated circuits as well. The circuit shows an i-f frequency of 9 MHz, but the filter can be used at any desired frequency below 9 MHz by altering the crystal frequencies and the tuned circuits. Commercial versions of the 9-MHz lattice filter are available at moderate cost.[1] War-surplus FT-241 crystals in the 455-kHz range are inexpensive and lend themselves nicely to this type of circuit.

Mechanical filters can be built at frequencies below 1 MHz. They are made up of three sections; an input transducer, a mechanically resonant filter

[1]Spectrum International, P. O. Box 87, Topsfield, MA 01983. Also, McCoy Electronics Co., Mount Holly Springs, PA.

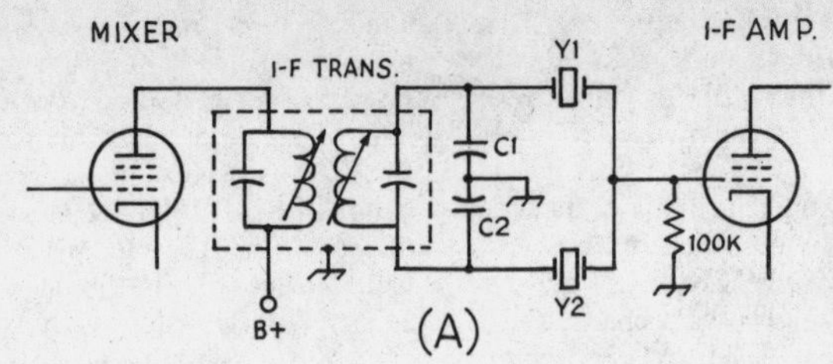

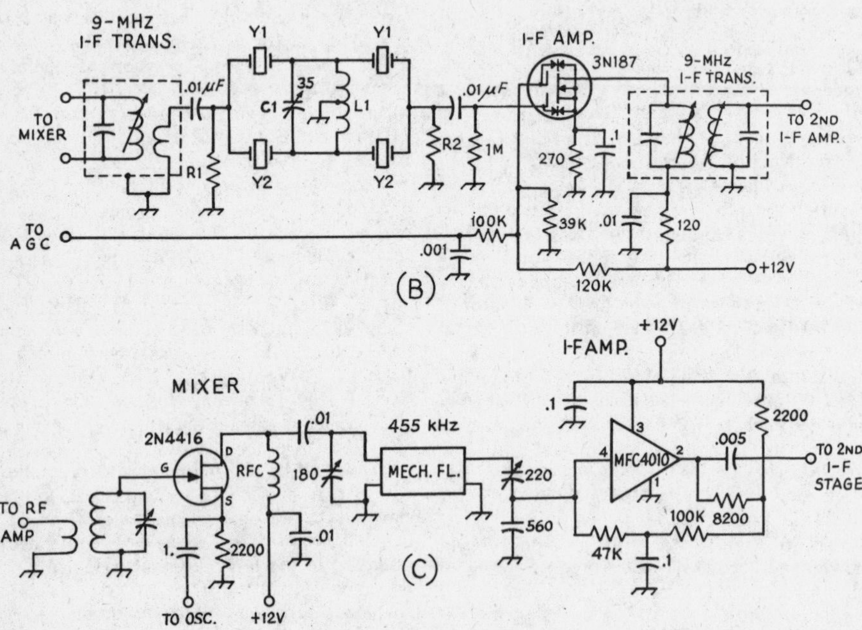

Fig. 8-25 – A half-lattice bandpass filter at A; B shows two half-lattice filters in cascade; C shows a mechanical filter.

section, and an output transducer. The transducers use the principle of magneto-striction to convert the electrical signal to mechanical energy, then back again. The mechanically resonant section consists of carefully machined metal disks supported and coupled by thin rods. Each disk has a resonant frequency dependent upon the material and its dimensions, and the effective Q of a single disk may be in excess of 2000. Consequently, a mechanical filter can be built for either narrow or broad passband with a nearly rectangular curve. Mechanical filters are available commercially and are used in both receivers and single-sideband transmitters. They are moderately priced.

The signal-handling capability of a mechanical filter is limited by the magnetic circuits to from 2 to 15 volts rms, a limitation that is of no practical importance provided it is recognized and provided for. Crystal filters are limited in their signal-handling ability only by the voltage breakdown limits, which normally would not be reached before the preceding amplifier tube was overloaded. A more serious practical consideration in the use of any high-selectivity component is the prevention of coupling "around" the filter, externally, which can only degrade the action of the filter.

The circuit at Fig. 8-25C shows a typical hookup for a mechanical filter. FL1 is a Collins 455-FB-21, which has an ssb band-pass characteristic of 2.1 kHz. It is shown in a typical solid-state receiver circuit, but can be used equally as well in a tube-type application.

Placement of the BFO signal with respect to the passbands of the three circuits at A, B, and C, is the same. Either a crystal-controlled or self-excited oscillator can be used to generate the BFO signal and the usual practice is to place the BFO signal at a frequency that falls at the two points which are approximately 20 dB down on the filter curve, dependent upon which sideband is desired. Typically, with the filter specified at C, the center frequency of FL1 is 455 kHz. To place the BFO at the 20-dB points (down from the center-frequency peak) a signal at 453 and 456 kHz is required.

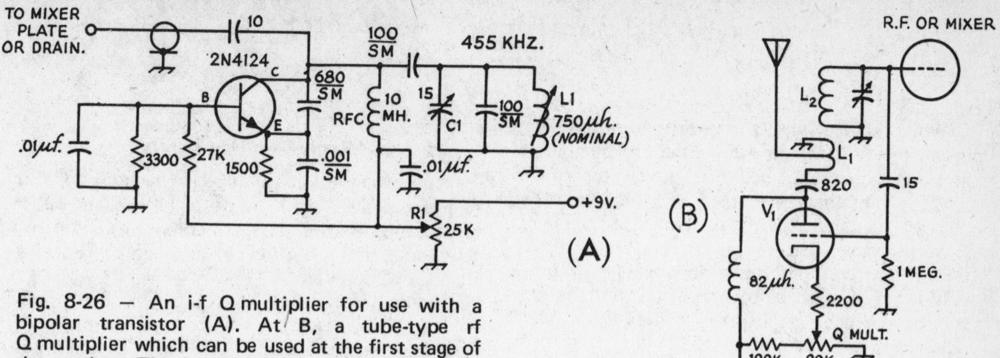

Fig. 8-26 – An i-f Q multiplier for use with a bipolar transistor (A). At B, a tube-type rf Q multiplier which can be used at the first stage of the receiver. The antenna coil is used for feedback to V1, which then introduces "negative resistance" to L2.

Q Multiplier

The "*Q* Multiplier" is a stable regenerative stage that is connected in parallel with one of the i-f stages of a receiver. In one condition it narrows the bandwidth and in the other condition it produces a sharp "null" or rejection notch. A "tuning" adjustment controls the frequency of the peak or null, moving it across the normal passband of the receiver i-f amplifier. The *shape* of the peak or null is always that of a single tuned circuit (Fig. 2-42) but the effective *Q* is adjustable over a wide range. A *Q* Multiplier is most effective at an i-f of 500 kHz or less; at higher frequencies the rejection notch becomes wide enough (measured in Hz) to reject a major portion of a phone signal. Within its useful range, however, the *Q* Multiplier will reject an interfering carrier without degrading the quality of the desired signal.

In the "peak" condition the *Q* Multiplier can be made to oscillate by advancing the "peak" (regeneration) control far enough and in this condition it can be made to serve as a beat-frequency oscillator. However, it cannot be made to serve as a selective element and as a BFO *at the same time.* Some inexpensive receivers may combine either a *Q* Multiplier or some other form of regeneration with the BFO function, and the reader is advised to check carefully any inexpensive receiver he intends to buy that offers a regenerative type of selectivity, in order to make sure that the selectivity is available when the BFO is turned on.

A representative circuit for a transistorized *Q*-multiplier is given in Fig. 8-26A. The constants given are typical for i-f operation at 455 kHz. L1 can be a J. W. Miller 9002 or 9102 slug-tuned inductor. A 25,000-ohm control, R1, permits adjustment of the regeneration. C1 is used to tune the *Q*-multiplier frequency back and forth across the i-f passband for peaking or notching adjustments. With circuits of this type there is usually a need to adjust both R1 and C1 alternately for a peaking or notching effect, because the controls tend to interlock as far as the frequency of oscillation is concerned. A *Q*-multiplier should be solidly built in a shielded enclosure to assure maximum stability.

Q multipliers can be used at the front end of a receiver also, as shown at B in Fig. 8-26. The enhancement of the *Q* at that point in a receiver greatly reduces image problems because the selectivity of the input tuned circuit is increased markedly. The antenna coil, L1, is used as a feedback winding to make V1 regenerative. This in effect adds "negative resistance" to L2, increasing its *Q*. A 20,000-ohm control sets the regeneration of V1, and should be adjusted to a point just under regeneration for best results. Rf *Q* multiplication is not a cure for a poor-quality inductor at L2, however.

T-Notch Filter

At low intermediate frequencies (50 – 100 kHz) the T-notch filter of Fig. 8-27 will provide a sharp tunable null.

The inductor *L* resonates with *C* at the rejection frequency, and when $R = QX_L/4$ the rejection is maximum. (X_L is the coil-reactance and *Q* is the coil *Q*.) In a typical 50-kHz circuit, *C* might be 3900 pF making *L* approximately 2.6 mH. When *R* is greater than the maximum-attenuation value, the circuit still provides some rejection, and in use the inductor is detuned or shorted out when the rejection is not desired.

At higher frequencies, the T-notch filter is not sharp enough with available components to reject only a narrow band of frequencies.

T-NOTCH

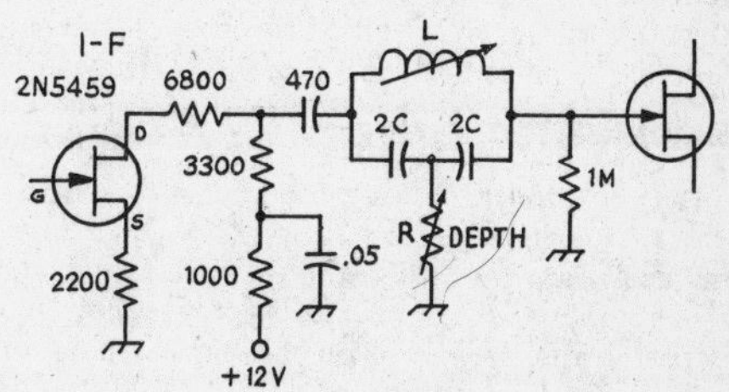

Fig. 8-27 – Typical T-notch (bridged-T) filter, to provide a sharp notch at a low i-f. Adjustment of L changes the frequency of the notch; adjustment of R controls the notch depth.

RADIO-FREQUENCY AMPLIFIERS

While selectivity to reduce audio-frequency images can be built into the i-f amplifier, discrimination against radio-frequency images can only be obtained in tuned circuits or other selective elements ahead of the first mixer or converter stage. These tuned circuits are usually used as the coupling networks for one or more vacuum tubes or transistors, and the combinations of circuits and amplifying devices are called radio-frequency amplifiers. The tuned circuits contribute to the rf-image rejection and the amplifying device(s) determines the noise figure of the receiver.

Knowing the Q of the coil in each tuned circuit between the antenna and the first mixer or converter stage, the image rejection capability can be computed by using the chart in Fig. 2-50. The Q of the input tuned circuit (coupled to the antenna) should be taken as about one-half the unloaded Q of that circuit, and the Q of any other tuned circuit can be assumed to be the unloaded Q to a first approximation (the vacuum tubes will reduce the circuit Q to some extent, especially at 14 MHz and higher).

In general, receivers with an i-f of 455 kHz can be expected to have some noticeable image response at 14 MHz and higher if there are only two tuned circuits (or one rf stage) ahead of the mixer or converter. Regeneration in the rf amplifier will reduce image response, but regeneration usually requires frequent readjustment when tuning across a band. Regeneration is, however, a useful device for improving the selectivity of an rf amplifier without requiring a multiplicity of tuned circuits.

With three tuned circuits between the antenna and the first mixer, and an i-f of 455 kHz, no images should be encountered up to perhaps 25 MHz. Four tuned circuits or more will eliminate any images at 28 MHz when an i-f of 455 kHz is used.

Obviously, a better solution to the rf selectivity problem (elimination of image response) is to use an i-f higher than 455 kHz, and most modern receivers use an i-f of 1600 kHz or higher. The owner of a receiver with a 455-kHz i-f amplifier can enjoy image-free reception on the higher frequencies by using a crystal-controlled converter ahead of the receiver and utilizing the receiver as a "tunable i-f amplifier" at 3.5 or 7.0 MHz.

For best selectivity rf amplifiers should use high-Q circuits and tubes with high input and output resistance. Variable-μ pentodes and field-effect transistors (JFET and MOSFET) are practically always used, although triodes (neutralized or otherwise connected so that they won't oscillate) are often used on the higher frequencies because they introduce less noise. However, their lower plate resistance will load the tuned circuits. Pentodes and FETs are better where maximum image rejection is desired, because they have less loading effect on the tuned circuits.

Representative Circuits

An example of a typical vacuum-tube rf amplifier using a remote-cutoff pentode and agc is given in Fig. 8-28 at A. The manual rf gain control, R1, varies the bias on the stage, thereby changing the gain of the tube.

In the circuit at B, two junction field-effect transistors are used as a cascade rf amplifier. If sufficient isolation is provided between the input and output tuned circuits, neutralization is seldom required below 30 MHz. Agc potential is applied to the gate of the second JFET. For efficient operation as an rf amplifier, the transistors chosen should have an f_T rating somewhat above the desired operating frequency.

A dual-gate MOSFET with built-in transient protection is used in the circuit at C. Negative agc voltage is applied to gate 2. Zener diodes contained within the 40673, bridged between the gates and the source/substrate connection, provide protection from transient voltages (up to 10 V pk-pk) that might otherwise damage the device. The gate-1 and drain connections are tapped down on their associated tuned circuits, a technique which produces stability without neutralization with only a slight reduction in gain.

The rf amplifier shown in Fig. 8-28D is a broad-band type which produces approximately 12 dB of gain from 0.5 to 50 MHz. Because of the high drain-to-gate capacitance of high-current FETs such as the CP651, the transistor is operated in a grounded-gate circuit to avoid the need for neutralization. A passive input circuit and 4-to-1 balun output transformer are employed. Details of the construction of balun transformers are given in Chapter 6.

FEEDBACK

Feedback giving rise to regeneration and oscillation can occur in a single stage or it may appear as an overall feedback through several stages that are on the same frequency. To avoid feedback in a single stage, the output must be isolated from the input in every way possible, with the vacuum tube or transistor furnishing the only coupling between the two circuits. An oscillation can be obtained in an rf or i-f stage if there is any undue capacitive or inductive coupling between output and input circuits, if there is too high an impedance between cathode and ground or screen and ground, or if there is any appreciable impedance through which the grid and plate currents can flow in common.

To avoid overall feedback in a multistage amplifier, attention must be paid to avoid running any part of the output circuit back near the input circuit without first filtering it carefully. Since the signal-carrying parts of the circuit can't be filtered, the best design for any multistage amplifier is a straight line, to keep the output as far away from

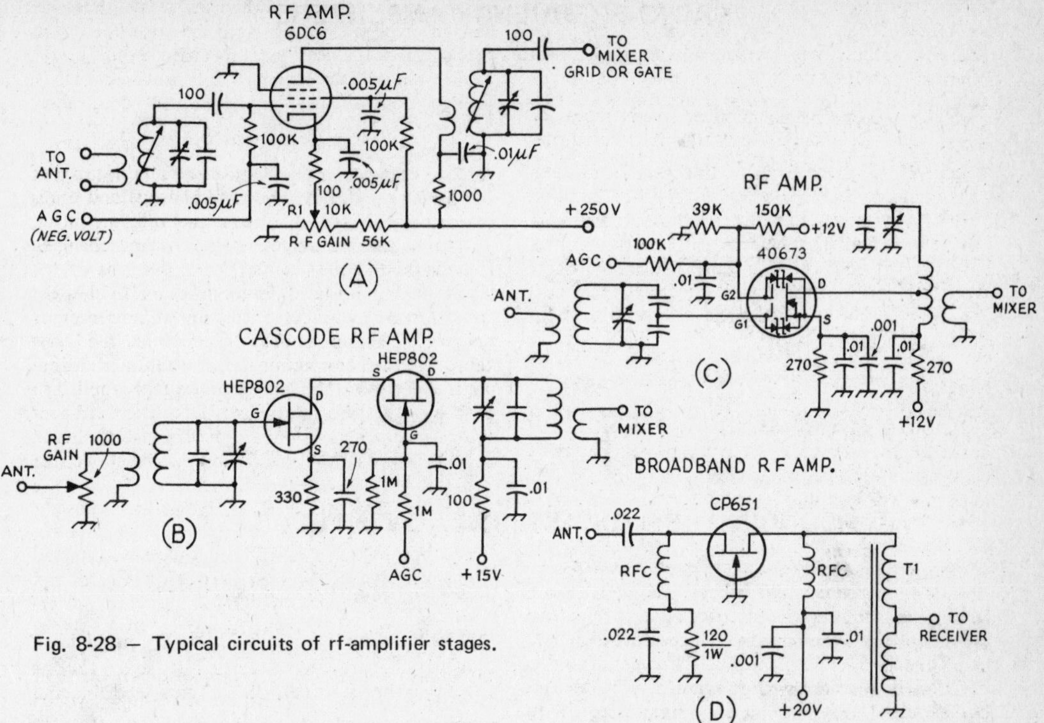

Fig. 8-28 – Typical circuits of rf-amplifier stages.

the input as possible. For example, an rf amplifier might run along a chassis in a straight line, run into a mixer where the frequency is changed, and then the i-f amplifier could be run back parallel to the rf amplifier, provided there was a very large frequency difference between the rf and the i-f amplifiers. However, to avoid any possible coupling, it would be better to run the i-f amplifier off at right angles to the rf amplifier line, just to be on the safe side. Good shielding is important in preventing overall oscillation in high-gain-per-stage amplifiers, but it becomes less important when the stage gain drops to a low value. In a high-gain amplifier, the power leads (including the heater circuit) are common to all stages, and they can provide the overall coupling if they aren't properly filtered. Good bypassing and the use of series isolating resistors will generally eliminate any possibility of coupling through the power leads. Rf chokes, instead of resistors, are used in the heater leads where necessary.

CROSS MODULATION

Since a one- or two-stage rf amplifier will have a bandwidth measured in hundreds of kHz at 14 MHz or higher, strong signals will be amplified through the rf amplifier even though it is not tuned exactly to them. If these signals are strong enough, their amplified magnitude may be measurable in *volts* after passing through several rf stages. If an undesired signal is strong enough after amplification in the rf stages to shift the operating point of a tube or transistor (by driving the grid into the positive region), the undesired signal will modulate the desired signal. This effect is called **cross modulation**, and is often encountered in receivers with several rf stages working at high gain. It shows up as a superimposed modulation on the signal being listened to, and often the effect is that a signal can be tuned in at several points. It can be reduced or eliminated by greater selectivity in the antenna and rf stages (difficult to obtain), the use of FETs or variable-μ tubes in the rf amplifier, reduced gain in the rf amplifier, or reduced antenna input to the receiver. The 6BJ6, 6BA6 and 6DC6 are recommended for rf amplifiers where cross modulation may be a problem.

A receiver designed for minimum cross modulation will use as little gain as possible ahead of the high-selectivity stages, to hold strong unwanted signals below the cross-modulation point. Cross modulation often takes place in double-conversion superheterodynes at the *second* converter stage because there is insufficient selectivity up to this point and at this point the signals have quite appreciable amplitudes. Whenever interference drops out quite suddenly with a reduction in the setting of the gain control, cross modulation should be suspected. Normally, of course, the interference would reduce in amplitude in proportion to the desired signal as the gain setting is reduced.

RF Gain Control

To avoid cross modulation and other overload effects in the mixer and rf stages, the gain of the rf stages is usually made adjustable. This is accomplished by using variable-μ tubes and varying the dc grid bias, either in the grid or cathode circuit. If the gain control is automatic, as in the case of agc, the bias is controlled in the grid circuit. Manual control of rf gain is generally done in the cathode circuit. A typical rf amplifier stage with the two types of gain control is shown in schematic form in Fig. 8-28A. The agc control voltage (negative) is derived from rectified carrier or signal at the detector before the audio amplifier, or in the case of a cw or ssb receiver it can be derived from rectified audio. The manual-gain control voltage (positive with respect to chassis) is usually derived from a potentiometer across the B+ supply, since the bias can be changed even though little plate current is being drawn.

Tracking

Tracking refers to the ability of a receiver to have all of its front-end stages – usually the rf amplifier, the mixer, and the oscillator – tune over a given range while each stage remains tuned to its proper frequency at any specified point in the tuning range. This arrangement provides a single tuning control for bandset and bandspread adjustments. To achieve proper tracking, it is usually necessary to have variable inductors and variable trimmer and padder capacitors for each of the tuned circuits. A two- or three-section variable capacitor is used for the tuning control.

Most modern receivers use a separate tuning control for the local oscillator and this is called the "main tuning." The rf and mixer stages are tracked and use a two-section variable for front-end peaking adjustments. This control is frequently called "preselector tuning." If the main tuning control is moved, the preselector is readjusted for a peak signal response at the new frequency.

REDUCING BROADCAST STATION INTERFERENCE

Some receivers, particularly those that are lacking in front-end selectivity, are subject to cross talk and overload from adjacent-frequency ham or commercial stations. This condition is particularly common with simple receivers that use bipolar transistors in the rf and mixer stages. With the latter, the range of linear operation is small compared to that of vacuum tubes. Large signals send the transistors into the nonlinear operating region, causing severe crosstalk.

The most common cross-talk problem in ham radio is that which is caused by the presence of nearby broadcast stations in the 550- to 1600-kHz range. In some regions, the ham bands – when tuned in on even the best receivers – are a mass of distorted "pop" music, garbled voices, and splatter. It should be pointed out at this juncture that the broadcast stations themselves seldom are at fault, (although in isolated instances they are capable of generating spurious output if operating in a faulty manner).

The most direct approach to the problem of broadcast-station interference is to install a rejection filter between the antenna feed line and

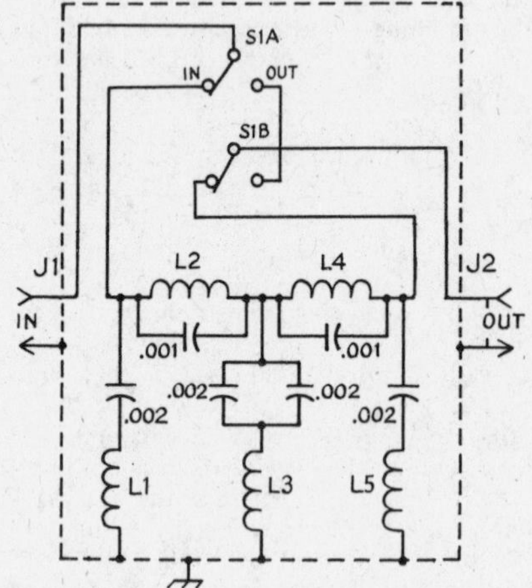

Fig. 8-30 – Capacitance is in pF. Capacitors are disk or tubular ceramic.

J1, J2 – Phono jack.

L1, L5 – 10-μH inductor, 43 turns, No. 26 enam. wire on Amidon T-50-2 toroid core (available from Amidon Associates, 12033 Ostego St., North Hollywood, CA 91607).

L2, L4 – 33-μH inductor, 75 turns, No. 30 enam. wire on Amidon T-68-2 toroid core.

L3 – 4.7-μH inductor, 30 turns, No. 26 enam. wire on Amidon T-50-2 toroid core.

S1 – Spst toggle.

Fig. 8-29 – Inside view of the broadcast trap.

the input terminals of the receiver. Such a filter, if capable of providing sufficient attenuation, prevents the broadcast-station signals from reaching the ham receiver's front end, thus solving the cross-talk problem.

An effective band-rejection filter, containing two constant-*k* sections in cascade, is shown in Fig. 8-30. It offers sharp rejection to signals in the 500- to 1600-kHz range but does not impair reception above or below the broadcast band. It is designed for use in low-impedance lines, particularly those that are 50 to 75 ohms.

The band-rejection filter is housed in a 3 1/2 X 2 1/8 X 1 5/8-inch Minibox. Phono connections are used for J1 and J2 – an aid to cost reduction. Different-style fittings can be used if the builder wishes. Standard-value components are used throughout the filter and the values specified must be used if good results are to be had.

In situations where a *single* broadcast station is involved in the cross-talk problem, a simple series- or parallel-tuned wave trap, tuned to the frequency of the interfering station, may prove adequate in solving the problem. (Such a trap can be installed as shown in Fig. 8-31.) The trap inductors can be made from ferrite-bar broadcast radio loop antennas and tuned to resonance by means of a 365-pF variable capacitor. Traps of this type should be enclosed in a metal box, as is true of the band-rejection filter.

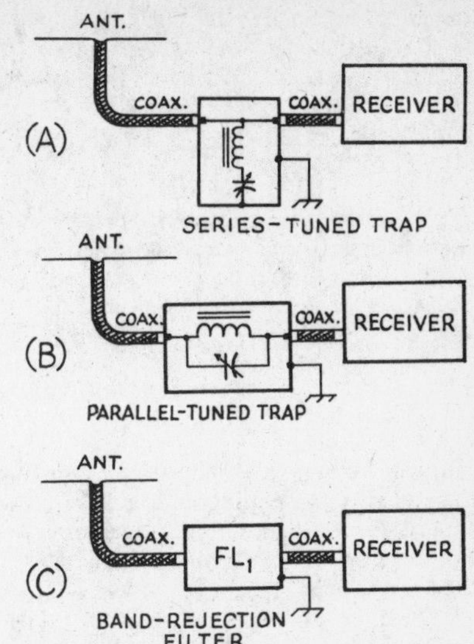

Fig. 8-31 – Examples of series- and parallel-tuned single-frequency traps (installed) are shown at A and B. At C, FL1 represents the band-rejection filter described in the text. If possible, the filter used should be bolted to the chassis or case of the receiver. The receiver should have a good earth ground connected to it.

FRONT-END OVERLOAD PROTECTION FOR THE RECEIVER

It is not uncommon to experience front-end overloading when the station receiver is subjected to an extremely strong signal. Frequently, it becomes necessary to install some type of external attenuator between the antenna and the input of the receiver to minimize the bad effects caused by the strong signal, or signals. Ideally, such an attenuator should be designed to match the impedance of the antenna feed line and the input impedance of the receiver. Also, the attenuator should be variable, enabling the user to have some control over the amount of attenuation used. Manufacturers of some modern receiving equipment build attenuators into the front end of their receivers, offering benefits that are not available from the normal rf gain-control circuit.

Examples of two such attenuators are given in Figs. 8-34 and 8-35. In Fig. 8-35 a ladder-type attenuator gives a 0- to 40-decibel range of control in five steps. A precision step attenuator is illustrated in Fig. 8-34. The latter offers an attenuation range of 3 to 61 decibels in 3-dB steps by closing one or more of five toggle switches. Both units are designed for use in low-impedance lines. The one in Fig. 8-35 is designed for a midrange impedance of 60 ohms, making it satisfactory for use with receivers having a 50- or 75-ohm input. Although designed for an impedance of 50 ohms, the attenuator of Fig. 8-34 will work satisfactorily with 75-ohm receiver inputs if accurate attenuation steps are not required.

Standard-value 1/2-watt resistors are used in the simple attenuator, which will give good results from the broadcast band to 30 MHz. Isolation between sections is not good enough to make this unit particularly effective above 30 MHz. The

Fig. 8-32 – Two attenuators for receiver front-end protection.

Fig. 8-33 – Inside view of the attenuators. In the upper unit the resistors are mounted directly on the switch, using short pigtails wherever possible. Wide strips of copper are used for the input and output leads. The lower unit has each attenuator section individually shielded. The entire assembly is made up of double-sided circuit board material, cut to form the necessary sections and soldered on all abutting edges. All resistors should be connected with the shortest possible leads. A U-shaped piece of aluminum forms the base.

precision step attenuator, if carefully constructed to reduce leakage to a minimum, will be effective to 150 MHz or higher. The smaller 1/4-watt resistors are used as they have less inductance than the 1/2-watt types.

Either attenuator can be used ahead of the receiver, or can be built into the receiver as an integral part of the circuit. Such a device is particularly useful ahead of receivers that do not have an rf gain control, such as simple regenerative receiving sets.

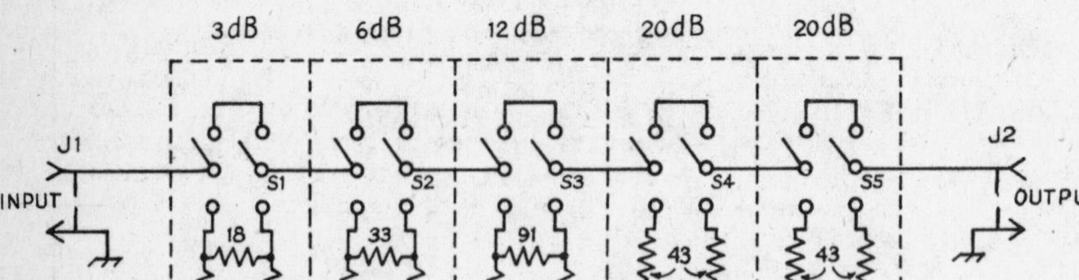

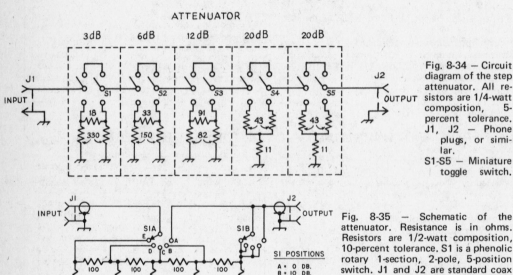

Fig. 8-34 – Circuit diagram of the step attenuator. All resistors are 1/4-watt composition, 5-percent tolerance.
J1, J2 – Phone plugs, or similar.
S1-S5 – Miniature toggle switch.

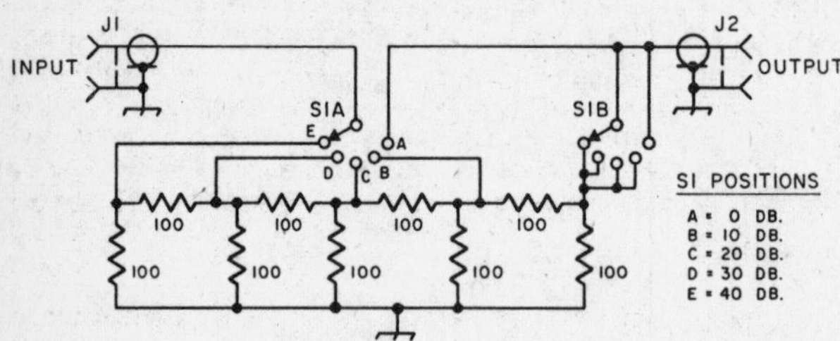

Fig. 8-35 – Schematic of the attenuator. Resistance is in ohms. Resistors are 1/2-watt composition, 10-percent tolerance. S1 is a phenolic rotary 1-section, 2-pole, 5-position switch. J1 and J2 are standard coax connectors. Approximate attenuation in decibels is given for each switch position.

IMPROVING RECEIVER SENSITIVITY

The sensitivity (signal-to-noise ratio) of a receiver on the higher frequencies (above 20 MHz) is dependent upon the bandwidth of the receiver and the noise contributed by the front end of the receiver. Neglecting the fact that image rejection may be poor, a receiver with no rf stage is generally satisfactory, from a sensitivity point, in the 3.5- and 7-MHz bands. However, as the frequency is increased and the atmospheric noise becomes less, the advantage of a good front end becomes apparent. Hence at 14 MHz and higher it is worth while to use at least one stage of rf amplification ahead of the first detector for best sensitivity as well as image rejection. The multigrid converter tubes have very poor noise figures, and even the best pentodes and triodes are three or four times noisier when used as mixers than they are when used as amplifiers.

If the purpose of an rf amplifier is to improve the receiver noise figure at 14 MHz and higher, a good FET, or a high-g_m pentode or triode should be used. Among the pentodes, the best tubes are the 6EH7, 6BZ6, and 6AK5. Of the triodes, the 6AN4, 6CW4, and 6DS4 are best. Among the better field-effect transistors are the MPF102, 2N4417, 3N128, CP625, 3N200, and 40673.

When a receiver is satisfactory in every respect (stability and selectivity) except sensitivity on 14 through 30 MHz, the best solution for the amateur is to add a **preamplifier**, a stage of rf amplification designed expressly to improve the sensitivity. If image rejection is lacking in the receiver, some selectivity should be built into the preamplifier (it is then called a preselector). If, however, the receiver operation is poor on the higher frequencies but is satisfactory on the lower ones, a converter is the best solution.

Some commercial receivers that appear to lack sensitivity on the higher frequencies can be improved simply by tighter coupling to the antenna. This can be accomplished by changing the antenna feed line to the right value (as determined from the receiver instruction book) or by using a simple matching device.

Gain Control

In a receiver front end designed for best signal-to-noise ratio, it is advantageous in the reception of weak signals to eliminate the gain control from the first rf stage and allow it to run "wide open" all the time. If the first stage is controlled along with the i-f (and other rf stages, if any), the signal-to-noise ratio of the receiver will suffer. As the gain is reduced, the g_m of the first tube is reduced, and its noise figure becomes higher. A good receiver might well have two gain controls, one for the first rf stage and another for the i-f (and any other rf) stages. The first rf stage gain would be reduced only for extremely strong signals, thus assuring a good noise figure.

THE 80-10 FET PRESELECTOR

It is often necessary to put new life into tired or inexpensive receivers, especially when operation is marginal on the three higher hf bands – 14, 21 and 28 MHz. A preselector of the type described here can pep up the front end of such receivers while at the same time offering additional selectivity on all the hf bands. The latter helps to reduce images and generally improves the reception on some of the low-cost receivers. Often, signals heard on the amateur bands actually originate on quite different frequencies. They appear on ham sections of the dial as a result of image reception or overload of a receiver mixer.

Circuit Details

This preselector is self-contained, except for the power supply, and no modifications are required in the receiver used. The diagram of the unit is shown in Fig. 8-37. Input and output tuned circuits consist of the preselector tuning capacitor, C1, and high-*Q* coils wound on small toroid cores. Each coil has a trimmer capacitor for alignment purposes. A secondary winding is added which serves as the input or output 50-ohm link. Band changing is accomplished by S1, a multipole miniature switch. An "off" position is included so that the preselector may be bypassed when it is not required.

Two JFETs are operated in a cascode circuit. The advantage of this arrangement is that the capacitance between input and output is only a fraction of a picofarad – so low that neutralization is not required in the hf range. Current drain is low, so the preselector may be operated from a 9-volt transistor-radio battery if desired, with only a slight loss of gain and dynamic range. Otherwise, a 12-volt miniature power supply, such as the type sold for battery replacement, should be used. If battery operation is contemplated it would be well to add a power on/off switch; otherwise, current will be drawn all of the time.

The gain for each band has been set at approximately 20 dB by adjustment of the turns ratio on the rf transformers. Although the cascode circuit can provide up to 30 dB of gain, care must be taken so that the preselector does not overload the succeeding stages in the receiver.

Construction

The preselector is built on a 4 X 5-inch etched circuit board which is housed in a 7 X 5 X 3-inch homemade cabinet. The enclosure is made from two U-shaped pieces of aluminum stock. Any of the popular commercially made cabinets may be substituted. Also, point-to-point wiring using terminal strips may be employed in place of the etched board. Whatever the assembly technique chosen, good isolation between the input and output tuned circuits is of prime importance. Any stray coupling can cause instability. If trouble

Fig. 8-36 – The 80- to 10-meter preselector is constructed in a cabinet made from two U-shaped pieces of sheet aluminum. Press-on feet are used. Panel decals (obtained from H. H. Smith) lend a "finished" appearance to the unit.

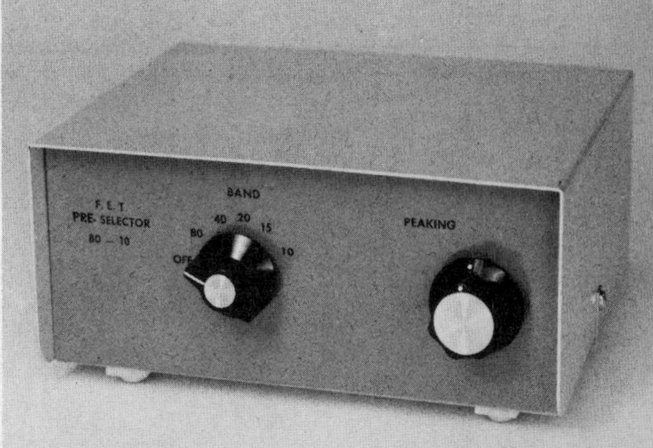

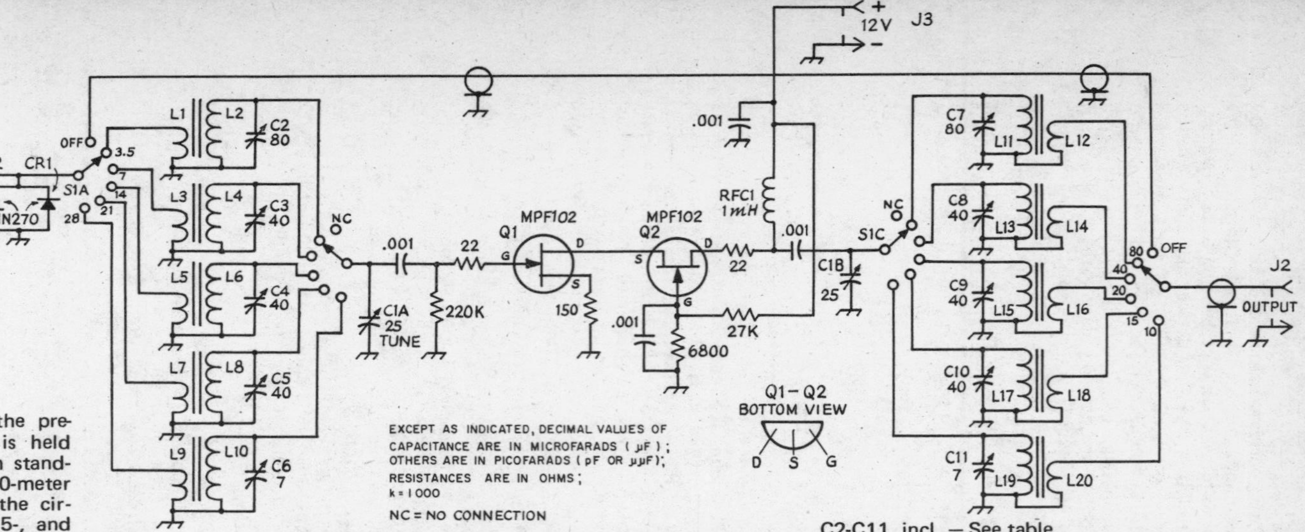

Fig. 8-37 — Schematic diagram of the selective preselector. Unless otherwise indicated, decimal values of capacitance are in µF; others are in pF. Resistors are 1/4- or 1/2-watt composition and fixed-value capacitors are disk ceramic.

C1 — Split-stator variable, dual section (Hammarlund HFD-25).

C2-C11, incl. — See table.

CR1-CR2 — High-speed switching diodes.

J1-J3, incl. — Phone jack, panel mount.

L1-L20, incl. — See table.

Q1, Q2 — HEP 802 or 2N5486.

RFC1 — Miniature choke (Miller 70F103A1).

S1 — Ceramic miniature rotary switch, 4 pole, 6 position, 2 section (Centralab PA-2011).

Fig. 8-38 — Inside view of the preselector. The circuit board is held off the chassis with 1/4-inch standoff pillars. The 80- and 40-meter coils are along the rear of the circuit board, with the 20-, 15-, and 10-meter input coils to the right of the switch while the output coils for the 14- to 28-MHz bands are to the left. Q1 is on the bottom left of the circuit board, with Q2 just above. ▼

COIL TABLE

80	L1, L12 — 5 turns No. 30 enam. over L2, L11, respectively.	L2, L11 — 85 turns No. 30 enam. on Amidon T-50-2 core.	C2, C7 — 7-80-pF compression trimmer, Calectro A1-247
40	L3, L14 — 3 turns No. 30 enam. over L4, L13, respectively.	L4, L13 — 40 turns No. 30 enam. on Amidon T-50-2 core.	C3, C8 — 4-40-pF compression trimmer, Calectro A1-246
20	L5, L16, — 2½ turns No. 22 enam. over L6, L15, respectively.	L6, L15 — 20 turns No. 22 enam. on Amidon T-50-2 core.	C4, C9 — 4-40-pF compression trimmer, Calectro A1-246
15	L7, L18 — 2 turns No. 22 enam. over L8, L17, respectively.	L8, L17 — 13 turns No. 22 enam. on Amidon T-50-6 core.	C5, C10 — 4-40-pF compression trimmer, Calectro A1-246
10	L9, L20 — 1½ turns No. 22 enam. over L10, L19, respectively.	L10, L19 — 10 turns No. 22 enam. on Amidon T-50-6 core.	C6, C11 — 0.9-7-pF compression trimmer, Calectro A1-245
Note: Amidon Associates, 12033 Otsego Street, North Hollywood, CA 91607			

develops, a shield between Q1 and Q2 may be of help.

The band switch, S1, is mounted on an aluminum bracket which is, in turn, mounted at the center of the circuit board. The toroid coils are held in place with a drop of epoxy cement. The shield that separates the two sections of C1 must be grounded to the etched board with a short lead. This metal strip provides vital shielding between sections A and B. The PRESELECTOR capacitor is mounted directly to the front panel using hardware supplied with the unit. All of the trimmer capacitors are mounted on the circuit board.

During assembly, whether or not a circuit board is used, a heat sink should always be employed when soldering the transistor leads. If excessive heat reaches the body of the transistor, the device can be ruined.

The input, output, and power jacks are mounted on the rear apron of the chassis. The rf protection diodes, CR1CR2, are connected right across J1. Subminiature coax (RG-174A/U) is used to connect the input and output jacks to the circuit board. Sockets for the transistors were included in the original model to facilitate experimentation; they may be omitted if desired.

Alignment

The completed preselector is best adjusted with a signal generator. However, if no test equipment is available, on-the-air signals may be used. The antenna or generator should be connected to J1 and a short patch cord run from J2 to the receiver. Start with the 10-meter band, and set C2 with the plates fully unmeshed. Then tune in a signal at the uppermost point in the band. Adjust trimmers C6 and C11 for maximum indication on the receiver S meter. Repeat this procedure for the other bands, setting the appropriate trimmers. The lower-frequency bands will appear to tune more broadly. However, the selectivity provided by the high-*Q* rf transformers is about the same on each band.

If this preselector is to be used with a transceiver, the unit will have to be switched *out* of the antenna line when transmitting. Otherwise severe damage will result to the coils and transistors in the unit. If the transceiver has a separate receiving-antenna input, as some do, the preselector can be connected to this jack, and the feeder switched with an external antenna-changeover relay.

SQUELCH CIRCUITS

An audio squelch is one that cuts off the receiver output when no signal is coming through the receiver. A squelch is useful in mobile equipment where the no-signal receiver hiss noise may be as loud as some of the weak signals being copied. Noise of this kind, when listened to over a sustained period, can cause considerable operator fatigue. A squelch is useful with certain types of fixed-station equipment too, especially where continuous monitoring of a fixed vhf or uhf frequency is desired.

A practical vacuum-tube squelch circuit is given in Fig. 8-39 at A. A twin triode (12AX7) serves as an audio amplifier and a control tube. When the agc voltage is low or zero, the lower (control) triode draws plate current. The consequent voltage drop across the adjustable resistor in the plate circuit cuts off the upper (amplifier) triode and no signal or noise is passed. When the agc voltage rises to the cutoff value of the control triode, the tube no longer draws current and the bias on the amplifier triode is now only its normal operating bias, furnished by the 1000-ohm resistor in the cathode circuit. The tube now functions as an ordinary amplifier and passes signals. The relation between the agc voltage and the signal turn-on point is adjusted by varying the resistance in the plate circuit of the control triode.

The circuit shown at B employs a Schmitt-trigger input to achieve positive on-off gating of the audio signal. For ssb operation, the length of the squelch-gate on time after the input signal disappears is increased by switching in an electrolytic capacitor. The dc signal from the squelch gate controls an emitter follower which is connected between the receiver detector and the first audio amplifier.

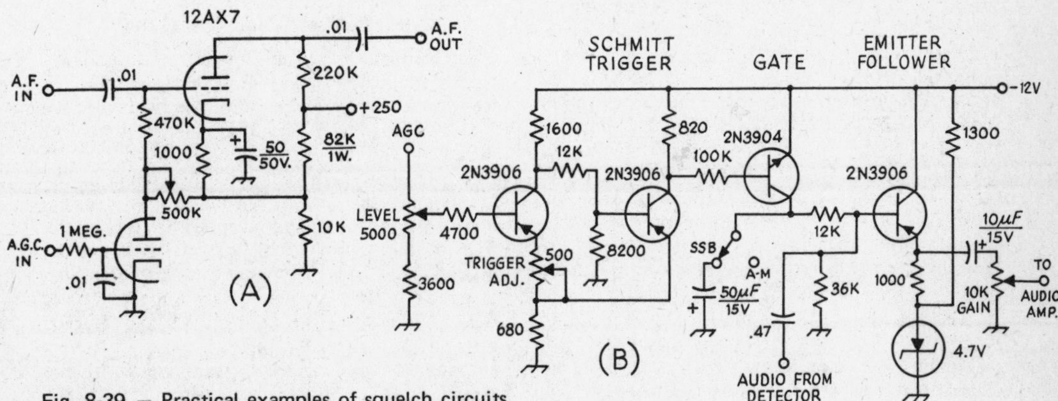

Fig. 8-39 — Practical examples of squelch circuits for cutting off the receiver output when no signal is present.

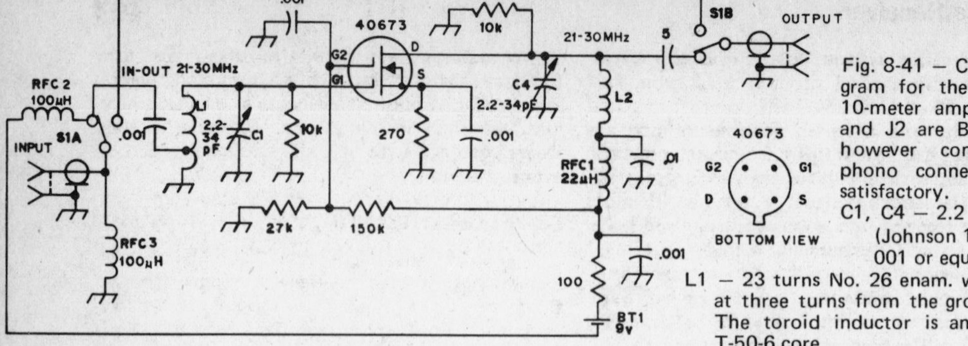

Fig. 8-41 – Circuit diagram for the 15- and 10-meter amplifier. J1 and J2 are BNC type, however conventional phono connectors are satisfactory.
C1, C4 – 2.2 to 34 pF (Johnson 193-0010-001 or equiv.).
L1 – 23 turns No. 26 enam. with a tap at three turns from the ground end. The toroid inductor is an Amidon T-50-6 core.
L2 – 20 turns No. 26 enam. on an Amidon T-50-6 core.
RFCl – 22 μH (Millen J302-22 or equiv.).

Fig. 8-40 – Inside of the receiver preamplifier. The battery is held in position with a clamp fabricated from a small strip of aluminum.

AN RF AMPLIFIER FOR 10 AND 15 METERS

Many receivers are deficient in gain when operated on the higher hf amateur bands. The problem becomes very apparent when the receiver is used as an i-f for vhf converters. The preamplifier given in Fig. 8-41 will provide a gain of about 14 dB and will perk up the performance of almost any receiver on the 15- and 10-meter amateur bands.

With the shield placed between C1 and C4, the preamplifier shows no signs of instability. The range of the capacitor-inductor combinations is sufficient to peak the output on either 10 meters or 15 meters. A band switch is not needed. Some adjustment of the turns spacing on the toroid inductors may be necessary to allow each corresponding capacitor to tune the full frequency range of the unit.

TUNING A RECEIVER

CW Reception

In a receiver without selectivity, it doesn't much matter where the BFO is set, so long as it is within the pass band of the receiver. However, in a receiver with selectivity, the BFO should be offset, to give single-signal code reception. The proper setting of the BFO is easy to find. In the absence of incoming signals, it will be found that, as the BFO control is tuned, the pitch of the background noise will go from high to low and back to high again. The setting that gives the lowest pitch represents the setting of the BFO in the *center* of the pass band. Setting the BFO for a higher pitch (to the noise) will give more or less single-signal effect on incoming signals, depending upon the selectivity of the receiver. If the receiver uses a crystal filter that has a "rejection notch" or "phasing" control, setting the notch on the audio image will improve the single-signal effect.

The best receiver condition for the reception of code signals will have the first rf stage running at maximum gain, the following rf mixer and i-f stages operating with just enough gain to maintain the signal-to-noise ratio, and the audio gain set to give comfortable headphone or speaker volume. The audio volume should be controlled by the audio gain control, not the i-f gain control. Under the above conditions, the selectivity of the receiver is being used to best advantage, and cross modulation is minimized. It precludes the use of a receiver in which the gains of the rf and i-f stages are controlled simultaneously.

Single-Sideband Phone Reception

The receiver is set up for ssb reception in a manner similar to that for single-signal code reception, except that a suitable bandwidth for ssb (2 to 3 kHz) is used. The BFO *must* be set off to one side of the passband if good use is to be made of the selectivity. To determine which side to set it, remember this rule: A selective receiver can be set up for *lower*-sideband reception by setting the BFO so that there is little or no signal on the *low*-frequency side of zero beat when tuning through a steady carrier or cw signal. Lower sideband is customarily used on 3.9 and 7 MHz, upper on the higher frequencies.

Unless the receiver has an agc system suitable for ssb reception (fast attack, slow decay), the operator must be very careful not to let the receiver overload. If the receiver does overload, it will be impossible to obtain good ssb reception.

Run the receiver with as little rf gain as possible, consistent with a good signal-to-noise ratio, and run the audio gain high.

Carefully tune in an ssb signal using only the main tuning dial. When the voice becomes natural sounding and understandable, the signal is properly tuned. If the incoming signal is on lower sideband, tuning the receiver to a lower frequency will make the voice sound lower pitched. An upper-sideband signal will sound higher pitched as the receiver is tuned to a lower frequency.

If the receiver has excellent selectivity, 2.1 kHz or less, it will be desirable to experiment slightly with the BFO setting, remembering that each adjustment of the BFO calls for a similar adjustment of the main tuning control. If the selectivity is quite high, setting the BFO too far from the pass band will limit the incoming signal to the high audio frequencies only. Conversely, setting it too close will limit the response to the low audio frequencies.

A-M Phone Reception

In reception of a-m phone signals, the normal procedure is to set the rf and i-f gain at maximum, switch on the agc, and use the audio gain control for setting the volume. This insures maximum effectiveness of the agc system in compensating for fading and maintaining constant audio output on either strong or weak signals. On occasion a strong signal close to the frequency of a weaker desired station may take control of the agc, in which case the weaker station may disappear because of the reduced gain. In this case better reception may result if the agc is switched off, using the manual rf gain control to set the gain at a point that prevents "blocking" by the stronger signal.

When receiving an a-m signal on a frequency within 5 to 20 kHz from a single-sideband signal it may also be necessary to switch off the agc and resort to the use of manual gain control, unless the receiver has excellent skirt selectivity.

A crystal filter will help reduce interference in phone reception. Although the high selectivity cuts sidebands and reduces the audio output at the higher audio frequencies, it is possible to use quite high selectivity without destroying intelligibility. As in code reception, it is advisable to do all tuning with the filter in the circuit. Variable-selectivity filters permit a choice of selectivity to suit interference conditions.

An undesired carrier close in frequency to a desired carrier will heterodyne with it to produce a beat note equal to the frequency difference.

Spurious Responses

Spurious responses can be recognized without a great deal of difficulty. Often it is possible to identify an image by the nature of the transmitting station, if the frequency assignments applying to the frequency to which the receiver is tuned are known. However, an image also can be recognized by its behavior with tuning. If the signal causes a heterodyne beat note with the desired signal and is actually on the same frequency, the beat note will not change as the receiver is tuned through the signal; but if the interfering signal is an image, the beat will vary in pitch as the receiver is tuned. The beat oscillator in the receiver must be turned off for this test. Using a crystal filter with the beat oscillator on, an image will peak on the side of zero beat opposite that on which desired signals peak.

Harmonic response can be recognized by the "tuning rate," or movement of the tuning dial required to give a specified change in beat note. Signals getting into the i-f via high-frequency oscillator harmonics tune more rapidly (less dial movement) through a given change in beat note than do signals received by normal means.

Harmonics of the beat oscillator can be recognized by the tuning rate of the beat-oscillator pitch control. A smaller movement of the control will suffice for a given change in beat note than that necessary with legitimate signals. In poorly designed or inadequately shielded and filtered receivers it is often possible to find BFO harmonics below 2 MHz, but they should be very weak or nonexistent at higher frequencies.

ALIGNMENT AND SERVICE OF SUPERHETERODYNE RECEIVERS

I-F Alignment

A calibrated signal generator or test oscillator is a useful device for alignment of an i-f amplifier. Some means for measuring the output of the receiver are required See Fig. 8-40. If the receiver has a tuning meter, its indications will serve. Lacking an S meter, a high-resistance voltmeter or a vacuum-tube voltmeter can be connected across the second-detector load resistor, if the second detector is a diode. Alternatively, if the signal generator is a modulated type, an ac voltmeter can be connected across the primary of the transformer feeding the speaker, or from the plate of the last audio amplifier through a 0.1-μF blocking capacitor. Lacking an ac voltmeter, the audio output can be judged by ear, although this method is not as accurate as the others. If the tuning meter is used as an indication, the agc of the receiver should be turned on, but any other indication requires that it be turned off. Lacking a test oscillator, a steady signal tuned through the input of the receiver (if the job is one of just touching up the i-f amplifier) will be suitable. However, with no oscillator and tuning an amplifier for the first time, one's only recourse is to try to peak the i-f transformer on "noise," a difficult task if the transformers are badly off resonance, as they are apt to be. It would be much better to haywire together a simple oscillator for test purposes.

Initial alignment of a new i-f amplifier is as follows: The test oscillator is set to the correct frequency, and its output is coupled through a capacitor to the grid of the last i-f amplifier tube. The trimmer capacitors of the transformer feeding

Fig. 8-42 – Receiver alignment requires a stable signal source (a signal generator) and voltmeter. Alignment of communications receivers should be checked at least once a year.

the second detector are then adjusted for maximum output, as shown by the indicating device being used. The oscillator output lead is then clipped on to the grid of the next-to-the-last i-f amplifier tube, and the second-from-the-last transformer trimmer adjustments are peaked for maximum output. This process is continued, working back from the second detector, until all of the i-f transformers have been aligned. It will be necessary to reduce the output of the test oscillator as more of the i-f amplifier is brought into use. It is desirable in all cases to use the minimum signal that will give useful output readings. The i-f transformer in the plate circuit of the mixer is aligned with the signal introduced to the grid of the mixer. Since the tuned circuit feeding the mixer grid may have a very low impedance at the i-f, it may be necessary to boost the test generator output or to disconnect the tuned circuit temporarily from the mixer grid.

If the i-f amplifier has a crystal filter, the filter should first be switched out and the alignment carried out as above, setting the test oscillator as closely as possible to the crystal frequency. When this is completed, the crystal should be switched in and the oscillator frequency varied back and forth over a small range either side of the crystal frequency to find the exact frequency, as indicated by a sharp rise in output. Leaving the test oscillator set on the crystal peak, the i-f trimmers should be realigned for maximum output. The necessary readjustment should be small. The oscillator frequency should be checked frequently to make sure it has not drifted from the crystal peak.

A modulated signal is not of much value for aligning a crystal-filter i-f amplifier, since the high selectivity cuts sidebands and the results may be inaccurate if the audio output is used as the tuning indication. Lacking the agc tuning meter, the transformers may be conveniently aligned by ear, using a weak unmodulated signal adjusted to the crystal peak. Switch on the beat oscillator, adjust to the suitable tone, and align the i-f transformers for maximum audio output.

An amplifier that is only slightly out of alignment, as a result of normal drift or aging, can be realigned by using any steady signal, such as a local broadcast station, instead of the test oscillator. One's 100-kHz standard makes an excellent signal source for "touching up" an i-f amplifier. Allow the receiver to warm up thoroughly, tune in the signal, and trim the i-f for maximum output as noted on the S meter, or by tuning for peak af output.

Rf Alignment

The objective in aligning the rf circuits of a gang-tuned receiver is to secure adequate tracking over each tuning range. The adjustment may be carried out with a test oscillator of suitable frequency range, with harmonics from your 100-kHz standard or other known oscillator, or even on noise or such signals as may be heard. First set the tuning dial at the high-frequency end of the range in use. Then set the test oscillator to the frequency indicated by the receiver dial. The test-oscillator output may be connected to the antenna terminals of the receiver for this test. Adjust the oscillator trimmer capacitor in the receiver to give maximum response on the test-oscillator signal, then reset the receiver dial to the low-frequency end of the range. Set the test-oscillator frequency near the frequency indicated by the receiver dial and tune the test oscillator until its signal is heard in the receiver. If the frequency of the signal indicated by the test-oscillator calibration is higher than that indicated by the receiver dial, more inductance (or more capacitance in the tracking capacitor) is needed in the receiver oscillator circuit; if the frequency is lower, less inductance (less tracking capacity) is required in the receiver oscillator. Most commercial receivers provide some means for varying the inductance of the coils or the capacitance of the tracking capacitor, to permit aligning the receiver tuning with the dial calibration. Set the test oscillator to the frequency indicated by the receiver dial, and then adjust the tracking capacitance or inductance of the receiver oscillator coil to obtain maximum response. After making this adjustment, recheck the high-frequency end of the scale as previously described. It may be necessary to go back and forth between the ends of the range several times before the proper combination of inductance and capacitance is secured. In many cases, better overall tracking will result if frequencies near but not actually at the ends of the tuning range are selected, instead of taking the extreme dial settings.

After the oscillator range is properly adjusted, set the receiver and test oscillator to the high-frequency end of the range. First adjust the mixer trimmer capacitor for maximum hiss or signal, then the rf trimmers. Reset the tuning dial and test oscillator to the low-frequency end of the range, and repeat; if the circuits are properly designed, no change in trimmer settings should be necessary. If it is necessary to increase the trimmer capacitance in any circuit, more indicatance is needed; conversely, if less capacitance resonates the circuit, less inductance is required.

Tracking seldom is perfect throughout a tuning range, so that a check of alignment at intermediate points in the range may show it to be slightly off. Normally the gain variation will be small, however, and it will suffice to bring the circuits into line at both ends of the range. If most reception is in a particular part of the range, such as an amateur band, the circuits may be aligned for maximum performance in that region, even though the ends of the frequency range as a whole may be slightly out of alignment.

RECEIVER SELECTION

Beginning amateurs often find themselves faced with the dilemma of choosing between a home-built or store-bought receiver. Ideally, the new ham would elect to build his own complete amateur station, extracting the maximum value from the project through the knowledge he would gain about electronics. Additionally, home-built equipment is more familiar in detail to its owner than is a manufactured receiver. Thus, he can service his unit more rapidly and does not have to consult with the manufacturer about servicing details. If he wishes to add new circuits to the home-built receiver, or to modify existing circuitry, he need not worry about destroying the resale value of the equipment. For this reason the owner may be encouraged to experiment more with circuits, enhancing his overall knowledge of electronics.

Conversely, single-lot quantities of small parts are quite expensive these days, sometimes causing the constructor to spend more money on a simple home-built receiver than he would on a complicated commercially built unit. Modifications to factory-built ham gear generally degrade its resale value, discouraging the owner from making circuit improvements or improving his knowledge by experimenting.

The complexity of the receiver need only be such as to fill the operator's needs. Some very basic home-made receivers perform better than poorly designed multitube commercial units. The receivers described later in this chapter have been designed with the radio amateur's needs in mind, yet no unnecessary circuitry has been added simply to make them appear to be highly sophisticated. Many of the parts used in these receivers can be obtained from junked TV sets, war surplus stores, junked war surplus equipment, and from the workshop junk box. These possibilities should not be overlooked, for a considerable amount of money can be saved by garnering small parts in this manner.

The final decision whether to buy or build will of course be up to the operator. If you're only interested in being a "communicator," then a store-bought receiver will probably suffice. If, however, you want to experience the thrill of communicating by means of home-constructed equipment, and if you want to *learn by doing*, then home-made receiving equipment should be considered. Such forthright endeavors are often the stepping stones to higher plateaus – a satisfying career in electronics, or the needed background to qualify for radio schooling when in the military service. Just having a good working knowledge of one's own station is rewarding in itself, and such knowledge contributes to an amateur's value during public service and emergency operations.

AUDIO FILTERS FOR HUM AND HISS REJECTION (CRUD-O-JECT)

Many amateurs, in their search for a good headset, find the comfort and sensitivity of hi-fi "cans" very desirable. Since these phones are available within almost any price range and from many local dealers, they are quite popular. Although the typical headset designed for hi-fi use is comfortable and sensitive, it has certain characteristics which are *undesirable* from an amateur standpoint. The most undesirable feature is the frequency response. Hi-fi enthusiasts are interested in hearing not only very low frequencies, but very high-pitched tones, too. For amateur communications, the high and low frequencies can be classed as *CRUD* (*C*ontinuous *R*andom *U*nwanted *D*isturbances) because they do not contribute to communications effectiveness. Most hi-fi phones are of low impedance, and it is usually desirable to connect the headset to the receiver speaker terminals. This allows a good match for the headset, but it also provides a higher hum level than is heard with limited-frequency-range earphones.

A very sharp filter response can be obtained easily with surplus toroidal inductors. While these filters can (and do) eliminate CRUD, they may also have "super" selectivity leading to a monotone and even ringing performance. The CRUD-O-Ject is a band-pass filter which will eliminate the crud but not be ringing sharp.

The Cw Circuit

The original cw CRUD-O-Ject model was described in February, 1972, *QST*. The schematic diagram is given in Fig. 1. The heart of the circuit is a 3-pole large-percentage band-pass filter having a Butterworth response. It is designed for an input and output impedance of 600 ohms, with 600 Hz as its center frequency. The impedance value of 600 ohms was chosen to match the output which is available on many receivers. Most ardent cw operators, when receiving, prefer to hear a tone lower than the 800- to 1000-Hz range of the many filters previously published. The center frequency of 600 Hz was picked in preference to the higher tones. The filter design also makes use of six surplus 88-mH toroidal inductors for L1, rather than a single inductor which would not be readily available on the surplus market and would cost 8 or 9 dollars new.

The theoretical 3-dB bandwidth of the filter is 362 Hz, and the 30-dB bandwidth is 1160 Hz, for a ratio of 3.2 to 1. As was explained earlier, a narrow bandwidth with steep skirts was *not* the objective

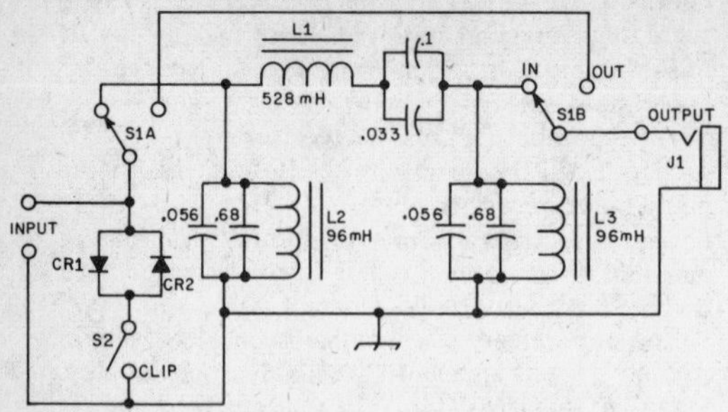

Fig. 1 — Schematic diagram of the cw CRUD-O-JECT. All capacitances are in microfarads (μF), and all capacitors should be of high quality paper or polyester dielectric with 75-V or higher ratings. (Sprague type 255P "orange drop" capacitors were used in the unit photographed.) Parallel capacitor combinations of stock values are shown in the filter section, but other values of individual components may be used to obtain the desired total capacitance.

CR1, CR2 — Silicon rectifier, Mallory M 2.5 A, 1N4001, or similar. Avoid using small-signal diodes.

J1 — Phone jack.

L1 — 528 mH, made by connecting six 88-mH toroids in series (New England Engineering 8888 or equiv.).

L2, L3 — Modified 88-mH toroid; add 40 turns No. 30 enam. wire, wound in same direction as original windings. (New England Engineering[1] 8896).

S1 — Dpdt toggle.

S2 — Spst toggle.

when designing this filter. The attenuation of 120-Hz power supply hum is in excess of 50 dB. Hum resulting from 60-Hz pickup in the receiver audio system is attenuated by more than 70 dB.

Silicon diodes CR1 and CR2, connected across the input when S2 is closed, limit the amplitude of signals reaching the output of the CRUD-O-Ject to approximately 1.2 volts pk-pk, no matter what the input level may be. Thus, the audio power-output level is limited to approximately 24 milliwatts. This is a comfortable listening level for most operators who use sensitive headphones. With S1 and S2, selection of filtering or clipping may be made independently, or both may be used simultaneously. The insertion loss of the filter is approximately 2 dB, so when switching the filter in or out, the change in volume is just barely noticeable in the headset.

Operation

Connecting the filter to the station receiver is simple if the receiver has a 600-ohm output terminal. The anti-VOX system in most transmitter-receiver systems is of this value. If a 600-ohm source is not available, an audio line transformer may be used to transform the speaker 4- or 8-ohm output to 600 ohms. Likewise, the same kind of transformer may be used to match the output of the filter to a low-impedance headset (or the station speaker) if 600-ohm "cans" are not available. Transformers similar to those used for the ssb version could be constructed easily.

This filter is one of the few station accessories which does not require "operator technique." On cw, it is turned on; on phone it is turned off. The two front-panel switches are used for disabling the clipper and bypassing the filter. There are occasions when the operator may want to listen to a low-frequency beat note, such as when tuning the receiver to zero the calibrator. In order to hear the low-pitched tone near zero beat, it is necessary to switch out the filter. The clipper should be left in; otherwise, the operator takes the chance of getting his ears thumped *severely* by an unusually loud signal.

The Phone Version

This filter has a theoretical 3-dB ripple in the passband, 355 to 2530 Hz, with a band pass of 2175 Hz at the 3-dB points. In this design, the Q_u of the toroids was ignored. The actual response is given in the original article presented in *QST* for May, 1974.

Impedance Matching

The cw CRUD-O-Ject design has 600 ohms as the input and output impedances. With the phone version it was decided to use unmodified standard 44- and 88-mH toroid inductors and allow the terminal impedances to be what they may. The final result was 254 ohms. One hundred turns of fine magnet wire are required to achieve 4 to 8 ohms output impedance (see Fig. 3). Lab tests indicate the impedances of T1 and T2 to vary across the passband of the system, as expected, over a range of 5.2 to 8.7 ohms *when the filter is properly terminated.* The CRUD-O-Ject must be connected to the four- or eight-ohm terminal on

[1] New England Engineering, P.O. Box 145, Wethersfield, CT 06109.

Fig. 2 — Inside view of the cw CRUD-O-Ject. The inductors are mounted with special retaining hardware. This model uses a combination of three capacitors across L2 and L3 to make up the required capacitance. The circuit board is mounted using a two-inch section of angle aluminum bolted to the top of the cover.

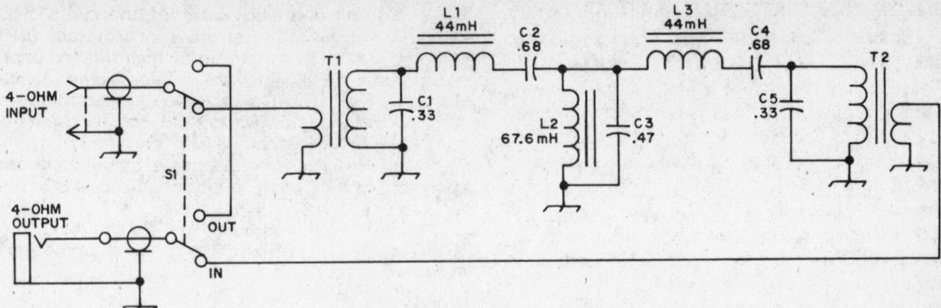

Fig. 3 – Circuit diagram for the ssb CRUD-O-Ject. The capacitors should be of good quality, as mentioned in the text. A complete set of inductors, trimmed and checked, along with two transformers (T1 and T2) are available from New England Engineering.[2]

L1, L3 – 44-mH toroid inductor (New England Engineering 8844 or equiv.).
L2 – Modified 88-mH toroid inductor. A total of 94 turns must be removed from the winding (New England Engineering 8867).
S1 – Dpdt toggle.
T1, T2 – Modified 88-mH toroid inductor. See text. (New England Engineering 8804).

the station receiver (not the headphone jack unless it is designed for low-impedance use) and a speaker or low-impedance (four to sixteen ohms) headset. Headphones suitable for hi-fi operation are generally low impedance and will operate with the filter very nicely. Incidentally, this filter eliminates the major objection most operators have to hi-fi earphones; the reproduction of high- and low-pitched tones as well as audio hum. Hi-fi "cans" respond to receiver hum and hiss extremely well if these noises are allowed to reach them.

If the operator has a favorite set of phones which are not of low impedance, he could use a small audio transformer to match the filter output to a high-impedance load. If the headphone impedance is unknown a multitap transformer could be obtained and the proper tap determined by trial and error for the most volume. The important point to remember is that the filter must be matched correctly to the headset or speaker.

Construction

The entire unit is self-contained in an aluminum utility box which measures 2-1/4 × 3-1/2 × 6 inches (57 × 89 × 152 mm) HWD. The capacitors used for this project should be of good quality with a tolerance not greater than plus or minus ten percent. The Orange Drop style was used here. Disk-ceramic capacitors should be avoided.

Operation

To check the bandpass-characteristics, connect the filter to a receiver, connect a speaker or headset to the output, and tune through the crystal-calibrator signal first with the filter out of the line, and then with it switched in. Take note of the very low and high notes. Then tune in an ssb signal. It will be apparent at first that the audio response is somewhat restricted. Any 60- or 120-Hz hum along with most audio hiss, will completely disappear.

Features

Several characteristics of the CRUD-O-Ject are not apparent at first glance. The filter is a passive device which means no operational voltage is needed! There are no batteries, no interconnections to the receiver to sample dc voltages, and no cable harness. The unit is connected directly between the receiver speaker terminals and the station speaker or headphones. The CRUD-O-Ject is immune to rf pickup, making it usable for break-in cw operation, although the sharper cw model described earlier performs this task considerably better.

Low and high-pitched ssb QRM is reduced when the filter is in the line. The amount of the reduction depends on the overall characteristics of the station receiver i-f selectivity circuits. If the station transceiver has a 2.7-kHz band-pass filter, the addition of the circuit described here will make a noticeable improvement.

Many speakers (and even some headphones) tend to distort low-frequency energy. The har-

[2] See footnote 1.

Fig. 4 – Inside view of the CRUD-O-Ject. The circuit board has been turned up for a better view of the toroid inductors.

monic distortion can give the impression of QRM that is actually not there! The simplest way to eliminate low-frequency harmonic distortion is to prevent the low-frequency energy from reaching the speaker. The other advantage to removing the base response is the reduction of any tendency for a large heavy-magnet speaker to become "boomy." The restriction of high-pitched noise from reaching the speaker (especially a small speaker which will accent the high-frequency energy) makes listening to ssb transmissions for long periods of time more pleasurable.

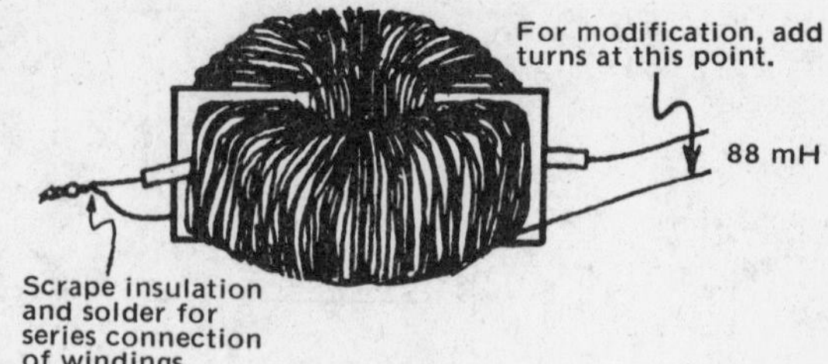

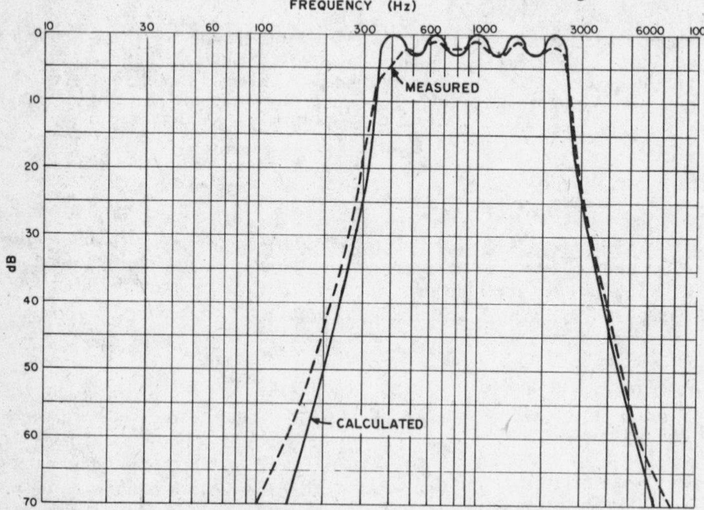

Fig. 2 — Calculated and measured curves for the phone filter.

A "UNIVERSAL" HF RECEIVING CONVERTER

The receiving converter shown in Fig. 8-49 can be used as a "down converter" with an i-f output of 3.5 to 4 MHz, as an "up converter" with an i-f of 28 to 28.5 MHz, or as a front end for a multiband hf receiver. The tuned circuits at the front end will cover all of the hf amateur bands – 1.6 to 29.6 MHz. Thus, it is only necessary to select an appropriate output network for the mixer tuned circuits, for the crystal oscillator, and crystals for the desired frequency coverage. WWV or WWVH reception at 5, 10, 15 or 20 MHz may be added. With the band-switch arrangement shown, five amateur bands and one WWV frequency can be selected with S1. A second switch, S2, allows bypassing the converter. Suitable coil and capacitor combinations are given in the chart, Fig. 8-50, for all of the bands mentioned above. Other 500-kHz segments in the range from 1.6 to 30 MHz may be covered with an appropriate conversion crystal and oscillator-tank circuit.

Front view of the hf converter. The upper knob controls the PRESLECTOR capacitor, while the lower control is for the band switch. The small switch to the lower right disconnects the converter from the antenna line.

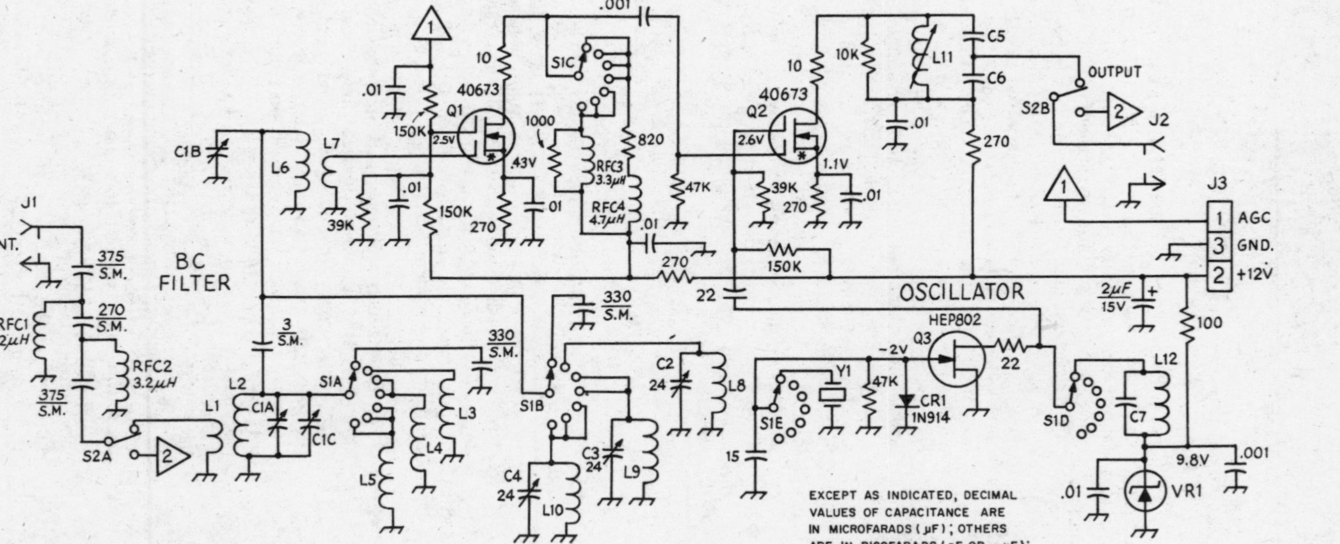

Fig. 8-49 — Schematic diagram of the hf converter. Capacitors are disk ceramic and resistors are 1/2-watt composition, unless otherwise noted. Capacitors with polarity marked are electrolytic. A template is available from the ARRL Technical Department for fifty cents and a large self-addressed stamped envelope.

C1 — Broadcast-type air variable, dual section, 365 pF per section, gear-reduction drive (J. W. Miller 565-8).

C2-C4, incl. — Air variable, pc mount (Johnson 189-0509-005).

C5, C6 — For 3.5 MHz, 45 and 470 pF, respectively. For 28 MHz, 15 and 150 pF. May be silver mica or disk ceramic.

C7 — See table (Fig. 8-50).

CR1 — High-speed silicon switching diode.

J1, J2 — Phono type, chassis mount.

J3 — 3-terminal strip, screw type (Millen E303).

L1 — 6 turns No. 28 enam. wound over L2.

L2, L6 — 52 turns No. 28 enam. on Amidon T-68-2 toroid core (Amidon Associates, 12033 Ostego St., North Hollywood, CA 91607).

L3, L8 — 46 turns No. 28 enam. wound on Amidon T-68-2 core.

L4, L9 — 20 turns No. 20 enam. wound on Amidon T-50-2 core.

L5, L10 — 13 turns No. 20 enam. wound on Amidon T-50-6 core.

L7 — 13 turns No. 28 enam. wound over L6.

L11 — For 3.5 MHz, 22-µH slug-tuned coil; for 28 MHz, 1.2-µH slug-tuned coil, pc mount (J. W. Miller 46A225CPC and 46A126CPC, respectively).

L12 — See table.

Q1, Q2 — RCA dual-gate MOSFET.

Q3 — Motorola JFET.

RFC1, RFC2 — Solenoid-wound rf choke, one turn removed (J. W. Miller 74F336AP).

RFC3 — Solenoid-wound rf choke (J. W. Miller 74F336AP).

RFC4 — Solenoid-wound rf choke (J. W. Miller 74F476AP).

S1 — Assembly consisting of one Centralab PA-302 index section and 5 Centralab PA-1001 1-pole, 11-position phenolic sections.

S2 — Dpdt toggle.

VR1 — Zener diode, 9.8 V, 1 W.

Y1 — See table.

		1.8 MHz	3.5 MHz	7 MHz	10 MHz	14 MHz	15 MHz	21 MHz	25 MHz	28 MHz	28.5 MHz
For 3.5-4 MHz i-f	Y1	5.8 MHz	N/A	11 MHz	14 MHz	10.5 MHz	11 MHz	17.5 MHz	29 MHz	32 MHz	32.5 MHz
	L12	7.5 μH		4.25 μH	2.5 μH	4.8 μH	4.25 μH	2.5 μH	1.5 μH	1.5 μH	1.5 μH
		46A826CPC	N/A	46A476CPC	46A276CPC	46A476CPC	46A476CPC	46A276CPC	46A156CPC	46A156CPC	46A156CPC
	C7	100 pF	N/A	39 pF	47 pF	39 pF	39 pF	18 pF	10 pF	5 pF	5 pF
For 28-28.5 MHz i-f	Y1	30.3 MHz	32 MHz	35.5 MHz	38 MHz	42.5 MHz	43 MHz	49.5 MHz	53 MHz	N/A	N/A
	L12	1.5 μH	1.5 μH	1.2 μH	1.0 μH	0.82 μH	0.82 μH	0.54 μH	0.55 μH	N/A	N/A
		46A156CPC	46A156CPC	46A126CPC	46A106CPC	46A827CPC	46A827CPC	46A576CPC	46A576CPC		
	C7	7 pF	5 pF	5 pF	5 pF	5 pF	5 pF	5 pF	5 pF	N/A	N/A

Fig. 8-50 – Table of values for the hf converter.

Design

The design of the converter has been optimized for strong-signal performance. All of the rf selectivity has been placed *before* the rf amplifier, insuring maximum rejection of out-of-band signals. The tuned circuits exhibit some loss, a limiting factor that determines the sensitivity of the converter. Average sensitivity is about 0.5 μV for a 10-dB signal-plus-noise-to-noise ratio (S + N/N).

A second dual-gate MOSFET, Q2, functions as the mixer. The amplified rf signal is fed to gate 1 of this device while gate 2 is coupled to the hf oscillator, Q3. The dual-gate MOSFET is an excellent transistor for mixer service as it has good conversion gain, provides isolation between the signal and oscillator inputs, and performs well when handling strong signals. The mixer has a low-*Q* output tank to permit nearly constant gain over a 500-kHz tuning range, even when a 3.5 to 4 MHz i-f is chosen. A capacitive divider provides the impedance transformation necessary to match 52-ohm cable. A short length of RG-58A/U is suitable as an interconnecting cable to the associated receiver.

The bottom view reveals the shielding sections which provide a mount for the switch, as well as isolating the stages of the converter. These shields are made from 3 X 2-inch sections of double-sided circuit board. C2, C3 and C4 are mounted on the bottom side of the main board so that they can be reached easily for alignment purposes.

Construction

All components, except for the dual-section TUNING capacitor and the chassis-mount connectors, are installed on a 3 1/2 X 8-inch etched circuit board. A foil pattern and parts-placement template may be obtained from the ARRL Technical Department (see Fig. 8-49). A length of sheet-aluminum stock, bent to form a 3 1/2 X 8 X 2-inch rectangle (with a 1/4-inch lip around the top), provides a base for the pc board. Sheet-metal screws are used to secure the board to the base. The dual-section input-tuning capacitor, C1, is mounted on a small shelf supported by the 6 1/2 X 3 1/2-inch front panel – see the rear-view photograph. C1 has a built-in reduction drive which facilitates tuning on the 21- and 28-MHz bands. The frame of C1 contains two small trimmer capacitors, one for each section. The trimmer closest to the tuning shaft is retained, but the second one is disabled by removing the screw. Trimmers C2, C3 and C4 are used instead to align the front end for proper tracking. Three 25-pF miniature variable capacitors are employed and are mounted on the bottom side of the circuit board. Before installation, the two solder tabs on each capacitor are bent out at right angles to the capacitor body. Correct positioning of these capacitors is shown in the parts-layout diagram offered in Fig. 8-49.

Alignment

Before applying 12 volts to the converter, check to see that the transistors are properly oriented in their sockets and that no solder bridges are shorting the foil sections on the pc board. Check the resistance from J3 (pin 3) to ground; it should be 250 ohms or higher. A low-resistance reading indicates a fault which should be corrected before power is applied.

The hf crystal oscillator is aligned first. Some means of detecting the oscillator signal, such as an hf oscilloscope, general-coverage receiver or wavemeter, will be needed. Whatever the indicating device used, it should be loosely coupled to the oscillator tank circuit to be checked. Oscillation is started by varying the inductance of the tank inductor, moving the slug in the coil form. Best operation is achieved when the slug is set just above the point of maximum oscillator output, on the high frequency side of resonance. After an oscillator coil has been set, the 12-volt supply should be switched on and off a few times to see that the oscillator starts reliably. If not, try a setting that provides slightly less inductance.

Adjustment of the mixer-output circuit is the next alignment task. The mixer tank circuit is adjusted by moving the slug in L11, which should be set for maximum output noise when the receiver is tuned to the center of the i-f band to be used. A broad peak will be obtained. This is normal and desirable.

Peaking the front-end circuits requires a weak-signal source; a signal generator or on-the-air signal may be employed. Align the 40-meter band first. Using C1, peak the incoming signal for maximum S-meter reading on the associated receiver. Next, peak C1C, the trimmer that is part of the TUNING capacitor, and C2. Then, rotate C1 and observe that only one peak occurs on the S meter. If a double peak is obtained, repeat the adjustments of C1C and C2. Then align C3 and C4 on the 20- and 10-meter bands, respectively. (Don't move the setting of C1C during these adjustments.)

On the 160-, 40- and 10-meter bands the oscillator operates at a higher frequency than does the incoming signal. The receiver tunes in the reverse direction, when using an 80-meter i-f. Thus, 7 MHz is heard at 4 MHz and 7.5 MHz at 3.5 MHz.

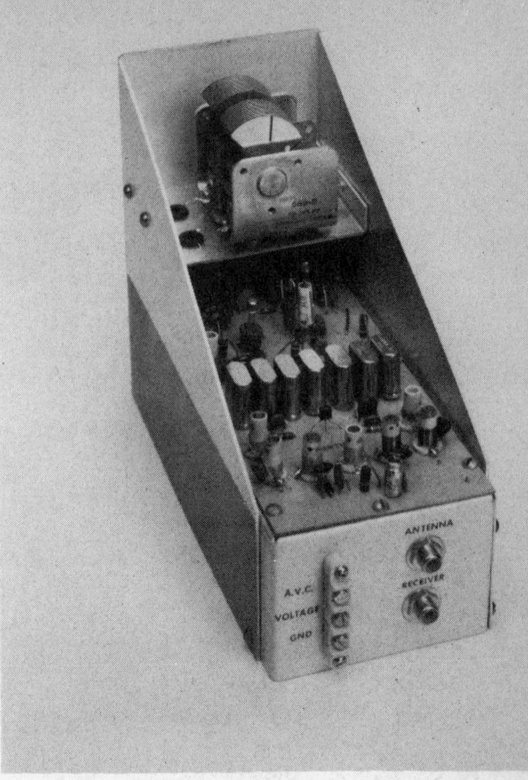

Fig. 8-51 – The front-end tuning capacitor, C1, is mounted on a small shelf just above the toroid coils. The rear section of the main circuit board contains the crystal oscillator. The crystals are soldered directly into the board. The capacitors that go with the oscillator-tank coils are connected across the terminals of the pc-mount coil forms. Most of the chokes and resistors are mounted vertically to save space.

Because the 20- and 15-meter bands have the oscillator set on the low-frequency side, they will tune in the conventional manner. If the values shown in the chart are chosen for a 28-MHz i-f, all bands will tune from 28.5 to 28 MHz, as the signal is always lower in frequency than that of the hf crystal oscillator.

A RECEIVING PACKAGE FOR 160 TO 15 METERS

This solid-state receiver will enable the operator to tune the amateur cw bands from 160 to 15 meters. The main portion of the package consists of a single-conversion tunable i-f which covers the lower portion of the 160-meter band. Converters for each additional desired band may be built into the same package. This approach combines the virtues of high performance, moderate complexity, and reasonable cost with plenty of flexibility. Although the receiver makes a fine unit for fixed-station use, its small size, corresponding light weight, and low power consumption make it an ideal candidate for a quality portable receiver.

Tunable I-F Section

A tuning range of 1800 to 1900 kHz was chosen for the tunable i-f portion of the receiver.

A tunable front-end filter is used to assure rejection of out-of-band signals on 160 meters . . . particularly those of local bc stations. Inexpensive ferrite loopstick inductors are used. They were obtained from Radio Shack at two for $1.19. It was necessary to remove 125 turns of wire from each so that they would be suitable for tuning from 1800 to 1900 kHz with the split-stator variable used in the filter. The unloaded *Q* of each, after modification, is 125 at 1.9 MHz.

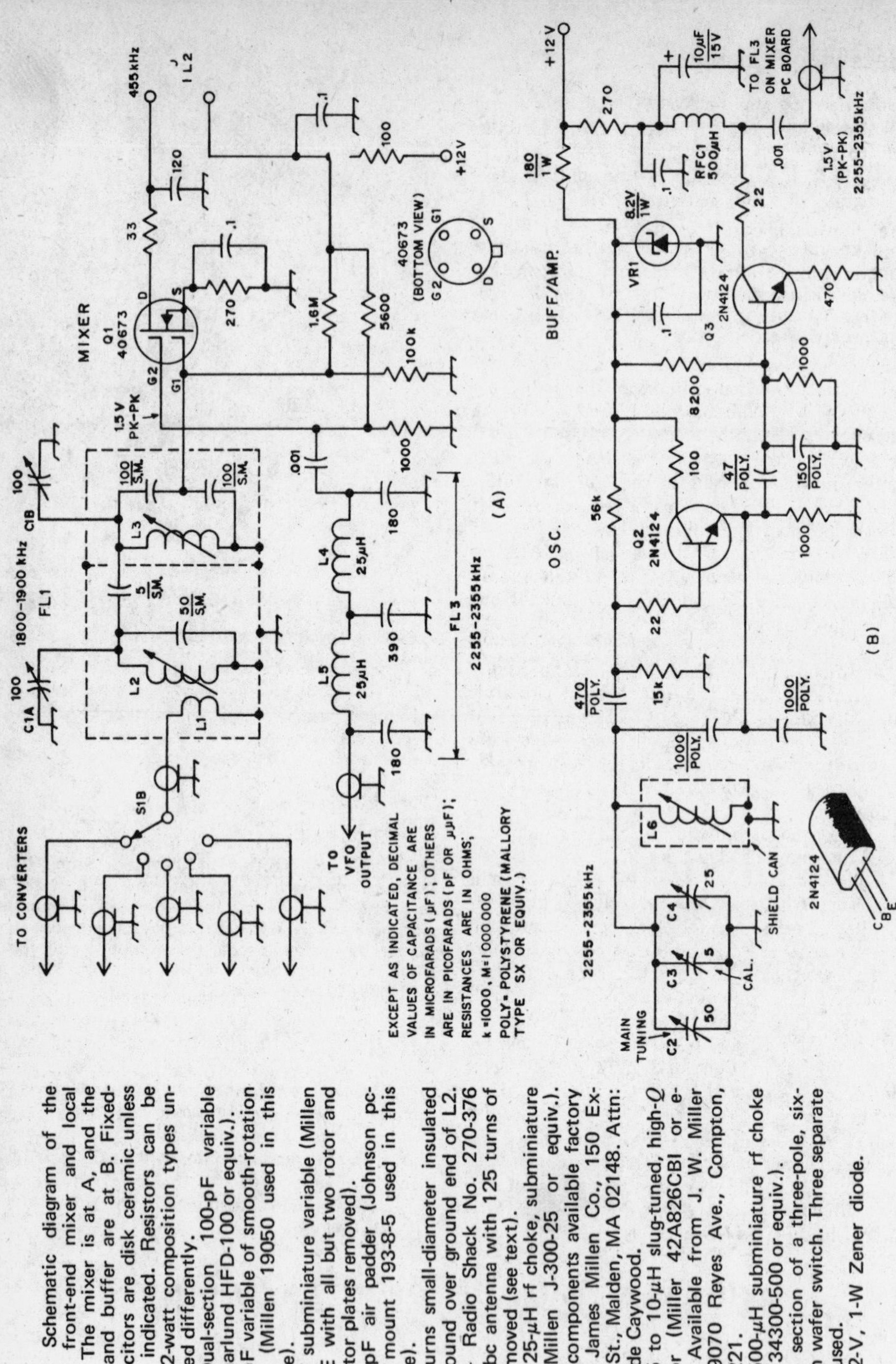

Fig. 1 — Schematic diagram of the 160-meter front-end mixer and local oscillator. The mixer is at A, and the oscillator and buffer are at B. Fixed-value capacitors are disk ceramic unless otherwise indicated. Resistors can be 1/4- or 1/2-watt composition types unless specified differently.

C1 — Dual-section 100-pF variable (Hammarlund HFD-100 or equiv.).

C2 — 50-pF variable of smooth-rotation variety (Millen 19050 used in this example).

C3 — 5-pF subminiature variable (Millen 25012E with all but two rotor and two stator plates removed).

C4 — 25-pF air padder (Johnson pc-board mount 193-8-5 used in this example).

L1 — 3 turns small-diameter insulated wire wound over ground end of L2.

L2, L3 — Radio Shack No. 270-376 ferrite bc antenna with 125 turns of wire removed (see text).

L4, L5 — 25-μH rf choke, subminiature type (Millen J-300-25 or equiv.). Millen components available factory direct. James Millen Co., 150 Exchange St., Malden, MA 02148. Attn: Mr. Wade Caywood.

L6 — 4.45 to 10-μH slug-tuned, high-*Q* inductor (Miller 42A826CBI or equiv.). Available from J. W. Miller Co., 19070 Reyes Ave., Compton, CA 90221.

RFC1 — 500-μH subminiature rf choke (Millen 34300-500 or equiv.).

S1 — One section of a three-pole, six-position wafer switch. Three separate wafers used.

VR1 — 8.2-V, 1-W Zener diode.

An active mixer was chosen for the first stage of the tunable i-f section to limit the number of receiver stages required for suitable overall gain. A passive mixer of the diode-quad type (doubly balanced) would probably have been acceptable, and would be superior to the dual-gate MOSFET type with respect to IMD and overloading. However, such a mixer has a typical conversion loss of 8 dB, and this was not desired. Q1, the dual-gate MOSFET, operates with the signal gate tapped down on FL1 to reduce the possibility of overloading and cross modulation. The conversion gain is roughly 10 dB, and that more than compensates for the insertion loss of the tunable filter; FL1. It

A Receiving Package

Interior view of the receiver. The U-shaped pc board (lower left) contains the i-f, agc, BFO, and audio preamplifier circuits. Mounted edgewise behind the S meter is an MFJ Enterprises 1-watt audio-amplifier module. The subassembly in the center is the VFO. The shield can is a cut-down 35-mm film container. To the right of the VFO, mounted on end, is the front-end tunable filter and 160-meter mixer. An MFJ crystal calibrator is visible at the upper right. One of the hf-band converters is shown in place at the lower right. The others mount ahead of it.

is wise to keep the signal voltage at gate 1 as low as practicable to assure good mixer performance. A small amount of forward bias is applied to both gates of the 40673 mixer to increase the linearity and conversion gain of that stage. A 33-ohm resistor is used in the drain to prevent vhf parasitic oscillations.

Local Oscillator

Stability is especially vital in a local oscillator when a narrow i-f bandwidth is used – 400 Hz in this example. Although the photograph shows silver-mica capacitors in the frequency-determining part of the VFO, they were changed later to the more stable polystyrene kind. Polystyrene capacitors are rated to hold their values within 1.3 percent over a temperature excursion of -10 to +70°C. Furthermore, they are sealed against moisture, and have a tolerance of 5 percent with respect to the marked value. They are no more expensive than dipped silver micas, and have proved to be far more stable than the latter when used in the writer's circuits. Silver-mica capacitors have unpredictable drift characteristics. The polystyrene capacitors stabilize quickly and maintain their values.

It can be seen from Fig. 1B that a conventional Colpitts oscillator is used. The *L* and *C* values were selected to provide *exactly* 100 kHz of tuning range – 2255 to 2355 kHz, thereby providing receiver coverage of 1800 to 1900 kHz. This feature enables the builder to use a dial mechanism of low cost (0 to 100 dial-face markers) and small size. Linearity is quite good, providing 1-kHz accuracy per division up to 50 on the dial plate. At the high end of the tuning range (100 on the dial) there is an error of 2 kHz. A 5-pF variable is used in parallel with the 50-pF main-tuning capacitor to correct for the error when tuning from 1850 to 1900 kHz.

A buffer/amplifier follows the oscillator to increase the rf output and prevent "pulling" of the frequency when the front end is peaked. Output from the buffer is filtered by means of a half-wave network to assure pure sine-wave injection to the mixer. VFO noise was measured as being better than 80 dB down from the peak value of the rf output. The 500-μH rf choke in the collector of Q2 is broadly resonant with the stray circuit capacitance at the VFO operating frequency. FL3 is designed for a Q_L of 3 and a bilateral impedance of 1000 ohms.

I-F Strip

U1 and U2 of Fig. 2 are preceded by an FET i-f preamplifier, the gain of which has been compromised purposely by tapping the gate down on the output of FL2. This stage, Q4, compensates for the insertion loss of FL2 and establishes the noise figure of the i-f strip. An MPF102 was selected because of its low-noise characteristics. It is unconditionally stable without being neutralized, because the gate is tapped down at low impedance. A single-tuned 455-kHz i-f transformer is used to couple the output from Q4 to the input of U1.

RCA CA3028A integrated circuits were chosen for use in the i-f chain because they are inexpensive and easy to work with. In this circuit they are connected as differential amplifiers. Audio-derived agc is applied to terminal 7 of each IC (+2.5 to +9 volts), the constant-current-source bases. The dynamic range of the i-f system is approximately 60 dB.

A passive product detector was chosen over an active one because of its simplicity and good signal-handling capability. A pair of high-speed switching diodes (1N914) were chosen because of their low cost and widespread availability. BFO injection to the product detector is 7 volts pk-pk.

Audio-Derived AGC

Audio output from the product detector is split into two channels, one line feeding the agc strip and the other running to the audio amplifier circuit. An MFC4010A low-cost IC provides 60 dB of gain and serves as the agc amplifier (U3 of Fig. 2). Output from U3 is rectified by means of a voltage doubler consisting of two 1N914 diodes. Because of the high gain capability of U3 it tends to be unstable at frequencies above the audio range. Addition of the .01-μF bypass from terminal 2 to ground cured all signs of unstable operation in this circuit. Stubborn cases may require some additional bypassing at terminal 4 of U3. If so, use only that amount necessary to ensure stability.

Rectified audio voltage from CR4 and CR5 is supplied to a two-transistor dc amplifier, Q7 and Q8. Agc voltage is taken from the emitter of Q8. Its amount varies with the incoming signal level, and changes as the current-caused voltage drop across the 1500-ohm emitter resistor, R6, shifts in

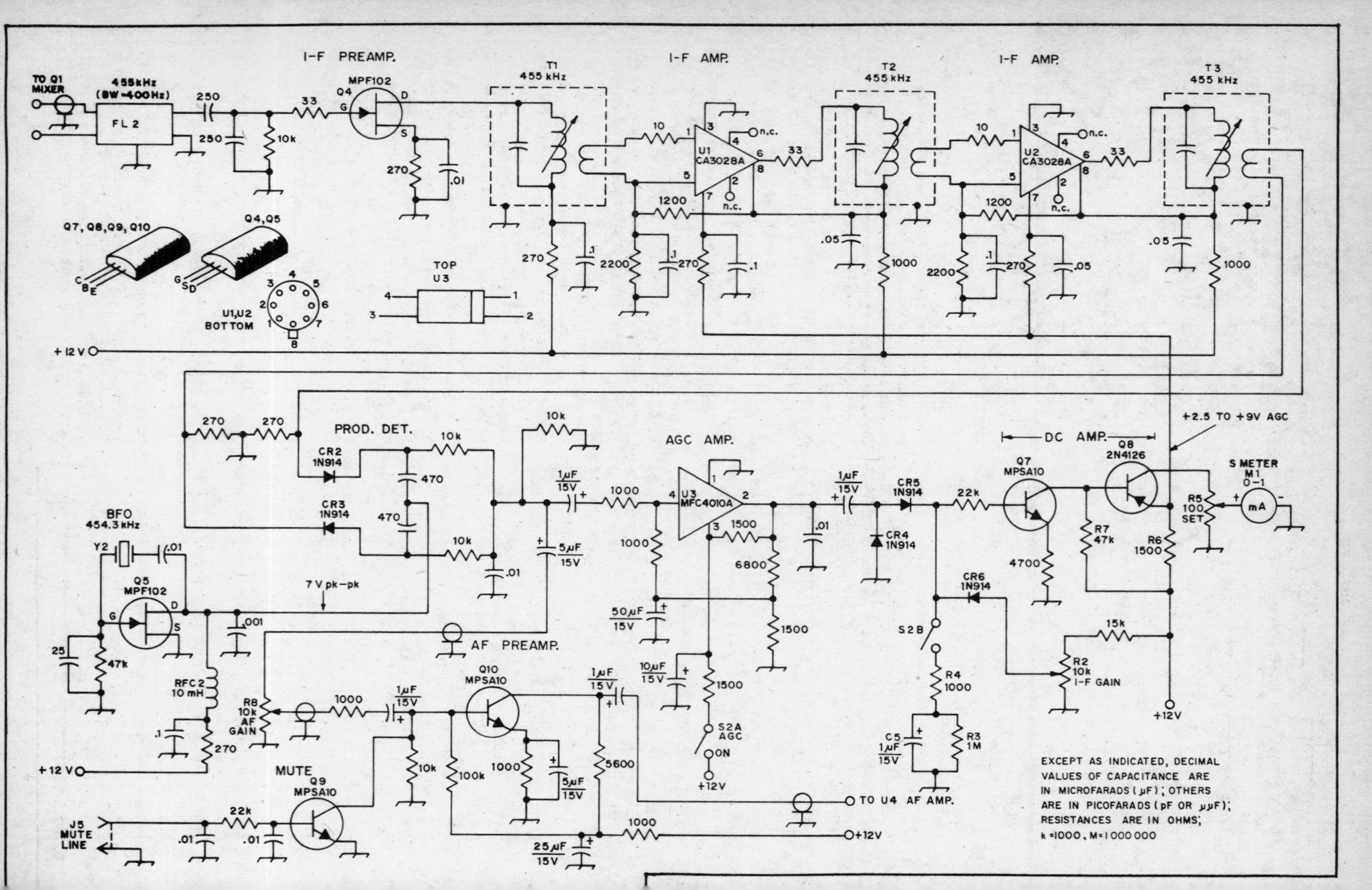
I-F PREAMP.
I-F AMP.
I-F AMP.
TO Q1 MIXER
455kHz (BW-400Hz)
FL 2
MPF102
Q4
T1 455 kHz
T2 455 kHz
T3 455 kHz
U1 CA3028A
U2 CA3028A
n.c.
Q7, Q8, Q9, Q10
Q4, Q5
TOP U3
U1, U2 BOTTOM
+ 12 V
PROD. DET.
CR2 1N914
CR3 1N914
AGC AMP.
U3 MFC4010A
DC AMP.
+2.5 TO +9V AGC
Q7 MPSA10
Q8 2N4126
S METER M1 0-1
mA
R5 100 SET
R6 1500
R7 47k
CR5 1N914
CR4 1N914
CR6 1N914
S2 B
R4 1000
R3 1M
C5 1µF 15V
R2 10k I-F GAIN
BFO 454.3 kHz
Y2
Q5 MPF102
7 V pk-pk
AF PREAMP.
Q10 MPSA10
RFC2 10 mH
R8 10k AF GAIN
S2A AGC
ON
MUTE Q9 MPSA10
J5 MUTE LINE
TO U4 AF AMP.
EXCEPT AS INDICATED, DECIMAL VALUES OF CAPACITANCE ARE IN MICROFARADS (µF); OTHERS ARE IN PICOFARADS (pF OR µµF); RESISTANCES ARE IN OHMS; k=1000, M=1000 000

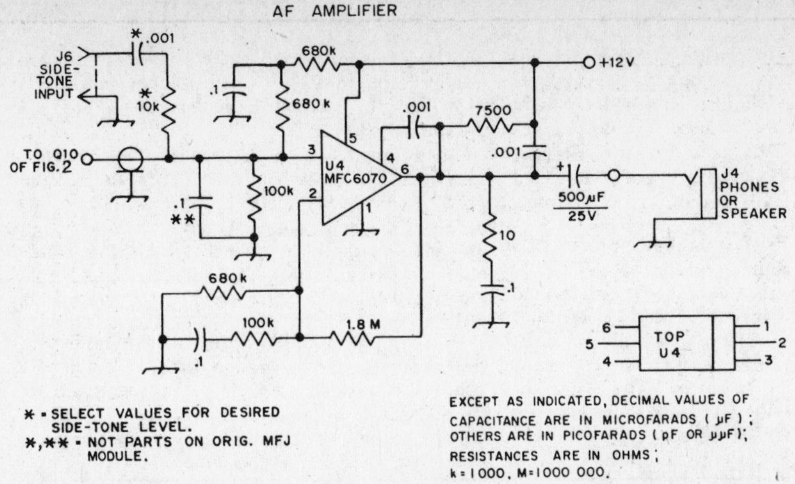

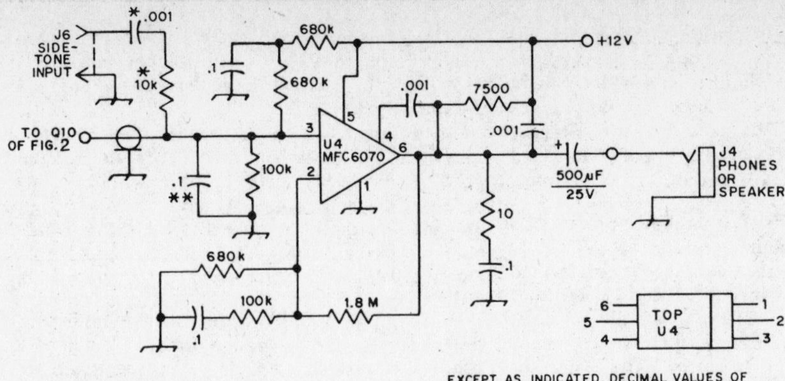

Fig. 3 — Schematic diagram of the MFJ Enterprises 1-watt audio module used in the receiver.

* = SELECT VALUES FOR DESIRED SIDE-TONE LEVEL.
*,** = NOT PARTS ON ORIG. MFJ MODULE.

EXCEPT AS INDICATED, DECIMAL VALUES OF CAPACITANCE ARE IN MICROFARADS (µF) ; OTHERS ARE IN PICOFARADS (pF OR µµF); RESISTANCES ARE IN OHMS ; k = 1000, M = 1000 000.

value. S meter M1 follows the same excursions in current at Q8.

Manual i-f gain control is possible by means of potentiometer R2. It supplies dc voltage to the base of Q7, thereby causing a voltage drop across R7, which causes Q8 to conduct more heavily. As a result, the voltage drop across R6 increases and reduces the agc voltage to lower the gain of the i-f system. The same action takes place during normal agc action. Diode CR6 acts as a gate to prevent the dc voltage provided by CR4 and CR5 from being disturbed by the presence of R2. Maximum i-f gain occurs when the arm of R2 is closest to ground.

R3 and C5 establish the agc time constant. The value of R4 can be tailored to provide the attack-time characteristics one prefers. Slower or faster agc time constants can be obtained by changing the values of R3 and C5. The final values will be a matter of operator preference; no two people seem to agree on which time constant is best.

Fig. 2 — Schematic diagram of the i-f, agc, and audio preamplifier circuits. Capacitors are disk ceramic except those with polarity marked, which are electrolytic. Fixed-value resistors can be 1/4- or 1/2-watt composition unless otherwise noted. Numbered components not appearing in the parts list are so numbered for text discussion.

CR2-CR6, incl. — High-speed silicon switching diode, 1N914 or equiv.

FL2 — 455-kHz Collins mechanical filter, 400-Hz bandwidth. No. F455FD-04, Collins Radio Co., 4311 Jamboree Blvd., Newport Beach, CA 92663. Those wishing to use a 300-Hz-bandwidth Collins filter (slightly larger physical size) can obtain one from New England Engineering, P.O. Box 145, Wethersfield, CT 06109.

J5 — Phono jack, single-hole mount.

M1 — 0 to 1-mA meter (Simpson No. 1521 edge-mount type used in this receiver). Builder may use any 0 to 1-mA meter of his choice.

R2, R8 — 10,000-ohm linear-taper control.

R5 — 100-ohm pc-board-mount control (Mallory MTC-12L1 or equiv.).

RFC2 — 10-mH subminiature rf choke (Millen J302-10,000 or equiv.).

S2 — Two-pole, single-throw toggle. Subminiature type used in this example.

T1-T3, incl. — Single-tuned miniature 455-kHz i-f transformer, 30,000-ohm primary to 500-ohm secondary (Radio Shack No. 273-1383). Use the black core at T1, yellow core at T2, and white core at T3.

U1, U2 — RCA integrated circuit.

U3 — Motorola integrated circuit.

Y2 — 454.3-kHz crystal in HC-6/U style holder (International Crystal Co., type EX. 10 N. Lee St., Oklahoma City, OK 73102).

The Audio System

Low-cost components are used in the audio system of Fig. 2. The circuit performs well and delivers undistorted af output up to one watt in level. An MPSA10 transistor is employed as an audio preamplifier. Muting is provided for by means of another MPSA10, Q9. A positive-polarity voltage is fed to the base of Q9 from the transmitter changeover system to saturate the muting transistor. When in the saturated mode, Q9 shorts out the base of Q10 to silence the receiver. The audio output circuit, U4 of Fig. 3, was borrowed from MFJ Enterprises and is that used in their 1-watt module, No. 1000. Those wishing to do so may order the assembly direct from MFJ.

Provisions are made for feeding a side-tone signal into terminal 3 of U4. This will permit monitoring one's sending even though the receiver is muted by means of Q9. U4 remains operative at all times.

BFO

An MPF102 JFET functions in a Pierce crystal-controlled BFO, Q5 of Fig. 2. The BFO frequency is 700 Hz away from the center frequency of the i-f system (454.3 or 455.7 kHz).

HF-Band Converters

The same pattern is followed for the individual crystal-controlled converters used from 40 through 15 meters (Fig. 4). The 80-meter design is slightly different and is seen in Fig. 5. Separate converters were incorporated to eliminate the need for complicated band switching, and also to permit optimization of circuit values for each band of interest. The system used in this receiver calls for switching of only dc and 50-ohm circuitry. Low-impedance switching eliminates problems caused by long switch leads. Switching at high-impedance points, which is the usual technique in multiband receivers, can impair the quality of the tuned circuits and makes isolation of critical circuits more difficult.

A common-gate JFET rf amplifier provides 10 dB of gain in these converters, and has good IMD and overload immunity. A 40673 MOSFET is used as the mixer in each converter. Output is taken at the 1.8- to 1.9-MHz i-f from a broadly resonant circuit formed by a 500-μH rf choke and an rf voltage divider which uses a series capacitor combination (25 and 50 pF). The divider provides a low-impedance pickoff point for the i-f output line to the tunable i-f receiver section.

The 40- through 15-meter converters employ simple Colpitts oscillators. A high-beta transistor is used for the oscillator. It has an f_T of approximately 200 MHz.

A different design is used in the 80-meter converter, wherein a bandpass filter is used as the input fixed-tuned circuit. This technique was necessary to assure ample bandwidth from 3.5 to 3.6 MHz without the need to have a panel-mounted peaking control. The bandwidth is ample for an 80- and 75-meter frequency spread of 1 MHz.

No rf amplifier is used in the 80-meter converter. As is true of operation on 160 meters, atmospheric and man-made noise levels almost always exceed the noise of the receiver. Therefore, in the interest of good mixer performance (minimum IMD and overloading) the rf stage was

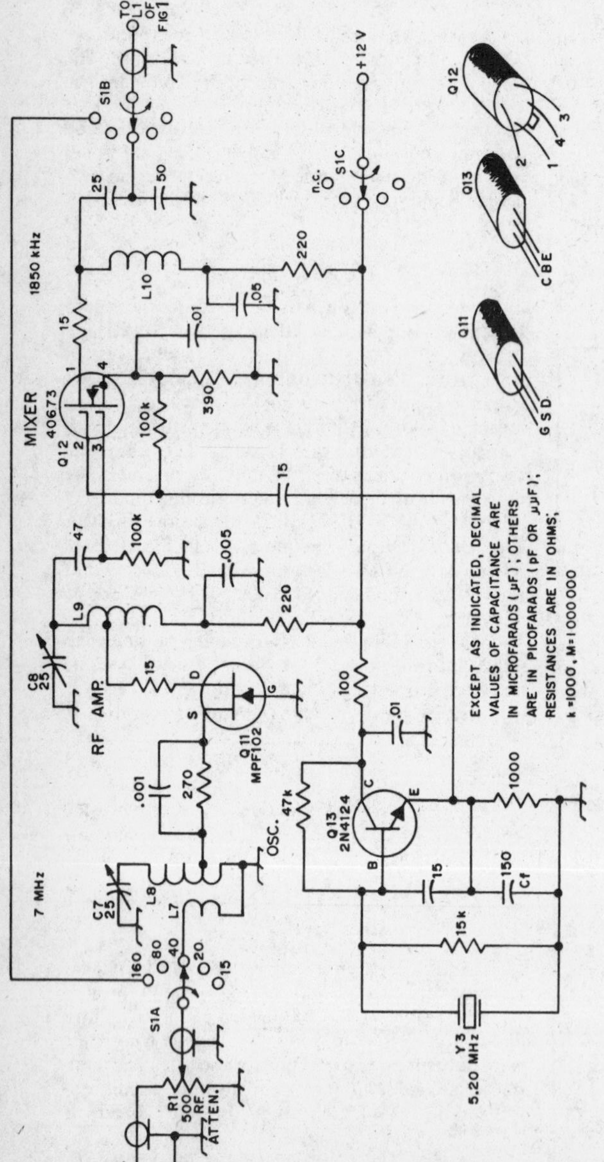

Fig. 4 — Schematic diagram of the 40-meter converter. Capacitors are disk ceramic (fixed-value types). Resistors can be 1/4- or 1/2-watt composition types.
C7, C8 — Miniature ceramic or compression trimmer, 5- to 25-pF range.
C_f — 39 pF for 20-, and 15-meter converters.
J1 — Coax connector of builder's choice.
L7 — 2 turns No. 28 enam. wire over grounded end of L8 for 40, 20, and 15 meters.
L8 — 40 meters, 50 turns No. 28 enam. on Amidon T-50-2 toroid core. Tap 8 turns above ground (13 μH, Q_u = 180). 20 meters, 44 turns No. 28 enam. on Amidon T-50-6 toroid core. Tap 6 turns above ground (8 μH, Q_u = 180). 15 meters, 25 turns No. 28 enam. on Amidon T-50-6 toroid core. Tap 4 turns above ground (4 μH, Q_u = 150).
L9 — 40 meters, same as L8, but tap at 25 turns. 20 meters, same as L8, but tap at 22 turns. 15 meters, same as L8, but tap at 12 turns.
L10 — 500-μH miniature rf choke (Millen J302-500 or equiv.).
Q11, Q13 — Motorola transistor.
Q12 — RCA dual-gate MOSFET.
R1 — 500-ohm. linear-taper composition control.
S1 — Three-pole, 6-position wafer switch. Three separate wafer sections are recommended.
Y3 — Type GP crystal in FM-1 holder, fundamental mode. 40 meters, 5.20 MHz. 20 meters, 12.20 MHz. 15 meters, 19.2 MHz (International Crystal Co., 10 N. Lee St., Okla. City, OK 73102).

omitted. The front-end bandpass filter was designed for a characteristic bilateral impedance of 600 ohms. The series-resonant element is tapped midway on the parallel-tuned elements in order to realize practical *L* and *C* values (150-ohm points). A Pierce oscillator is used in the 80-meter front-end module to assure plenty of feedback for the 1700-kHz crystal.

Construction Notes

The cabinet and chassis for this receiver were formed by hand from No. 16 aluminum sheeting. The cabinet dimensions (HWD) are 2-3/4 × 10 × 8 inches.

The converters and audio module are mounted vertically and are held in place by means of No. 6 spade bolts (two per module). Spade bolts are used also to fasten the 160-meter front-end assembly to the chassis. The remainder of the circuit boards are mounted parallel to the chassis on short metal standoff posts. Kurz-Kasch ribbed-aluminum knobs are used on the controls.

To assure good mechanical stability of the VFO an aluminum brace is attached between the rear and front panels near the top center. The brace is 2-1/2 inches wide. One No. 6 sheet-metal screw is used to secure the lid of the cabinet to the center of the brace. The lower right- and left-hand sides of the lid are affixed to the chassis by using No. 6 sheet-metal screws. L brackets are mounted on the right and left edges of the chassis to permit fastening the cover securely at those points.

The circuit-board material used in this receiver is the glass-epoxy variety. This type of board is recommended in the interest of longevity, minimum warping, and high dielectric factor. Double-sided pc board has been used for all modules but those of the converters and VFO. The copper surface on the side where the components are mounted serves as a ground plane for the circuit, and greatly reduces the possibility of instability problems. This technique is not recommended for the VFO circuit because changes in temperature will cause small variations in capacitance between the two sides of the board, thereby encouraging unwanted frequency changes in the VFO output.

Adjustment

The 160-meter tunable i-f receiver should be tuned up before the converters are checked out. If a signal generator is not available, couple a wire from the receiver antenna jack to the local oscillator of a broadcast-band radio. Tune the radio to 1345 kHz to obtain an 1800-kHz output from its local oscillator. Use that signal to set the VFO for reception at 1800 kHz (VFO on 2255 kHz). Reception at 1900 kHz, can be verified by tuning the a-m radio to 1445 kHz, at which time its local oscillator will be on 1900 kHz. Next, set the broadcast radio for 1395 kHz to place its local

Fig. 5 — Schematic diagram of the 80-meter converter. Capacitors are disk ceramic. Resistors can be 1/4- or 1/2-watt composition types.

L11 — 4 turns No. 28 enam. wire over grounded end of L12.

L12 — 36 turns No. 28 enam. wire on Amidon T-50-2 toroid core (5.5 μH, Q_u = 175). Tap at 18 turns.

L13 — 68-μH miniature rf choke (Q_u of 50 or greater). Millen 34300-68 used in this example.

L14 — Same as L12.

L15 — 500-μH miniature rf choke (Millen J302-500 or equiv.).

Q14 — RCA dual-gate MOSFET.

Q15 — Motorola transistor.

Y4 — Type GP crystal in F-700 holder, 1700 kHz (International Crystal Co.).

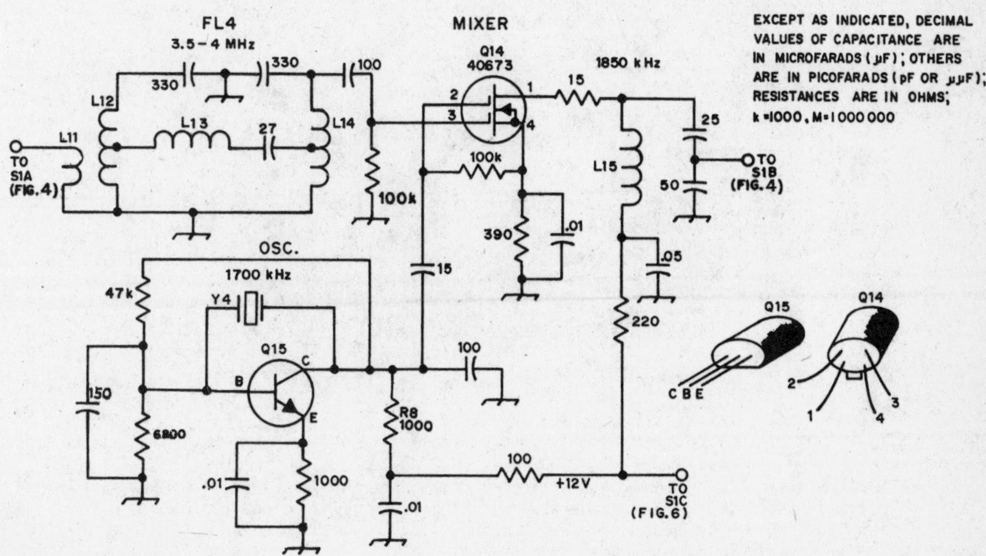

oscillator at 1850 kHz. Tune in this signal and peak the tuned circuits in FL1 for maximum response as heard in the speaker of the homemade receiver. Repeat the peaking process several times until the filter is optimized.

Now, tune T1, T2, and T3 for maximum signal output as heard in the speaker. All that remains to be adjusted is the S-meter control, R5. With the agc on, but with the i-f gain (R2) set at *minimum* sensitivity, adjust R5 to give full-scale deflection of M1. This procedure will complete the tune-up of the main portion of the receiver.

Checkout of the converters is similarly easy. The trimmers should be adjusted for peak signal response at 3550, 7050, 14,050, 21,050, and 28,050 kHz. On-the-air signals, preferably weak ones, will suffice for this part of the tune-up.

Performance

VFO drift from a cold start to full stabilization (5 minutes) was measured as 70 Hz. Sensitivity on all of the bands covered is such that a 0.1-μV signal from a model 80 generator (50-ohm, 6-dB pad inserted) is discernible in the receiver output. Agc action is more than ample for normal reception. Agc response begins at a signal amount of approximately 4 μV and levels off to remain constant when the signals reach 10 μV. No change in audio-output level could be observed when varying the input signal from 10 to 10,000 μV.

Because no trimmers are used to "net" the converter oscillators it is necessary to recalibrate the main-tuning dial for each band above 1.8 MHz by adjusting C3, the panel-mounted trimmer.

Current drain of this receiver is 50 mA on 160 meters when no signal is being received. The drain increases to 65 mA when any one of the converters is activated. Maximum current drain when signals are being received is approximately 75 mA when 600-ohm phones are being used. It will swing as high as 100 mA on peaks when a 4-ohm speaker is used in place of the phones.

Templates for the pc boards used in this receiver, plus a parts-placement guide, can be obtained by sending $1 and a large self-addressed, stamped envelope to ARRL Hq. A list of circuit-board suppliers will be included in the package for those who wish to purchase ready-made boards.

A HIGH-PERFORMANCE SOLID-STATE RECEIVER

The design is based on the "D.C. 80-10 Receiver" described in *QST* for May, 1969. Changes and improvements include the addition of a stage of rf amplification and the use of a single integrated-circuit audio stage. The emphasis is on high performance at minimum cost.

Plug-in converters for 80, 40, and 15 meters are used to provide three-band coverage for the Novice. The lower 300 kHz of each band are covered so that all of the cw segments are included. Two circuit boards, one for the converter and the other for the product detector, beat frequency oscillator (BFO), and audio stages, comprise the receiver. The detector and the BFO tune 2.2 to 2.5 MHz – the intermediate frequency (i-f) of the converters. An audio filter, employing an 88-mH telephone toroid, provides good cw selectivity. Ssb signals may also be tuned in and a-m reception is possible by zero-beating the desired a-m signal. The receiver may be run for relatively long periods of time from

Exterior view of the three-band beginner's receiver. The dimensions are 11 × 5-1/2 × 7 inches. The vernier dial is calibrated for 10 kHz per division. The front panel is finished in dark blue. White press-on decals are used to identify the gain control and phone jack. The receiver was built by WA1CQW.

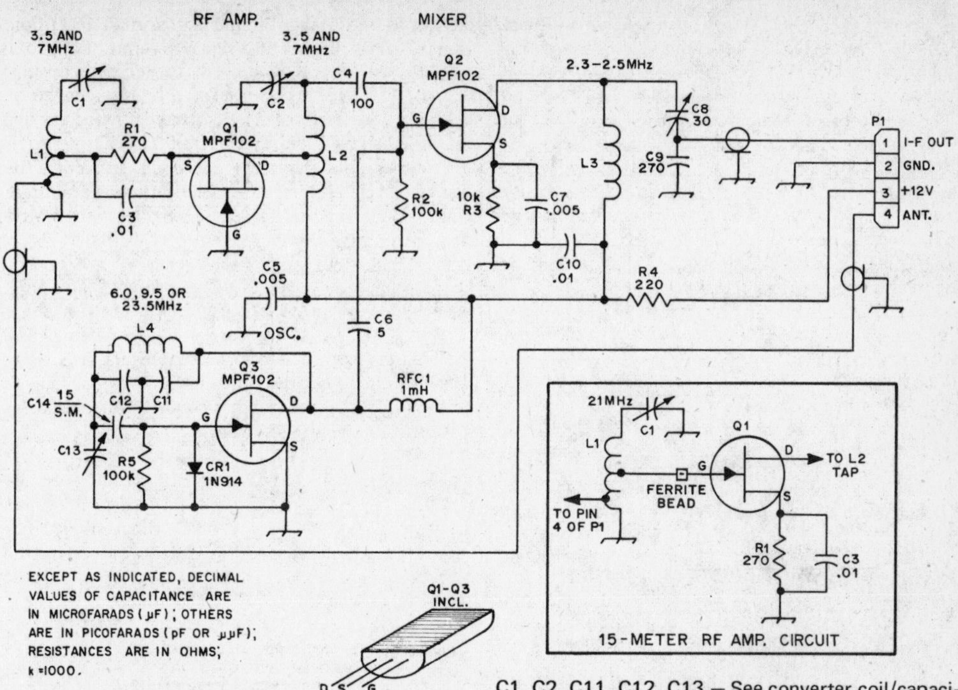

Fig. 1 — Schematic diagram of the plug-in converter front end. Rf amplifier Q1 is wired differently for operation on 21 MHz (see inset), otherwise the circuit is the same for all three bands. Resistors are 1/2-watt composition. Fixed-value capacitors are disk ceramic unless otherwise noted. Numbered components not listed below are identified for circuit-board layout purposes.

C1, C2, C11, C12, C13 — See converter coil/capacitor table.
C8 — 3 to 30-pF mica compression trimmer.
L1, L2, L4 — See converter coil/capacitor table.
L3 — 150-μH inductor; 90 turns No. 30 enamel wire wound on Amidon Assoc. T-80-3 toriod core (Amidon Assoc., 12033 Otsego Street, N. Hollywood, CA 91607).
RFC1 — 1-mH rf choke (James Millen J300-1000 or equiv.).

a battery supply, because of its low dc current drain.

The use of only two controls (frequency tuning and audio gain) keep the operation of the receiver simple. More than enough audio is available to drive a pair of high-impedance headphones, which are connected to a jack on the front panel.

Circuit Information

The design is fairly uncomplicated. A block diagram in Fig. 3 shows the basic stages of the receiver. An rf amplifier tuned to the appropriate amateur bands amplifies incoming signals. The mixer "shifts", or heterodynes, these signals down to the intermediate-frequency range (2.2 to 2.5 MHz), which is the difference between the oscillator frequency and the signal frequency. In the product detector, the BFO signal beats with the i-f signal to produce low-level audio output. Audio amplification is then necessary to raise the audio output to a level sufficient for headphone operation.

The converters for the three bands are basically alike. The rf amplifier, mixer, and oscillator stages each employ a JFET (junction field-effect transistor). The rf amplifier operates in a grounded-gate configuration, except in the 15-meter converter where a grounded-source hookup is employed to provide greater gain. Although a crystal-controlled oscillator could have been used, a fixed-tuned self-excited oscillator was chosen to minimize cost. It is stable and easy to adjust.

The basic receiver is laid out on a separate circuit board, and consists of the integrated-circuit product detector, a JFET BFO, and an integrated-circuit audio amplifier. The detector tunes from 2.2 to 2.5 MHz by means of L2, C1, C2, and C3A. Use of the integrated circuit helps reduce size, cost, and complexity of this stage. The BFO tunes the same frequency range as the detector. The beat-frequency oscillator signal, injected through a 5-pF capacitor, mixes with incoming i-f signals to provide a beat note for cw reception or furnishes a carrier for ssb reception. The two stages are gang-tuned by means of C3, a dual-section 100-pF variable capacitor. The Zener diodes, VR1 and VR2, help provide greater electrical stability by regulating the supply voltages for both stages.

The audio stage employs an operational amplifier – an integrated circuit capable of high gain. Its level of output furnishes plenty of audio for high-impedance headphone operation.

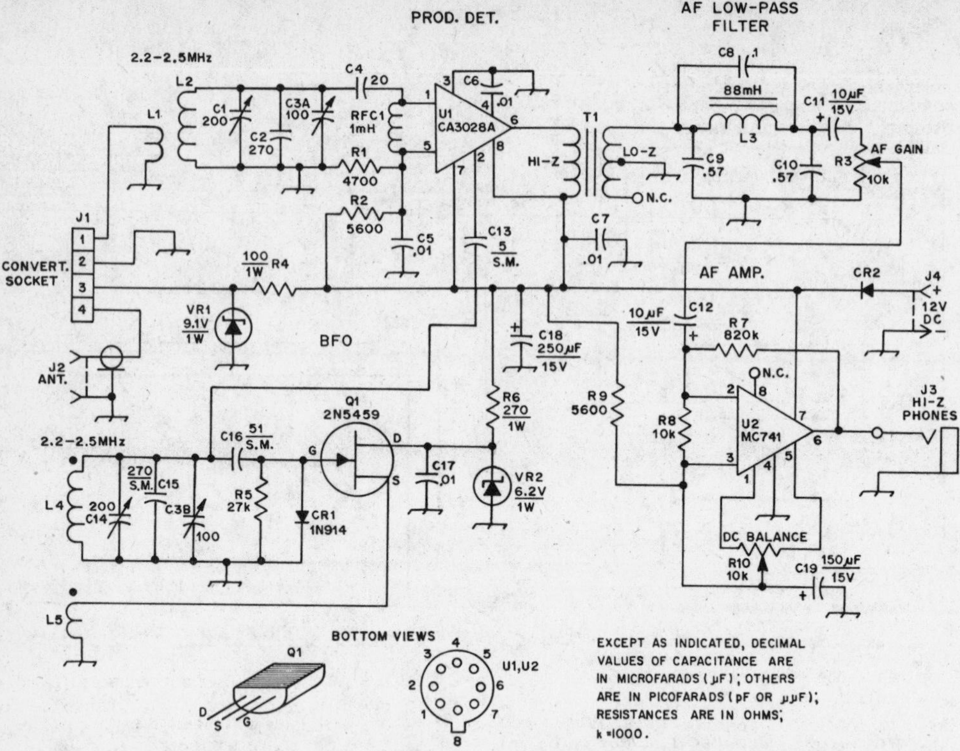

Fig. 2 – Schematic diagram of the tunable i-f portion of the receiver. Capacitors with polarity marked are electrolytic. Fixed-value capacitors are disk ceramic unless otherwise noted. Numbered parts not appearing below are so identified for pc-board layout purposes only.

C1, C14 – 24 to 200-pF mica compression trimmer (Elmenco Type 42 or equiv.).
C3 – Air variable, 100 pF per section, split stator (James Millen 26100 RM or equiv.). (James Millen Mfg. Co., 150 Exchange St., Malden, MA. Direct orders accepted.)
CR2 – Silicon rectifier, 50 PRV at 1 A (IOR 1N4001, Motorola HEP161, or equiv.).
J1 – 4-pin female chassis-mount socket to mate with P1 of Fig. 1 (Amphenol 77MIP4 or equiv.).
J2 – Chassis-mount coax receptacle, type SO-239.
J3 – 2-conductor phone jack (Switchcraft Little-Jax or equiv.).
J4 – RCA phono connector, single-hole mounting.
L1 – 5 turns No. 24 enameled wire wound over ground end of L2.
L2, L4 – 45 turns No. 24 enamel wire on Amidon Assoc. T-80-2 toroid core.
L3 – 88-mH telephone-type toroidal inductor (see *QST* Ham Ads for suppliers).
L5 – 14 turns No. 24 enameled wire over ground end of L4. Observe polarity of L4 and L5 as discussed in the text.
Q1 – Motorola junction FET, 2N5459/MPF105.
R3 – 10,000-ohm, audio-taper, carbon control.
R10 – 10,000-ohm, linear-taper, pc-board-mount control (Mallory MTC14L1 or equiv.).
RFC1 – 1-mH rf choke (James Millen J300-1000 or equiv.).
T1 – Miniature audio transformer, 10,000-ohm pri. to 1000-ohm secondary (Lafayette Radio 00T6124 or equiv., use 1/2 of secondary winding).
U1 – RCA CA3028A integrated circuit.
U2 – Motorola MC741 integrated circuit.
VR1 – 9.1-volt Zener diode, 1 watt (IOR 1N1770, Motorola HEP104, or equiv.).
VR2 – 6.2-volt Zener diode, 1 watt (IOR 1N3828, Motorola HEP103, or equiv.).
Note: Most of the components used in this receiver are available from Allied Electronics (see *QST* for July 1972, "The Ailing Emporium," for addresses of parts suppliers).

Between the dectector and audio stages is an *m*-derived audio low-pass filter. It is used to reject unwanted high-frequency responses to aid cw reception. It uses a single telephone-type surplus 88-mH toriod, which can be purchased from a number of surplus houses.

Diode CR4, at the 12-volt dc input, prevents accidental damage to the circuit should the operator connect the wrong-polarity voltage to the power supply terminal. The diode will conduct, and thus allow the receiver to operate only when a positive voltage is connected to the proper terminal.

Construction Notes

The converters are housed in 5 × 4 × 3-inch Miniboxes, such as a Bud CU-2105A. Each circuit board, 3 1/4 × 4 1/2 inches in size, is mounted on

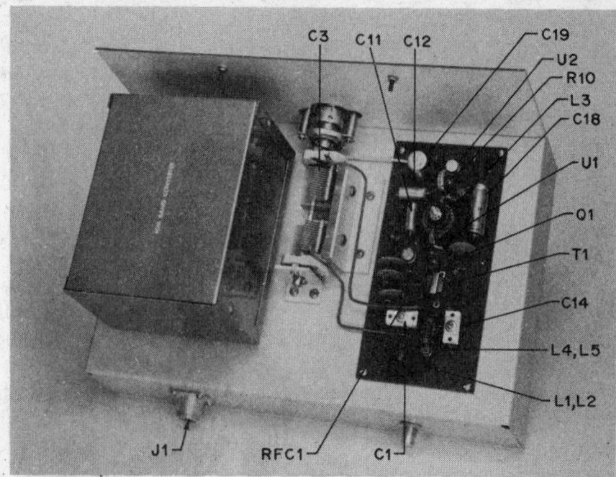

Top view of one of the converters. The completed pc board is mounted inside a Minibox. The assembly, with cover installed, plugs into the main chassis of the receiver. Significant parts are identified in this photo.

3/8-inch metal spacers. A four-prong plug is installed on the bottom of each Minibox so that the converters can be plugged into the main chassis of the receiver when changing bands. Q1, Q2, and Q3 are soldered directly to the board with leads as short as possible to minimize unwanted stray inductance. Plug-in sockets for the FETs are not recommended at these frequencies since the inductance in the leads can cause feedback and thus, unwanted oscillations. The circuit boards are prepared such that either the grounded-gate or the grounded-source rf amplifier can be used in the appropriate converters. It is only necessary to change two jumper wires to employ either configuration. Toroidal-wound coils are employed for all tuned circuits as their self-shielding property greatly reduces unwanted coupling between the circuits. L1 and L2 are held in place on the circuit board by their respective leads. L3 is secured by an insulating washer and a screw which is passed through the toroid core from underneath the board. L4 is fastened in a like manner to enhance the mechanical stability of the oscillator.

The detector, BFO, and audio circuitry are on a 3 × 6-inch circuit board which is mounted directly on top of the chassis. The chassis base, a Bud AC-407, measures 7 × 11 × 2 inches. The 5-1/2 × 11-inch front panel and the chassis cover were homemade, although the cover is not strictly desirable or necessary if one frequently plugs in and unplugs the converters to change bands. The eight-pin integrated circuits are soldered directly to the boards, although sockets can be used if desired. Full-size templates are given in *QST* for October, 1972.

The main-tuning capacitor C3 is mounted on top of the chassis base. A Millen 26100RM is used here although any equivalent dual-section capacitor can be used instead. The Millen model is fitted with its own Plexiglas mounting plate to insulate it from a metal chassis, but it was necessary to mount it on its side by means of two right-angle aluminum brackets (in back and on the side of the capacitor) because of complications in mounting the tuning dial. The use of two mounting brackets as opposed to one also reduces tuning backlash by minimizing

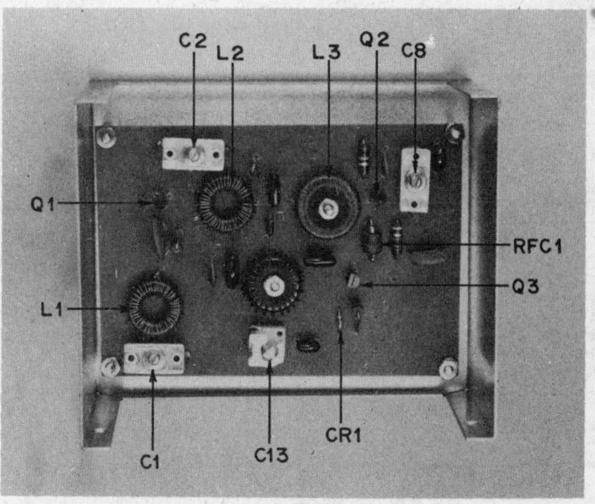

View of the completed receiver. The main-tuning capacitor is located at the center of the chassis. The pc board at the right is that of the tunable i-f, and audio section of the receiver. Antenna and power supply jacks are visible on the rear apron of the chassis.

wobbling of the capacitor. The front-panel tuning mechanism is a two-speed Miller MD-4 dial, which provides 6:1 and 36:1 drive ratios – slow enough that signals are easily tuned in. Any panel dial with a slow tuning rate can be used instead.

In lieu of an outboard power supply, eight size C flashlight batteries can be series connected and strap mounted inside the chassis base (there is ample room). The unit draws about 70 mA at 12 volts dc.

Testing and Alignment

First, the etched circuit boards should be inspected for possible breaks in the foil, unwanted solder bridges between adjacent conductors, or poor solder joints. The one may proceed with the alignment. A well-calibrated general-coverage receiver and an rf signal source, such as a grid-dip oscillator or a signal generator, are required.

It is first necessary to determine if the BFO is functioning. With power applied, listen for the BFO signal on the general-coverage receiver in the range of 2.2 to 2.5 MHz. The carrier should be strong enough that a few feet of wire will suffice as a pickup antenna for the monitor receiver. If no signal can be heard, check to see that L5 and L6 are wound in the *same* direction on their toroid core, i.e., both coils are wound counterclockwise, or both clockwise, but not in opposite directions. Once the signal is found, adjust the BFO frequency by means of trimmer capacitor C14 until the signal is heard at exactly 2.2 MHz with the dual-section main-tuning capacitor, C3, almost fully *meshed*. Then adjust C3 until it is fully *unmeshed*. The BFO signal should be found at 2.5 MHz or slightly higher (a little overlap of the 300-kHz segment is desirable to assure complete coverage of the desired tuning range).

Next adjust the balance control, R10, in the audio stage so the dc voltage appearing across the headphone jack is 6 volts (one half the dc supply voltage). Headphones can now be plugged into the receiver. With the audio gain turned up, some hiss should be clearly audible. If not, the audio stage is not working properly.

With converters unplugged, feed a 2.2– to 2.5-MHz signal into the detector through L1, either by direct connection to a signal generator output or by light coupling to a grid-dip oscillator. Adjust the main-tuning dial until the signal from the rf source is located. Peak trimmer capacitor C1 for maximum received signal strength. This ensures that the detector and BFO tuned circuits will track as they are tuned through their frequency range.

One of the converters may be plugged in now. Despite the different frequencies involved, adjustment of each converter is the same. To determine that the converter oscillator is working properly, listen on the general-coverage receiver for oscillator its signal at approximately the frequency on which it should be oscillating. Again the signal should be strong enough to be plainly audible on the general-coverage receiver. Adjust trimmer capacitor C13 until the oscillator frequency is "on the nose."

Converter Coil and Capacitor Table

Band	*80 Meters*	*40 Meters*	*15 Meters*
C11	470 pF, s.m.	220 pF, s.m.	100 pF, s.m.
C12	330 pF, s.m.	150 pF, s.m.	100 pF, s.m.
C1,C2	470 to 100-pF trimmer (Elmenco 423)	7 to 100-pF trimmer (Elmenco 423)	2 to 25-pF trimmer (Elmenco 421)
C13	1.8 to 16.7-pF min. air variable (Johnson) 189-0506-005).	1.5 to 11.6-pF min. air variable (Johnson 189-0504-005).	Same type as for 40 meters.
L1	55 μH. 100 turns No.28 enam. on Amidon T-80-2 toroid core. Ant. tap at 10 turns above gnd. Tap Q1 source at 50 turns above gnd.	10 μH. 42 turns No. 30 enam. on Amidon T-68-2 toroid core. Ant. tap at 4 turns above gnd. Q1 source tap at 21 turns above gnd.	5.5 μH. 30 turns No. 26 enam. on Amidon T-68-2 toroid core. Ant. tap at 3-1/2 turns above gnd. Q1 source tap at 12 turns above gnd.
L2	Same number of turns and core material as L1. Tap at 50 turns.	Same number of turns and material core as as L1. Tap at 21 turns	Same number of turns and core material as L1. Tap at 12 turns.
L4	3.4 μH. Use 23 turns No. 20 enam. on Amidon T-68-2 toroid core.	2.9 μH. Use 21 turns No. 20 enam. on Amidon T-68-2 toroid core.	0.9 μH. Use 10 turns No. 18 enam. on Amidon T-68-2 toroid core.

S.m. = silver mica. All toroid windings are spaced to occupy the entire core circumference, and as uniformly as possible.

Next, it is necessary to peak the converter by listening to a signal in the amateur band covered by the converter. Connect a signal source to the antenna input. The main-tuning capacitor should be set to approximately the center of its range, or to the segment of the band to be used most frequently. The 2.2-MHz i-f corresponds to the high-frequency end of each segment and 2.5-MHz to the low-frequency end. Tune the signal source to this frequency and adjust trimmer capacitors C1, C2, and C8 in the converter for maximum received signal strength. A definite peak should be noted when tuning each capacitor – otherwise the associated tuned circuits are not adjusted to resonance properly. If desired, an antenna may instead be connected directly to the converter and the converter can be peaked while listening to on-the-air signals in the amateur band. Some "pulling" of the converter oscillator frequency may be noted when peaking the rf and mixer capacitors because of a small amount of interaction between the three tuned circuits. C13 in the converter should then be retuned to bring the oscillator back on frequency. This completes alignment of the receiver.

The receiver is simple to operate as there are only two controls to adjust. The BFO is always on for both cw and ssb reception. High-impedance headphones should be used. Loudspeaker operation is possible if a suitable matching transformer is used. Its primary winding should be about 10,000 ohms and should be connected to the headphone jack connected to the speaker, should match the speaker impedance. The audio level from the loudspeaker is adequate for listening in a small, quite room.

To receive cw signals, one may tune to either side of zero beat of the desired cw signal, depending on which side is more QRM-free. Ssb reception may be accomplished by tuning to the proper sideband of the received signal and adjusting for the desired voice pitch. A-m may be received by *zero-beating* the station and thereby eliminating the beat note. Observe, however, that the audio filter is designed primarily for cw reception and attenuates audio frequencies above 1000 Hz. Hence a-m or ssb signals will have somewhat impaired audio quality, since effective voice frequencies extend to 2500 Hz or so.

Performance of this receiver compares favorably with that of many modern superheterodyne receivers. Measured sensitivity on 80 and 40 meters is 0.3 μV for a 10 dB signal-plus-noise to noise ratio. Electrical stability is good and circuit-board construction enhances mechanical stability so that drift and instability are insignificant even in the presence of mechanical vibrations. If desired, cw selectivity may be improved by addition of an outboard peak audio filter.

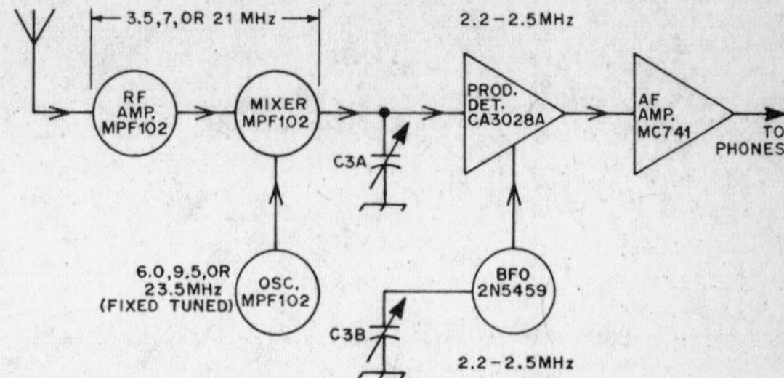

Fig. 5 – Block diagram of the receiver. The arrows indicate the direction of signal travel.

Chapter 9

VHF and UHF Receiving Techniques

Adequate receiving capability is essential in vhf and uhf communication, whether the station is a transceiver or a combination of separate transmitting and receiving units, and regardless of the modulation system used. Transceivers and fm receivers are treated separately in this *Handbook*, but their performance involves basic principles that apply to all receivers for frequencies above 30 MHz. Important attributes are good signal-to-noise ratio (low noise figure), adequate gain, stability, and freedom from overloading and other spurious responses.

Except where a transceiver is used, the vhf station often has a communications receiver for lower bands, with a crystal-controlled converter for the vhf band in question ahead of it. The receiver serves as a tunable i-f system, complete with detector, noise limiter, BFO and audio amplifier. Unless one enjoys work with communications receivers, there may be little point in building this part of the station. Thus our concern here will be mainly with converter design and construction.

Choice of a suitable communications receiver for use with converters should not be made lightly, however. Several degrees of selectivity are desirable: 500 Hz or less for cw, 2 to 3 kHz for ssb, 4 to 8 kHz for a-m phone and 12 to 36 kHz for fm phone are useful. The special requirements of fm phone are discussed in Chapter 14. Good mechanical design and frequency stability are important. Image rejection should be high in the range tuned for the converter output. This may rule out 28 MHz with receivers of the single-conversion type having 455-kHz i-f systems.

Broad-band receiving gear of the surplus variety is a poor investment at any price, unless one is interested only in local work. The superregenerative receiver, though simple to build and economical to use, is inherently lacking in selectivity. With this general information in mind, this section will cover vhf and uhf receiver "front ends" stage by stage.

RF AMPLIFIERS

Signal-to-Noise Ratio: Noise of one kind or another limits the ability of any receiving system to provide readable signals, in the absence of other kinds of interference. The noise problem varies greatly with frequency of reception. In the hf range man-made, galactic and atmospheric noise picked up by the antenna and amplified by all stages of the receiver exceeds noise generated in the receiver itself. Thus the noise figure of the receiver is not of major importance in weak-signal reception, up to at least 30 MHz.

At 50 MHz, external noise still overrides receiver noise in any well-designed system, even in a supposedly "quiet" location. The ratio of external to internal noise then drops rapidly with increasing signal frequency. Above 100 MHz or so external noise other than man-made is seldom a problem in weak-signal reception. Noise characteristics of transistors and tubes thus become very important in receivers for 144 MHz and higher bands, and circuit design and adjustment are more critical than on lower frequencies.

The noise figure of receivers using rf amplifiers is determined mainly by the first stage, so solving the internal-noise problem is fairly simple. Subsequent stages can be designed for selectivity, freedom from overloading, and rejection of spurious signals, when a good rf amplifier is used.

Gain: It might seem that the more gain an rf amplifier has, the better the reception, but this is not necessarily true. The primary function of an rf amplifier in a vhf receiver is to establish the noise figure of the system; that is, to override noise generated in later stages. One good rf stage is usually enough, and two is the usual maximum requirement.

Once the system noise figure is established, any further gain required may be more readily obtained in the intermediate frequency stages, or even in the audio amplifier. Using the minimum rf gain needed to set the overall noise figure of the receiver is helpful in avoiding overloading and spurious responses in later circuits. For more on rf gain requirements, see the following section on mixers.

Stability: Neutralization or unilaterialization (see chapter on semiconductors) may be required in rf amplifiers, except where the grounded-gate circuit or its tube equivalent is used. Amplifier neutralization is accomplished by feeding the energy from the output circuit back into the input, in such amount and phase as to cancel out the effects of device capacitance and other unwanted input-output coupling that might cause oscillation or other regenerative effects. Inductive neutralization is shown in Fig. 9-1B and C. Capacitive arrangements are also usable. Examples of both will be seen later in this chapter.

An rf amplifier may not actually oscillate if operated without neutralization, but noise figure and bandwidth of the amplifier may be better with

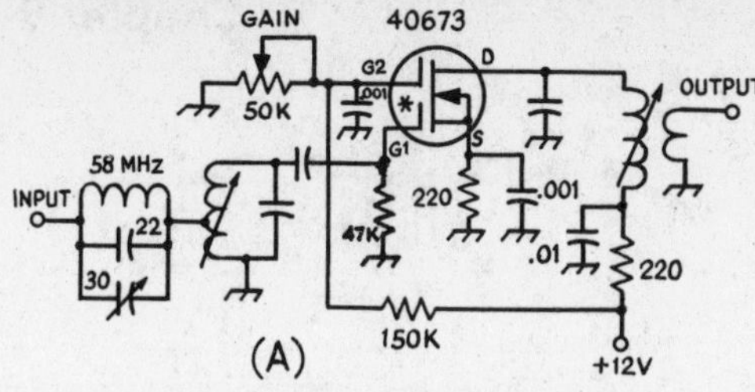

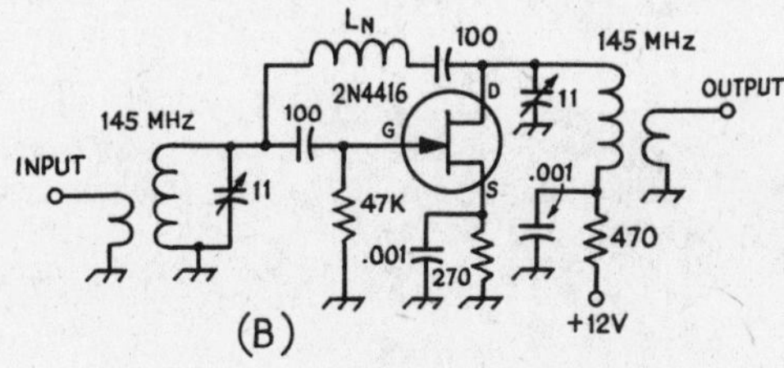

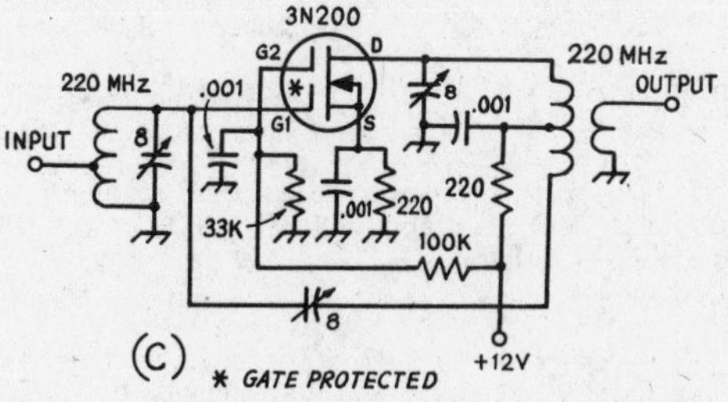

Fig. 9-1 – Typical grounded-source rf amplifiers. The dual-gate MOSFET,A, is useful below 500 MHz. The junction FET,B, and neutralized MOSFET,C, work well on all vhf bands. Except where given, component values depend on frequency.

it. Any neutralization adjustment reacts on the tuned circuits of the stage, so the process is a repetitive cut-and-try one. The objective should be greatest margin of signal over noise, rather than maximum gain without oscillation. A noise generator is a great aid in neutralization, but a weak signal can be used if the job is done with care.

Overloading and Spurious Signals: Except when some bipolar transistors are used, the rf amplifier is not normally a major contributor to overloading problems in vhf receivers, though excessive rf gain can cause the mixer to overload more readily. Overloading is usually a matter of mixer design, with either transistors or tubes. Images and other spurious responses to out-of-band signals can be kept down by the use of double-tuned circuits between the rf and mixer stages, and in the rf amplifier input circuit. In extreme cases, such as operation near to fm or TV stations, coaxial or other high-*Q* input circuits are helpful in rejecting unwanted frequencies.

Using RF Preamplifiers

It is important to design the front-end stages of a vhf receiver for optimum performance, but we often want to improve reception with equipment already built. Thousands of fm receivers formerly in commercial service, now revamped for amateur work in the 50-, 144- and 420-MHz bands, were built before modern low-noise tubes and transistors were available. Though otherwise useful, these receivers have excessively-high noise figure. Many other commercial and home-built vhf converters and receivers are also not as sensitive as they might be.

Though it would be better to replace the rf stages of such equipment with more modern devices, the simpler approach is usually to add an outboard rf amplifier using a low-noise tube or transistor. In the fm example, the quieting level of some receivers can be improved by as much as 10 dB by addition of a simple transistor amplifier. Similar improvement in noise figure of some receivers for other modes is also possible; particularly band-switching communications receivers that have vhf coverage.

Common circuits for rf preamplifier service are shown in Figs. 9-1, 2 and 3. Examples of amplifier construction are given later in this chapter. Circuits shown in the vhf converters described can also be adapted to preamplifier service.

Circuit discussion is cumbersome if we use strictly-correct terms for all tube and transistor amplifiers, so tube terminology will be used here for simplification. The reader is asked to remember

Amplifier Circuitry

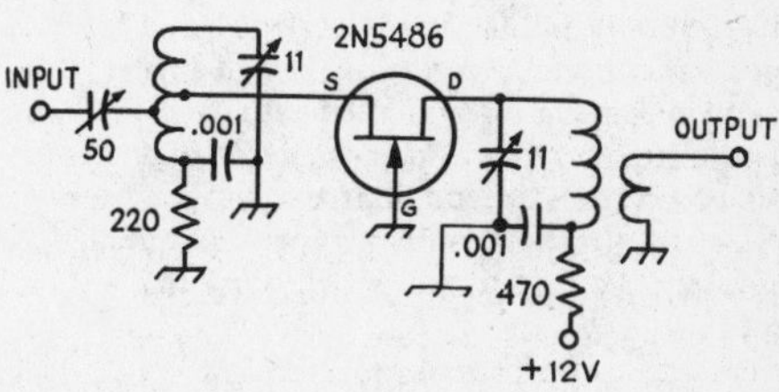

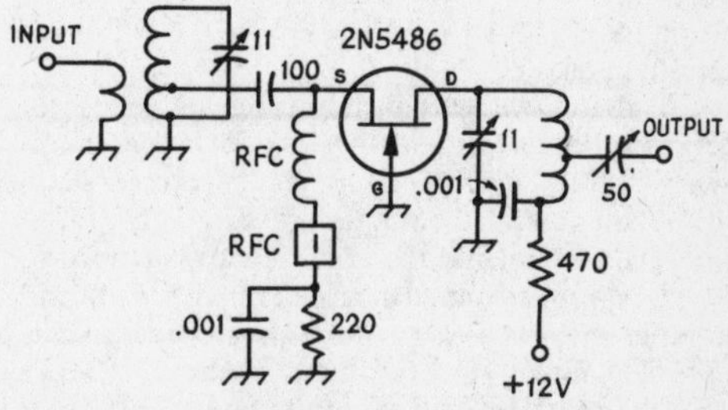

Fig. 9-2 – Grounded-gate FET preamplifier tends to have lower gain and broader frequency response than other amplifiers described.

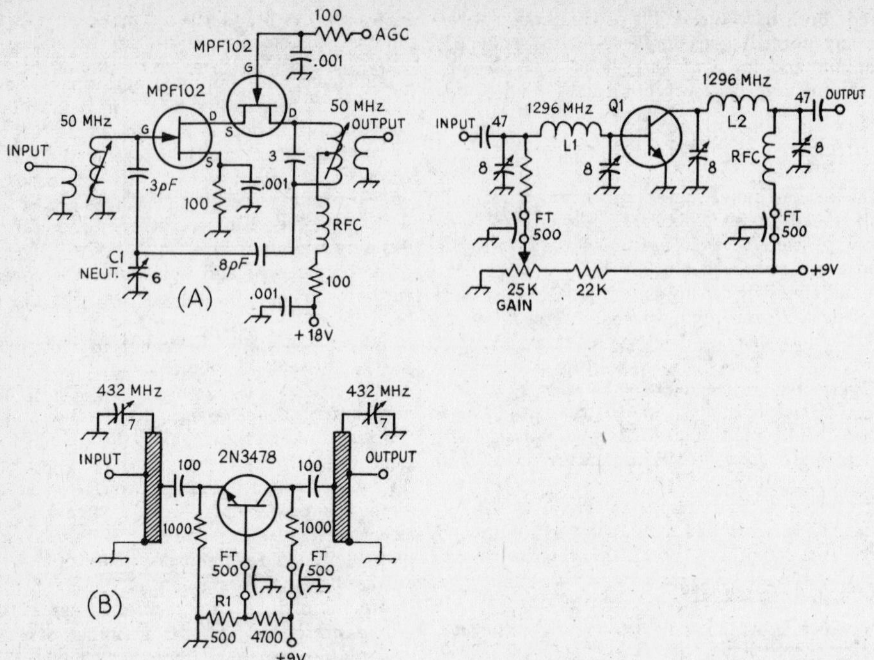

Fig. 9-3 – (A) Cascode amplifier circuit combines grounded-source and grounded-gate stages, for high gain and low noise figure. Though JFETs are shown, the cascode principle is usable with MOSFETs as well. (B and C) Examples of uhf preamplifier construction using bipolar transistors.

that "gate" may also imply "base" for bipolar transistors, or "grid" for tubes. "Source" should be read as "emitter" for the bipolar, and as "cathode" for the FET.

Amplifiers may be the grounded-source type, Fig. 9-1; grounded-gate, 9-2; or a combination of both, 9-3. The dual-gate MOSFET circuit, 9-1A, works well up to 300 MHz, but JFET and bipolar devices are superior for 420 MHz and higher. The gain and noise figure of a dual-gate MOSFET are adequate at 300 MHz, and it is simple and readily adapted to automatic gain control.

Triode tubes and FET transistors usually require neutralization for optimum noise figure with the grounded-cathode circuit. Inductive neutralization is shown in Fig. 9-1B, and the capacitive method shown at C works equally well. Examples will be seen later in this chapter. The 58-MHz trap circuit in Fig. 9-1A is discussed in the following section on mixers.

An alternative to neutralization lies in use of the grounded-gate circuit, Fig. 9-2. Its stage gain is lower and its bandwidth generally greater than with the grounded-cathode circuit. The input impedance is low, and the input circuit is tapped to provide a proper impedance match. A broad-band amplifier may be made with a low-impedance line connected directly to the input element, if selectivity is not required at this point for other reasons. Tubes designed for grounded-grid service include the 417A/5842, 416B, 7768 and the various "lighthouse" types, though almost any triode or triode-connected tetrode can be used. JFETs work well in grounded-gate circuits. In the grounded-grid amplifier, the tube heater becomes effectively a part of the tuned circuit, so some form of high-current rf choke is required. Ferrite-bead chokes work well.

The cascode circuit, Fig. 9-3, combined grounded-source and grounded-gate stages, securing some of the advantages of both. Fig. 9-3B shows a grounded-base bipolar transistor amplifer. The value of R1 should be chosen experimentally to achieve best sensitivity.

Front-End Protection

The first amplifier of a receiver is susceptible to damage or complete burnout through application of excessive voltage to its input element by way of the antenna. This can be the result of lightning discharges (not necessarily in the immediate vicinity), rf leakage from the station transmitter through a faulty send-receive relay or switch, or rf power from a nearby transmitter and antenna system. Bipolar transistors often used in low-noise uhf amplifiers are particularly sensitive to this trouble. The degradation may be gradual, going unnoticed until the receiving sensitivity has become very poor.

No equipment is likely to survive a direct hit from lightning, but casual damage can be prevented by connecting diodes back-to-back across the input circuit. Either germanium or silicon vhf diodes can be used. Both have thresholds of conduction well above any normal signal level, about 0.2 volt for germanium and 0.6 volt for silicon. The diodes used should have fast switching times. Computer diodes such as the IN914 and hot-carrier types are suitable. A check on weak-signal reception should be made before and after connection of the diodes.

RF SELECTIVITY

The weakest point in any vhf or uhf receiver is the front-end circuit. Solid-state devices with high sensitivity, wide dynamic range and freedom from overload are now available. Thus, the quality of a front-end circuit is usually determined by how the active devices are used and the degree of rf selectivity included. High selectivity at vhf and uhf is not easy to achieve. Many lumped-constant tuned circuits are needed for even a moderate degree of selectivity at the signal frequency. Several tuned circuits before the first active stage (rf amplifier or mixer) will have sufficient loss to limit the sensitivity of the receiver. If lumped-constant circuits are employed, rf amplifiers can be interspaced between the *LC* elements to make up losses. High gain is not needed or desirable, so FETs operated grounded-gate are preferred.

For improved rf selectivity a helical resonator, a device which consists of a shield and a coil may be employed. One end of the coil is attached to the shield, as shown in Fig. 9-4, and the other end is open-circuited, except for a tuning capacitor. Helical resonators are electrically equivalent to a

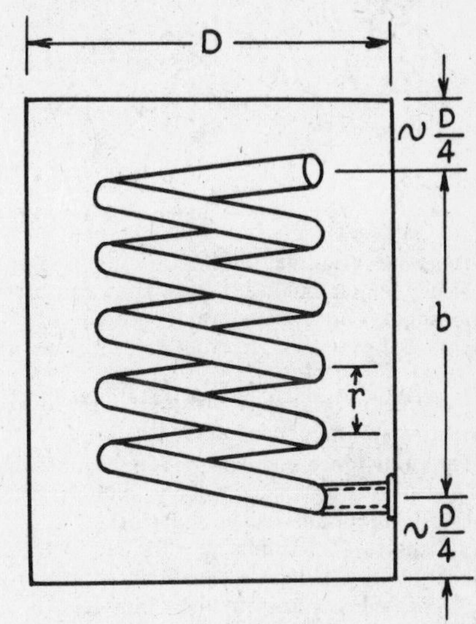

Fig. 9-4 – Outline sketch of resonator.

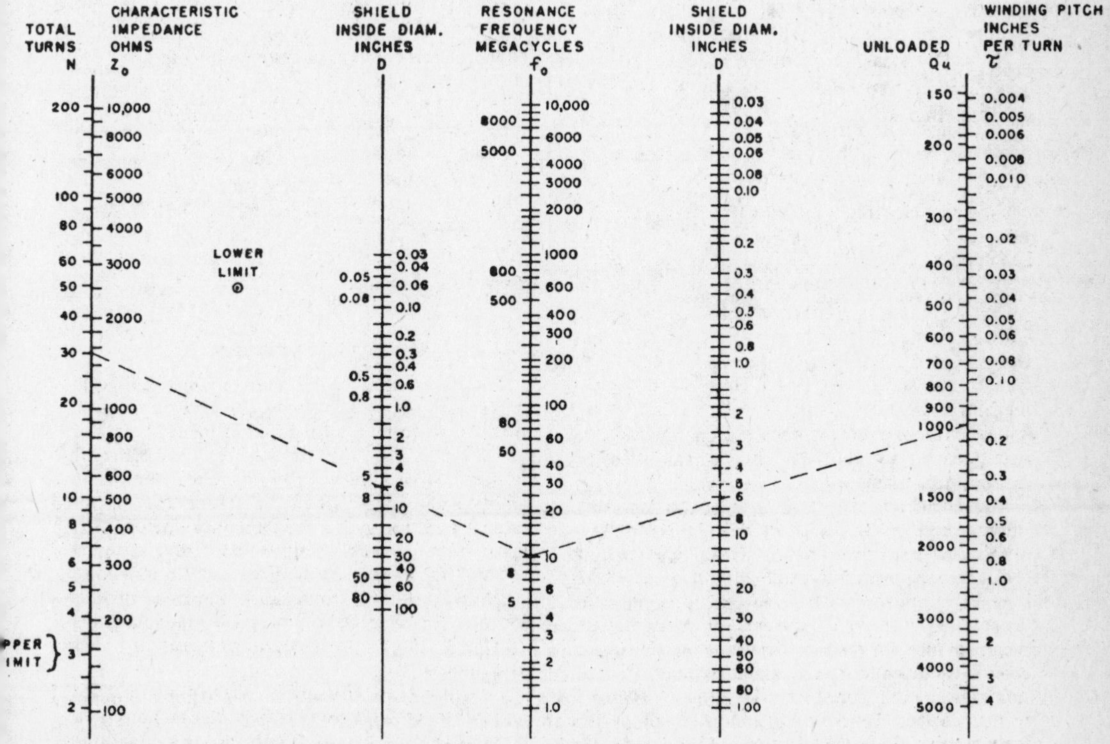

TOTAL TURNS N — CHARACTERISTIC IMPEDANCE OHMS Z_o — SHIELD INSIDE DIAM. INCHES D — RESONANCE FREQUENCY MEGACYCLES f_o — SHIELD INSIDE DIAM. INCHES D — UNLOADED Q_u — WINDING PITCH INCHES PER TURN τ

LOWER LIMIT

UPPER LIMIT

Fig. 9-5 – Design chart for quarter-wave helical resonators.

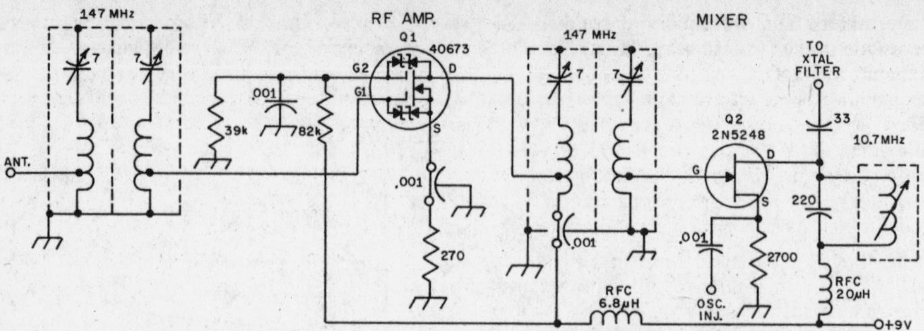

Fig. 9-6 – Schematic diagram of the Johnson 504 front-end circuit.

quarter-wave transmission-line resonator but are physically much smallter. Resonators can be built exhibiting *Q* of 1000 or more at vhf and uhf. Because the *Q* is so high, front-end circuits can be designed using helical resonators which provide a high degree of selectivity without high losses, at least a low and moderate power levels.

The inductance element in a helical resonator should be made as large as possible and capacitance kept to a minimum for best performance. Probe, tap or aperture coupling may be employed. The basic form of a helical resonator is shown in Fig. 9-4. A low-loss air-insulated trimmer or disk plunger may be used to tune the resonator. The capacitor must be much higher *Q* than the resonator to be useable. The usual precautions for fabricating high-Q coils must be observed when building a helical resonator. A protective silver plating is recommended for the coil and shield for units to be used above 100 MHz. The shield should be seamless and all joints should be effectively soldered to keep resistance to a minimum. The coil and shield should be made using heavy stock to assure mechanical stability.

Fig. 9-5 can be used to obtain approximate design information accurate to plus or minus ten percent. Complete design equations for helical resonators are beyond the scope of this text, but they may be found in Macapline and Schildknecht, "Coaxial Resonators with Helical Inner Conductor," *Proceeding of the IRE*, December, 1959.

Fig. 9-7 – Close-up view of the helical resonators with the covers removed. The rf amplifier stage is constructed on the outside wall of the upper-right-hand resonator. Details are given in the text.

An application of helical resonators in a 146-MHz front-end circuit is shown in Figs. 9-6 and 9-7. This circuit is used in the Johnson 504 transceiver. The helical resonators consist of 5-3/4 turns of No. 12 wire contained in a rectangular 1 × 1 × 2-inch cavity. Both the coil and enclosure are silver plated. The coil is 5/8 inch inside diameter and 5/8 inch long, tuned with a 7-pF miniature air-variable capacitor. The 50-ohm input tap is at 1/4 turn from the ground end of the coil, an indication of the high impedance achieved. Coupling between individual resonators is through a 1/2 × 1/4 -inch aperture, or "window." Layout details can be seen in Fig. 9-7.

MIXERS

Conversion of the received energy to a lower frequency, so that it can be amplified more efficiently than would be possible at the signal frequency, is a basic principle of the superheterodyne receiver. The stage in which this is done may be called a "converter," or "frequency converter," but we will use the more common term, *mixer*, to avoid confusion with *converter*, as applied to a complete vhf receiving accessory. Mixers perform similar functions in both transmitting and receiving circuits, and mixer theory and practice are treated in considerable detail elsewhere in this *Handbook.*

A receiver for 50 MHz or higher usually has at least two such stages; one in the vhf or uhf converter, and usually two or more in the communications receiver that follows it. We are concerned here with the first mixer.

Diode Mixer: There are many types of mixers, the simplest being merely a diode with the signal and energy on the heterodyning frequency fed into it, somewhat in the manner of the 1296-MHz example, Fig. 9-8A. The mixer output includes both the sum and difference frequencies. Either can be used, but in this application it is the difference, since we are interested in going lower in frequency.

With a good uhf diode in a suitable circuit, a diode mixer can have a fairly low noise figure, and this is almost independent of frequency, well into the microwave region. The effectiveness of most active mixers falls off rapidly above 400 MHz, so the diode mixer is almost standard practice in amateur microwave communication. All diode mixers have some conversion *loss.* This must be added to the noise figure of the i-f amplifier following, to determine the overall system noise figure. Low-noise design in the first i-f stage is thus mandatory, for good weak-signal reception with a diode mixer having no rf amplifier preceding it. Purity of the heterodyning energy and the level of injection to the mixer are other factors in the performance of diode mixers.

Balanced mixers using hot-carrier diodes are capable of noise figures 1 to 2 dB lower than the best point-contact diodes. Hot-carrier diodes are normally quite uniform, so tedious selection of matched pairs (necessary with other types of diodes) is eliminated. They are also rugged, and superior in the matter of overloading.

The i-f impedance of a balanced hot-carrier diode mixer (Fig. 9-8B) is on the order of 90 ohms, when the oscillator injection is about one milliwatt. Thus the mixer and a transistorized i-f amplifier can be separated physically, and connected by means of 93-ohm coax, without an output transformer.

Conversion loss, around 7 dB, must be added to the noise figure of the i-f system to determine the overall system noise figure. Unless a low-noise preamplifier is used ahead of it, a communications receiver may have a noise figure of about 10 dB, resulting in an overall noise figure of 17 dB or worse for a vhf system with any diode mixer. A good i-f preamplifier could bring the receiver noise figure down to 2 dB or even less, but the system noise figure would still be about 9 dB; too high for good reception.

An amplifier at the signal frequency is thus seen to be required, regardless of mixer design, for optimum reception above 50 MHz. The rf gain, to override noise in the rest of the receiver, should be greater than the sum of noise figures of the mixer and the i-f system. Since the noise figure of the better rf amplifiers will be around 3 dB, the gain should be at least 20 dB for the first example in the previous paragraph, and 12 dB for the second.

Tube and Transistor Mixers: Any mixer is prone to overloading and spurious responses, so a prime design objective should be to minimize these problems. FET mixers have become standard practice at vhf. JFETs are slightly better than MOSFETs, although the junction types require

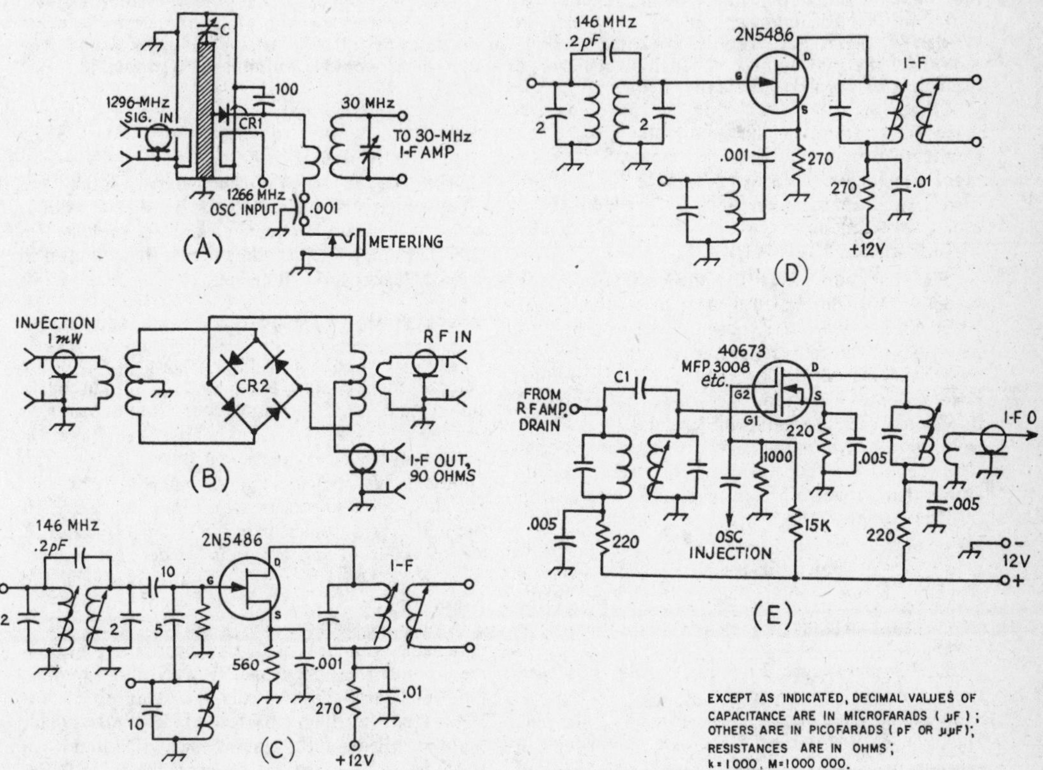

Fig. 9-8 — Vhf and uhf mixer circuits. A diode mixer for 1296 MHz, with a coaxial circuit for the signal frequency, is shown in A. CR1 is a uhf diode, such as the 1N21 series. A balanced mixer, as in B, gives improved rejection of the signal and injection frequencies. If hot-carrier diodes are used for CR2, sorting for matched characteristics is eliminated. Gate and source injection of a JFET mixer are shown at C and D, respectively.

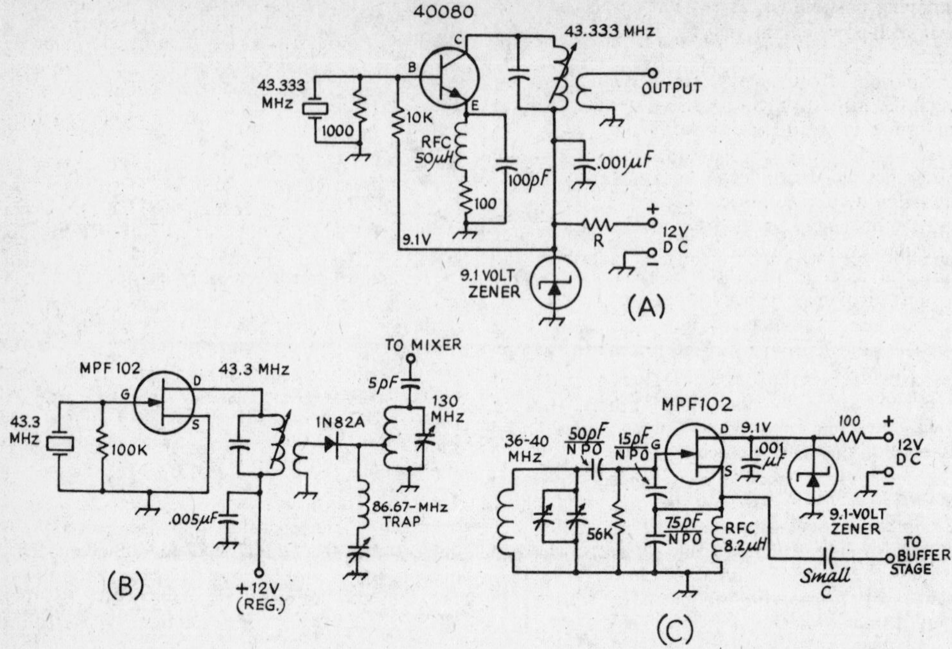

Fig. 9-9 – A simple overtone crystal oscillator for vhf converters, (A) has Zener voltage regulation. An FET overtone oscillator and diode multiplier, (B) supply injection for a 144-MHz converter with a 14-MHz i-f. Series trap absorbs unwanted second harmonic at 86 MHz. A triode oscillator would use essentially the same circuit. A tunable oscillator, as shown at C, would be suitable for a simple 50-MHz receiver with a broad i-f system.

more power from the injection source. When the local-oscillator frequency is far removed from the input frequency, the scheme of Fig. 9-8C can be used. The diagram at 9-8D is needed if the oscillator frequency is within 20 percent of the signal frequency.

The injection level from the oscillator affects mixer performance. Until it affects the mixer adversely in other ways, raising the injection level raises the mixer conversion gain. A simple check is made by observing the effect on signal-to-noise ratio as the injection is varied. At preferred injection levels, the gain will vary but the signal-to-noise ratio will not change. The injection should then be set for conversion gain a few decibels above that at which lower injection causes a drop in signal-to-noise ratio.

Double-tuned circuits in the mixer and the rf amplifier, as shown in several of the schematic diagrams in this chapter, help to keep down mixer response to signals outside the intended tuning range.

The insulated-gate FET is superior to other transistors for mixer service in the matter of overloading. An example is given in Fig. 9-8E. An objection to the MOSFET, the ease with which it can be damaged in handling, has been taken care of by building-in protective diodes in devices such as the MPF122, 40673, and 3N187. Units so designed require no special care in handling, and they work as well as their more fragile predeccessors. Insulated-gate MOSFETs have resistance to overloading which, while superior to most tubes, is not as good as the best JFETs.

Pentode or tetrode tubes make simple and effective mixers, up to 150 MHz or so. Triodes work well at any frequency, and are preferred in the high vhf range. Diode mixers are common in the 420-MHz band and higher.

INJECTION STAGES

Oscillator and multiplier stages that supply heterodyning energy to the mixer should be as stable and free of unwanted frequencies as possible. Stability is no great problem in crystal-controlled converters, if the oscillator is run at low input and its supply voltage is regulated. Simple Zener regulation, as in Fig. 9-9A, is adequate for a transistorized overtone oscillator. A higher order of regulation is needed for tunable oscillators. See Chapter 5 for suitable regulated power supplies.

Unwanted frequencies generated in the injection stages can beat with signals that are outside the intended tuning range. In a typical example, Fig. 9-9B, an FET overtone oscillator on 43.333 MHz feeds a diode tripler to 130 MHz. This frequency beats with signals between 144 and 148 MHz, to give desired responses at 14 to 18 MHz. The multiplier stage also has some output at twice the crystal frequency, 86.666 MHz. If allowed to reach the mixer, this can beat with fm broadcast signals in the 100-MHz region that leak through the rf circuits of the converter. There are many such annoying possibilities, as any vhf enthusiast living near high-powered fm and TV stations has found out.

Spurious frequencies can be kept down by using the highest practical oscillator frequency, no multiplier in a 50-MHz converter, and as few as possible for higher bands. Some unwanted harmonics are unavoidable, so circuit precautions are often needed to prevent both these harmonics and the unwanted signals from reaching the mixer. Selective coaxial or helical-resonator circuits are practical aids in uhf receivers. Trap circuits of various kinds may be needed to "suck out" energy on troublesome frequencies.

The series trap in Fig. 9-5B reduces the level of the 86-MHz second harmonic of the crystal frequency. A 58-MHz parallel-tuned trap, Fig. 9-1A, prevents the entry of Channel 2 TV signals that could otherwise beat with the second harmonic of a 36-MHz oscillator in a 50-MHz converter that works into a 14-MHz i-f (36 × 2 - 14=58).

Unwanted frequencies also increase the noise output of the mixer. This degrades performance in a receiver having no rf amplifier, and makes the job of an amplifier, if used, more difficult.

Frequency multipliers in vhf receivers generally follow transmitting practice, except for their low power level. The simple diode multiplier of Fig. 9-9B will often suffice. Its parallel-tuned 130-MHz circuit emphasizes the desired third harmonic, while the series circuit suppresses the unwanted second harmonic. The trap is tuned by listening to a spurious fm broadcast signal and tuning the series capacitor for minimum interference. The tripler circuit should be peaked for maximum response to a 2-meter signal. Do not detune this circuit to lower injection level. This should be controlled by the voltage on the oscillator, the coupling between the oscillator and multiplier, or by the coupling to the mixer from the 130-MHz circuit.

Tunable Oscillators

Any tunable vhf receiver must employ a variable oscillator. At this point the intermediate frequency is fixed, and the oscillator tunes a range higher or lower than the signal frequency by the amount of the i-f. In the interest of stability, it is usually lower. In Fig. 9-9C a simple JFET oscillator tunes 36 to 40 MHz, for reception of the 50-MHz band with a fixed 14-MHz i-f. Its stability should be adequate for a-m or fm reception with a relatively broad i-f, but it is unlikely to meet the requirements for ssb or cw reception, even for 50 MHz, and certainly not for higher bands.

Practically all vhf reception with high selectivity uses double-conversion schemes, with the tunable oscillator serving the second conversion. Such hf oscillators are treated in Chapter 6. They should run at the lowest practical input level, to minimize drift caused by heating. The supply should be well-regulated pure dc. Mechanically-rugged components and construction are mandatory. The circuits should be shielded from the rest of the receiver, and coupling to the mixer should be as light as practical. Drift cycling due to heating can be minimized if the oscillator is kept running continuously.

THE SUPERREGENERATIVE RECEIVER

Though the newcomer may not be too familiar with the superregenerative detector, the simple "rushbox" was widely used in early vhf work. Nothing of comparable simplicity has been found to equal its weak-signal reception, inherent noise-limiting and agc action, and freedom from overloading and spurious responses. But like all simple devices the superregenerator has limitations. It has little selectivity. It makes a high and unpleasant hissing noise, and it radiates a broad interfering signal around its receiving frequency.

Adding an rf amplifier will improve selectivity and reduce detector radiation. High-Q tuned circuits aid selectivity and improve stability. Use of superregeneration at 14 to 18, 26 to 30 MHz, or some similar hf range, in the tunable element of a simple superheterodyne receiver, works fairly well as a simple tuner for vhf converters. None of these steps corrects the basic weaknesses entirely, so the superregenerator is used today mainly where simplicity, low cost and battery economy are major considerations. Cw and narrow-band fm signals cannot be received using a superregenerative receiver.

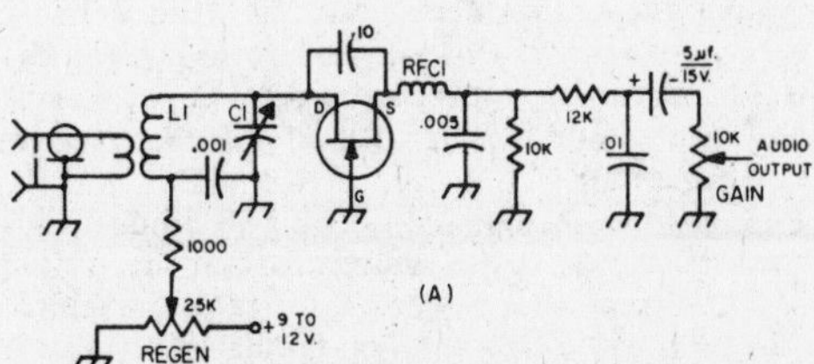

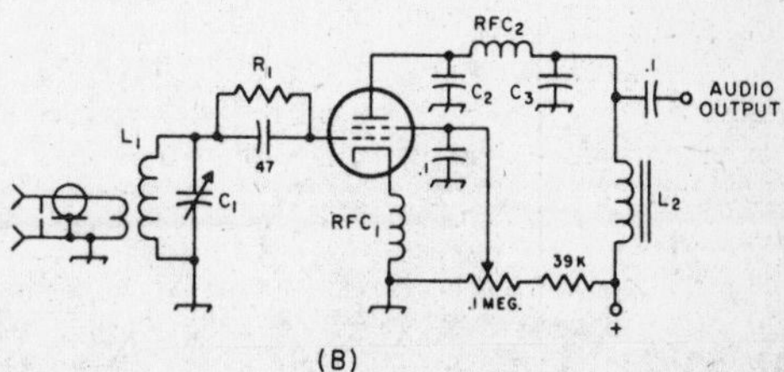

Fig. 9-10 – Circuits of typical superregenerative detectors using a field-effect transistor, A, and a tetrode tube, B. Regeneration is controlled by varying the drain voltage on the detector in the transistor circuit, and the screen voltage in the tetrode or pentode. Values of L1 and C1 should be adjusted for the frequency involved, as should the size of the rf choke, RFC1.

C2, C3 – .001-µF disk ceramic. Try different values up to .005 for desired audio quality.
R1 – 2 to 10 megohms.
L2 – Small audio or filter choke; not critical.
RFC1 – Single-layer rf choke, to suit frequency.
RFC2 – 85-mH rf choke.

Typical superregenerative detector circuits are shown in Fig. 9-10. High-transconductance FETs and high-beta vhf transistors are favored. The power source should be well-filtered and of low impedance. Fresh or well-charged batteries are ideal. Regeneration is controlled by varying the gain of the stage.

SERIES-RESONANT BYPASSING

Inexpensive disk-ceramic and "dog-bone" types of capacitors are relatively ineffective for bypassing above approximately 100 MHz. This is because of their considerable lead inductance, even when they are connected as close to the elements to be bypassed as possible. Actually this lead inductance can be used to advantage by selecting lead lengths that make the capacitor series-resonant at the frequency to be bypassed.

This approach is recommended by WA2KYF, who supplied the information in Table 9-I, showing capacitor and lead-length combinations for effective bypassing of rf energy at frequencies commonly encountered in vhf work. The values are not particularly critical, as a series-resonant circuit is broad by nature. The impedance of a series-resonant bypass is very close to zero ohms at the frequency of resonance, and it will be lower than most conventional capacitors for a considerable range of frequency either side of resonance.

A high-capacitance short-lead combination is preferable to a lower value with longer leads, because the former will be less likely to allow unwanted coupling to other circuits. For example, a 100-pF capacitor with 1/4-inch leads is a better bet than a 25-pF with 1-inch leads, for bypassing at 144 MHz. The series-resonant bypass is worth a try in any circuit where instability is troublesome, and conventional bypassing has been shown to be ineffective.

TABLE 9-I

Values of capacitance in pF required for resonance of frequencies commonly encountered in amateur-band vhf work, for leads of 1/4, 1/2 and 1 inch in length.

Frequency MHz	*1/4-Inch Leads*	*1/2-Inch Leads*	*1-Inch Leads*
48–50	800	400	200
72	390	180	91
96	220	100	56
144	100	47	25
220	39	20	10

MOSFET PREAMPLIFIERS FOR 10, 6, AND 2 METERS

Where an hf or vhf receiver lacks gain, or has a poor noise figure, an external preamplifier can improve its ability to detect weak signals. This preamplifier uses an RCA 40673 dual-gate MOSFET. Designs for using this device as a mixer or as a preamplifier abound and many of them are excellent.

When it comes to simplicity, small size, good performance, low cost, and flexibility, a design by Gerald C. Jenkins, W4CAH, certainly qualifies.

Where the preamplifier really shines is in pepping up the performance of some of the older ten-meter receivers that many have pressed into service. A six-meter version is also very useful for any of the modes of communication available on that band.

The voltage dropping resistor, R4, and the Zener diode, VR1, may be of the value necessary to obtain 9 to 12 V dc for operation of the unit. By increasing the resistance and dissipation rating of R4 and VR1, the preamplifier may be operated from the 150- to 200-V supply found in many tube-type receivers.

The layout of the board is so simple that it is hardly worth the effort of making a negative for the photo-etch process. A Kepro resist-marking pen was used with success on several boards. Another approach – and one that is highly recommended –

Two versions of the preamplifier. The one in the box is for 2-meter use. Toroids are used in the six-meter version (right) and in the ten-meter preamplifier (not shown). Input is at the right on both units. The extra rf choke and feedthrough capacitor on the right end of the Minibox are for decoupling a crystal-current metering circuit that is part of a 2304-MHz mixer.

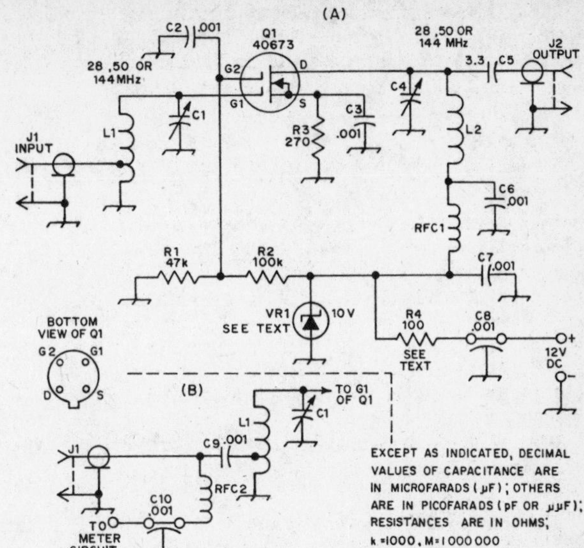

Fig. 1 — Schematic diagram for the preamplifier. Part designations not listed below are for pc board placement purposes. Alternative input circuit for use with microwave diode mixer is shown at B.

C1, C4 — See Table I.
C2, C3, C5, C6, C7, C9 — Disk ceramic.
C8 — .001 feedthrough capacitor.
J1, J2 — Coaxial connectors. Phono-type, BNC or SO-239 acceptable.
L1, L2 — See Table I.
R4 — 3 turns No. 28 enam. on ferrite bead. A 220-ohm, 1/2-watt resistor may be substituted.
RFC2 — 33 μH, iron-core inductor. Millen J300-33 or J. W. Miller 70F335A1.

is to cover the copper with masking tape, transfer the pattern with carbon paper, then cut away the tape to expose the part to be etched. On small, simple boards the masking-tape method is hard to beat.

The pc board may be mounted in almost any small enclosure. Construction is not tricky or difficult. It should take only a few minutes to complete the unit after the board is prepared. The board is fastened in the enclosure by means of one metal standoff post and a No. 4 screw and nut. Input and output connectors are not critical; phono-type jacks may be used in the interest of low cost.

Adjustment is so easy that it almost needs no description. After connecting the amplifier to a receiver, simply tune the input (C1) and the output (C4) for maximum indication on a weak signal. One possible area of concern might be that the toroids used in the ten- and six-meter versions are not always uniform in permeability, as purchased from various suppliers. However, it is an easy matter to add capacitance or remove a turn as required to make the circuits resonate at the correct frequency.

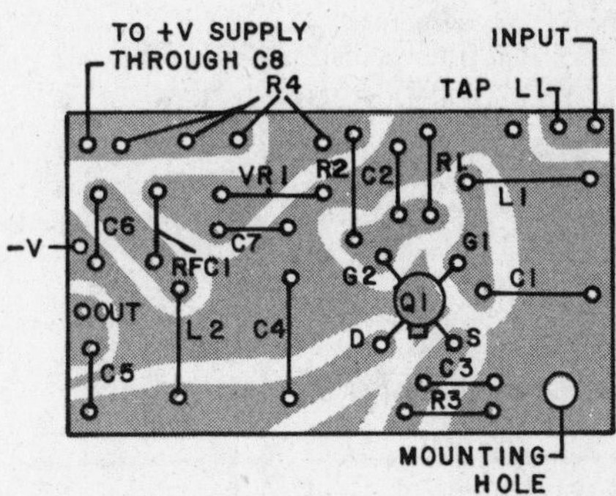

Fig. 2 — Full-scale layout and parts placement guide for the pc board. Foil side shown.

Table I

	28 MHz	*50 MHz*	*144 MHz*
L1	17 turns No. 28 enam. on Amidon T-50-6 core. Tap at 6 turns from ground end	12 turns No. 26 enam. on Amidon T-37-10 core. Tap at 5 turns from ground end.	5 turns No. 20 tinned 1/2-inch ID × 1/2-inch long. Tap at 2 turns from ground end.
L2	Same as L1, without tap.	Same as L1, without tap.	4 turns No. 20 tinned like L1, without tap.
C1, C4,	15 to 60-pF ceramic trimmer. Erie 538-002F.	1.8- to 16.7-pF air variable. E. F. Johnson 189-506-005.	1.5- to 11.6-pF air variable. E. F. Johnson 189-504-005.

Fig. 1 — Completed six- and two-meter converters (left and center) with power supply.

CONVERTERS FOR 50 AND 144 MHz

The converters described here are designed by the Rochester VHF Group and details are presented by W2DUC and K2YCO.

Because of the nature of the project, a universal circuit-board design is used. One circuit board serves for either band, with only slight modification. Other specific design goals were:

1) Low noise figure, less than 3 dB.

2) State-of-the-art freedom from cross modulation.

3) Sufficient gain to override the front-end noise of most receivers.

4) Double-tuned bandpass interstage and output circuits to achieve a flat response over a two-MHz portion of either band.

5) Filtering of the local oscillator chain in the two-meter model to reduce spurious responses.

6) Small size and low power consumption.

7) Freedom from accidental mistuning during the life of the converter.

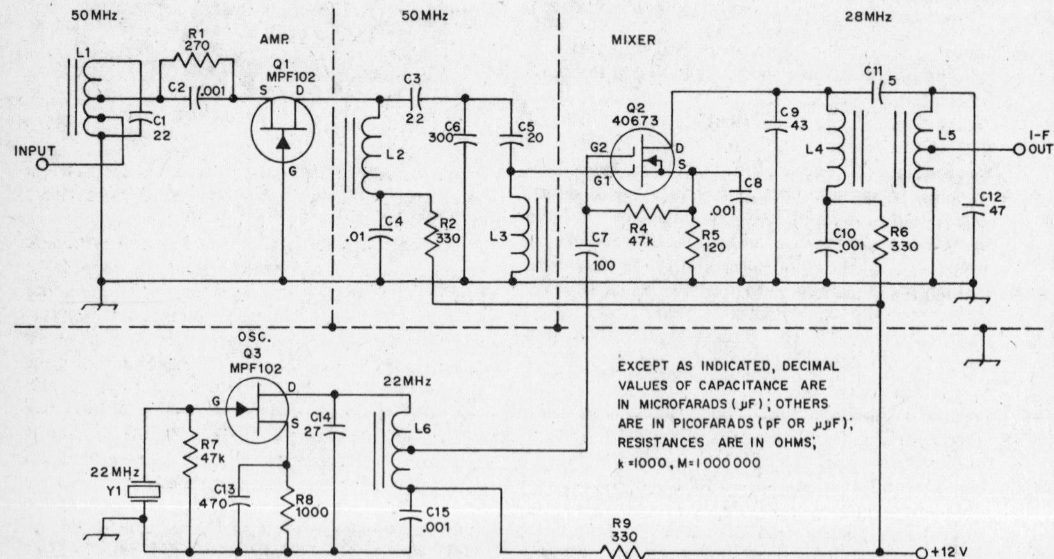

Fig. 2 — Schematic diagram of the six-meter converter. All resistors are 1/4-watt composition. C2, C8, C10 and C15 are .001 µF disk ceramic. C4 is .01-µF disk ceramic. All other capacitors are dipped mica.

L1-L6, incl. — All No. 28 enam. wire wound on Amidon T-30-6 cores as follows: L1, 14 turns tapped at 4 turns and 6 turns; L2, 13 turns; L3, 12 turns; L4, 18 turns; L5, 18 turns tapped at 4 turns from cold end; L6, 26 turns tapped at 6 turns from hot end.

Y1 — 22-MHz crystals. International Crystal Mfg. Co. type EX.

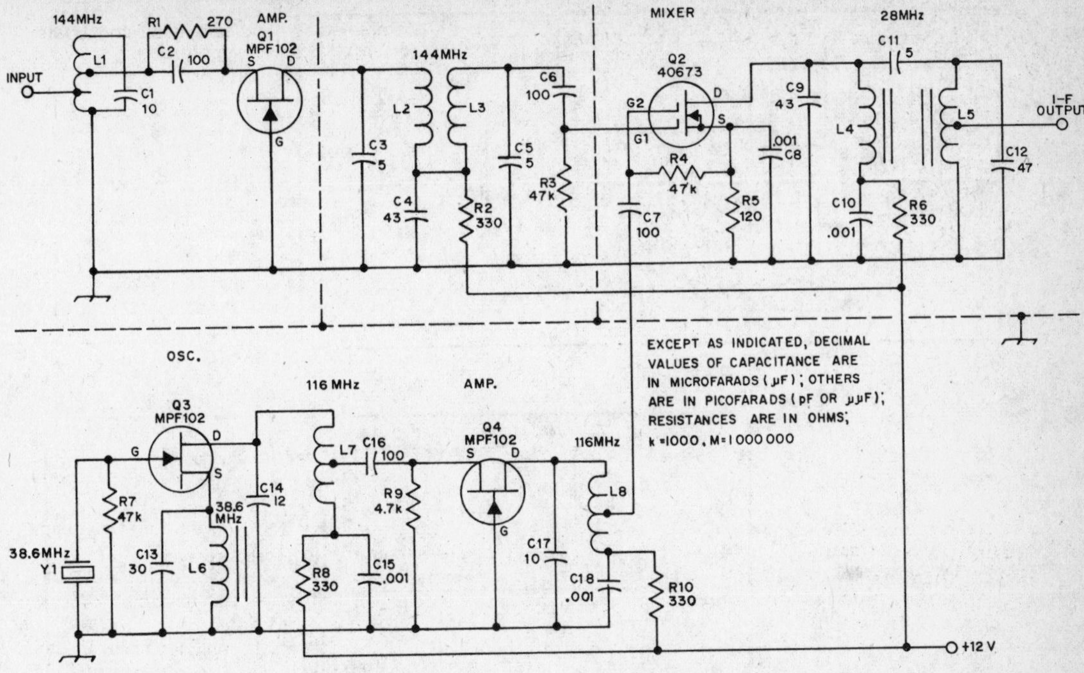

Fig. 3 — Schematic diagram of the two-meter converter. All resistors are 1/4-watt composition. C8, C10, C15 and C18 are .001-μF disk ceramic. All other capacitors are dipped mica units.

L1, L2, L3, L7, L8 — All No. 20 enam. wire formed by using the threads of a 1/4-20 bolt as a guide. L1, 5 turns tapped at 1-3/4 turns and 3/4 turn from cold end; L2, 5 turns; L3, 4 turns; L7, and L8, 5 turns tapped at 2 turns from hot end.

L4 — 18 turns No. 28 enam. wound on Amidon T-30-6 core.

L5 — 18 turns like L4, tapped at 4 turns from cold end.

L6 — 0.68 μH miniature inductor. Delevan 1025 series or J. W. Miller 9230-16.

Y1 — 38.666-MHz crystal. International Crystal Mfg. Co. type EX.

Other points considered were such things as freedom from the necessity of neutralization and the use of moderately priced transistors.

Several breadboard models were constructed and tested as the design evolved. Fig. 1 shows two completed converters and a power supply.

Circuit Design

A schematic diagram for the six-meter converter is shown in Fig. 2, and for the two-meter model in Fig. 3. The configuration of the rf and mixer portions of the circuit are virtually identical for six and two meters, with the values of the frequency-determining components being scaled appropriately. The major difference between the two converters is a change in the local oscillator chain. A minor change in the method of interstage coupling was necessary to prevent stray-capacitance effects from making the alignment critical on the six-meter converter.

All inductors in the six-meter model and the two-meter output circuit are wound on Amidon T-30-6 toroid cores. The tuned circuits are aligned by spreading or compressing the turns around the toroid core. After alignment the coils are glued in place with Silastic compound (sold as bathtub caulk).

The rf amplifier, Q1, is used in a grounded-gate configuration. The input circuit is tapped to provide a proper match between the antenna and source of the FET while maintaining a reasonable *Q*. The six-meter interstage coupling network consists of C3, C5, L2, and L3. Band-pass coupling is controlled by the capacitive T network of C3 and C5 in ratio with C6. A 40673 dual-gate MOSFET is used in the mixer circuit (Q2). Gate 1 receives the signal, while gate 2 has the local -oscillator injection voltage applied to it through C7. A slight amount of positive bias is applied to gate 2 through R2. A top-coupled configuration, using toroid inductors, serves as the 28-MHz output circuit of both converters.

The oscillator circuit in the six-meter model is straightforward, relying on the drain-to-gate capacitance of the FET for feedback. A tap at four turns from the hot end of the toroid winding provides the injection to the mixer through capacitor C7. In the two-meter converter, Fig. 3, the rf stage is identical to the six-meter version except for

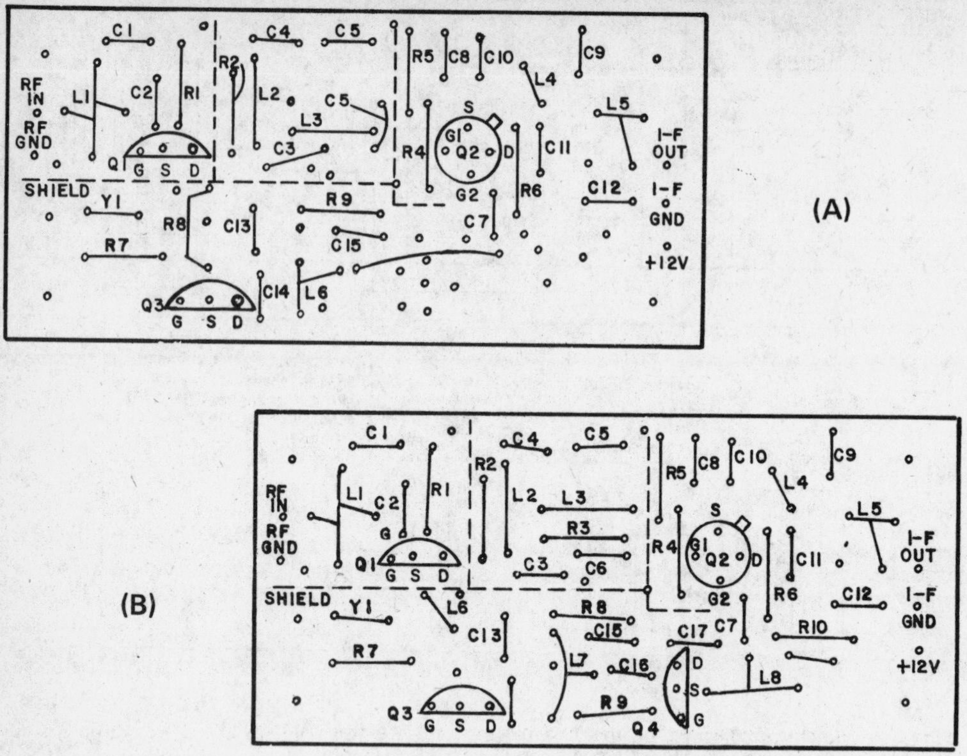

Fig. 4 — Parts-placement guide for the six-meter converter, A, and the two-meter converter, B. View is from the foil side of the board. Dashed lines show the location of shields that are soldered to short pieces of wire which project through holes in the pc board. The shields may be fabricated from sheet brass or copper, or scraps of copper-clad board material.

the tuning networks. L1, L2, and L3 are air wound, self-supporting, and are formed initially by winding wire around the threads of a 1/4-20 bolt. The turns of L1 are spread to permit adding taps prior to mounting on the board. The degree of interstage coupling in the two-meter model is controlled by the positions of L2 and L3. Since they are mounted at right angles, the coupling is very light. By changing the angle between these two coils, the passband may be optimized.

In the two-meter oscillator stage, Q3 is changed to an oscillator/tripler by replacing the source bias resistor with L6. Replace bypass capacitor, C13,

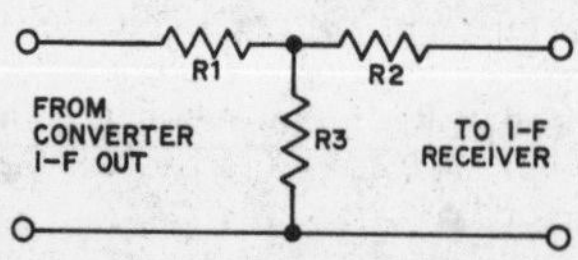

Fig. 5 — An i-f attenuator may be necessary if the receiver following the converter is exceptionally hot. Values for 6 dB: R1, R2 — 18 ohms; R3 — 68 ohms. For 10 dB: R1, R2 — 27 ohms; R3 — 39 ohms.

with a 30-pF value to resonate L6 near the crystal frequency. Source-to-gate capacitance provides the feedback in this case. The drain tank is modified to provide output at the third harmonic, thus eliminating the need for a separate tripler stage. Q4 is used as an isolation amplifier running at very low current level (as controlled by R9) to provide attenuation of the adjacent harmonics. This stage is not needed for amplification of the oscillator signal but without the additional filtering, severe "birdies" may result from nearby fm or TV stations. In both the six- and two-meter versions, a number of printed-circuit pads will be left over when construction is completed. These are the result of providing both bands on a common pc layout. For example, the isolation amplifier following the oscillator is not used on six meters. Therefore, this stage is bypassed by a jumper wire from L6 to C7. Five additional holes are located in the ground area along the centerline of the board and between rf and mixer stages. Component lead clippings are soldered into these holes to provide a mounting for the shield partitions, which are soldered to the wires where they extend through the board. Fig. 4 shows the parts layout for the six- and two-meter converters. Notice that one lead of

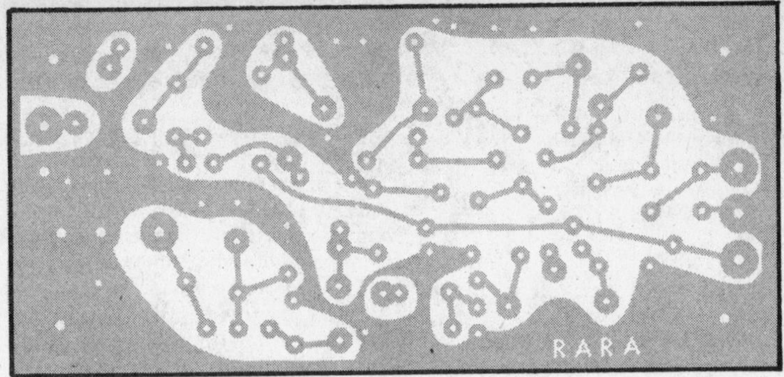

Fig. 6 – Scale-size layout for the pc board. The same pattern is used for either band. Foil side shown here.

Table I – Performance Specifications

Parameter	*6 Meters*	*2 Meters*
Noise figure, dB	1.8 – 2.3	2.0 – 2.4
Conversion gain, dB	22 – 28	17 – 24
Spurious responses, dB	–80*	–60*
	* Has a response at 6 MHz	* Responses at 107 & 181 MHz
Freq. response, ± 1 dB	49.8 – 51.5 MHz	143.9 – 146.4 MHz
Current at 12 V dc	12 – 18 mA	14 – 20 mA

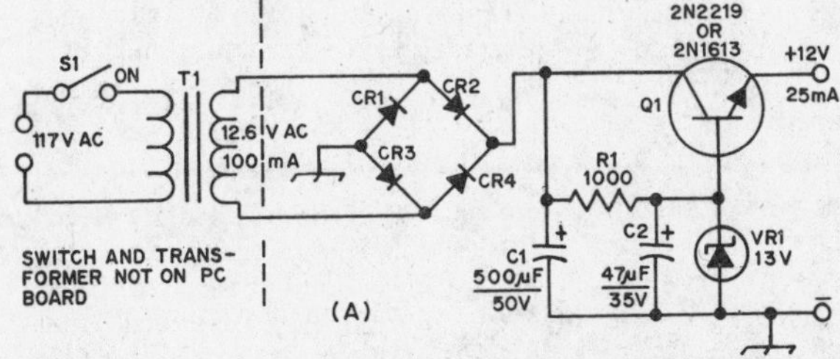

Fig. 7 – Schematic diagram and parts-placement guide for the power supply to the converters. The transformer is mounted external to the board. Pc board size is identical to the one used for the converters.

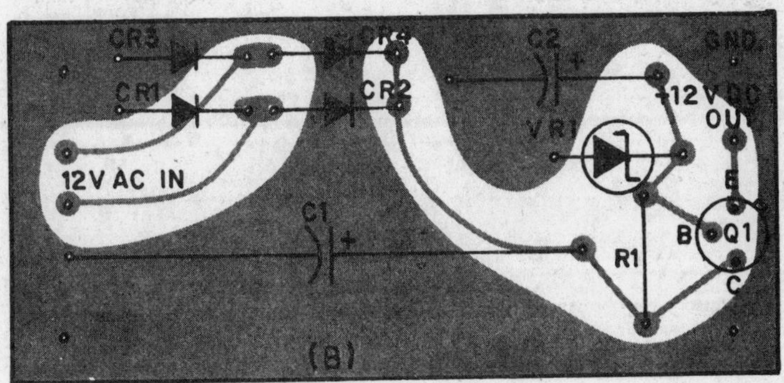

C3 must reach past the ground hole and connect to the foil. R3 is not used on the six-meter converter.

Alignment and Test

Perhaps the most difficult task in the project was the test and tune-up of the finished converter. A single test setup using a sweep generator, diode probe, and oscilloscope was a necessity to assure the flat response over the tuning range. Commercial attenuators were used to calibrate each converter by the substitution method.

Tuning of the air-wound rf circuit for two meters was accomplished by spreading or compressing the turns of the coils. After alignment, the windings were secured by a bead of Silastic compound along the oil to hold the turns in place. The noise figure of each converter was checked using the Monode noise-generator technique.[1] A final sensitivity check using a receiver (NC300) and a model 80 calibrated signal generator completed the checkout.

[1] Guentzler, "The Monode Noise Generator," *QST*, April 1967.

The transistors used in the rf stage were also subject to some variation in noise figure. When this occurred, an rf FET was carefully traded with an oscillator FET, since performance of the FET as an oscillator was always satisfactory.

The performance specification range for the converters is seen in Table I.

Small ceramic trimmers can be used in place of the fixed-value mica capacitors in the tuned circuits of these converters. The midrange of the trimmer should be approximately the value of the mica capacitors replaced. This procedure may simplify the tuning process of the converters where a sweep generator setup is not available. A little careful tweaking should give a reasonably flat response.

If trimmers are used, the rf input circuit should be tuned to the center of the desired response, 50.5 MHz as an example. This circuit tunes broadly and is not too critical. The rf interstage circuits should be stagger tuned, one at 50.0 MHz and the other at 51.0 MHz, as an example, the output i-f circuits can be tuned in a manner similar to the interstage circuits.

HIGH PERFORMANCE 2-METER CONVERTER

How effective is your vhf converter? Experienced vhf operators know that good results in receiving weak signals are proportional to the performance of the converter being used. A mediocre- quality vhf receiving setup will almost always negate the good features of the rest of the station equipment.

Unfortunately, many homemade converters are poor performers at best. Some are simply of inferior design, while others are so touchy that they will not maintain alignment from day to day. Thoughtful design can serve to eliminate most of the performance problems common to vhf converters, and the measures that need to be taken are not expensive or difficult. This section describes a smooth-performing solid-state 144-MHz converter that is free of spurious responses, is unconditionally stable, and has a low noise figure plus considerable overall gain. Construction and align-

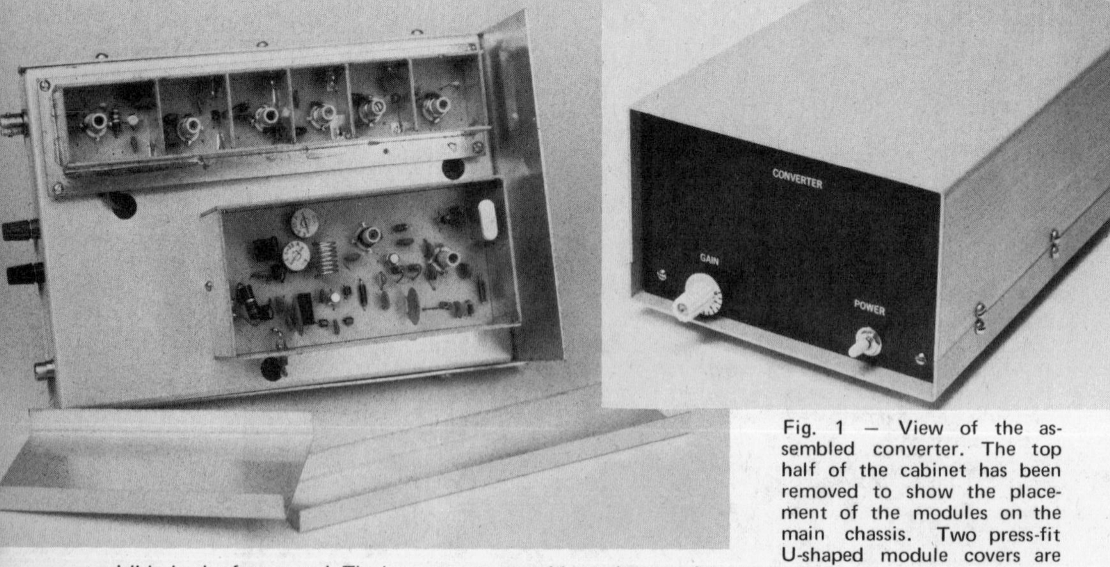

Fig. 1 — View of the assembled converter. The top half of the cabinet has been removed to show the placement of the modules on the main chassis. Two press-fit U-shaped module covers are visible in the foreground. The long narrow assembly at the top of the photo is the rf and mixer portion of the converter. The oscillator chain is contained in the shielded box at the lower right. A 12-volt power supply or IC i-f amplifier (see text) can be built in the vacant space at the lower left of the chassis. The completely assembled unit is shown in the inset.

ment should be within the capability of anyone who has had a moderate amount of experience in assembling ham equipment.

RF and Mixer Circuits

Junction FETs are used in a cascaded common-gate rf amplifier, Fig. 2. Source bias (R1 and R2) is used in each rf stage to reduce overloading in the presence of strong signals. The JFETs are able to sustain up to 80 volts pk-pk from gate to source before junction damage occurs. Therefore, protective diodes aren't needed at the antenna input if a good changeover relay is used for antenna switching. The rf stages, as stated earlier, are unconditionally stable in the common-gate mode, thus eliminating the need for neutralization circuits. A properly-adjusted common-gate rf amplifier (one stage) can provide up to 16 dB of gain and have a low noise figure.

The antenna is tapped down on L1 for lowest noise figure. The source of Q1 is tapped near the center of L1 to effect an impedance match. A three-section bandpass tuned circuit, lightly coupled, is used between Q1 and Q2 to establish a 2-MHz passband (144 to 146 MHz). Inductors L1 through L5 are stagger-tuned to provide a uniform response across that range. Shield compartments separate the tuned circuits to prevent mutual coupling, and to discourage input-output coupling at Q1 and Q2. The latter conditionion could cause instability of the rf amplifiers. Networks R2-C4 and R4-C12 prevent unwanted ac coupling between the stages via the 12-volt line. The combined gain of the rf amplifiers (after coupling losses through the tuned circuits) is approximately 18 dB.

The mixer circuit, Q3, is by no means unique. It employs an RCA 40673 dual-date MOSFET (metal-oxide silicon field-effect transistor) with built-in gate-protection Zener diodes. Either gate will handle up to 10 volts pk-pk (gate to source) before damage occurs. Other MOSFETs, such as the 3N200 (uhf type), 3N187, or MFE3008, can be used at Q3. The 40673 proved to be a good performer at 144 MHz, so it was used in this unit.

FETs, when compared to bipolar transistors, offer superior overload and cross-modulation characteristics and perform almost as well as do the best vacuum tubes. Gate 2 of Q3 is connected to its source through R6 to obtain its bias. A separate resistive divider can be used across the 12-volt line to obtain a more specific and stable bias voltage, but the method used here proved adequate for the performance characteristics desired. Low-impedance output to the tunable i-f receiver is provided by means of a capacitive divider across L6. Conversion gain of this mixer is approximately 12dB.

Oscillator Strip

The toughest aspect of converter design usually centers in the oscillator strip. This part of the circuit can make or break an otherwise good converter. Injection to the mixer should be provided by a single path – the intended one. The wave form being supplied to the mixer should be pure, Fig. 2. Many converters rely on a diode multiplier after the oscillator, and output from the multiplier is fed to the mixer without benefit of selective circuits. Other circuits feed the oscillator output into a transistor multiplier, and then to the mixer . . . again without filtering. When this is done many frequencies are contained in the mixer injection voltage. This can result in birdies and poor mixer performance. Furthermore, when the injection is taken from a doubler or tripler it is often too low in level (at the desired frequency) to provide suitable mixer performance.

The oscillator chain in Fig. 2 was designed for high performance. It has more output capability than is needed, the output waveform is pure, and there are no spurious oscillations in the circuit. The strip is contained in its own shielded enclosure to prevent coupling to the rf and mixer stages of the converter by stray paths.

Oscillator Q4 operates in the third-overtone mode. An optional frequency-trimmer capacitor, C36, is shown in dashed lines. Those wishing to place the oscillator dead on frequency may add this component. The crystal should be a high-accuracy commercial-standard type if this is done, and should be ground for a load capacitance of 20 pF. Capacitor C36 can be an NPO ceramic trimmer, mounted on the side wall of the oscillator box near Y1.

Zener-diode regulaion of the oscillator supply voltage is provided by CR1. The forward bias to Q5 is also regulated by CR1. Regulation of this part of the supply is desirable if the main 12-volt source is unregulated. This will help to keep the oscillator on frequency.

Low-cost 40637 (careful, *not* 40673) bipolar transistors are used at Q5 and Q6. Other types can be substituted if necessary, and performance should be about the same with the component values shown. Likely substitutes can include types 2N4124, MPS3563, and HEP-53.

The output level from the strip can be varied by changing the value of R13. With the 470-ohm resistor shown, in excess of 100 mW can be taken from amplifier Q6. In fact, this strip will work nicely as a transmitter or exciter by changing R13 to 100 ohms. With that value of resistance the output was measured at 0.5 watt!

Output stage Q6 operates Class C. A 58-MHz parallel trap is used to filter out the oscillator energy which feeds through the doubler and amplifier stages. Following the trap is a half-wave low-pass filter whose center frequency is 116 MHz. This filter removes any harmonic energy that is present in the output of Q6.

Construction Technique

Modular construction assures proper isolation between the two sections of the converter. Each piece is assembled on an etched-circuit board, and

Fig. 2 – Schematic diagram of the high-performance converter. Numbered components not appearing below are so designated for pc-board layout purposes. Other fixed-value capacitors are disk ceramic. Resistors, unless noted otherwise, are 1/2-watt carbon. Dashed lines denote shielding.

C5, C7, C31 – Silver-mica type.

C29, C30 – 5- tp 25-pF ceramictrimmer (Erie 557 with phenolic flange trimmed off).

C35 – .001-μF feedthrough capacitor mounted on wall of shield compartment.

C36 – 25-pF miniature air variable or ceramic trimmer (Eire 557 NPO suitable).

CR1 – 9.1-volt 1-watt Zener diode.

J1 – Chassis-mount coax fitting, type BNC.

J2 – Single-hole-mount phono jack.

J3, J4 – Binding post, one red, one black. (Johnson 111-102 and 111-103 used here.)

L1-L5, incl. – 4 1/2 turns No. 22 tinned-copper wire. Space one wire dia between turns. Wind on 1/4-in. dia ceramic form with brass slug (J. W. Miller 46A013-5 form. Address: 19070 Reyes Ave., Compton, CA 90224). L1 tapped at 1 (ant.) and 2 (source) turns above ground. L4 tapped at 2 turns. See text.

L6 – 2.96 to 3.64-μH slug-tuned inductor (J. W. Miller 46A336CPC).

L7 – 7 1/2 turns No. 26 enam. wire, close-wound at base end of Miller 46A013-4 form.

L8 – 4 1/2 turns No. 22 enam., close-wound at base end of Miller 46A013-4 form.

L9 – 16 turns No. 22 enam., close-wound, self-supporting, 3/16-in. dia.

L10 – 6 turns No. 20 tinned copper wire, 3/8-in. dia x 5/8 in. long.

L11 – 6 turns No. 22 enam., 3/16-in. dia, close-wound. See text.

L12, L13 – 4 turns No. 22 enam., 3/16-in. dia, close-wound. See text.

R13 – Select value to provide required output from Q6. See text.

RFC1, RFC2 – 8.2-μH rf choke (James Millen J300-8.2 or equiv.).

RFC3-RFC5, incl. – 10-μH rf choke. 4 turns No. 30 enam. wire looped through Amidon ferrite bead (Amidon Assoc., 12033 Otsego St., N. Hollywood, CA 91607).

S1 – Spst toggle.

Y1 – 58-MHz 3rd-overtone crystal. (International Crystal type GP.) Case style F-605. International Crystal PC-board socket F-605.

both units are enclosed in boxes made from double-sided circuit board. The modules can be mounted on a U-shaped piece of aluminum plate, or a chassis and cabinet arrangement of the type shown here can be used. The esthetic qualities of the converter are of secondary importance, and can best be decided by the constructor.

The oscillator section is contained in a box which measures 2 1/2 × 5 1/4 × 1 3/4 inches. The pc board is recessed into the compartment 1 1/4 inches. No. 6 spade bolts, 6 each, secure the box to the chassis. The corners of the box are soldered together by means of a 100-watt iron with a slender tip. The bottom (foil side) of the pc board is soldered to the box walls on all four sides. Capacitor C35 is mounted on the box wall just above L13.

The rf amplifiers and mixer are contained in a long shield box which measures 7 3/4 × 1 3/8 × 7/8 inches. The main pc board is slightly longer and wider than the box to provide a base on which to solder the upper shield compartment. The main pc board for this module is double-sided, as is the material used for the shield box. The layout patterns of Fig.6 show both sides of the board. The top foil provides copper segments to which the walls of the box and the internal dividers can be soldered. It is suggested that the compartment and its dividers be soldered in place prior to parts installation. The completed assembly is mounted above the main chassis on four 1/4-inch metal spacers.

Both shield boxes have their top openings enclosed by press-fit U-shaped aluminum covers.

Fig. 3 – Interior view of the rf amplifier and mixer section. The input stage is at the far left, and the mixer compartment is at the extreme right. Double-sided pc board is used to make the shield box and its compartment dividers. The main pc board is also double-sided.

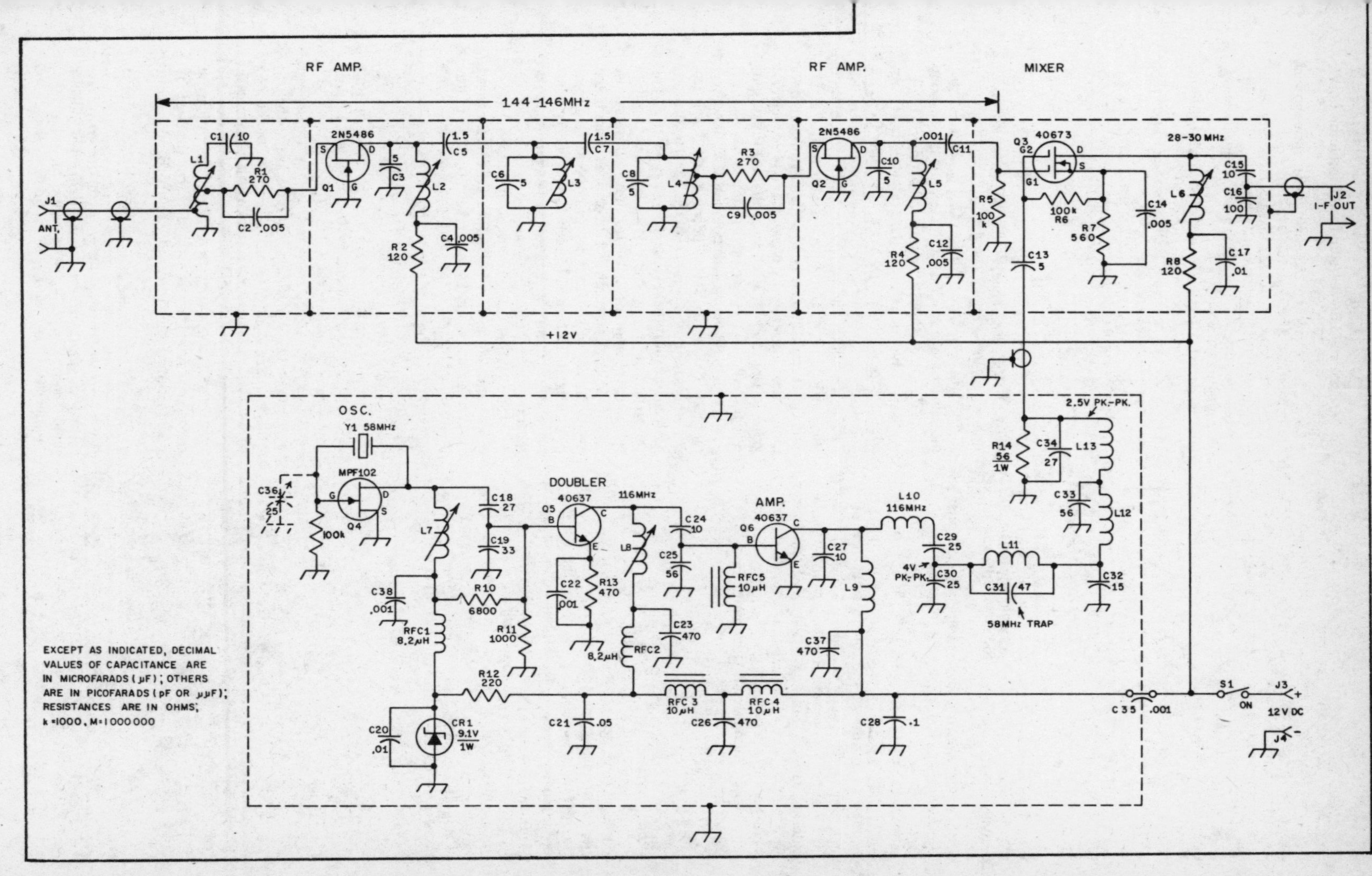
RF AMP.
RF AMP.
MIXER
144-146MHz
28-30 MHz
J1
ANT.
C1 10
L1
R1 270
C2 .005
2N5486
Q1
C3 5
C5 1.5
L2
R2 120
C4 .005
C6 5
L3
C7 1.5
C8 5
L4
R3 270
C9 .005
2N5486
Q2
C10 5
.001 C11
L5
R4 120
C12 .005
Q3 40673
R5 100 k
100k R6
R7 560
C13 5
C14 .005
L6
R8 120
C17 .01
C15 10
C16 100
J2 I-F OUT
+12V
OSC.
Y1 58MHz
MPF102
Q4
C36 25
100k
L7
C18 27
C19 33
C38 .001
R10 6800
R11 1000
RFC1 8.2µH
R12 220
C20 .01
CR1 9.1V 1W
DOUBLER
Q5 40637
116MHz
L8
C22 .001
R13 470
8.2µH
RFC2
C23 470
C24 10
C25 56
C21 .05
RFC 3 10µH
C26 470
AMP.
Q6 40637
RFC5 10µH
C27 10
L9
C37 470
RFC 4 10µH
C28 .1
L10 116MHz
C29 25
4V PK.-PK.
C30 25
L11
C31 47
58MHz TRAP
R14 56 1W
C34 27
L13
2.5V PK.-PK.
C33 56
L12
C32 15
C35 .001
S1
ON
J3
12V DC
J4
EXCEPT AS INDICATED, DECIMAL
VALUES OF CAPACITANCE ARE
IN MICROFARADS (µF); OTHERS
ARE IN PICOFARADS (pF OR µµF);
RESISTANCES ARE IN OHMS;
k=1000, M=1000 000

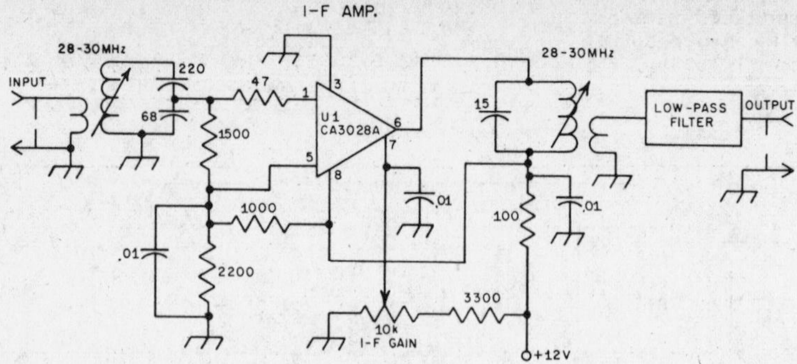

Fig. 4 – Circuit for an IC i-f amplifier that has manual gain control, and which can be used between the converter of Fig. 1 and the tunable i-f receiver. See the text for a discussion of this circuit. This amplifier can provide an additional 25 dB of gain.

The supply-voltage terminals and the input and output connectors are mounted on the rear lip of the main chassis. The shield boxes shown here were silver plated to prevent tarnishing and to make soldering easier. This step, however, is not necessary.

Converter Alignment

This converter draws 100 mA when connected to a 12-volt dc supply. The supply should be reasonably free from hum to prevent the oscillator strip from being modulated by ripple.

With operating voltage applied to the converter, couple a wavemeter to L7 and adjust the tuned circuit for maximum output. Turn the supply on and off a few times to make sure the oscillator starts rapidly each time. If not, choose a slug setting for L7 that allows fast starts. Next, couple the wavemeter to L8 and adjust its slug for maximum output at 116 MHz. Adjust C29 and C30 at Q6 for the same condition.

A grid-dip meter will be needed for adjustment of the 58-MHz trap. Spread or compress the turns of L11 for resonance at 58 MHz. In the same manner adjust coils L12 and L13 for resonance at 116 MHz. Now, readjust C29 and C30 for maximum output. When the circuit it working properly there should be approximately 1.5 volts pk-pk at the junction of L13 and C34. If not, adjust trap coil L11 for a clean waveform. Coils L2 and L13 can be tweaked for maximum output at 116 MHz while observing the waveform. Should the particular set of transistors you install at Q5 and Q6 exhibit unusually high beta, you may have more than 2.5 volts pk-pk at R14. If so, select a value of resistance at R13 that will limit the output of Q6 to the value specified.

A signal generator will be helpful during alignment of the rf amplifiers and mixer. If one is not available, tune in a weak 2-meter signal and use it for tune-up purposes. Connect a receiver to J2 and set it up for tuning from 28 to 30 MHz. Apply a signal to J1 and adjust L1 for maximum response at 145 MHz. Then, adjust L2 for peak response at 144 MHz. Trim L3 for a peak at 146 MHz, L4 for 144 MHz, and L5 for 145 MHz. There will be some interaction, so repeat the process a couple of times. Set the slug in L6 for peak output at 29 MHz.

Optimization of the noise figure requires a noise generator and careful adjustment of the input circuit. The taps of L1 must be moved until the lowest noise figure is obtained. *Do not adjust the taps or the slugs of L1 and L2 for maximum sensitivity.* The lowest noise figure seldom coincides with maximum gain. If you do not have a noise generator, adjustment can be brought to a ball-park figure by adjusting the taps on L1 while listening to a weak signal.

This converter can be tuned up for a narrower segment of the 2-meter band if coverage of the full 2-MHz spread is not desired. When set for the 144 to 146-MHz range, overall gain of the converter is approximately 30 dB. The gain will increase somewhat if the bandpass is decreased. Full band coverage from 144 to 148 MHz can be had by stagger tuning the front-end circuits. However, the

Fig. 5 – Interior view of the oscillator strip. The crystal oscillator is at the far right. The output stage and harmonic filter are at the left. Double-sided pc board is used to form the shield box.

Fig. 6 — Circuit-board patterns and layout for the two modules. These drawings are 1/2 scale.

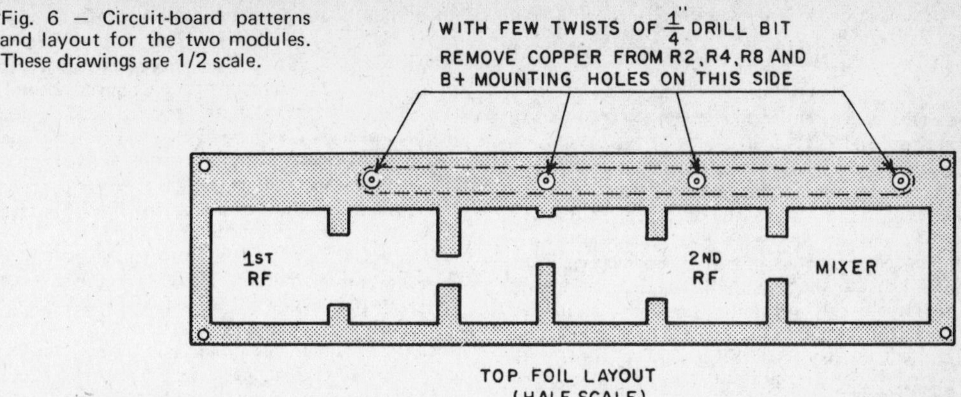

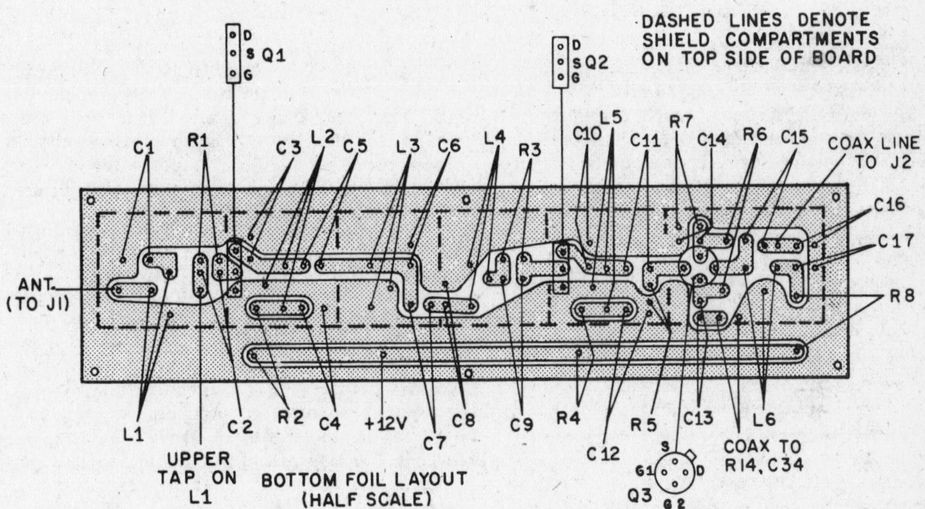

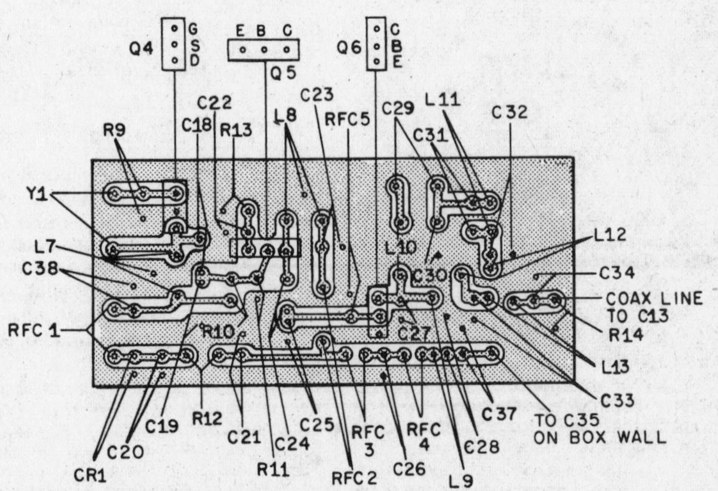

overall gain of the unit will drop to roughly 20 dB if this is done.

Some Comments

This converter was tried with a Collins 51S1 receiver and an older Hallicrafters SX-71. No birdies could be detected in the 28 to 30-MHz tuning range. Some spurious responses were noted, however, when using the converter with some receivers whose i-f was 455 kHz. This resulted from the receiver local oscillator being relatively close (455 kHz) to the tunable i-f frequency. The local oscillator energy apparently reached the converter along the coupling cable and beat with the converter oscillator energy at the mixer. A cure for this resulted from the addition of an i-f amplifier stage at the converter output. Though the extra gain was not needed, the stage helped to isolate the receiver from the converter mixer. The circuit used is shown in Fig. 4. In some instances this effect can work in reverse. Energy from the converter oscillator strip can leak past the mixer and enter the tunable receiver front end to cause sum and difference frequencies when beating with the tunable oscillator in the receiver. An effective cure for this is the installation of a low-pass filter between the converter output and the receiver input.

The noise figure of this converter can be set for the lowest value obtainable with the transistor used at Q1. In this instance it is somewhere between 2 and 2.5 dB . . . more than adequate for work on 144 MHz. Though this circuit may seem somewhat more complex than need be, the performance realized is well worth the few extra parts used.

COMPACT CONVERTER FOR 220 MHz

With the recent increase in repeater planning and, in some cases, activity on 220 MHz, there is a need for receiving systems on that frequency. Many past designs for 220-MHz converters have suffered from bulkiness in size, and complexity of circuits, that has made them unattractive for most mobile installations. The converter described here is small enough to be mounted in or near most mobile receivers.

One decision that must be made when designing a converter is what frequency to use as an i-f. For fm use the field is narrowed somewhat by the availability of surplus equipment. Much of this equipment is in the "low-band" range of 30 to 50 MHz, or in the "high-band" range of 148 to 170 MHz. It has been common practice to convert these rigs to work in the amateur 6- or 2-meter bands. Therefore, a most useful converter design would be one that could be adapted to use either of these bands as an i-f. This converter can be constructed for either i-f with only small differences in the components needed.

Fig. 1 – The 220-MHz converter is mounted in a box made from sheet aluminum. A phono jack at the lower left is the input connection. Another jack at the upper right is the output to the receiver. The i-f output coil shown here is for use with a low-band receiver. Changes necessary to work into a 2-meter receiver are explained in the parts list and text.

Circuit Considerations

One of the important features of this converter is the crystal oscillator and the multiplier stage that follows it. As shown in Fig. 2, Q3 is the oscillator and quadrupler. By using a crystal frequency of 19.25 MHz, and tuning the collector circuit to 77 MHz, the transistor stage provides the injection voltage to the mixer for an i-f of 147 MHz, or high-band. For a low-band i-f, only one more stage is needed – a frequency doubler. With a crystal frequency of 21.5 MHz, the output of Q3 is 86 MHz. Q4 doubles this to 172 MHz, which is the injection frequency for an i-f of 52 MHz. The foreqoing figures assume an input or signal frequency of 224 MHz. Crystal frequencies for other input or output frequencies can be calculated as follows:

For a low-band i-f, $f_o = \frac{f_s - f_1}{8}$

For a high-band i-f, $f_o = \frac{f_s - f_1}{4}$

Where f_o is the crystal frequency, f_s is the signal frequency to be received, and f_1 is the i-f. If the receiver to be used has several channels, an extra one can be set up for use with the converter. Where the choice of channels is limited, the one with least likelihood of feedthrough interference should be used. The severity of such interference will depend on the sensitivity of the receiver, shielding, grounding of the chassis, and the strength of the repeater signal.

A 40673 dual-gate MOSFET is used for the mixer, with the gate 2 connection tapped on the

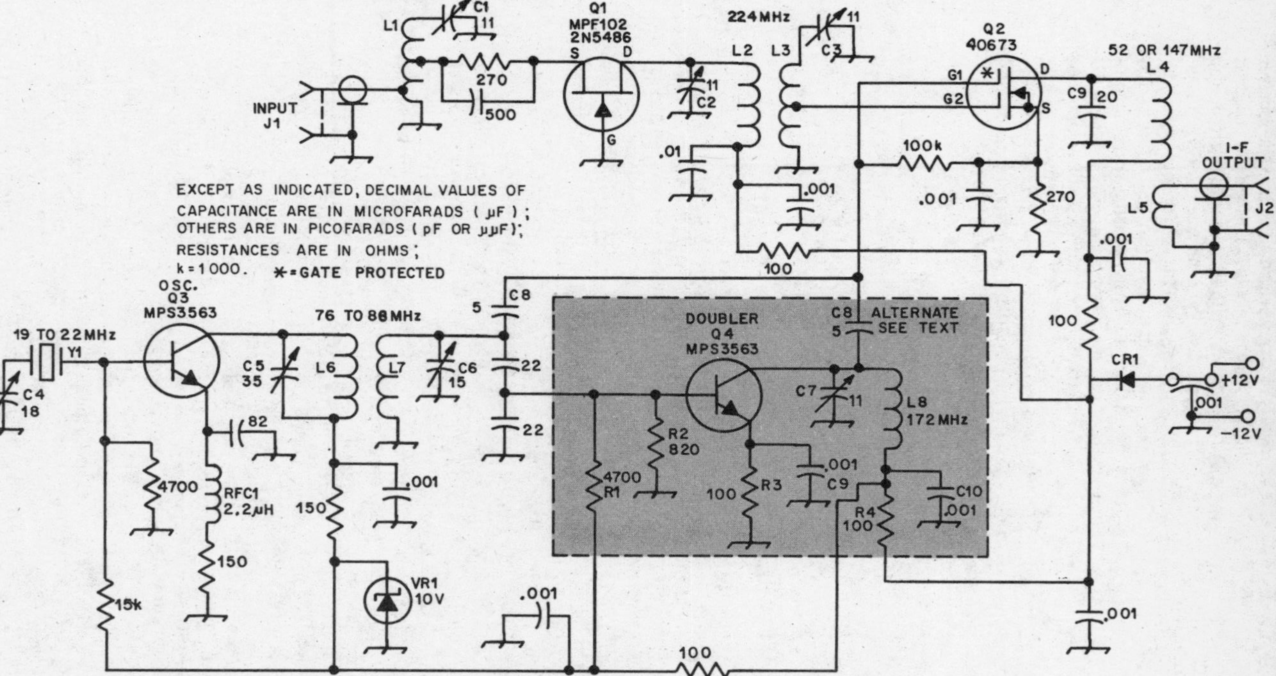

Fig. 2 — Schematic diagram of the 220-MHz converter. The components shown in the shaded area are the frequency-doubler circuit and can be omitted if the converter is built for use with a 2-meter receiver. Note that the connection point for C8 is also changed for a high-band i-f.

C1, C2, C3, C7 — 1.7- to 11-pF miniature variable (E. F. Johnson 187-0106-105).
C4 — 5.5- to 18-pF ceramic trimmer (Erie 538-002A-5.5-18 or equiv.).
C5 — 9- to 35-pF ceramic trimmer (Erie 538-002D-9-35 or equiv.).
C6 — 1.9- to 15.7-pF miniature variable (E.F. Johnson 187-0109-105).
C8 — 5-pF ceramic (see text).
C9 — For 52 MHz, 20 pF ceramic; for 146 MHz, 10 pF ceramic.
CR1 — Silicon diode, 50 PRV, 200 mA or greater.
J1, J2 — Coaxial connector, phono or other type.
L1 — 4 turns No. 20 tinned wire, 1/4-in. ID × 3/8-in. long, tapped 1-1/2 and 2-1/4 turns from ground end.
L2 — 4 turns No. 18 enam. wire, 1/4-in. ID × 1/2-in. long.
L3 — 3 turns No. 20 tinned wire, 1/4-in. ID × 3/8-in. long, tap 1-1/2 turns from ground end.
L4 — For 52 MHz, 9 turns No. 20 enam. wire, 1/4-in. ID × 5/8-in. long; for 146 MHz, 5 turns No. 20 enam. wire, 1/4-in. ID × 3/8-in. long.
L5 — For 52 MHz, 3 turns No. 20 enam. wire, 1/4-in. ID, closewound; for 146 MHz, 2 turns No. 20 enam. wire, 1/4-in. ID, closewound.
L6 — 6 turns No. 20 enam. wire, 1/4-in. ID × 1/2-in. long.
L7 — 7 turns No. 20 enam. wire, 1/4-in. ID × 1/2-in. long.
L8 — 5 turns No. 18 enam. wire, 3/16-in. ID × 3/8-in. long.
RFC1 — 2.2 μH choke, (J. W. Miller 70F225AI).
Y1 — Crystal, 19- to 22-MHz fundamental (International Crystal type CS or equiv.). The etched board layout will accept either 0.486 or 0.275 pin spacing.

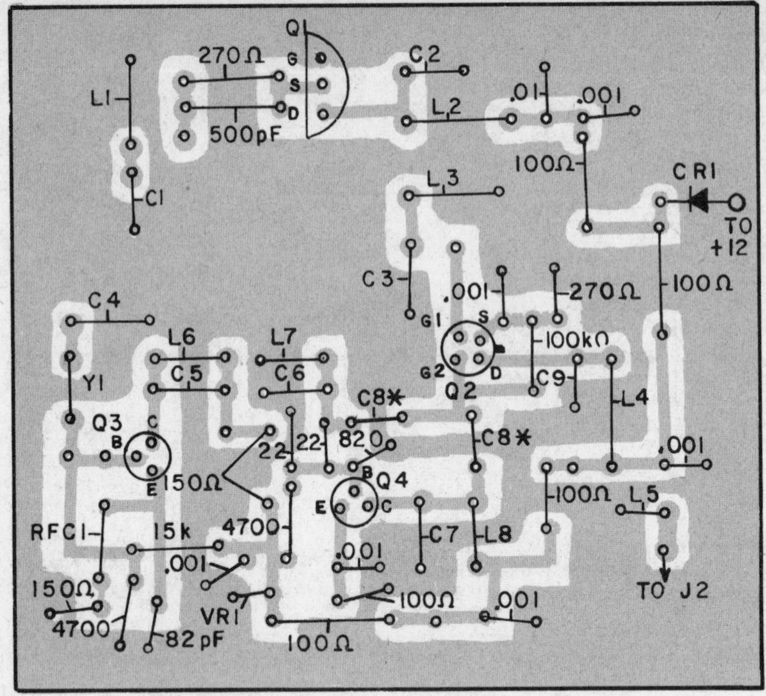

✱ CONNECT C8 ACCORDING TO TEXT

Fig. 3 — Scale drawing of the pc-board pattern for the 220-MHz converter. Foil side shown.

input-frequency coil. GATE 1 obtains injection voltage via a 5-pF capacitor from the output of the oscillator multiplier chain. The i-f output circuit is connected to the drain of the MOSFET. This circuit is fixed-tuned for simplicity's sake. It can be peaked for maximum output by squeezing or stretching the coil.

The rf amplifier uses an MPF102 or 2N5486 JFET in a grounded-gate configuration. The latter device will give slightly better performance. A word of advice when using these transistors in such a circuit: The gate must be connected to ground with the *shortest* possible lead length. A stubborn case of self-oscillation in the converter described here was cured by leaning the 2N5486 over so that the gate lead was just long enough to reach through the board and connect to the ground foil.

Construction

The converter is built on a piece of glass-epoxy board, 8.8-cm wide by 9.9-cm long. In inches, that works out to be just under 3-7/16 × 4. An aluminum box, 9-cm wide, 10-cm long, and 5-cm high was constructed as a housing. If the converter is to be installed inside a receiver, the box may not be necessary. However, care should be taken to assure that the converter is not mounted close to circuits that would couple unwanted signals into it. Such circuits might be the oscillator, multiplier, or rf amplifier stages of the i-f receiver.

Metal stand-off posts at each corner of the board serve to mount the converter and provide a good ground to the chassis. Phono connectors are used for input and output. The 12-volt dc supply is connected to a feedthrough capacitor on the wall of the bos. A silicon diode in the supply lead offers protection against damage caused by reversing the polarity, although in most mobile installations this should not be a problem.

The circuit board has been designed to include parts placement for either high- or low-band i-f. For an output at 147 MHz, the injection coupling capacitor, C8, is connected from the top of L7 to gate 1 of the 40673. For a 52-MHz i-f, Q4 is added to the board, along with its associated resistors, capacitors, and L8. When the doubler is used, C8 must be connected in the alternative position (from the top of L8 to gate 1) to provide injection voltage.

All of the coils are wound with wire large enough to be self-supporting. Vibration should not be a problem, but a few drops of coil dope can be applied to each winding for further stiffening. Some of the resistors are installed flat and some are upright, depending on the space available. Power consumption of each stage is low enough that 1/4-watt resistors can be used, resulting in a more neat-appearing board.

Tune-up and Performance

As with most construction projects of this type, a grip-dip oscillator is an almost indispensable tool to aid in getting the tuned circuits on the correct frequency. A good quality crystal should be used for Y1. There is no oven to keep the crystal at a constant temperature, so a good commercial-grade crystal is worth the price. If the oscillator has a low output or shows a reluctance to start, it might need a feedback capacitor connected from emitter to base. Something in the range from 10 to 30 pF should do, but use the smallest value that will assure oscillation. Most of the transistors tried in this circuit did not require extra feedback. The oscillator performance should be checked to be sure that its output is on the 4th harmonic of the crystal, and not the third or fifth.

After the frequency multipliers are tuned for maximum injection to the mixer, the converter can be connected to the input of a receiver. If a transceiver is to be used, the converter must be ahead of the receiver portion only. Accidental keying of a transmitter with the converter connected to it can ruin several hours work! The rf amplifier and mixer stages can be peaked up on a signal while monitoring the limiter current in the receiver. The spacing between L2 and L3 should be adjusted a small amount at a time, and each circuit retuned for maximum limiter current. The ultimate in adjustment requires a calibrated signal generator and an audio-output meter to measure the amount of quieting that a given signal will provide. When this converter was used ahead of a Motorola strip on 52 MHz, sensitivity was such that 0.28-microvolt into the converter produced the sought-after 20 dB of quieting. Under these condtions 0.1 microvolt would open the squelch of the receiver. Performance like this makes the converter equal to many of the two- meter receivers now in use, and better than some. Image rejection was more than 70 dB.

An i-f amplifier was not needed with the strip used to test the converter. If the receiver needs a bit of help in the sensitivity department, it is an easy metter to add a small amplifier. Single-stage premaplifiers for 6 or 2 meters should be adequate. Examples of such amplifiers can be found earlier in this chapter.

A LOW-NOISE 432-MHz CONVERTER

There is usually great emphasis on the need for a good low-noise uhf transistor in at least the first stage of a 432-MHz converter, but the rf stage or stages cannot do the whole job. Good front-end design is often hampered by deficiencies elsewhere in the converter. These can include inadequate injection to the mixer, and poor noise figure in the stage immediately following the mixer. The converter described here does well with a single rf amplifier stage, because the mixer has plenty of injection, and it is followed by a low-noise i-f amplifier. The latter is especially important when the intermediate frequency is in the 28-MHz range, as some communications receivers have rather poor noise figure and gain in this region.

Circuit

The rf amplifier uses a 2N5032 uhf bipolar transistor, with grounded emitter, and neutralization. This gives more gain than the commonly used grounded-base circuit, so only one rf stage is needed to override mixer noise and establish the noise figure of the system. Tuned lines are used in the input, collector and mixer-input circuits, for some selectivity and rejection of unwanted frequencies. The segment of the band near 432 MHz used for weak-signal work is so narrow that rf selectivity presents no problems. The amplifier collector current is adjusted for optimum signal-to-noise ratio by varying the base bias, by means of R1. The bias source is Zener-regulated by CR1.

The mixer is a Schottky-barrier diode, CR2. It works into a 28-MHz i-f amplifier stage using an integrated circuit. The amplifier may not be needed with communications receivers that work well in the 10-meter range, but it adds little to the cost and complexity of the converter, and its gain control, R2, is handy for setting the converter gain to the optimum level for any receiver.

The injection system uses more transistors and components than most converters have for this purpose, but the string of doublers is easy and inexpensive to build, and it produces injection voltage to spare. Use of a starting frequency of 50.5 MHz makes checking the oscillator a simple

Fig. 1 – The 432-MHz converter is built on the cover plate of a standard aluminum chassis. The "cigar-box effect" results from application of contact paper with simulated wood-grain finish to all exposed surfaces.

Fig. 2 – Interior of the 432-MHz low-noise converter, showing the rf and i-f amplifier assemblies. Strip-lines in the rf assembly are, left to right, L1, L3 and L4. The wire loop coupled to L3 is the neutralizing device, L2, with a capacitor tab coupling to L1. The small mixer diode is just visible, close to the right side of the rf assembly. The 28-MHz i-f amplifier is the square circuit board at the lower right.

matter if the builder has a 50-MHz receiver. A tuned-line filter, loosely-coupled to the last doubler, helps to suppress unwanted products of the multiplier system.

Construction

The converter is built in three principal subassemblies, mounted on an aluminum plate that fits the top of a 5 X 9 1/2 X 2-inch chassis, thereby providing complete shielding. An L-shaped bracket, 1 7/8 inches high and 8 1/2 inches long, supports the oscillator-multiplier assembly. The injection circuit board is mounted with 3-48 screws and short metal spacers, to provide lead clearance. Output from the tuned-line filter, C14L17, is taken off through L18 and small coax to the mixer.

Small screws and spacers are also used to mount the i-f amplifier to the cover plate. A small pc-type control, R2, reached through a hole in the side of the chassis, is used for gain adjustment. If the converter is to be used with several receivers, a shaft-type control could be substituted, and mounted on the cover or chassis, to facilitate readjustment, as needed. Lead lengths to R2 are not critical.

The rf amplifier enclosure and tuned lines are made of flashing copper. Dimensions are shown in Fig. 6. All holes should be drilled before cutting the metal and bending it to shape. Corners are soldered for rigidity and rf shielding. The lines, L1, L3 and L4, should be laid out and drilled before cutting the strips apart, as it is difficult to drill a clean hole in a narrow strip of flashing copper. The ends of the strips are bent up and soldered to the inside of the box.

A shield partition isolates the input line from the collector line, and also supports the transistor, Q1, which is mounted in a small hole near one end of the shield. The emitter lead is connected to the input side of the shield and the case lead to the collector side. Both leads are grounded by a 2-56 screw and nut, with no soldering needed. The entire assembly (the shield, Q1, R1, C2 and L2) can be completed before it is fastened in place with small sheetmetal screws. Note the "sense" of the neutralizing loop, L2. The grounded end is toward the transistor, and the hot end goes through a hole in the shield, toward the grounded end of the tuned lines. Cover the wire with insulating sleeving where it passes through the hole.

The coupling capacitor C4 is supported by its own leads, between L3 and L4. The mixer diode, CR2, is tapped on L4, through a hole in the side of the enclosure, and is supported on a small tie-strip, outside the assembly. The 3-pF injection-coupling capacitor, one end of RFC2, and the end of the small coax from the injection board are also supported by this strip.

Adjustment

Alignment of the oscillator-multiplier chain requires a dip meter or calibrated absorption wavemeter. To protect the amplifier transistor, Q1, do not apply voltage to it, or the bias-adjusting network, until all other stages are checked out. The oscillator should be checked to be sure that it is working only on the marked frequency. Improper adjustment of the coil L9 may allow oscillation on the crystal fundamental, about 16.83 MHz, and output at 50.5 MHz will be much too low to drive the following stages properly. There should be no evidence of rf in the 16-MHz region, or on twice the fundamental frequency. Be sure that the core tunes L9 *through* the crystal frequency.

Peak each doubler stage for maximum output at the desired frequency. If no indicator for 404 MHz is available, a simple Lecher-Wire[1] setup can be used, with a diode and milliammeter, to be sure

[1] A Lecher-Wire device is described in *The Radio Amateur's VHF Manual*, Chapter 14. A slotted line that can be used for uhf frequency measurement is described in *QST* for January, 1969.

Fig. 3 – The oscillator-multiplier assembly is on a circuit board mounted on a full-length aluminum bracket that provides both support and shielding. The crystal oscillator is at the right end. The strip-line at the left end is L17, the tuned circuit of a 404-MHz filter in the output of the last doubler stage.

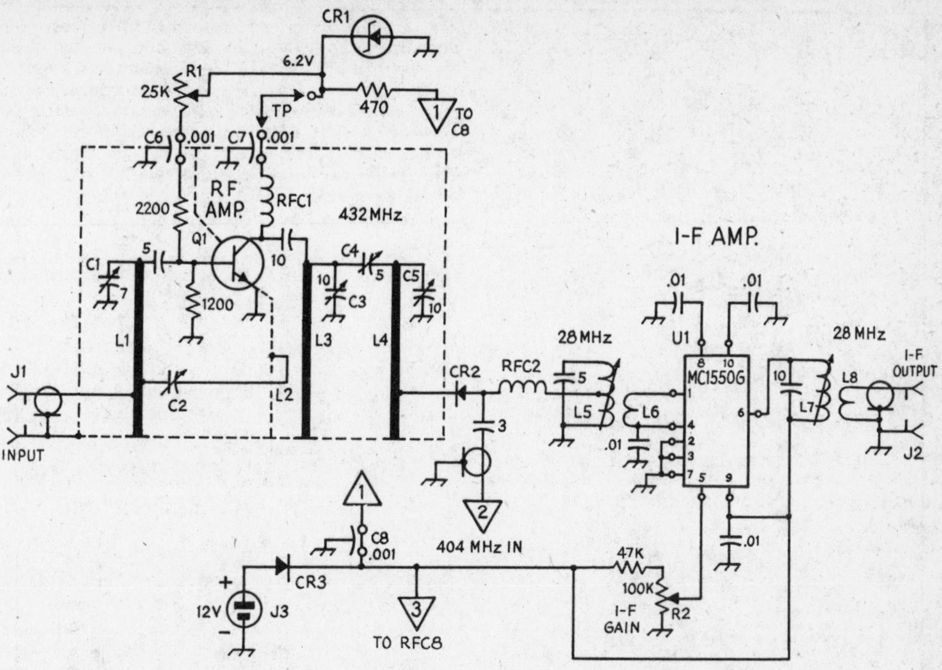

Fig. 4 — Schematic diagram and parts information for the rf and i-f portions of the 432-MHz converter.

C1 — 7-pF cylindrical trimmer (Centralab 829-7).
C2 — Copper tab 1/4 inch square, about 1/8 inch over L1, 1 5/8 inches from ground end. Adjust spacing for neutralization.
C3, C5 — 10-pF cylindrical trimmer (Centralab 829-10).
C4 — 5-pF piston trimmer.
C6, C7, C8 — .001-μF feedthrough (Erie 662-003-102K). C7 and a lug on the tie-strip serve as test points, and should be joined by a jumper when no meter is connected.
CR1 — 6.2-volt Zener diode.
CR2 — Hot-carrier diode (Hewlett-Packard 2811).
CR3 — 1-A, 100-PRV diode (Int. Rect. 5A1).
J1, J2 — BNC coaxial jack.
J3 — 2-pin polarized power connector.
L1 — Copper strip 3/8 by 2 1/4 inches after bending. Tap at 7/8 and 1 3/4 inches from ground end.
L2 — No. 24 enamel 1 11/16 inches long, bent as shown in Figs. 9-28 and 32.
L3, L4 — Copper strip 3/8 by 2 9/16 inches long after bending. Tap L4 3/4 inch from ground end.
L5, L7 — 20 turns No. 30 enamel on .162-inch slug-tuned form (Miller 27A013-7). Tap L5 10 turns from ground end.
L6, L8 — 3 turns small enameled wire over cold ends of L5 and L7.
Q1 — Low-noise uhf npn transistor, Motorola 2N5032.
R1 — 25K control, pc-type mounting (CTS R253B — Allied).
R2 — 100K control, pc-type mounting (CTS R104B — Allied).
RFC1 — .22-μH rf choke (Miller 4584).
RFC2 — 6 turns No. 26 enamel 1/8-inch dia, 3/8 inch long.
U1 — Motorola MC1550G integrated circuit.

TABLE 9-II

Crystal frequencies recommended for use with popular vhf and uhf converter i-fs

Band MHz	*Crystal frequency for i-f range from* 7 MHz	14 MHz	28 MHz	30.5 MHz
50	43.0 MHz	36 MHz	22.0 MHz	19.5 MHz
144	45.667 MHz	43.333 MHz	38.667 MHz	37.833 MHz
220	53.25 MHz	51.5 MHz	48.0 MHz	47.375 MHz
432	——	46.44 MHz	44.9 MHz	44.611 MHz

Other i-f tuning ranges can be used, but will require different crystal frequencies and suitable L-C combinations in the multiplier chain to effect proper resonance.

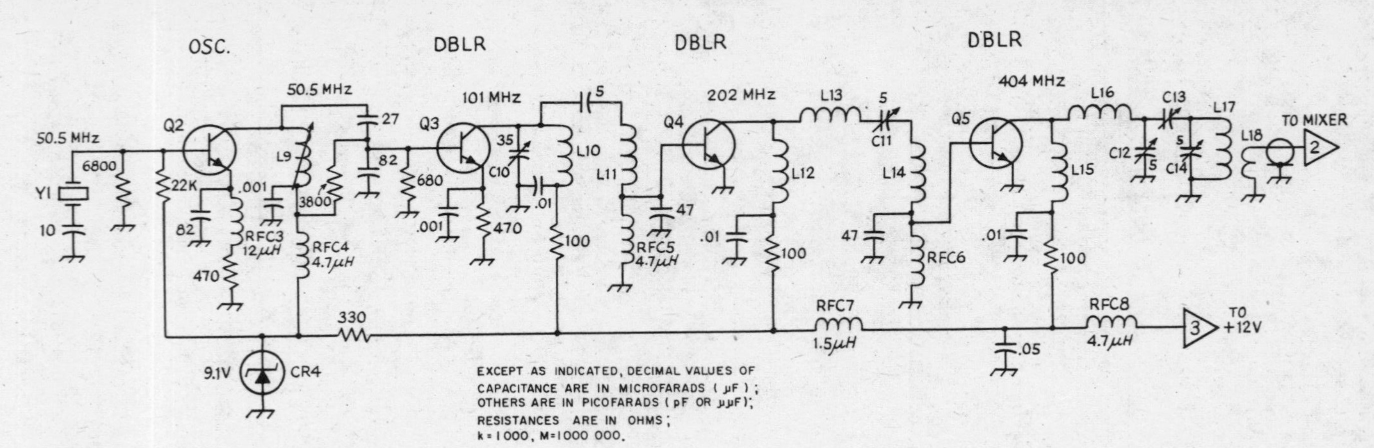

Fig. 5 – Schematic diagram and parts information for the oscillator-multiplier stages of the 432-MHz converter.

C10 – 35-pF ceramic trimmer.
C11, C12, C14 – 5-pF miniature trimmer (Johnson 189-504-5).
C13 – 1/4 by 3/8-inch copper tab. See Fig. 9-32 and text.
CR4 – 9.1-volt Zener diode.
L9 – 6 turns No. 26 enamel on .162-inch slug-tuned form (Miller 27A013-7).
L10 – 6 turns No. 22, 3/16-inch dia, 1/2 inch long.
L11 – 7 turns No. 24 enamel, 3/16-inch dia, closewound.
L12, L14 – 4 turns No. 22, 3/16-inch dia, 3/8 inch long.
L13 – 4 turns No. 22, 1/4-inch dia, 3/8 inch long.
L15 – 5 turns No. 28 enamel, on 1/2-watt resistor.
L16 – 4 turns No. 22, 1/2-inch dia, 1/2 inch long.
L17 – Copper strip, 5/16 by 2 1/2 inches. Bend at ground end, so that when run through the circuit board it will lie parallel to it, at the height of the stator of C14. See Fig. 9-29.
L18 – Hairpin loop, No. 24 enamel. Portion coupling to L17 is 3/8 inch wide and 5/8 inch long. Mount on small tie-strip at upper left corner, as seen in Fig. 9-29.
Q2-Q5, incl. – Vhf npn transistor (Motorola MPS3563).
RFC3, RFC4, RFC5, RFC7, RFC8 – Small rf chokes, values as indicated on drawing.
RFC6 – 2 turns No. 26 enamel through ferrite bead.
Y1 – Third-overtone crystal, 50.5 MHz (International Crystal Type EX).

TABLE 9-III

Required mixer injection frequencies from the oscillator chain when using the tunable i-f ranges listed in Table 9-II. Ordinarily, the crystal frequency is multiplied 3 times in 144-MHz converters, 4 times for 220 MHz and 9 times for 432.

Band	*Injection frequencies for i-fs of*			
MHz	*7 MHz*	*14 MHz*	*28 MHz*	*30.5 MHz*
50	43 MHz	36 MHz	22 MHz	19.5 MHz
144	137 MHz	130 MHz	116 MHz	113.5 MHz
220	213 MHz	206 MHz	192 MHz	189.5 MHz
432	——	418 MHz	404 MHz	401.5 MHz

that this circuit peaks properly. Injection on the proper frequency should also cause a noise increase in the communications receiver, at 28 MHz. The copper tab, C13, provides loose coupling to the stator of C12. Adjustment is not critical, and a spacing of about 1/8 inch should be about right. There is some coupling between the tuned line and the chassis, causing detuning and loss of injection, when the converter is assembled in its case. The circuit can be repeaked through a small hole drilled in the bottom of the chassis.

Moving the i-f gain control through its range should cause a smooth change in noise level at 28 MHz. L5 and L7 can be peaked roughly on noise, or on a 28-MHz signal.

The mixer tuning should result in a small noise increase as C5 is peaked. This adjustment can be made by using a harmonic of the dip oscillator, or the third harmonic of a 2-meter transmitter, for a test signal.

The rf amplifier can now be adjusted. Before voltage is applied to this stage, a 50-ohm resistor should be connected across J1, or a signal generator with a built-in termination should be used. The bias-adjusting control, R1, should be set at maximum resistance, and a 10-mA meter connected in place of the jumper across the test points in the lead to RFC1. Be sure that solid connections are made, as accidental application of base bias, with no collector voltage, can ruin the transistor. A safer arrangement might be to use a lower-range meter, with a suitable permanent shunt connected between the test points. The meter can then be removed from the circuit safely.

The collector current should be set to around 2 mA by adjustment of R1. Tune C1, C3, C4 and C5 for maximum response to the test signal, watching the collector current for any sign of change. Such fluctuation, or bursts of noise or rough-sounding notes in the receiver, indicates oscillation in the rf stage. The positions of the coupling loop, L2, and the capacitor tab, C2, should be adjusted to stop oscillation, if any is encountered.

After the converter has been stabilized, adjust the collector current for best signal-to-noise ratio, using a weak test signal. The data sheet for the 2N5032 indicates that best noise figure should be obtained with about 1 mA. Other good uhf transistors may require different values of collector current. Usually it will be found that highest gain will occur with somewhat more collector current than that giving the best signal-to-noise ratio, so it

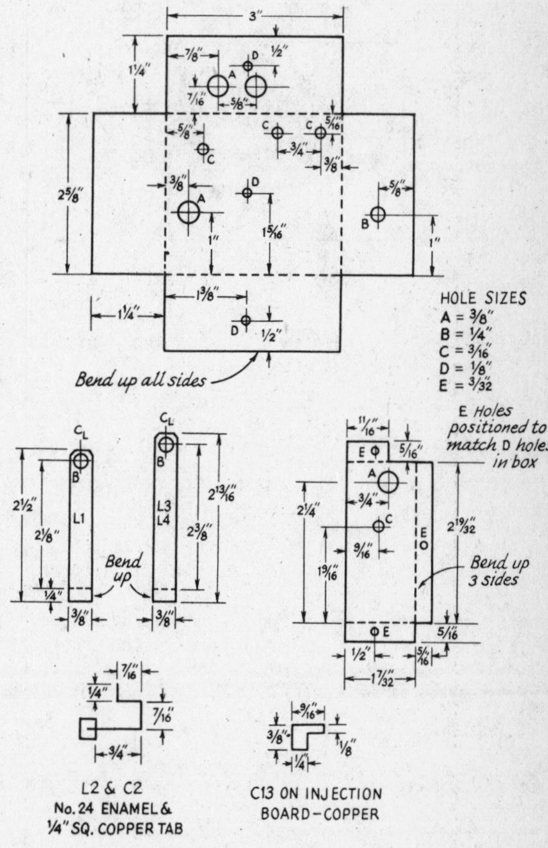

Fig. 6 – Details of the copper parts of the rf amplifier and mixer assembly. It is suggested that layout work and drilling be done before the sheet of flashing copper is cut, as drilling of small pieces of thin metal is difficult.

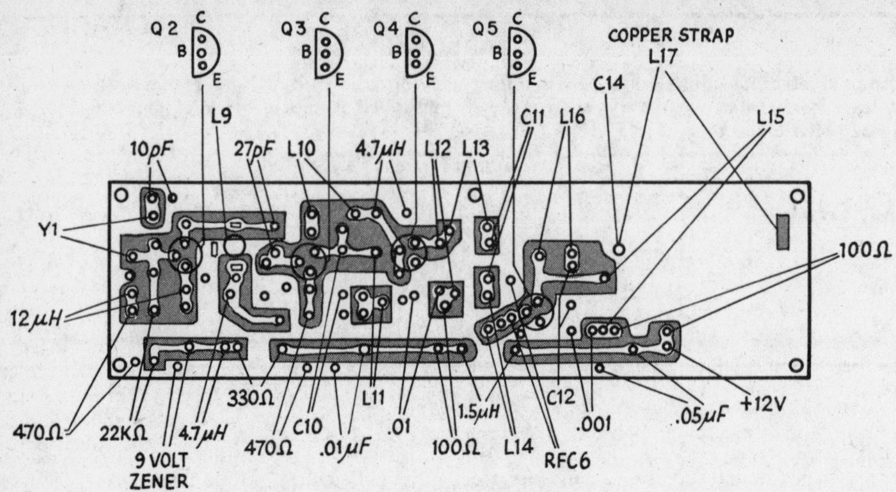

Fig. 9-7 — Half-scale drawing of the injection board, foil side.

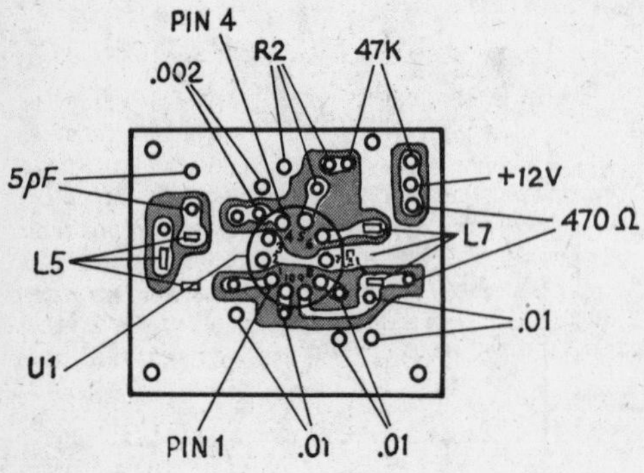

Fig. 9-8 — Half-scale drawing of the i-f amplifier board, foil side.

is important to make all tuning adjustments and current setting for the latter quality. Gain can be made up in the i-f stage.

An additional check can be made to be sure that the oscillator-multiplier string is giving the mixer adequate injection voltage. If it is, and if the rf stage is working properly, the injection can be reduced enough to cause the converter gain to drop several dB, before the signal-to-noise ratio is adversely affected. If adequate gain is available elsewhere in the converter, the best overall performance will generally be obtained with the injection level toward the lowest that will give good signal-to-noise ratio.

CHAPTER 10

Mobile and Portable/Emergency Equipment and Practices

MOBILE AND PORTABLE EQUIPMENT

Amateur mobile and portable operation provides many opportunities for one to exercise his skill under less than ideal conditions. Additionally, the user of such equipment is available for public-service work when emergencies arise in his community – an important facet of amateur-radio operation. Operating skill must be better than that used at most fixed locations because the mobile/portable operator must utilize inferior antennas, and must work with low-power transmitters in many instances.

Most modern-day hf-band mobile work is done while using the ssb mode. Conversely, the fm mode is favored by mobile and portable vhf operators, though ssb is fully practical for vhf service. Some amateurs operate cw mobile, much to the consternation of local highway patrolmen, but cw operation from a *parked car* should not be overlooked during emergency operations.

High-power mobile operation has become practical on ssb because of the low duty cycle of voice operation, and because low-drain solid-state mobile power supplies lessen battery drain over that of dynamotors or vibrator packs. Most mobile a-m and fm operation is limited to 60 watts for reasons of battery drain.

Portable operation is popular on ssb, cw and fm while using battery-powered equipment. Ordinarily, the power of the transmitter is limited to less than five-watts dc input for practical reasons. Solid-state equipment is the choice of most modern amateurs because of its compactness, reliability, and low power consumption. High-power portable operation is practical and desirable when a gasoline-powered ac generator is employed.

The secret of successful operation from portable sites is much the same as that from a fixed station – a good antenna, properly installed. Power levels as low as 0.5 watt are sufficient for covering thousands of miles during hf-band ssb and cw operation. In the vhf and uhf region of operation it is common to work distances in excess of 100 miles – line of sight – with less than one watt of transmitter output power. Of course it is important to select a high, clear location for such operation on vhf, and it is beneficial to use an antenna with as much gain as is practical. Low-noise receiving equipment is the ever-constant companion of any low-power portable transmitter that provides successful long-distance communications. Careful matching of the portable or mobile antenna to obtain the lowest possible SWR is another secret of the successful operator.

All portable and mobile equipment should be assembled with more than ordinary care, assuring that maximum reliability under rough-and-tumble conditions will prevail. All solder joints should be made well, stranded hookup wire should be used for cabling (and in any part of the equipment subjected to stress). The cabinets for such gear should be rugged, and should be capable of protecting the components from dust, dirt, and moisture.

ELECTRICAL-NOISE ELIMINATION

One of the most significant deterrents to effective signal reception during mobile or portable operation is electrical impulse noise from the automotive ignition system. The problem also arises during the use of gasoline-powered portable ac generators. This form of interference can completely mask a weak signal, thus rendering the station ineffective. Most electrical noise can be eliminated by taking logical steps toward suppress-

Fig. 10-1 – Effective portable operation can be realized when using lofty locations for vhf or uhf. Here, W1CKK is shown operating a battery-powered, 150-mW output, 2-meter transceiver. With only a quarter wavelength antenna it is possible to communicate with stations 25 miles or more away. Low-power transistor equipment like this unit will operate many hours from a dry-cell battery pack.

Fig. 10-2 — High-power portable/emergency operation can be made possible on all amateur bands by using vacuum-tube transmitters, and powering them from a gasoline-operated ac generator of one or more kW rating. (Shown here is VE7ARV/7 during a Field Day operation.)

ing it. The first step is to clean up the *noise source* itself, then utilize the receiver's built-in noise-reducing circuit as a last measure to knock down any noise pulses from passing cars, or from other man-made sources.

Spark-Plug Noise

Spark-plug noise is perhaps the worst offender when it comes to ignition noise. There are three methods of eliminating this type of interference — resistive spark-plug suppressors, resistor spark plugs, or resistance-wire cabling. By installing Autolite resistor plugs a great deal of the noise can be stopped. Tests have proved, however, that suppressor cable between the plugs and the distributor, and between the distributor and ignition coil, is the most effective means of curing the problem. Distributed-resistance cable has an approximate resistance of 5000 ohms per foot, and consists of a carbon-impregnated sheath followed by a layer of insulation, then an outer covering of protective plastic sheathing. Some cars come equipped with suppressor cable. Those which do not can be so equipped in just a matter of minutes. Automotive supply stores sell the cable, and it is not expensive. It is recommended that this wiring be used on all mobile units. The same type of cable can be installed on gasoline-powered generators for field use. A further step in eliminating plug noise is the addition of shielding over each spark-plug wire, and over the coil lead. It should be remembered that each ignition cable is an antenna by itself, thus radiating those impulses passing through it. By fitting each spark-plug and coil lead with the shield braid from a piece of RG-59/U coax line, grounding the braid at each end to the engine block, the noise reduction will be even greater. An additional step is to encase the distributor in flashing copper, grounding the copper to the engine block. This copper is quite soft and can be form-fit to the contour of the distributor. (Commercially-manufactured shielded ignition cable kits are also available.) The shield braid of the spark-plug wires should be soldered to the distributor shield if one is used. Also, the ignition coil should be enclosed in a metal shield since the top end of many of these coils is made of plastic. A small tin can can often be used as a top cover for the coil or distributor. It should be soldered to the existing metal housing of the coil. Additional reduction in spark-plug noise can be effected by making certain that the engine hood makes *positive* contact with the frame of the car when it is closed, thus offering an additional shield over the ignition system The engine block should also be bonded to the frame at several points. This can be done with the shield braid from coax cable. Feedthrough (hi-pass) capacitors should be mounted on the coil shield as shown in Fig. 10-6 to filter the two small leads leaving the assembly.

Other Electrical Noise

The automotive generator system can create an annoying type of interference which manifests itself as a "whine" when heard in the receiver. This noise results from the brushes sparking as the commutator passes over them. A dirty commutator is frequently the cause of excessive sparking, and can be cleaned up by polishing its surface with a fine grade of emery cloth. The commutator grooves should be cleaned out with a small, pointed instrument. A coaxial feedthrough capacitor of 0.1- to 0.5-μF capacitance should be mounted on the generator frame and used to filter the generator *armature* lead. In stubborn cases of generator noise a parallel L/C tuned trap can be used in place of the capacitor, or in addition to it, tuned to the receiver's operating frequency. This is probably the most effective measure used for curing generator noise.

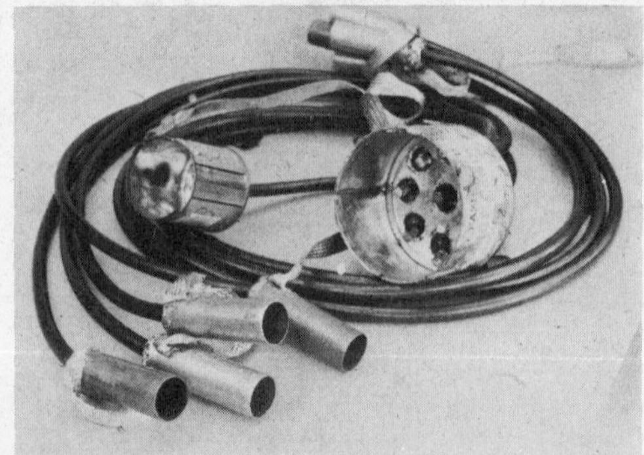

Fig. 10-3 — A typical homemade shielding kit for an automotive ignition system. Tin cans have been put to use as shields for the spark coil and distributor. Additional shields have been mounted on the plug ends of the wires for shilding the spark plugs. The shield braid of the cabling protrudes at each end of the wires and is grounded to the engine block.

Fig. 10-4 – A close-up view of the distributor shield can. The shield braid over each spark-plug wire is soldered to the top of the can, and the can is grounded to the engine block.

Voltage regulators are another cause of mobile interference. They contain relay contacts that jitter open and closed when the battery is fully charged. The noise shows up in the receiver as a ragged, "hashy" sound. Coaxial feedthrough capacitors can be mounted at the *battery* and *armature* terminals of the regulator box to filter those leads. The *field* terminal should have a small capacitor and resistor, series-connected, from it to chassis ground. The resistor prevents the regulator from commanding the generator to charge constantly in the event the bypass capacitor short-circuits. Such a condition would destroy the generator by causing overheating.

Alternators should be suppressed in a similar manner as dc generators. Their slip rings should be kept clean to minimize noise. Make sure the brushes are making good contact inside the unit. A coaxial feedthrough capacitor and/or tuned trap should be connected to the output terminal of the alternator. Make certain that the capacitor is rated to handle the output current in the line. The same rule applies to dc generators. *Do not connect a capacitor to the alternator or generator field terminals.* Capacitor values as high as 0.5 μF are suitable for alternator filtering.

Some alternator regulator boxes contain solid-state circuits, while others use single or double contact relays. The single-contact units require a coaxial capacitor at the *ignition* terminal. The double-contact variety should have a second such capacitor at the *battery* terminal. If noise still persists, try shielding the field wire between the regulator and the generator or alternator. Ground the shield at both ends.

Instrument Noise

Some automotive instruments are capable of creating noise. Among these gauges and senders are the heat- and fuel-level indicators. Ordinarily, the addition of a 0.5-μF coaxial capacitor at the sender element will cure the problem.

Other noise-gathering accessories are turn signals, window-opener motors, heating-fan motors and electric windshield-wiper motors. The installation of a 0.25-μF capacitor will usually eliminate their interference noise.

Frame and Body Bonding

Sections of the automobile frame and body that come in contact with one another can create additional noise. Suspected areas should be bonded together with flexible leads such as those made from the shield braid of RG-8/U coaxial cable. Trouble areas to be bonded are:

1 – Engine to frame.
2 – Air cleaner to engine block.
3 – Exhaust lines to car fame and engine block.
4 – Battery ground terminal to frame.
5 – Steering column to frame.
6 – Hood to car body.
7 – Front and rear bumpers to frame.
8 – Tail pipe to frame.
9 – Trunk lid to frame.

Wheel and Tire Static

Wheel noise produces a ragged sounding pulse in the mobile receiver. This condition can be cured by installing static-collector springs between the spindle bolt of the wheel and the grease-retainer cap. Insert springs of this kind are available at automotive supply stores.

Tire static has a ragged sound too, and can be detected when driving on hard-surface highways. If the noise does not appear when driving on dirt roads it will be a sure indication that tire static exists. This problem can be resolved by putting

Fig. 10-5 – Gasoline-powered ac generators used for portable/emergency operation should be treated for ignition noise in the same manner as automobile engines are. The frame of the gas generator should be connected to an earth ground, and the entire unit should be situated as far from the operating position as possible. This will not only reduce ignition noise, but will minimize ambient noise from the power unit. (Shown here is K1GTK during Field Day operations.)

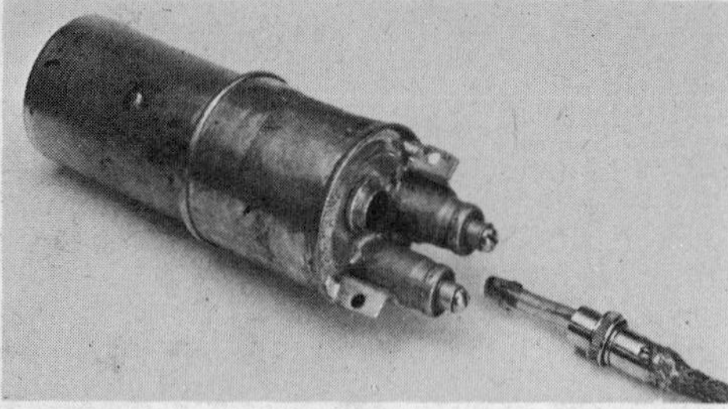

Fig. 10-6 – The automobile ignition coil should be shielded as shown here. A small tin can has been soldered to the metal coil case, and coaxial feed through capacitors have been soldered to the top of the can. The "hot" lead of the coil enters the shield can through a modified audio connector.

antistatic powder inside each tire. This substance is available at auto stores, and comes supplied with an injector tool and instructions.

Corona-Discharge Noise

Some mobile antennas are prone to corona build-up and discharge. Whip antennas which come to a sharp point will sometimes create this kind of noise. This is why most mobile whips have steel or plastic balls at their tips. But, regardless of the structure of the mobile antenna, corona build-up will frequently occur during or just before a severe electrical storm. The symptoms are a high-pitched "screaming" noise in the mobile receiver, which comes in cycles of one or two minutes duration, then changes pitch and dies down as it discharges through the front end of the receiver. The condition will repeat itself as soon as the antenna system charges up again. There is no cure for this condition, but it is described here to show that it is not of origin within the electrical system of the automobile.

Electronic Noise Limiters

Many commercially built mobile transceivers have some type of built-in noise clipping or cancelling circuit. Those which do not can be modified to include such a circuit. The operator has a choice of using af or rf limiting. Circuits of this type are described in the theory section of the hf receiving chapter.

Simple superregenerative receivers, by nature of their operation, provide noise-limiting features, and no additional circuit is needed. Fm receivers, if operating properly, do not respond to noise pulses of normal amplitude; hence no additional circuitry is required.

THE MOBILE ANTENNA

The antenna is perhaps the most important item in the successful operation of the mobile installation. Mobile antennas, whether designed for single or multiband use, should be securely mounted to the automobile, as far from the engine compartment as possible (for reducing noise pickup), and should be carefully matched to the coaxial feed line which connects them to the transmitter and receiver. All antenna connections should be tight and weatherproof. Mobile loading coils should be protected from dirt, rain, and snow if they are to maintain their Q and resonant frequency. The greater the Q of the loading coil, the better the efficiency, but the narrower will be the bandwidth of the antenna system.

Though bumper-mounted mobile antennas are favored by some, it is better to place the antenna mount on the rear deck of the vehicle, near the rear window. This locates the antenna high and in the clear, assuring less detuning of the system when the antenna moves to and from the car body. *Never use a base-loaded antenna on a bumper mount* if an efficient system is desired. Many operators avoid cutting holes in the car body for fear of devaluation when selling the automobile. Such holes are easily filled, and few car dealers, if any, lower the trade-in price because of the holes.

The choice of base or center loading a mobile antenna has been a matter of controversy for many years. In theory, the center-loaded whip presents a slightly higher base impedance than does the base-loaded antenna. However, with proper impedance-matching techniques employed there is no discernible difference in performance between the two methods. A base-loading coil requires fewer turns of wire than one for center loading, and this is an electrical advantage because of reduced coil

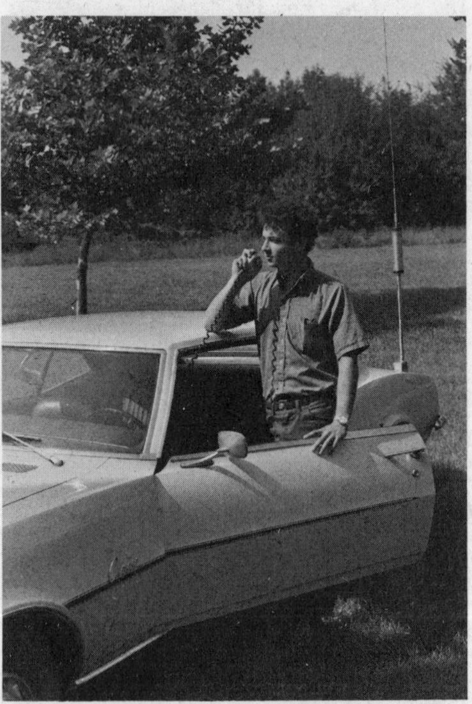

Fig. 10-7 – Here a mobile station is used as a portable/emergency station. As such, it can be connected to a full-size stationary antenna for maximum effectiveness. The engine should be noise-suppressed, and should be kept running during operation of the station to assure full battery power. (WA3EQK operating.)

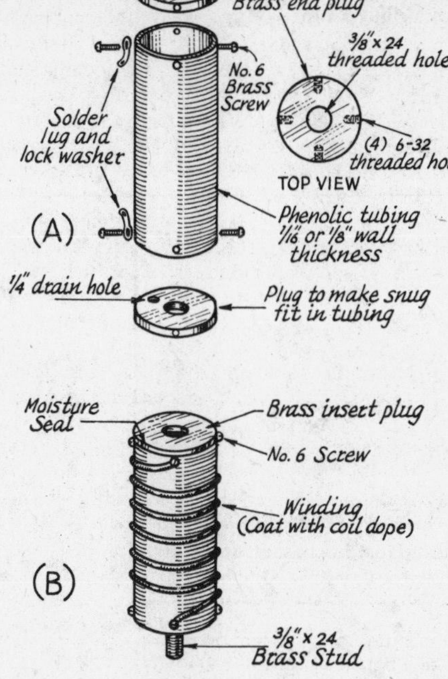

Fig. 10-8 – Details for making a home-built mobile loading coil. A breakdown view of the assembly is given at A. Brass end plugs are snug-fit into the ends of the phenolic tubing, and each is held in place by four 6-32 brass screws. Center holes in the plugs are drilled and tapped for 3/8-24 thread. The tubing can be any diameter from one to four inches. The larger diameters are recommended. Illustration B shows the completed coil. Resonance can be obtained by installing the coil, applying transmitter power, then pruning the turns until the lowest SWR is obtained. Pruning the coil for maximum field-strength-meter indication will also serve as a resonance indication. The chart in Fig. 10-10 will serve as a guide in determining the number of turns required for a given frequency of operation.

losses. A base-loaded antenna is more stable from the standpoint of wind loading and sway. If a homemade antenna system is contemplated, either system will provide good results, but the base-loaded antenna may be preferred for its mechanical advantages.

Loading Coils

There are many commercially built antenna systems available for mobile operation, and some manufacturers sell the coils as separate units. Air-wound coils of large wire diameter are excellent for use as loading inductors. Large Miniductor coils can be installed on a solid phenolic rod and used as loading coils. Miniductors, because of their turns spacing, are easy to adjust when resonating the mobile antenna, and provide excellent circuit *Q*. Phenolic-impregnated paper or fabric tubing of large diameter is suitable for making homemade loading coils. It should be coated with liquid fiber glass, inside and out, to make it weather proof. Brass insert plugs can be installed in each end, their centers drilled and tapped for a 3/8 X 24 thread to accommodate the mobile antenna sections. After the coil winding is pruned to resonance it should be coated with a high-quality, low-loss compound to hold the turns securely in place, and to protect the coil from the weather. Liquid polystyrene is excellent for this. It can be made by dissolving chips of solid polystyrene in carbon-tetrachloride. *Caution*: Do not breathe the chemical fumes, and do not allow the liquid to come in contact with the skin. *Carbon tetrachloride is hazardous to health.* Dissolve sufficient polystyrene material in the liquid to make the remaining product the consistency of Q-dope or pancake syrup. Details for making a home-built loading coil are given in Fig. 10-8.

Impedance Matching

Fig. 10-9 illustrates the shunt-feed method of obtaining a match between the antenna and the coaxial feed line. For operation on 75 meters with a center-loaded whip, L2 will have approximately 18 turns of No. 14 wire, spaced one wire thickness between turns, and wound on a 1-inch diameter form. Initially, the tap will be approximately 5 turns above the ground end of L2. Coil L2 can be inside the car body, at the base of the antenna, or it can be located at the base of the whip, outside the car body. The latter method is preferred. Since L2 helps determine the resonance of the overall antenna, L1 should be tuned to resonance in the desired part of the band with L2 in the circuit. The

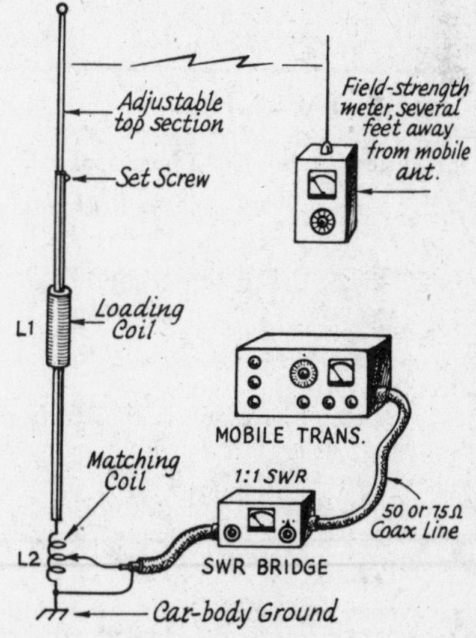

Fig. 10-9 – A mobile antenna using shunt-feed matching. Overall antenna resonance is determined by the combination of L1 and L2. Antenna resonance is set by pruning the turns of L1, or adjusting the top section of the whip, while observing the field-strength meter or SWR indicator. Then, adjust the tap on L2 for lowest SWR.

Approximate Values for 8-foot Mobile Whip

Base Loading

f kHz	*Loading* *L*μH	R_C*(Q50)* *Ohms*	R_C*(Q300)* *Ohms*	R_R *Ohms*	*Feed R** *Ohms*	*Matching* *L*μH*
1800	345	77	13	0.1	23	3
3800	77	37	6.1	0.35	16	1.2
7200	20	18	3	1.35	15	0.6
14,200	4.5	7.7	1.3	5.7	12	0.28
21,250	1.25	3.4	0.5	14.8	16	0.28
29,000	--------	-----	—	—	36	0.23
Center Loading						
1800	700	158	23	0.2	34	3.7
3800	150	72	12	0.8	22	1.4
7200	40	36	6	3	19	0.7
14,200	8.6	15	2.5	11	19	0.35
21,250	2.5	6.6	1.1	27	29	0.29

R_C = Loading-coil resistance; R_R = Radiation resistance.
* Assuming loading coil Q = 300, and including estimated ground-loss resistance.
Suggested coil dimensions for the required loading inductance are shown in a following table.

Fig. 10-10 — Chart showing inductance values used as a starting point for winding homemade loading coils. Values are based on an approximate base-loaded whip capacitance of 25 pF, and a capacitance of 12 pF for center-loaded whips. Large-diameter wire and coils, plus low-loss coil forms, are recommended for best Q.

TABLE 10-I

Suggested Loading-Coil Dimensions

Req'd L μH	*Turns*	*Wire Size*	*Dia In.*	*Length In.*
700	190	22	3	10
345	135	18	3	10
150	100	16	2 1/2	10
77	75	14	2 1/2	10
77	29	12	5	4 1/4
40	28	16	2 1/2	2
40	34	12	2 1/2	4 1/4
20	17	16	2 1/2	1 1/4
20	22	12	2 1/2	2 3/4
8.6	16	14	2	2
8.6	15	12	2 1/2	3
4.5	10	14	2	1 1/4
4.5	12	12	2 1/2	4
2.5	8	12	2	2
2.5	8	6	2 3/8	4 1/2
1.25	6	12	1 3/4	2
1.25	6	6	2 3/8	4 1/2

adjustable top section of the whip can be telescoped until a maximum reading is noted on the field-strength meter. The tap is then adjusted on L2 for the lowest reflected-power reading on the SWR bridge. Repeat these two adjustments until no further increase in field strength can be obtained; this point should coincide with the lowest SWR. The number of turns needed for L2 will have to be determined experimentally for 40- and 20-meter operation. There will be proportionately fewer turns required.

MATCHING WITH AN *L* NETWORK

Any mobile antenna that has a feed-point impedance less than the characteristic impedance of the transmission line can be matched to the line by means of a simple L network, as shown in Fig. 10-11. The network is composed of C_M and L_M. The required values of C_M and L_M may be determined from the following:

$$C_M = \frac{\gamma \, R_A (R_O - R_A) \times 10^9}{2\pi f \, \text{kHz} \, R_A \, R_O} \text{ pF and}$$

$$L_M = \frac{\gamma \, R_A (R_O - R_A) \times 10^3}{2\pi f \, \text{kHz}} \, \mu\text{H}$$

where R_A is the antenna feed-point impedance and R_O is the characteristic impedance of the transmission line.

As an example, if the antenna impedance is 20 ohms and the line is 50-ohm coaxial cable, then at 4000 kHz,

$$C_M = \frac{\sqrt{20\,(50 - 20) \times 10^9}}{(6.28)\,(4000)\,(20)\,(50)}$$

$$= \frac{\sqrt{600 \times 10^4}}{(6.28)\,(4)\,(2)\,(5)}$$

$$= \frac{24.1}{251.2} \times 10^{4} = 974 \text{ pF}$$

$$L_M = \frac{\sqrt{20\,(50 - 20) \times 10^3}}{(6.28)\,(4000)}$$

$$= \frac{\sqrt{600}}{25.12} = \frac{24.5}{25.12} = 0.97\ \mu\text{H}$$

The chart of Fig. 10-12 shows the capacitive reactance of C_M, and the inductive reactance of L_M necessary to match various antenna impedances to 50-ohm coaxial cable.

In practice, L_M need not be a separate inductor. Its effect can be duplicated by adding an equivalent amount of inductance to the loading coil, regardless of whether the loading coil is at the base or at the center of the antenna.

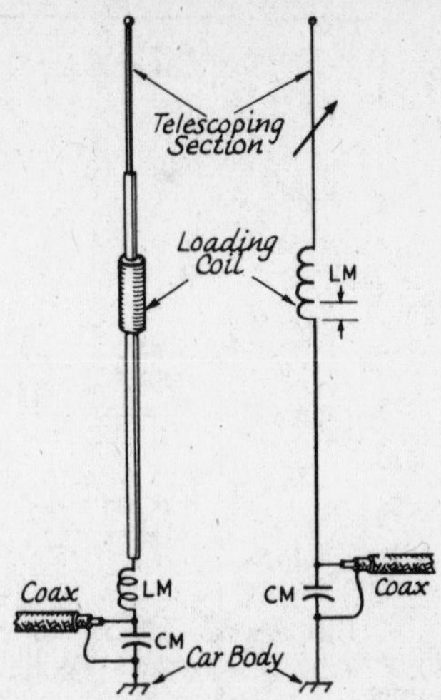

Fig. 10-11 – A whip antenna may also be matched to coax line by means of an L network. The inductive reactance of the L network can be combined in the loading coil, as indicated at the right.

Adjustment

In adjusting this system, at least part of C_M should be variable, the balance being made up of combinations of fixed mica capacitors in parallel as needed.

A small one-turn loop should be connected between C_M and the chassis of the car, and the loading coil should then be adjusted for resonance at the desired frequency as indicated by a GDO coupled to the loop at the base. Then the transmission line should be connected, and a check made with an SWR bridge connected at the transmitter end of the line.

With the line disconnected from the antenna again, C_M should be readjusted and the antenna returned to resonance by readjustment of the loading coil. The line should be connected again, and another check made with the SWR bridge. If the SWR is less than it was on the first trial, C_M should be readjusted in the same direction until the point of minimum SWR is found. Then the coupling between the line and the transmitter can be adjusted for proper loading. It will be noticed from Fig. 10-12 that the inductive reactance varies only slightly over the range of antenna resistances likely to be encountered in mobile work. Therefore, most of the necessary adjustment is in the capacitor.

The one-turn loop at the base should be removed at the conclusion of the adjustment and slight compensation made at the loading coil to maintain resonance.

Fig. 10-12 – Curves showing inductive and capacitive reactances required to match a 50-ohm coax line to a variety of antenna resistances.

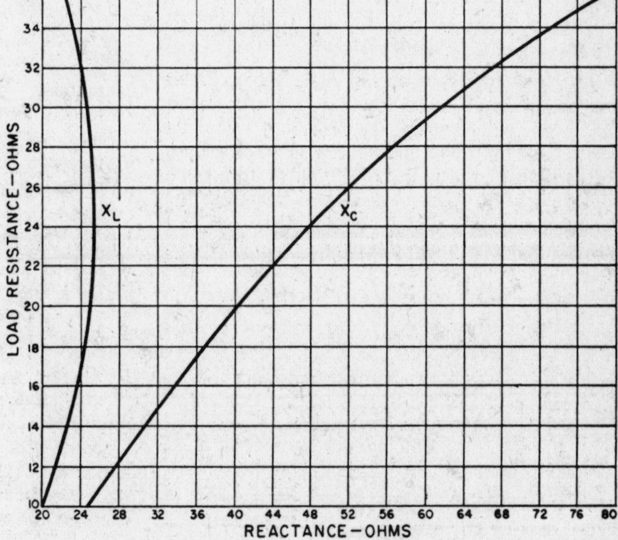

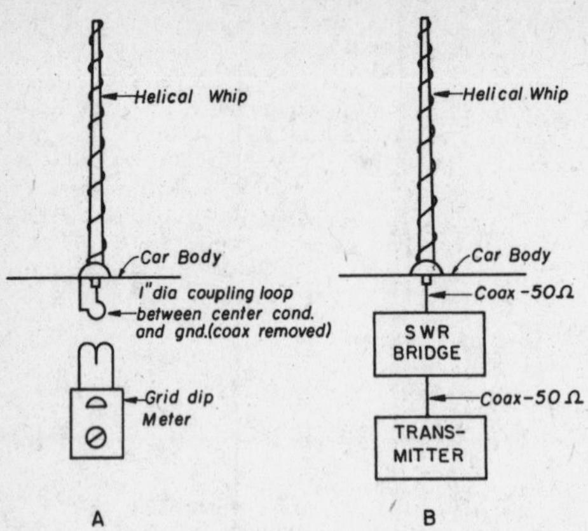

Fig. 10-13 – The resonant frequency of the antenna can be checked (A) with a grid-dip meter or (B) by finding the frequency at which minimum feed-line SWR occurs. The latter method is more accurate at high frequencies because it eliminates the effect of the coupling loop required in A.

CONTINUOUSLY-LOADED HELICAL WHIPS

A continuously-loaded whip antenna of the type shown in Fig. 10-14 is thought to be more efficient than a center- or base-loaded system (*QST*, May 1958, W9KNK). The feed-point impedance of the helically-wound whip is somewhat greater than the previously described mobile antennas, and is on the order of 20 ohms, thus providing an SWR of only 2.5 when 50-ohm coaxial feed line is used. The voltage and current distribution is more uniform than that of lumped-constant antennas. The low SWR and this feature make the antenna more efficient than the center- or base-loaded types. Antennas of this variety can be wound on a fiber glass fishing rod, then weatherproofed by coating them with liquid fiber glass, or by encapsulating them with shrinkable vinyl-plastic tubing.

Tapered Pitch

On frequencies below 28 MHz the radiation resistance falls off so rapidly that for the desired 4- and 6-foot whip lengths the resistance values are not suitable for direct operation with 50-ohm lines. It is desirable to raise the feed-point *R* to a value, approaching 50 ohms so that a matched line condition will exist. Based on extensive experimentation, a *tapered*-pitch continuous-loading antenna is recommended. Since it is not feasible to wind the helix with continuously varying pitch, a "step-tapered" design is best. A typical step-tapering technique for a variable-pitch helical whip antenna is to divide the total length of the radiator, say 4 feet, into 6 equal parts of 8 inches each. The helix is then wound with a 2-inch pitch for the first 8 inches, pitches of 1, 1/2, 1/4 and 1/8 inch, respectively, for the next four 8-inch sections, and finished with close winding of the final section. The resonant frequency will depend upon the rod diameter, wire size and number of turns. However, the variable-pitch 6-step taper approaches the ideal continuously-variable condition closely enough to give a good 50-ohm match with a 4-foot antenna at frequencies between 20 and 30 MHz.

Adjustment

With this design it is difficult to adjust the resonant frequency by changing the turns near the base; however, the frequency may be adjusted very readily by cutting off sections of the tightly-wound portion near the top of the whip. The technique to follow is to design for a frequency slightly lower than desired and then to bring the unit in on frequency by cutting small sections off the top until it resonates at the desired frequency. Resonance can be checked either by the use of a grid-dip meter or by the use of a transmitter and SWR bridge. Reflected power as low as 2 to 5 percent can easily be obtained with the units properly resonated even though it may mean cutting an inch or two off the top closely wound section to bring the unit in on frequency. These values can be obtained in the 10- and 15-meter band with overall lengths of 4 feet and in the 20- and 40-meter bands with a length of 6 feet. In the 75-meter band it has been possible to obtain an SWR of 1.5 using a 6-foot tapered-pitch helical winding, although the bandwidth is restricted to about 60 kHz. This affords operation comparable to the center coil loaded 12-foot whips. In general, the longer the radiator (in wavelengths), the greater the bandwidth. By arbitrarily restricting the physical length to 6 feet, or less, we obtain the following results:

Band	*Length*	*Resonant Freq.*	*SWR*	*Bandwidth for SWR = 2.0*
10 meters	4 feet	29.00 MHz	1.3	800 kHz
15 meters	4 feet	21.30 MHz	1.4	500 kHz
20 meters	6 feet	14.25 MHz	1.3	250 kHz
40 meters	6 feet	7.25 MHz	1.5	100 kHz
75 meters	6 feet	3.90 MHz	1.5	60 kHz

In the 15-, 20- and 40-meter bands the bandwidths of the taper-pitch designs are good enough to cover the entire phone portions of the bands. The bandwidths have been arbitrarily

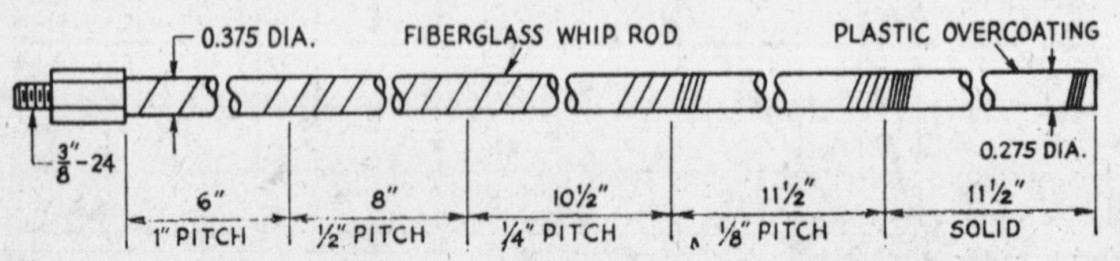

Fig. 10-14 – Dimensions for a 15-meter stepped-pitch whip, wound with No. 20 enameled wire.

Fig. 10-15 – K1MET prunes a capacity hat for antenna resonance at the low end of the 160-meter band. The Webster Big-K antenna is first tuned for the high segment of the band. The capacity hat is clipped on when operation on the "low end" is desired. Fine adjustments can be made by increasing or decreasing the spacing between the two No. 10 wires.

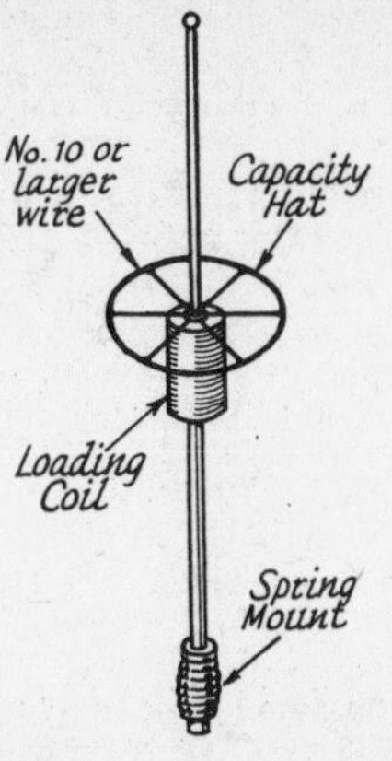

Fig. 10-16 – A capacitance "hat" can be used to improve the performance of base- or center-loaded whips. A solid metal disk can be used in place of the skeleton disk shown here.

selected as that frequency spread at which the SWR becomes 2 on a 50-ohm line, although with most equipment SWR values up to 2.5 can be tolerated and loading accomplished with ease.

Top-Loading Capacitance

Because the coil resistance varies with the inductance of the loading coil, the resistance can be reduced, beneficially, by reducing the number of turns on the coil. This can be done by adding capacitance to that portion of the mobile antenna that is *above* the loading coil. To achieve resonance, the inductance of the coil is reduced proportionally. Capacity "hats," as they are often called, can consist of a single stiff wire, two wires or more, or a disk made up from several wires, like the spokes of a wheel. A solid metal disk can also be used. The larger the capacity hat, in terms of mass, the greater the capacitance. The greater the capacitance, the smaller the amount of inductance needed in the loading coil for a given resonant frequency.

There are two schools of thought concerning the attributes of center-loading and base-loading. It has not been established that one system is superior to the other, especially in the lower part of the hf spectrum. For this reason both the base- and center-loading schemes are popular. Capacity-hat loading is applicable to either system. Since more inductance is required for center-loaded whips to make them resonant at a given frequency, capacity hats should be particularly useful in improving their efficiency.

REMOTE ANTENNA RESONATING

Fig. 10-17 shows circuits of two remote-control resonating systems for mobile antennas. As shown, they make use of surplus dc motors driving a loading coil removed from a surplus ARC-5 transmitter. A standard coil and motor may be used in either installation at increased expense.

The control circuit shown in Fig. 10-17A is a three-wire system (the car frame is the fourth conductor) with a double-pole double-throw switch and a momentary (normally off) single-pole single-throw switch. S2 is the motor reversing switch. The motor runs so long as S1 is closed.

The circuit shown in Fig. 10-17B uses a latching relay, in conjunction with microswitches, to reverse automatically the motor when the roller reaches the end of the coil. S3 and S5 operate the relay, K1, which reverses the motor. S4 is the

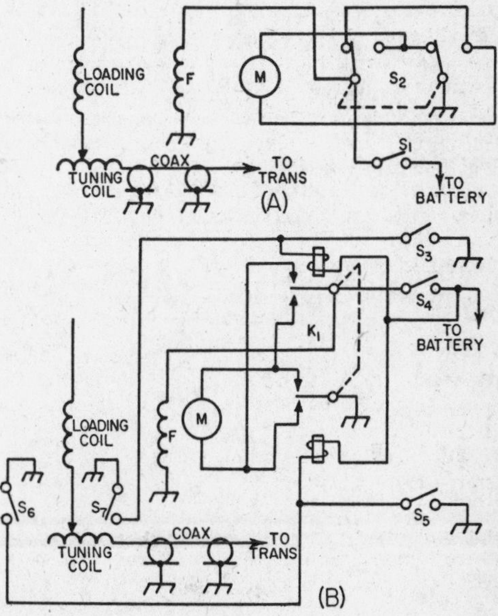

Fig. 10-17 – Circuit of the remote mobile-whip tuning systems.
K1 – Dpdt latching relay.
S1, S3, S4, S5 – Momentary-contact spst, normally open.
S2 – Dpdt toggle.
S6, S7 – Spst momentary-contact microswitch, normally open.

motor on-off switch. When the tuning coil roller reaches one end or the other of the coil, it closes S6 or S7, as the case may be, operating the relay and reversing the motor.

The procedure in setting up the system is to prune the center-loading coil to resonate the antenna on the highest frequency used without the base-loading coil. Then, the base-loading coil is used to resonate at the lower frequencies. When the circuit shown in Fig. 10-17A is used for control, S1 is used to start and stop the motor, and S2, set at the "up" or "down" position, will determine whether the resonant frequency is raised or lowered. In the circuit shown in Fig. 10-17B, S4 is used to control the motor. S3 or S5 is momentarily closed (to activate the latching relay) for raising or lowering the resonant frequency. The broadcast antenna is used with a wavemeter to indicate resonance. (Originally described in *QST*, December 1953.)

VHF MOBILE ANTENNAS

The three most popular vhf mobile antennas are the so-called halo, the turnstile, and the 1/4-wavelength vertical. The same rules apply to the installation and use of these antennas as for antennas operated in the hf bands – mounted as high and in the clear as possible, and with good electrical connections throughout the system.

The polarization chosen – vertical or horizontal – will depend upon the application and the area of the USA where operation will take place. It is best to use whatever polarity is in vogue for your region, thus making the mobile signal compatible with those of other mobiles or fixed stations. Vertically-polarized mobile antennas are more subject to pattern disturbance than horizontal types. That is to say, considerably more flutter will be inherent on the signal than with horizontal antennas. This is because such objects as trees and power poles, because of their vertical profile, tend to present a greater path obstacle to the vertical antenna. It is becoming common practice, however, to use omnidirectional, vertically-polarized vhf mobile antennas in connection with fm/repeater mobile service, even in areas where horizontal antennas are favored.

Both the turnstile and halo antennas are horizontally polarized. The halo is physically small, but is less effective than a turnstile. It is a half-wavelength dipole bent into a circle, and because the ends are in close proximity to one another, some signal cancellation occurs. This renders the antenna less efficient than a straight center-fed dipole. Halos do not offer a perfectly circular radiation pattern, though this has been a popular belief. Tests indicate that there is definite directivity, though broad, when a halo is rotated 360 degrees over a uniform plane surface.

Turnstile antennas of the type shown in Fig. 10-20 more closely approach the desired circular pattern of radiation, though the pattern is somewhat like a poorly defined four-leaf clover. Here two dipoles are fed with a 90-degree phase difference, and the antenna has a gain equal to, or better than a straight dipole. Of the three types discussed in the foregoing text, the latter is recommended.

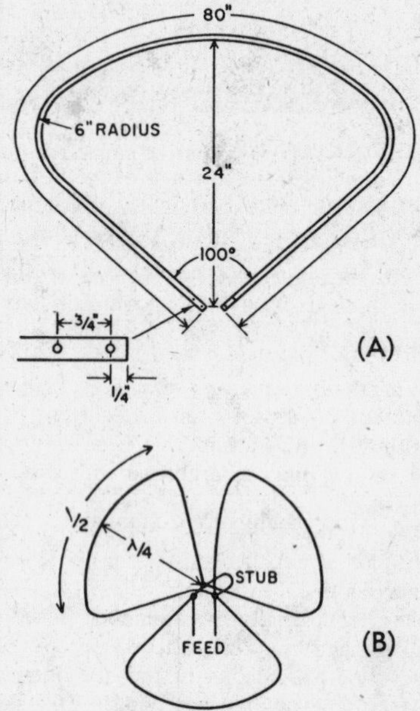

Fig. 10-19 – Schematic representation of the Big Wheel at B. Three one-wavelength elements are connected in parallel. The resulting low feed impedance is raised to 52 ohms with an inductive stub. Illustration A shows the bend details of one element for 144-MHz use.

Fig. 10-18 – The Big Wheel, an omnidirectional horizontal antenna for the 144-MHz band designed by W1FVY and W1IJD. Radiating elements occupy an area approximately 40 inches in diameter.

Fig. 10-20 – Two-meter turnstile antenna shown mounted on the front of an automobile. The miniature coax cable which feeds the antenna is taped to its 1/4-inch diameter steel supporting rod. The ends of the antenna elements should be flattened, or rounded, to make them safer in the event of accidental contact with the human body.

If one does not object to having an antenna that is likely to become a conversation piece because of its size and shape, it would be well to consider using the "Big Wheel" antenna, designed by W1FVY and W1IJD (September and October *QST*, 1961, and *ARRL Radio Amateur's VHF Manual*). The "wheel" consists of three one-wavelength elements, Fig. 10-19, connected in parallel and arranged as a cloverleaf. The antenna has a low feed-point impedance which is raised to 50 ohms by means of an inductive stub. Each clover leaf is 80 inches long overall (144 MHz), and can be made from aluminum tubing. Though the radiation pattern is not perfectly circular, it offers a good approach to that goal. Its performance greatly surpasses that of the three previously described antennas. It showed an increase in signal strength, from a selected test site, of several dB over the vertical whip, the halo, and the turnstile. Polarization is horizontal, as was the fixed-station antenna used in the tests.

TWO-METER 5/8-WAVELENGTH VERTICAL

Probably the most popular antenna used by the fm group is the 5/8-wavelength vertical. As stated previously, this antenna has some gain when compared to a dipole. The antenna can be used in either a fixed location with radials or in a mobile installation. An inexpensive antenna of this type can be made from a modified CB whip. The antenna shown in Figs. 1 and 2 is a 5/8-wavelength, 2-meter whip.

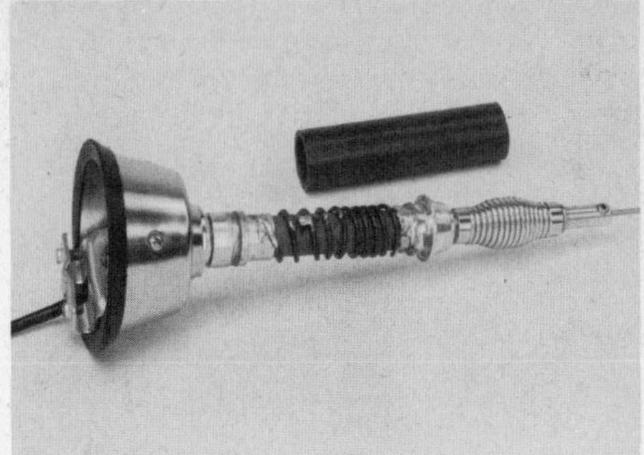

Fig. 1 – The new coil is tapped two turns from the base end. It may be necessary to file the coil ends so that the assembly will fit in the phenolic covering.

There are a number of different types of CB mobile antennas available. This particular antenna to be modified consists of a clamp-on trunk mount, a base loading coil, and a 39-inch spring-mounted, stainless-steel whip.

The modification consists of removing the loading-coil inductance, winding a new coil, and mounting a 3-30 pF trimmer in the bottom housing. The capacitor is used for obtaining a precise match in conjunction with the base coil tap.

The first step is to remove the weatherproof phenolic covering from the coil. Remove the base housing and clamp the whip side of the antenna in a vise. Insert a knife blade between the edge of the whip base and the phenolic covering. Gently tap the knife edge with a hammer to force the housing away from the whip section.

Next, remove the coil turns and wind a new coil using No. 12 wire. The new coil should have nine turns, equally spaced. The tap point is two turns up from the base (ground) end on the antenna as

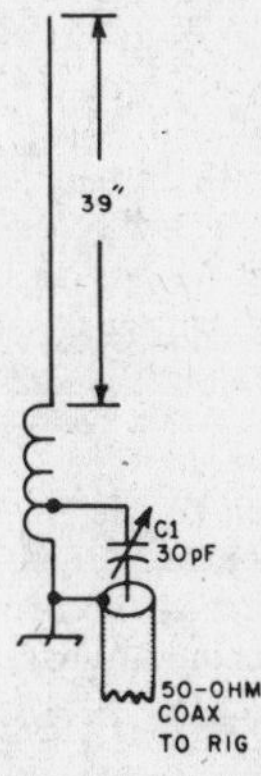

Fig. 2 – Circuit diagram of the whip antenna. C1 is a 3- to 30-pF trimmer.

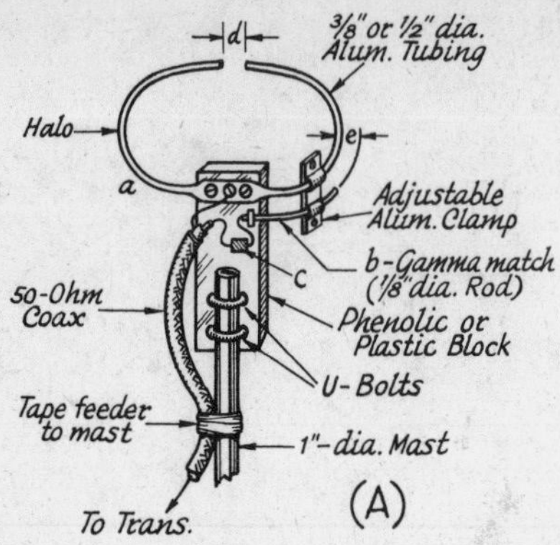

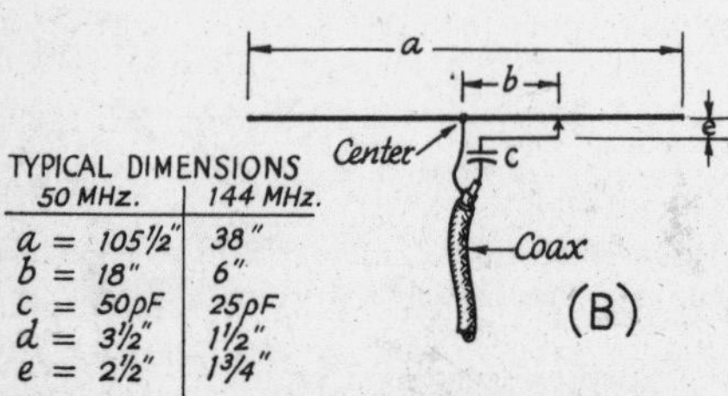

TYPICAL DIMENSIONS

	50 MHz.	144 MHz.
a =	105 1/2"	38"
b =	18"	6"
c =	50pF	25pF
d =	3 1/2"	1 1/2"
e =	2 1/2"	1 3/4"

Fig. 10-22 – Details for building a halo antenna for 6- or 2-meter use are shown at A. Other mechanical methods are possible, and the construction technique used will be up to the builder. The open end of the coax cable should be sealed against the weather. At B, a schematic representation of the halo. Dimension *a* is set for 1/2 wavelength at the operating frequency. The chart gives approximate dimensions in inches, and will serve as a guide in building a halo.

modified. The trimmer capacitor is mounted on a terminal strip which is installed in the base housing. A hole must be drilled in the housing to allow access to the capacitor adjustment screw.

Initially, the tap on the coil was tried at three turns from the bottom. The antenna was mounted on the car, an SWR indicator was inserted in the feed line, and C1 and the whip height were adjusted for a match. A match was obtained, but when the phenolic sleeve was placed over the coil, it was impossible to obtain an adjustment that proved a match. Apparently the dielectric material used in the coil cover has an effect on the coil. After some experimenting it was found that with the tap two turns up from the bottom, and with the cover over the coil, it was possible to get a good match with 50-ohm line.

This antenna can be used in a fixed location by adding radials. The radials, three or four, should be slightly longer than 1/4-wave and should be attached to the base mounting section.

THE QUARTER-WAVELENGTH VERTICAL

Ideally, the vhf vertical antenna should be installed over a perfectly flat plane reflector to assure uniform omnidirectional radiation. This suggests that the center of the automobile roof is the best place to mount it. Alternatively, the flat portion of the auto's rear trunk deck can be used, but will result in a directional pattern because of car-body obstruction. Fig. 10-23 illustrates at A and B how a Millen high-voltage connector can be used as a roof mount for a 144-MHz whip. The hole in the roof can be made over the dome light, thus providing accessability through the upholstery. RG-59/U and matching section *L*, Fig. 10-23C, can be routed between the car roof and the ceiling upholstery and brought into the trunk compartment, or down to the dashboard of the car. Some operators install an SO-239-type coax connector on the roof for mounting the whip. The method is similar to that of drawing A.

VHF HALO ANTENNAS

The antenna of Fig. 10-22 can be built from aluminum tubing of medium tensile strength. The one-half-wavelength dipole is bent into a circle and fed with a gamma match. Capacitor *c* is shown as a fixed value, but a variable capacitor mounted in a weatherproof box will afford more precise

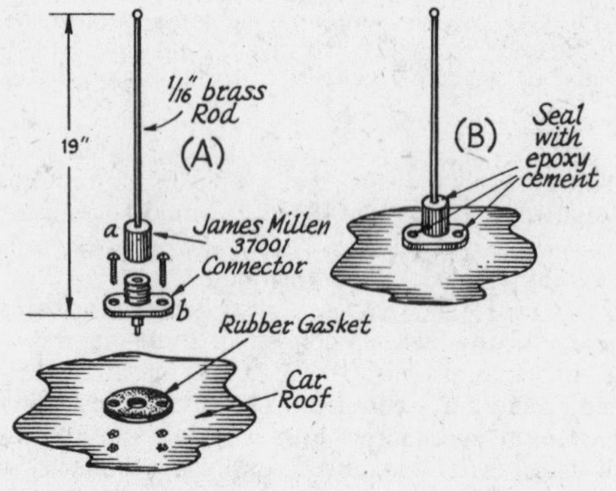

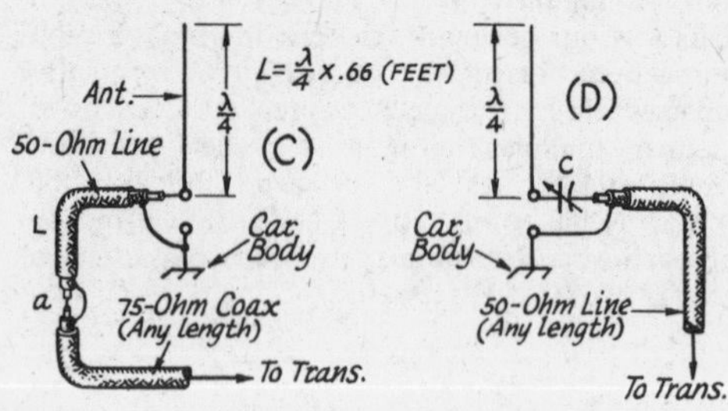

Fig. 10-23 – At A and B, an illustration of how a quarter-wavelength vertical antenna can be mounted on a car roof. The whip section should be soldered into the cap portion of the Millen connector, then screwed to the base socket. This handy arrangement permits removing the antenna when desired. Epoxy cement should be used at the two mounting screws to prevent moisture from entering the car. Diagrams C and D are discussed in the text.

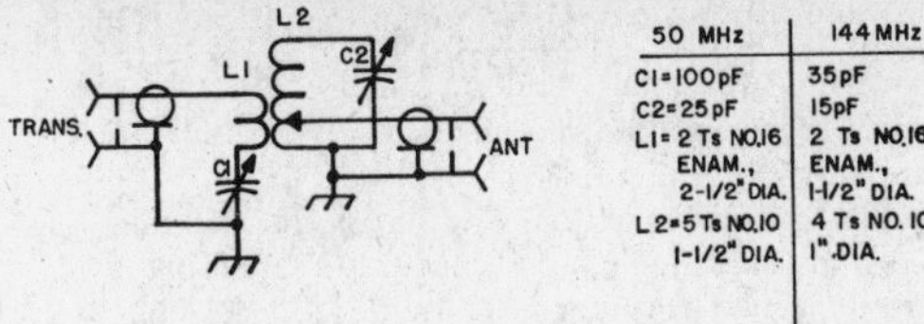

50 MHz	144 MHz
C1=100pF	35pF
C2=25pF	15pF
L1=2 Ts NO.16 ENAM., 2-1/2" DIA.	2 Ts NO.16 ENAM., 1-1/2" DIA.
L2=5 Ts NO.10 1-1/2" DIA.	4 Ts NO. 10 1" DIA.

Fig. 10-24 – Schematic diagram of the 6- or 2-meter antenna-matching circuit for use at the base of the quarter-wavelength vertical antenna. It can be housed in a Minibox and mounted permanently at the antenna base, inside or outside the car. If used outside, it should be sealed against dirt and moisture.

adjustment of the SWR. Or, a variable capacitor can be used initially for obtaining a 1:1 match, then its value can be measured at that setting to determine the required value for fixed capacitor *c*. Fixed-value capacitor *c* should be a dipped silver mica. A 75-pF variable should be used for 6-meter antennas, and a 35-pF variable will suffice for 144 MHz.

The tubing of *a* can be flattened to provide a suitable mounting surface for attachment to the insulating block of Fig. 10-22A. Gamma rod *b* can be secured to the same block by flattening its end and bolting it in place with 4-40 brass hardware. The spacing at *d* can be varied during final adjustment to secure the lowest SWR. Better physical stability will result if a high-dielectric insulator is connected across area *d*. Steatite material is recommended if an insulator/stabilizer is used.

If 75-ohm transmission line is used for the vertical, a quarter-wavelength matching transformer, L, can be used to match the feed impedance of the whip – approximately 30 ohms – to that of the feed line. A section of 50-ohm coax inserted as shown provides a close match to the antenna. Coax fittings can be used at junction *a* to assure a flat line, and to provide mechanical flexibility. BNC connectors are ideal for use with small coax lines. Illustration D shows how a series capacitor can be used to tune the reactance out of the antenna when using 50-ohm feed line. For 144-MHz use it should be 35 pF. A 75-pF variable will suffice for 6-meter antennas. An SWR bridge should be connected in the line while *c* is tuned for minimum reflected-power indication.

A more precise method of matching the line to the antenna is shown in Fig. 10-24. This antenna coupler can match 50- or 75-ohm lines to any antenna impedance from 20 ohms to several hundred ohms. It should be installed *at* the base of the vertical, and with an SWR bridge in the line C1 and C2 should be adjusted for the lowest SWR possible. The tap near the ground end of L2 should then be adjusted for the lowest SWR, readjusting C1 and C2 for minimum reflected power each time the tap is moved. A very compact tuner can be built by scaling down the coil dimensions appropriately. Trimmer capacitors can be used for C1 and C2 if power levels of less than 50 watts are used.

MOBILE POWER SUPPLIES

Most modern-day mobile installations utilize commercially-built equipment. This usually takes the form of a transceiver for ssb on the hf bands, and ssb or a-m for vhf operation. For fm operation in the vhf bands, most transceivers are surplus units which were originally used by commercial land-mobile services. Some home-built equipment is still being used, and it is highly recommended that one consider building his own mobile installation for the technical experience and satisfaction such a project can afford.

Many mobile transceivers contain their own power supplies for 6- and 12-volt dc operation. Some internal power supplies will also work off the 117-V mains. Vibrator power supplies are quite popular for low and medium power levels, but solid-state supplies are more reliable and efficient. Dynamotors are still used by some operators, but are bulky, noisy, and inefficient. The latter imposes an extremely heavy drain on the car battery, and does not contribute to long-term mobile or emergency operation without having the engine running at fairly high rpm to maintain the charge level of the battery.

Dynamotors

A dynamotor differs from a motor generator in that it is a single unit having a double armature winding. One winding serves for the driving motor, while the output voltage is taken from the other. Dynamotors usually are operated from 6-, 12-, 28- or 32-volt storage batteries and deliver from 300 to 1000 volts or more at various current ratings.

Commutator noise is a common cause of poor reception when dynamotors are used. It can usually be cured by installing .002-μF mica bypass capacitors from the dynamotor brushes (high-voltage end of armature) to the frame of the unit, preferably inside the cover. The high-voltage output lead from the dynamotor should be filtered by placing a .01-μF capacitor in shunt with the line (a 1000-V disk), followed by a 2.5-mH rf choke (in series with the line) of adequate current rating for the transmitter or receiver being powered by the dynamotor. This network should be followed by a smoothing filter consisting of two 8-μF electrolytic capacitors and a 15- or 30-H choke having a low dc resistance. The commutator and its grooves, at both ends of the armature, should be kept clean to further minimize noise. Heavy, direct leads should be used for connecting the dynamotor to the storage battery.

Vibrator Power Supplies

The vibrator type of power supply consists of a special step-up transformer combined with a

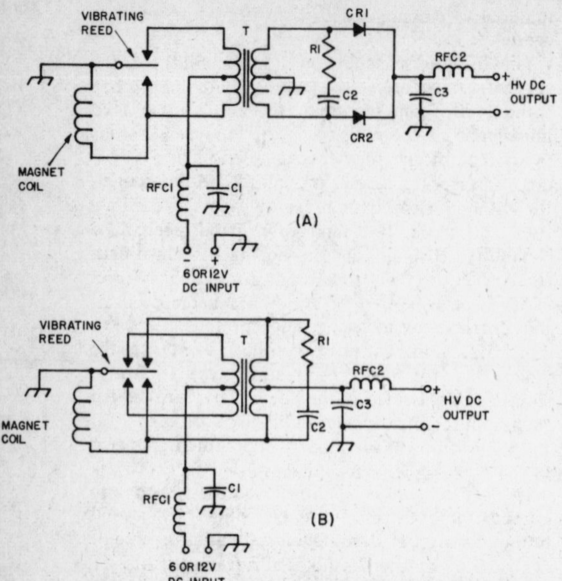

Fig. 10-25 – Basic types of vibrator power supplies. A – Nonsynchronous. B – Synchronous.

vibrating interrupter (**vibrator**). When the unit is connected to a storage battery, plate power is obtained by passing current from the battery through the primary of the transformer. The circuit is made and reversed rapidly by the vibrator contacts, interrupting the current at regular intervals to give a changing magnetic field which induces a voltage in the secondary. The resulting square-wave dc pulses in the primary of the transformer cause an alternating voltage to be developed in the secondary. This high-voltage ac in turn is rectified, either by silicon diode rectifiers or by an additional synchronized pair of vibrator contacts. The rectified output is pulsating dc, which may be filtered by ordinary means. The smoothing filter can be a single-section affair, but the output capacitance should be fairly large – 16 to 32 μF.

Fig. 10-25 shows the two types of circuits. At A is shown the **nonsynchronous** type of vibrator. When the battery is disconnected the reed is midway between the two contacts, touching neither. On closing the battery circuit the magnet coil pulls the reed into contact with one contact point, causing current to flow through the lower half of the transformer primary winding. Simultaneously, the magnet coil is short-circuited, de-energizing it, and the reed swings back. Inertia carries the reed into contact with the upper point, causing current to flow through the upper half of the transformer primary. The magnet coil again is energized, and the cycle repeats itself.

The synchronous circuit of Fig. 10-25B is provided with an extra pair of contacts which rectifies the secondary output of the transformer, thus eliminating the need for a separate rectifier tube. The secondary center tap furnishes the positive output terminal when the relative polarities of primary and secondary windings are correct. The proper connections may be determined by experiment.

The buffer capacitor, C2, across the secondary of T, absorbs spikes that occur on breaking the current, when the magnetic field collapses almost instantly and hence causes high voltages to be induced in the secondary. Without C2 excessive sparking occurs at the vibrator contacts, shortening the vibrator life. Resistor R1 is part of the buffer and serves as a fuse if C2 should short out, thus protecting the vibrator and transformer from damage. Values between 1000 and 5600 ohms, 1 watt, are commonly used. Correct values for C2 lie between .005 and .03 μF, and for 220-350-V supplies the capacitor should be rated at 2000 V or better, dc. The exact capacitance is critical, and should be determined experimentally while observing the output waveform on an oscilloscope for the least noise output. Alternatively, though not as effective a method, the capacitor can be selected for least sparking at the vibrator contacts.

Vibrator-transformer units are available in a variety of power and voltage ratings. Representative units vary from one delivering 125 to 200 volts at 100 mA to others that have a 400-volt output rating at 150 mA. Most units come supplied with "hash" filters, but not all of them have built-in ripple filters. The requirements for ripple filters are similar to those for ac supplies. The usual efficiency of vibrator packs is in the vicinity of 70 percent, so a 300-volt 200-mA unit will draw approximately 15 amperes from a 6-volt storage battery. Special vibrator transformers are also available from transformer manufacturers so that the amateur may build his own supply if he so desires. These have dc output ratings varying from 150 volts at 40 mA to 330 volts at 135 mA.

"Hash" Elimination

Sparking at the vibrator contacts causes rf interference ("hash," which can be distinguished from hum by its harsh, sharper pitch) when used with a receiver. To minimize this, rf filters are incorporated, consisting of RFC1 and C1 in the battery circuit, and RFC2 with C3 in the dc output circuit.

Equally as important as the hash filter is thorough shielding of the power supply and its connecting leads, since even a small piece of wire or metal will radiate enough rf to cause interference in a sensitive amateur receiver.

TRANSISTORIZED POWER SUPPLIES

Most present-day mobile equipment is powered by solid-state dc-to-dc converters. They are somewhat similar to vibrator supplies in that they use power transistors to switch the primary voltage of the transformer. This technique eliminates sparking in the switching circuit, and offers greater reliability and efficiency. The switching transistors can be made to oscillate, by means of a feedback winding on the transformer, and by application of forward bias on the bases of the switching transistors. The switching rate can be set for any frequency between 50 Hz and several thousand Hz and depends to a great extent upon the inductance of the transformer windings. The switching waveform is a square wave. Therefore, the supply is capable of causing a buzzing sound in transmitter or receiver output in much the same fashion as with a vibrator supply. Rf filtering should be employed as a corrective measure. At higher switching rates the buzz becomes a whine which sounds like that from a dynamotor. High-frequency switching rates are preferred for dc-to-dc converters because smaller transformer cores can be used, and because less output filtering is required. The efficiency of a well-designed solid-state power suuply is on the order of 80 percent, an improvement over the usual 60 to 70 percent of vibrator supplies, or the miserable 30 to 40 percent of dynamotors.

A typical transistorized supply is shown in Fig. 10-26. The supply voltage is fed into the emitter circuit of Q1-Q2. A resistive divider is used to obtain forward bias for the transistors through base-feedback-winding 1. The primary switching takes place between the emitter and collector of each transistor. Q1 and Q2 are connected in push-pull and conduct on alternate half cycles. As each transistor is driven into conduction it saturates, thus forming a closed contact in that leg of the circuit. The induced voltage is stepped up by T, and high-voltage appears across winding 3. Zener diodes CR1 and CR2 protect Q1 and Q2 from voltage spikes. They should be rated at a voltage slightly lower than the Vce of the transistors. Diodes CR3 through CR6 form a bridge rectifier to provide dc output from winding 3. Some supplies operate at a switching rate of 2000 to 3000 Hz. It is possible to operate such units without using output rectifiers, but good filtering is needed to remove the ripple from the dc output.

Transistor Selection

The switching transistors should be able to handle the primary current of the transformer. Since the feedback will diminish as the secondary load is increased, the beta of the transistors, plus

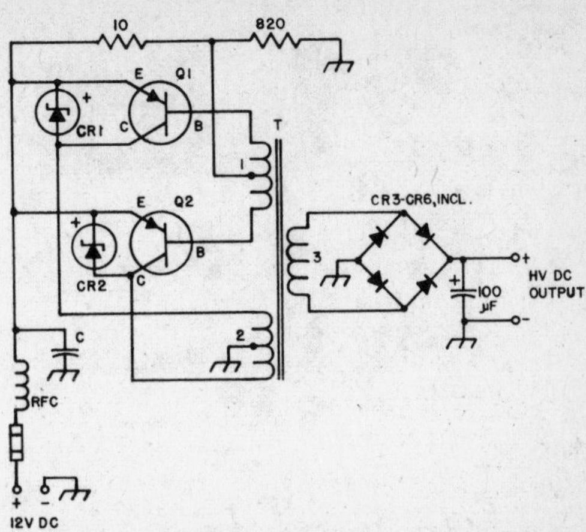

Fig. 10-26 – Typical dc-to-dc converter. Ratings for CR3-CR6, and the 100-µF filter capacitor can be selected from data in the power-supply chapter.

the design of the feedback circuit, must be sufficient to sustain oscillation under full-load conditions. During no-load conditions, the feedback voltage will reach its highest peak at the bases of Q1 and Q2. Therefore, the transistors must be rated for whatever base-emitter reverse voltage that occurs during the cutoff period. Since the transistors must be able to handle whatever peak voltage occurs during the switching process, it is wise to stay on the safe side. Choose transistors that have a Vceo rating of three or four times the supply voltage, keeping in mind that fully charged automobile batteries can deliver as much as 14 volts. Heat sinks should be used on Q1 and Q2 to prevent damage from excessive heating. The larger the heat sink, the better. Under full-load conditions the transistors should only be slightly warm to the touch. If they are running hot, this will indicate inadequate heat sinking, too great a secondary load, or too much feedback. *Use only enough feedback to sustain oscillation under full loading*, and to assure rapid starting under the same conditions.

MOBILE POWER SUPPLY FOR TRANSCEIVERS

Transceivers, such as the Heath SB-102, and the Drake TR-4 require a separate power supply when operated from 12-volts dc. Additionally, linear amplifiers can be run from a separate dc supply to allow increased power operation from relatively low-power transceivers. The unit described here, when operated from 12-volts dc, will deliver approximately 900-volts dc at 300 mA, 250-volts dc at 200 mA, negative 150-volts dc at 40 mA, and an adjustable bias voltage from 10 to 150 volts of dc.

The Circuit

A common-emitter configuration is used with diodes to provide a return path for the feedback winding, as shown in Fig. 10-28. Assuming that Q2 conducts first, the base is driven negative by the feedback winding (connections 6 and 7 on T1). CR15 then conducts, thereby protecting the base of Q1. CR14 is back-biased to an open circuit when Q2 is conducting. When T1 saturates producing a square wave, the voltage at pins 6 and 7 of T1 reverses turning on Q1. When Q2 conducts, current flows through the primary of T2 in one direction and as Q1 conducts, current flows through the primary of T2 in the other direction. This reversal of current in the primary of T2 provides an alternating square-wave voltage which is stepped up by the secondary winding. Full-wave rectification with current limiting is used with each secondary winding.

Fig. 10-27 – The heat sinks are mounted on an aluminum panel. When installing a power supply of this type, be sure to keep the heat sink fins in a vertical position to provide best air circulation. All of the filter capacitors are mounted in a row across the front of the chassis. RFC1 is located next to the transformer. Two sockets are mounted on the chassis side wall to accept an interconnecting cable from the transceiver. To the left of these sockets is the bias voltage adjustment control, R3. This model of the power supply was built by W8HS and assistance was given by W8DDO, W9IWJ (of Delco Radio Corp.), and Jim Osborne (of Osborne Transformer Co.).

The supply oscillates at about 1000 Hz and audible noise is low. The main power to the supply is applied through K1B. K1A can be connected in parallel with the filament supply in the transceiver.

Hash filtering is provided by RFC1 and its associated bypass capacitors in the primary lead. Transient suppression is assured by CR13, CR16 and CR17. Bleeder resistors are used on each supply leg to provide a constant minimum load for the circuit. The supply can be operated without being connected to its load without fear of damaging the diodes or transistors, although this is not considered good practice. Input and output connectors for interconnection to the battery and the transceiver can be selected to meet the needs of the particular installation.

Construction

This circuit requires that the transistors be insulated from the heat sink. Suitable insulators are included with the devices. Silicone grease should be used to help conduct the heat away from the transistors.

No attempt has been made to make the supply small. It is built on a 12 X 6 X 3-inch chassis which allows plenty of room for the heavy conductors. The capacitors are mounted in a row along one side

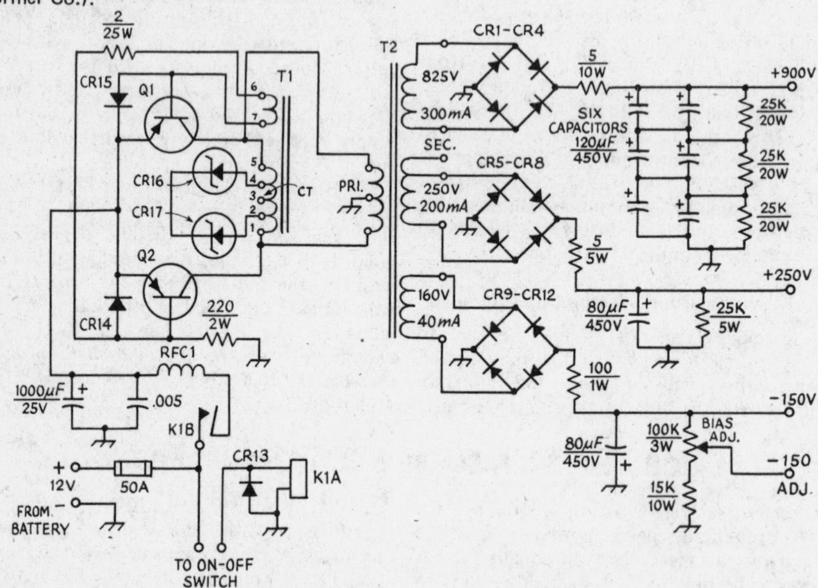

Fig. 10-28 – Circuit diagram of the mobile power supply. Polarized capacitors are electrolytic, others are paper or mica. Resistances are in ohms. Component designations not listed below are for text reference.

CR1-CR13, incl. – 1000-PRV, 1.5-A silicon diode (Mallory MR 2.5 A or equiv.).

CR14, CR15 – 50-PRV, 3-A silicon diode (G.E. A15F).

CR16, CR17 – 18-volt, 1-watt, Zener diode (Motorola 1N4746).

K1 – Spst contactor relay, 60-A, 12-volt dc coil (Potter and Brumfield MB3D).

Q1, Q2 – Delco 2N1523 transistor (substitutions not recommended). Delco insulator kits (No. 7274633) are required. The heat sinks are Delco part No. 7281366.

R3 – 100,000-ohm, 3-watt, linear-taper control.

RFC1 – 20 turns, No. 10 enam. wire on a 1/4-inch dowel.

T1 – Feedback transformer, 1000-Hz (Osborne 6784).

T2 – Hipersil transformer, 1000-Hz (Osborne 21555).

of the chassis. The heat sinks, shown in the photograph, are mounted on a 1/8-inch-thick aluminum back plate.

The leads from the battery to the relay, and from the relay to the transistors and T1, should be No. 6 or No. 8 conductors. All ground leads should be connected to one point on the chassis. The wiring layout is uncritical and no other special precautions are necessary.

Operation

The power supply should be mounted as close to the battery terminals as possible to minimize voltage drop. If the supply is trunk mounted, 1/4-inch conductors should be used to connect it to the battery. A 300-volt tap is available on the secondary of T2. If the transciever requires more than 250 volts for proper operation, this tap can be used.

DC-TO-AC INVERTERS

It is possible to convert the automotive battery voltage from 12-volt dc to 117-volt ac, 60 Hz, by using an inverter. The principle of operation is substantially the same as for dc-to-dc converters, but larger transformers are needed to handle the lower switching rate. The primary circuit is the same as for the dc converters, but the secondary voltage is not rectified. Square-wave output is obtained, though some commercial inverters are available with sine-wave output. The latter is recommended for operating motor-driven equipment. The square-wave types introduce some buzz into the equipment they power, but a brute-force line filter can be used to knock down some of the harmonic energy from the square-wave output. Inverters are useful for powering soldering irons, light bulbs during portable/emergency operations, and to power small ac-operated transceivers. They are commercially available at power levels up to 500 watts or more, but the larger the unit the greater the demand on the car battery.

Fig. 10-29 – Top view of the dc-to-ac inverter. The transistors and their heat sink are at the right. Two ac outlets are used, offering greater convenience than would be possible with a single receptacle. A neon lamp lights when the unit is operation.

A HOME-MADE 175-WATT INVERTER

The unit shown here provides 60-Hz output, square wave, and has taps for 110, 117 or 125-volts. Because of the square-wave output, some hash noise may appear in the output of transmitters or receivers that are operated from the supply. If so, some form of filtering may be necessary at the output of the inverter.[1]

Construction

The inverter is built on a homemade base which measures 8 X 6 X 2 inches. A Bud CU-3009-A Minibox can be used as a chassis. Rubber feet are attached to the bottom cover of the Minibox to help prevent the assembly from scratching the automobile's finish if it is to be placed on the hood or trunk.

A large heat sink is used for cooling Q1 and Q2. The unit shown here is 4 inches long, 3 inches wide, and 2 inches high. It was manufactured by Delco Radio (part number 7281366). Any heat sink of similar dimensions will work satisfactorily. Because the circuit is operated in a common-collector configuration, the transistors need not be insulated from the heat sink, nor is it necessary to insulate the heat sink from the chassis. Silicone grease is used between the transistors and the heat sink, and between the heat sink and the chassis. This contributes to efficient heat transfer between the transistors and the thermal hardware.

All leads carrying primary current should be of large circular-mil size in order to prevent a voltage drop in that part of the circuit. Parallel sections of ac zip cord are used in this model. They are used between the input terminal block and the fuse holder, between the fuse holder and the toggle switch, and between the switch and the primary leads of T1. A dpst toggle switch is used at S1 to permit both sections to be used in parallel, increasing the current-handling capacity.

Two ac outlets are located on the top-front of the chassis so that more than one piece of equipment can be plugged in at the same time.

1 A brute-force line filter is often helpful in reducing this type of hash. Commercial units of this kind are available from most wholesale houses (J. W. Miller Co., No. 7818). A homemade filter might consist of two scramble-wound inductors containing 10 feet (each) of No. 12 enameled copper wire. A coil would be placed in each leg of the ac output. Four 0.1-μF 600-volt paper capacitors would be needed. They would be connected between the ends of each coil and ground. Such a filter could be built on the inverter chassis, or contained in its own case, outboard fashion.

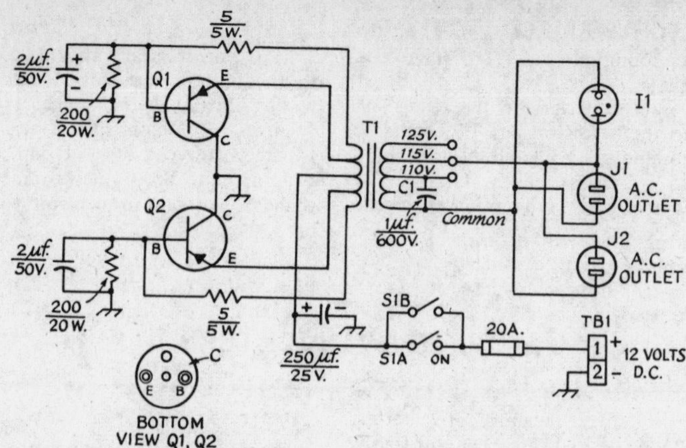

Fig. 10-30 – Schematic diagram of the inverter. Capacitance is in µF. Polarized capacitors are electrolytic. Resistance is in ohms.

C1 – 1-µF 600-volt capacitor (paper type only).

DS1 – Neon panel-lamp assembly with built-in dropping resistor.

J1, J2 – Standard female-type ac outlet socket.

Q1, Q2 – High-wattage power transistor. 2N278 used here. (2N678, 2N1146, 2N173 suitable.)

S1 – Dpdt toggle switch with sections in parallel.

T1 – Inverter transformer, 12 volts dc to 117 volts ac (Triad TY-75A).

TB1 – Two-terminal connector (Millen 37302 suitable).

Operation

In using the inverter, it is wise to have some kind of a load connected across the output of the unit when it is turned on. Without a secondary load, voltage peaks can occur and cause the destruction of the switching transistors, Q1 and Q2. The best procedure is to attach the equipment to the inverter's outlet receptacle, turn the equipment on, then activate the inverter by turning it on with S1. In turning the system off, this process should be reversed – turning the inverter off first, then the equipment.

Motor-operated equipment such as tape recorders and record players will not function satisfactorily from this inverter and should not be used with it. Also, make certain that the equipment which is to be operated from the inverter does not draw more than 100 watts if continuous-duty operation is planned. The inverter should safely handle intermittent loads of up to 175 watts.

For maximum efficiency, the inverter should be connected directly to the car-battery terminals by means of large-diameter conductors. The shorter the conductor length, the less voltage drop there will be in the line.

Fig. 10-31 – A look at the underside of the chassis. The resistors and capacitors are mounted between insulated terminal strips. Ac zip cord, paralleled, is used for the heavy-duty primary wiring.

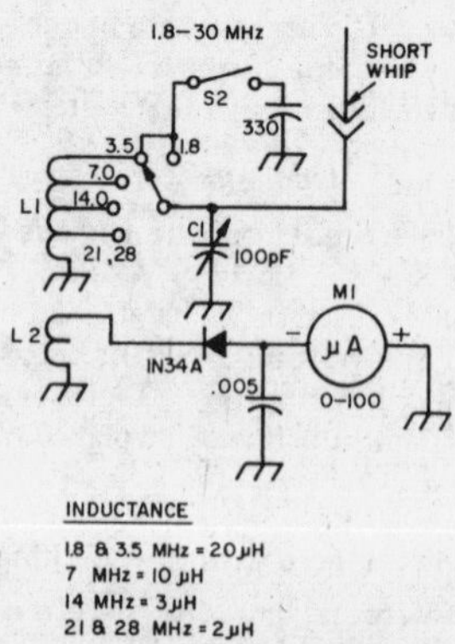

Fig. 10-32 – A band-switched field-strength meter for tuning up the hf-band mobile antenna. It should be assembled in a metal box. In use, it should be placed several feet from the antenna under test. C1 is tuned for a peak meter reading at the operating frequency. It can be detuned for varying the sensitivity.

A BAND-SWITCHING FIELD-STRENGTH METER

The circuit of Fig. 10-32 can be used for tuning the mobile antenna system to resonance. It covers a range from 1.8 to 30 MHz. A single toroidal inductor is used in the tuned circuit. The coil is tapped to provide band switching by means of S1. C1 is tuned for a peak meter reading at the transmitter's output frequency. The unit should be housed in a metal utility box. A banana jack can be used for attaching the short whip antenna.

An Amidon Associates E-core, No. T-68-2, is wound with 50 turns of No. 26 enamel wire. It is tapped 10 turns from ground for 15- and 10-meter use, 18 turns from ground for 20 meters, and 36 turns above ground for 40 meters. The entire 50 turns are used for 80 and 160 meters. S2 adds a 330-pF capacitor for 160-meter operation. S1 can be a single wafer, single-pole, 5-position rotary switch of phenolic or ceramic insulation. S2 can be a spst slide switch. C1 is a Hammarlund HF-100 capacitor, or equivalent. (Amidon cores can be obtained from Amidon Associates, 12033 Otsego St., N. Hollywood, CA 91607.)

A DIRECT-CONVERSION KILOGRAM FOR 20 AND 40 METERS

When portability, low current drain, and simplicity are required in a receiver, it is hard to beat the technique of direct conversion. The unit described here covers the cw portion of both 20 and 40 meters. As total power consumption is on the order of 0.6 watt, battery operation is practical. Packaged in an aluminum box only 6 × 7 × 3 inches (HWD), the receiver weighs in at about one kilogram (2.2 pounds) and fits easily inside a suitcase. The receiver is designed to be compatible with the low-power solid-state transmitter described in Chapter 6.

Circuit Overview

This approach to direct conversion uses an FET as a fixed-tuned rf amplifier, switchable between 20 and 40 meters. An IC transistor array serves as the heart of a band-switched local oscillator. A differential amplifier IC functions as a product detector. The audio channel uses an FET to establish a low noise figure, followed by a high-gain wide-band IC amplifier. Audio selectivity is achieved through the use of a two-stage active filter. A signal strength indication is obtained through the use of an audio-derived S-meter circuit.

Circuit Description

Q1 operates as a grounded-gate rf amplifier. C1, a front-panel mounted broadcast type variable capacitor, peaks the input of the stage for 40- or 20-meter reception. The output of the stage is tuned to 20 meters by L3-C3. One pole of S1 switches additional capacitance in parallel with C3 for 40-meter operation. L4 couples rf energy to the input of the product detector, U1. Local-oscillator injection is applied to pin 2 of U1, the base of the internal constant-current source transistor. The local oscillator is built around a CA3046 IC transistor array, and is identical to the VFO used in the companion transmitter described in Chapter 6.

The CA3046 contains three independent NPN

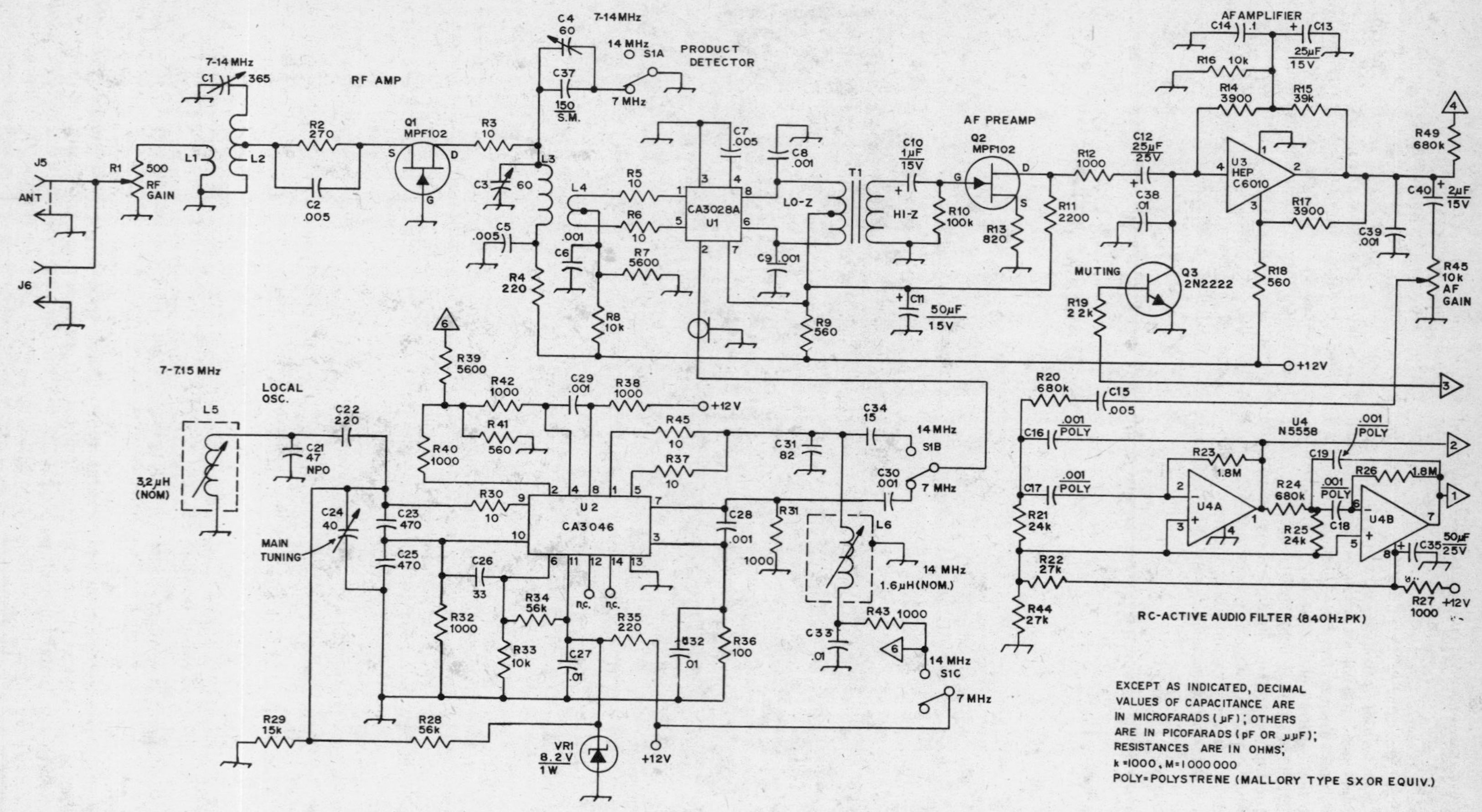
RF AMP
PRODUCT DETECTOR
AF PREAMP
AF AMPLIFIER
MUTING
LOCAL OSC.
MAIN TUNING
RC-ACTIVE AUDIO FILTER (840Hz PK)
EXCEPT AS INDICATED, DECIMAL VALUES OF CAPACITANCE ARE IN MICROFARADS (μF); OTHERS ARE IN PICOFARADS (pF OR μμF); RESISTANCES ARE IN OHMS; k=1000, M=1000000
POLY=POLYSTRENE (MALLORY TYPE SX OR EQUIV.)

silicon transistors plus one differentially connected transistor pair, and is available in a 14 pin dual inline package. The RCA CA3045 is directly interchangeable with the CA3046, and they are available surplus very inexpensively. The ICs have identical pin connections and electrical characteristics, and the only difference between the two is that the CA3046 is packaged in a ceramic case, while the CA3045 is packaged in a plastic case.

In this application, one transistor is used in a Colpitts VFO circuit operating at 7 MHz, one transistor is used as a phase splitter, and the differential pair is used as a push-push doubler to produce output at 14 MHz. One transistor is unused. The 7-MHz output is taken from the emitter of the phase splitter. The devices in the

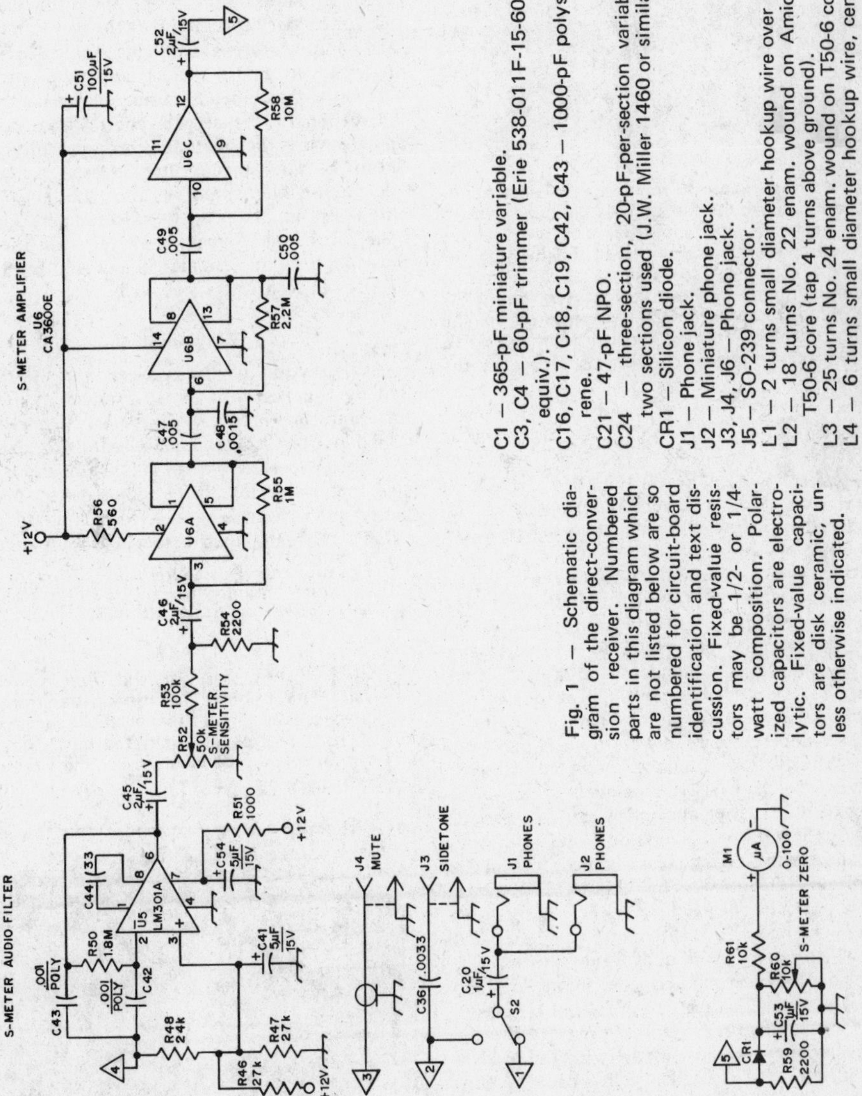

Fig. 1 — Schematic diagram of the direct-conversion receiver. Numbered parts in this diagram which are not listed below are so numbered for circuit-board identification and text discussion. Fixed-value resistors may be 1/2- or 1/4-watt composition. Polarized capacitors are electrolytic. Fixed-value capacitors are disk ceramic, unless otherwise indicated.

C1 — 365-pF miniature variable.
C3, C4 — 60-pF trimmer (Erie 538-011F-15-60 or equiv.).
C16, C17, C18, C19, C42, C43 — 1000-pF polystyrene.
C21 — 47-pF NPO.
C24 — three-section, 20-pF-per-section variable, two sections used (J.W. Miller 1460 or similar).
CR1 — Silicon diode.
J1 — Phone jack.
J2 — Miniature phone jack.
J3, J4, J6 — Phono jack.
J5 — SO-239 connector.
L1 — 2 turns small diameter hookup wire over L2.
L2 — 18 turns No. 22 enam. wound on Amidon T50-6 core (tap 4 turns above ground).
L3 — 25 turns No. 24 enam. wound on T50-6 core.
L4 — 6 turns small diameter hookup wire, center tapped, over L3.
L5 — 3.0-7.0 μH shielded variable inductor (J.W. Miller 9051 or equiv.).
L6 — 1.5-3.0 μH shielded variable inductor. (J.W. Miller 9050 or equiv.).
M1 — 100 microamperes full scale.
Q1, Q2 — MPF-102.
Q3 — 2N2222 or equiv.
S1 — 4pdt slide switch (Radio Shack 275-405).
S2 — spdt toggle switch.
T1 — Miniature interstage transformer, 2000-ohm ct to 10,000 ohms (Radio Shack 273-1378).
U1 — CA3028A.
U2 — CA3046 or CA3045.
U3 — HEP C6010 or MFC 4010A.
U4 — Dual 741 op amp (Radio Shack 276-038 or equiv.).
U5 — LM301A op amp.
U6 — CA3600E.
VR1 — 8.2-volt, 1-watt Zener diode.

Fig. 2 — Inside view of the receiver. Most of the components are mounted on a 4- × 6-inch printed-circuit board. The rf amplifier and product detector components are grouped together at the upper left corner of the board, while the audio channel occupies the left foreground. The VFO main-tuning capacitor, C24, is centered in the cabinet, and is positioned directly over the VFO. The S-meter amplifier circuitry is visible at the right.

CA3046 have a rated F_T of 550 MHz. R30, R37, and R45 are used to prevent vhf parasitic oscillations from occurring. S1B may be used to select either 40- or 20-meter output from the local oscillator, and S1C applies 12 volts dc to the frequency doubler portion of the oscillator for 20-meter operation. With the component values shown, the receiver covers 7.0 to 7.15 MHz and 14.0 to 14.3 MHz. A miniature interstage transformer, T1, is used to couple the output of the product detector to the audio channel. Q2 functions as a moderate-gain, low-noise audio preamplifier, which is followed by the integrated high-gain amplifier U3. Q3 has been included to allow for muting of the receiver during transmitting periods by the application of 12 volts dc to R19 (in series with the base of Q3) by means of a contact on the transmitter's T-R relay. This biases Q3 into conduction and effectively breaks the circuit path between Q2 and U3. A miniature pot is used at R45, which serves as the af gain control. The setting of R45 determines the input level to U4A-U4B. A small part of the output of U3 (taken off before the af gain control) is used to drive the S-meter circuitry. Audio selectivity for the receiver is provided by two cascaded active filter sections consisting of a dual 741 op amp, U4A-U4B, plus associated passive components. With the values shown in the schematic each individual filter section will have a peak response at 840 Hz and a bandwidth of 375 Hz (measured at 6 dB below peak response). When two sections are cascaded, a narrower filter with a bandwidth of 200 Hz results. It is advantageous to match the peak frequency response of each filter section closely by hand picking component values[1] to achieve optimum filter performance. Provision is made for using either a broad or a narrow response by using S2 to switch the headphones to either the output of U4A or U4B, respectively. The active filter drives a pair of high-impedance headphones directly. Provision for monitoring the transmitter sidetone is included by introducing the tone into the audio channel beyond the muting transistor, Q3. The audio-derived S-meter circuit uses a single-stage audio filter, followed by a meter amplifier. The filter is similar to one section of the audio channel filter and is necessary to assure that the meter indication is a function of the signal being monitored and not the result of extraneous signals at the output of U3. Thus, the S-meter reading does not vary with the setting of the af gain control, and does not operate while the sidetone is being monitored. The output of the S-meter filter drives a three-section integrated-circuit amplifier, U6. The rectified amplifier output drives a 100 micorampere full-scale meter for the signal strength indication. Pc mounted pots are used at R52 and R60 for S-meter adjustment (sensitivity and zero).

Construction

Construction of the receiver is greatly simplified by the use of an etched printed-circuit board for mounting most of the parts. A template is available from ARRL for 50 cents and an s.a.s.e. The entire receiver fits on a 4- × 6-inch board. If no S-meter is desired, it is a simple matter to adjust the layout to fit on a 4- × 4-1/2-inch board leaving out U5, U6, and their associated components. A

[1] **Components plus a circuit board for the audio filter may be obtained from MFJ Enterprises, P.O. Box 494, Mississippi State, MS 39762**

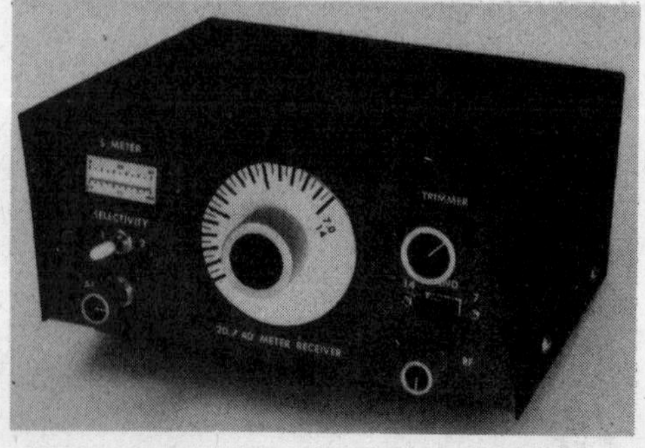

Fig. 3 — Front view of the direct-conversion receiver. The cabinet is homemade from two U-shaped pieces of .040-inch thick sheet aluminum. The front panel is painted battleship gray, and white "press-on" labels mark the function of the controls.

photo-etch process was used to produce the original board although it may be duplicated by other methods as long as sufficient care is taken in the vicinity of the IC pins and other high-density areas of the pattern to avoid the appearance of unwanted foil bridges. The prototype receiver was built on double-sided G-10 glass epoxy board, 1/16-inch thick. The circuit pattern is etched on the bottom of the board while the top is left as a continuous ground plane broken only where component leads project through the board. The ground plane is an aid to stability and interstage isolation. An easy technique for removing the ground plane around the component leads (after the bottom of the board has been drilled) is to use a large diameter drill (1/4-inch is satisfactory) and make a shallow hole in the top side of the board at every lead location. This may be done by hand, or very carefully with a drill press. The prototype receiver board was silver plated before component assembly, a step which while not required, makes soldering easier, and improves the appearance of the final product. Part of the key to building a compact receiver is the use of parts which are physically small. The use of small 50-volt disk ceramic capacitors can go a long way toward increasing packing density. Using miniature low-voltage electrolytic capacitors, toroidal inductors,

Fig. 4 — Parts placement and board layout for the receiver. R34, C8 and C26 are mounted on the foil side.

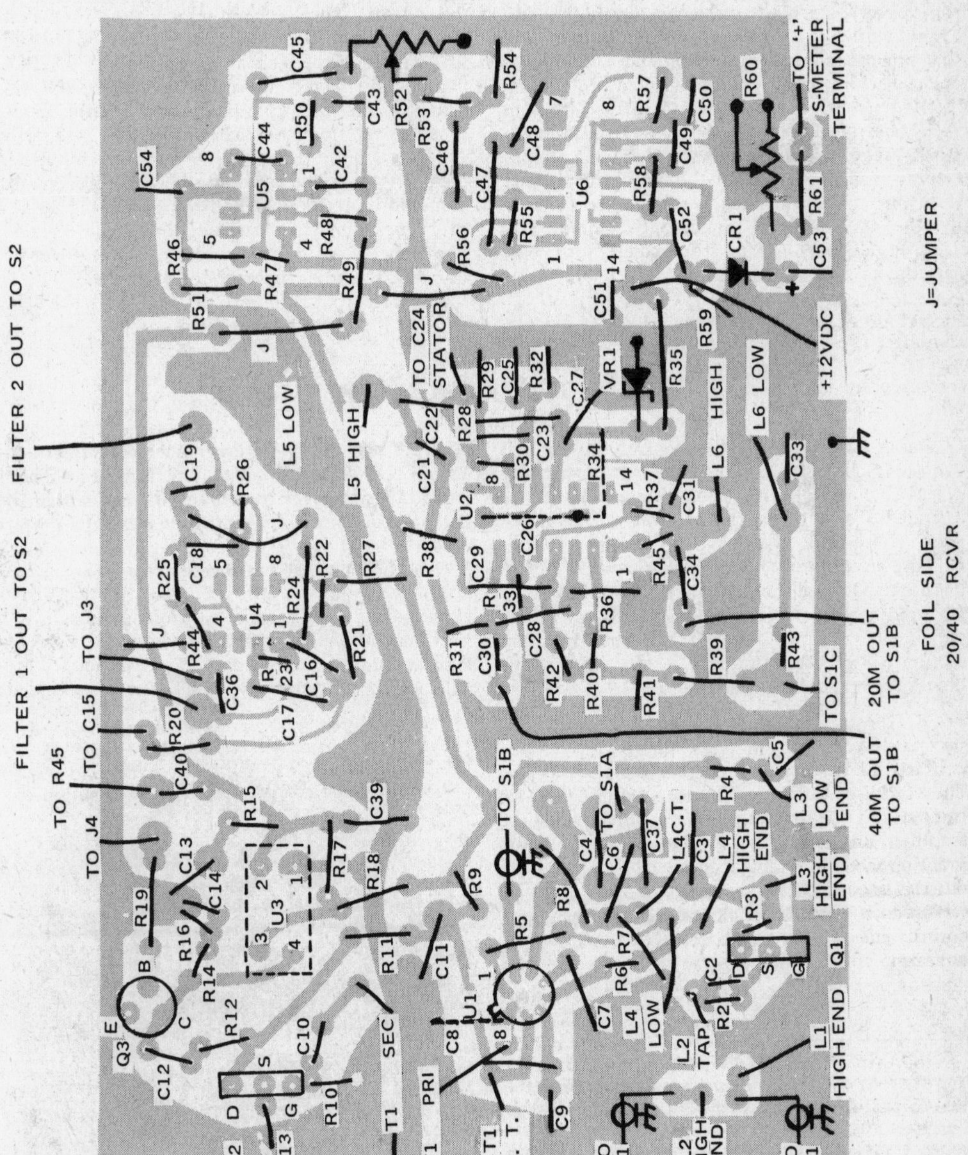

and 1/4-watt instead of 1/2-watt resistors where applicable will make construction much easier for the builder of portable equipment.

The placement of the front- and rear-panel-mounted parts is determined as much by symmetry as by the criterion of short leads. In the author's receiver, the S-meter, controls for af and rf gain, the band switch, input trimmer capacitor, selectivity switch, and the main tuning knob are located on the front panel. The rear panel includes banana jacks for the 12-volt dc input, phono jacks for sidetone and muting inputs from the transmitter, and a phone jack for headphones. For operating convenience, an SO-239 coax receptacle and a female phono jack wired in parallel were used as antenna connectors. The VFO tuning capacitor, C24, is mounted on an aluminum bracket from the front panel to achieve mechanical stability. The capacitor drive is a modified imported vernier dial. The original escutcheon, calibrated 0-100, was replaced with a homemade plastic dial. Fifty- and 25-kHz markers on the dial are made with thin black tape of the type usually used for printed-circuit artwork. The homemade U-shaped cabinet is spray painted with battleship gray enamel and white pressure-sensitive labels were added to identify the controls. The top cover is painted flat black. Professional-looking front-panel knobs complete the mechanical assembly.

Initial Adjustment

The local oscillator should be checked first for proper operation on 40 meters. With C24 almost fully meshed, L5 may be adjusted with a nonmetallic tool to set the output frequency to 7.000 MHz. A drop of melted wax will be sufficient to hold the slug in place. The frequency doubler portion of the local oscillator should be checked with an oscilloscope. L6 may be adjusted to provide the cleanest 14-MHz waveform. A signal generator and an oscilloscope may be used to verify that the audio channel is functioning. Assuming that parts tolerances were adhered to closely, the audio filter width and center frequency in both the broad and narrow positions should be comparable to the results mentioned above. With the aid of a signal generator or a weak on-the-air signal, the front-end response should be peaked first on 20 meters by adjusting C1 and C3, and then on 40 meters by adjusting C1 and C4. In actual operation, C1 is a front-panel control, and is tuned to the frequency band of interest. After C3 and C4 are set, it should not be necessary to repeak them. If the product detector is working correctly it should be possible to hook a pair of headphones to J1 or J2 and make these adjustments by ear. The S-meter zero and sensitivity controls can be adjusted according to operator preference.

A PORTABLE TRANSCEIVER FOR 144 MHz

Here's a vhf transceiver that's truly portable, is easy to build, and is capable of spanning many miles when used with a good antenna. It can be operated from its internal 12-volt flashlight-cell pack, from the cigar lighter of any 12-volt negative-ground car, or from an ac-operated 12-volt dc pack. The transmitter and the two-stage FET superregenerative receiver are assembled on etched circuit boards to simplify construction. The audio section is a prewired "import" – also on a circuit board. (From *QST*, August 1968.)

Receiver-Section Circuit

Two FETs are used in the simple receiver circuit of Fig. 3. A JFET (junction field-effect transistor), Q4, operates as a common-gate rf amplifier and offers a fair amount of detector isolation while providing a few decibels of gain. Its output is coupled to the detector, Q5, through C19, which is a "gimmick" capacitor. The latter consists of three turns of insulated hookup wire wrapped around the ground end of L8. The opposite end of the wire is soldered to the drain end of L7. A junction-type FET is used at Q4 to make it less subject to rf burnout than would be the case if an IGFET (insulated-gate FET) were used.

An IGFET is used as the detector, Q5. Since it is isolated from the antenna circuit there is little chance of its being harmed by strong rf fields.

Quench-frequency voltage is provided by R14 and C26 in the source lead of Q5. Feedback for the detector is between gate and source, making it

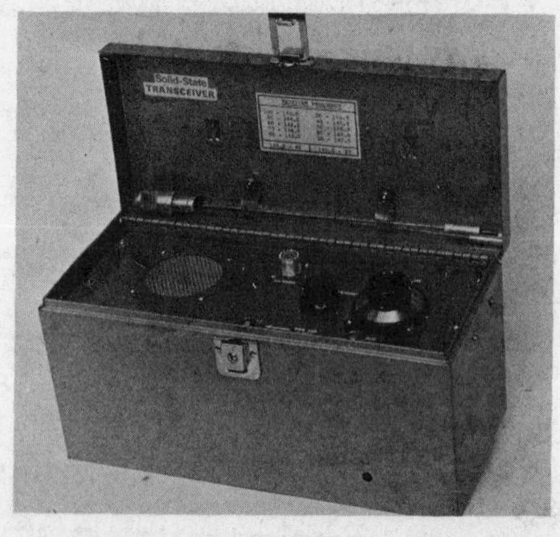

Fig. 1 – The 2-meter transceiver is housed in a legal-bond box. A homemade dial-calibration chart for the receiver is pasted on the inside of the lid. Two plastic cable clamps serve as holders for the two-section 1/4-wavelength whip antenna (inside lid) when the unit is not in use. The antenna is held together at the center by a homemade 1/4-inch diameter threaded coupling.

Fig. 2 — Top-chassis layout of the transceiver. The receiver section is at the left. Controls for regeneration and modulation are in the foreground near the center of the chassis. The audio module is at the lower right, and the transmitter board is near the panel, directly under the loudspeaker. The home-made heat sinks are visible at the left end of the audio board.

necessary to keep the source above rf ground by means of RFC4.

Af output from the detector is taken from the drain through a quench-frequency filter consisting of C24, C25, RFC5 and C27. The filter prevents the quench voltage from reaching the audio amplifier. L9 isolates the af signal from the B-plus line, and R15 varies the drain-supply voltage to control superregeneration. R16 is the af gain control.

A word of caution at this point: When soldering the IGFET, Q5, into the circuit, be sure to connect a clip lead between the tip of the soldering iron and a good earth ground. This will help prevent damage to the gate of the 3N128 should static charges be present. Also, *do not handle* the leads of Q5. The leads should be removed from their shorting collar by means of a non-plastic or nonmetallic tool. A wooden toothpick is recommended for this, and for spreading the leads apart. Once Q5 is soldered in place, it should be quite safe from static-charge damage.

Transmitter Circuit

Referring again to Fig. 3, the transmitter section starts out with a Colpitts oscillator, Q1, which uses 72-MHz overtone crystals. C1 and the internal base-emitter capacitance of Q1 control the feedback. RFC1 keeps the emitter above rf ground. Bandpass coupling is used between Q1 and Q2 to reduce harmonics in the driving signal to Q2. A capacitive divider, C5 and C6, is used to match the collector of Q1 to the low base impedance of Q2. The high value of capacitance between the base of Q2 (C6) and ground helps to further reduce harmonic energy in that part of the circuit. Both Q1 and Q2 are low-cost Motorola transistors designed for amplifier or oscillator use at frequencies up to 500 MHz. They have a beta spread of 20 to 200, and have a collector-dissipation rating of 500 milliwatts. Other transistors can be substituted provided they have similar specifications. Resistors R5 and R6 establish Class A bias for Q2, making it easier to drive with the low output of Q1.

An RCA 2N3512 is used in the power amplifier, Q3. It was selected because of its low cost ($1.08) and high maximum dissipation rating of 4 watts. It is designed for high-speed switching applications and has an f_T of 375 MHz. Its h_{FE} rating is approximately 10. The low h_{FE} makes it easier to stabilize than would be the case if a high-beta transistor were used. Other transistors can also be used at Q3; a 40290, an HEP-75, and a 2N3553 were tried and performed as well as the 2N3512, but are more costly. To assure good heat dissipation at Q3, a heat sink is clipped to the transistor body. A Wakefield Engineering NF205 costs 27 cents and is ideal.

A capacitive divider, C10 and C11, matches the output of Q2 to the base of Q3. C10 tunes L3 to resonance. Forward bias is used on the base of Q3 to establish Class AB conditions. This provided greater output from Q3 than resulted with Class-C operation, as is usually the case when the driver stage has low output. The collector tank of Q3 is a combination *L* and pi network. The *L* network, C12 and L4, matches the load to the collector. The pi network is used for harmonic reduction, a necessary provision when clean output is desired from transistorized transmitters. C12 tunes the PA tank to resonance; C15 serves as a loading control.

In order to assure suitable stability, the power leads of the stages are decoupled by means of C3, C9 and C14 in combination with R4, R8 and R11. The three resistors also serve as current-limiting devices to protect Q1, Q2 and Q3.

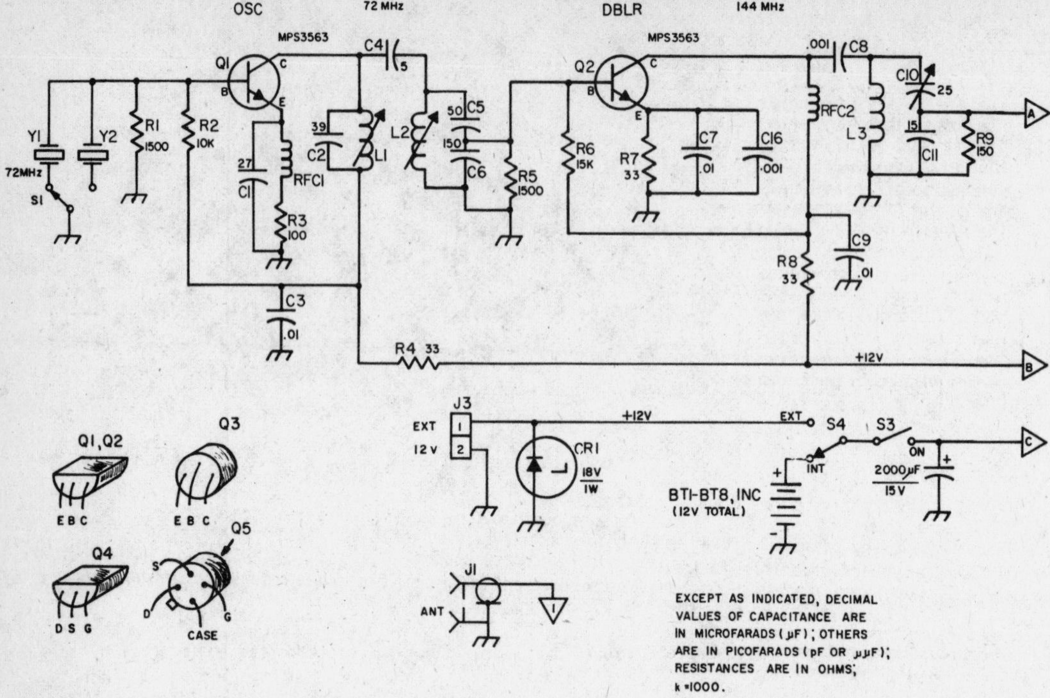

Fig. 3 — Schematic of the 2-meter transceiver. Fixed-value capacitors are disk ceramic except those with polarity marking, which are electrolytic. Resistors are 1/2-watt composition. Component numbering is for identification of parts on the circuit-board templates. Significant parts are listed below in the usual manner.

AR1 — 200-milliwatt audio module (Round Hill Associates Model AA-100*).

BT1-BT8, incl. — Eight 1.5-volt size-D flashlight cells, series-connected and mounted inside box by means of four Keystone No. 176 dual-battery clips.

C10, C12 — 5- to 25-pF ceramic trimmer (Erie 822-CN or equiv). (Midget 3- to 30-pF mica trimmer also suitable.)

C15 — 8- to 50-pF ceramic trimmer (Erie 822-AN or equiv). (Midget 8- to 60-pF mica trimmer also suitable.)

C19 — Gimmick-type capacitor. See text.

C20 — 15-pF subminiature variable (E. F. Johnson 160-107).

C22 — 5-pF min. variable (Hammarlund MAPC-15B, all but one rotor and one stator plate removed).

CR1 — 18-volt 1-watt Zener diode (used for transient protection during mobile operation).

J1 — SO-239 coax fitting (chassis mount).

J2, J3 — Two-terminal single-contact audio connector (Amphenol 75PC1M or similar).

L1, L2 — 3 turns No. 22 enam. wire spaced to occupy 1/2 inch on 1/4-inch dia ceramic slug-tuned form (J. W. Miller 4500-4*).

L3 — 4 turns No. 20 bare wire, 1/2 inch long, 5/16 inch ID.

L4 — 6 turns No. 20 bare wire, 1/2 inch long 5/16 inch ID.

L5 — Same as L3.

L6 — 8 turns No. 20 bare wire, 1 inch long, 5/16 inch ID. Tap 5 turns from source lead of Q4.

L7 — 5 turns No. 22 enam. wire, close-wound on 1/4-inch dia ceramic slug-tuned form (J. W. Miller 45005).

L8 — 4 turns No. 10 bare copper wire, 1 inch long, 3/8-inch ID. (The tap shown is not a physical one; see text discussion of C19.)

L9 — Total primary winding of 500-ohm ct transistor output transformer. The 8-ohm secondary winding not used. (Argonne AR-164 or similar.)

R15-R17, incl. — 100,000-ohm audio-taper carbon control.

RFC1 — Miniature 50-µH choke (Millen 34300-50*).

RFC2-RFC4, incl. — Miniature 2.7-µH rf choke (Millen 34300-2.7).

RFC5 — Subminiature 10-mH rf choke (J. W. Miller 73F102AF).

S1, S4 — Spdt slide switch.

S2 — 4-pole 2-position phenolic single-section rotary wafer switch. (Mallory 3142J.)

S3 — Spst slide switch.

Y1, Y2 — 72-MHz overtone crystal (International Crystal Co. in HC-6/U holder*).

* Round Hill Assoc., Inc., 434 Sixth Ave., NY, NY 10011.

* J. W. Miller Co., 19070 Reyes Ave., Compton, CA 90221.

* International Crystal Co., 10 N. Lee St., Oklahoma City, OK 73102.

* James Millen Mfg. Co., 150 Exchange St., Malden, MA 02148.

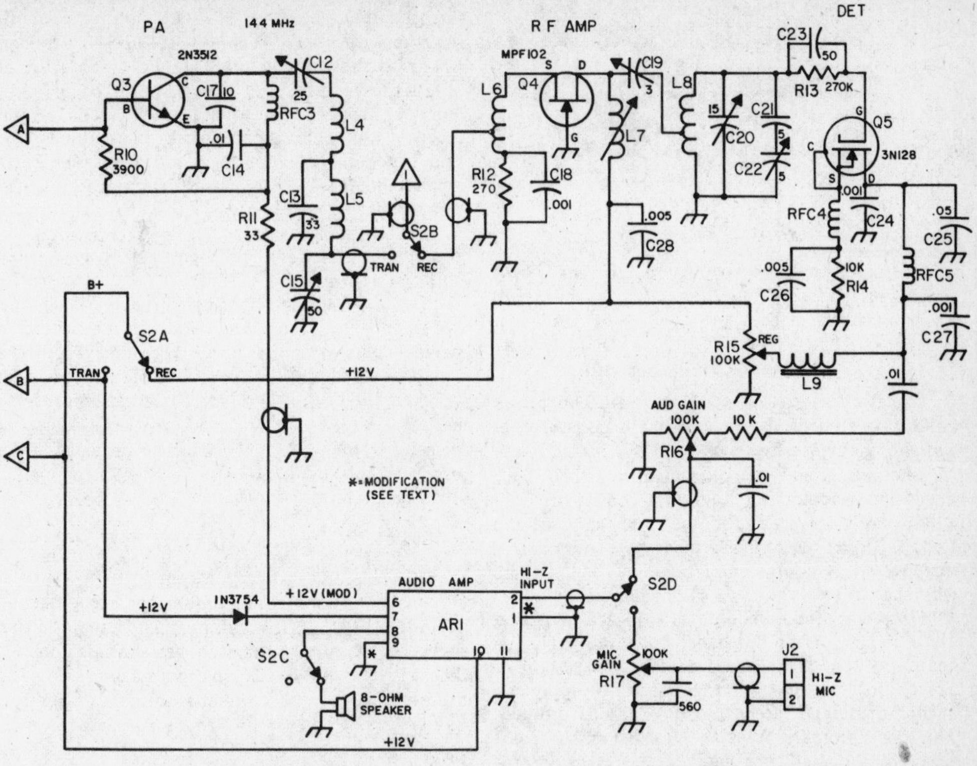

The Audio Section

The audio channel, AR1, can be purchased for approximately $8.00. It has a 200-milliwatt output rating at 9 volts, but by increasing the operating voltage to 12, and adding heat sinks to the two output transistors, slightly more than 300 milliwatts of output are available. This was done in the circuit of Fig. 10

AR1 has two input impedances – 50 ohms and 100,000 ohms. Two output impedances are available, providing a 500-ohm transformer winding for modulator service, and an 8-ohm winding for driving a loudspeaker. The high-impedance input connects to the microphone gain control, R17, during transmit, and is switched to the receiver gain control, R16, during receive. The 50-ohm tap is not used.

Because the module is designed for a positive-ground bus (pnp transistors are used), it is necessary to "float" the entire assembly above chassis ground to prevent short-circuiting the

Fig. 4 – Bottom view of the chassis. The receiver board is at the right. The transmitter board is at the upper left. A 2000-μF 15-volt electrolytic is mounted near the rear lip of the chassis.

Fig. 5 – Details of the homemade heat sinks for AR1.

power supply. Information on the mounting techniques and some modifications to the board are given later.

Building the Transceiver

The packaging of this circuit can be up to the builder. In this instance a standard legal-bond box was chosen. It measures 5 X 6 X 11 1/2 inches.

The chassis and panel are made from 16-gauge aluminum sheeting. An aluminum cookie tin from a hardware store can be the source of the panel and chassis stock. Many are made of heavy-gauge material and are large enough to assure that there will be excess stock. The chassis measures 11 1/4 X 4 X 1 inch. The panel is 11 1/4 inches by 4 3/4 inches. After the panel holes are drilled, a coating of zinc chromate should be sprayed on it. Then, after thorough drying, a coat of spray-can enamel or lacquer can be added for the final touch. The zinc chromate helps the finish coat of paint adhere to the aluminum sheeting.

The receiver and transmitter are built on etched circuit boards, but point-to-point wiring could be used if done neatly and with short connections. Etched-circuit templates are available from the ARRL if desired.[1] They are to scale and show where the various parts are mounted.

AR1 is insulated from the main chassis to prevent short-circuiting the power supply. It has a plus-ground bus; the rest of the transceiver circuit uses a negative ground. A piece of cardboard is mounted between the circuit board and the chassis to prevent accidental contact between AR1 and the chassis. AR1 is bolted to the chassis at four points. The four mounting holes in the main chassis contain small rubber grommets, each serving as an insulator. Terminals 1 and 9 of the audio board are common to its plus-ground bus. These terminals must be disconnected from the ground bus by removing the thin copper connecting strip which joins the circuits. A pocket knife works nicely for this job; the copper can then be peeled off.

To operate AR1 at 12 volts it is necessary to add heat sinks to the two transistors nearest the output transformer. The sinks can be fashioned from pieces of thin brass, copper, or aluminum. They are 1 1/2 inches long and each is formed by warping the stock around a drill bit which is slightly smaller in diameter than the body of the transistor.

All interconnecting rf leads are made with subminiature coax cable, RG-174/U (Belden 8216). Shielded audio cable should be used for all af wiring which is more than a couple of inches in length. A bargain-house import is used for the receiver tuning dial. No slippage was noted with the 2-inch-diameter model used here. The next smaller model is not recommended because it will not handle the torque of the tuning capacitor.

A 2 1/2-inch-diameter loudspeaker is used. Its protective grille can be made from perforated aluminum.

Two 3-inch-long brass angle brackets, each with 3/4-inch sides, are used as mounts for the panel-chassis assembly inside the box. Two 6-32 nuts are soldered to the bottom side of each bracket, directly under No. 10 access holes. Four 6-32 X 3/8-inch screws hold the transceiver in place. The brackets are attached to the sides of the box with 4-40 hardware.

Tune-Up and Use

The receiver should be tested first. With an antenna connected to J1, apply operating voltage and adjust R15 until a rushing noise is heard in the speaker. Do not advance R15 beyond this point as the sensitivity of the receiver will decrease. Next, tune in a weak signal from another ham station (or

Fig. 6 – Eight size D cells are series connected to provide 12 volts. They are mounted in Keystone holders on the back wall of the bond box. The 1/4-inch diameter hole in the front of the cabinet (upper right of photo) permits final calibration of the receiver (C20) after the installation is completed. The hole is opposite the shaft of C20.

[1] Scale circuit-board templates and parts placement guide are available from ARRL for 25 cents and an s.a.s.e. Ready-made boards are often available commercially. For a list of suppliers, send ARRL an s.a.s.e.

from a signal generator) and tune L7 for a peak response. Chances are that when the peak is reached, the detector will stop oscillating. If this happens, advance R15 until the hiss returns. If it does not, detune L7 slightly until a compromise is reached (L7 usually loads the detector somewhat when it is tuned to the operating frequency). Alternatively, a 1000-ohm swamping resistor can be connected across L7 to reduce its effect on the detector. Trimmer C20 is used to set the tuning range of C22. The turns of L8 can be spread or compressed for additional frequency adjustment. The receiver should tune the entire 4-MHz of the 2-meter band, or nearly so.

A No. 49 pilot lamp makes a suitable dummy load for visual tune-up of the transmitter, though somewhat reactive at 144 MHz. First, determine that the oscillator, Q1, is operating by coupling a wavemeter (or grid-dip meter in the diode-detector position) to L1 and look for an indication of output. Adjust the slug in L1 for maximum output, then turn the transmitter on and off a few times to make sure the crystal always kicks in. If not, detune L1 slightly toward the high-frequency side of resonance until the oscillator does start each time. Next, peak L2, C10, C12 and C15 for maximum indication on the bulb. There will be some interaction between the circuits, so the foregoing steps should be repeated a few times to assure maximum output. Final adjustments should be made with the antenna connected, and with an SWR indicator in the line.[2]

[2] A highly sensitive SWR indicator is needed at this power level. One of the Monimatch indicators with a 4-inch or longer line (air-dielectric element type) can provide full-scale readings if a 100-μA meter is installed. Alternatively, see *QST* August, 1967 for a low-power bridge. Also, see the "Monimatch Mark II," *QST*, February, 1957.

AN ULTRAPORTABLE CW STATION FOR 40 METERS

Operating under emergency or portable conditions usually requires the equipment to be low powered and lightweight. Shown in the photographs is a 40-meter transceiver designed and built by W7ZOI and K7TAU.

Receiver Circuit

Shown in Fig. 1 is a schematic diagram of the receiver section. Following current trends, a straightforward direct-conversion design is used with a dual-gate MOSFET, Q1, as the product detector. The usual *LC* low-pass audio filter is eliminated. Instead, *RC* filtering is employed throughout the three-stage audio amplifier, yielding an audio bandwidth of approximately 2.5 kHz. The audio amplifier is stable and delivers a little more than 90 dB gain. An extra transistor, Q6, is included in the audio amplifier and is saturated when the T-R switch is in the transmit position. This serves to mute the receiver completely.

The local oscillator is a Colpitts circuit using a single pnp transistor. In order to achieve mechanical simplicity, the oscillator is varactor tuned by a potentiometer which is mounted on the from panel. Varactor diodes are not needed since the collector-base junctions of readily available 2N3053 transistors accomplish the same purpose. The back-to-back diode arrangement assures that the 2N3053s never conduct on any part of the rf cycle, thus minimizing loading of the oscillator. With the components shown, the tuning range of the receiver is 70 kHz eliminating the need for vernier drive on the tuning control.

The receiver sensitivity is adequate for use with the low-power transmitter. A one-microvolt signal is easily copied and the selectivity is suitable for most portable work. A high-performance audio filter connected between the receiver output and the headphones is a useful accessory for home station operation.[1] The receiver requires about 14 mA at 12 volts.

[1] Hayward, "An RC Active Audio Filter for CW," *QST*, May 1970.

Top view of the W7ZOI and K7TAU 40-meter transceiver built by WA1JLD.

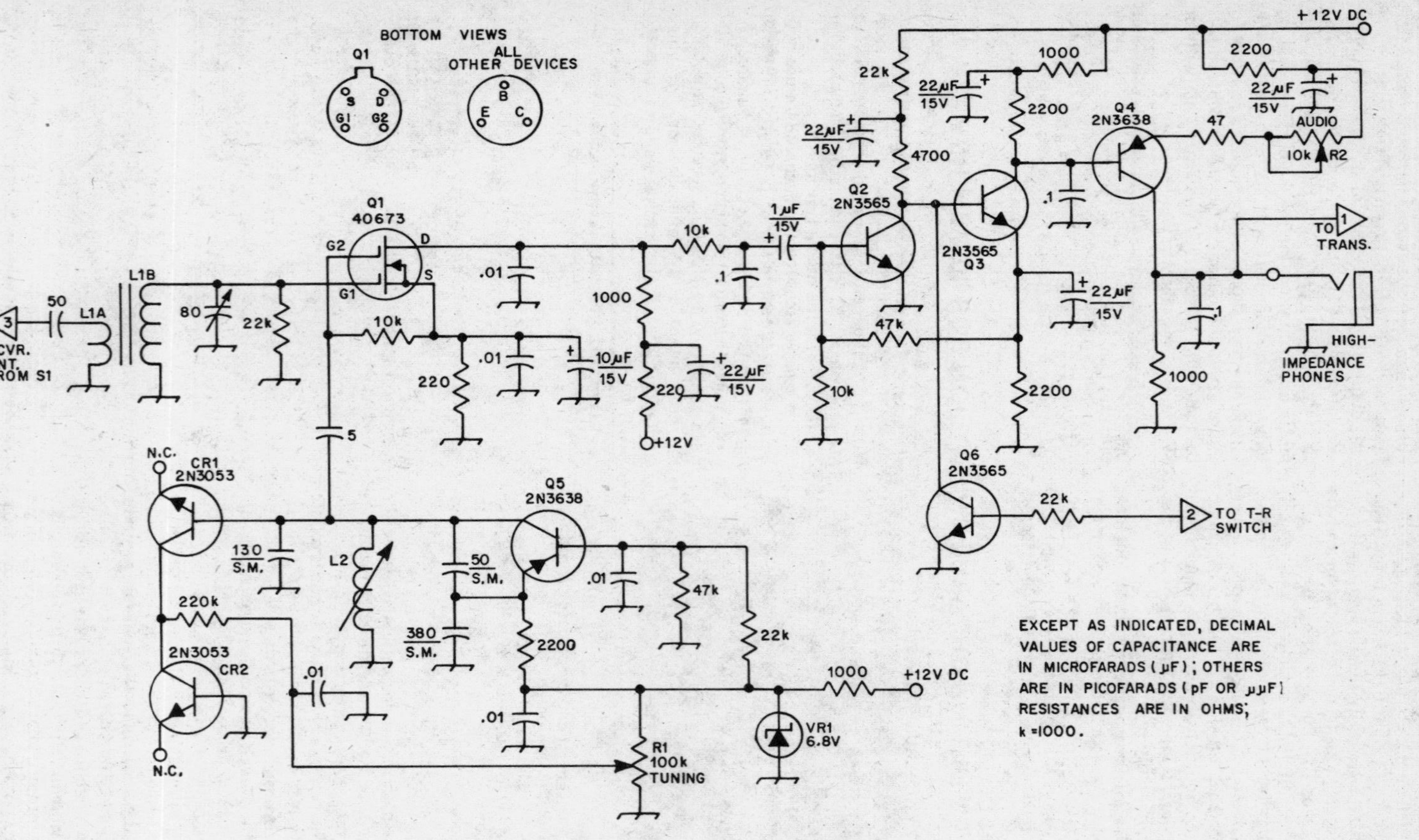

Fig 1 — Circuit diagram for the receiver section of the Mountaineer. Component designations not listed below are for text reference. CR1 and CR2 are the collector-base junctions of 2N3053s and are labeled D1 and D2 respectively on the pc-layout sheets available from the authors.

L1 — 44 turns No. 28 enam. on Amidon T-50-2 core.

L1B — 4 turns No. 28 enam. over L1A.

L2 — 1.6-3.1 μH, 19 turns No. 28 enam. on 1/4-inch dia ceramic form (J. W. Miller 4404 or equiv.).

R1, R2— Linear taper, compostion.

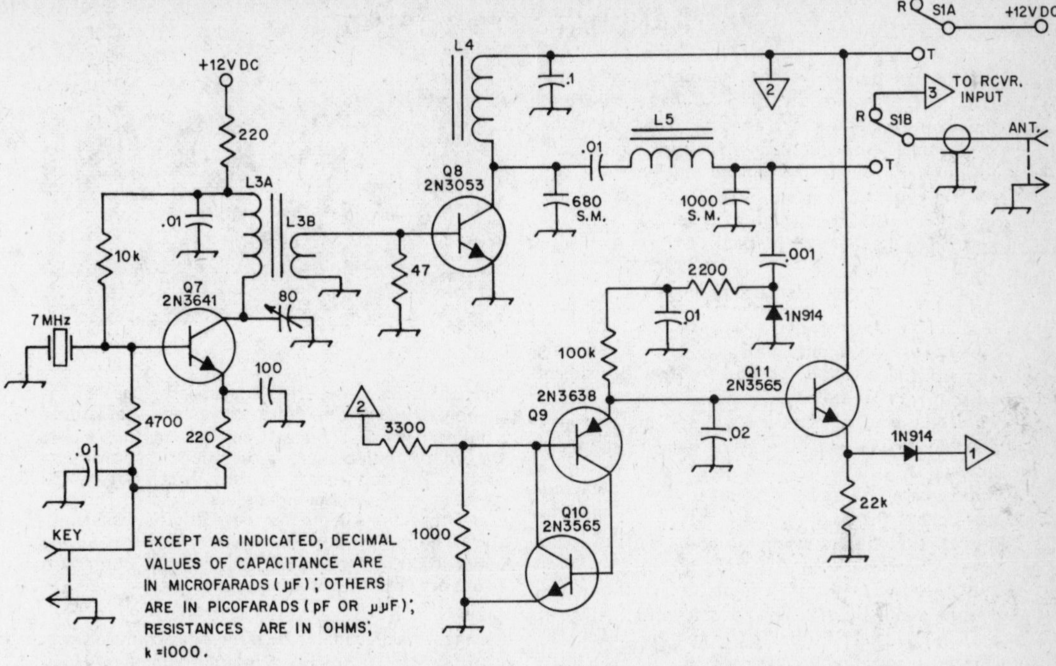

Fig. 2 — Circuit diagram for the transmitter. Component designations not listed below are for text reference.
L3A — 44 turns No. 28 enam. on Amidon T-50-2 core.
L3B — 4 turns No. 28 enam. over L3B.
L4 — 60 turns No. 28 enam. on T-50-2 Amidon core.
L5 — 14 turns No. 22 enam. on T-50-2 Amidon core.
S1 — Spdt slide.

Transmitter Design

Shown in Fig. 2 is the circuit diagram for the transmitter. Q7 operates as a keyed crystal oscillator and is used to drive Q8, the power amplifier. The matching circuit in the amplifier output is a pi network designed for a *Q* of 3. When terminated in 50 ohms, a load resistance of about 80 ohms is presented to the collector of Q8. In spite of the rig's simplicity, the output is exceptionally clean. The second and third harmonics are 32 and 60 dB below the fundamental output respectively. With a 12.5-volt supply, the output power is 650 milliwatts and the total key-down current drain is approximately 100 mA.

The sidetone oscillator consists of Q9 and Q10 which forms a relaxation oscillator similar to the type used as a clock in an electronic keyer. Q11 is an impedance-transforming follower to drive the headphones. The oscillator is activated by a voltage which is derived from the transmitter output. The sidetone frequency is directly proportional to the rf output voltage. Hence, the circuit serves a dual role as a cw monitor and a sensitive output indicator. It eliminates the need for a meter. The diode in the output of Q11 isolates the receiver from the sidetone oscillator.

Also shown in Fig. 2 are the details of the T-R switching circuit. Supply voltage is always applied to the oscillator. However, power is applied to the amplifier only during transmit periods. Hence, during receive, pressing the key turns on Q7, providing a convenient "spot" signal.

Construction and Operation

Printed-circuit techniques are used exclusively. The receiver easily fits on a 3 × 5-inch board. A smaller 1.8 × 4.8-inch board is used for the transmitter and sidetone oscillator. The entire transceiver (including a hand key) will fit conveniently inside a standard 2 × 5 × 7-inch chassis. With a little effort, 8 size AA penlight cells and a suitable electronic keyer could be contained in the same enclosure. The electrolytic capacitors are dipped solidtantalum similar to the Kemet series E. Silvered mica capacitors are used in the receiver local oscillator; mica compression trimmers tune the receiver input and transmitter oscillator.

Adjustment is very straightforward. The receiver local oscillator is adjusted while listening to the home station receiver. The input circuit of Q1 is peaked for maximum signal with an antenna connected to J1. The tuning capacitor in the transmitter is adjusted for maximum power output and clean keying into a 50-ohm dummy load. Should there by any power-amplifier instability, the 47-ohm base resistor may be reduced in value. The transmitter output network limits the power to less than one watt.

A TRANSMATCH FOR QRP RIGS

This equipment permits matching low-power (five watts) transmitters to a wide range of impedances encountered when using random-length, single-wire antennas of the type common to portable and emergency operation. The unit will also match the transmitter to any coax line regardless of the mismatch reflected from the antenna to the feed end of the line.

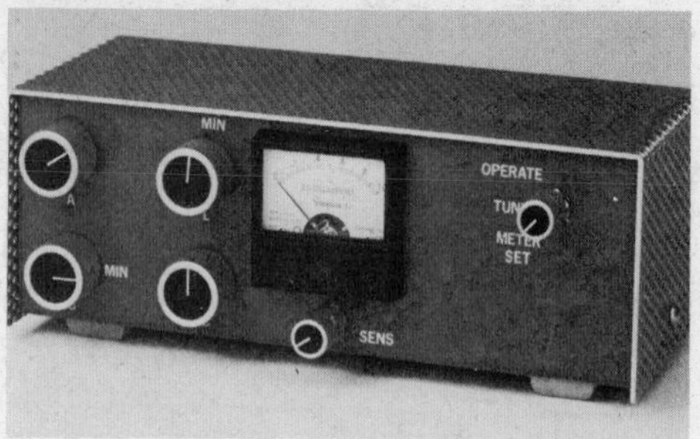

Exterior view of the QRP Transmatch. The cabinet is homemade from solid sheet and perforated aluminum stock. The two controls at the far left are 365-pF variables, as is the one at the lower left of the Simpson meter. At the upper left of the meter is the variable-inductance control. Directly under the meter is the meter-sensitivity potentiometer. The bridge function switch is visible at the upper right of the panel. Kurz-Kasch aluminum knobs are used on the controls.

Construction

The use of separate capacitors at C1 and C2, Fig. 1, requires slightly more manipulation during tune-up than would be the case with ganged capacitors, but once ball-park settings are found for each operating band it is a simple matter to log them for future use. C2 and C3 must be mounted so that their rotor and stator sections are above chassis ground. This is accomplished easily by assembling them on a small piece of phenolic insulating board and using insulating shaft couplers (Allied Electronics No. 920-0120).

Three small toroidal inductors and one air-wound coil comprise the variable-inductor leg of the circuit, L1-L4, inclusive, and S2. With the constants specified for the circuit of Fig. 1 the tuner will give good performance from 80 through 10 meters. S2 is a low-cost imported component.

M1 can be any 1-mA instrument. A Simpson No. 2121 is shown in the photos, but may be a trifle too dear in terms of cost for those wishing to do the job at minimum investment. Many imported meters (Radio Shack No. 22-018 for one) can be purchased at a fraction of the cost common to high-quality American made instruments.

S1, in the unit pictured, is a double-pole, four-position, two-section ceramic wafer switch of the subminiature species. A piece of double-clad pc board is visible between the wafer sections. It was added to function as an rf shield between the two sections of S1, thereby helping to isolate the input and output ports of the resistance bridge. Any shorting-type double-pole, three-position switch should be suitable, ceramic or phenolic insulation. S1 and S2 are the shorting variety, thus preventing momentary no-load conditions from being seen by the transmitter. The package dimensions are 7-1/2 × 2-3/4 × 2-3/4 inches (18 × 6-1/2 × 6-1/2 cm). A cover was made from a section of surplus perforated-aluminum stock. Solid aluminum stock would be just as good. In fact, the entire enclosure could be constructed from galvanized furnace ducting, often available in scrap sizes from furnace repair shops. Rf shielding is not imperative when building housings for Transmatches.

Preparation for Use

It will be noted that the components for the resistance bridge are mounted on a piece of single-sided pc board. This is not mandatory. Point-to-point wiring (keeping the leads ultra short) can be used if desired. Multilug terminal strips should be fine for the latter. Whatever technique is adopted, the completed bridge should be tested prior to attaching it to the rf section of the Transmatch. This can be done easily by placing S1 in the METER SET position, adjusting R4 for minimum meter sensitity (arm near ground), then applying rf power from the transmitter at J1. Adjust the transmitter for peak output (5 watts maximum!), then advance R4 until full-scale deflection occurs on M1. Now, connect a 50-ohm resistive load between the CR1-R1 junction and ground. If all is well, the meter reading should drop to zero, indicating a null at 50 ohms. Values of load resistance above and below 50 ohms will cause

Interior view of the Transmatch. The three variable capacitors are grouped at the right. Note that two of them are mounted on insulating board. Just to the right of the meter one can see the inductance switch on which three toroids and one air-wound coil are mounted. The resistance bridge and function switch are located at the far left of the chassis.

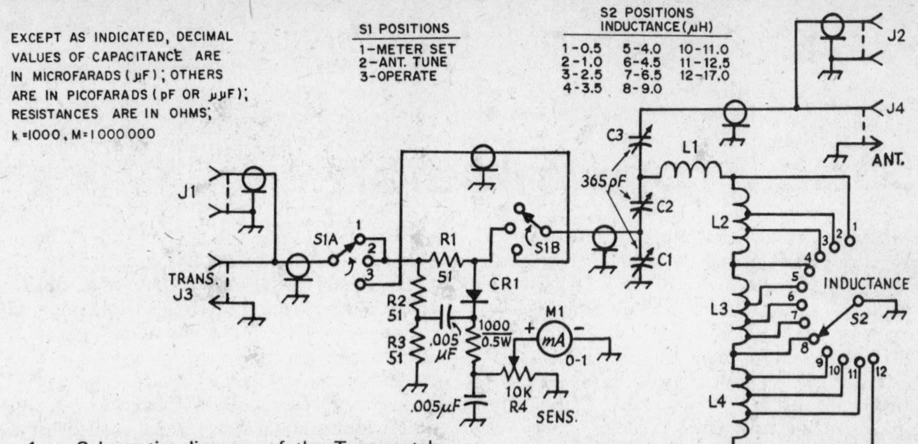

Fig. 1 — Schematic diagram of the Transmatch. Fixed-value capacitors are desk ceramic. Fixed-value resistors are composition types.

C1-C3, incl. — Miniature 365-pF variable (Archer/Radio Shack No. 272-1341 or equiv.).

CR1 — High-speed silicon diode, 1N914 or equiv.

J1, J2 — Phono connector, single-hole chassis mount.

J3, J4 — SO-239 style coax connector.

L1 — 15 turns No. 24 enam. wire, close-wound on 1/4-inch ID form. Remove form after winding.

L2 — 28 turns No. 24 enam. wire on Amidon T-50-6 toroid core. Tap 7 turns from each end.

L3 — 27 turns No. 24 enam. wire on Amidon T-50-2 toroid core. Tap at 5, 10 and 15 turns from L2 end.

L4 — 26 turns No. 24 enam. wire on Amidon T-68-2 toroid core. Tap at 6, 12 and 18 turns from L3 end.

M1 — 0- to 1-mA dc meter, 1-1/2 inches square. See text.

R1-R3, incl. — 51-ohm, 2-watt, 5-percent tolerance.

R4 — Miniature 10,000-ohm control, audio or linear taper suitable.

S1 — Two-pole, three-position, shorting-type rotary wafer switch. See text.

S2 — Single-pole, 12-position, rotary wafer switch, shorting type (Radio Shack No. 277-1385 or Calectro No. E-2-162).

the meter to deflect in accordance with the SWR that prevails.

Connect the output port of the bridge to the remainder of the circuit. Attach a 50-ohm load at J2. Place S1 in the ANT. TUNE position and juggle the settings of C1, C2, C3 and S2 until zero deflection is indicated at M1. Repeat this process for each band of interest. If the meter can be made to read zero on each band, all is as it should be. Tuning the circuit with the antenna or feed line connected to J2 is done in the same manner as with a dummy load. After the load is matched to the transmitter, turn S1 to the OPERATE position. This bypasses the bridge, which, if left in the line, will consume precious rf power. *A word of caution:* Always use the least amount of tuned-circuit inductance (L1 through L4) that will provide an SWR of 1. This will assure maximum power transfer to the antenna. A matched condition can be realized at several settings of the controls, but only the foregoing procedure should be followed in tuning the system.

Summarization

Rf connections within the box should be made with RG-174/U subminiature coax cable to assure satisfactory isolation between the input and output ports of the bridge. Be sure to ground the shield braid at each end of each length of cable. Leads less than one inch in length need not be shielded.

Those wishing to utilize the bridge portion of this unit for adjusting antenna matching sections can add a coax connector on the rear panel and connect it to the middle terminal of S1B. This will permit the bridge to operate independently of the rf-matching network which attaches to the arm of S1B. The function switch would be placed in the METER SET position for independent use of the bridge. Similarly, with S1 in that position, the impedance-matching portion of the Transmatch can be used separately by connecting the open terminal of S1B to still another coax jack. The estimated cost of the parts used in this project is $12, provided low-priced imported components are used where applicable.

Code Transmission

Keying a transmitter properly involves much more than merely turning it on and off with a fast manually operated switch (the key). If the output is permitted to go from zero to full instantaneously (zero "rise" time), side frequencies, or **key clicks**, will be generated for many kilohertz either side of the transmitter frequency, at the instant the key is closed. Similarly, if the output drops from full to zero instantaneously (zero "decay" time), side frequencies will be generated at the instant of opening the key. The amplitude of the side-frequency energy decreases with the frequency separation from the transmitter frequency. To avoid key clicks and thus to comply with the FCC regulations covering spurious radiations, the transmitter output must be "shaped" to provide finite rise and decay times for the envelope. The longer the rise and decay times, the less will be the side-frequency energy and extent.

Since the FCC regulations require that " . . . the frequency of the emitted wave shall be as constant as the state of the art permits," there should be no appreciable change in the transmitter frequency while energy is being radiated. A *slow* change in frequency is called a frequency **drift**; it is usually the result of thermal effects on the oscillator. A *fast* frequency change, observable during each *dit* or *dah* of the transmission, is called a **chirp**. Chirp is usually caused by a nonconstant load on the oscillator or by dc voltage changes on the oscillator during the keying cycle. Chirp may or may not be accompanied by drift.

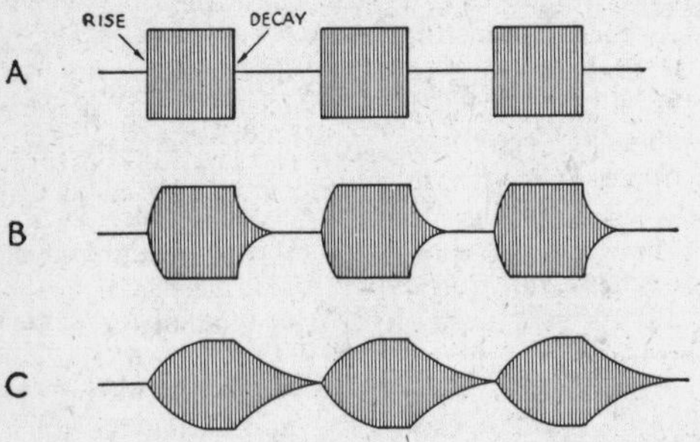

Fig. 11-1 — Typical oscilloscope displays of a code transmitter. The rectangular-shaped dots or dashes (A) have serious key clicks extending many kHz either side of the transmitter frequency. Using proper shaping circuits increases the rise and decay times to give signals with the envelope form of B. This signal would have practically no key clicks. Carrying the shaping process too far, as in C, results in a signal that is too "soft" and is not quite as easy to copy as B.

Oscilloscope displays of this type are obtained by coupling the transmitter rf to the vertical plates and using a slow sweep speed synchronized to the dot speed of an automatic key.

If the transmitter output is not reduced to zero when the key is up, a **backwave** (sometimes called a "spacing wave") will be radiated. A backwave is objectionable to the receiving operator if it is readily apparent; it makes the signal slightly harder to copy. However, a slight backwave, 40 dB or more below the key-down signal, will be discernible only when the signal-to-noise ratio is quite high. Some operators listening in the shack to their own signals and hearing a backwave think that the backwave can be heard on the air. It isn't necessarily so, and the best way to check is with an amateur a mile or so away. If he doesn't find the backwave objectionable on the S9+ signal, you can be sure that it won't be when the signal is weaker.

When any circuit carrying dc or ac is closed or opened, the small or large spark (depending upon the voltage and current) generates rf during the instant of make or break. This rf click covers a frequency range of many megahertz. When a transmitter is keyed, the spark at the key (and relay, if one is used) causes a click in the receiver. *This click has no effect on the transmitted signal.* Since it occurs at the same time that a click (if any) appears on the transmitter output, it must be eliminated if one is to listen critically to his own signal within the shack. A small rf filter is required at the contacts of the key (and relay); typical circuits and values are shown in Fig. 11-2. To check the effectiveness of the rf filter, listen on a band lower in frequency than the one the transmitter is tuned to, with a short receiving antenna and the receiver gain backed off.

What Transmitter Stage To Key

A satisfactory code signal, free from chirp and key clicks, can be amplified by a *linear* amplifier without affecting the keying characteristics in any way. If, however, the satisfactory signal is amplified by one or more nonlinear stages (e.g., a Class C multiplier or amplifier), the signal envelope will be modified. The rise and decay times will be decreased, possibly introducing significant key clicks that were not present on the signal before amplification. It is possible to compensate for the effect by using longer-than-normal rise and decay times in the excitation and letting the amplifier(s) modify the signal to an acceptable one.

Many two-, three- and even four-stage VFO-controlled transmitters are incapable of chirp-free output-amplifier keying because keying the output stage has an effect on the oscillator frequency and "pulls" it. Keying the amplifier presents a variable load to its driver stage, which in turn is felt as a variable load on the previous stage, and so on back

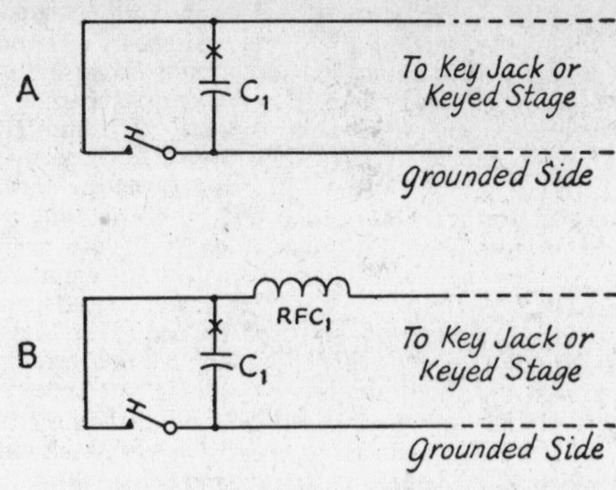

Fig. 11-2 – Typical filter circuits to apply at the key (and relay, if used) to minimize rf clicks. The simplest circuit (A) is a small capacitor mounted at the key. If this proves insufficient, an rf choke can be added to the ungrounded lead (B). The value of C1 is .001 to .01 μF; RFC1 can be 0.5 to 2.5 mH, with a current-carrying ability sufficient for the current in the keyed circuit. In difficult cases another small capacitor may be required on the other side of the rf choke. In all cases the rf filter should be mounted right at the key or relay terminals; sometimes the filter can be concealed under the key. When cathode or center-tap keying is used, the resistance of the rf choke or chokes will add cathode bias to the keyed stage, and in this case a high-current low-resistance choke may be required, or compensating reduction of the grid-leak bias (if it is used) may be needed. Shielded wire or coaxial cable makes a good keying lead.

A visible spark on "make" can often be reduced by the addition of a small (10 to 100 ohms) resistor in series with C1 (inserted at point "x"). Too high a value of resistance reduces the arc-suppressing effect on "break."

to the oscillator. Chances of **pulling** are especially high when the oscillator is on the same frequency as the keyed output stage, but frequency multiplication is no guarantee against pulling. Another source of reaction is the variation in oscillator supply voltage under keying conditions, but this can usually be handled by stabilizing the oscillator supply with a VR tube. If the objective is a completely chirp-free transmitter, the first step is to make sure that keying the amplifier stage (or stages) has no effect on the frequency. This can be checked by listening on the oscillator frequency while the amplifier stage is keyed. Listen for chirp on either side of zero beat, to eliminate the possibility of a chirpy receiver (caused by line-voltage changes or BFO pulling).

An amplifier can be keyed by any method that reduces the output to zero. Neutralized stages can be keyed in the cathode circuit, although where powers over 50 or 75 watts are involved it is often desirable to use a keying relay or vacuum tube keyer, to minimize the chances for electrical shock. Tube keying drops the supply voltages and adds cathode bias, points to be considered where maximum output is required. Blocked-grid keying is applicable to many neutralized stages, but it presents problems in high-powered amplifiers and requires a source of negative voltage. Output stages that aren't neutralized, such as many of the tetrodes and pentodes in widespread use, will usually leak a little and show some backwave regardless of how they are keyed. In a case like this it may be necessary to key two stages to eliminate backwave. They can be keyed in the cathodes, with blocked-grid keying, or in the screens. When screen keying is used, it is not always sufficient to reduce the screen voltage to zero; it may have to be taken to some negative value to bring the key-up plate current to zero, unless fixed negative control-grid bias is used. It should be apparent that where two stages are keyed, keying the earlier stage must have no effect on the oscillator frequency if completely chirp-free output is the goal.

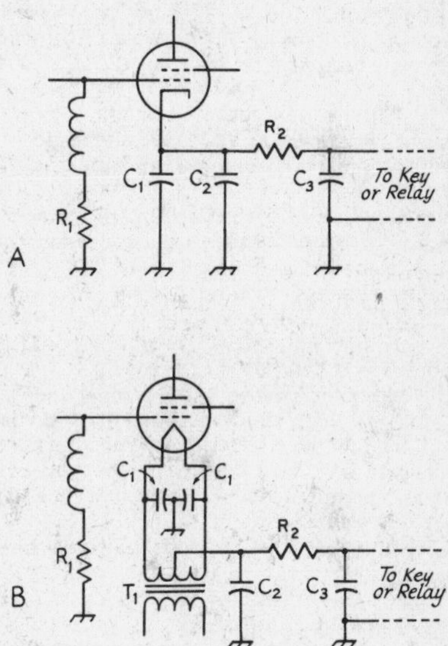

Fig. 11-3 – The basic cathode (A) and center-tap (B) keying circuits. In either case C1 is the rf return to ground, shunted by a larger capacitor, C2, for shaping. Voltage ratings at least equal to the cutoff voltage of the tube are required. T1 is the normal filament transformer. C1 and C3 can be about .01 μF.

The shaping of the signal is controlled by the values of R2 and C2. Increased capacitance at C2 will make the signal softer on break; increased resistance at R2 will make the signal softer on make.

Values at C2 will range from 0.5 to 10 μF, depending upon the tube type and operating conditions. The value of R2 will also vary with tube type and conditions, and may range from a few to one hundred ohms. When tetrodes or pentodes are keyed in this manner, a smaller value can sometimes be used at C2 if the screen-voltage supply is fixed and not obtained from the plate supply through a dropping resistor. If the resistor decreases the output (by adding too much cathode bias) the value of R1 should be reduced.

Oscillators keyed in the cathode can't be softened on break indefinitely by increasing the value of C2 because the grid-circuit time constant enters into the action.

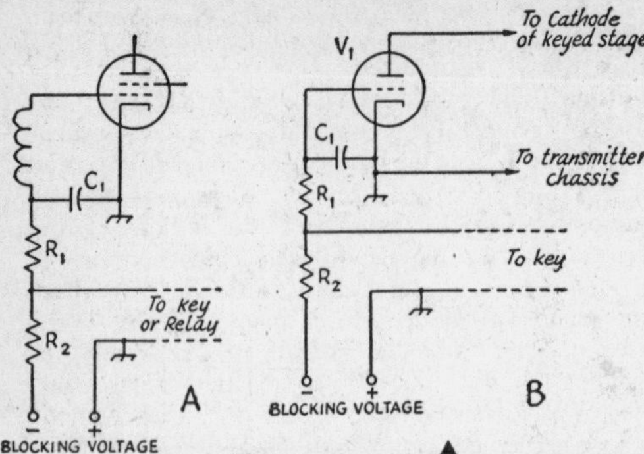

Fig. 11-4 – The basic circuit for blocked-grid keying is shown at A. R1 is the normal grid leak, and the blocking voltage must be at least several times the normal grid bias. The click on make can be reduced by making C1 larger, and the click on break can be reduced by making R2 larger. Usually the value of R2 will be 5 to 20 times the resistance of R1. The power supply current requirement depends upon the value of R2, since closing the key circuit places R2 across the blocking voltage supply.

An allied circuit is the vacuum-tube keyer of B. The tube V1 is connected in the cathode circuit of the stage to be keyed. The values of C1, R1 and R2 determine the keying envelope in the same way that they do for blocked-grid keying. Values to start with might be 0.47 megohm for R1, 4.7 megohms for R2 and .0047 μF for C1.

The blocking voltage supply must deliver several hundred volts, but the current drain is very low. A 6Y6 or other low plate-resistance tube is suitable for V1. To increase the current-carrying ability of a tube keyer, several tubes can be connected in parallel.

A vacuum-tube keyer adds cathode bias and drops the supply voltages to the keyed stage and will reduce the output of the stage. In oscillator keying it may be impossible to use a VT keyer without changing the oscillator dc grid return from ground to cathode.

Fig. 11-5 – When the driver-stage plate voltage is roughly the same as the screen voltage of a tetrode final amplifier, combined screen and driver keying is an excellent system. The envelope shaping is determined by the values of L1, C4, and R3, although the rf bypass capacitors C1, C2 and C3 also have a slight effect. R1 serves as an excitation control for the final amplifier, by controlling the screen voltage of the driver stage. If a triode driver is used, its plate voltage can be varied for excitation control.

The inductor L1 will not be too critical, and the secondary of a spare filament transformer can be used if a low-inductance choke is not available. The values of C4 and R3 will depend upon the inductance and the voltage and current levels, but good starting values are 0.1 μF and 50 ohms.

To minimize the possibility of electrical shock, it is recommended that a keying relay be used in this circuit, since both sides of the circuit are "hot." As in any transmitter, the signal will be chirp-free only if keying the driver stage has no effect on the oscillator frequency. (The Sigma 41FZ-35-ACS-SIL 6-volt ac relay is well-suited for keying applications.) ▼

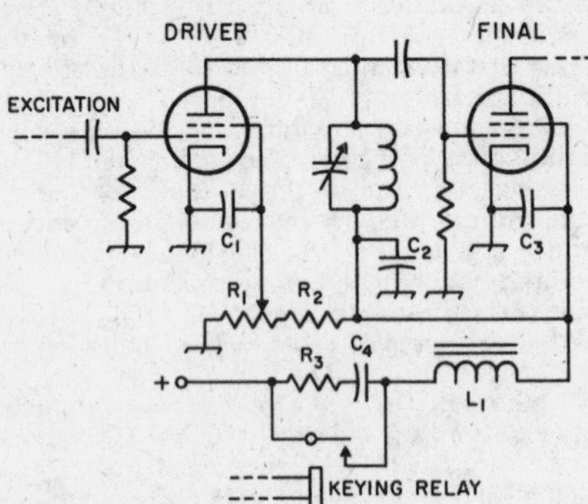

Shaping of the keying is obtained in several ways. Vacuum-tube keyers, blocked-grid and cathode-keyed systems get suitable shaping with proper choice of resistor and capacitor values, while screen-grid keying can be shaped by using inductors or resistors and capacitors. Sample circuits are shown in Figs. 11-3, 11-4, and 11-5, together with instructions for their adjustment. There is no "best" adjustment, since this is a matter of personal preference and what you want your signal to sound like. Most operators seem to like the make to be heavier than the break. All of the circuits shown here are capable of a wide range of adjustment.

If the negative supply in a grid-block keyed stage fails, the tube will draw excessive key-up current. To protect against tube damage in this eventuality, an overload relay can be used or, more simply, a fast-acting fuse can be included in the cathode circuit.

OSCILLATOR KEYING

One may wonder why oscillator keying hasn't been mentioned earlier, since it is widely used. A sad fact of life is that excellent oscillator keying is infinitely more difficult to obtain than is excellent amplifier keying. If the objective is no detectable chirp, it is probably *impossible* to obtain with oscillator keying, particularly on the higher frequencies. The reasons are simple. Any keyed-oscillator transmitter requires shaping at the oscillator, which involves changing the operating conditions of the oscillator over a significant period of time. The output of the oscillator doesn't rise to full value immediately so the drive on the following stage is changing, which in turn may reflect a variable load on the oscillator. No oscillator has been devised that has no change in frequency over its entire operating voltage range and with a changing load. Furthermore, the shaping of the keyed-oscillator envelope usually has to be exaggerated, because the following stages will tend to sharpen up the keying and introduce clicks unless they are operated as linear amplifiers.

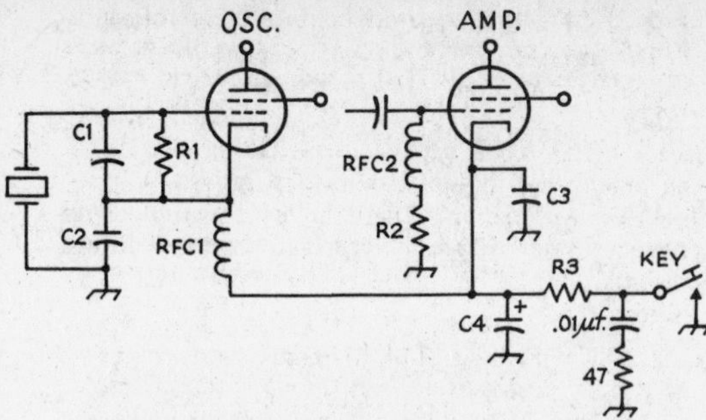

Fig. 11-6 – Simple differential-keying circuit for a crystal-controlled oscillator and power-amplifier transmitter.

Most simple crystal-controlled transmitters, commercial or home-built, return the oscillator grid-leak resistor, R1, to chassis, and "cathode keying" is used on the oscillator and amplifier stages. By returning the oscillator grid leak to the cathode, as shown here, negative power-supply-lead keying is used on the oscillator. A good crystal oscillator will operate with only 5 to 10 volts applied to it.

Using the above circuit, the signal is controlled by the shaping circuit, C4-R3. Increasing the value of R3 will make the signal "softer" on make; increasing the capacitance of C4 will make the signal softer on make and break. The oscillator will continue to operate after the amplifier has cut off, until the charge in C4 falls below the minimum operating voltage for the oscillator.

The .01-μF capacitor and 47-ohm resistor reduce the spark at the key contacts and minimize "key clicks" heard in the receiver and other nearby receivers. They *do not* control the key clicks associated with the signal miles away; these clicks are reduced by increasing the values of R3 and C4.

Since the oscillator may hold in between dots and dashes, a back wave may be present if the amplifier stage is not neutralized.

C1, C2 – Normal oscillator capacitors.
C3 – Amplifier rf cathode bypass capacitor.
C4 – Shaping capacitor, typically 1 to 10 μF, 250 volts, electrolytic
R1 – Oscillator grid leak; return to cathode instead of chassis ground.
R2 – Normal amplifier grid leak; no change.
R3 – Typically 47 to 100 ohms.
RFC1, RFC2 – As in transmitter, no change.

Break-in Keying

The usual argument for oscillator keying is that it permits break-in operation (see subsequent sections, also Chapter 23). If break-in operation is not contemplated and as near perfect keying as possible is the objective, then keying an amplifier or two by the methods outlined earlier is the solution. For operating convenience, an automatic transmitter "turner-onner" (see Campbell, *QST* Aug., 1956), which will turn on the power supplies and switch antenna relays and receiver muting devices, can be used. The station switches over to the complete "transmit" condition where the first dot is sent, and it holds in for a length of time dependent upon the setting of the delay. It is equivalent to voice-operated phone of the type commonly used by ssb stations. It does not permit hearing the other station whenever the key is up, as does full break-in.

Full break-in with excellent keying is not easy to come by, but it is easier than many amateurs think. Many use oscillator keying and put up with a second-best signal.

Differential Keying

The principle behind "differential" keying is to turn the oscillator on fast before a keyed amplifier stage can pass any signal and turn off the oscillator fast after the keyed amplifier stage has cut off. A number of circuits have been devised for accomplishing the action. The simplest, which should be applied *only* to a transmitter using a voltage-stable (crystal-controlled) oscillator is shown in Fig. 11-6. Many "simple" and kitted Novice transmitters can be modified to use this system, which approaches the performance of the "turner-onner" mentioned above insofar as the transmitter performance is concerned. With separate transmitting and receiving antennas, the performance is comparable.

A simple differential-keying circuit that can be applied to any grid-block keyed amplifier or tube-keyed stage by the addition of a triode and a VR tube is shown in Fig. 11-7. Using this keying

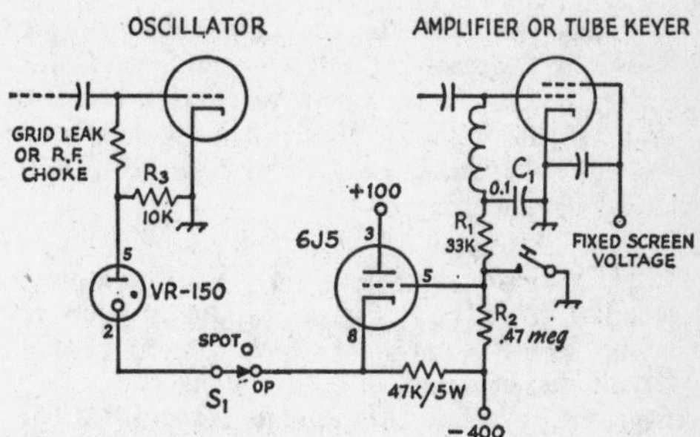

Fig. 11-7 – When satisfactory blocked-grid or tube keying of an amplifier stage has been obtained, this VR-tube break-in circuit can be applied to the transmitter to furnish differential keying. The constants shown here are suitable for blocked-grid keying of a 6146 amplifier; with a tube keyer the 6J5 and VR tube circuitry would be the same.

With the key up, sufficient current flows through R3 to give a voltage that will cut off the oscillator tube. When the key is closed, the cathode voltage of the 6J5 becomes close to ground potential, extinguishing the VR tube and permitting the oscillator to operate. Too much shunt capacity on the leads to the VR tube and too large a value of grid capacitance in the oscillator may slow down this action, and best performance will be obtained when the oscillator (turned on and off this way) sounds "clicky." The output envelope shaping is obtained in the amplifier, and it can be made softer by increasing the value of C1. If the keyed amplifier is a tetrode or pentode, the screen voltage should be obtained from a fixed voltage source or stiff voltage divider, not from the plate supply through a dropping resistor.

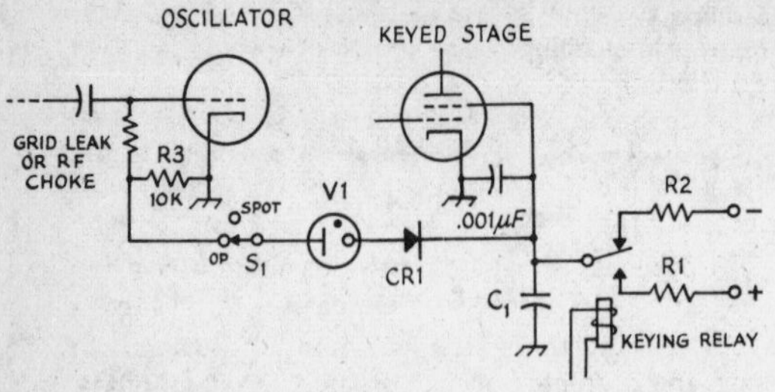

Fig. 11-8 – VR-tube differential keying in an amplifier screen circuit.

With key up and current flowing through V1 and CR1, the oscillator is cut off by the drop through R3. The keyed stage draws no current because its screen grid is negative. C1 is charged negatively to the value of the – source. When the relay is energized, C1 charges through R1 to a + value. Before reaching zero (on its way +) there is insufficient voltage to maintain ionization in V1, and the current is broken in R3, turning on the oscillator stage. As the screen voltage goes positive, the VR tube cannot reignite because the diode, CR1, will not conduct in that direction. The oscillator and keyed stage remain on as long as the relay is closed. When the relay opens, the voltage across C1 must be sufficiently negative for V1 to ionize before any bleeder current will pass through R3. By this time the screen of the keyed stage is so far negative that the tube has stopped conducting. (See Fig. 11-5 for suitable relay.)

system for break-in, the keying will be chirp-free if it is chirp-free with the VR tube removed from its socket to permit the oscillator to run all of the time. If the transmitter can't pass this test, it indicates that more isolation is required between keyed stage and oscillator.

Another VR-tube differential-keying circuit, useful when the screen-grid circuit of an amplifier is keyed, is shown in Fig. 11-8. The normal screen keying circuit is made up of the shaping capacitor C1, the keying relay (to remove dangerous voltages from the key), and the resistors R1 and R2. The + supply should be 50 to 100 volts higher than the normal screen voltage, and the – voltage should be sufficient to ignite the VR tube, V1, through the drop in R2 and R3. Current through R2 will be determined by the voltage required to cut off the oscillator; if 10 volts will do it the current will be 1 mA. For a desirable keying characteristic, R2 will usually have a higher value than R1. Increasing the value of C1 will soften both "make" and "break."

The tube used at V1 will depend upon the available negative supply voltage. If it is between 120 and 150, a 0A3/VR75 is recommended. Above this a 0C3/VR105 can be used. The diode, CR1, can be any unit operated within its ratings. A type 1N4005, for example, may be used with screen voltages under 600 and with far greater bleeder currents than are normally encountered – up to 1 ampere.

Clicks in Later Stages

It was mentioned earlier that key clicks can be generated in amplifier stages following the keyed stage or stages. This can be a puzzling problem to an operator who has spent considerable time adjusting the keying in his exciter unit for clickless keying, only to find that the clicks are bad when the amplifier unit is added. There are two possible causes for the clicks: low-frequency parasitic oscillations and amplifier "clipping."

Under some conditions an amplifier will be momentarily triggered into low-frequency parasitic oscillations, and clicks will be generated when the amplifier is driven by a keyed exciter. If these clicks are the result of low-frequency parasitic oscillations, they will be found in "groups" of clicks occurring at 50- to 150-kHz intervals either side of the transmitter frequency. Of course low-frequency parasitic oscillations can be generated in a keyed stage, and the operator should listen carefully to make sure that the output of the exciter is clean before he blames a later amplifier. Low-frequency parasitic oscillations are usually caused by poor choice in rf choke values, and the use of more inductance in the plate choke than in the grid choke for the same stage is recommended.

When the clicks introduced by the addition of an amplifier stage are found only near the transmitter frequency, amplifier "clipping" is indicated. It is quite common when fixed bias is used on the amplifier and the bias is well past the "cut-off" value. The effect can usually be minimized by using a combination of fixed and grid-leak bias for the amplifier stage. The fixed bias should be sufficient to hold the key-up plate current only to a low level and not to zero.

A linear amplifier (Class AB1, AB2 or B) will amplify the excitation without adding any clicks, and if clicks show up a low-frequency parasitic oscillation is probably the reason.

KEYING SPEEDS

In radio telegraphy the basic code element is the dot, or unit pulse. The time duration of a dot and a space is that of two unit pulses. A dash is three unit pulses long. The space between letters is three unit pulses; the space between words or groups is seven unit pulses. A speed of one **baud** is one pulse per second.

Assuming that a speed key is adjusted to give the proper dot, space and dash values mentioned above, the code speed can be found from

$$Speed\ (wpm) = \frac{dots/min.}{25} = 2.4 \times dots/sec.$$

E.g.: A properly adjusted electronic key gives a string of dots that count to 10 dots per second. Speed = 2.4 X 10 = 24 wpm.

Many modern electronic keyers use a clock or pulse-generator circuit which feeds a flip-flop dot generator. For these keyers the code speed may be determined directly from the clock frequency

$$Speed\ (wpm) = 1.2 \times clock\ frequency\ (Hz).$$

For a quick and simple means of determining the code speed, send a continuous string of dashes and count the number of dashes which occur in a 5-second period. This number, to a close approximation, is the code speed in words per minute.

BREAK-IN OPERATION

Smooth cw break-in operation involves protecting the receiver from permanent damage by the transmitter power and assuring that the receiver will "recover" fast enough to be sensitive between dots and dashes, or at least between letters and words.

Separate Antennas

Few of the available antenna transfer relays are fast enough to follow keying, so the simplest break-in system is the use of a separate receiving antenna. If the transmitter power is low (25 or 50 watts) and the isolation between transmitting and receiving antennas is good, this method can be satisfactory. Best isolation is obtained by mounting the antennas as far apart as possible and at right angles to each other. Feed-line pickup should be minimized, through the use of coaxial cable or 300-ohm Twin-Lead. If the receiver recovers fast enough but the transmitter clicks are bothersome (they may be caused by the receiver overload and so exist only in the receiver) their effect on the operator can be minimized through the use of input and output limiters (see Chapter 8).

ELECTRONIC TRANSMIT-RECEIVE SWITCHES

When powers above 25 or 50 watts are used, where two antennas are not available, or when it is desired to use the same antenna for transmitting and receiving (a "must" when directional antennas are used), special treatment is required for quiet break-in operation on the transmitter frequency. A means must be provided for limiting the power that reaches the receiver input. This can be either a direct short-circuit, or may be a limiting device like an electronic switch used in the antenna feed line. The word "switch" is a misnomer in this case; the transmitter is connected directly to the antenna at all times. The receiver is connected to the antenna through the T-R switch, which functions to protect the receiver's input from transmitted power. In such a setup, all the operator need do is key the transmitter, and all the switching functions are taken care of by the T-R switch.

With the use of a T-R switch some steps should be taken to prevent receiver blocking. Turn off the agc or avc, decrease the rf gain setting, and advance the audio gain control. Use the rf gain control for obtaining the desired listening level. A little experimenting with the controls will provide the receiver settings best suited to individual operating preferences. A range of settings can usually be found, just on the threshold of receiver blocking, where comfortable levels of received signals are heard, and where, without adjusting the controls, the receiver can be used as a monitor during transmission. Usually no modification to the receiver is required, but if annoying clicks and thumps or excess volume occur at all settings of the receiver controls during transmission, their effect can be reduced with output audio limiting (see Chapter 8).

Fig. 11-9 – Proper method of interconnecting T-R switch with various other station accessory equipment.

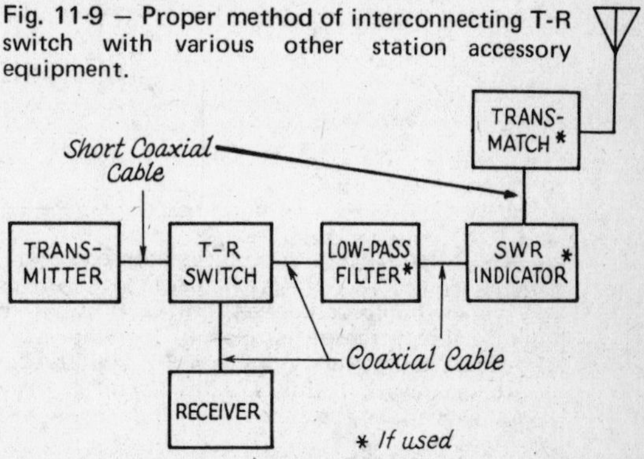

TVI and T-R Switches

T-R switches generate harmonics of the transmitted signal because of rectification of the energy reaching the input of the switch. These harmonics can cause TVI if steps are not taken to prevent it. Any T-R switch should be very well shielded, and should be connected with as short as possible a cable length to the transmitter. In addition, a low-pass filter may be required in the transmission line between the T-R switch and the antenna. Fig. 11-9 shows the proper method of interconnecting the various station accessory equipment.

Reduction of Receiver Gain During Transmission

For absolutely smooth break-in operation with no clicks or thumps, means must be provided for momentarily reducing the gain through the receiver. The system shown in Fig. 11-10 permits quiet break-in operation of high-powered stations. It may require a simple operation on the receiver, although many commercial receivers already provide the connection and require no internal modification. The circuit is for use with a T-R switch and a single antenna. R1 is the regular receiver rf and i-f gain control. The ground lead is run to chassis ground through R2. A wire from the junction runs to the keying relay, K1. When the key is up, the ground side of R1 is connected to ground through the relay arm, and the receiver is in its normal operating condition. When the key is closed the relay closes, which breaks the ground connection from R1 and applies additional bias to the tubes in the receiver. This bias is controlled by R2. When the relay closes, it also closes the circuit to the transmitter keying circuit. A simple rf filter at the key suppresses the local clicks caused by the

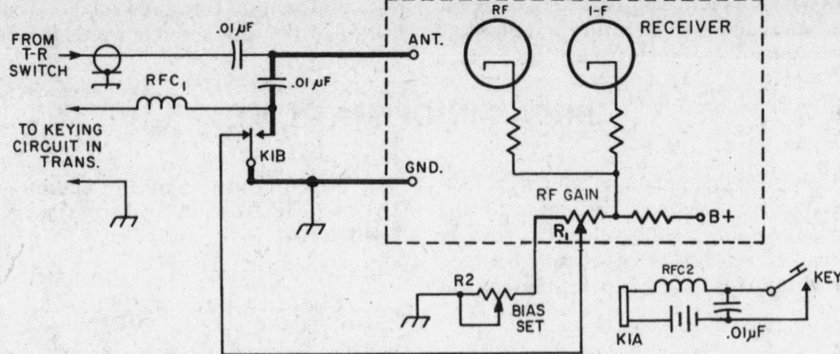

Fig. 11-10 – circuit for smooth break-in operation, using an electronic T-R switch. The leads shown as heavy lines should be kept as short as possible, to minimize direct transmitter pickup.

K1 – Spdt keying relay (Sigma 41FZ-10000-ACS-SIL or equiv.). Although battery and dc relay are shown, any suitable ac or dc relay and power source can be used.

R1 – Receiver manual gain control.

R2 – 5000- or 10,000-ohm wire-wound potentiometer.

RFC1, RFC2 – 1- to 2 1/2-mH rf choke, current rating adequate for application.

relay current. This circuit is superior to any working on the agc line of the receiver because the cathode circuit(s) have shorter time constants than the agc circuits and will recover faster. A similar circuit may be used in the emitters or source leads of transistorized receivers.

TESTING AND MONITORING OF KEYING

In general, there are two common methods for monitoring one's "fist" and signal. The first type involves the use of an audio oscillator that is keyed simultaneously with the transmitter.

The second method is one that permits receiving the signal through one's receiver, and this generally requires that the receiver be tuned to the transmitter (not always convenient unless working on the same frequency) and that some method be provided for preventing overloading of the receiver, so that a good replica of the transmitted signal will be received. Except where quite low power is used, this usually involves a relay for simultaneously shorting the receiver input terminals and reducing the receiver gain.

An alternative is to use an rf-powered audio oscillator. This follows the keying very closely (but tells nothing about the quality – chirps or clicks – of the signal).

The easiest way to find out what your keyed signal sounds like on the air is to trade stations with a near-by ham friend some evening for a short QSO. If he is a half mile or so away, that's fine, but any distance where the signals are still S9 will be satisfactory.

After you have found out how to work his rig, make contact and then have him send slow dashes, with dash spacing (the letter "T" at about 5 wpm). With minimum selectivity, cut the rf gain back just enough to avoid receiver overloading (the condition where you get crisp signals instead of mushy ones) and tune slowly from out of beat-note range on one side of the signal through to zero and out the other side. Knowing the tempo of the dashes, you can readily identify any clicks in the vicinity as yours or someone else's. A good signal will have a thump on "make" that is perceptible only where you can also hear the beat note, and the click on "break" should be practically negligible at any point. If your signal is like that, it will sound good, provided there are no chirps. Then have your friend run off a string of fast dots with the bug – if they are easy to copy, your signal has no "tails" worth worrying about and is a good one for any speed up to the limit of manual keying. Make one check with the selectivity in, to see that the clicks off the signal frequency are negligible even at high signal level.

If you don't have any friends with whom to trade stations, you can still check your keying, although you have to be a little more careful. The transmitter output should be fed into a shielded dummy load. Ordinary incandescent lamps are unsatisfactory as lamp resistance varies too much with current. The thermal lag may cause the results to be misleading.

The first step is to get rid of the rf click at the key. This requires an rf filter (mentioned earlier). With no clicks from a spark at the key, disconnect the antenna from your receiver and short the antenna terminals with a short piece of wire. Tune in your own signal and reduce the rf gain to the point where your receiver doesn't overload. Detune any antenna trimmer the receiver may have. If you can't avoid overload with the rf gain-control range, pull out the rf amplifier tube and try again. If you still can't avoid overload, listen to the second harmonic as a last resort. An overloaded receiver can generate clicks.

Describing the volume level at which you should set your receiver for these "shack" tests is a little difficult. The rf filter should be effective with

These photos show cw signals as observed on an oscilloscope. At A is a dot generated at a 46-baud rate with no intentional shaping, while at B the shaping circuits have been adjusted for approximately 5-ms rise and decay times. Vertical lines are from a 1-kHz signal applied to the Z or intensity axis for timing. Shown at C is a shaped signal with the intensity modulation of the pattern removed. For each of these photos, sampled rf from the transmitter was fed directly to the deflection plates of the oscilloscope.

At D may be seen a received signal having essentially no shaping. The spike at the leading edge is typical of poor power-supply regulation, as is also the immediately following dip and rise in amplitude. The clicks were quite pronounced. This pattern is typical of many observed signals, although not by any means a worst case. The signal was taken from the receiver's i-f amplifier (before detection) using a hand-operated sweep circuit to reduce the sweep time to the order of one second. (Photos from *QST* for October and November 1966.)

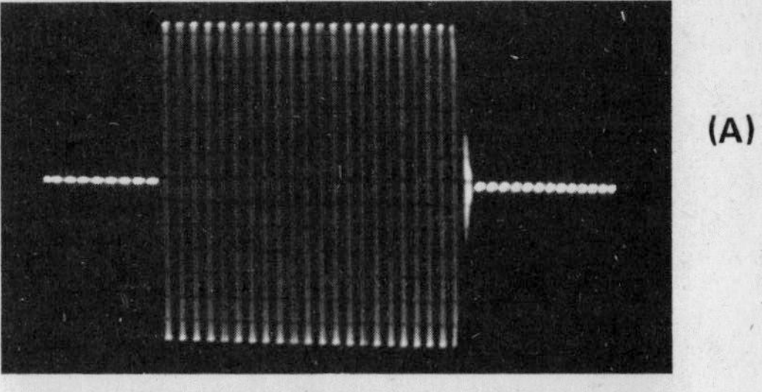

(A)

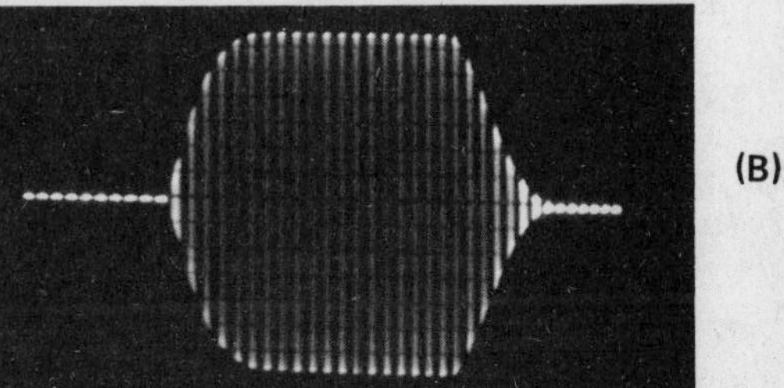

(B)

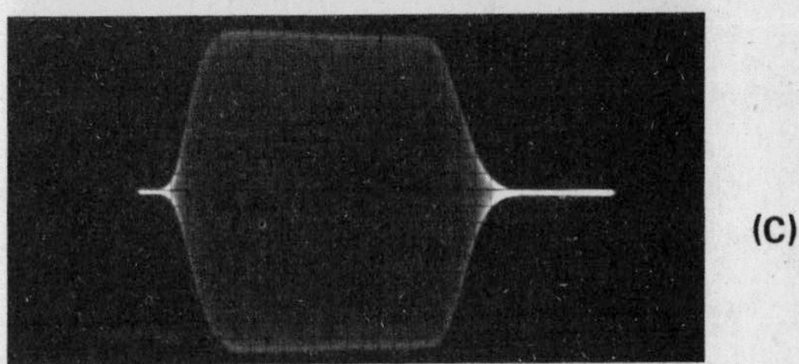

(C)

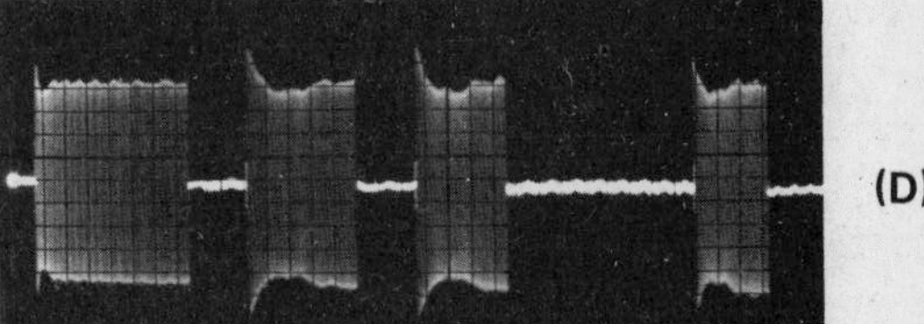

(D)

the receiver running wide open and with an antenna connected. When you turn on the transmitter and take the steps mentioned to reduce the signal in the receiver, run the audio up and the rf down to the point where you can just hear a little "rushing" sound with the BFO off and the receiver tuned to the signal. This is with the selectivity in. At this level, a properly adjusted keying circuit will show no clicks off the rushing-sound range. With the BFO on and the same gain setting, there should be no clicks outside the beat-note range. When observing clicks, make the slow-dash and dot tests outlined previously.

Now you know how your signal sounds on the air, with one possible exception. If keying your transmitter makes the lights blink, you may not be able to tell too accurately about the chirp on your signal. However, if you are satisfied with the absence of chirp when tuning *either side of zero beat*, it is safe to assume that your receiver isn't chirping with the light flicker and that the observed signal is a true representation. No chirp either side of zero beat is fine. Don't try to make these tests without first getting rid of the rf click at the key, because clicks can mask a chirp.

The least satisfactory way to check your keying is to ask another ham on the air how your keying sounds. It is the least satisfactory because most hams are reluctant to be highly critical of another amateur's signal. In a great many cases they don't actually know what to look for or how to describe any aberrations they may observe.

AN RF-ACTUATED CW MONITOR

This unit permits the operator to monitor his cw sending. Also, it can be used as a code-practice oscillator. As an oscillator, connect a key to TB1, and plug a set of phones into J3. To use the speaker, close S1 and advance R2. For use as a monitor, connect coax from your transmitter to J1 and route the antenna feed to J2. Set R1 so that the arm of the control is at the ground end. Connect a VTVM between terminal 1 on TB1 and the chassis. Next, tune up the rig to the input and adjust R1 so that the VTVM reads -7 or -8 volts. The monitor should be generating a tone, and if you have S1 turned on the audio gain control, R2, turned up, you should hear a note. See Fig. 11-11.

For headphone use, plug the phones into J3 and plug P1 into the receiver headphone jack. When receiving, the audio from the receiver will be piped through the monitor. When going to transmit, you'll hear the multivibrator oscillator tone in the phones. The battery drain is about 2 mA; it is a good idea to leave S1 switched off when the speaker is not in use. You don't have to disconnect the monitor from the rf line in order to use the unit as a code practice oscillator. (From *QST*, Nov. 1968.)

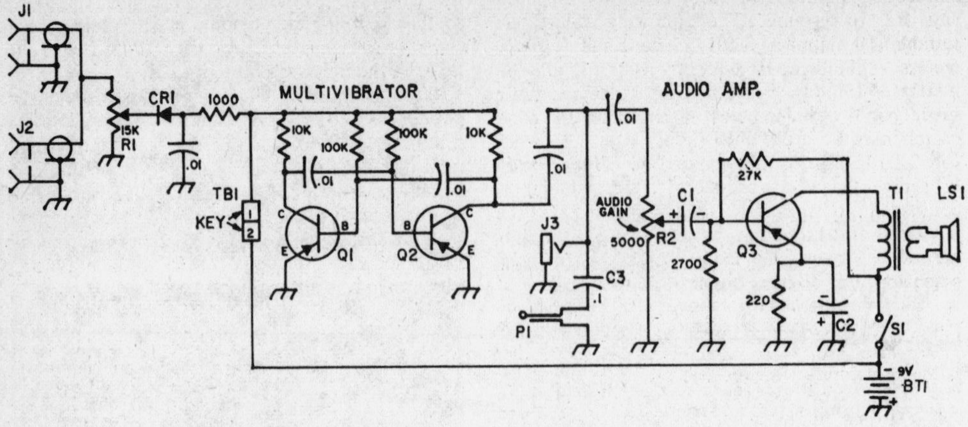

Fig. 11-11 – Circuit diagram of the cw monitor. Unless specified, all resistors are 1/2 watt; resistances are in ohms (K = 1000). All values of capacitors are in microfarads (µF, all .01-µF capacitors are disk ceramic). Capacitors marked with polarity are electrolytic.

BT1 – 9-volt battery.
C1, C2 – 25-µF electrolytic, 25 working volts or more.
C3 – 0.1 µF paper, 25 working volts or more.
CR1 – 1N277 or 1N34A.
J1, J2 – Coax chassis receptacle, type SO-239.
J3 – Open-circuit phone jack.
LS1 – Speaker, 3-inch diameter, 4-ohm type.
P1 – Phone plug.
Q1, Q2, Q3 – 2N406, SK3003, or equiv.
R1 – 15,000-ohm, 2-watt control.
R2 – 5000-ohm control with single-pole, single-throw switch, S1, mounted on rear.
T1 – Output transformer, 2000- to 5000-ohm primary, 4- to 10-ohm voice-coil secondary; see text (Lafayette 99 H 6101 or similar).
TB1 – Two-terminal connector.

A SOLID-STATE T-R SWITCH

One of the simplest approaches to T-R switch construction is illustrated in Figs. 1 and 2. This circuit was designed by W4ETO and originally described by W1ICP in *QST* for April, 1971. A gate-protected dual-gate MOSFET couples an incoming signal to the receiver. When the transmitter is keyed, a sample of the signal is used to turn Q1 off. The dc voltage required to operate Q1 is obtained by rectifying 6.3 volts ac from the transmitter filament line. Connection to the line should be made to the ungrounded side of the heater supply.

Fig. 1 – The solid-state T-R switch constructed on an etched circuit board of the pattern shown in *QST* for April, 1971, p. 32. The circuit could also be built on a piece of insulated or perforated board.

Installation

Mount the T-R switch close to the transmitter PA tank. The coupling capacitor, C1, which should have a voltage rating of at least twice the plate voltage of the transmitter PA stage, should be connected with one end to the input side of the pi-network coil, as shown in Fig. 2. Mount a coax chassis fitting on the back of the transmitter chassis, and run a connecting line of coax from the fitting to the T-R switch. (This length of coax is shown in Fig. 1, extending out the right-hand side of the photograph.) Make sure the coax braid is grounded at the fitting and at the T-R switch. The receiver antenna terminals can then be connected, using coax, to the T-R coax terminal on the transmitter.

With high-power transmitters, near the kilowatt level, the value of C1 should be changed to no more than 1 pF. Because of this light coupling, a broadly resonant input circuit may be required on the T-R switch in order to have adequate gain during reception. This may be obtained by connecting an inductor from the junction of C1 and R1 to ground. The following values are suitable; 10 meters – 3 μH; 15 meters – 5 μH; 20 meters – 11 μH; 40 meters – 40 μH; and 80 meters – 130 μH. For operation on more than a single band, a single-pole 5-position rotary band switch may be used, with inductor values of 3.1 μH, 2.1 μH, 6.0 μH, 29 μH, and 90 μH connected in series. One end of the 3.1-μH inductor is connected to the T-R switch input, and the junction of this and the 2.1-μH inductor is grounded through the band switch for 10-meter operation. For 15-meter operation, the junction of the 2.1- and 6-μH inductors is grounded, and so on, so that for 80-meter operation all 5 inductors in series are connected from the T-R switch input through the bandswitch to ground.

One thing about this type of device should be pointed out. The T-R switch is connected to the transmitter's tank circuit via C1, a low-value capacitor. If, as in the case of Class AB linear amplifiers, the amplifier plate current is not cut off when receiving, there may be enough noise generated in the amplifier tube to be objectionable during receive. Such noise should not be noticeable with Class C or with cathode-keyed amplifiers.

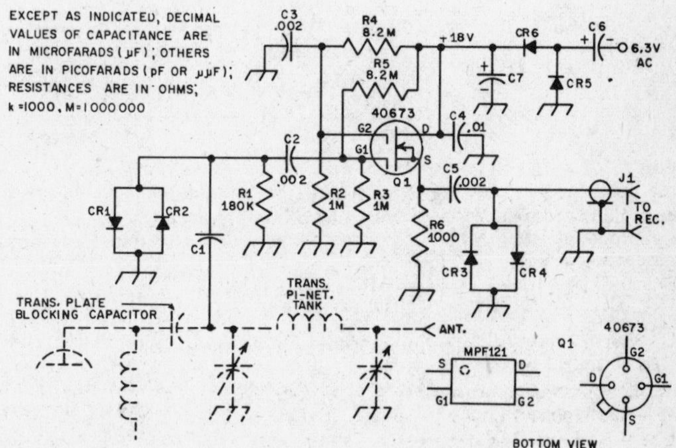

Fig. 2 – Circuit diagram of the T-R switch. All resistors are 1/2-watt composition. Parts not listed below are for circuit-board identification.
C1 – 5- to 10-pF.
C6, C7 – 100-μF, 25-volt electrolytic.
CR1, CR2, CR3, CR4 – 1N914 or equiv.
CR5, CR6 – 100 PRV, 100-mA silicon diode.
J1 – Coax chassis fitting.
Q1 – Gate-protected dual-gate MOSFET (RCA 40673 or Motorola MPF121).

SELF-CONTAINED ALL-BAND ELECTRONIC T-R SWITCH

This vacuum-tube T-R switch differs in several ways from the preceding example. It contains its own power supply and consequently can be used with any transmitter/receiver combination without "borrowing" power. It will add gain and front-end selectivity to the receiver. A homemade switch-coil-capacitor is shown in the unit, enabling the constructor to build his own.

In the circuit diagram of Fig. 2, one triode of a 12AU7 is used as an amplifier stage, followed by the other triode as a cathode-follower stage to couple between the tuned circuit and the receiver. The triodes are biased during transmission periods by rectified grid current, and insufficient power is fed to the receiver to damage its input circuit.

The T-R switch is intended to mount behind the transmitter near its output terminal, so that the connecting cable is short. The lead from the T-R switch to the receiver can be any reasonable length. Components are mounted above and below the chassis. In wiring the switch, a length of RG-58/U should be used between the cathode-follower load (resistor and rf choke) and the output jack J2, to minimize "feedthrough" around the tube. A pair of .01 μF capacitors across the ac line where it enters the chassis helps to hold down the rf that might otherwise ride in on the ac line.

In operation, it is only necessary to switch the unit to the band in use and peak capacitor C4 for maximum signal or background noise. A significant increase in signal or background noise should be observed on any band within the range of the coil/capacitor combination.

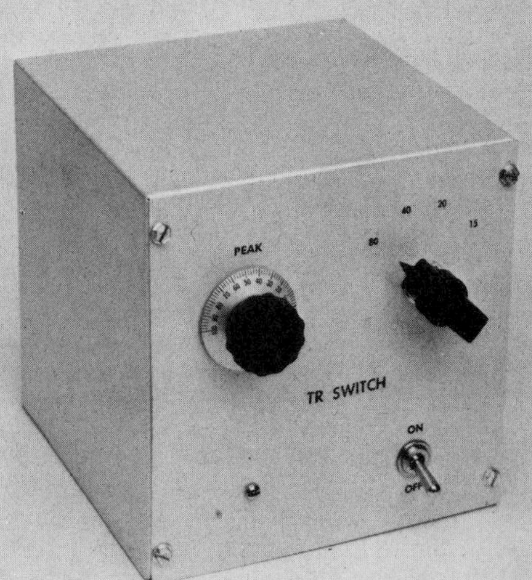

Fig. 1 – The knob at the left is used for peaking the tuned circuit. At the right is the bandswitch. Only four positions are shown; the 15-meter position also covers 10 meters.

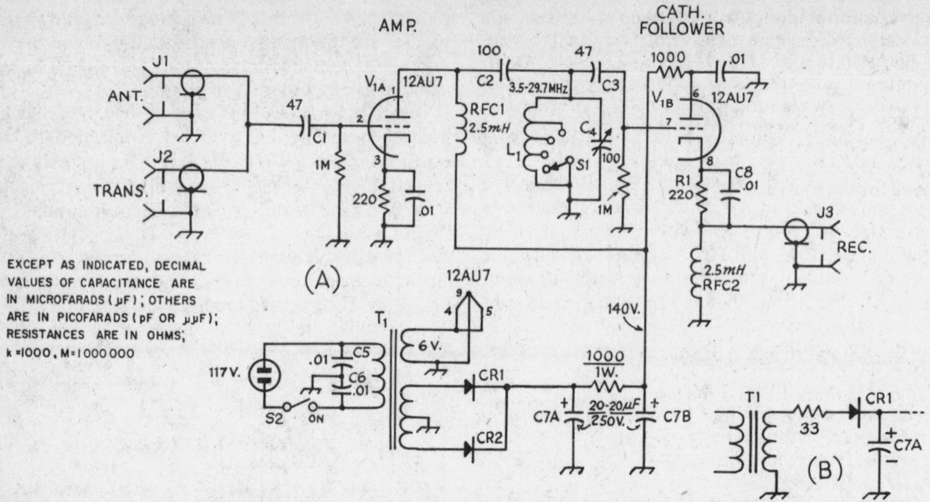

Fig. 2 – Circuit diagram of the T-R switch. Unless otherwise specified, resistors are 1/2 watt; decimal value fixed capacitors are disk ceramic, others are mica with the exception of C7, which is electrolytic. B – method of using a half-wave transformer for T1. Circuit designations not listed below are for text reference.

C4 – 100 pF variable (Millen 20100 or similar).
C7A, C7B – 20/20-μF electrolytic 250 volts or more.
CR1, CR2 – Silicon rectifier, 400 volts or more, any current rating over 40 mA.
J1, J2, J3 – Coax chassis receptacle, type SO-239.
L1 – See Fig. 3.
S1 – Single-pole, four-position wafer switch (Mallory 3115J, 3215J, or similar).
S2 – Spst toggle switch.
T1 – Power transformer, full-wave, 125-0-125 25 mA, 6.3 volts, 1 A (Stancor PS-8416, Knight 54A2008). B – half-wave, 125 V, 15 mA, 6 volts, 0.6 A (Stancor PS-8415, Knight 54-A1410).

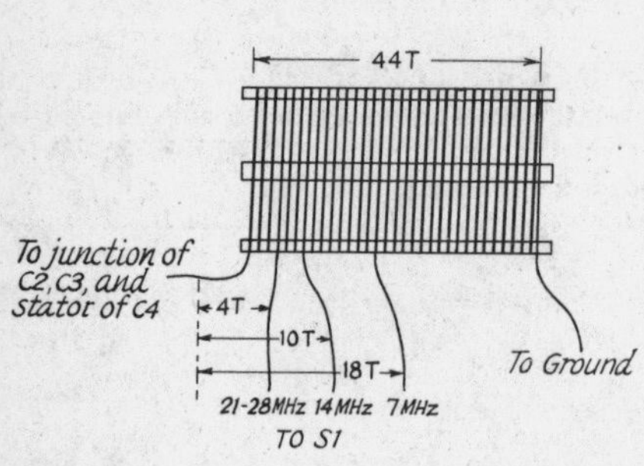

Fig. 3 – L1 and associated taps. L1 is 44 turns of No. 24, 32 turns per inch, 1 inch diameter (Miniductor 3016, Air Dux 832T). To solder the tap leads, indent each turn adjacent to the tap point. This will allow soldering room.

Fig. 4 – The power transformer and filter components are mounted at the upper right. Just to the bottom of center is the socket for the 12AU7.

DELUXE ALL-SOLID-STATE KEYER

The Accu-Keyer is a modern keying device with deluxe features available on only the most expensive of commercially available instruments, but it may be built for less than $25.

The basic circuit uses seven TTL integrated circuits which may be purchased at "bargain" suppliers for less than $3. Optional features which may be incorporated at the builder's discretion are a stiffly regulated power supply, a keying monitor, and provisions for solid-state keying of cathode-keyed transmitters.

The Accu-Keyer was designed with these features in mind:

1) Self-completing dots and dashes
2) Dot and dash memories

This version of the WB4VVF Accu-Keyer contains all optional circuit features described in the text. It is housed in a 9 × 2-1/2 × 3-1/8-inch Apollo aluminum "shadow box," type BB (available from Apollo Products, Box 245, Vaughnsville, OH 45893). The low-profile cabinet with its black crinkle finish and simulated walnut front panel provides an attractive as well as a very functional keyer for the ham shack.

3) Iambic operation
4) Dot and dash insertion
5) Automatic character space (with switching provided to defeat this feature)
6) 5-50 wpm speed range
7) Low cost

A synchronized clock provides uniform starting for constant-width characters. Also the dot-dash decision is made at the end of the space following the bit, allowing maximum leeway in paddle operation.

Logic Description

Three types of gates are used in the logic section of the keyer. There are three 7474 edge-triggered type *D* flip-flops, three 7400 quad two-input NAND gates, and one 7410 triple three-input NAND gate, for a total of seven dual-in-line packages.

The 7474 is a clocked edge-triggered type *D* flip-flop which has two modes of operation, synchronous and nonsynchronous. Nonsynchronous inputs are the SET (pin 1) and the RESET (pin 4) connections. These inputs can be used to force the Q and $\overline{Q}$ outputs into either a high or low condition. SET, when grounded, forces the Q output high and RESET, when grounded, forces the Q output low. The $\overline{Q}$ output is always in an opposite state from the Q output.

A synchronous input is provided (pin 2). If both the SET and RESET inputs are high and the clock pulse (pin 3) goes positive, the state of the *D* input (pin 3) will be transferred to the Q output, i.e., if *D* was high, Q will go high. This transition can occur only on the positive-going edge of the clock pulse.

The two- and three-input gates are NAND-type gates. Outputs of these gates are low only if all the inputs to the gates are high.

Block Diagrams

Fig. 1 shows that the keyer is composed of four sections. In the nonsychronous section the gates change logic state when the paddle is moved, while in the synchronous section the logic changes in step with the clock signal. The output driver changes the logic levels into voltages that will key the transmitter. The +5 volts is developed in the Zener-diode-regulated power supply.

The flip-flops and gates that perform the functions in the circuit are shown in the blocks. In the discussion that follows, a bit is defined as a single dot or dash and the space following.

The present-bit memories store the information as to which bit is being sent. These memories start the bit by enabling the start-stop gates. These outputs are fed through an OR gate to the output driver. A counter is also enabled at the start of a bit and disables the output at the beginning of the bit space.

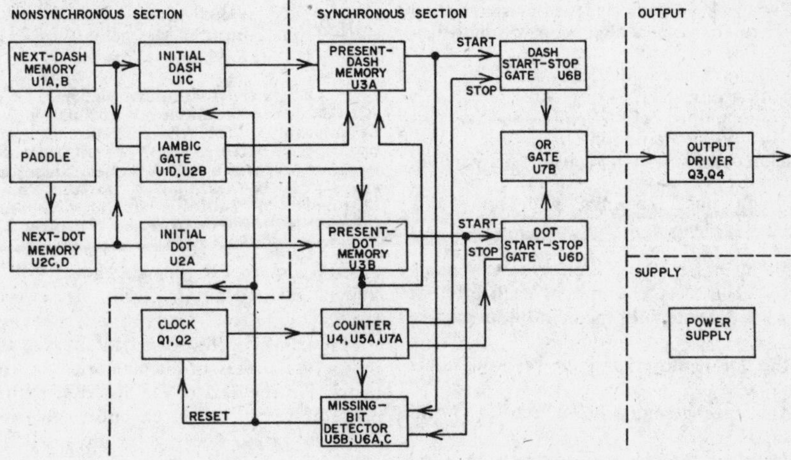

Fig. 1 — Block diagram of the Accu-Keyer.

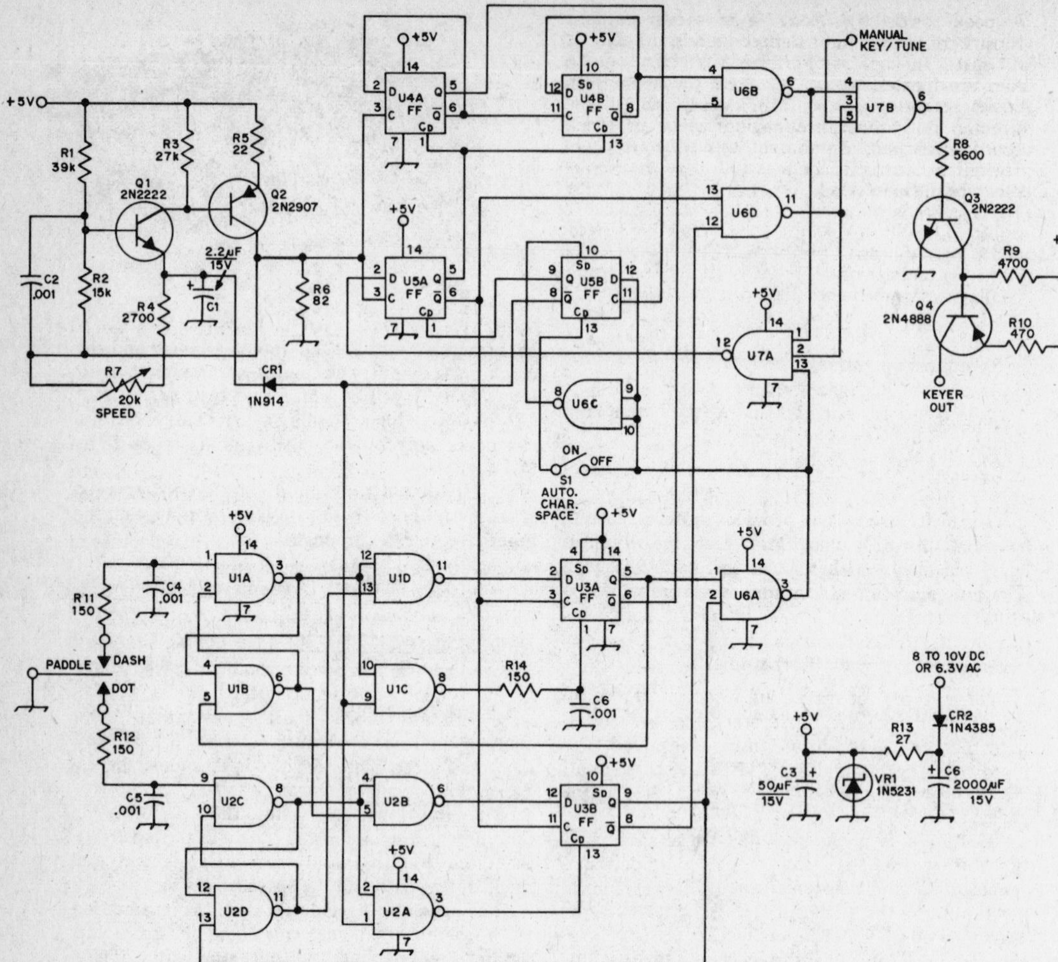

Fig. 2 — Schematic diagram of the Accu-Keyer. Resistances are in ohms; k = 1000. All capacitances are in microfarads. All resistors may be 1/4 watt except R13, which should have a 2-W rating. Capacitors with polarity indicated are electrolytic; all others are disk ceramic. Parts not listed below are for text reference and circuit-board identification.

CR1 — Small-signal silicon diode.
CR2 — Rectifier diode, 1/2 A or greater.
Q1, Q3 — Silicon npn, 250-mW, high-speed switching or rf-amplifier transistor.
Q2 — Silicon pnp, 250-mW, high-speed switching or rf-amplifier transistor.
Q4 — Silicon pnp, 250-mW, high-voltage af-amplifier transistor.
R7 — Reverse-log-taper control; Mallory U-28 suitable.
S1 — Spst toggle.
U1, U2, U6 — Quad 2-input NAND gate, type 7400.*
U3, U4, U5 — Dual type *D* flip-flop, type 7474.*
U7 — Triple 3-input NAND gate, type 7410.*
VR1 — 5.1-V, 0.5-W Zener diode.

*** All ICs are dual-in-line package, 14 pin. Note: All ICs are available from various manufactuerers or as surplus. Motorola part numbers are prefixed by *MC* and suffixed by *P*. Texas Instruments parts have an *SN* prefix and *N* suffix. Signetics ICs have an *N* prefix and an *A* suffix. For example, Motorola's MC7400P is equivalent to Texas Instruments' SN7400N orSignetics' N7400A.**

Next-bit memories allow the keyer to remember one bit ahead. At the end of each bit four conditions are possible with the next-bit memories.

1) If the dot memory is on, the keyer will start a dot.

2) If the dash memory is on, the keyer will start a dash.

3) If both are on, the keyer will produce the opposite bit from the one it is sending.

4) If neither is on, the keyer will assume a missing bit and automatically give two additional spaces.

The iambic gate is used to produce the correct input to the present-bit memories for condition 3 above. At the end of condition 4, the missing-bit detector resets the clock and enables the initial dash-dot gates. These gates are used to start the keyer and synchronize the clock with the first bit sent.

A peek inside the Accu-Keyer shows compact construction in this deluxe version built by W1RML. The ac-operated power supply components are located at the left, and the basic keyer board at the right. The keying monitor is constructed on a separate vertically mounted circuit board positioned near the center of the enclosure. The pitch control is mounted inside the keyer on this circuit board, as it is not adjusted frequently. The speaker is mounted over a "grille" formed by drilling many holes at the bottom of the enclosure, and is nearly hidden by the filter capacitor in this view. On the rear panel, in TO-3 style cases, are the 5-volt regulator IC and the cathode keying transistor.

The Circuit

The schematic diagram of the Accu-Keyer is shown in Fig. 2. The voltage applied to CR2 for powering the keyer may be either 8 to 10 volts dc or 6.3 volts ac, such as from the filament supply of a transmitter or receiver. If dc is applied, C6 is not required. If ac is applied to CR2, VR1 functions more to protect the ICs from overvoltage by limiting the amplitude of the ripple than it does for voltage regulation. If a well-filtered and regulated supply is desired, the circuit of Fig. 3A may be used in place of CR2, R13, and VR1 and associated capacitors. Constructed with the components shown, that supply will handle the keyer requirements with power to spare.

Should a keying monitor be desired, the diagram of Fig. 3B may be used to construct a circuit which will afford plenty of volume and a stable, pleasing tone. The circuit is a modified version of the code-practice oscillator appearing in Chapter 1. Equipped with such a monitor, the Accu-Keyer becomes ideal for conducting code practice sessions for small and medium-sized groups.

Fig. 3C shows a circuit which may be used for cathode-keyed or solid-state "QRP" transmitters. The Delco keying transistor will safely handle two amperes of current and a collector-to-emitter potential of 800 V, and yet its cost is less than that of a new mercury-wetted relay. The use of a transistor offers advantages over both vacuum-tube keying and relay keying of cathode-keyed rigs; the voltage drop across the transistor when saturated introduces negligible grid-cathode bias to the keyed stage, and the keying is softened somewhat over relay keying because the transistor cannot go from cutoff to saturation (or vice versa) instantaneously. For QRP transmitters, Q6 may be a 300- or 500-mW silicon npn transistor, such as a 2N2222 or 2N4123.

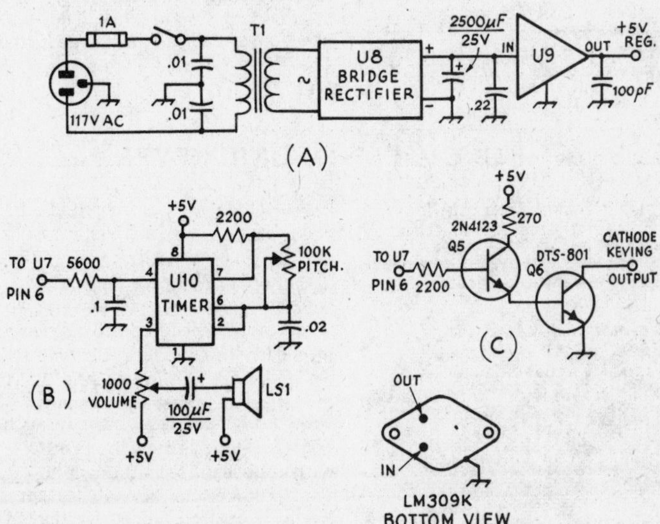

Fig. 3 — At A, optional ac-operated power supply circuit for the Accu-Keyer; At B, an optional monitor, and at C a circuit for cathode keying.

LS1 — Miniature speaker, 4-, 8- or 16-ohm impedance.

Q6 — High-voltage high-current silicon npn power transistor (Delco DTS-801, -802, or -804 or equiv.).

T1 — Surplus filament transformer, 12.6-V 1-A secondary rating.

U8 — Full-wave rectifier bridge, 1-A 50-V (Motorola 920-2, HEP 175, or equiv.). Four rectifier diodes in a bridge arrangement may be used instead.

U9 — Voltage-regulator IC, 5-volt (National Semiconductor LM309K or equiv.).

U10 — Signetics NE555 timer IC.

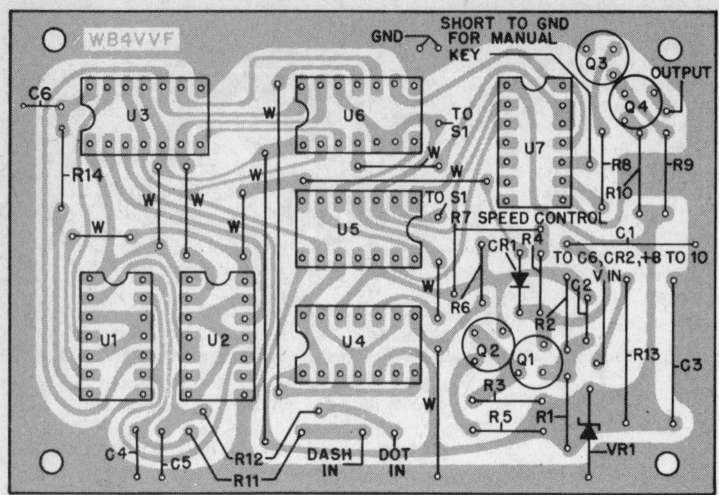

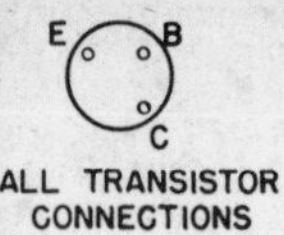

W = WIRE JUMPER

Fig. 4 — Etching pattern and parts-layout diagram for the Accu-Keyer. Pattern is actual size, shown from *foil side* of board.

Construction and Operation

A ready-made circuit board is available for the basic circuit of the Accu-Keyer. [1] Fig. 4 is an actual-size board layout and parts-placement guide. If the builder elects to use none of the optional circuit features of Fig. 3, the complete keyer may be built into a 3 × 2 × 5-inch Minibox. The board pattern in Fig. 4 contains all parts of Fig. 2 except the controls, the filter capacitor, and the rectifier in the power supply.

It is essential that all leads to the keyer be shielded from rf. RG-174/U coax may be used. A .01-μF bypass capacitor is provided on the power input to remove rf. As shown on the diagram, the inputs from the paddle are filtered by 150-ohm resistors bypassed by .001-μF capacitors. In stubborn cases it may be necessary to bypass the paddle contacts at the paddle itself.

Substitution of transistors for Q1 and Q2 may require changing the value of R5 to make the first clock pulse the same length as the rest. Both should be transistors with a beta of at least 60. Q3 is noncritical, and any good silicon transistor should work. Q4 should be capable of withstanding the transmistter key-up voltage. Any pnp silicon device having a reasonable beta and meeting this requirement should work. The value of C1 may be juggled to change the range of the speed control. The value specified gives a range of approximately 5 to 50 wpm.

[1] A glass-epoxy board, pre-drilled, is available for $3.50 from James M. Garrett, WB4VVF, 126 W. Buchanon, Orlando, FL 32809.

A SINGLE-IC ELECTRONIC KEYER

Electronic keyers, depending on the features they offer, can be quite simple or they can be rather complex. This is a simple digital electronic keyer which uses only a single integrated circuit and a single transistor, yet it makes the sending of perfect code a rather easy task. The dots and dashes are self-completing, and code may be sent at any speed between 10 and 40 wpm with adjustment of the speed control. A weighting control is provided, too, a desirable feature to compensate for variations in wave shaping and time sequencing in different transmitter circuits. Keying is done with a high-voltage transistor, connected for use with grid-block-keyed transmitters or transmitters with equivalent solid-state circuits.

The keyer can be built for approximately $12. By using batteries to power the circuit, the cost of

The single-IC keyer is contained in a 2-1/8 × 3 × 5-1/4-inch metal box. The power switch is mounted on the ratio or weighting control. Jacks for the paddle and output keying, located on the rear of the box, are not visible in this view.

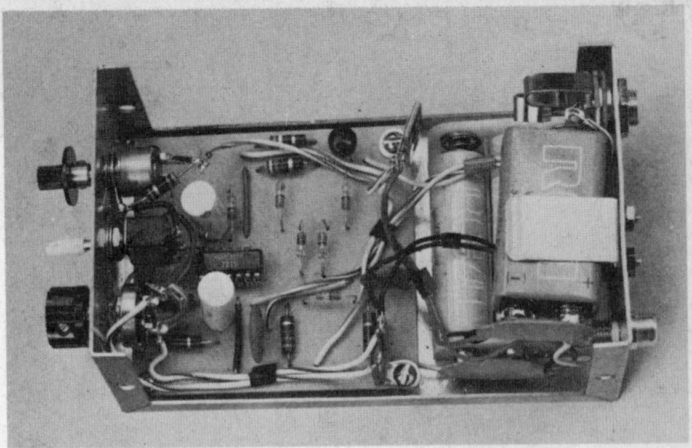

Because there are relatively few components in the keyer, there is ample room even with the batteries mounted inside the box. Although an etched circuit board was used in this keyer built by W1RML, perforated board and point-to-point wiring may be used in construction.

a power transformer is eliminated. The IC is available for approximately $2 at industrial electronic supply houses.

The method of construction is shown in the photographs. An etched circuit board was used for this version, but perforated board and point-to-point wiring work just as well if one uses care in making connections to the IC. The builder may find it desirable to use a socket for the IC, rather than to attempt to solder directly to the IC pins. The controls, jacks, and holders for the batteries are mounted directly on the metal box. The IC and the transistor, along with their associated components, are mounted on the circuit board.

The power switch, S1, must be of a double-pole type, to provide complete electrical isolation of the negative terminals of the two battery supplies with power off. Leaving these terminals connected together and ungrounding the common connection with a single-pole switch is not satisfactory, as current will still flow from the batteries. In the keyer shown in the photographs, S1 is located on the rear of the weight control. When the keyer is energized, the response is almost instantaneous, as there is nothing which must warm up before operation can commence.

The speed range of the keyer is determined by the values of the two electrolytic capacitors, shown as 22 μF in the schematic diagram. If the builder desires to change the range, these values may be changed, always keeping the two equal. Smaller values will provide for an increase in the range.

To avoid the possibility of rf entering the keying enclosure, the key line should be shielded, with the shield conductor providing the ground return. Small-diameter coax such as RG-58/U or RG-59/U, or the smaller RG-174/U, is ideal for this purpose. The paddle line may be a twisted pair with shield, and the shield should provide the ground or common connection at the paddle itself. The two .01-μF bypass capacitors shown for the paddle leads should be installed where the wires from the paddle enter the keyer enclosure.

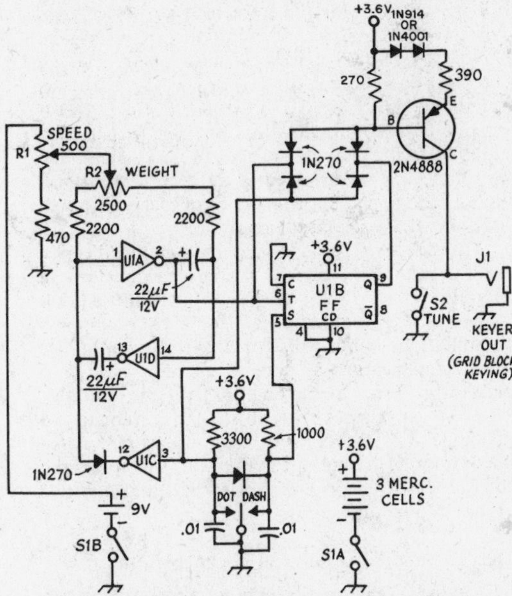

Fig. 1 — Schematic diagram of the single-IC keyer; circuit courtesy of W9HFM. Resistances are in ohms; k = 1000. All fixed resistors are 1/2-watt 10-percent tolerance.

Q1 — Silicon pnp, 300-mW, 150-V af-amplifier transistor.

R1, R2 — Linear taper.

S1 — Dpst. (Type shown in photograph is Mallory US27, mounted on rear of R2, which is Mallory type U6.)

S2 — Spst toggle.

U1 — Multifunction RTL IC, 1 *J-K* flip-flop, 1 inverter, 2 buffers (Motorola MC787P or HEP-C2503P or equiv.).

Bibliography

Source material and more extended discussions of topics covered in this chapter can be found in the references given below. In addition, a detailed bibilography of electronic keyer information is available upon request from ARRL Hq. Please enclose a stamped self-addressed business-size envelope.

Garrett, "The WB4VVF Accu-Keyer," *QST*, Aug., 1973.

Grammer, "Oscilloscope Setups for Transmitter Testing," *QST*, October, 1964; "V.F.O. Stability – Recap and Postscript," *QST*, Sept. and Oct., 1966; "Why Key Clicks?" *QST* Oct., 1966; "Low-Level Blocked-Grid Keying," *QST*, Nov., 1966.

McCoy, "Clicks and Chirps – Let's Clean 'Em Up!" *QST* Sept., 1967; "An R.F.-Actuated C.W. Monitor," *QST*, Nov., 1968; "Simplified Antenna Switching," *QST*, April, 1971.

Wooten, "A Code Practice Oscillator for the Beginner," *QST*, Nov., 1972.

"A Relay Driver for Use with Solid-State Keyers," Gimmicks and Gadgets, *QST*, Oct., 1971. Also Feedback, *QST* for April, 1972.

Chapter 12

Amplitude Modulation and Double-Sideband Phone

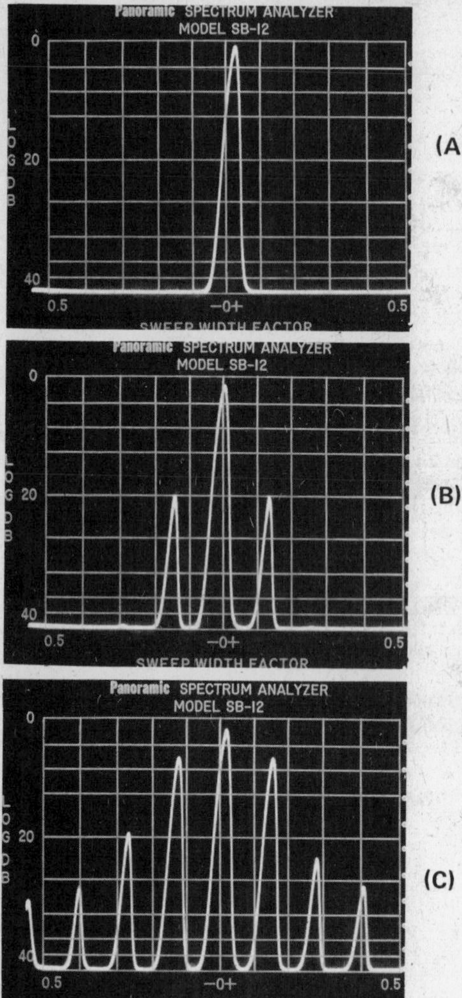

Fig. 12-1 – Spectrum-analyzer display of the rf output of an a-m transmitter. Frequency is presented on the horizontal axis (7-kHz total display width) versus relative amplitude of the signal component on the vertical axis. Shown at A is the unmodulated carrier, which occupies but a single frequency. At B the carrier is 20-percent modulated with a 1000-Hz tone. Each sideband may be seen to be at a level approximately 20 dB below the carrier. The signal bandwidth in this case is twice the modulating frequency, or 2 kHz. Shown at C is the widened channel bandwidth resulting from splatter caused by overmodulation. New frequencies, audio harmonics of the 1000-Hz modulating tone, extend for several kilohertz either side of the carrier.

As described in the chapter on circuit fundamentals, the process of modulation sets up groups of frequencies called **sidebands**, which appear symmetrically above and below the frequency of the unmodulated signal or **carrier.** If the instantaneous values of the amplitudes of all these separate frequencies are added together, the result is called the **modulation envelope.** In **amplitude modulation (a-m)** the modulation envelope follows the amplitude variations of the signal that is used to modulate the wave.

For example, modulation by a 1000-Hz tone will result in a modulation envelope that varies in amplitude at a 1000-Hz rate. The actual rf signal that produces such an envelope consists of three frequencies – the carrier, a side frequency 1000 Hz higher, and a side frequency 1000 Hz lower than the carrier. See Fig. 12-1. These three frequencies easily can be separated by a receiver having high selectivity. In order to reproduce the original modulation the receiver must have enough bandwidth to accept the carrier and the sidebands simultaneously. This is because an a-m detector responds to the modulation envelope rather than to the individual signal components, and the envelope will be distorted in the receiver unless all the frequency components in the signal go through without change in their amplitudes.

In the simple case of tone modulation the two side frequencies and the carrier are constant in amplitude – it is only the envelope amplitude that varies at the modulation rate. With more complex modulation such as voice or music the amplitudes and frequencies of the side frequencies vary from instant to instant. The amplitude of the modulation envelope varies from instant to instant in the same way as the complex audio-frequency signal causing the modulation. Even in this case the *carrier* amplitude is constant if the transmitter is properly modulated.

A-M Sidebands and Channel Width

Speech can be electrically reproduced, with high intelligibility, in a band of frequencies lying between approximately 100 and 3000 Hz. When these frequencies are combined with a radio-frequency carrier, the sidebands occupy the frequency spectrum from about 3000 Hz below the carrier frequency to 3000 Hz above – a total band or **channel** of about 6 kHz.

Actual speech frequencies extend up to 10,000 Hz or more, so it is possible to occupy a 20-kHz channel if no provision is made for reducing its width. For communication purposes such a channel width represents a waste of valuable spectrum space, since a 6-kHz channel is fully adequate for intelligibility. Occupying more than the minimum channel creates unnecessary interference.

THE MODULATION ENVELOPE

In Fig. 12-2 the drawing at A shows the unmodulated rf signal, assumed to be a sine wave of the desired radio frequency. The graph can be taken to represent either voltage or current.

In B, the signal is assumed to be modulated by the audio frequency shown in the small drawing above. This frequency is much lower than the carrier frequency, a necessary condition for good modulation. When the modulating voltage is "positive," (above its axis) the envelope amplitude is increased *above* its unmodulated amplitude; when the modulating voltage is "negative," the envelope amplitude is *decreased.* Thus the envelope grows larger and smaller with the polarity and amplitude of the modulating voltage.

The drawing at C shows what happens with stronger modulation. The envelope amplitude is doubled at the instant the modulating voltage reaches its positive peak. On the negative peak of the modulating voltage the envelope amplitude just reaches zero.

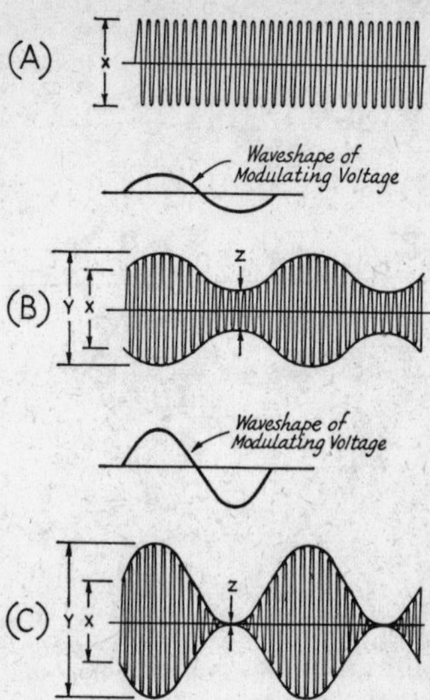

Fig. 12-2 — Graphical representation of (A) rf output unmodulated, (B) modulated 50 percent, (C) modulated 100 percent. The modulation envelope is shown by the thin outline on the modulated wave.

Percentage of Modulation

When a modulated signal is detected in a receiver, the detector output follows the modulation envelope. The stronger the modulation, therefore, the greater is the useful receiver output. Obviously, it is desirable to make the modulation as strong or "heavy" as possible. A wave modulated as in Fig. 12-2C would produce more useful audio output than the one shown at B.

The "depth" of the modulation is expressed as a percentage of the unmodulated carrier amplitude. In either B or C, Fig. 12-2, X represents the unmodulated carrier amplitude, Y is the maximum envelope amplitude on the modulation uppeak, and Z is the minimum envelope amplitude on the modulation downpeak.

In a properly operating modulation system the modulation envelope is an accurate reproduction of the modulating wave, as can be seen in Fig. 12-2 at B and C by comparing one side of the outline with the shape of the modulating wave. (The lower outline duplicates the upper, but simply appears upside down in the drawing.)

The **percentage of modulation** is

$$\% \text{ Mod.} = \frac{Y - X}{X} \times 100 \text{ (upward modulation), or}$$

$$\% \text{ Mod.} = \frac{X - Z}{X} \times 100 \text{ (downward modulation)}$$

If the two percentages differ, the larger of the two is customarily specified. If the wave shape of the modulation is such that its peak positive and negative amplitudes are equal, then the modulation percentage will be the same both up and down, and is

$$\% \text{ Mod.} = \frac{Y - Z}{Y + Z} \times 100.$$

Power in Modulated Wave

The amplitude values shown in Fig. 12-2 correspond to current and voltage, so the drawings may be taken to represent instantaneous values of either. The power in the wave varies as the *square* of either the current or voltage, so at the peak of the modulation upswing the instantaneous power in the envelope of Fig. 12-2C is four times the unmodulated carrier power (because the current and voltage both are doubled). At the peak of the downswing the power is zero, since the amplitude is zero. These statements are true of 100-percent modulation no matter what the wave form of the modulation. The instantaneous envelope power in the modulated signal is proportional to the square of its envelope amplitude at every instant. This fact is highly important in the operation of every method of amplitude modulation.

It is convenient, and customary, to describe the operation of modulation systems in terms of sine-wave modulation. Although this wave shape is seldom actually used in practice (voice wave shapes depart very considerably from the sine form) it lends itself to simple calculations and its use as a standard permits comparison between systems on a common basis. With sine-wave modulation the *average* power in the modulated signal over any number of full cycles of the modulation frequency is found to be 1-1/2 times the power in the unmodulated carrier. In other words, the power output increases 50 percent with 100-percent modulation by a sine wave.

This relationship is very useful in the design of modulation systems and modulators, because any such system that is capable of increasing the *average* power output by 50 percent with sine-wave

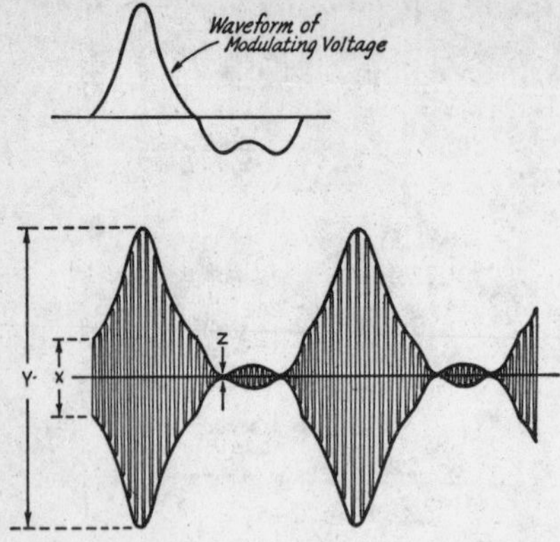

Fig. 12-3 – Modulation by an unsymmetrical wave form. This drawing shows 100-percent downward modulation along with 300-percent upward modulation. There is no distortion, since the modulation envelope is an accurate reproduction of the wave form of the modulating voltage.

modulation automatically fulfills the requirement that the *instantaneous* power at the modulation uppeak be four times the carrier power. Consequently, systems in which the additional power is supplied from outside the modulated rf stage (e.g., plate modulation) usually are designed on a sine-wave basis as a matter of convenience. Modulation systems in which the additional power is secured from the modulated rf amplifier (e.g., grid modulation) usually are more conveniently designed on the basis of peak envelope power rather than average power.

The extra power that is contained in a modulated signal goes entirely into the sidebands, half in the upper sideband and half into the lower. As a numerical example, full modulation of a 100-watt carrier by a sine wave will add 50 watts of sideband power, 25 in the lower and 25 in the upper sideband. With lower modulation percentages, the sideband power is proportional to the *square* of the modulation percentage, i.e., 50-percent modulation will add 12.5 watts of sideband power, 6.25 watts in each sideband. Supplying this additional power for the sidebands is the object of all of the various systems devised for amplitude modulation.

No such simple relationship exists with complex wave forms. Complex wave forms such as speech do not, as a rule, contain as much average power as a sine wave. Ordinary speech wave forms have about half as much average power as a sine wave, for the same peak amplitude in both wave forms. Thus for the same modulation percentage, the sideband power with ordinary speech will average only about half the power with sine-wave modulation, since it is the peak envelope amplitude, not the average power, that determines the percentage of modulation.

Unsymmetrical Modulation

In an ordinary electric circuit it is possible to increase the amplitude of current flow indefinitely, up to the limit of the power-handling capability of the components, but it cannot very well be decreased to less than zero. The same thing is true of the amplitude of an rf signal; it can be modulated *upward* to any desired extent, but it cannot be modulated *downward* more than 100 percent.

When the modulating wave form is unsymmetrical it is possible for the upward and downward modulation percentages to be different. A simple case is shown in Fig. 12-3. The positive peak of the modulating signal is about 3 times the amplitude of the negative peak. If, as shown in the drawing, the modulating amplitude is adjusted so that the peak downward modulation is just 100 percent ($Z = 0$) the peak upward modulation is 300 percent ($Y = 4X$). The carrier amplitude is represented by X, as in Fig. 12-2. The modulation envelope reproduces the wave form of the modulating signal accurately, hence there is no distortion. In such a modulated signal the increase in power output with modulation is considerably greater than it is when the modulation is symmetrical. In Fig. 12-3 the peak envelope amplitude, Y, is four times the carrier amplitude, X, so the peak-envelope power **(PEP)** is 16 times the carrier power. When the upward modulation is more than 100 percent the power capacity of the modulating system obviously must be increased sufficiently to take care of the much larger peak amplitudes. Such a system of modulation, often called "supermodulation," was popular among amateurs in the early 1950s. (See bibliography at the end of this chapter.)

Overmodulation

If the amplitude of the modulation on the downward swing becomes too great, there will be a period of time during which the rf output is entirely cut off. This is shown in Fig. 12-4. The shape of the downward half of the modulating wave is no longer accurately reproduced by the modulation envelope, consequently the modulation is distorted. Operation of this type is called **overmodulation.**

The distortion of the modulation envelope causes new frequencies (harmonics of the modulating frequency) to be generated. These combine

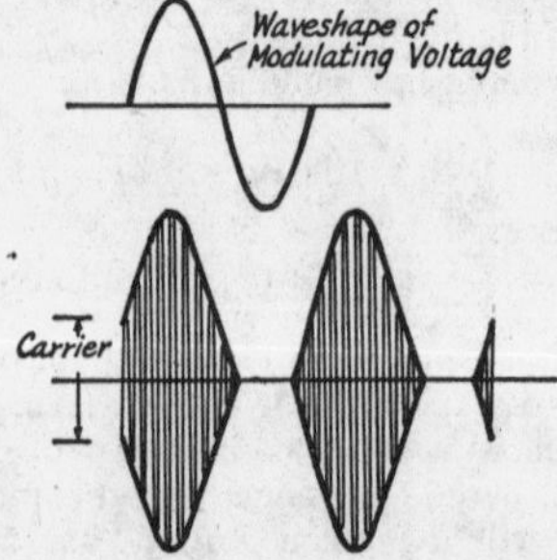

Fig. 12-4 – An overmodulated signal. The modulation envelope is not an accurate reproduction of the wave form of the modulating voltage. This, or any type of distortion occurring during the modulation process, generates spurious sidebands or "splatter."

with the carrier to form new side frequencies that widen the channel occupied by the modulated signal, as shown in Fig. 12-1C. These spurious frequencies are commonly called "splatter."

It is important to realize that the channel occupied by an amplitude-modulated signal is dependent *on the shape of the modulation envelope.* If this wave shape is complex and can be resolved into a wide band of audio frequencies, then the channel occupied will be correspondingly large. An overmodulated signal splatters and occupies a much wider channel than is necessary because the "clipping" of the modulating wave that occurs at the zero axis changes the envelope wave shape to one that contains high-order harmonics of the original modulating frequency. These harmonics appear as side frequencies separated by, in some cases, many kilohertz from the carrier frequency.

Because of this clipping action at the zero axis, it is important that care be taken to prevent applying too large a modulating signal in the downward direction. Overmodulation downward results in more splatter than is caused by most other types of distortion in a phone transmitter.

AMPLITUDE MODULATION METHODS

MODULATION SYSTEMS

As explained in the preceding section, amplitude modulation of a carrier is accompanied by an increase in power output, the additional power being the "useful" or "talk power" in the sidebands. This additional power may be supplied from an external source in the form of audio-frequency power. It is then added to the unmodulated power input to the amplifier to be modulated, after which the combined power is converted to rf. This is the method used in plate or collector modulation. It has the advantage that the rf power is generated at the high-efficiency characteristic of Class C amplifiers – of the order of 65 to 75 percent – but has the accompanying disadvantage that generating the audio-frequency power is rather expensive.

An alternative that does not require relatively large amounts of audio-frequency power makes use of the fact that the power output of an amplifier can be controlled by varying the potential of a tube or transistor element – such as a control or screen grid or a transistor base – that does not, in itself, consume appreciable power. In this case the additional power during modulation is secured by sacrificing carrier power; in other words, a tube is capable of delivering only so much total power within its ratings, and if more must be delivered at full modulation, then less is available for the unmodulated carrier. Systems of this type must of necessity work at rather low efficiency at the unmodulated carrier level. As a practical working rule, the efficiency of the modulated rf amplifier is of the order of 30 to 35 percent, and the unmodulated carrier power output obtainable with such a system is only about one-fourth to one-third that obtainable from the same amplifier with plate modulation.

PLATE OR COLLECTOR MODULATION

Fig. 12-5 shows a system of plate modulation, in this case with a triode rf tube. A balanced (push-pull Class A, Class AB or Class B) **modulator** is transformer coupled to the plate circuit of the modulated rf amplifier. The audio-frequency power generated by the modulator is combined with the dc power in the modulated-amplifier plate circuit by transfer through the coupling transformer, T. For 100-percent modulation the audio-frequency power output of the modulator and the turns ratio of the coupling transformer must be such that the voltage at the plate of the of the modulated amplifier varies between zero and twice and dc operating plate voltage, thus causing corresponding variations in the amplitude of the rf output. The tubes of Fig. 12-5 may be replaced with transistors, either bipolar or FET, for collector or drain modulation.

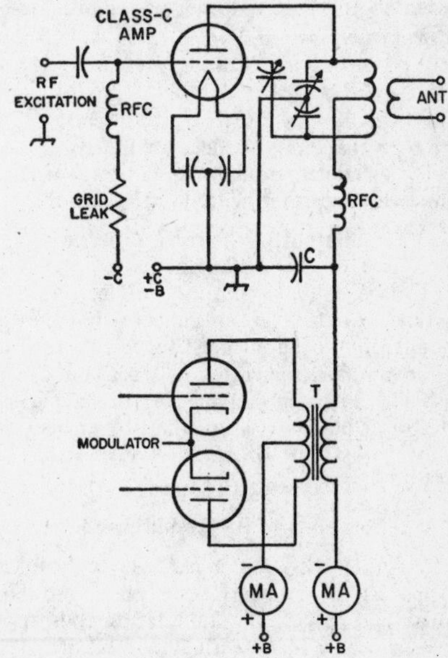

Fig. 12-5 – Plate modulation of a Class C rf amplifier. The rf plate bypass capacitor, C, in the amplifier stage should have reasonably high reactance at audio frequencies. A value of the order of .001 μF to .005 μF is satisfactory in practically all cases for vacuum-tube circuits. A considerably higher value will be required if the vacuum tubes are replaced by transistors – in the order of a few microfarads.

Audio Power

As stated earlier, the average power output of the modulated stage must increase during modulation. The modulator must be capable of supplying to the modulated rf stage sine-wave audio power equal to 50 percent of the dc input power. For example, if the dc input power to the rf stage is 100 watts, the sine-wave audio power output of the modulator must be 50 watts.

Although the total power input (dc plus audio-frequency ac) increases with modulation, the dc plate or collector current of a modulated amplifier should not change when the stage is modulated. This is because each increase in voltage and current is balanced by an equivalent decrease in voltage and current on the next half cycle of the modulating wave. Dc instruments cannot follow the af variations, and since the average dc plate or collector current and voltage of a properly operated amplifier do not change, neither do the meter readings. A change in current with modulation indicates nonlinearity. On the other hand, a thermocouple rf ammeter connected in the antenna, or transmission line, will show an increase in rf current with modulation, because instruments of this type respond to power rather than to current or voltage.

Modulating Impedance; Linearity

The **modulating impedance,** or load resistance presented to the modulator by the modulated rf amplifier, is equal to

$$Z_m = \frac{E_b}{I_p} \times 1000 \text{ ohms}$$

where E_b = Dc plate or collector voltage
I_p = Dc plate or collector current (mA)
E_b and I_p are measured without modulation.

The power output of the rf amplifier must vary as the square of the instantaneous plate or collector voltage (the rf output voltage must be proportional to the plate or collector voltage) for the modulation to be linear. This will be the case when the amplifier operates under Class C conditions. The linearity depends upon having sufficient grid or base excitation and proper bias, and upon the adjustment or circuit constants to the proper values.

Screen-Grid RF Amplifiers

Screen-grid tubes of the pentode or beam-tetrode type can be used in Class C plate-modulated amplifiers by applying the modulation to both the plate and screen grid. The usual method of feeding the screen grid with the necessary dc and modulation voltages is shown in Fig. 12-6. The dropping resistor, R, should be of the proper value to apply normal dc voltage to the screen under steady carrier conditions. Its value can be calculated by taking the difference between plate and screen voltages and dividing it by the rated screen current.

The modulating impedance is found by dividing the dc plate voltage by the sum of the plate and screen currents. The plate voltage multiplied by the sum of the two currents gives the power input to be used as the basis for determining the audio power required from the modulator.

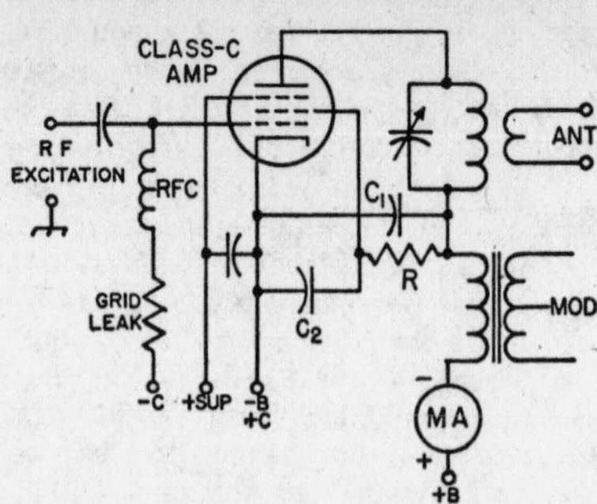

Fig. 12-6 – Plate and screen modulation of a Class C rf amplifier using a screen-grid tube. The plate rf bypass capacitor, C1, should have reasonably high reactance at all audio frequencies; a value of .001 to .005 μF is generally satisfactory. The screen bypass, C2, should not exceed .002 μF in the usual case.

Modulation of the screen along with the plate is necessary because the screen voltage has a much greater effect on the plate current than the plate voltage does. The modulation characteristic is nonlinear if the plate alone is modulated.

Choke-Coupled or Heising Modulation

One of the oldest types of plate modulating systems is the choke-coupled Class A or **Heising** modulator shown in Fig. 12-7. Because of the relatively low power output and plate efficiency of a Class A amplifier, the method is rarely used now except for a few special applications.

The audio power output of the modulator is combined with the dc power in the plate circuit through the modulation choke, L1, which has a high impedance at audio frequencies. This technique of modulating the rf signal is similar to the case of the transformer-coupled modulator but there is considerably less freedom in adjustment since no transformer is available for matching impedances. The dc input power to the rf stage must not exceed twice the rated af power output of the modulator, and for 100-percent modulation the plate voltage on the modulator must be higher than the plate voltage on the rf amplifier. This is because the af voltage developed by the modulator cannot swing to zero without a great deal of distortion. R1 provides the necessary dc voltage drop between the modulator and the rf amplifier. The voltage drop across this resistor must equal the minimum instantaneous plate voltage on the modulator tube under normal operating conditions. C1, an audio-frequency bypass across R1, should have a capacitance such that its reactance at 100 Hz is not more than about one-tenth the resistance of R1. Without R1-C1 the percentage of modulation is limited to 70 to 80 percent in the average case.

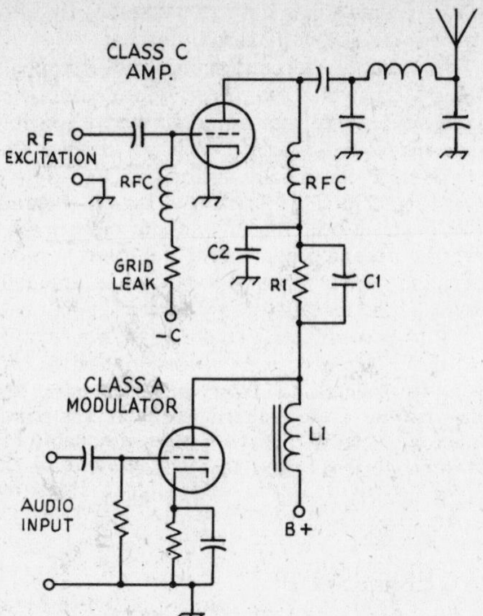

Fig. 12-7 – Choke-coupled Class A modulator. The modulation choke, L1, should have a value of 5 H or more. A value of .001 to .005 μF is satisfactory for C2. See text for discussion of C1 and R1.

GRID MODULATION

The principal disadvantage of plate modulation is that a considerable amount of audio power is necessary. This requirement can be avoided by applying the modulation to a grid element in the modulated amplifier. However, serious disadvantages of grid modulation are the reduction in the carrier power output obtainable from a given rf amplifier tube and the more rigorous operating requirements and more complicated adjustment.

The term "grid modulation" as used here applies to all types – control grid, screen, or suppressor – since the operating principles are exactly the same no matter which grid is actually modulated. (Screen-grid modulation is the most commonly used technique of the three types listed here.) With grid modulation the plate voltage is constant, and the increase in power output with modulation is obtained by making both the plate current and plate efficiency vary with the modulating signal. The efficiency obtainable at the envelope peak depends on how carefully the modulated amplifier is adjusted, and sometimes can be as high as 80 percent. It is generally less when the amplifier is adjusted for good linearity, and under average conditions a round figure of 2/3, or 66 percent, is representative. The efficiency without modulation is only half the peak efficiency, or about 33 percent. This low average efficiency reduces the permissible carrier output to about one-fourth the power obtainable from the same tube in cw operation, and to about one-third the carrier output obtainable from the tube with plate modulation.

The modulator is required to furnish only the audio power dissipated in the modulated grid under the operating conditions chosen. A speech amplifier capable of delivering 3 to 10 watts is usually sufficient.

Grid modulation does not give quite as linear a modulation characteristic as plate modulation, even under optimum operating conditions. When misadjusted the nonlinearity may be severe, resulting in considerable distortion and splatter.

Screen Grid Modulation

Screen modulation is probably the simplest and most popular form of grid modulation, and the least critical of adjustment. The most satisfactory way to apply the modulating voltage to the screen is through a transformer.

With practical tubes it is necessary to drive the screen somewhat negative with respect to the cathode to get complete cutoff of rf output. For this reason the peak modulating voltage required for 100-percent modulation is usually 10 percent or so greater than the dc screen voltage. The latter, in turn, is approximately half the rated screen voltage recommended by the manufacturer under maximum ratings for radiotelegraph operation. The audio power required for 100-percent modulation is approximately one-fourth the dc power input to the screen in cw operation, but varies somewhat with the operating conditions.

Controlled Carrier

As explained earlier, a limit is placed on the output obtainable from a grid-modulation system by the low rf-amplifier plate efficiency (approximately 33 percent) under unmodulated carrier

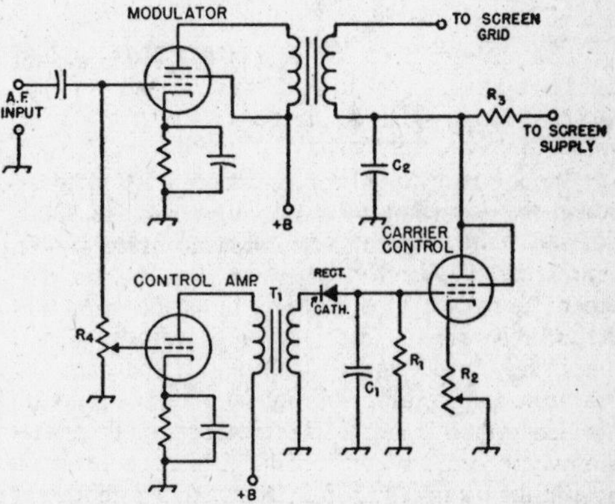

Fig. 12-8 – Circuit for carrier control with screen modulation. A small triode such as the 6C4 can be used as the control amplifier and a 6Y6G is suitable as a carrier-control tube. T1 is an interstage audio transformer having a 1-to-1 or larger turns ratio. R4 is a 0.5-megohm volume control and also serves as the grid resistor for the modulator. A germanium diode may be used as the rectifier. R3 may be the normal screen dropping resistor. C1-R1 and C2-R3 should have a time constant of about 0.1 second.

conditions. The plate efficiency increases with modulation, since the output increases while the dc input remains constant, and reaches a maximum in the neighborhood of 50 percent with 100-percent sine-wave modulation. If the power input to the amplifier can be reduced during periods when there is little or no modulation, thus reducing the plate loss, advantage can be taken of the higher efficiency at full modulation to obtain higher effective output. This can be done by varying the dc power input to the modulated stage in accordance with *average* variations in voice intensity, in such a way as to maintain just sufficient carrier power to keep the modulation high, but not exceeding 100 percent, under all conditions. Thus the carrier amplitude is controlled by the average voice intensity. Properly utilized, controlled carrier permits increasing the carrier output at maximum level to a value about equal to the rated plate dissipation of the tube, twice the output obtainable with constant carrier.

It is desirable to control the power input just enough so that the plate loss, without modulation, is safely below the tube rating. Excessive control is disadvantageous because the distant receiver's avc system must continually follow the variations in average signal level. The circuit of Fig. 12-8 permits adjustment of both the maximum and minimum power input, and separates the functions of modulation and carrier control. A portion of the audio voltage at the modulator grid is applied to a Class A "control amplifier," which drives a rectifier circuit to produce a dc voltage negative with respect to ground. C1 filters out the audio variations, leaving a dc voltage proportional to the average voice level. This voltage is applied to the grid of a "clamp" tube to control the dc screen voltage and thus the rf carrier level.

DOUBLE-SIDEBAND GENERATORS

The a-m carrier can be suppressed or nearly eliminated by using a balanced modulator. The basic principle in any balanced modulator is to introduce the carrier in such a way that it does not appear in the output but so that the sidebands will. This requirement is satisfied by introducing the audio in push-pull and the rf drive in parallel, and connecting the output in push-pull. Balanced modulators can also be connected with the rf drive and audio inputs in push-pull and the output in parallel with equal effectiveness.

Vacuum-tube balanced modulators can be operated at high power levels and the double-sideband output can be used directly into the antenna. Past issues of *QST* have given construction details on such transmitters (see, for example, Rush, "180-Watt D.S.B. Transmitter," *QST* July, 1966). A dsb signal can be copied by the same methods that are used for single-sideband signals, provided the receiver has sufficient selectivity to reject one of the sidebands. In any balanced-modulator circuit, no rf output will exist with no audio signal. When audio is applied, the balance of the modulator is upset so that sum and difference frequencies (sidebands) appear at the output. Further information on balanced modulators is presented in Chapter 13.

CHECKING A–M PHONE OPERATION

USING THE OSCILLOSCOPE

Proper adjustment of a phone transmitter is aided immeasurably by the oscilloscope. The scope will give more information, more accurately, than almost any collection of other instruments that might be named. Furthermore, an oscilloscope that is entirely satisfactory for the purpose is not necessarily an expensive instrument; the cathode-ray tube and its power supply are about all that are needed. Amplifiers and linear sweep circuits are by no means necessary.

In the simplest scope circuit, radio-frequency voltage from the modulated amplifier is applied to the vertical deflection plates of the tube, usually through blocking capacitors, and audio-frequency voltage from the modulator is applied to the horizontal deflection plates. As the instantaneous amplitude of the audio signal varies, the rf output of the transmitter likewise varies, and this produces a wedge-shaped pattern or **trapezoid** on the screen. If the oscilloscope has a built-in horizontal sweep, the rf voltage can be applied to the vertical plates as before, and the sweep will produce a pattern that follows the modulation envelope of the transmitter output, provided the sweep frequency is lower than the modulation frequency. This produces a **wave-envelope** modulation pattern.

The Wave-Envelope Pattern

The connections for the wave-envelope pattern are shown in Fig. 12-9A. The vertical deflection plates are coupled to the amplifier tank coil (or an antenna coil) through a low-impedance (coax, twisted pair, etc.) line and pickup coil. As shown in the alternative drawing, a resonant circuit tuned to the operating frequency may be connected to the vertical plates, using link coupling between it and the transmitter. This will eliminate rf harmonics, and the tuning control provides a means for adjustment of the pattern height.

If it is inconvenient to couple to the final tank coil, as may be the case if the transmitter is tightly shielded, the pickup loop may be coupled to the tuned tank of a matching circuit or antenna coupler. Any method (even a short antenna coupled to the tuned circuit shown in the "alternate input connections" of Fig. 12-9A) that will pick up enough rf to give a suitable pattern height may be used.

The position of the pickup coil should be varied until an unmodulated carrier pattern, Fig. 12-10A, of suitable height is obtained. The horizontal sweep voltage should be adjusted to make the width of the pattern somewhat more than half the diameter of the screen. When voice modulation is applied, a rapidly changing pattern of varying height will be obtained. When the maximum height of this pattern is just twice that of the carrier alone, the wave is being modulated 100 percent. This is illustrated by Fig. 12-10C.

If the height is greater than twice the unmodulated carrier amplitude, as illustrated in Fig. 12-10D, the wave is overmodulated in the upward direction. Overmodulation in the downward direction is indicated by a gap in the pattern at the reference axis, where a single bright line appears on the screen. Overmodulation in either direction may take place even when the modulation in the other direction is less than 100 percent.

The Trapezoidal Pattern

Connections for the trapezoid or wedge pattern as used for checking a-m are shown in Fig. 12-9B. The vertical plates of the CR tube are coupled to the transmitter tank through a pickup loop, preferably using a tuned circuit, as shown in the upper drawing, adjustable to the operating frequency. Audio voltage from the modulator is applied to the horizontal plates through a voltage divider, R1-R2. This voltage should be adjustable so a suitable pattern width can be obtained; a 0.25-megohm volume control can be used at R2 for this purpose.

The resistance required at R1 will depend on the dc voltage on the modulated element. The total resistance of R1 and R2 in series should be about 0.25 megohm for each 100 volts. For example, if a plate-modulated amplifier operates at 1500 volts, the total resistance should be 3.75 megohms, 0.25 megohm at R2 and the remainder, 3.5 megohms, in R1. R1 should be composed of individual resistors not larger than 0.5 megohm each, in which case 1-watt resistors will be satisfactory.

For adequate coupling at 100 Hz, the capacitance in microfarads of the blocking capacitor, C, should be at least .05/R, where R is the total resistance (R1 + R2) in megohms. In the example above, where R is 3.75 megohms, the capacitance should be .05/3.75 = .013 μF or more. The voltage rating of the capacitor should be at least twice the dc voltage applied to the modulated element.

Trapeziodal patterns for various conditions of modulation are shown in Fig. 12-10, each alongside the corresponding wave-envelope pattern. With no signal, only the cathode-ray spot appears on the screen. When the unmodulated carrier is applied, a vertical line appears; the length of the line should be adjusted, by means of the pickup-coil coupling, to a convenient value. When the carrier is modulated, the wedge-shaped pattern appears; the higher the modulation percentage, the wider and more pointed the wedge becomes. At 100-percent modulation it just makes a point at one end of the horizontal axis, and the height at the other end is equal to twice carrier height. Overmodulation in the upward direction is indicated by increased height, at one end, and downward by an extension along the horizontal axis at the pointed end.

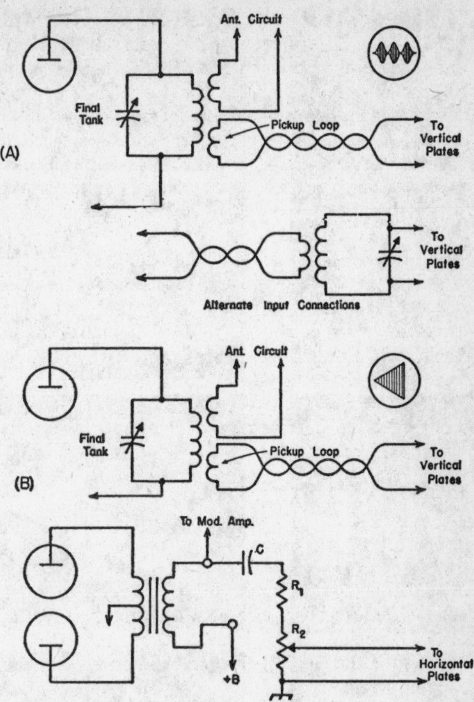

Fig. 12-9 — Methods of connecting the oscilloscope for modulation checking. A — connections for wave-envelope pattern with any modulation method; B — connections for trapezoidal pattern with plate or screen modulation.

CHECKING A-M TRANSMITTER PERFORMANCE

The trapezoidal pattern is generally more useful than the wave-envelope pattern for checking the operation of the phone transmitter. However, both types of patterns have their special virtues, and the best test setup is one that makes both available. The trapezoidal pattern is better adapted to showing the performance of a modulated amplifier from the standpoint of inherent linearity, without regard to the wave form of the audio modulating signal, than is the wave-envelope pattern. Distortion in the audio signal also can be detected in the trapezoidal pattern, although experience in analyzing scope patterns is required to recognize it.

If the wave-envelope pattern is used with a sine-wave audio modulating signal, distortion in the

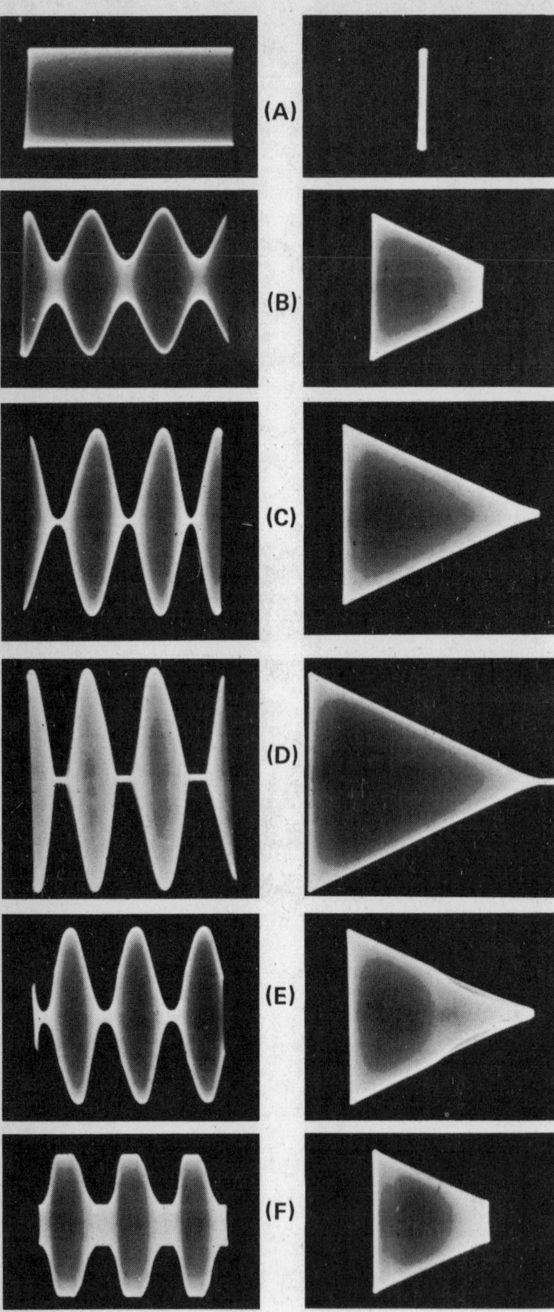

Fig. 12-10 — Oscilloscope patterns showing various forms of modulation of an rf amplifier. At left, wave-envelope patterns; at right, corresponding trapezoidal patterns. The wave-envelope patterns were obtained with a linear oscilloscope sweep having a frequency one-third that of the sine-wave audio modulating frequency, so that three cycles of the modulation envelope may be seen. Shown at A is an unmodulated carrier, at B approximately 50-percent modulation, and at C, 100-percent modulation. The photos at D show modulation in excess of 100 percent. E and F show the results of improper operation or circuit design. See text.

modulation envelope is easily recognizable; however, it is difficult to determine whether the distortion is caused by lack of linearity of the rf stage or by af distortion in the modulator. If the trapezoidal pattern shows good linearity in such a case, the trouble obviously is in the audio system. It is possible, of course, for both defects to be present simultaneously. If they are, the rf amplifier should be made linear first; then any distortion in the modulation envelope will be the result of improper operation in the speech amplifier or modulator, or in coupling the modulator to the modulated rf stage.

Rf Linearity

The trapezoidal pattern is a graph of the modulation characteristic of the modulated amplifier. The sloping sides of the wedge show the rf amplitude for every value of instantaneous modulating voltage. If these sides are perfectly straight lines, the modulation characteristic is linear. If the sides show curvature, the characteristic is nonlinear to an extent shown by the degree to which the sides depart from perfect straightness. This is true regardless of the modulating wave form. If these edges tend to bend over toward the horizontal at the maximum height of the wedge, the amplifier is "flattening" on the modulation uppeaks. This is usually caused by attempting to get too large a carrier output, and can be corrected by tighter coupling to the antenna or by a decrease in the dc screen voltage. The slight "tailing off" at the modulation downpeak (point of the wedge) can be minimized by careful adjustment of excitation and plate loading.

Several types of improper operation are shown in Fig. 12-10. The patterns at E show the effect of a too long time constant in the screen circuit, in an amplifier getting its screen voltage through a dropping resistor, both plate and screen being modulated. The "double-edged" pattern is the result of audio phase shift in the screen circuit combined with varying screen-to-cathode resistance during modulation. This effect can be reduced by reducing the screen bypass capacitance, and also by connecting resistance (to be determined experimentally, but of the same order as the screen dropping resistance) between screen and cathode.

The pictures at the bottom, F, show the effect of insufficient audio power. Although the trapezoidal pattern shows good linearity in the rf amplifier, the wave-envelope pattern shows flattened peaks (both positive and negative) in the modulation envelope even though the audio signal applied to the amplifier was a sine wave. More speech-amplifier gain merely increases the flattening without increasing the modulation percentage in such a case. The remedy is to use a larger modulator or less input to the modulated rf stage. In some cases the trouble may be caused by an incorrect modulation-transformer turns ratio, causing the modulator to be overloaded before its maximum power output capabilities are reached.

GENERAL-PURPOSE AMPLITUDE MODULATORS

The two modulator circuits shown in Figs. 12-11 and 12-12 can be employed to deliver from 3 to 70 watts of audio power. The basic designs are taken from RCA's *Audio Design Phase 2.* The complementary-symmetry circuit, Fig. 12-11, is characterized by a Class A driver and a complementary pair (npn/pnp) of output transistors. The primary advantages of this circuit are simplicity and economy. Common conduction is minimized because the transistor which is "off" during half of the audio cycle is reverse biased. The output transistors are operated at zero bias, providing excellent dc stability. Elaborate regulated power supplies are not required. The complementary-symmetry amplifier is limited to about 20 watts output because of the high level of heat that the driver stage must dissipate. Component values and transistor types are given in Table 12-I for 3-, 5-, 12-, and 20-watt designs.

For higher power levels, the quasi-complementary circuit (Fig. 12-12) is usually chosen. Here a Class A predriver feeds a Class B npn/pnp driver

TABLE 12-I

PARTS VALUES FOR COMPLEMENTARY – SYMMETRY CIRCUIT

Power (Watts)	R1	R3	R5	R7	R8	R9	R10	R13	R14	R16	R17	C1 µF	C3 pF	C6 pF	Q4	Q5	Q6	T1	
3	91k	68k	2.7k	3.9k	620	33k	5.6k	120	150	22	22k	0.1/6V	10	100	40611	40610	40609	15V, 1A	(Stancor TP-4)
5	51k	68k	3.3k	3.9k	620	27k	3.6k	110 (1W)	110 (1W)	27	22k	0.25/6V	5	150	40616	40615	40614	17V, 1A	(Stancor TP-4)
12	16k	91k	7.5k	2.7k	390	18k	1.8k	91 (2W)	91 (2W)	56	–	1/6V	10	220	40389	40622	40050	25V, 1A	(Stancor TP-4)
20	8.2k	91k	8.2k	2.2k	360	22k	1.3k	100 (2W)	100 (2W)	100	–	2/6V	10	270	40628	40627	40626	32V, 1A	(C. P. Elec. 10596)

TABLE 12-II

PARTS VALUES FOR QUASI-COMPLEMENTARY-SYMMETRY CIRCUIT

Power (Watts)	R3	R7	R8	R10	R11	R22 R23	Q4	Q5	Q6 Q7	T1		
25	12k	680	1800	2200	270	0.43(5W)	2N3568	2N3638	40632	37V	1.5A	(C. P. Elec. 10596)
40	15k	560	2200	2700	390	0.39(5W)	40635	40634	40633	46V	2A	(C. P. Elec. 10596)
70	18k	470	2700	3300	470	0.33(5W)	40594	40595	40636	60V	2.5A	(C. P. Elec. 10598)

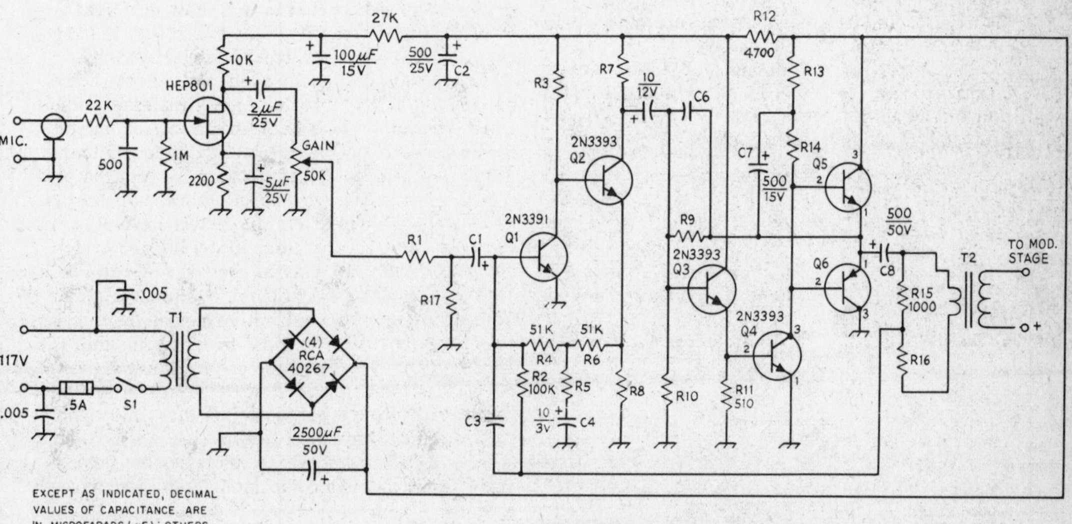

Fig. 12-11 — General-purpose amplitude modulator for 3 to 20 watts of audio power. Capacitors with polarity indicated are electrolytic. See Table 12-I for parts not listed below.
S1 — Spst toggle.
T2 — See text.

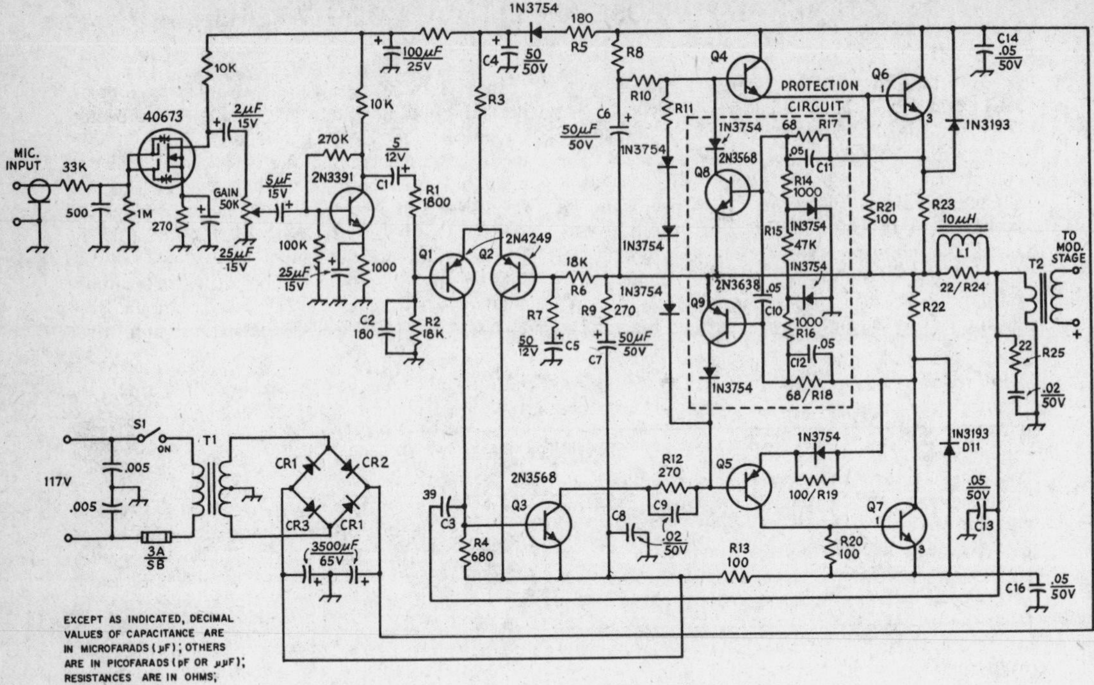

Fig. 12-12 – General-purpose amplitude modulator for 25 to 70 watts of audio power. Capacitors with polarity indicated are electrolytic. See Table 12-II for parts not listed below.

L1 – J. W. Miller 4622 or equiv.
S1 – Spst toggle.
T2 – See text.

pair, which, in turn, activates the npn output transistors. The danger of damage to the output stage from a short circuit is high, so protection is included. Table 12-II includes parts information for three power levels: 25, 40, and 70 watts.

All amplifiers are designed for an 8-ohm output, so T2 can be a standard audio output transformer in "reverse." The secondary impedance will depend on the impedance of the stage to be modulated.

Bibliography

Audio Design Phase 2, RCA, Somerville, NJ, 1970.

Preiss, "The '2-Meter QRP Mountain Topper'," *QST*, May, 1970.

Rush, "180-Watt D.S.B. Transmitter," *QST*, July, 1966.

Villard, " 'Supermodulation' – An Evaluation and Explanation," *QST*, December, 1950.

Chapter 13

Single-Sideband Transmission

GENERATING THE SSB SIGNAL

A fully modulated a-m signal has two thirds of its power in the carrier and only one third in the sidebands. The sidebands carry the intelligence to be transmitted; the carrier "goes along for the ride" and serves only to demodulate the signal at the receiver. By eliminating the carrier and transmitting only the sidebands, or just one sideband, the available transmitter power is used to greater advantage. To recover the intelligence being transmitted, the carrier must be reinserted at the receiver, but this is no great problem with a proper detector circuit.

Assuming that the same final-amplifier tube or tubes are used either for normal a-m or for single sideband, carrier suppressed, it can be shown that the use of ssb can give an effective gain of up to 9 dB over a-m – equivalent to increasing the transmitter power 8 times. Eliminating the carrier also eliminates the heterodyne interference that so often spoils communication in congested phone bands.

Filter Method

Two basic systems for generating ssb signals are shown in Fig. 13-2. One involves the use of a bandpass filter having sufficient selectivity to pass one sideband and reject the other. Mechanical filters are available for frequencies below 1 MHz. From 0.2 to 10 MHz, good sideband rejection can be obtained with filters using four or more quartz crystals. Oscillator output at the filter frequency is combined with the audio signal in a balanced modulator, and only the upper and lower sidebands appear in the output. One of the sidebands is passed by the filter and the other rejected, so that an ssb signal is fed to the mixer. The signal is mixed with the output of a high-frequency rf oscillator to produce the desired output frequency. For additional amplification a linear rf amplifier must be used. When the ssb signal is generated around 500 kHz it may be necessary to convert twice to reach the operating frequency, since this simplifies the problem of rejecting the "image" frequencies resulting from the heterodyne process. The problem of image frequencies in the frequency conversions of ssb signals differs from the problem in receivers because the beating-oscillator frequency becomes important. Either balanced mixers or sufficient selectivity must be used to attenuate these frequencies in the output and hence minimize the possibility of unwanted radiations. (Examples of filter-type exciters can be found in various issues of *QST* and in *Single Sideband for the Radio Amateur.*)

Phasing Method

The second system is based on the phase relationships between the carrier and sidebands in a modulated signal. As shown in the diagram, the audio signal is split into two components that are identical except for a phase difference of 90 degrees. The output of the rf oscillator (which may be at the operating frequency, if desired) is likewise split into two separate components having a 90-degree phase difference. One rf and one audio component are combined in each of two separate balanced modulators. The carrier is suppressed in the modulators, and the relative phases of the sidebands are such that one sideband is balanced out and the other is augmented in the combined output. If the output from the balanced modulators is high enough, such an ssb exciter can work directly into the antenna, or the power level can be increased in a following amplifier.

Generally, the filter-type exciter is easier to adjust than is the phasing exciter. Most home built ssb equipment uses commercially made filters these days. The alignment is done at the factory, thus relieving the amateur of the sometimes tedious task of adjusting the filter for suitable bandpass characteristics. Filter-type exciters are more popular than phasing units and offer better carrier suppression and alignment stability. It is still practical for the builder to fabricate his own crystal-lattice filter by utilizing low-cost surplus crystals. This possibility should not be overlooked if the builder is interested in keeping the overall cost of the home-built exciter at a minimum.

BALANCED MODULATORS

The carrier can be suppressed or nearly eliminated by using a balanced modulator or an extremely sharp filter. In ssb transmitters it is common practice to use both devices. The basic principle of any balanced modulator is to

Fig. 13-1 – Single sideband is the most popular of all the modes for amateur hf communication.

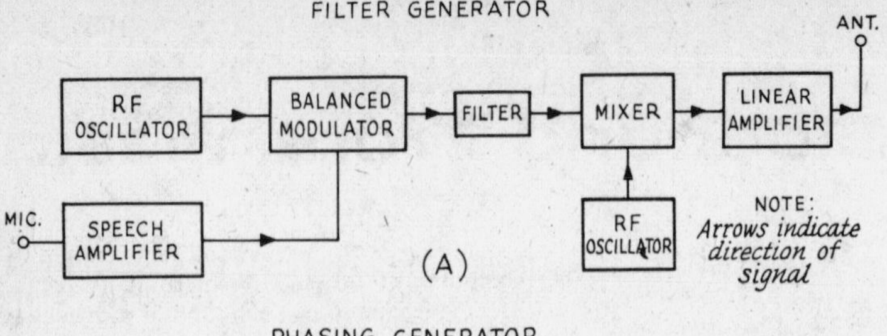

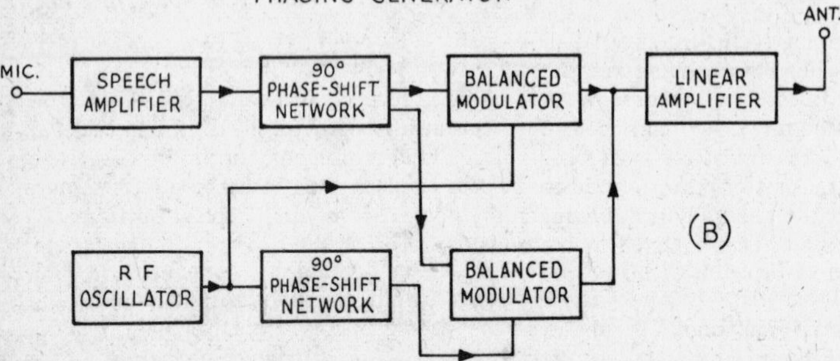

Fig. 13-2 — Two basic systems for generating single-sideband suppressed carrier signals.

introduce the carrier in such a way that it does not appear in the output, but so that the sidebands will. The type of balanced-modulator circuit chosen by the builder will depend upon the constructional considerations, cost, and whether diodes or transistors are to be employed.

In any balanced-modulator circuit there will be no output with no audio signal. When audio is applied, the balance is upset, and one branch will conduct more than the other. Since any modulation process is the same as "mixing" in receivers, sum and difference frequencies (sidebands) will be generated. The modulator is not balanced for the sidebands, and they will appear in the output.

In the rectifier-type balanced modulators shown in Fig. 13-3, at A and B, the diode rectifiers are connected in such a manner that, if they have equal forward resistances, no rf can pass from the carrier source to the output circuit via either of the two possible paths. The net effect is that no rf energy appears in the output. When audio is applied, it unbalances the circuit by biasing the diode (or diodes) in one path, depending upon the instantaneous polarity of the audio, and hence some rf will appear in the output. The rf in the output will appear as a double-sideband suppressed-carrier signal.

In any diode modulator, the rf voltage should be at least 6 to 8 times the peak audio voltage for minimum distortion. The usual operation involves a fraction of a volt of audio and several volts of rf. Desirable diode characteristics for balanced modulator and mixer service include: low noise, low forward resistance, high reverse resistance, good temperature stability, and fast switching time (for high-frequency operation). Fig. 13-4 lists the different classes of diodes, giving the ratio of forward-to-reverse resistance of each. This ratio is an important criterion in the selection of diodes. Also, the individual diodes used should have closely matched forward and reverse resistances; an ohmmeter can be used to select matched pairs or quads.

One of the simplest diode balanced modulators in use is that of Fig. 13-3A. Its use is usually limited to low-cost portable equipment in which a high degree of carrier suppression is not vital. A ring balanced modulator, shown in Fig. 13-3B, offers good carrier suppression at low cost. Diodes CR1 through CR4 should be well matched and can be 1N270s or similar. C1 is adjusted for best rf phase balance as evidenced by maximum carrier null. R1 is also adjusted for the best carrier null obtainable. It may be necessary to adjust each control several times to secure optimum suppression.

Varactor diodes are part of the unusual circuit shown in Fig. 13-3C. This arrangement allows single-ended input of near-equal levels of audio and carrier oscillator. Excellent carrier suppression, 50 dB or more, and a simple method of unbalancing the modulator for cw operation are features of this design. CR1 and CR2 should be rated at 20 pF for a bias of -4 V. R1 can be adjusted to cancel any mismatch in the diode characteristics, so it isn't necessary that the varactors be well matched. T1 is wound on a small-diameter toroid core. The tap on the primary winding of this transformer is at the center of the winding.

A bipolar-transistor balanced modulator is shown in 13-3D. This circuit is similar to one used by Galaxy Electronics and uses closely matched transistors at Q1 and Q2. A phase splitter (inverter) Q3, is used to feed audio to the balanced modulator in push-pull. The carrier is supplied to the circuit in parallel and the output is taken in push-pull. CR1 is a Zener diode and is used to stabilize the dc voltage. Controls R1 and R2 are adjusted for best carrier suppression.

The circuit at E offers superior carrier suppression and uses a 7360 beam-deflection tube as a balanced modulator. This tube is capable of

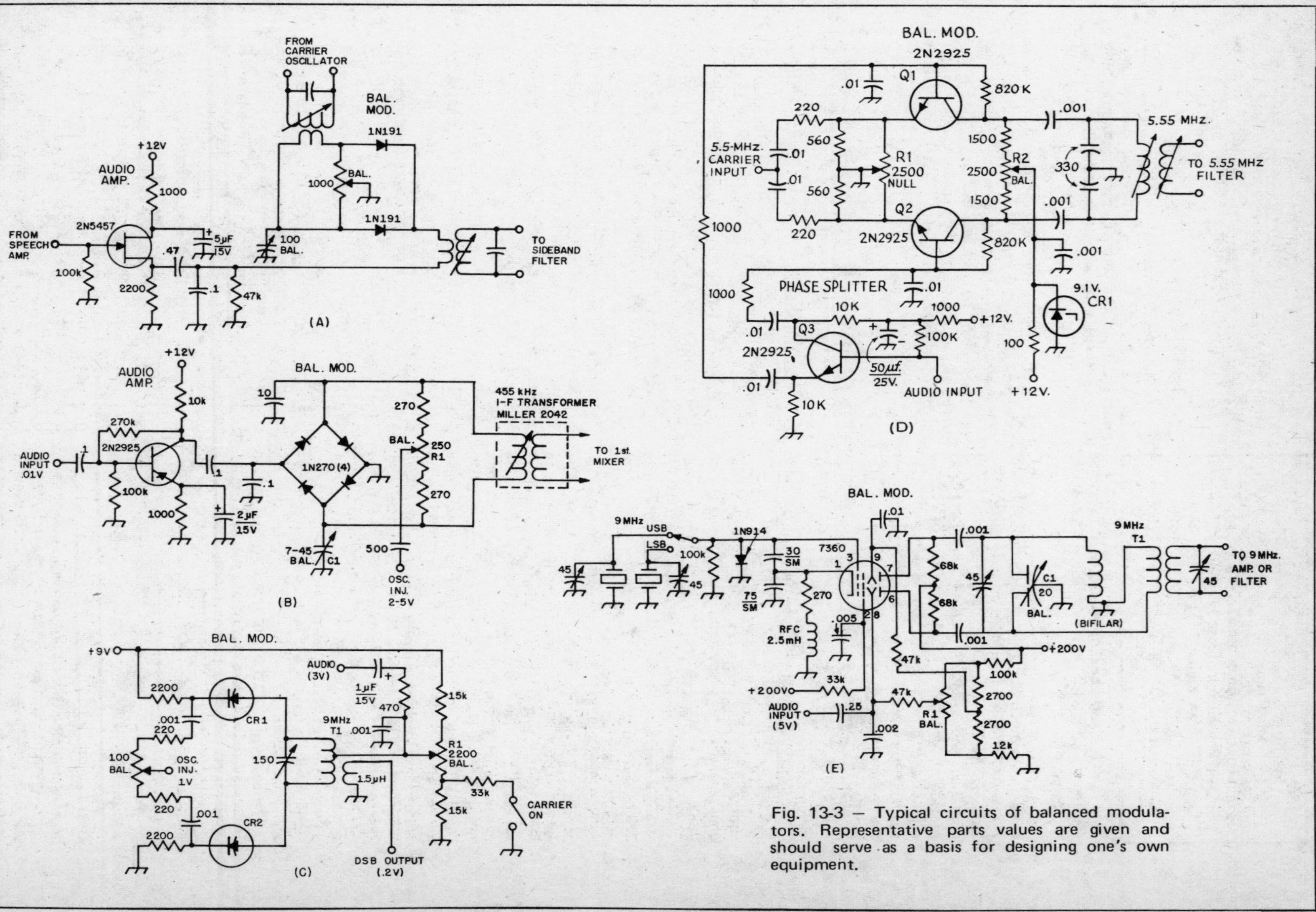

Fig. 13-3 — Typical circuits of balanced modulators. Representative parts values are given and should serve as a basis for designing one's own equipment.

Diode Type	Ratio (M = 1,000,000)
Point-contact germanium (1N98)	500
Small-junction germanium (1N270)	0.1M
Low-conductance silicon (1N457)	48M
High-conductance silicon (1N645)	480M
Hot-carrier (HPA-2800)	2000M

Fig. 13-4 – Table showing the forward-to-reverse resistance ratio for the different classes of solid-state diodes.

providing as much as 60 dB of carrier suppression. When used with mechanical or crystal-lattice filters the total carrier suppression can be as great as 80 dB. Most well-designed balanced modulators can provide between 30 and 50 dB of carrier suppression; hence the 7360 circuit is highly desirable for optimum results. The primary of transformer T1 should be bifilar wound for best results.

IC Balanced Modulators

Integrated circuits (ICs) are presently available for use in balanced-modulator and mixer circuits. A diode array such as the RCA CA3039 is ideally suited for use in circuits such as that of Fig. 13-5A. Since all diodes are formed on a common silicon chip, their characteristics are extremely well matched. This fact makes the IC ideal in a circuit where good balance is required. The hot-carrier diode also has closely matched characteristics and excellent temperature stability. Using broad-band toroidal-wound transformers, it is possible to construct a circuit similar to that of Fig. 13-6 which will have 40 dB of carrier suppression without the need for balance controls. T1 and T2 consist of trifilar windings, 12 turns of No. 32 enam. wire wound on a 1/2-inch toroid core. Another device with good inherent balance is the special IC made for modulator/mixer service, such as the Motorola MC1496G or Signetics S5596. A sample circuit using the MC1496 can be seen in Fig. 13-5B. R1 is adjusted for best carrier balance. The amount of energy delivered from the carrier generator effects the level of carrier suppression; 100 mV of injection is about optimum, producing up to 55 dB of carrier suppression. Additional information on balanced modulators and other ssb-generator circuits is given in the texts referenced at the end of this chapter.

FILTERS

A home-built crystal lattice filter suitable for use in an ssb generator is shown in Fig. 13-7. This unit is composed of three half-lattice sections, with 2 crystals in each section, made with surplus hf crystals. The 330-ohm resistor between sections two and three reduces interaction and smooths the passband response. The leakage reactance between the two halves of L2 and L3 is tuned out by the capacitors connected in series with the center taps of these coils. L1 and L4, the input and output coils, resonate with the calculated value of terminating capacitance at 5060 kHz and reflect the needed inductance across the crystals. The 2000-ohm resistors complete the termination.

All the crystals were purchased as 5500-kHz FT-243s and etched to the desired frequencies with hydrofluoric acid. It is best to wash each crystal with soap and water and measure its frequency before etching. The crystals in each set of three should be as close to each other in frequency as possible, and the separation between the two groups should be about 1500 Hz.

Tuning the filter is quite simple since all four adjustements can be peaked for maximum output at a fixed alignment frequency. This frequency should be on the high side of the pass band and can be the carrier frequency used for lower-sideband transmission (5505.5 kHz in the case of the filter described). Using the carrier frequency it is only necessary to unbalance the balanced modulator to obtain a cw alignment signal. Of course, a signal generator and rf-probe-equipped VTVM can also be used. C1, C2, L1 and L4 are adjusted for maximum output.

A slightly better shape factor can be had by detuning the carrier oscillator to a lower alignment frequency corresponding to about the 4-dB-down point on the high-frequency side of the pass band. Fig. 13-8 shows the measured performance of the filter when aligned at 5505.2 kHz. The 6-dB bandwidth is 2750 Hz.

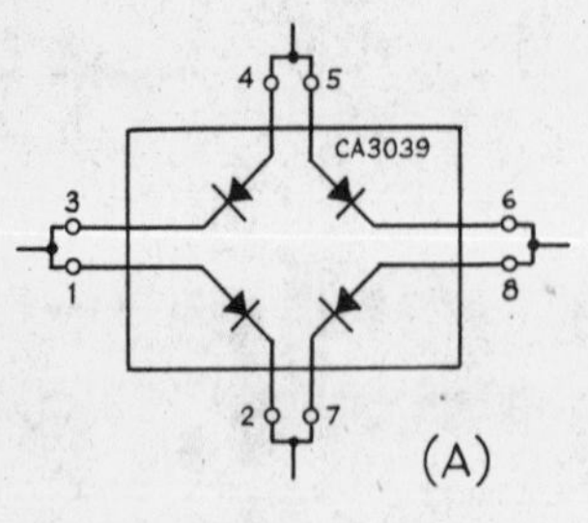

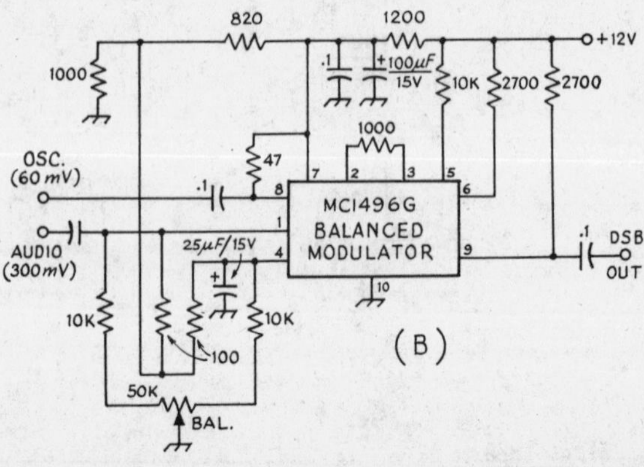

Fig. 13-5 – Additional balanced-modulator circuits in which integrated circuits are used.

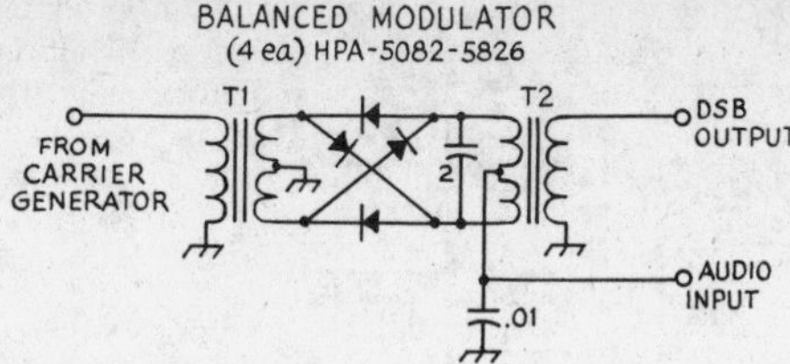

Fig. 13-6 – Balanced modulator design using hot-carrier diodes.

The (suppressed) carrier frequency must be adjusted so that it falls properly on the slope of the filter characteristic. If it is too close to the filter mid frequency the sideband rejection will be poor; if it is too far away there will be a lack of "lows" in the signal.

Ordinarily, the carrier is placed on one side of the curve, depending upon which sideband is desired, which is approximately 20 dB down from the peak. It is sometimes helpful to make provisions for "rubbering" the crystal of the carrier oscillator so that the most natural voice quality can be realized when making initial adjustments.

Using Commercial Crystal Filters

Some builders may not have adequate testing facilities for building and aligning their own filters. In such instances it is possible to purchase ready-made units which are prealigned and come equipped with crystals for upper- and lower-sideband use. Spectrum International[1] has two types for use at 9 MHz. Another manufacturer, McCoy Electronics Co.,[2] sells 9-MHz models for amateur use, and other filters are available surplus.[3]

Mechanical Filters

Mechanical filters contain elements that vibrate and establish resonance mechanically. In crystal filters the coupling between filter sections is achieved by electrical means. In mechanical filters, mechanical couplers are used to transfer the vibrations from one resonant section to the next. At the input and output ends of the filter are transducers which provide for electrical coupling to and from the filter. Most mechanical filters are designed for use from 200 to 600 kHz, the range near 455 kHz being the most popular for amateur use. Mechanical filters suitable for amateur radio circuits are manufactured by the Collins Radio Co. and can be purchased from some dealers in amateur radio equipment.

[1] McCoy Electronics Company, Mt. Holly Springs, PA.

[2] Spectrum International, Topsfield, MA.

[3] E. S. Electronic Labs, 31 Augustus, Excelsior Springs, MO.

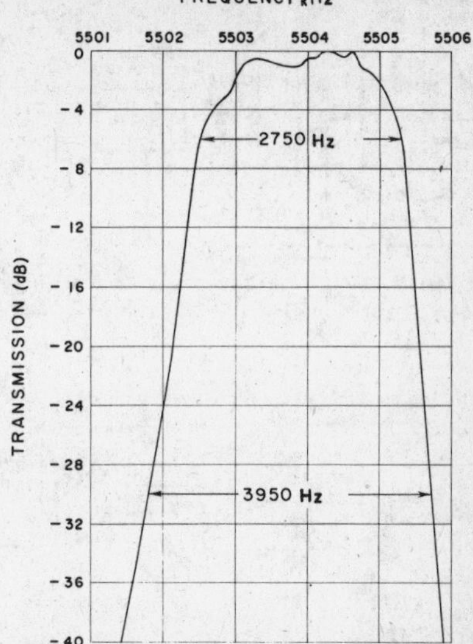

Fig. 13-8 – Measured selectivity characteristic of the filter when aligned at 5505.2 kHz. The 6-dB bandwidth is 2750 Hz and the 30-dB/6-dB shape factor is 1.44.

FILTER APPLICATIONS

Methods for using typical sideband filters are shown schematically in Fig. 13-9. In the circuit of

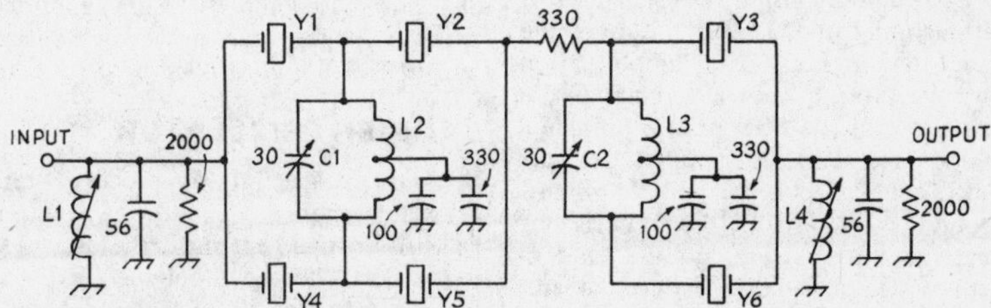

Fig. 13-7 – Circuit diagram of a filter. Resistances are in ohms, and resistors are 1/2-watt composition; capacitors are disk ceramic except as noted.

C1, C2 – Mica trimmer.
L1, L4 – 50 turns No. 38 enamel, close-wound on 17/64-inch dia ceramic slug-tuned form (CTC LS-6, National XR-81 or similar).
L2, L3 – 60 turns No. 38 enamel, close wound on 17/64-inch ceramic form (CTC LS-6, National XR-81 or similar with powered-iron core removed), center tapped.
Y1, Y2, Y3 – All same frequency (near 5500 kHz).
Y4, Y5, Y6 – All same frequency and 1500 to 1700 Hz different from Y1, Y2, Y3.

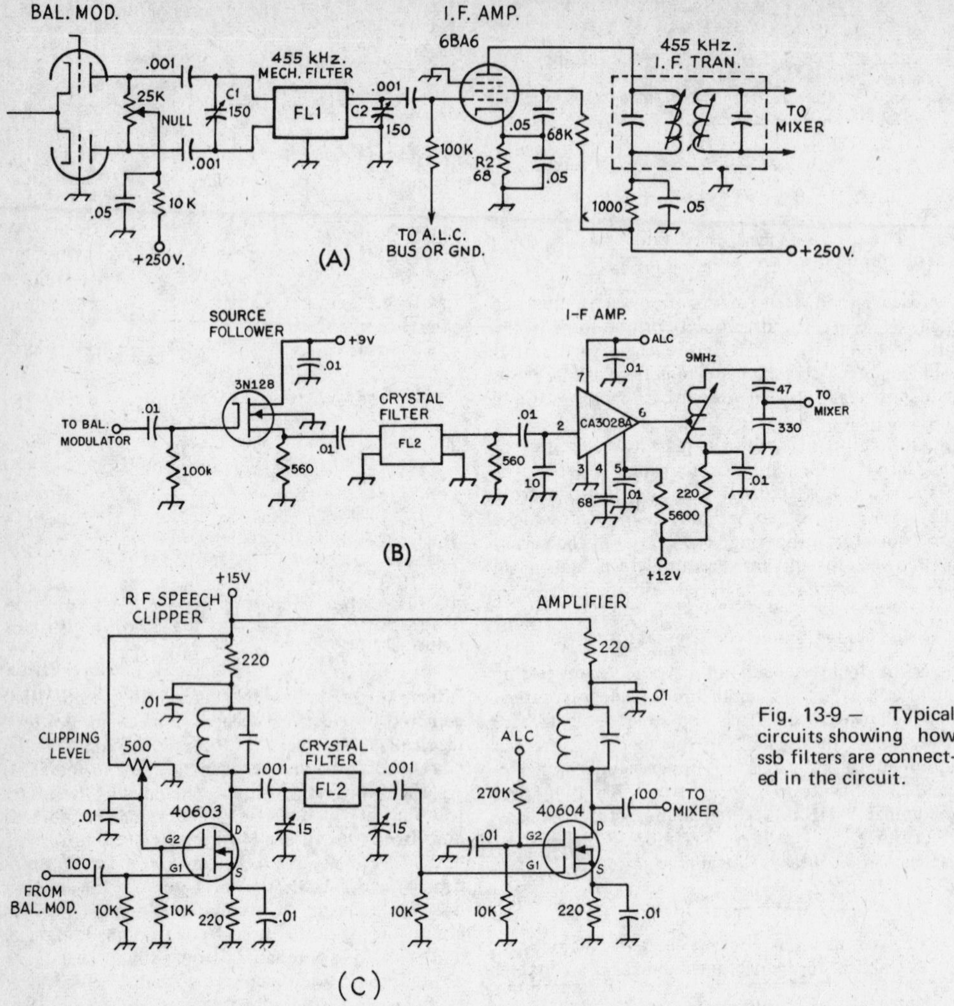

Fig. 13-9 — Typical circuits showing how ssb filters are connected in the circuit.

Fig. 13-9A a 455-kHz mechanical filter is coupled to the balanced modulator by means of two dc isolating capacitors. C1 is used to tune the input of FL1 to resonance (if a Collins type 455-FB-21 is used). Frequently, a fixed-value 120-pF capacitor will suffice at each end of the filter. C2 tunes the output of the filter. A stage of i-f amplification usually follows the filter, as shown, to compensate for the insertion loss of the filter and to provide a stage to which agc can be applied for alc (automatic level control) purposes. In the circuit shown the operator can ground R1 if alc is not used. R2 can be lifted from ground and a 5000-ohm control can be placed between it and ground to provide a means of manual gain control for providing the desired signal level to the mixer.

The circuit of Fig. 13-9B uses a 9-MHz crystal filter, followed by an IC i-f amplifier. Either the McCoy or Spectrum International filters are suitable. Most commercial ssb filters are supplied with a data sheet which shows recommended input and output circuits for matching the impedance of the filter. All are adaptable to use with tubes or transistors.

Another circuit which uses an hf crystal filter, preceded by a dual-gate MOSFET operating as an rf speech clipper, is shown in Fig. 13-9C. The advantages of rf clipping are explained later in this chapter. A second MOSFET amplifies the signal from the filter and provides a variable level of output which is controlled by the alc line.

CARRIER OSCILLATOR

The ssb-generation process starts with a crystal-controlled oscillator, as shown in Fig. 13-2. In a filter-type generator, the oscillator frequency is set on the low-frequency side of the filter bandpass to produce upper sideband and on the upper side when lower-sideband operation is desired. Suitable oscillator circuits are shown in Chapter 6.

MIXER

A single-sideband signal, unlike fm or cw, cannot be frequency multiplied. One or more mixer stages are employed in an ssb exciter to

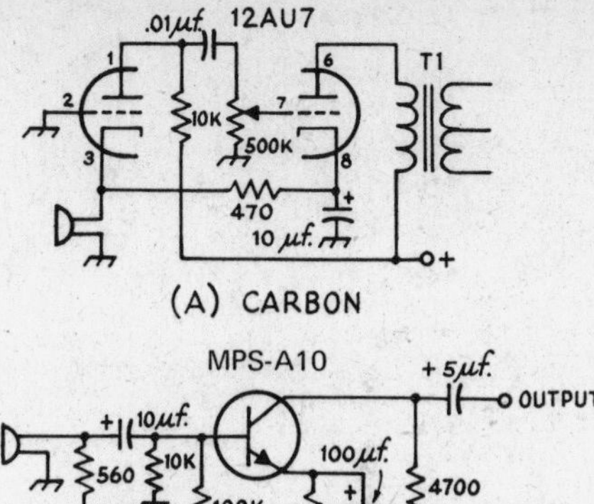

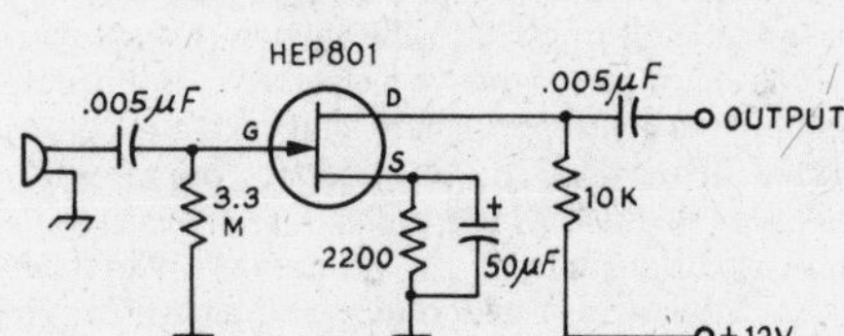

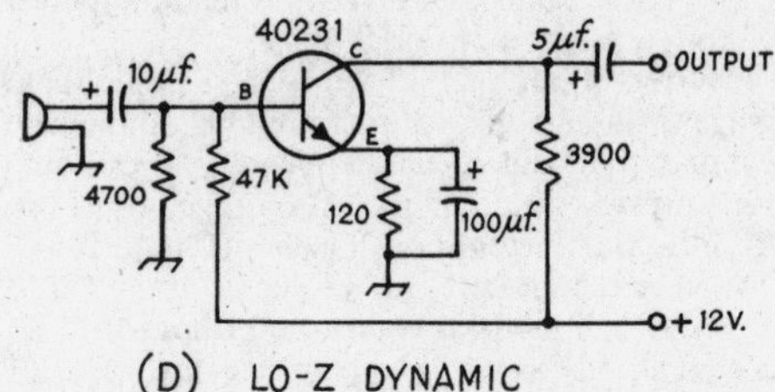

Fig. 13-10 – Speech circuits for use with standard-type microphones. Typical parts values are given.

heterodyne the output of a fixed-frequency ssb generator to the desired operating frequency. See Chapter 8 for details of mixer design and sample mixer circuits.

THE SPEECH AMPLIFIER

The purpose of a speech amplifier is to raise the level of audio output from a microphone to that required by the modulator of a transmitter. In ssb and fm transmitters the modulation process takes place at low levels, so only a few volts of audio are necessary. One or two simple voltage-amplifier stages will suffice. A-m transmitters often employ high-level plate modulation requiring considerable audio power, as described in Chapter 12. The microphone-input and audio voltage-amplifier circuits are similar in all three types of phone transmitters, however.

When designing speech equipment it is necessary to know (1) the amount of audio power the modulation system must furnish and (2) the output voltage developed by the microphone when it is spoken into from normal distance (a few inches) with ordinary loudness. It then becomes possible to choose the number and type of amplifier stages needed to generate the required audio power without overloading or undue distortion anywhere in the system.

MICROPHONES

The level of a microphone is its electrical output for a given sound intensity. The level varies somewhat with the type. It depends to a large extent on the distance from the sound source and the intensity of the speaker's voice. Most commercial transmitters are designed for the median level. If a high-level mike is used, care should be taken not to overload the input amplifier stage. Conversely, a microphone of too low a level must be boosted by a preamplifier.

The frequency response (fidelity) of a microphone is its ability to convert sound uniformly into alternating current. For high articulation it is desirable to reproduce a frequency range of 200-3500 Hz. When all frequencies are reproduced equally, the microphone is considered "flat." Flat response is highly desirable as peaks (sharp rises in the reproduction curve) limit the swing or modulation to the maximum drive voltage, whereas the usable energy is contained in the flat part of the curve.

Microphones are generally omnidirectional, and respond to sound from all directions, or unidirectional, picking up sound from one direction. If a microphone is to be used close to the operator's

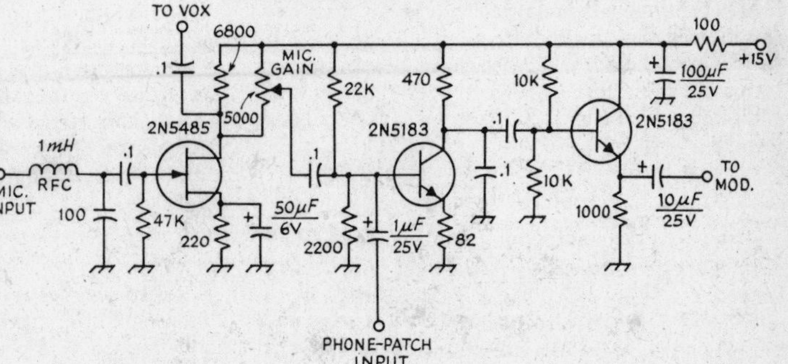

Fig. 13-11 – A resistance-coupled speech amplifier. Component values are representative of a typical circuit.

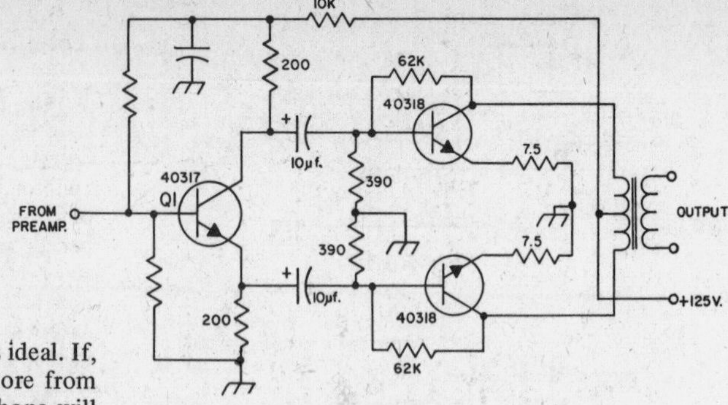

Fig. 13-12 – Typical phase-inverter circuits for transistor amplifier applications.

mouth, an omnidirectional microphone is ideal. If, however, speech is generated a foot or more from the microphone, a unidirectional microphone will reduce reverberation by a factor of 1.7:1. Some types of unidirectional microphones have proximity effect in that low frequencies are accentuated when the microphone is too close to the mouth.

Carbon Microphones

The carbon microphone consists of a metal diaphragm placed against a cup of loosely packed carbon granules. As the diaphragm is actuated by the sound pressure, it alternately compresses and decompresses the granules. When current is flowing through the button, a variable dc will correspond to the movement of the diaphragm. This fluctuating dc can be used to provide grid-cathode voltage corresponding to the sound pressure.

The output of a carbon microphone is extremely high, but nonlinear distortion and instability has reduced its use. The circuit shown in Fig. 13-10 will deliver 20-30 volts at the transformer secondary.

Piezoelectric Microphones

Piezoelectric microphones make use of the phenomena by which certain materials produce a voltage by mechanical stress or distortion of the material. A diaphragm is coupled to a small bar of material such as Rochelle salt or ceramic made of barium titanate or lead zirconium titanate. The diaphragm motion is thus translated into electrical energy. Rochelle-salt crystals are susceptible to high temperatures, excessive moisture, or extreme dryness. Although the output level is higher, their use is declining because of their fragility.

Ceramic microphones are impervious to temperature and humidity. The output level is adequate for most modern amplifiers. They are capacitive devices and the output impedance is high. The load impedance will affect the low frequencies. To provide attenuation, it is desirable to reduce the load to 0.25 megohm or even lower, to maximize performance when operating ssb, thus eliminating much of the unwanted low-frequency response.

Dynamic Microphones

The dynamic microphone somewhat resembles a dynamic loudspeaker. A lightweight coil, usually made of aluminum wire, is attached to a diaphragm. This coil is suspended in a magnetic circuit. When sound impinges on the diaphragm, it moves the coil through the magnetic field generating an alternating voltage.

Electret Microphones

The electret microphone has recently appeared as a feasable alternative to the carbon, piezoelectric or dynamic microphone. An electret is an insulator which has a quasi-permanent static electric charge trapped in or upon it. The electret operates in a condenser fashion which uses a set of biased plates whose motion, caused by air pressure variations, creates a changing capacitance and accompanying change in voltage. The electret acts as the plates would, and being charged, it requires no bias voltage. A low voltage provided by a battery used for an FET impedance converter is the only power required to produce an audio signal.

Electrets traditionally have been susceptable to damage from high temperatures and high humidity. New materials and different charging techniques have lowered the chances of damage, however. Only in extreme conditions (such as 120 degrees F at 90 percent humidity) are problems present. The output level of a typical electret is higher than that of a standard dynamic microphone.

VOLTAGE AMPLIFIERS

The important characteristics of a voltage amplifier are its **voltage gain**, maximum undistorted **output voltage**, and its **frequency response.** The voltage gain is the voltage-amplification ratio of the stage. The output voltage is the maximum af voltage that can be secured from the stage without distortion. The amplifier frequency response should be adequate for voice reproduction; this requirement is easily satisfied.

The voltage gain and maximum undistorted output voltage depend on the operating conditions of the amplifier. The output voltage is in terms of *peak* voltage rather than rms; this makes the rating independent of the waveform. Exceeding the peak value causes the amplifier to distort, so it is more useful to consider only peak values in working with amplifiers.

Resistance Coupling

Resistance coupling generally is used in voltage-amplifier stages. It is relatively inexpensive, good frequency response can be secured, and there

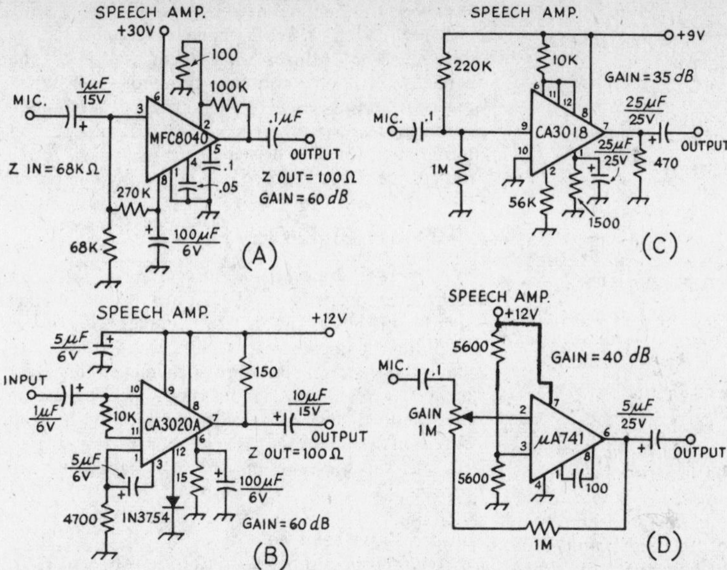

Fig. 13-13 – Typical speech amplifier using integrated circuits.

is little danger of hum pick-up from stray magnetic fields. It is the most satisfactory type of coupling for the output circuits of pentodes and high-μ triodes, because with transformers a sufficiently high load impedance cannot be obtained without considerable frequency distortion. A typical circuit is given in Fig. 13-11.

Phase Inversion

Push-pull output may be secured with resistance coupling by using **phase-inverter** or **phase-splitter** circuits as shown in Fig. 13-12. In this circuit the voltage developed across the emitter resistor of Q1 is equal to, but 180 degrees out of phase with, the voltage swing across the collector resistor. Thus, the following two stages are fed equal af voltages. The gain of Q1 will be quite low, if indeed the stage exhibits any gain at all.

Transformer Coupling

Transformer coupling between stages ordinarily is used only when power is to be transferred (in such a case resistance coupling is very inefficient), or when it is necessary to couple between a single-ended and a push-pull stage.

Several types of ICs have been developed for use in speech amplifiers. The Motorola MFC8040 features very low noise, typically 1 μV, (Fig. 13-13A), while the RCA CA3020 has sufficient power output – 500 mW – to drive low-impedance loads (Fig. 13-13B). A transistor IC array can also be put to work in a speech amplifier, as shown in Fig. 13-13C. This circuit uses an RCA CA3018, with a high-gain Darlington pair providing high gain and high input impedance. A second transistor within the IC functions as an emitter follower, for low-impedance output. Most of the operational-amplifier ICs will work as high-gain speech amplifiers, using a minimum of external parts as shown in Fig. 13-13D. The μA741 has internal frequency compensation, but the popular 709 series of operational amplifiers requires external frequency compensation to prevent self-oscillation.

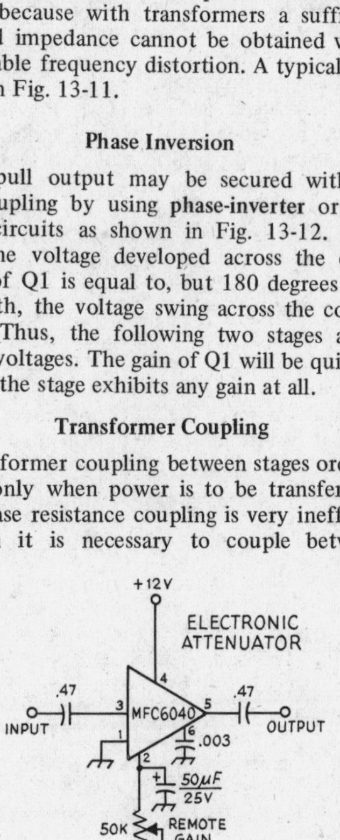

Gain Control

A means for varying the over-all gain of the amplifier is necessary for keeping the final output at the proper level for modulating the transmitter. The common method of gain control is to adjust the value of ac voltage applied to the base or grid of one of the amplifiers by means of a voltage divider or potentiometer.

The gain-control potentiometer should be near the input end of the amplifier, at a point where the signal voltage level is so low there is no danger that the stages ahead of the gain control will be overloaded by the full microphone output. In a high-gain amplifier it is best to operate the first stage at maximum gain, since this gives the best signal-to-hum ratio. The control is usually placed in the input circuit of the second stage.

Remote gain control can also be accomplished with an electronic attenuator IC, such as the Motorola MFC6040. A dc voltage varies the gain of the IC from +6 dB to -85 dB, eliminating the need

Fig. 13-14 – A dc voltage controls the gain of this IC, eliminating the need for shielded leads to the gain control.

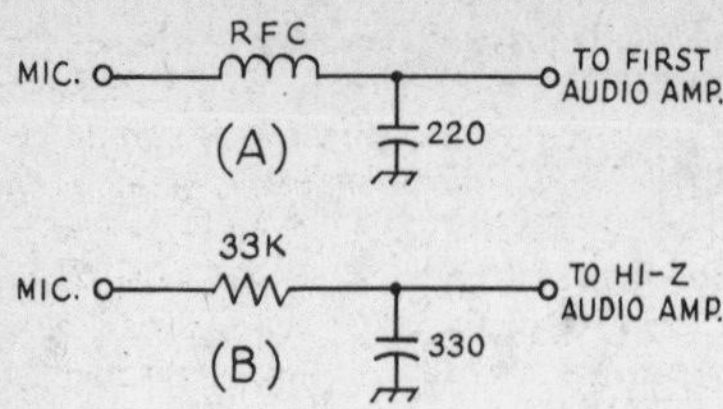

Fig. 13-15 – Rf filters using *LC* (A) and *RC* (B) components, which are used to prevent feedback caused by rf pickup on the microphone lead.

for shielded leads to a remotely located volume control. A typical circuit is shown in Fig. 13-14.

Speech-Amplifier Construction

Once a suitable circuit has been selected for a speech amplifier, the construction problem resolves itself into avoiding two difficulties – excessive hum, and unwanted feedback. For reasonably humless operation, the hum voltage should not exceed about 1 percent of the maximum audio output voltage – that is, the hum and noise should be at least 40 dB below the output level.

Unwanted feedback, if negative, will reduce the gain below the calculated value; if positive, is likely to cause self-oscillation or "howls." Feedback can be minimized by isolating each stage with decoupling resistors and capacitors, by avoiding layouts that bring the first and last stages near each other, and by shielding of "hot" points in the circuit, such as high-impedance leads in low-level stages.

If circuit-board construction is used, high-impedance leads should be kept as short as possible. All ground returns should be made to a common point. A good ground between the circuit board and the metal chassis is necessary. Complete shielding from rf energy is always required for low-level solid-state audio circuits. The microphone input should be decoupled for rf with a filter, as shown in Fig. 13-15. At A, an rf choke with a high impedance over the frequency range of the transmitter is employed. For high-impedance inputs, a resistor may be used in place of the choke.

When using paper capacitors as bypasses, be sure that the terminal marked "outside foil," often indicated with a black band, is connected to ground. This utilizes the outside foil of the capacitor as a shield around the "hot" foil. When paper or mylar capacitors are used for coupling between stages, always connect the outside foil terminal to the side of the circuit having the lower impedance to ground.

DRIVER AND OUTPUT STAGES

Few ssb transmitting mixers have sufficient output to properly drive an output stage of any significant power level. Most modern-day linear amplifiers require at least 30 to 100 watts of exciter output power to drive them to their rated power input level. It follows, then, that an intermediate stage of amplification should be used between the mixer and the pa stage of the exciter.

The vacuum-tube mixers of Chapter 8 will provide 3 to 4 peak volts of output into a high-impedance load. Since most AB_1 exciter output stages need from 25 to 50 volts of swing on their grids for normal operation, it is necessary to employ a driver stage to amplify the mixer output. There are several high-transconductance pentode tubes that work well as drivers. Among them are the 6CL6, the 12BY7, the 6EH7, and the 6GK6. Since all of these tubes are capable of high gain, instability is sometimes encountered during their use. Parasitic suppression should be included as a matter of course, and can take the form of a low-value noninductive resistor in series with the grid, or a standard parasitic choke installed directly at the plate of the tube. Some form of neutralization is recommended and is preferred to resistive loading of the tuned circuits. The latter method lowers the tuned-circuit *Q*. This in turn lowers the stage selectivity and permits spurious responses from the mixer to be passed on to the following stage of the exciter.

A typical driver and PA stage for modern exciters is shown in Fig. 13-16. The PA is set up for AB_1 amplification. The AB_1 mode is preferred because it results in less distortion than does the AB_2 or Class-B modes, and because driving power is not needed for AB_1 operation. A 6146 tube is used but an inexpensive TV sweep tube may be employed if a higher level of IMD is permissible.

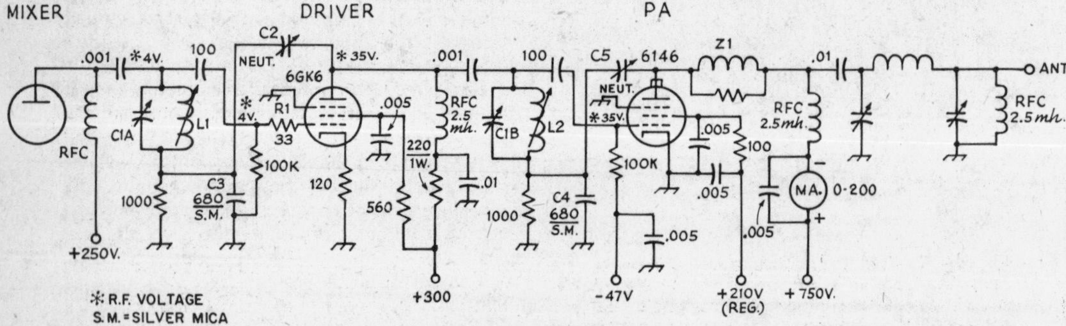

Fig. 13-16 – Schematic diagram of a typical driver and final stage for ssb exciter. Neutralization and parasitic-suppression circuits have been included.

Some sweep tubes are capable of producing less IMD than others, but if not overdriven most of them are satisfactory for ham use. Among the sweep tubes useful as AB_1 amplifiers are the following: 6DQ5, 6GB5, 6GE5, 6HF5, 6JE6, 6JS6, 6KD6, 6KG6, 6LF6 and 6LQ6.

A Practical Circuit

In the circuit of Fig. 13-16, a 6GK6 and a 6146 are shown in a typical driver-amplifier arrangement. Each stage is stabilized by means of R1 in the driver grid, and Z1 in the PA plate, both for parasitic suppression. C2 and C5 are neutralizing capacitors and can take the form of stiff wires placed adjacent to, and in the same plane as the tube anode. Varying the spacing between the neutralizing stubs and the tube envelopes provides the adjustment of these capacitors. Parallel dc feed is used in the mixer and driver stages to prevent the tuned-circuit Q from being lowered by dc current flow through L1 and L2. C1A and C1B are ganged, and slug-tuned inductors are used at L1 and L2 to permit tracking of the mixer and driver plate tanks. C3 and C4 form part of the neutralizing circuits. The values shown are suitable for operation on 3.5 MHz but may require modification for use on the other bands. Regulated dc voltage is recommended for the screen grids of the driver and rf stages. Typical rf voltages (measured with a diode rf probe and VTVM are identified with an asterisk. A circuit of this type is capable of up to 60 watts PEP output. For more information on linear amplifiers for sideband service, see Chapter 6.

POWER RATINGS OF SSB TRANSMITTERS

Fig. 13-17 is more or less typical of a few voice-frequency cycles of the modulation envelope of a single-sideband signal. Two amplitude values associated with it are of particular interest. One is the *maximum peak amplitude*, the greatest amplitude reached by the envelope at any time. The other is the *average amplitude*, which is the average of all the amplitude values contained in the envelope over some significant period of time, such as the time of one syllable of speech.

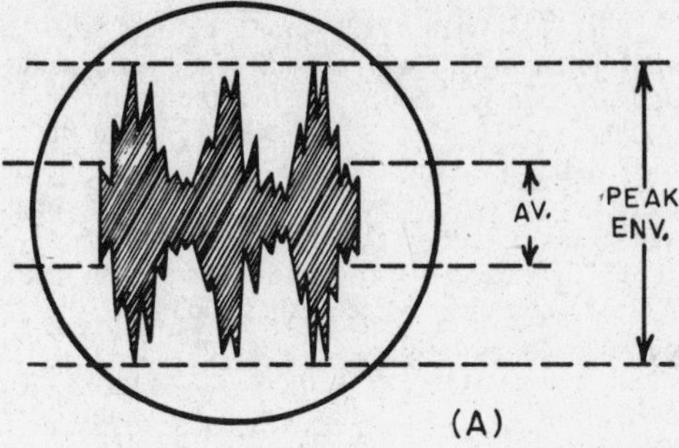

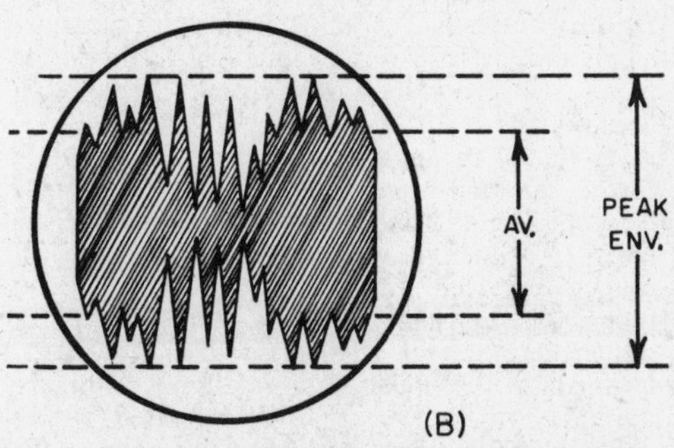

Fig. 13-17 — (A) Typical ssb voice-modulated signal might have an envelope of the general nature shown, where the rf amplitude (current or voltage) is plotted as a function of time, which increases to the right horizontally. (B) Envelope pattern after speech processing to increase the average level of power output.

The power contained in the signal at the maximum peak amplitude is the basic transmitter rating. It is called the *peak-envelope power*, abbreviated PEP. The peak-envelope power of a given transmitter is intimately related to the distortion considered tolerable. The lower the signal-to-distortion ratio the lower the attainable peak-envelope power, as a general rule. For splatter reduction, an S/D ratio of 25 dB is considered a border-line minimum, and higher figures are desirable.

The signal power, S, in the standard definition of S/D ratio is the power in *one* tone of a two-tone test signal. This is 3 dB below the peak-envelope power in the same signal. Manufacturers of amateur ssb equipment usually base their published S/D ratios on PEP, thereby getting an S/D ratio that looks 3 dB better than one based on the standard definition. In comparing distortion-product ratings of different transmitters or amplifiers, first make sure that the ratios have the same base.

When the output of an ssb transmitter is viewed on a spectrum analyzer, the display shows the power in the two tones separately, so that the level of distortion products is 6 dB below the level of either tone. However, commercial analyzers usually have a scale over the display tube which is calibrated directly in dB below a single-tone test. Readings may be converted to dB below the PEP level by subtracting 6 dB from the indicated distortion levels.

Peak vs. Average Power

Envelope peaks occur only sporadically during voice transmission, and have no direct relationship with meter readings. The meters respond to the amplitude (current or voltage) of the signal averaged over several cycles of the modulation envelope. (This is true in practically all cases, even though the transmitter rf output meter may be *calibrated* in watts. Unfortunately, such a calibra-

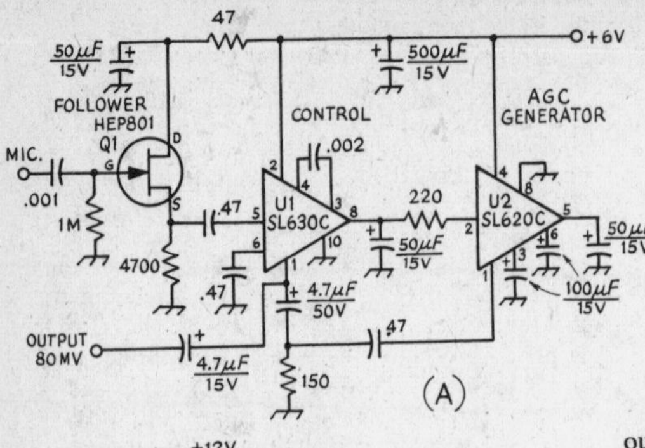

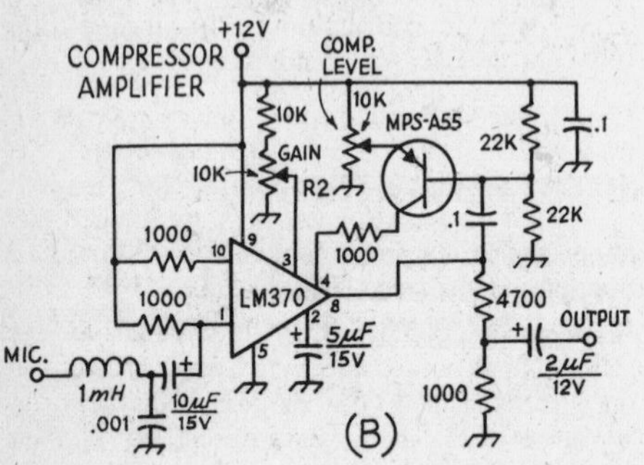

Fig. 13-18 – Typical solid-state compressor circuit.

tion means little in voice transmission since the meter can be calibrated in watts only by using a sine-wave signal – which a voice-modulated signal definitely is not.)

The ratio of peak-to-average amplitude varies widely with voice of different characteristics. In the case shown in Fig. 13-17A the average amplitude, found graphically, is such that the peak-to-average ratio of amplitudes is almost 3 to 1. The ratio of peak *power* to average *power* is something else again. There is no simple relationship between the meter reading and actual average power, for the reason mentioned earlier.

DC Input

FCC regulations require that the transmitter power be rated in terms of the dc input to the final stage. Most ssb final amplifiers are operated Class AB_1 or AB_2, so that the plate current during modulation varies upward from a "resting" or no-signal value that is generally chosen to minimize distortion. There will be a peak-envelope value of plate current that, when multiplied by the dc plate voltage, represents the instantaneous tube power input required to produce the peak-envelope output. This is the "peak-envelope dc input" or "PEP input." It does not register on any meter in the transmitter. Meters cannot move fast enough to show it – and even if they did, the eye couldn't follow. What the plate meter *does* read is the plate current averaged over several modulation-envelope cycles. This multiplied by the dc plate voltage is the number of watts input required to produce the *average* power output described earlier.

In voice transmission the power input and power output are both continually varying. The power input peak-to-average ratio, like the power-output peak-to-average ratio, depends on the voice characteristics. Determination of the input ratio is further complicated by the fact that there is a resting value of dc plate input even when there is no rf output. *No exact figues are possible.* However, experience has shown that for many types of voices and for ordinary tube operating conditions where a moderate value of resting current is used, the ratio of PEP input to average input (during a modulation peak) will be in the neighborhood of 2 to 1. That is why many amplifiers are rated for a PEP input of 2 kilowatts even though the maximum legal input is 1 kilowatt.

PEP Input

The 2-kilowatt PEP input rating can be interpreted in this way: The amplifier can handle dc peak-envelope inputs of 2 kw, presumably with satisfactory linearity. But it should be run up to such peaks if – and *only* if – in doing so the dc plate current (the current that shows on the plate meter) multiplied by the dc plate voltage does not at any time exceed 1 kilowatt. On the other hand, if your voice has characteristics such that the dc peak-to-average ratio is, for example, 3 to 1, you should not run a greater dc input during peaks than 2000/3, or 660 watts. Higher dc input would drive the amplifier into nonlinearity and generate splatter.

If your voice happens to have a peak-to-average ratio of less than 2 to 1 with this particular amplifier, you cannot run more than 1 kilowatt dc input even though the envelope peaks do not reach 2 kilowatts.

It should be apparent that the dc input rating (based on the *maximum* value of dc input developed during modulation, of course) leaves much to be desired. Its principal virtues are that it can be measured with ordinary instruments, and that it is consistent with the method used for rating the power of other types of emission used by amateurs. The meter readings offer no assurance that the transmitter is being operated within linearity limits, unless backed up by oscilloscope checks using *your* voice.

It should be observed, also, that in the case of a grounded-grid final amplifier, the 1-kilowatt dc input permitted by FCC regulations must include the input to the driver stage as well as the input to the final amplifier itself. Both inputs are measured as described above.

SPEECH PROCESSING

Four basic systems, or a combination thereof, can be used to reduce the peak-to-average ratio, and thus, to raise the average power level of an ssb signal. They are: compression or clipping of the af wave before it reaches the balanced modulator, and compression or clipping of the rf waveform after the ssb signal has been generated. One form of rf compression, commonly called alc (automatic level control) is almost universally used in amateur ssb transmitters. Audio processing is also used to increase the level of audio power contained in the sidebands of an a-m transmitter and to maintain constant deviation in an fm transmitter. Both compression and clipping are used in a-m systems, while most fm transmitters employ only clipping.

Volume Compression

Although it is obviously desirable to keep the voice level as high as possible, it is difficult to maintain constant voice intensity when speaking into the microphone. To overcome this variable output level, it is possible to use automatic gain control that follows the *average* (not instantaneous) variations in speech amplitude. This can be done by rectifying and filtering some of the audio output and applying the rectified and filtered dc to a control electrode in an early stage in the amplifier.

A practical example of an audio compressor circuit is shown in Fig. 13-18A. Q1 is employed as an impedance converter, providing coupling between a high-impedance microphone and the input terminal of the Plessey SL630C audio-amplifier IC. Low-impedance microphones can be connected directly to the input of the SL630C. U1 has an agc terminal which allows logarithmic control of the output level with a variable dc voltage. High-frequency cutoff is accomplished by connecting a .002-μF capacitor between pins 3 and 4. Manual gain control is effected by applying a dc voltage to pin 8.

Agc voltage for U1 is developed by the SL620C. A suitable time constant for voice operation is established by the capacitors connected to pins 3, 4 and 6, respectively. The IC provides a fast-attack, slow-decay characteristic for the agc voltage when voice signals are applied and a short burst of agc voltage when a short noise burst occurs. Twenty transistors and four diodes are used in U2.

The compressor will hold the output level constant within 2 dB over a 40-dB range of input signal. The nominal output level is 80 mV; the microphone used should develop at least 3 mV at the gate of Q1.

Fig. 13-18B shows an IC audio compressor circuit using the National Semiconductor LM-370. This IC has two gain-control points, pins 3 and 4; one is used for the input gain adjustment while the other receives agc voltage whenever the output level exceeds a preset norm. R2 establishes the point at which compression starts.

Speech Clipping and Filtering

In speech wave forms the average power content is considerably less than in a sine wave of the same peak amplitude. If the low-energy peaks are clipped off, the remaining wave form will have a considerably higher ratio of average power to peak amplitude. Although clipping distorts the wave form and the result therefore does not sound exactly like the original, it is possible to secure a worthwhile increase in audio power without sacrificing intelligibility. Once the system is properly adjusted *it will be impossible to overdrive* the modulator stage of the transmitter because the maximum output amplitude is fixed.

By itself, clipping generates high-order harmonics and therefore will cause splatter. To prevent this, the audio frequencies above those

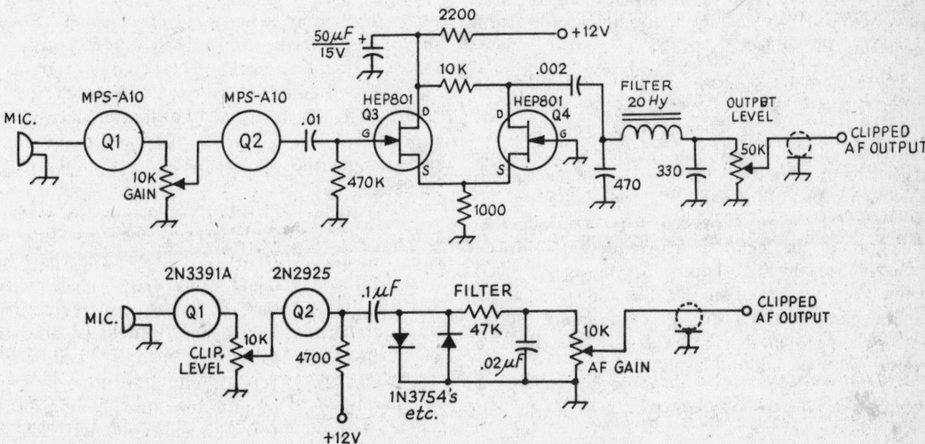

Fig. 13-19 – This drawing illustrates use of JFETs or silicon diodes to clip positive and negative voice peaks.

needed for intelligible speech must be filtered out, *after* clipping and *before* modulation. The filter required for this purpose should have relatively little attenuation below about 2500 Hz, but high attentuation for all frequencies above 3000 Hz.

The values of L and C should be chosen to form a low-pass filter section having a cutoff frequency of about 2500 Hz, using the value of the terminating resistor load resistance. For this cutoff frequency the formulas are:

$$L1 = \frac{R}{7850} \text{ and } C1 = C2 = \frac{63.6}{R}$$

where R is in ohms, L1 in henrys, and C1 and C2 in microfarads.

There is a loss in naturalness with "deep" clipping, even though the voice is highly intelligible. With moderate clipping levels (6 to 12 dB) there is almost no change in "quality" but the voice power is increased considerably.

Before drastic clipping can be used, the speech signal must be amplified several times more than is necessary for normal modulation. Also, the hum and noise must be much lower than the tolerable level in ordinary amplification, because the noise in the output of the amplifier increases in proportion to the gain.

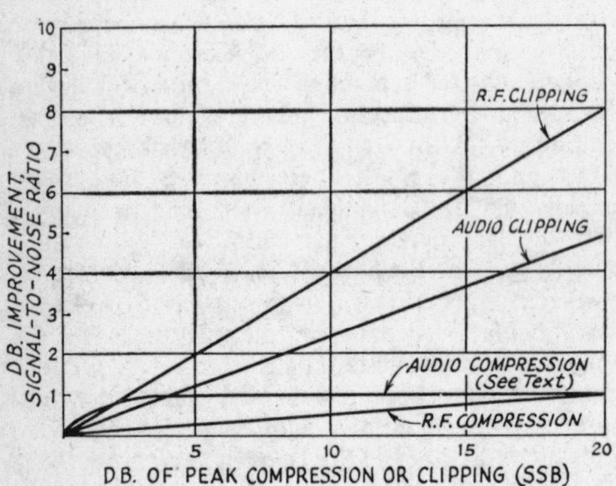

Fig. 13-20 – The improvement in received signal-to-noise ratio achieved by the simple forms of signal processing.

In the circuit of Fig. 13-19B a simple diode clipper is shown following a two-transistor preamplifier section. The 1N3754s conduct at approximately 0.7 volt of audio and provide positive- and negative-peak clipping of the speech wave form. A 47,000-ohm resistor and a .02-μF capacitor follow the clipper to form a simple R-C filter for attenuating the high-frequency components generated by the clipping action, as discussed earlier. Any top-hat or similar silicon diodes can be used in place of the 1N3754s. Germanium diodes (1N34A type) can also be used, but will clip at a slightly lower peak audio level.

SSB SPEECH PROCESSING

Compression and clipping are related, as both have fast attack times, and when the compressor release time is made quite short, the effect on the wave from approaches that of clipping. Speech processing is most effective when accomplished at radio frequencies, although a combination of af clipping and compression can produce worthwhile results. The advantage of an outboard audio speech processor is that no internal modifications are necessary to the ssb transmitter with which it will be used.

(A)

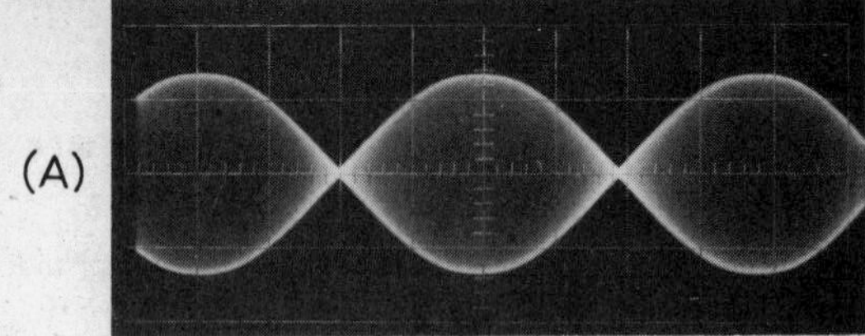

(B)

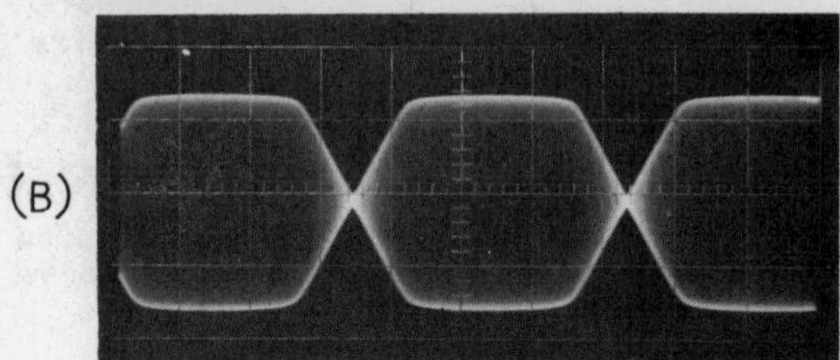

(C)

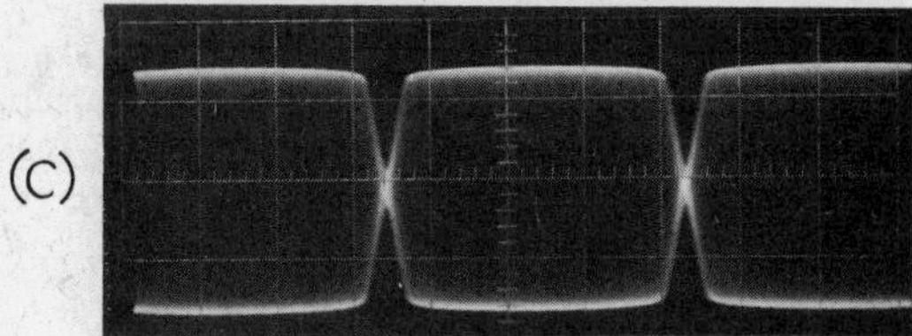

(D)

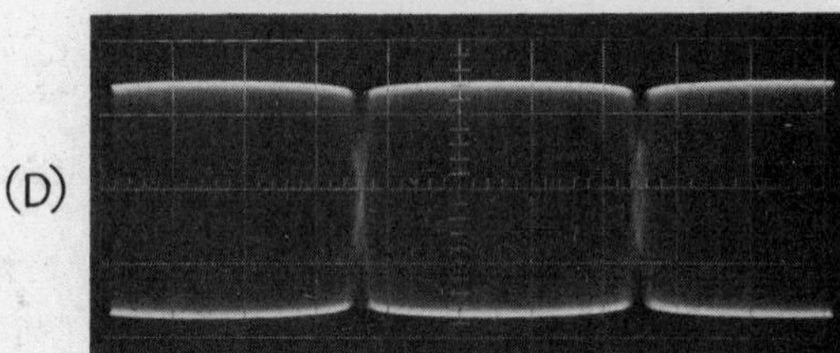

Fig. 13-21 – Two-tone envelope patterns with various degrees of rf clipping. All envelope patterns are formed using tones of 600 and 1000 Hz. (A) At clipping threshold; (B) 5 dB of clipping; (C) 10 dB of clipping; (D) 15 dB of clipping.

To understand the effect of ssb speech processing, review the basic rf waveforms shown in Fig. 13-17A. Without processing, they have high peaks but low average power. After processing, Fig. 13-17B, the amount of average power has been raised considerably. Fig. 13-20 shows an advantage of several dB for rf clipping (for 20 dB of processing) over its nearest competitor.

Investigations by W6JES reported in *QST* for January, 1969, show that, observing a transmitted signal using 15 dB of audio clipping from a remote receiver, the intelligibility threshold was improved nearly 4 dB over a signal with no clipping.

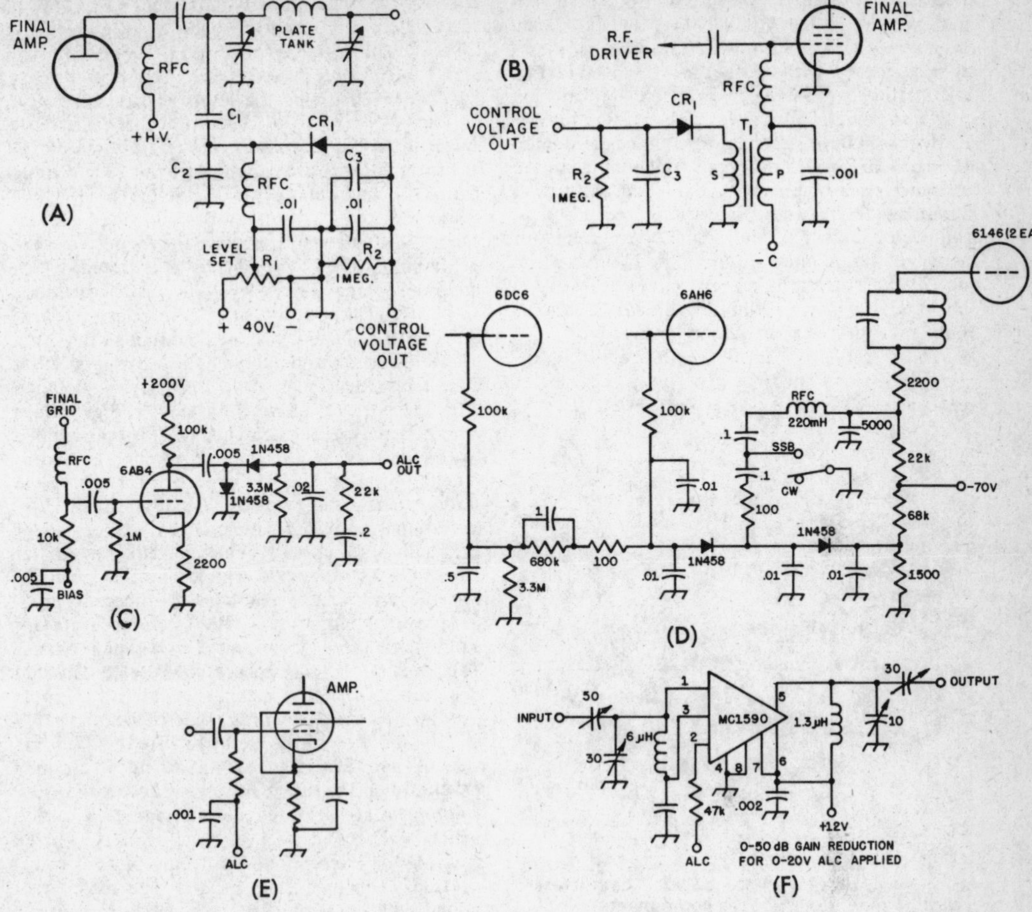

Fig. 13-22 – (A) Control voltage obtained by sampling the rf output voltage of the final amplifier. The diode back bias, 40 volts or so maximum, may be taken from any convenient positive voltage source in the transmitter. R1 may be a linear control having a maximum resistance of the order of 50,000 ohms. CR1 may be a 1N34A or similar germanium diode.
(B) Control voltage obtained from grid circuit of a Class AB_1 tetrode amplifier. T1 is an interstage audio transformer having a turns ratio, secondary to primary, of 2 or 3 to 1. An inexpensive transformer may be used since the primary and secondary currents are negligible. CR1 may be a 1N34A or similar; time constant R2C3 is discussed in the text.
(C) Control voltage is obtained from the grid of a Class AB_1 tetrode amplifier and amplified by a triode audio stage.
(D) Alc system used in the Collins 32S-3 transmitter.
(E) Applying control voltage to the tube or (F) linear IC controlled amplifier.

Increasing the af clipping level to 25 dB gave an additional 1.5 dB improvement in intelligibility. Audio compression was found to be valuable for maintaining relatively constant average-volume speech, but such a compressor added little to the intelligibility threshold at the receiver, only about 1-2 dB.

Evaluation of rf clipping from the receive side with constant-level speech, and filtering to restore the original bandwidth, resulted in an improved intelligibility threshold of 4.5 dB with 10 dB of clipping. Raising the clipping level to 18 dB gave an additional 4-dB improvement at the receiver, or 8.5-dB total increase. The improvement of the intelligibility of a weak ssb signal at a distant receiver can thus be substantially improved by rf clipping. The effect of such clipping on a two-tone test pattern is shown in Fig. 13-21.

Automatic level control, although a form of rf speech processing, has found its primary application in maintaining the peak rf output of an ssb transmitter at a relatively constant level, hopefully below the point at which the final amplifier is overdriven, when the audio input varies over a considerable range. These typical alc systems, shown in Fig. 13-22, by the nature of their design time constants offer a limited increase in transmitted average-to-PEP ratio. A value in the region of 2-5 dB is typical. An alc circuit with shorter time constants will function as an rf syllabic compressor, producing up to 6 dB improvement in the intelligibility threshold at a distant receiver. The Collins Radio Company uses an alc system with dual time constants (Fig. 13-22D) in their S/Line transmitters, and this has proven to be quite effective.

Heat is an extremely important consideration in the use of any speech processor which increases the average-to-peak power ratio. Many transmitters, in particular those using television sweep tubes, simply are not built to stand the effects of increased average input, either in the final-amplifier tube or tubes or in the power supply. If heating in the final tube is the limiting factor, adding a cooling fan may be a satisfactory answer.

AN AUDIO SPEECH PROCESSOR

Inside view of the audio processor. A circuit board is used to mount most of the components.

One hears the terms clipping, compression, limiting and rf clipping regularly on the hf amateur bands. Each of these systems represents a different technique to accomplish a common goal: increase the average level of the human voice, and correspondingly the ssb transmitter output signal. The voice waveform is modified either at the audio level before it is delivered to the microphone connector or after the ssb signal is generated at radio frequencies. The former has the advantage of processing the energy before it reaches the transmitter. The latter, while eliminating the harmonic distortion component, requires the owner to "operate" on the exciter and interconnect the system at some point in the rf amplifier chain (usually at the i-f).

While some authorities insist that rf clipping is superior to audio processing, the advantages of installing a device between the microphone and the mic-input connector on the transmitter are hard to overlook. Impedance matching, rf feedback and hum problems are almost nonexistent. Setting the proper level to the exciter is simple, especially if the the transmitter is equipped with provisions to monitor the transmitting alc voltage. If the audio energy is filtered properly (and this is the key to success), the effect of the processing generates only a very small degree of distortion. Proper filtering also eliminates excessive transmitter-signal bandwidth (assuming the levels are set correctly).

Fig. 1 gives the block diagram for the Logarithmic Limiter shown schematically in Fig. 2. A preamplifier is used to increase the audio energy from the microphone to a suitable level which overcomes the loss through its following high-pass filter. A potentiometer at the input of the preamplifier allows the gain to be adjusted, which determines the drive level to the logarithmic amplifier. The output of U2 is relatively low; however it remains constant even though the input level varies considerably. The low-pass filter attenuates the signal even further, but does an effective job of eliminating any energy above approximately 2950 Hz. This signal is then applied to the input of another amplifier which is used to set the output level of the processor for driving the station transmitter properly. Readily available 741 operational amplifiers are used to perform all of the active functions. The overall amount of amplitude limiting is determined by the setting of R4, the preamplifier gain control. A second input is provided for use with station accessory equipment like a phone patch or a tape recorder. The level of the accessory input is set by R7 and operates in a similar manner as R4. Both inputs may be used simultaneously, if desired.

The function of the high-pass filter (C4, C5, C6, C8, L1 and L2) is to eliminate any 60-Hz hum developed in the audio system *or in the accessory equipment*. It also reduces harmonic distortion which is generated by a very low-frequency energy entering the microphone (a deeply pitched voice) or from hum picked up by the tape recorder or phone patch. R5 and R6 are included to load the input and output of the high-pass filter and reduce band-pass ripple created by the use of standard-value components rather than a combination of several components to obtain a specific calculated one. The same technique is used with the low-pass filter (C10, C11, C12, C13, L3, L4 and L5).

The gain of op amp U2 is determined by CR1 and CR2 which display a logarithmic response to the audio amplitude appearing at the input. The gain decreases as the input amplitude increases. Output from this amplifier remains nearly constant with signal input variations of more than 20 dB. The output signal contains a certain amount of harmonic distortion which would, if not properly filtered, cause an excessively broad signal on the air. The low-pass filter, however, serves to cut off any energy above approximately three kHz, eliminating the primary source for a broad signal. If the transmitter is operated correctly, the signal will be no broader with this processor turned on than with the microphone hooked directly to the transmitter in a conventional manner.

Construction Details

Building the processor is straightforward. A

circuit board is used to mount all of the components except for the jacks and controls.[1] The chassis is homemade and measures (HWD) 2 × 5 × 8 inches (51 × 127 × 203 mm). A simple cover is fabricated from sheet aluminum. The enclosure is two-tone spray painted to give the unit a professional appearance. The cover is fastened to the chassis by means of three self-tapping No. 6 screws.

The switch to activate the processor should contain three poles to allow the power to be applied at the same time the audio switching is accomplished. This is to assure that the battery supply is turned off when the processor is not being used. An LED is connected in *series* with the battery primary lead to act as a panel lamp. It glows as a result of the nominal current drain of the processor. The circuit draws approximately 10 mA with no audio input, and reaches 18 mA during voice peaks. Alkaline batteries will last approximately 200 hours in continuous operation, and probably twice that amount during intermittent operation. This is an appreciable fraction of a year for the normally active amateur. The batteries are included in favor of an ac supply to eliminate any unwanted hum within the system and to make the processor completely self-contained. The home constructor could add his own ac-operated 18-volt supply, but should be careful not to introduce any mechanical or electrical hum into the early stages of the processor. Any low-level hum will be "processed" and appear at the output as a rather annoying disturbance.

All of the component values are standard except those of the toroidal inductors. These need to be modified, as explained in Fig. 2, to obtain the proper filter characteristics. The LED is a surplus type, but a suitable Allied/Radio Shack replacement should not be difficult to obtain. The op-amp integrated circuits are soldered directly on the pc board. If the builder has no opportunity to test the devices prior to their installation on the pc board, it would be wise to purchase a few sockets to make troubleshooting easy.

Alignment

While no test equipment is needed for initial adjustment, a simple audio oscillator and an oscilloscope are handy tools for determining the proper settings of R2, R17, and R19. A sine wave of approximately one kilohertz should be applied to the processor input connector. An amplitude of 500 mV is adequate to drive the limiter correctly. Connect an oscilloscope to the output jack (J2), and adjust each of the three pots (R2, R17, and R19) for minimum distortion of the waveform displayed. Stages may be set independently by connecting the scope to pin six of each op amp and performing the corresponding pot adjustment. The output of U2 will be a square wave. The adjustment of R19 is made to assure symmetry. The LIMITER control should be set to near maximum when positioning R19.

The OUTPUT control is used to adjust the drive to the transmitter. Adjustment capability of the model shown in the photographs provides a range from zero output to several volts. If test equipment is not available to make the foregoing initial adjustments, the builder could connect a microphone to the processor, connect the processor to an ssb transmitter, and adjust the three pots while listening for minimum distortion of the transmitted signal on a communications receiver.

Operation of the Processor

The use of this device is simple, especially if a Monitorscope (or similar unit) is used as part of the station equipment. The first step is to tune the transmitter properly for operation in the ssb mode. This is accomplished with the processor turned off. The transmitted-signal waveform should appear nearly the same as the one shown in Fig. 3A. If an alc monitor is included with the transmitter (alc meter position), the mic gain of the transmitter should be set so that the alc meter reading responds in accordance with the instruction manual (usually about 1/3 scale deflection). Then the processor may be switched on. The LIMITER gain should be set initially at maximum gain and the OUTPUT level of the processor adjusted for the same alc meter reading as obtained with the processor off. There is no need to readjust the transmitter gain control after it has been set initially. When the alc reading appears to be the same with the processor in the line as it is with it out of the line, the output level of the processor will have been set to match the output of the

[1] A scale template is available from ARRL Hq. for fifty cents and an s.a.s.e.

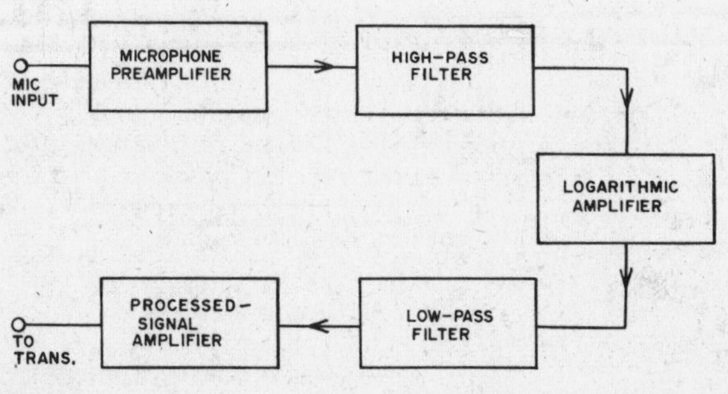

Fig. 1 — Block diagram for the logarithmic processor.

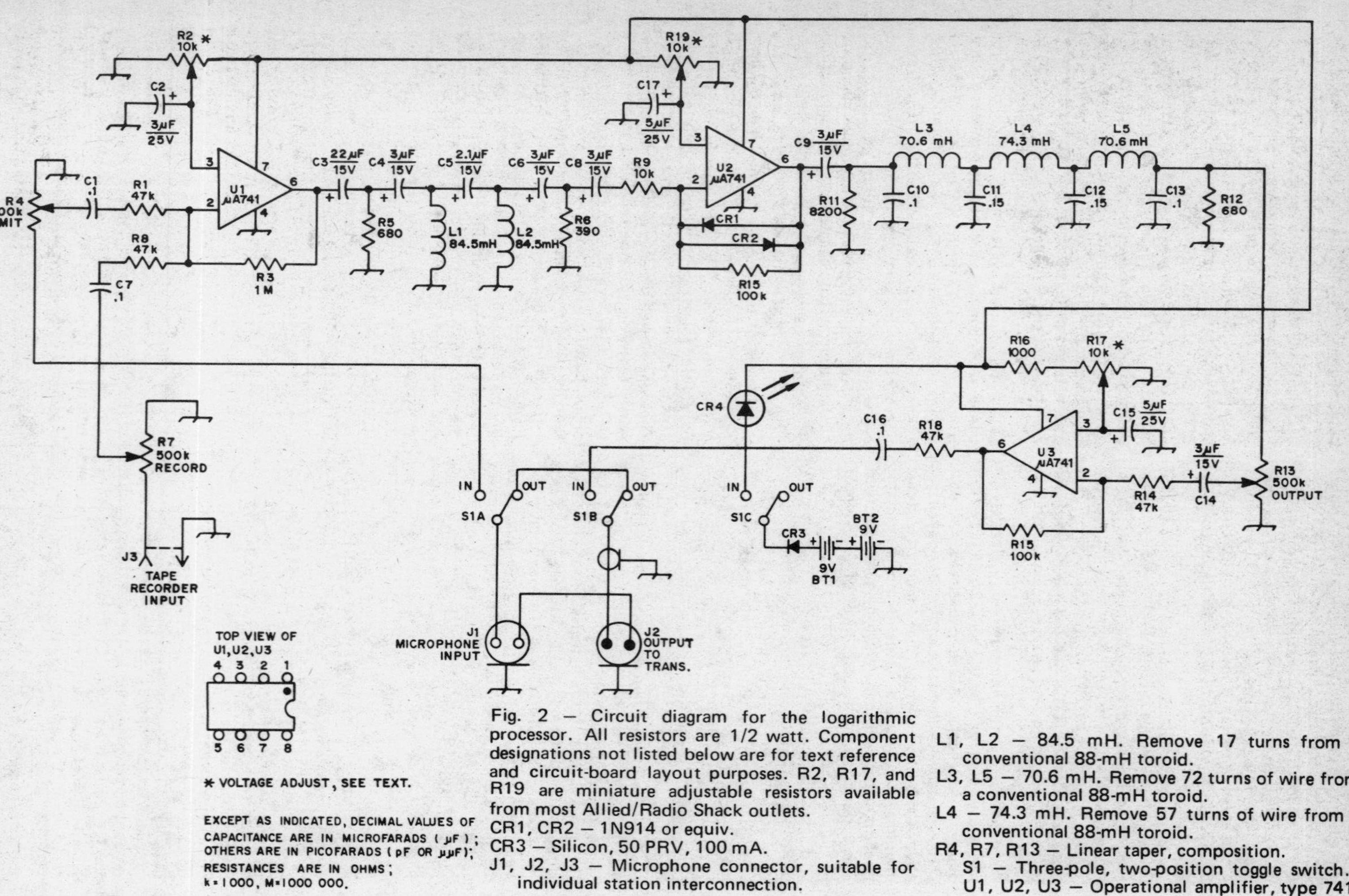

Fig. 2 — Circuit diagram for the logarithmic processor. All resistors are 1/2 watt. Component designations not listed below are for text reference and circuit-board layout purposes. R2, R17, and R19 are miniature adjustable resistors available from most Allied/Radio Shack outlets.

CR1, CR2 — 1N914 or equiv.
CR3 — Silicon, 50 PRV, 100 mA.
J1, J2, J3 — Microphone connector, suitable for individual station interconnection.
L1, L2 — 84.5 mH. Remove 17 turns from a conventional 88-mH toroid.
L3, L5 — 70.6 mH. Remove 72 turns of wire from a conventional 88-mH toroid.
L4 — 74.3 mH. Remove 57 turns of wire from a conventional 88-mH toroid.
R4, R7, R13 — Linear taper, composition.
S1 — Three-pole, two-position toggle switch.
U1, U2, U3 — Operational amplifier, type 741.

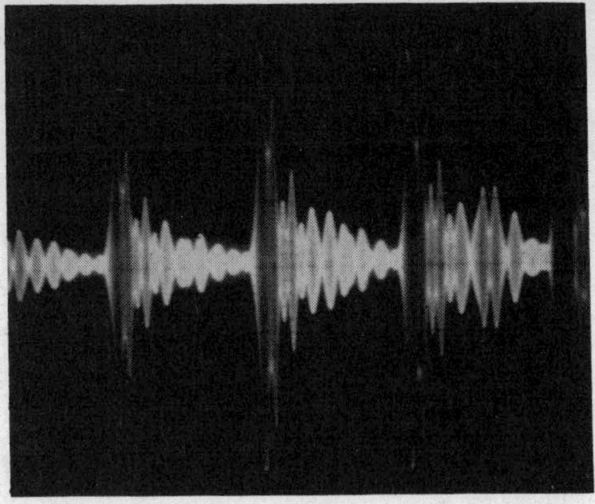

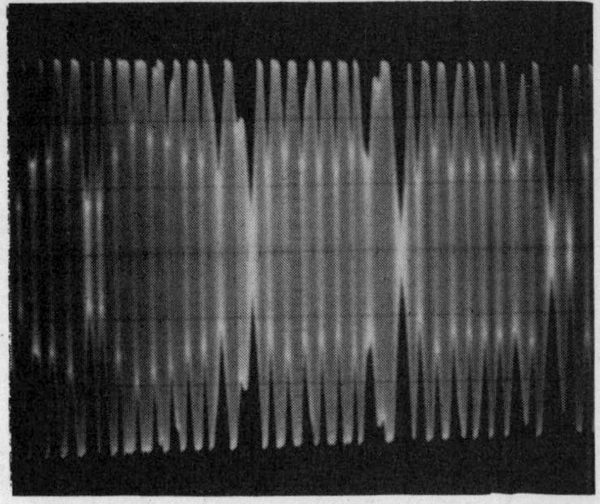

Fig. 3 – Waveform displayed at the output of a Kenwood TS-520 transceiver. The word "hello" is being spoken in each case. (A) Unprocessed signal with the TS-520 set for maximum amplitude display. (B) TS-520 output under fully limited conditions set by the Quasi-Logarithmic Limiter Processor. (The TS-520 was provided by Henry Radio, Inc.)

microphone. Then, the LIMITER control should be turned back to near minimum until a point is reached where the waveform pattern reaches a peak display. This waveform should be similar to the unprocessed one in the pattern shown in Fig. 3A. This is the point at which limiting will begin to take over as the gain is advanced. The amount of limiting will be determined by how far beyond this point the control is set. When viewing the display on a Monitorscope, one should set the LIMITER control to fill in the waveform pattern. The condition of maximum limiting is shown in Fig. 3B.

The alignment of the carrier oscillator is not identical in all ssb transmitters. There have been a few isolated cases of restricted audio characteristics when the Logarithmic Limiter is used in conjunction with some individual ssb transmitters (not specific models). If the band-pass range of the Logarithmic Limiter does not match the range of the ssb filtering system in the transmitter, the result can be a hollow sounding signal (the talking-in-a-barrel effect). In most cases this is caused by the transmitter filter cutting off the high-frequency energy and the Logarithmic Limiter restricting the low-frequency response. The simple way to solve the problem, if it exists, (without disturbing the alignment of the transmitter) is to omit the high-pass filter in the Logarithmic Limiter. There will be no noticeable change in the performance of the system except the capability to reduce hum introduced by an ac-operated power supply or from the accessory equipment. The battery supply is highly recommended. The removal of the high-pass filter has not caused difficulty with any of the test models built in the ARRL Lab.

To remove the high-pass filter, omit parts R5, R6, C4, C5, C6, C8, L1 and L2. Run a jumper wire between C3 (where C3 and C4 join) and R9 (where C8 and R9 join).

There is no substitute for on-the-air reports to confirm proper adjustment of the level controls. Stations both near and far should be asked for comments to determine the best level setting of the limiter control.

SINGLE-SIDEBAND TRANSCEIVERS

A "transceiver" combines the functions of transmitter and receiver in a single package. In contrast to a packaged "transmitter-receiver," it utilizes many of the active and passive elements for both transmitting and receiving. Ssb transceiver operation enjoys widespread popularity for several justifiable reasons. In most designs the transmissions are on the same (suppressed-carrier) frequency as the receiver is tuned to. The only practical way to carry on a rapid multiple-station "round table" or net operation is for all stations to transmit on the same frequency. Transceivers are ideal for this, since once the receiver is properly set the transmitter is also. Transceivers are by nature more compact than transmitter-receivers, and thus lend themselves well to mobile and portable use.

Although the many designs available on the market differ in detail, there are of necessity many points of similarity. All of them use the filter type of sideband generation, and the filter unit furnishes the receiver i-f selectivity as well. The carrier oscillator doubles as the receiver (fixed) BFO. One or more mixer or i-f stage or stages will be used for both transmitting and receiving. The receiver S meter may become the transmitter plate-current or output-voltage indicator. The VFO that sets the receiver frequency also determines the transmitter frequency. The same signal-frequency tuned circuits may be used for both transmission and reception, including the transmitter pi-network output circuit.

Usually the circuits are switched by a

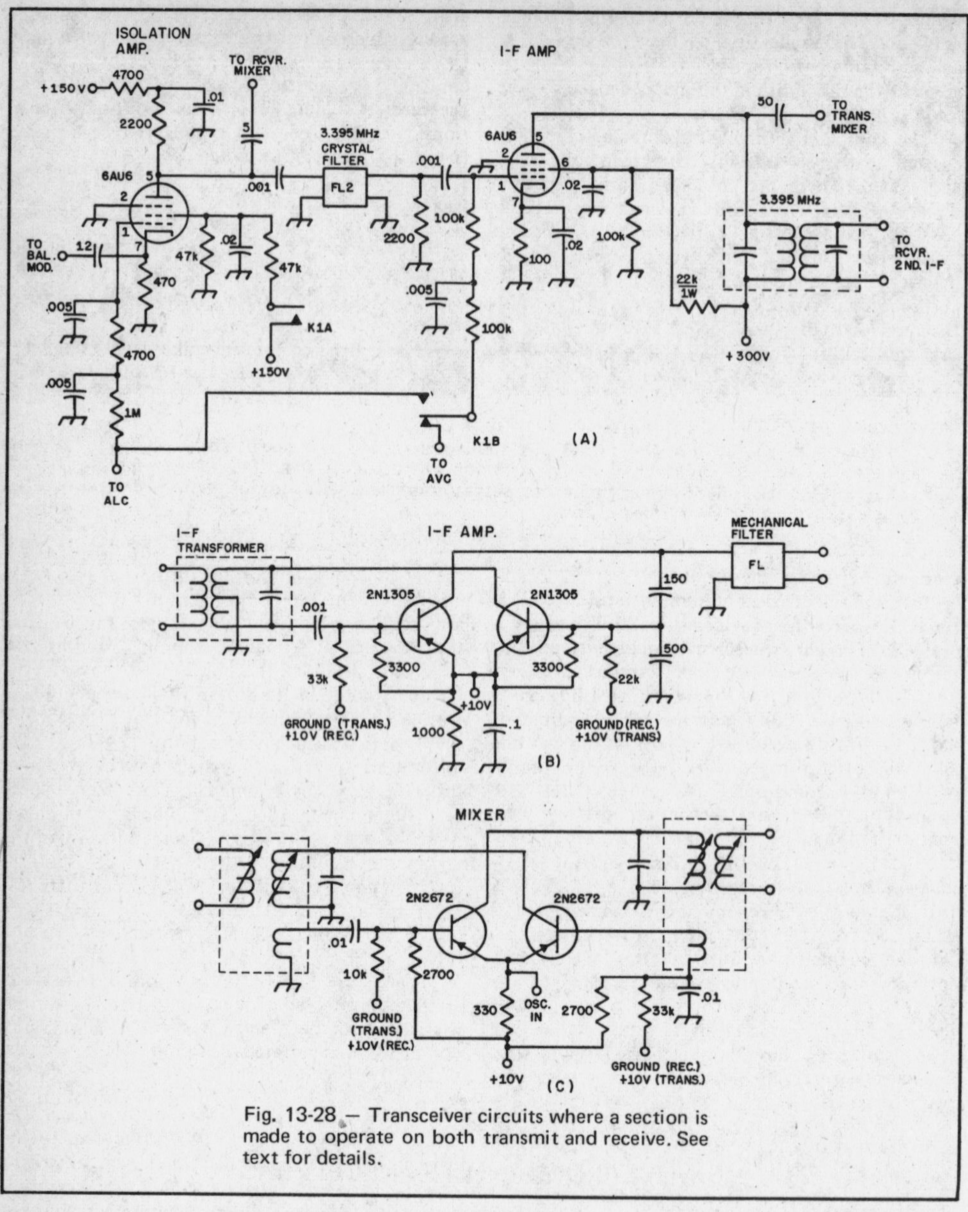

Fig. 13-28 – Transceiver circuits where a section is made to operate on both transmit and receive. See text for details.

multiple-contact relay, which transfers the antenna if necessary and also shifts the biases on several stages. Most commercial designs offer **VOX** (voice-controlled operation) and **MOX** (manual operation). Which is preferable is a controversial subject; some operators like VOX and others prefer MOX.

Circuits

The use of a filter-amplifier combination common to both the transmitter and receiver is shown in Fig. 13-28A. This circuit is used by the Heath Company in several of their transceiver kits. When receiving, the output of the hf mixer is coupled to the crystal filter, which, in turn, feeds the first i-f amplifier. The output of this stage is transformer coupled to the second i-f amplifier. During transmit, K1 is closed, turning on the isolation amplifier that links the balanced modulator to the band-pass filter. The single-sideband output from the filter is amplified and capacitance-coupled to the transmitter mixer. The relay contacts also apply alc voltage to the first i-f stage and remove the screen voltage from the second i-f amplifier, when transmitting.

Bilateral amplifier and mixer stages, first used by Sideband Engineers in their SBE-33, also have found application in other transceiver designs. The circuits shown in Fig. 13-28B and C are made to work in either direction by grounding the bias divider of the input transistor, completing the bias network. The application of these designs to an amateur transceiver for the 80-10 meter bands is given in the 5th Edition of *Single Sideband for the Radio Amateur.*

The complexity of a multiband ssb transceiver is such that most amateurs buy them fully built and tested. There are, however, some excellent designs available in the kit field, and any amateur able to handle a soldering iron and follow instructions can save himself considerable money by assembling an ssb transceiver kit.

Some transceivers include a feature that permits the receiver to be tuned a few kHz either side of the transmitter frequency. This consists of a voltage-sensitive capacitor, which is tuned by varying the applied dc voltage. This can be a useful device when one or more of the stations in a net drift slightly. The control for this function is usually labled **RIT** for *receiver independent tuning.* Other transceivers include provision for a crystal-controlled transmitter frequency plus full use of the receiver tuning. This is useful for "DXpeditions" where net operation (on the same frequency) may not be desirable.

SSB Bibliography

Single Sideband for the Radio Amateur, by the American Radio Relay League, 5th Edition, 1970.

Hennebury, *Single Sideband Handbook*, Technical Material Corporation, 1964.

Pappenfus, Bruene and Schoenike, *Single Sideband Principles and Circuits*, McGraw-Hill, 1964.

Amateur Single Sideband, by Collins Radio Company, 1962.

TESTING A SIDEBAND TRANSMITTER

To observe the rapidly changing levels in a sideband transmitter an oscilloscope is absolutely necessary. No meter can keep up with the dynamic variations encountered with the human voice. There are monitor scopes sold that will fill the bill completely, or any shop-type scope which has an internal horizontal sweep generator and external vertical deflection-plate connections may be used with the tuning unit to be described. Several inexpensive scope kits are also available.

An audio generator is the other piece of test equipment required. The standard sort of audio generator will do; one often can be borrowed from local RTTYers or high-fi buffs, or a simple audio generator may be constructed to give a selection of frequencies. See Chapter 17.

The generator should have good sine-wave output and low distortion. A two-tone generator makes testing even easier.

For the service-type oscilloscope an rf pickup unit is used to sample the output of the transmitter, and a tuned circuit builds up the rf voltage to provide adequate vertical deflection for the scope. See Figs. 13-29 and 13-31. The pickup unit is constructed in a 4 × 2 1/2 × 2 1/2-inch Minibox. The tuning unit has link-coupled input; each link is made by winding turns of hookup wire around the center of the coil and cementing it down. The shaft of the variable capacitor must be insulated from ground. In the unit in the photograph, the capacitor is mounted on a 3/4-inch standoff insulator.

Only a small amount of energy is used by the tuning unit, so the pickup may be left in the transmitter-output line for on-the-air monitoring.

A typical test setup is shown in Fig. 13-30. All testing should be done with a dummy load. The audio or two-tone generator is connected to the microphone jack of the transmitter, except when a mike is used for speech patterns. The generator should be adjusted so that its output is about at the level of the microphone normally used. Gain adjustments should be made at the transmitter with the mike gain control. The pickup unit is inserted between the transmitter and dummy load, and the tuning unit should be placed so short connections can be made to the scope. Don't forget to ground the scope to the tuning unit. A length of RG-58/U or RG-59/U is used to connect the tuning unit to the pickup unit.

The transmitter to be tested should be tuned up in the cw position, or in the sideband position with a single audio tone injected for normal input. Then adjust the tuning unit to give about half-scale deflection on the scope face, and adjust on the horizontal sweep generator in the oscilloscope.

Fig. 13-29 – An oscilloscope adaptor permits monitoring of the output rf envelope from an hf transmitter. Any shop-type oscilloscope may be used.

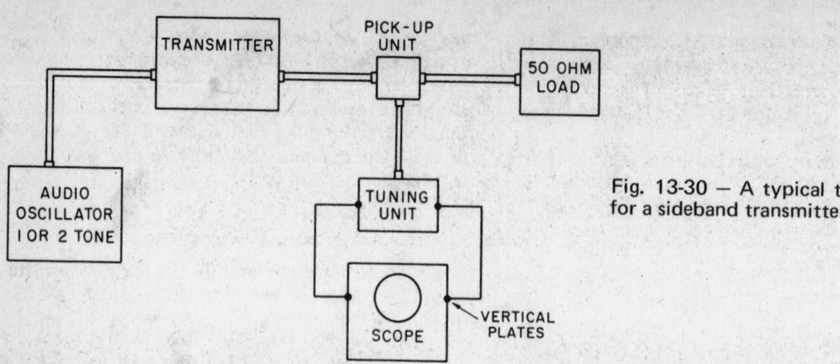

Fig. 13-30 — A typical test setup for a sideband transmitter.

Speech Patterns

Speech patterns offer a rather poor way of telling what is going on in the sideband transmitter because they come and go so fast. Yet with a little experience one can learn to recognize signs of transmitted carrier and flattening. These are useful later in monitoring on-the-air operation with a scope.

Connect a microphone to the transmitter, set the oscilloscope sweep for about 30 Hz and say a few words. The number "five" will produce a "Christmas tree" pattern similar to Fig. 13-33. Each different word will produce a different pattern, which is one of the reasons why speech patterns are so hard to interpret. The important thing here is to observe the peaks to see if they are sharp, as in Fig. 13-33A. Fig. 13-33B is the number "five" again but this time the mike gain is set way too high; the final stage is being overdriven resulting in clipping of the voice peaks as the final tube reaches plate-current saturation. Underloading the final stage will produce the same result. Operating a transmitter this way will produce a lot of splatter, making you unpopular with your neighbors on the band. Usually, reducing the gain control setting a little will remove all signs of flattening. Try different settings of the gain control until you can tell a correct pattern from one showing clipping.

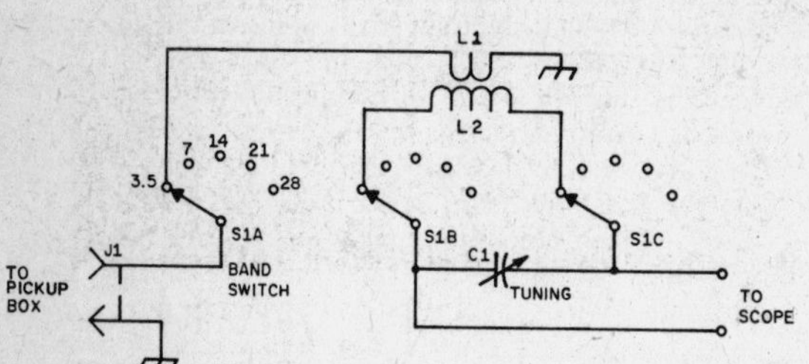

Fig. 13-31 — Schematic diagram of the oscilloscope adaptor. Output connections are made through nylon binding posts (Johnson 111-102). Capacitance is in picofarads (pF).

C1 — Small variable (Hammarlund HF-100).
J1 — Phono type.
L1 — Link wound over L2 using hookup wire as follows: 3.5 MHz, 3 turns; 7 MHz, 2 turns; 14, 21 and 28 MHz, 1 turn.
L2 — 3.5 MHz: 35 turns No. 24, 1 1/4-inch dia., 32 turns per inch (B&W Miniductor 3020). 7 MHz: 21 turns No. 20, 1-inch dia., 16 turns per inch (B&W 3015). 14 MHz: 6 turns No. 20, 3/4-inch dia., 16 turns per inch (B&W 3011). 21 MHz: 8 turns No. 18, 5/8-inch dia., 8 turns per inch (B&W 3006). 28 MHz: 4 turns No. 18, 1/2-inch dia., 4 turns per inch (B&W 3001).
S1 — Phenolic rotary type, 3-pole, 3-section, 2-6 position (5 used) non-shorting contacts (Centralab 1421).

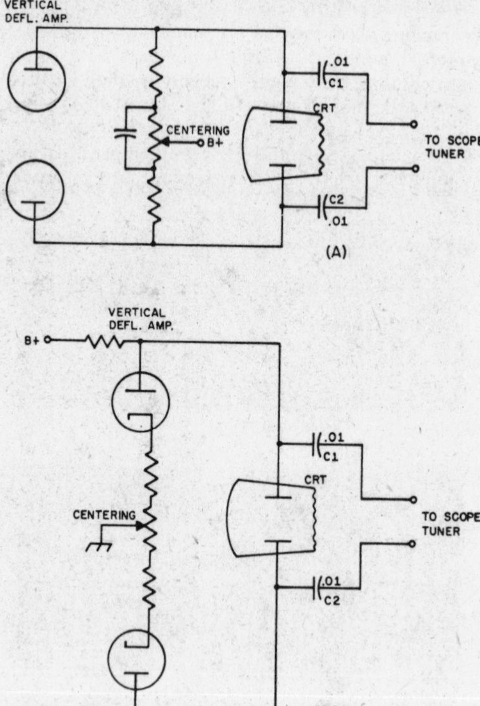

Fig. 13-32 — Modifications to a general-purpose oscilloscope to allow direct input to the vertical deflection plates. A, connection for a scope where centering is done in the B-plus lead and B, where centering is accomplished at the cathodes of the vertical amplifier tubes. The capacitors used for C1 and C2 should have a rating of 1000 volts or more. Connections can be brought out to the front or rear panel of the oscilloscope.

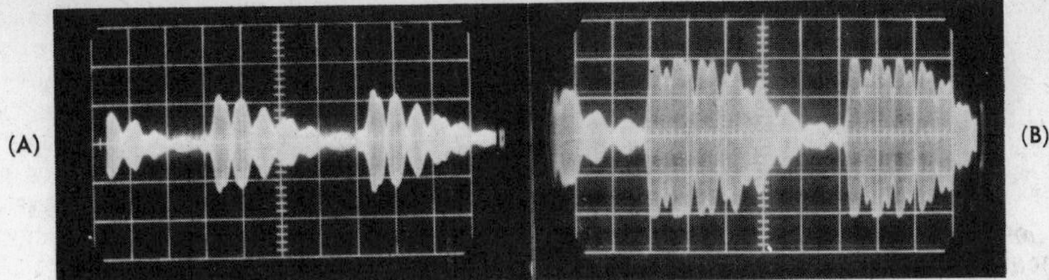

Fig. 13-33 – (A) Speech pattern of a correctly adjusted sideband transmitter. (B) The same transmitter with excessive drive causing peak clipping in the final amplifier.

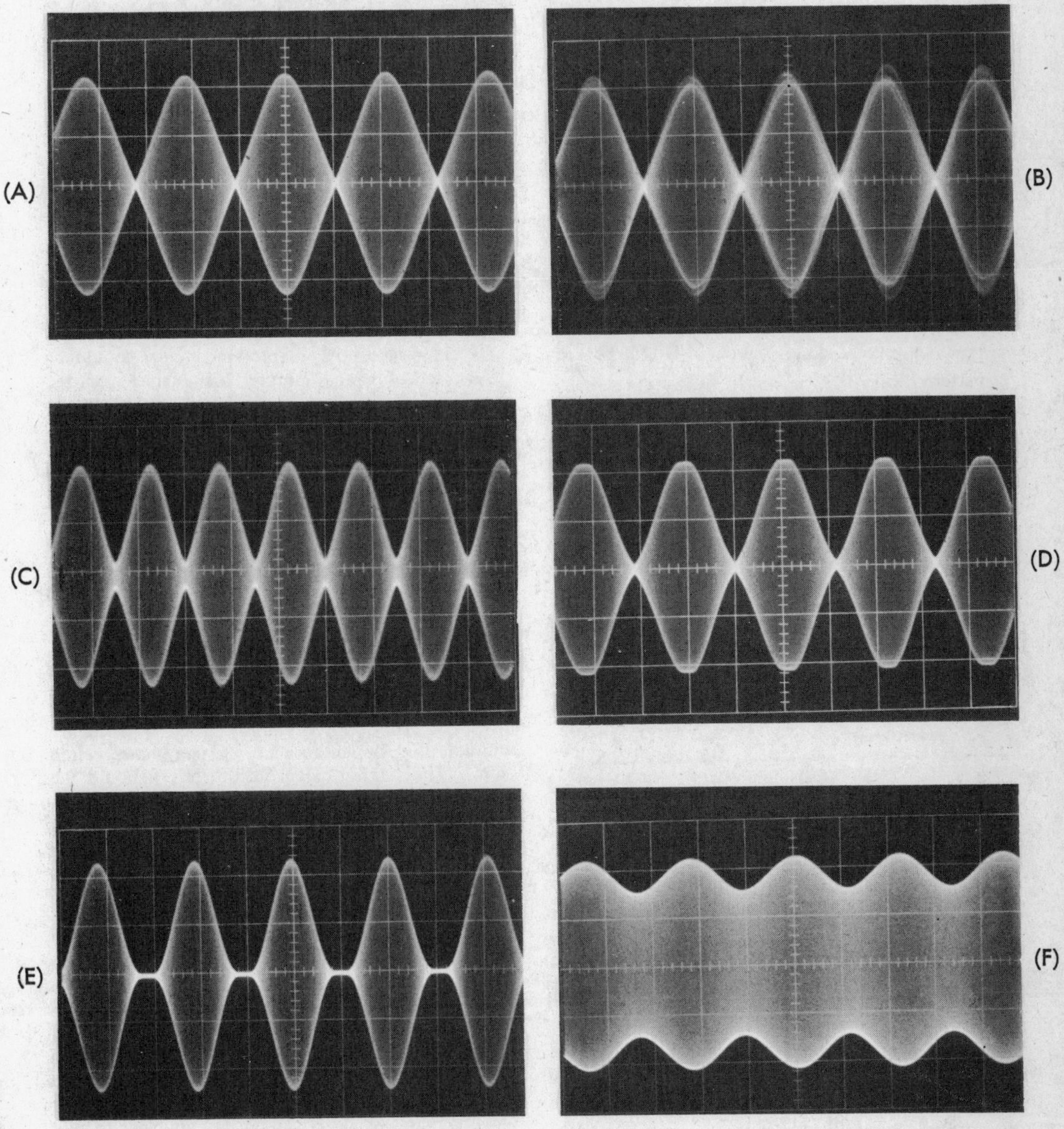

(A) (B)

(C) (D)

(E) (F)

Fig. 13-34 – Sideband two-tone test patterns. (A) Output pattern of a properly-adjusted transmitter. (B) A similar pattern to A, but showing hum on the signal. (C) Unequal tones (see text). (D) Excessive drive, causing flattopping and distortion. (E) Final amplifier incorrectly biased. (F) Single-tone showing modulation pattern caused by a partially suppressed carrier.

Fig. 13-35 – Interior view of the tuning unit and its pickup box. The variable capacitor is used to adjust the vertical deflection on the scope. The tuning unit should be mounted near the scope so that short interconnecting leads may be used. The pickup box consists of a No. 16 conductor forming a single-turn loop. Next to this loop is placed a two-turn second loop of plastic-covered hookup wire.

If, when the mike gain is reduced to zero, the scope pattern shows you still have some output, you may be transmitting carrier. Adjustment of the balanced modulator, which will be covered later, will be necessary.

Two-Tone Tests

A sideband transmitter should be a linear device from mike jack to output connector – for each audio frequency put in you should get out an rf frequency with no distortion of the wave form. The basis of a two-tone test is that you inject two audio signals, from which you should get out only two rf signals; No tube is ever perfectly linear, so some mixing of the two tones will occur, but all of the new signals produced should be so weak in comparison with the main output of the transmitter that you cannot detect their presence in a scope pattern. What you will see is the pattern of two sine-wave signals as they add and subtract, forming peaks and valleys.

A two-tone test's main advantage is that it will produce a stationary pattern that may be examined for defects. It is not easy to tell with your eye exactly what is a pure sine wave on a scope. Complex patterns are even more difficult, so it is a good idea to draw the correct pattern carefully on a piece of tracing paper, which may be placed over the actual pattern on the scope face for comparison. Remember that this test will show major defects in the transmitter only.

To make the test, apply the output of the two-tone generator to the mike jack, set the 'scope sweep for about 200 Hz, and check the pattern to see that both tones are of equal level. If they are not equal level, the valleys of the wave form will not meet at a single point on the zero line. Fig. 13-34A shows the correct pattern; note that the crossover is in the form of an X. Another way to obtain a two-tone test signal is to use a single audio tone and unbalance the carrier to the point where it forms the pattern shown in Fig. 13-34A.

Examine closely Fig. 13-34A – this is the correct pattern. Note the clean rounded peaks and straight sides of the envelopes, and again how an X is formed at the crossover. Fig. 13-34D shows mild flattening of the peaks. The cause is an amplifier stage being overdriven or underloaded. Cutting the drive level or increasing the loading should result in the Fig. 13-34A pattern.

Incorrect bias adjustment can also cause a stage to be nonlinear. This defect will show up as rounding of the crossover points as in Fig. 13-34E. The manufacturer's instruction manual should be consulted for the proper bias value and the location of the bias control. This control should be adjusted for the proper operating bias. Incorrect bias will also show up as high or low values of resting plate current. If a correct resting current and pattern cannot be obtained the tube may be bad and should be replaced.

If the two tones used are not of equal amplitude, the pattern of Fig. 13-34C results. Fig. 13-34B is a correct pattern showing hum modulation.

Carrier Balance

For carrier-balance adjustments only one tone is used. The carrier shows up as a sine-wave modulation, similar to what you may have seen in a-m. The carrier-balance control(s) should be adjusted until the sine-wave modulation disappears. Fig. 13-34A shows the single-tone test with sine-wave modulation caused by a partially suppressed carrier.

The location of the carrier-balance controls may be found in the instruction manual if they are not located on the front panel. Phasing rigs usually have two controls, while the filter types have one control and a variable capacitor. In either case the action of these adjustments is somewhat interlocking. The first should be adjusted, then the second, repeating in turn until the carrier is nulled out.

Carrier balance may also be adjusted with the aid of a communications receiver if it has an S meter. The receiver should be coupled to the transmitter so you have a strong, S9 signal. Then adjust the balanced modulator as before for the least amount of indicated signal on the S meter. During this test the mike gain should be reduced to zero, so no modulation appears on the carrier.

TRANSISTORIZED VOX

Voice-operated relay (VOX) provides automatic transmit-receive switching. It is a useful accessory, and one that can add to the pleasure of operating. Owners of commercially made transmitters that have been designed only for push-to-talk operation, and home constructors who are "rolling their own" rigs, will find that this unit, shown in Fig. 13-36, provides excellent VOX operation and that it can be used with their existing station equipment.

The Circuit

Operation of a VOX circuit is not complicated. A JFET transistor, Q1 in Fig. 13-36, operates as the first audio amplifier. The high input impedance of this type of transistor is desirable, because the use of high-impedance microphones is nearly universal in the amateur service. Q2 and Q3 provide additional amplification of the audio signal. The gain of these two stages is high. But, if additional gain is needed, bypass capacitor C7 may be added across the emitter resistor of Q2. With all but the low-output dynamic microphones, however, this capacitor should not be necessary. The audio output from Q3 is rectified by CR1 and CR2.

The dc output from the audio-signal rectifier is amplified by Q5 and fed to Q6. With no signal on its base, Q6 draws no collector current, holding the voltage on the base of Q7 near zero until the input signal reaches a sufficient level to turn the transistor on. Q7 will then turn on, drawing collector current through the relay coil, closing K1. The transistor that operates the relay is protected by CR5 from transient spikes generated as the current changes in the coil of K1. Provision is made for turning K1 on with a front-panel switch, S1, which holds the relay closed for a period of transmitter tuning or other adjustments.

A delay circuit, borrowed from ON5FE, is included to hold K1 closed for a short time after the audio-signal input ceases. This delay keeps the relay from chattering or opening during the short pauses between words or syllables. The length of the time delay is determined by the value of C15 and the setting of the DELAY control, R22. The advantage of ON5FE's circuit is that a relatively low value of capacitance can be used. Other circuits, which use delay capacitors of 50- to 200-μF, have slow turn-on action because series resistances used in the circuits prevent the large-value delay capacitor from charging instantaneously. A slow turn-on time is definitely undesirable, as it results in clipping of the first word spoken.

Audio output from a station receiver can key the VOX; to prevent this problem, an anti-VOX circuit is included. A sample of the receiver audio is amplified by Q4 and rectifed by CR3 and CR4. The output of this rectifier is negative in polarity and opposes the positive voltage developed by CR1 and CR2. Thus, when controls R19 and R20 are correctly set, any pickup from the speaker does not activate the VOX, as the positive and negative voltages cancel, and Q5 does not operate. A short time constant is desirable on the output of the anti-VOX rectifier; C11 provides this function. Receivers with 4- to 16-ohm speakers require amplification of the audio signal sampled across the speaker leads. If the receiver audio is taken

Interior view. With the exception of the controls, connection jacks, and rf bypass capacitors, all components are mounted on an etched-circuit board.

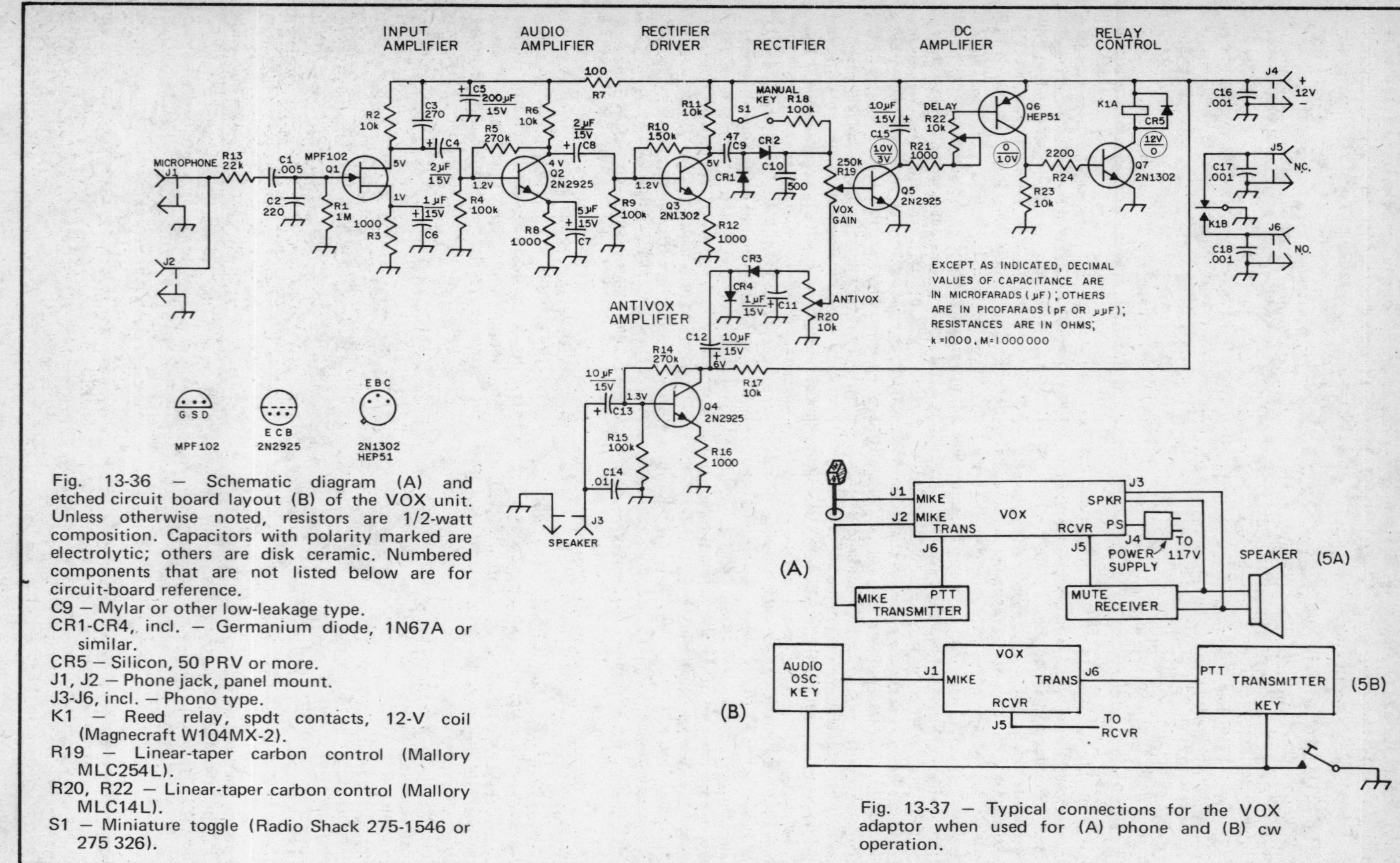

Fig. 13-36 — Schematic diagram (A) and etched circuit board layout (B) of the VOX unit. Unless otherwise noted, resistors are 1/2-watt composition. Capacitors with polarity marked are electrolytic; others are disk ceramic. Numbered components that are not listed below are for circuit-board reference.

C9 — Mylar or other low-leakage type.
CR1-CR4, incl. — Germanium diode, 1N67A or similar.
CR5 — Silicon, 50 PRV or more.
J1, J2 — Phone jack, panel mount.
J3-J6, incl. — Phono type.
K1 — Reed relay, spdt contacts, 12-V coil (Magnecraft W104MX-2).
R19 — Linear-taper carbon control (Mallory MLC254L).
R20, R22 — Linear-taper carbon control (Mallory MLC14L).
S1 — Miniature toggle (Radio Shack 275-1546 or 275 326).

Fig. 13-37 — Typical connections for the VOX adaptor when used for (A) phone and (B) cw operation.

from a 600-ohm speaker lead, or if the receiver has a high-impedance audio output, the Q4 amplifier stage may not be necessary.

Construction

The VOX unit, except for the controls and connection jacks, is built on a small etched circuit board. This board has a long, narrow shape, giving a modern shape factor to the VOX housing. Parts layout is not critical and it may be adjusted to suit one's individual requirements.

The case for the VOX is homemade. Two pieces of sheet aluminum, cut to size, are bent into U shapes. Small L brackets, fastened to each end of the base, are the points into which the sheet-metal screws that hold the cover are fastened. The overall size of the housing is 1 1/2 X 7 X 3 inches. Phone jacks are used for the microphone connections, and other input connections are made through phono-type jacks. The types of connectors used should mate with the other plugs and jacks used in an individual's ham shack. Unwanted rf pickup is always a potential hazard with transistor equipment. So, standard rf suppression techniques are used on the circuit board, and all connection points to the unit are bypassed.

A wide variety of npn transistors can be used; almost any of the small-signal, high-beta types are suitable. The bias resistors for the 2N2925s may have to be changed if a different type of transistor is substituted, however. When soldering connections to the etched board, care should be exercised, as excessive heat can damage transistors and diodes, as well as cause the copper foil to lift off the board. Also, correct polarity should be observed when installing the electrolytic capacitors. The unit's power supply is a 12-volt transistor-radio-battery eliminator, the Midland 18-112. Any of the 9- or 12-volt supplies sold for use with portable radios or tape recorders should do. A "stiff" supply is not necessary. The VOX does draw quite a bit of current, however, so small batteries are not suitable. Tests indicate that any voltage between 5 and 15 volts will provide satisfactory operation.

Operation

Connecting the VOX is easy. The microphone is plugged into one of the mic jacks, J1 or J2, and a patch cord is used to connect the remaining mic jack to the transmitter, as shown in Fig. 13-37A. The relay contact leads are connected to the transmitter PTT input, from J6. If a separate receiver is to be used, connect a cable from J5 to the receiver mute connections. The receiver audio can be sampled at the speaker terminals and fed to J3. The GAIN control, R19, should be advanced until even softly spoken words produce VOX operation. The DELAY time (R22) can be set to suit one's personal preference. The anti-VOX adjustment is set last. Place the microphone near the speaker, and tune in a loud signal. Then, advance the ANTIVOX control until the signal from the speaker does not operate the relay, even during periods when loud pops and static crashes are present.

A VOX adaptor can also be put to work to provide semibreak-in for cw operation. The connections for this are shown in Fig. 13-37B. Output from an audio oscillator or the audio signal from the monitor in an automatic keyer is needed to key the VOX. Only a low-level sample of the oscillator output is required; .01 volt will assure good operation. If no oscillator is available, one can be built from a commercial kit such as the RCA KC4002. Of course, both the audio oscillator and the transmitter must be keyed simultaneously.

A TRANSVERTER FOR 1.8 MHZ

Owners of five-band transceivers often get the urge to try "top band." Converting a transceiver to cover a frequency range for which the rig was not designed is difficult indeed. A far better approach is to build an outboard transverter, such as the one described here. This particular system requires one watt of drive power at either 21 or 28 MHz. Many transceivers can provide this low-level output along with the power supply voltages through an accessory socket.

The Circuit

A schematic diagram of the transverter is given in Fig. 1. Q1 operates as a crystal oscillator, to produce the local oscillator energy for the receive (Q5) and transmit (Q2) mixing stages, which runs continuously. During transmit 21.1 MHz ssb or cw energy is supplied to the emitter of Q2 through a power divider network. This signal is mixed with

Top view of transverter with cover removed. Final amplifier circuit is at the left. The rear apron has an accessory socket for an external power supply (transceiver), rf, and remote-keying connectors. The plate meter is at the lower left.

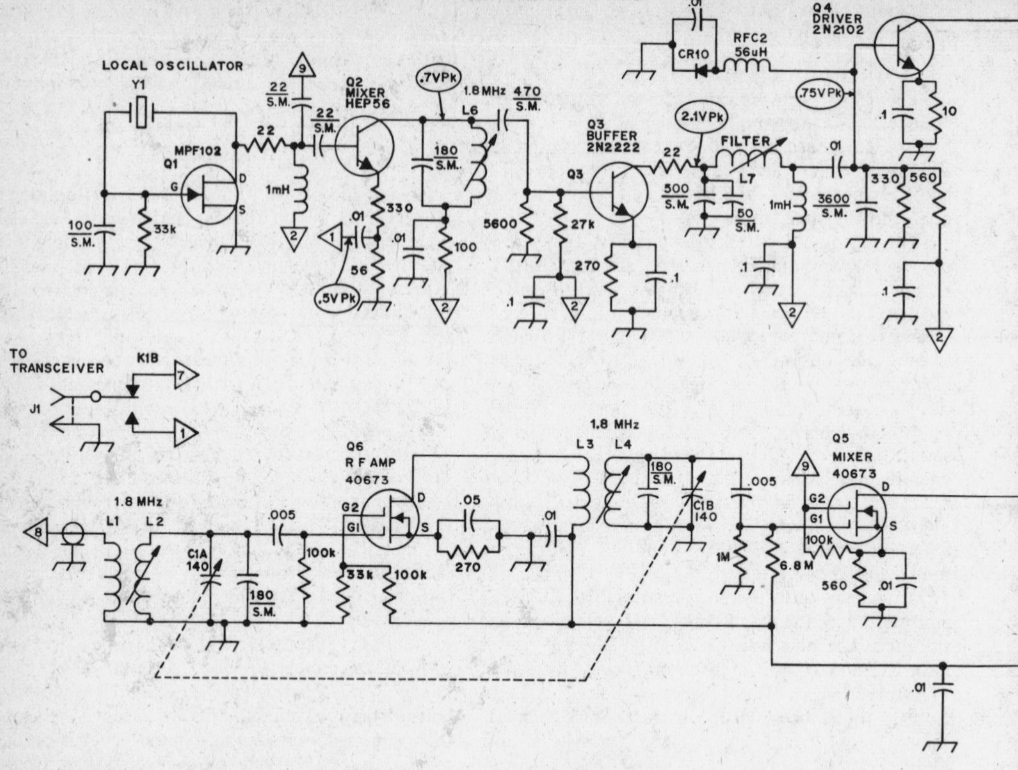

Fig. 1 – Schematic diagram for the transverter. Resistors are 1/2-watt composition and capacitors are disk ceramic, unless otherwise noted.

C1 – Dual-section air variable, 140 pF per section, or two 150 pF air variable units.
C2 – Air variable (Millen 19280).
C3 – Dual-section broadcast variable, 365 pF per section, both sections connected in parallel.
CR1 – Zener diode, 6.8-volt, 1-watt (1N4736).
CR10 – Silicon, 50 PRV, 100 mA.
J1 – Phono type, chassis mount.
J2 – Coaxial receptacle, chassis mount.
K1, K2 – 12 V dc, 2-A contacts, dpdt relay (Radio Shack 275-206).
L1 – 11 turns of No. 28 enam. wire wound over L2.
L2, L4 – 19.5-24.3 μH variable inductor (Miller 46A225CPC).
L3 – 22 turns of No. 38 enam. wire wound on L4 coil form.
L5 – 18.8-41.0 μH variable inductor (Miller 42A335CPC).
L6, L8 – 35-43.0 μH variable inductor (Miller 46A395CPC).
L7 – 13.2-16.5 μH variable inductor (Miller 46A155CPC).
L9 – 10.8-18.0 μH adjustable coil (Miller 21A155RBI).
L10 – 42 turns, No. 16 enam. wire equally spaced on a T-200 Amidon core.
M1 – 500 mA, panel mount (Simpson 17443 or similar),
Q5, Q6 – RCA MOSFET.
RFC1 – 1 mH. 500 mA rf choke (Johnson 102-572).
RFC2 – 56 μH rf choke (Millen J-302-56).
Y1 – 19.3-MHz crystal is used for a 21-MHz i-f, 26.5-MHz crystal for a 28-MHz i-f.
Z1, Z2 – 2 turns, No. 18 enam. wound over 47-ohm, 2-watt composition resistor.

the 19.3-MHz output from the LO producing 1.8 MHz power which is amplified by Q3, followed by a filter network. Q4 provides adequate drive to the pair of 6146Bs. The PA stage operates class AB1 which will deliver in excess of 100 watts PEP output.

During receive, an incoming signal is amplified by Q6, a dual-gate, diode-protected MOSFET. The output from the rf amplifier is mixed with local-oscillator energy at Q5 to produce a receiving i-f of 21 MHz. The frequency of the crystal is the only change required to make this system useable at 28 MHz. Changeover from transmit to receive is accomplished by K1 and K2 which are controlled by the associated transceiver. If the LO frequency is 19.3 MHz, the 1.8 to 2.0 MHz band will correspond with 21.1 to 21.3 MHz on the transceiver dial. Likewise, with a 26.5 MHz crystal in the LO circuit, the 160-meter band will appear between 28.3 and 28.5 MHz.

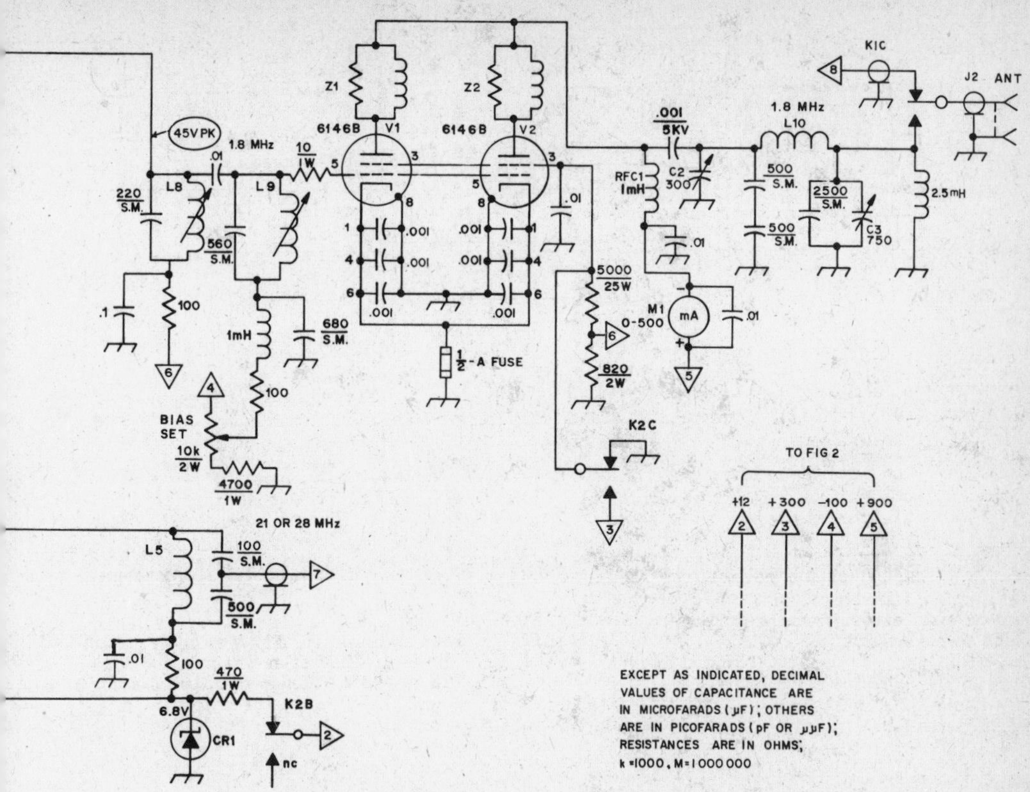

EXCEPT AS INDICATED, DECIMAL VALUES OF CAPACITANCE ARE IN MICROFARADS (µF); OTHERS ARE IN PICOFARADS (pF OR µµF); RESISTANCES ARE IN OHMS; k = 1000, M = 1 000 000

If the various supply voltages can not be obtained from the transceiver, an economy power supply shown in Fig. 2 can be used. The 6.3- and 5-volt windings of T1 are series-connected to provide 11.5 volts to power K1 and K2, the receiving converter and the predriver stages of the transmitting section. The windings must be phased properly to prevent cancellation of the voltages. If no output is obtained when the windings are connected, reverse the leads of one winding. The 11.3-volt ac is rectified by CR6.

Bias voltage is obtained for V1 and V2 by connecting a 6.3-volt filament transformer in back-to-back fashion with the 6.3-volt winding of T1. The 125-volt ac output from T2 is rectified, filtered, and then routed to the bias-adjust control, R1, to establish a PA resting plate current of 50 mA.

The metering circuit consists of a 500 mA meter connected in the plate voltage line. Other meters may be employed by using the proper shunts, as described in the Measurements Chapter.

The bottom view of the chassis, the sockets for the 6146B tubes are at the lower center. The etched-circuit board is above the final amplifier tube sockets and the T-R relays at the upper right. The different supply voltages are obtained from the associated transceiver.

Construction

An aluminum chassis which measures 7 × 11 × 2 inches is used as the base for the transverter. A homemade panel and cabinet enclose the unit. The front panel is 8 × 7-1/4 inches. The layout employed should be apparent from the photographs. All long runs of rf wiring should be made with subminiature coaxial cable (RG-174/U or similar).

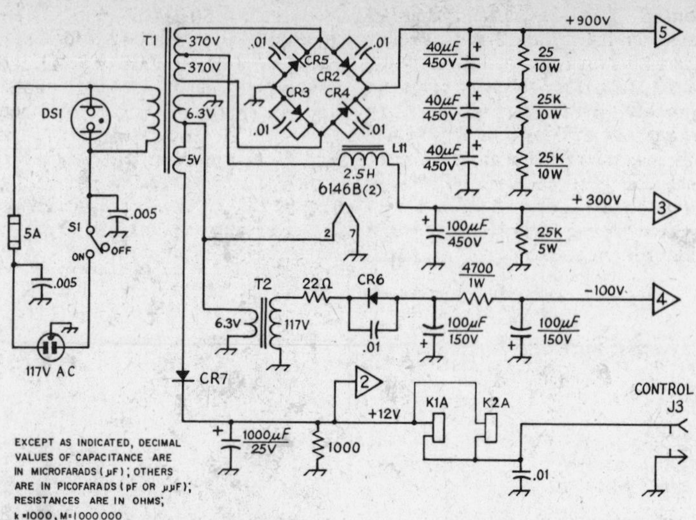

Fig. 2 – Diagram of the power-supply section. Resistors are 1/2-watt composition. Capacitors are disk ceramic, except those with polarity marked which are electrolytic.
CR2-CR5, incl. – Silicon, 1000 PRV, 1 A.
CR6, CR7 – Silicon, 400 PRV, 1 A.
J3 – Phono type, chassis mount.
K1, K2 – see Fig. 1.
L11 – Power choke, 130 mA (Allied 6X24HF or equiv.).
S1 – Spst toggle.
T1 – Power transformer, 117-V primary; secondary windings 740 V ct at 275 mA, 6.3 V at 7 A, and 5 V at 3 A (Stancor P-6315 or equiv.).
T2 – Filament transformer, 117-V primary; 6.3-V, 1-A secondary.

The receiver section, driver stages and local oscillator are constructed on a double-sided printed-circuit board measuring 3 × 3-1/2 inches. Inductors L1 and L2 are mounted on the chassis close to C1. Short leads are used from the circuit board to the PRESELECTOR capacitor and L1-L2 which are located on the underside of the chassis. The final tank inductor is wound on an Amidon T-200 toroid core. It is supported above the chassis by a ceramic standoff insulator and two pieces of Plexiglas.

Tune Up

Provision must be made to reduce the power output of most transceivers used with the transverter since only about one watt of drive power is required. Too much rf voltage can damage the HEP 56 and will "smoke" the input resistors. Some transceivers are capable of delivering sufficient drive by removing the screen voltage from the PA stage. Or, it may be practical to disable the PA and obtain a sample of driver output by a link-coupling circuit.

Before testing the transverter, assure that the changeover relays, K1 and K2, are connected to the remote-keying terminals of the transceiver. Then connect an antenna to J2 and listen for signals. Peak the incoming signals with the PRE-

Close-up view of the printed-circuit board. This board has the local oscillator, receiver, and low-level driver stages. The crystal socket and crystal for the LO are shown at the lower left.

SELECTOR control. The slugs of L2 and L4 should be adjusted for the highest S-meter reading on the transceiver. L5 should be set for maximum output at 21 or 28 MHz. If the receiving converter is functioning properly, it will be possible to copy a 0.1 μV signal without difficulty in areas where atmospheric and man-made noise are at a minimum. If no signals can be heard, check Q1 to make certain that it is working properly. A wavemeter or general-coverage receiver can be employed to see if the crystal oscillator is operating.

Attach a 50-ohm load to J2 before testing the transmitter section. Set R1 for an indicated resting plate current of 50 mA on M1. This adjustment should be made without drive applied but with K1 and K2 energized. Next, apply about one watt of 21.1-MHz cw drive power at J1. Tune L6, L7, L8 and L9 for maximum meter reading. While monitoring the plate current, tune C2 for a dip. C3 is the PA LOADING control. When the PA capacitors are properly adjusted, the plate current will be about 220 mA.

A LOW-POWER SSB/CW TRANSMITTER FOR 80 OR 20 METERS

A number of QRP transmitter designs have appeared in the past, mostly for cw-only operation. The unit to be described operates in both the ssb and cw modes. Using solid-state devices throughout, the transmitter is capable of delivering up to nine watts PEP output into a 50-ohm load. A 9-MHz i-f in conjunction with a VFO that tunes 5.0 to 5.5 MHz results in single-band operation on either 80 or 20 meters. A regulated 12-volt dc supply that can furnish at least two amperes is required to power the transmitter.

Construction Details

Four separate circuit board assemblies are used. Two boards, measuring 6 by 2-3/8 inches and 5-3/4 by 2-3/4 inches, contain most of the transmitter circuitry. The VFO and power output amplifier are included on separate boards, measuring 2 by 3 inches and 2-1/2 by 4 inches respectively. Double-clad circuit board should be used for all except the VFO board. The copper plane on the component side of each board provides a good rf ground and thus enhances stability in the unit. Component leads which are soldered to ground should be soldered to both the ground plane on the component side and the ground foil on the reverse side. To prevent other leads from shorting to the ground plane, their holes on the component side are drilled out slightly with a 1/4-inch drill before mounting. As can be seen in Fig. 2, shields, made from pieces of double-clad circuit board soldered to the main circuit boards, are used to isolate stages which are susceptible to stray rf pickup.

The VFO is housed in a four-walled enclosure formed by four pieces of circuit board soldered together at their common seams. The VFO board fits snugly inside and is soldered along its edges to the walls of the enclosure. The tuning capacitor, C6, mounts firmly against the front wall from which its shaft protrudes. Dc power connection is made via a feedthrough capacitor. A short length of subminiature RG-174/U coax connects the VFO output to U2.

If the 80-meter version of the unit is being constructed, Q11 and associated components in this amplifier stage are to be omitted from the board since the stage is required only for 20-meter operation. Instead, then, a jumper connection is made from common connection 4 (as indicated in the schematic diagram) directly to the base of Q12. In the 20-meter unit this stage is included and the jumper omitted.

Fig. 1 – Front view of the transmitter with cover in place. The two-piece chassis is made from sheet aluminum. The front panel, which measures 9-1/2 by 4 inches, is spray-painted orange and the cover is finished in brown. White decals are used to identify the power switch, mode switch, microphone gain control, and jack. For cw operation, the key plugs into a jack at the rear of the chassis. A two-speed vernier dial is employed for VFO tuning and stick-on rubber feet are fitted on the bottom of the chassis.

The broadband power output stage employs a 2N6367 rf power transistor rated for 9 watts PEP output with a –30 dB IMD specification. All rf-carrying leads associated with the base circuit of Q13 should be absolutely as short as possible. Because of the low base input impedance – two or three ohms – even small amounts of stray reactance cannot be tolerated. Leads as short as one inch can contribute a considerable amount of inductive reactance in the base circuit.

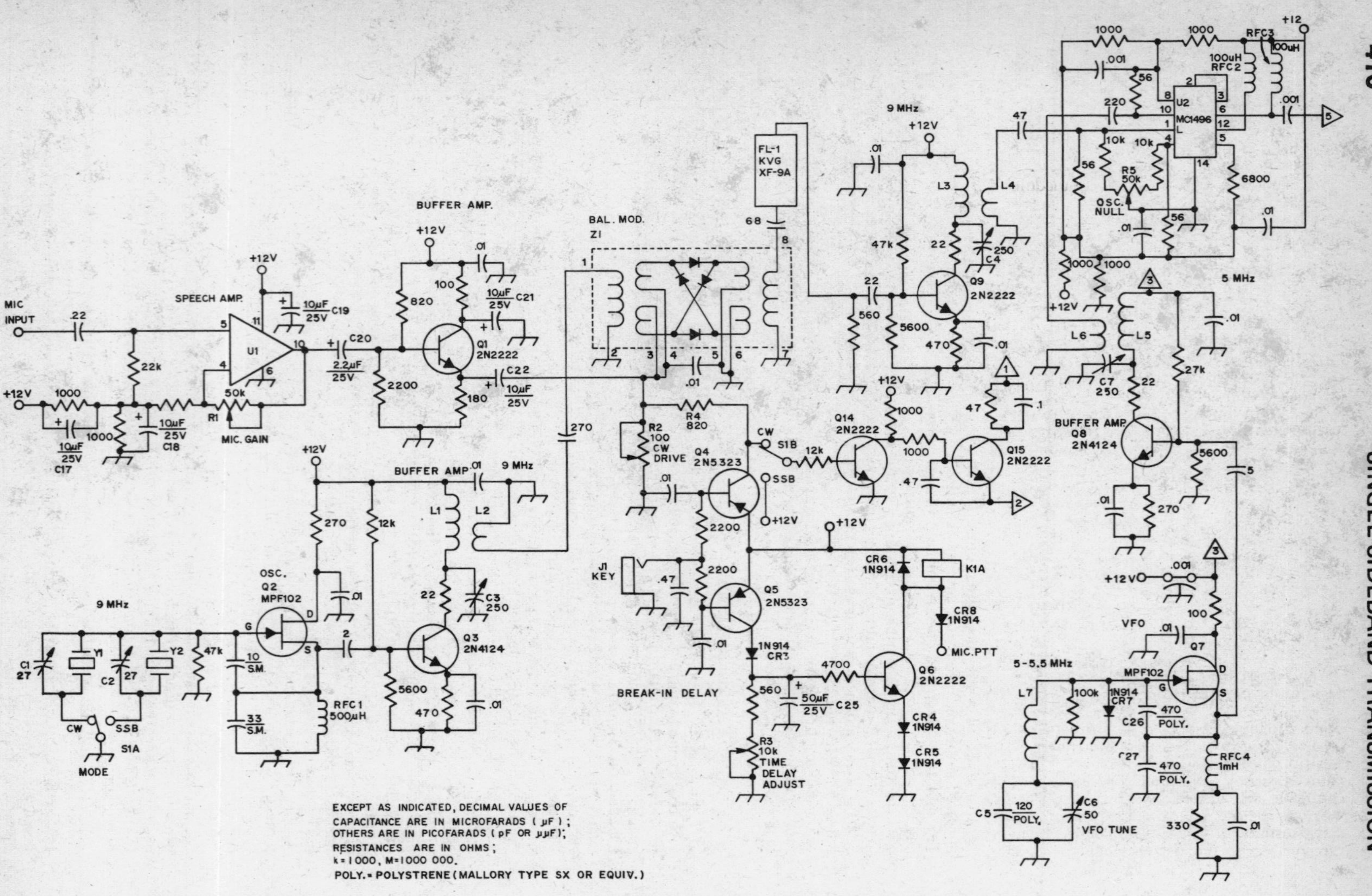
MIC INPUT
SPEECH AMP.
MIC. GAIN
BUFFER AMP.
BAL. MOD. Z1
FL-1 KVG XF-9A
CW DRIVE
BREAK-IN DELAY
TIME DELAY ADJUST
J1 KEY
MIC. PTT
OSC. NULL
5 MHz
9 MHz
5-5.5 MHz
VFO
VFO TUNE
MODE
EXCEPT AS INDICATED, DECIMAL VALUES OF CAPACITANCE ARE IN MICROFARADS (μF) ; OTHERS ARE IN PICOFARADS (pF OR μμF); RESISTANCES ARE IN OHMS; k=1000, M=1000 000.
POLY.= POLYSTRENE (MALLORY TYPE SX OR EQUIV.)

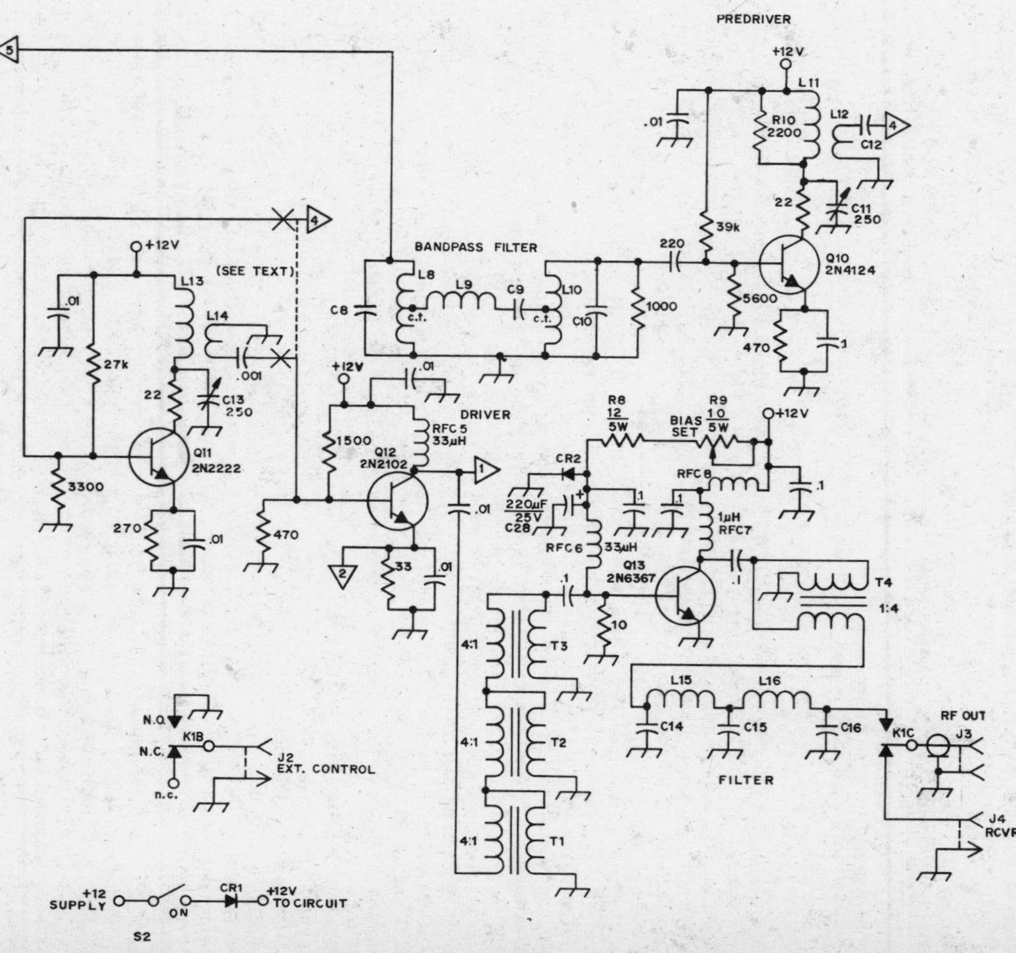

Fig. 2 — Schematic diagram of the 80- or 20-meter low-power ssb/cw transmitter. Capacitors with polarity marked are electrolytic. Fixed-value capacitors are ceramic unless otherwise noted. Resistors are 1/2-watt composition unless marked otherwise. Numbered parts not appearing below are so identified for pc-board layout purposes only.

C1, C2 — 2.0- to 27-pF printed-circuit air variable (E.F. Johnson No. 193-0008-005 or equiv.).
C3, C4, C7, C11, C13 — 250-pF max. trimmer (Arco Elmenco 426).
C6 — 50-pF air variable.
C8, C10 — 220-pF silver mica (80-meter unit); 100-pF silver mica (20-meter unit).
C9 — 68-pF silver mica (80-meter unit); 1.7- to 11-pF miniature air variable (E.F. Johnson No. 187-0106-005 or equiv. for 20-meter unit).
C12 — .001-μF (80-meter unit); 68-pF (20-meter unit).
C14 — 820-pF silver mica (80-meter unit); 680-pF silver mica (20-meter unit).
C15 — 1500-pF silver mica (80-meter unit); 470-pF silver mica (20-meter unit).
C16 — 820-pF silver mica (80-meter unit); 220-pF silver mica (20-meter unit).
CR1 — Silicon diode, 50 PRV, 1A (1N4001 or equiv.).
CR2 — Silicon diode, 50 PRV, 3A or greater, stud-mounting type (Motorola HEP R0130 or equiv.).
FL1 — 9-MHz, 2.5-kHz bandwidth crystal filter, KVG type XF-9A.
K1 — Dpdt 12 Vdc relay, contact rating of 1 ampere or greater (Radio Shack cat. No. 275-206 or equiv.).
L1, L3 — 2.5-μH, 25 turns No. 24 enam. on Amidon T-50-6 toroid core.
L2 — 2 turns No. 24 enam. wound over L1.
L4 — 2 turns No. 24 enam. wound over L3.
L5 — 4.6-μH, 34 turns No. 24 enam. on Amidon T-50-6 core.
L6 — 3 turns No. 24 enam. wound over L5.

(Continued on next page)

L7 — 7.8- to 12.0-μH slug-tuned coil (Miller 4309).
L8, L10 — 8.9-μH, 49 turns No. 26 enam. on Amidon T-50-6 core (80-meter unit); 1.2-μH, 17 turns No. 24 enam. on Amidon T-50-6 (20-meter unit).
L9 — 26.5-μH, 68 turns No. 28 enam. on Amidon T-68-2 toroid core (80-meter unit); 17.6-μH, 55 turns No. 28 enam. on Amidon T-68-2 core (20-meter unit).
L11 — 8.1-μH, 45 turns No. 26 enam. on Amidon T-50-6 core (80-meter unit); 0.68-μH, 13 turns No. 24 enam. on Amidon T-50-6 core (20-meter unit).
L12 — 3 turns No. 24 enam. wound over L11.
L13 — 0.68-μH, 13 turns No. 24 enam. on Amidon T-50-6 core (used in the 20-meter unit only).
L14 — 1 turn No. 24 enam. wound over L13.
L15, L16 — 2.6-μH, 25 turns No. 24 enam. on Amidon T-50-6 core (80-meter unit); 0.28-μH, 8 turns No. 24 enam. on Amidon T-50-6 core (20-meter unit).
RFC8 — 6 turns No. 28 enam. using Amidon Jumbo Ferrite Bead as toroid core.
S1 — Dpdt subminiature toggle switch (Radio Shack 275-1546 or equiv.).
S2 — Spst subminiature toggle switch (Radio Shack 275-324 or equiv.).
T1, T4 — 4:1 broadband transformer; 12 turns of 1 twisted pair of No. 24 enam. wire (6 turns per inch, not critical) wound on Amidon FT-61-301 toroid core.
T2 — 4:1 broadband transformer; 6 turns of 2 twisted pairs of No. 26 enam. wire (6 turns per inch) wound on Amidon FT-61-301 toroid core. In twisting the wires, a single turn consists of a full twist of all wires. The two wires at the ends of each pair are soldered together and each pair then comprises one winding of the transformer.
T3 — 4:1 broadband transformer; 4 turns of 4 twisted pairs of No. 26 enam. wire (6 turns per inch) wound on Amidon FT-61-301 toroid core. A single turn consists of a full twist of all wires. The two wires at the ends of each pair are soldered together, the ends of two pairs are soldered together, resulting in two 4-conductor wires. Each 4-conductor wire comprises one winding of the transformer.
U1 — 741 operational amplifier (Motorola MC1741, National Semiconductor LM741, Fairchild μA741 or equiv.), 14-pin DIP used here.
U2 — Balanced modulator IC (Motorola MC1496L or National Semiconductor LM1496L, Signetics 5596). 14-pin DIP used here.
Y1 — 8999.0-kHz crystal (KVG type XF 903).
Y2 — 8998.5-kHz crystal (KVG type XF 901).
Z1 — Double balanced mixer, model SRA-1 manufactured by Mini-Circuits Laboratory, 2913 Quentin Rd., Brooklyn, NY 11229.

Some care must be taken in mounting Q13. The power amplifier board is drilled out to allow the flange for heat-sink mounting to pass through the board. The transistor leads, which are short straps, then lie flush with the top surface of the board and the flange lies beneath the board. The leads are soldered to the board as close to the body of the transistor as possible and should not be bent. The heat sink consists of a 1/16-inch thick rectangular piece of sheet aluminum cut to the same size as the circuit board. The transistor requires two bolts for mounting to the heat sink. The use of silicone grease to improve thermal conductivity between the transistor and heat sink is recommended. CR2, a stud-mounting type diode, also mounts on the heat sink near the power transistor since good thermal contact with Q13 is necessary for CR2 to provide thermal compensation for the output transistor. Note also that in the driver stage, Q12 requires a heat sink.

The chassis is formed from a piece of sheet aluminum bent into a U-shape. The front panel measures 9-1/2 by 4 inches and the chassis is 7 inches deep. Except for the VFO enclosure, the circuit boards mount vertically on the chassis by means of spade bolts. An aluminum cover is formed to fit over the chassis. A Jackson Bros. No. 4103 dial mechanism is used for VFO tuning. Any similar mechanism with a slow tuning rate should be satisfactory. Front-panel controls are the microphone-gain control, VFO tuning, mode switch, and on-off switch. The key jack, rf-output connector, and dc-power connector are mounted at the rear of the chassis. The transmit-receive relay socket mounts inside the chassis and the spare set of contacts are brought out to a connector at the back of the unit.

Initial Adjustments and Operation

A well-calibrated general-coverage receiver, a VOM, and a VTVM with an rf probe (or better yet, a good rf oscilloscope) are required for making the initial adjustments on the transmitter. Connect a 12-volt dc supply to the transmitter (except the final power amplifier stage). With power turned on, check to see that the unit draws no more than about 200 mA from the supply. Any reading well in excess of this value indicates a wiring error or defective components.

Tune the receiver to 9 MHz to locate the heterodyne oscillator signal. A few feet of hookup wire placed near the circuit board should suffice for a receiving antenna. Switching the mode switch to change the oscillator crystals Y1 and Y2 should shift the oscillator frequency accordingly. Adjust C3 for maximum signal at the collector of Q3 as displayed on an oscilloscope or VTVM with rf probe.

Plug a key into the key jack and set cw drive control, R2, for minimum resistance. Place the mode switch in the cw position. Depress the key while monitoring the collector of Q9 for rf output with the oscilloscope or rf probe. Slowly increase the cw drive level until a 9-MHz signal appears at Q9. Adjust C4 for maximum signal at the collector. Tuning C1 allows a small variation of the cw frequency. Adjustment is not critical but it should be tuned to place the cw signal inside the passband of FL1. If the signal is too close to the edge of the passband, keying may cause the filter to "ring," producing key clicks at the output.

Tune the receiver between 5.0 and 5.5 MHz and vary the VFO tuning capacitor, C6, until the VFO signal is located. Slug-tuned coil L7, which resonates with C6, should then be adjusted so that an entire sweep of C6 covers the range of 5.0 to 5.5 MHz or slightly greater. While monitoring the collector of Q8 with the rf probe or the oscilloscope, adjust C7 for maximum signal.

At this point, an 80- or 20-meter signal should be generated when the transmitter is keyed. By tuning the monitor receiver to the appropriate amateur band, it should be possible to hear this signal. Tune C6 to place the signal in the center of the amateur band. If an oscilloscope is being used, adjust C11 for maximum signal at the base of Q11. Be careful not to peak this capacitor to a harmonic of the 80- or 20-meter signal or to another undesired frequency output from the mixer. If the 20-meter system is being tested, it is also necessary to peak the band-pass filter at the balanced mixer output for optimum frequency response. With the VFO set to the center of the 20-meter band, adjust C9 for maximum response, using an insulated tool so as not to introduce stray capacitance which could upset the filter tuning. Place the oscilloscope probe at the base of Q12. Next tune C13 for maximum signal amplitude. If an oscilloscope is not available, the above steps may be performed by listening to the radiated signal in a general-coverage receiver and using the receiver's S meter as a peak indicator.

The carrier null pot, R5, is adjusted to minimize any 5-MHz VFO signal appearing at the output of the balanced mixer. First disable the 9-MHz heterodyne oscillator by removing Y1 or Y2 from the socket. With the oscilloscope attached to the mixer output at pin 6 of the MC1496L, adjust R5 for minimum 5-MHz output. If an oscilloscope is not available R5 should be set to the middle of its range. Good suppression of the 5-MHz signal will result at the transmitter output in conjunction with the filtering in the following stages. It is difficult to perform this step with just a receiver alone since direct pickup from the VFO will obscure any null indication. Y1 or Y2 should be replaced in its socket.

A check should be made with the VOM or VTVM to assure that the dc voltage drop across R6 is approximately 4.4 volts. This indicates proper quiescent collector current at Q12 for linear operation.

Connect the power amplifier stage to the 12-volt supply but do not key the transmitter. R9 should temporarily be set at maximum resistance first. The VOM is temporarily inserted in series with the collector lead of Q13 to measure collector current. R9 should slowly be decreased to the point where the static collector current (no rf signal input) reaches 35 mA. The VOM is removed, the collector lead reconnected, and R9 left at this setting. If a silicon diode other than an HEP RO130 is used for CR2, it may be necessary to change the values of R8 and R9 to achieve the proper quiescent collector current. Some experimentation will determine the correct values, keeping in mind the resistor power dissipation requirements.

Finally, connect a 50-ohm dummy load to the antenna connector and a high-impedance microphone to the microphone jack. The gain control is adjusted in the same manner as with any conventional ssb transmitter. The setting is best determined with the aid of a Monitorscope at the transmitter output. R1 should never be advanced beyond the point where rf peak flattening begins. A slight readjustment of C2 may be necessary to center the ssb signal properly in the passband of the crystal filter. Improper centering will impair the audio frequency response. This adjustment can be made by listening to oneself in a receiver and tweaking C2 for proper response. Note that the ssb frequency will shift, too, as the setting of C2 is changed. The audio should be clean and free from distortion.

In cw operation, the cw drive control R2 should be brought up to the point where no further increase in rf output results. The break-in delay circuit provides semibreak-in operation for cw and push-to-talk operation for ssb. The setting of time delay adjustment R3 determines the length of time the transmit-receive relay K1 remains closed after the key is released. Adjust R3 for a delay time suitable for the keying speed being used. The spare set of contacts of K1 may be used for muting a receiver during transmit or for switching an outboard power amplifier. The transmitter should never be operated without a proper load at the output.

A set of templates for the four circuit boards is available from ARRL Headquarters, Newington, Conn. 06111 for $1.

Fig. 3 — View of the inside of the transmitter. The two main circuit boards are mounted vertically on the left side. Note the use of shields (made from double-clad circuit board) to provide isolation between stages on the boards. The VFO, the third circuit board assembly from the left, is housed in a four-sided enclosure fashioned from four pieces of circuit board. The power output amplifier board mounts over the sheet aluminum heat sink which is also mounted vertically on the chassis. Transmit-receive relay K1 is just visible behind the VFO.

A SOLID-STATE TRANSCEIVER FOR 160 METERS

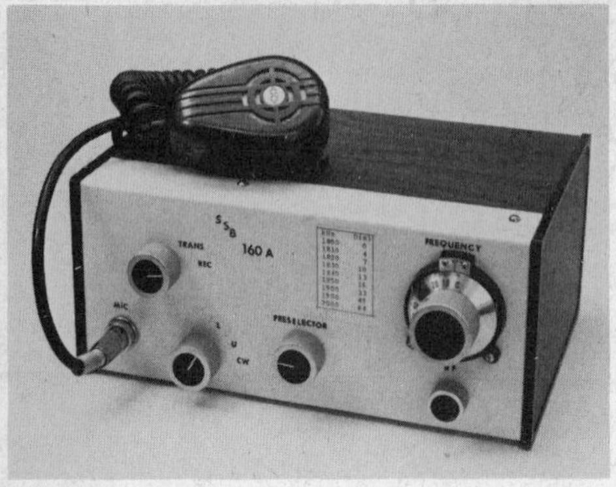

This ssb transceiver is suitable for QRP operation from batteries or as a main frame for fixed-station use. Its circuitry is simple enough to permit easy duplication (or substitution of components where necessary) by proficient builders with only limited experience in solid-state design.

Some 160 Notes

Technically speaking, 160 meters is interesting since it is the only amateur band in the mf range. Phone operation is similar to that encountered on the hf bands but the use of cw is somewhat different. Split-frequency operation is common and one should avoid transmitting within the DX "window" from 1825 to 1830 kHz when the band is open. While cw operation is possible with a transceiver, the above precaution should be noted. Because of the LORAN (Long Range Navigation) service, the band is split up according to geographical area and one should observe the frequency range and power limit for his region (See Chapter 1).

LORAN, proximity to the broadcast band, QRN, and interference from TV sets often imposes severe requirements on receiving devices for this band. While little can be done with sky-wave signals, experimentation with various antenna systems can reduce local interference to a great extent. Proximity and orientation of the antenna to the interfering source are the prime factors here. Because of latter consideration, separate transmitting and receiving antennas may be necessary. Hf-band dipoles, even though they may be electrically short on 160 meters, can still make excellent receiving antennas if a balancing network is used. The balancing transformer (T1) shown in Fig. 1 can be used for both transmitting and receiving, thus reducing ground-loop currents. A simple loading coil in one side of the feed line can be used to tune out the antenna capacitive reactance.

Adequate front-end selectivity is also necessary to assure that unwanted rf energy is rejected *before* it reaches the active elements in the receiving section of the transceiver. The preselector shown in Fig. 1 may be built from readily available parts. Some experimentation with the number of turns on L1 in receive-only applications may be necessary. Use the minimum number of turns that give sufficient sensitivity without signs of overloading. This preselector could also be used with existing receivers with inadequate front-end selectivity on 160.

Circuit Details

The circuit diagram of the transceiver is shown in Fig. 1 and Figs. 3 through 8 incl. The block diagram and switching logic of the transceiver are shown in Fig. 2. This arrangement eliminates the need for relays and provides excellent isolation around the 9-MHz filter board. The full capabilities of a good receiving filter may be reduced considerably by undesirable stray paths. Rf energy rejected by the filter goes around it through the unwanted paths. In the receive position, signals from 1.8 to 2 MHz are mixed with the LO (10.8 to 11 MHz) to give a 9-MHz i-f. Greater bandspread can be achieved by using a smaller value for C10 and increasing L5 or C11. This would reduce the band coverage, however. In the transmit position,

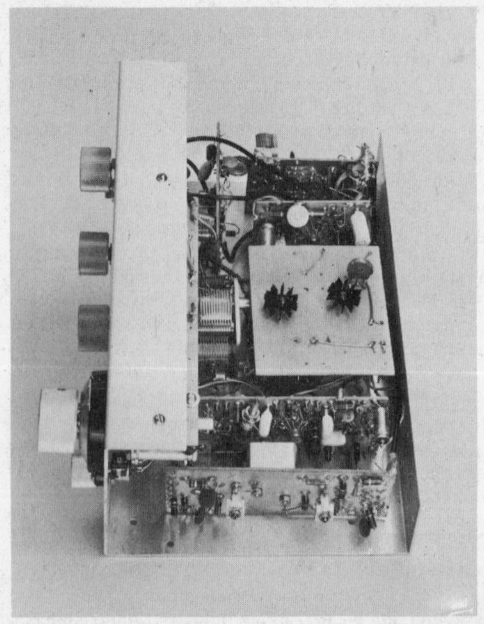

Interior view of the transceiver.

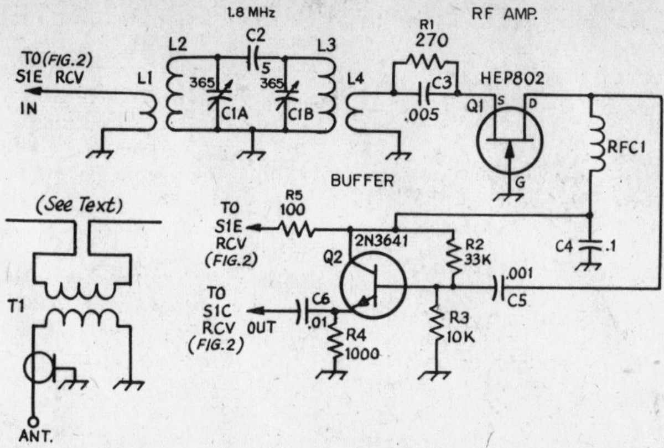

Fig. 1 — Schematic diagram of the rf amplifier and preselector. In this and succeeding diagrams, component designations not mentioned in the captions are for text and layout references only. Unless otherwise noted, resistors are 1/4- or 1/2-watt composition and capacitors are disk ceramic.

C1 — Air variable, 365 pF per section (J.W. Miller 2112 or equiv.).

L1, L4 — 2 turns of plastic-coated wire over cold ends of L2 and L3 respectively.

L2, L3 — Modified Ferri-Tenna Coil (Radio Shack No. 270-1430). Remove coupling coil and all but 35 turns of fine wire on core (see text).

RFC1 — 2.5 mH rf choke pc-board mounting type (Millen J302-2500).

T1 — 40 turns over Amidon T-68-3 toroid (gray core) of bifilar-wound No. 26 enamel wire.

the same mixer is used but rf energy from the balanced modulator and filter board at 9-MHz is converted to the 1.8-MHz band.

Because of the relationship between the LO and the i-f, a sideband inversion occurs. This means that the carrier oscillator crystals will be opposite that usually marked on the filter package. Cw operation is in the usb mode and both carrier-oscillator and VFO offset is used. The carrier-oscillator offset pulls the crystal frequency into the passband of the filter slightly, while the VFO offset can be adjusted for the desired tone on receiving. Keying is accomplished by unbalancing the 1496 IC balanced modulator. Waveshape is determined by the time constant of R62 and C59 in Fig. 7.

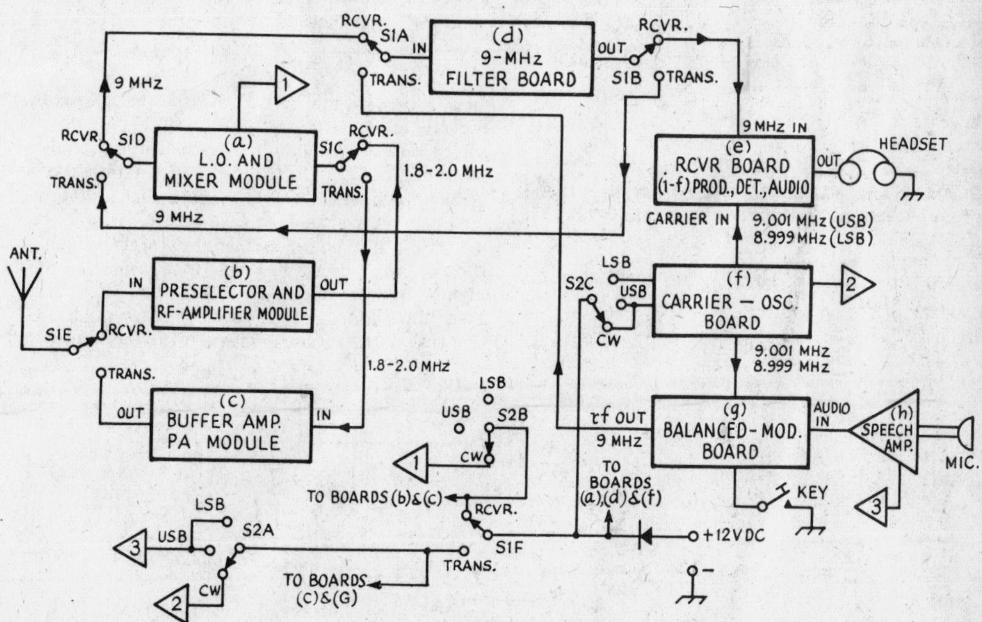

Fig. 2 — Block diagram & switching logic of the transceiver.

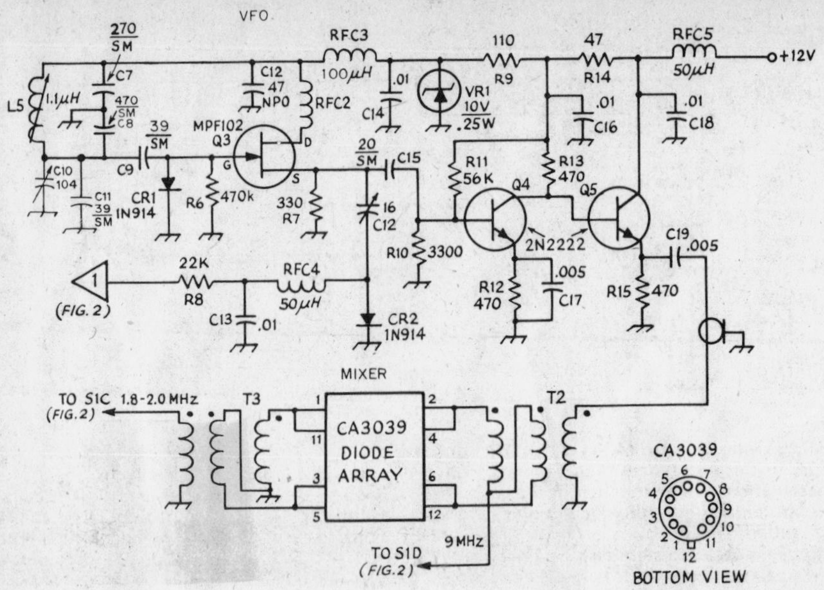

Fig. 3 – Schematic diagram of LO and mixer module. If greater bandspread is desired, a smaller value capacitor could be substituted for C10 with C11 increased by an appropriate amount to set the low-frequency end of the tuning range to 10.8 MHz.

C10 – Air variable, 104 pF maximum (J.W. Miller 2101 or equiv.).

L5 – 1.1-μH slug tuned (Millen 69054-0.91 or equiv.).

RFC2 – Three Amidon ferrite beads at drain terminal of Q3. Install on 1/2-inch length of No. 24 bare wire.

RFC3, RFC4, RFC5 – Miniature 50-μH choke (Millen Co. J300-50).

T2, T3 – 25 turns No. 28 (trifilar wound) on Amidon T-50-3 toroid core.

Fig. 4 – The 9-MHz filter board. Physical layout should keep input and output leads separated.

C22, C25 – 3- to 35- pF mica compression trimmer.

RFC6 – Miniature 100-μH choke (Millen Co. J300-100).

FL1 – 9-MHz crystal filter, 2.1-kHz bandwidth (KVG XF-9B Spectrum International, Box 87, Topsfield, MA 01983).

The low-pass filter shown in Fig. 8 is used to eliminate unwanted rf energy (LO, carrier oscillator, and other products) above 2 MHz before going to the buffer transistor Q11. While various transistors are suitable for cw service in the hf range, many will not perform well as linear power amplifiers. The variation in transistor current gain over a large dynamic range is too great. This results in distortion or imposes severe biasing problems. Generally speaking, uhf types are the best ones to use. The amplifier used with the transceiver is capable of approximately one-watt output with good IMD characteristics.

Construction

A modular-type layout was used that allows the builder to pretest various sections of the transceiver *before* installation in the cabinet. Single-sided pc board or Vectorbord construction should be avoided since unwanted capacitive and inductive coupling may cause spurious oscillations. Use double-sided pc board, or, as in the case of the unit shown, isolated-pad construction. The latter is highly recommended. The individual boards are then mounted in the cabinet with small "L" brackets or in the case of the VFO module, with screws.

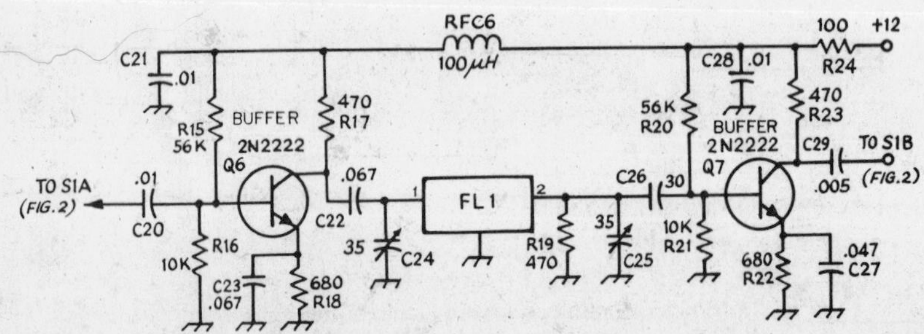

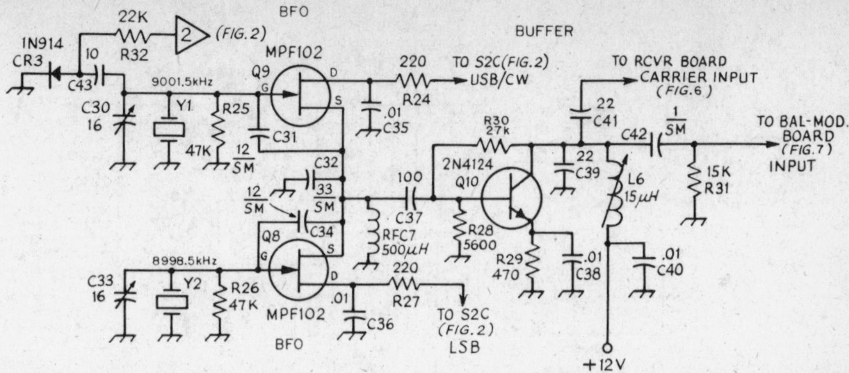

Fig. 5 – Carrier oscillator board.
C30, C33 – Miniature pc-mount air variable (Johnson 189-506-5, Allied Electronics 828-1219).
L6 – 15 μH nominal (Miller 4506 or equiv.).
RFC7 – 500-μH rf choke (Millen J300-500).
Y1, Y2 – KVG matching crystals for FL1.

Where interconnecting shielded cables are used (such as the connections on S1 and other rf leads), small coaxial cable is ideal. RG-174/U was used in the unit shown and it is good practice to tie the ground leads to one point where two or more cables come together. An example would be the switch connections at S1. Regular hook-up wire can be used for the power-supply leads going to each board.

While the general layout should not be critical, the one shown in the photograph is suggested. The cabinet is a Ten-Tec MW-10 and the dial assembly can be obtained from Allied/Radio Shack. The rootary switches for S1 and S2 are surplus miniature types with glass-epoxy insulation. The size of the various components available will determine the final layout but care should be taken to keep all leads as short as possible.

It is a good idea to start with the receiver portion of the transceiver (the rf amplifier and preselector is the simplest module to build). Carefully unwind (and save) the wire from the two ferrite-loop antenna coils.

Wind a one-layer coil (35 turns) back on each form and solder it in place. Paint each coil with *Q* dope to keep the turns from unwinding. Mount the completed coils (L2 and L3) using heavy wire leads on the 365-pF capacitor as shown in the photograph. L1 and L4 consist of 2 turns of hook up wire wound on the cold end of L2 and L3 respectively. Next, lay out the circuit board for the

Fig. 6 – Receiver board. This includes the i-f amplifier, product detector, and audio amplifier. Audio power is sufficient for high-impedance earphones.
L7 – Slug-tuned inductor, 1.6 μH nominal, 13 turns No. 26 enam. on 1/4-inch form.

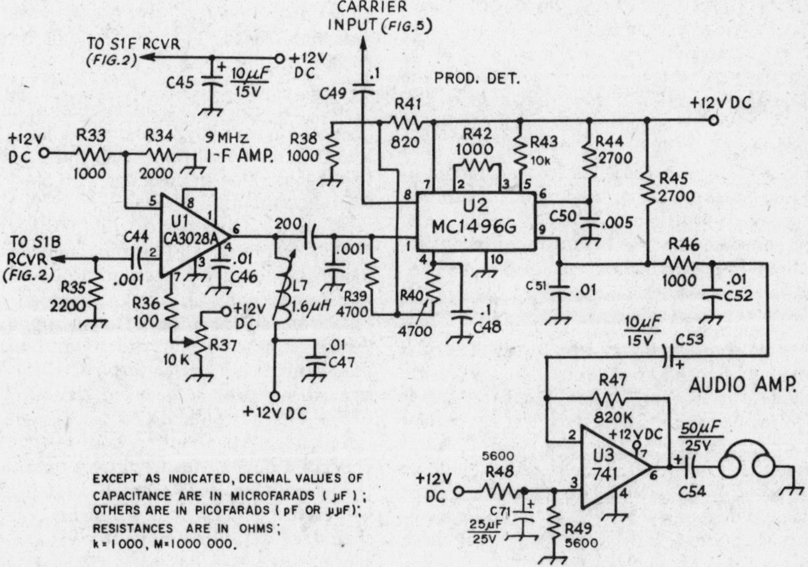

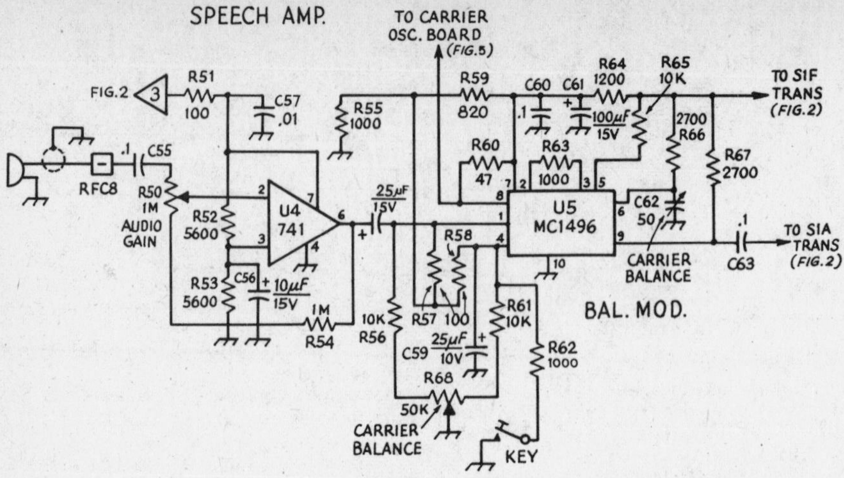

Fig. 7 – Schematic diagram of the speech amplifier and the balanced modulator boards.
C62 – Mica Compression trimmer, 50 pF.
R52, R68 – Control, pc-mounting type.
RFC8 – 3 ferrite beads over microphone-input lead.

rf amplifier, making it small enough to mount on the back of the capacitor with spacers and screws. Layout for this board (and the remaining ones) will be successful if the following rules are observed. First, keep all component leads as short as possible (especially IC leads) and second, lay out the stages in a straight line as shown in the photograph. Also assure that input and output leads are kept as far away from each other as is practical. If the isolated-pad construction technique is used, a drill press (bench style) is handy. However, either a hand-held electric drill or a crank-type hand drill may be used. Once the preselector module is completed, perform the alignment procedure before going on to the next board. Complete and test the remaining boards before mounting them permanently in the cabinet.

Alignment

While the transceiver could be tested after it is completed, the procedure outlined here will assure each module is working before the next one is mounted in the cabinet. Necessary test equipment includes a signal source and receiver covering 1.8 to 2.0 MHz, and 9 to 11 MHz. The receiver should be capable of receiving ssb signals. Other suggested equipment would be a VTVM, a monitor scope which can be used with the receiver to check modulation, and a frequency counter.

The preselector module should be aligned first. Connect a signal source to the general-coverage receiver and tune in the signal. Next, connect the preselector between the generator and the receiver and adjust the slugs until the signals peak. For correct alignment, C1 should be fully meshed at the low end (1.8 MHz) of the band. The VFO should be adjusted by setting its range for 10.8 to 11 MHz as indicated on either a general-coverage receiver or a frequency counter. The preselector and LO/mixer modules may be mounted inside the cabinet and interconnected. See blocks (a) and (b) in Fig. 2. The external receiver should be connected to the output of T2. When power is applied to the transceiver and S1 is set for RCV, signals and noise should be heard at 9 MHz as the VFO and preselector are tuned. The 9-MHz filter board should be installed and the receiver connection moved from T2 to the output of the filter. See block (d) in Fig. 2. Peak C24 and C25 for maximum signal. The carrier-oscillator board may be checked by listening with the general-coverage receiver to the two crystal frequencies (8.999 and 9.001). Mount the carrier-oscillator and receiver boards, connect a headphone set and adjust L7 for maximum receiver sensitivity. This completes the alignment of the receiver. See block (c) in Fig. 2 for details.

Refer to block (h) in Fig. 2 and mount the speech amplifier. Install the appropriate power, input and output connections. Couple a headset to the output of this circuit through a 0.5-µF capacitor and speak into the microphone. Speech should be heard. Install and connect the balanced-modulator board. Refer to block (g) in Fig. 2. Ssb signals should be detected at the output terminal of T3. Adjust R68 and C62 for minimum carrier. Interconnect the buffer and PA modules, and connect a dummy load (with an output indicator) to the antenna jack. A small pilot light (No. 47) will suffice if the PA shown in Fig. 8 is used. R73 should be set for minimum collector current. A short whistle into the microphone should produce

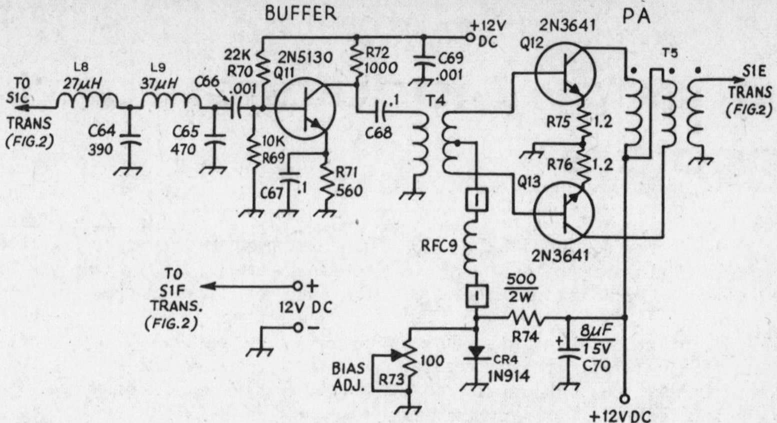

an output signal. Clear-sounding ssb signals should be heard when listening to the general-coverage receiver. This completes the ssb alignment.

Place a jumper from either the USB or LSB position of S2A to the CW position of S2A. Set the general-coverage receiver to the USB position. Turn the transceiver to the CW position and tune until a readable ssb signal is heard. Key the transceiver and depending upon the settings of C12 and C30, a tone should be heard. C30 will determine the amount of output. Adjust C12 until the desired sidetone is obtained. This will require retuning the receiver for readable usb after each adjustment. When the adjustment is correct, a proper-sounding ssb signal can be heard in the CW position and the desired note will also be heard when the transmitter is keyed. Remove the jumper from S2A. This completes alignment of the transceiver.

Fig. 8 – Schematic diagram of buffer and PA. If a broad-band amplifier or antenna circuit is to follow T5, a low-pass filter may be necessary to reduce unwanted harmonic energy.

L8 – 27 μH, 66 turns of No. 30 enam. wire on Amidon T-50-3 (gray) toroid core.

L9 – 37 μH, 76 turns No. 30 enam. on T-50-3 core.

R73 – Control, pc-mounting type.

RFC9 – 2.7 μH minimum. Slip a ferrite bead over each end of a small rf choke (Millen 34300).

T4 – Stack two Amidon Husky (7 mm) beads and wind a 5-turn primary and a 3 turn secondary through both cores. Use No. 26 enam. wire. Make a second transformer similar to the first one. Parallel the primaries, and series connect the secondaries observing the polarities shown on the diagram.

T5 – 24 turns No. 26 enam. wire (trifilar wound) on Amidon T-68-3 core.

Frequency Modulation and Repeaters

Methods of radiotelphone communication by frequency modulation were developed in the 1930s by Major Edwin Armstrong in an attempt to reduce the problems of static and noise associated with receiving a-m broadcast transmissions. The primary advantage of fm, the ability to produce a high signal-to-noise ratio when receiving a signal of only moderate strength, has made fm the mode chosen for mobile communications services and quality broadcasting. The disadvantages, the wide bandwidth required and the poor results obtained when an fm signal is propagated via the ionosphere (because of phase distortion), has limited the use of frequency modulation to the 10-meter band and the vhf/uhf section of the spectrum.

Fm has some impressive advantages for vhf operation, especially when compared to a-m. With fm the modulation process takes place in a low-level stage. The modulation equipment required is the same, regardless of transmitter power. The signal may be frequency multiplied after modulation, and the PA stage can be operated Class C for best efficiency, as the "final" need not be linear.

In recent years there has been increasing use of fm by amateurs operating around 29.6 MHz in the 10-meter band. The vhf spectrum now in popular use includes 52 to 53 MHz, 146 to 147.5 MHz, 222 to 225 MHz, and 440 to 450 MHz.

FREQUENCY AND PHASE MODULATION

It is possible to convey intelligence by modulating any property of a carrier, including its frequency and phase. When the frequency of the carrier is varied in accordance with the variations in a modulating signal, the result is **frequency modulation (fm).** Similarly, varying the phase of the carrier current is called **phase modulation (pm).**

Frequency and phase modulation are not independent, since the frequency cannot be varied without also varying the phase, and vice versa.

The effectiveness of fm and pm for communication purposes depends almost entirely on the receiving methods. If the receiver will respond to frequency and phase changes but is insensitive to amplitude changes, it will discriminate against most forms of noise, particularly impulse noise such as is set up by ignition systems and other sparking devices. Special methods of detection are required to accomplish this result.

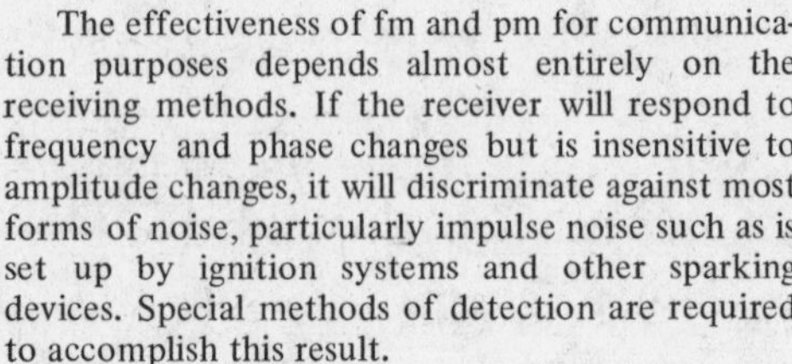

Modulation methods for fm and pm are simple and require practically no audio power. There is also the advantage that, since there is no amplitude variation in the signal, interference to broadcast reception resulting from rectification of the transmitted signal in the audio circuits of the bc receiver is substantially eliminated.

Frequency Modulation

Fig. 14-2 is a representation of frequency modulation. When a modulating signal is applied, the carrier frequency is increased during one half cycle of the modulating signal and decreased during the half cycle of opposite polarity. This is indicated in the drawing by the fact that the rf cycles occupy less time (higher frequency) when the modulating signal is positive, and more time (lower frequency) when the modulating signal is negative. The change in the carrier frequency **(frequency deviation)** is proportional to the instantaneous amplitude of the modulating signal, so the deviation is small when the instantaneous amplitude of the modulating signal is small, and is greatest when the modulating signal reaches its peak, either positive or negative.

As shown by the drawing, the amplitude of the signal does not change during modulation.

Phase Modulation

If the phase of the current in a circuit is changed there is an instantaneous frequency change during the time that the phase is being shifted. The amount of frequency change, or deviation, depends on how rapidly the phase shift is accomplished. It is also dependent upon the total amount of the phase shift. In a properly operating

Fig. 14-1 — The use of vhf fm mobile rigs in conjunction with repeaters has improved the communications of many amateur emergency groups. Here F2BQ relays traffic being received via 2-meter fm on a 40-meter ssb link.

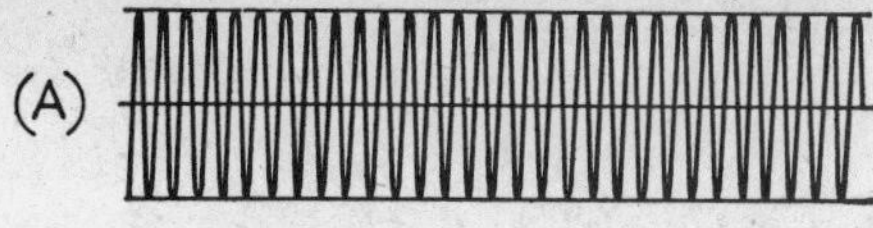

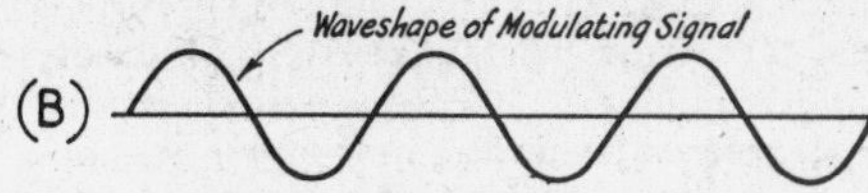

Fig. 14-2 – Graphical representation of frequency modulation. In the unmodulated carrier at A, each rf cycle occupies the same amount of time. When the modulating signal, B, is applied, the radio frequency is increased and decreased according to the amplitude and polarity of the modulating signal.

pm system the amount of phase shift is proportional to the instantaneous amplitude of the modulating signal. The rapidity of the phase shift is directly proportional to the frequency of the modulating signal. Consequently, the frequency deviation in pm is proportional to both the amplitude and frequency of the modulating signal. The latter represents the outstanding difference between fm and pm, since in fm the frequency deviation is proportional only to the amplitude of the modulating signal.

FM and PM Sidebands

The sidebands set up by fm and pm differ from those resulting from a-m in that they occur at integral multiples of the modulating frequency on either side of the carrier rather than, as in a-m, consisting of a single set of side frequencies for each modulating frequency. An fm or pm signal therefore inherently occupies a wider channel than a-m.

The number of "extra" sidebands that occur in fm and pm depends on the relationship between the modulating frequency and the frequency deviation. The ratio between the frequency deviation, in Hertz, and the modulating frequency, also in Hertz, is called the **modulating index.** That is,

$$\text{Modulation index} = \frac{\text{Carrier frequency deviation}}{\text{Modulating frequency}}$$

Example: The maximum frequency deviation in an f.m. transmitter is 3000 Hz. either side of the carrier frequency. The modulation index when the modulating frequency is 1000 Hz. is

$$\text{Modulation index} = \frac{3000}{1000} = 3$$

At the same deviation with 3000-Hz. modulation the index would be 1; at 100 Hz. it would be 30, and so on.

In pm the modulation index is constant regardless of the modulating frequency; in fm it varies with the modulating frequency, as shown in the above example. In an fm system the ratio of the *maximum* carrier-frequency deviation to the *highest* modulating frequency used is called the **deviation ratio.**

Fig. 14-3 shows how the amplitudes of the carrier and the various sidebands vary with the modulation index. This is for single-tone modulation; the first sideband (actually a pair, one above and one below the carrier) is displaced from the carrier by an amount equal to the modulating frequency, the second is twice the modulating frequency away from the carrier, and so on. For example, if the modulating frequency is 2000 Hz and the carrier frequency is 29,500 kHz, the first sideband pair is at 29,498 kHz and 29,502 kHz, the second pair is at 29,496 kHz and 29,504 kHz, the third at 29,494 kHz and 29,506 kHz, etc. The amplitudes of these sidebands depend on the modulation index, not on the frequency deviation.

Note that as shown by Fig. 14-3, the carrier strength varies with the modulation index. (In amplitude modulation the carrier strength is constant; only the sideband amplitude varies.) At a modulation index of approximately 2.4 the carrier disappears entirely. It then becomes "negative" at a higher index, meaning that its phase is reversed as compared to the phase without modulation. In fm and pm the energy that goes into the sidebands is taken from the carrier, the *total* power remaining the same regardless of the modulation index.

Since there is no change in amplitude with modulation, an fm or pm signal can be amplified without distortion by an ordinary Class C amplifier. The modulation can take place in a very low-level stage and the signal can then be amplified by either frequency multipliers or straight-through amplifiers.

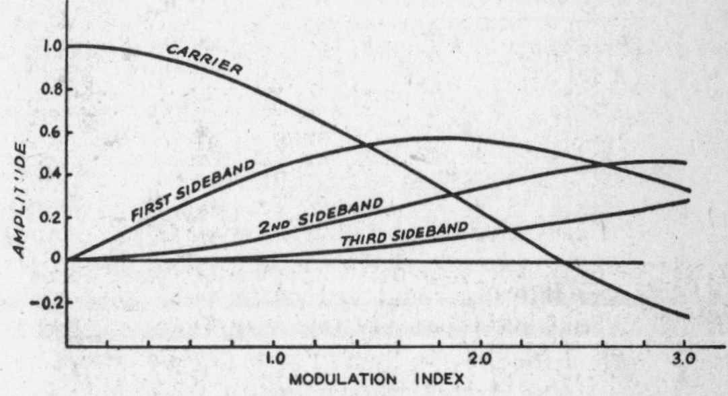

Fig. 14-3 – How the amplitude of the pairs of sidebands varies with the modulation index in an fm or pm signal. If the curves were extended for greater values of modulation index it would be seen that the carrier amplitude goes through zero at several points. The same statement also applies to the sidebands.

If the modulated signal is passed through one or more frequency multipliers, the modulation index is multiplied by the same factor that the carrier frequency is multiplied. For example, if modulation is applied on 3.5 MHz and the final output is on 28 MHz, the total frequency multiplication is 8 times, so if the frequency deviation is 500 Hz at 3.5 MHz it will be 4000 Hz at 28 MHz. Frequency multiplication offers a means for obtaining practically any desired amount of frequency deviation, whether or not the modulator itself is capable of giving that much deviation without distortion.

Bandwidth

FCC amateur regulations (Part 97.61) limit the bandwidth of F3 (frequency and phase modulation) to that of an a-m transmission having the same audio characteristics below 29.0 MHz and in the 50.1- to 52.5-MHz frequency segment. Greater bandwidths are allowed from 29.0 to 29.7 MHz and above 52.5 MHz.

If the modulation index (with single-tone modulation) does not exceed 0.6 or 0.7, the most important extra sideband, the second, will be at least 20 dB below the unmodulated carrier level, and this should represent an effective channel width about equivalent to that of an a-m signal. In the case of speech, a somewhat higher modulation index can be used. This is because the energy distribution in a complex wave is such that the modulation index for any one frequency component is reduced as compared to the index with a sine wave having the same peak amplitude as the voice wave.

The chief advantage of fm or pm for frequencies below 30 MHz is that it eliminates or reduces certain types of interference to broadcast reception. Also, the modulating equipment is relatively simple and inexpensive. However, assuming the same unmodulated carrier power in all cases, narrow-band fm or pm is not as effective as a-m *with the methods of reception used by many amateurs.* To obtain the benefits of the fm mode, a good fm receiver is required. As shown in Fig. 14-3, at an index of 0.6 the amplitude of the first sideband is about 25 percent of the unmodulated-carrier amplitude; this compares with a sideband amplitude of 50 percent in the case of a 100 percent modulated a-m transmitter. When copied on an a-m receiver, a narrow-band fm or pm transmitter is about equivalent to a 100-percent modulated a-m transmitter operating at one-fourth the carrier power. On a suitable (fm) receiver, fm is as good or better than a-m, watt for watt.

Three deviation amounts are now standard practice: 15, 5 and 2.5 kHz, which in the current vernacular of fm users, are known as wide band, narrow band, and sliver band, respectively. (See box above.) The 2.5-3 kHz deviation (called nbfm by OTs) was popular for a time on the vhf bands and 10 meters after World War II. Deviation figures are given for the frequency swing in one direction. The rule-of-thumb for determination of bandwidth requirements for an fm system is:

$$2\,(\triangle F) + F_{\mathrm{Amax}}$$

where $\triangle F$ is one half of the total frequency deviation, and F_{Amax} is the maximum audio frequency (3 kHz for communications purposes). Thus, for narrow-band fm, the bandwidth equals (2) 5 + 3 or 13 kHz. Wide-band systems need a 33-kHz receiver bandwidth.

Comparison of FM and PM

Frequency modulation cannot be applied to an amplifier stage, but phase modulation can; pm is therefore readily adaptable to transmitters employing oscillators of high stability such as the crystal-controlled type. The amount of phase shift that can be obtained with good linearity is such that the maximum practicable modulation index is about 0.5. Because the phase shift is proportional to the modulating frequency, this index can be used only at the highest frequency present in the modulating signal, assuming that all frequencies will at one time or another have equal amplitudes. Taking 3000 Hz as a suitable upper limit for voice work, and setting the modulation index at 0.5 for 3000 Hz, the frequency response of the speech-amplifier system above 3000 Hz must be sharply attenuated, to prevent excess splatter. (See Fig. 14-4.) Also, if the "tinny" quality of pm as received on an fm receiver is to be avoided, the pm must be changed to fm, in which the modulation index decreases in inverse proportion to the modulating frequency. This requires shaping the speech-amplifier frequency-response curve in such a way that the output voltage is inversely proportional to frequency over most of the voice range. When this is done the maximum modulation index can only be used to some relatively low audio frequency, perhaps 300 to 400 Hz in voice transmission, and must decrease in proportion to the increase in frequency. The result is that the maximum linear frequency deviation is only one or two hundred Hz, when pm is changed to fm. To increase the deviation for narrow band requires a frequency multiplication of 8 times or more.

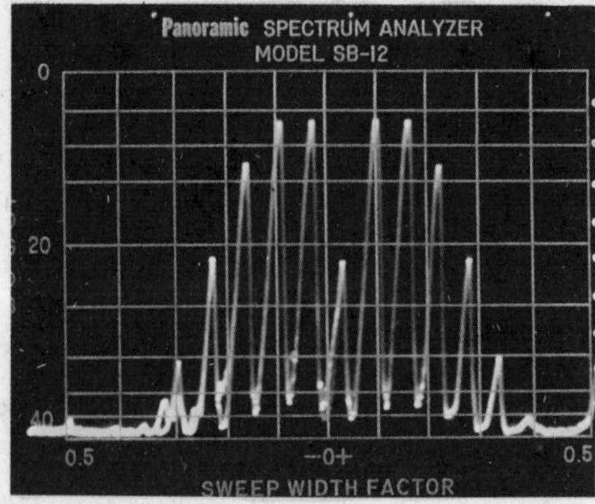

Fig. 14-4 — Output frequency spectrum of a narrow-band fm transmitter modulated by a 1-kHz tone.

It is relatively easy to secure a fairly large frequency deviation when a self-controlled oscillator is frequency-modulated directly. (True frequency modulation of a crystal-controlled oscillator results in only very small deviations and so requires a great deal of frequency multiplication.) The chief problem is to maintain a satisfactory degree of carrier stability, since the greater the inherent stability of the oscillator the more difficult it is to secure a wide frequency swing with linearity.

METHODS OF FREQUENCY MODULATION

Direct FM

A simple and satisfactory device for producing fm in the amateur transmitter is the reactance modulator. This is a vacuum tube or transistor connected to the rf tank circuit of an oscillator in such a way as to act as a variable inductance or capacitance.

Fig. 14-5A is a representative circuit. Gate 1 of the modulator MOSFET is connected across the oscillator tank circuit, C1L1, through resistor R1 and blocking capacitor C2. C3 represents the input capacitance of the modulator transistor. The resistance of R1 is made large compared to the reactance of C3, so the rf current through R1C3 will be practically in phase with the rf voltage appearing at the terminals of the tank circuit. However, the voltage across C3 will lag the current by 90 degrees. The rf current in the drain circuit of the modulator will be in phase with the grid voltage, and consequently is 90 degrees behind the current through C3, or 90 degrees behind the rf tank voltage. This lagging current is drawn through the oscillator tank, giving the same effect as though an inductance were connected across the tank. The frequency increases in proportion to the amplitude of the lagging plate current of the modulator. The audio voltage, introduced through a radio-frequency choke, varies the transconductance of the transistor and thereby varies the rf drain current.

The modulated oscillator usually is operated on a relatively low frequency, so that a high order of carrier stability can be secured. Frequency multipliers are used to raise the frequency to the final frequency desired.

A reactance modulator can be connected to a crystal oscillator as well as to the self-controlled type as shown in Fig. 14-5B. However, the resulting signal can be more phase-modulated than it is frequency-modulated, for the reason that the frequency deviation that can be secured by varying the frequency of a crystal oscillator is quite small.

The sensitivity of the modulator (frequency change per unit change in grid voltage) depends on the transconductance of the modulator transistor. It increases when R1 is made smaller in comparison with C3. It also increases with an increase in L/C ratio in the oscillator tank circuit. However, for highest carrier stability it is desirable to use the largest tank capacitance that will permit the desired deviation to be secured while keeping within the limits of linear operation.

A change in *any* of the voltages on the modulator transistor will cause a change in rf drain current, and consequently a frequency change. Therefore it is advisable to use a regulated power supply for both modulator and oscillator.

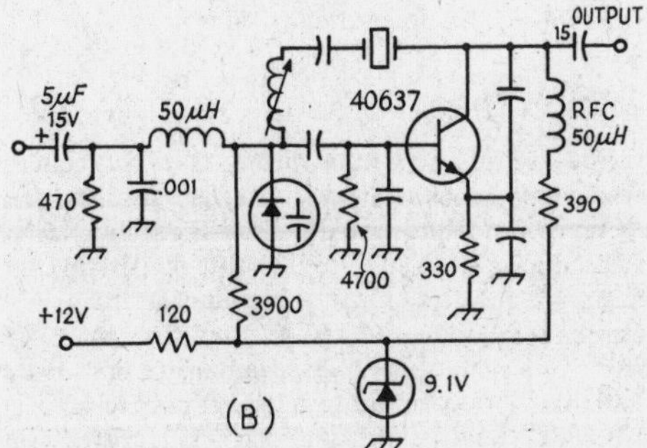

Fig. 14-5 — Reactance modulators using (A) a high-transconductance MOSFET and (B) a varactor diode.

Indirect FM

The same type of reactance-tube circuit that is used to vary the tuning of the oscillator tank in fm can be used to vary the tuning of an amplifier tank and thus vary the phase of the tank current for pm. Hence the modulator circuit of Fig. 14-5A or 14-6A can be used for pm if the reactance transistor or tube works on an amplifier tank instead of directly on a self-controlled oscillator. If audio shaping is used in the speech amplifier, as described above, fm instead of pm will be generated by the phase modulator.

The phase shift that occurs when a circuit is detuned from resonance depends on the amount of detuning and the *Q* of the circuit. The higher the

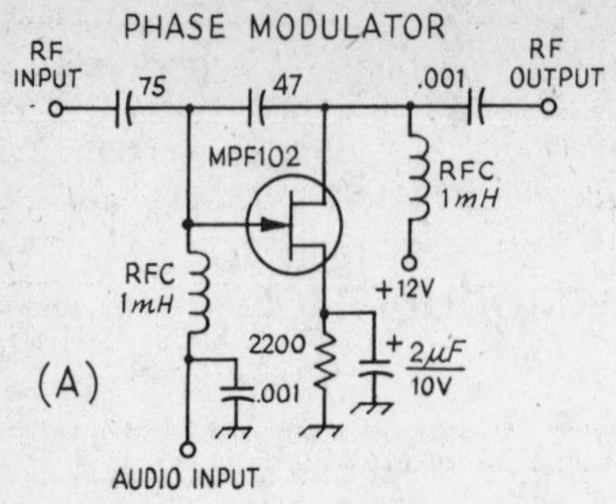

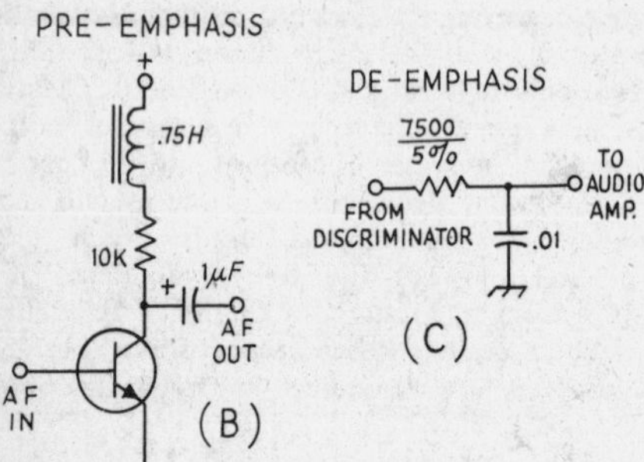

Fig. 14-6 – (A) The phase-shifter type of phase modulator. (B) Pre-emphasis and (C) de-emphasis circuits.

Q, the smaller the amount of detuning needed to secure a given number of degrees of phase shift. If the *Q* is at least 10, the relationship between phase shift and detuning (in kHz either side of the resonant frequency) will be substantially linear over a phase-shift range of about 25 degrees. From the standpoint of modulator sensitivity, the *Q* of the tuned circuit on which the modulator operates should be as high as possible. On the other hand, the effective *Q* of the circuit will not be very high if the amplifier is delivering power to a load since the load resistance reduces the *Q*. There must therefore be a compromise between modulator sensitivity and rf power output from the modulated amplifier. An optimum figure for *Q* appears to be about 20; this allows reasonable loading of the modulated amplifier and the necessary tuning variation can be secured from a reactance modulator without difficulty. It is advisable to modulate at a low power level.

Reactance modulation of an amplifier stage usually results in simultaneous amplitude modulation because the modulated stage is detuned from resonance as the phase is shifted. This must be eliminated by feeding the modulated signal through an amplitude limiter or one or more "saturating" stages – that is, amplifiers that are operated Class C and driven hard enough so that variations in the amplitude of the input excitation produce no appreciable variations in the output amplitude.

For the same type of reactance modulator, the speech-amplifier gain required is the same for pm as for fm. However, as pointed out earlier, the fact that the actual frequency deviation increases with the modulating audio frequency in pm makes it necessary to cut off the frequencies above about 3000 Hz before modulation takes place. If this is not done, unnecessary sidebands will be generated at frequencies considerably away from the carrier.

SPEECH PROCESSING FOR FM

The speech amplifier preceding the modulator follows ordinary design, except that no power is taken from it and the af voltage required by the modulator grid usually is small – not more than 10 or 15 volts, even with large modulator tubes, and only a volt or two for transistors. Because of these modest requirements, only a few speech stages are needed; a two-stage amplifier consisting of two bipolar transistors, both resistance-coupled, will more than suffice for crystal ceramic or hi-*Z* dynamic microphones. For more information on speech amplifiers see Chapter 13.

Several forms of speech processing produce worthwhile improvements in fm system performance. It is desirable to limit the peak amplitude of the audio signal applied to an fm or pm modulator, so that the deviation of the fm transmitter will not exceed a preset value. This peak limiting is usually accomplished with a simple audio clipper which is placed between the speech amplifier and modulator. The clipping process produces high-order harmonics which, if allowed to pass through to the modulator stage, would create unwanted sidebands. Therefore, an audio low-pass filter with a cut-off frequency between 2.5 and 3 kHz is needed at the output of the clipper. Excess clipping can cause severe distortion of the voice signal. An audio processor consisting of a compressor and a clipper, such as described in Chapter 13, has been found to produce audio with a better sound (i.e., less distortion) than a clipper alone.

To reduce the amount of noise in some fm communications systems, an audio shaping network called **pre-emphasis** is added at the transmitter to proportionally attenuate the lower audio frequencies, giving an even spread to the energy in the audio band. This results in an fm signal of nearly constant energy distribution. The reverse is done at the receiver, called **de-emphasis**, to restore the audio to its original relative proportions. Sample circuits are shown in Fig. 14-6.

FM EXCITERS

Fm exciters and transmitters take two general forms. One, shown at Fig. 14-7A, consists of a reactance modulator which shifts the frequency of an oscillator to generate an fm signal directly. Successive multiplier stages provide output on the desired frequency, which is amplified by a PA stage. This system has a disadvantage in that, if the oscillator is free running, it is difficult to achieve sufficient stability for vhf use. If a crystal-controlled oscillator is employed, unless the amount that the crystal frequency is changed is kept small, it is difficult to achieve equal amounts of frequency swing.

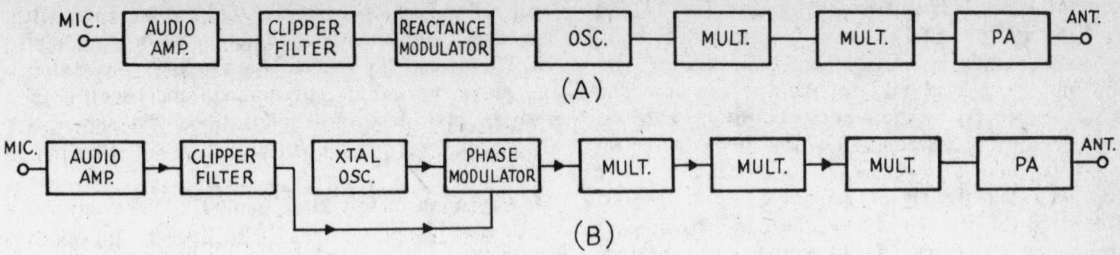

Fig. 14-7 — Block diagrams of typical fm exciters.

The indirect method of generating fm shown in Fig. 14-7B is currently popular. Shaped audio is applied to a phase modulator to generate fm. As the amount of deviation produced is very small, then a large number of multiplier stages is needed to achieve wide-band deviation at the operating frequency. In general, the system shown at A will require a less complex circuit than that at B, but the indirect method (B) often produces superior results.

TESTING AN FM TRANSMITTER

Accurate checking of the operation of an fm or pm transmitter requires different methods than the corresponding checks on an a-m or ssb set. This is because the common forms of measuring devices either indicate amplitude variations only (a milliammeter, for example), or because their indications are most easily interpreted in terms of amplitude.

The quantities to be checked in an fm transmitter are the linearity and frequency deviation and the output frequency., if the unit uses crystal control. The methods of checking differ in detail.

Frequency Checking

The crystal-controlled, channelized operation that is now popular with amateur fm users requires that a transmitter be held close to the desired channel, at least within a few hundred Hertz, even in a wide-band system. Having the transmitter on the proper frequency is particularly important when operating through a repeater. The rigors of mobile and portable operation make a frequency check of a channelized transceiver a good idea at three-month intervals.

Frequency meters generally fall in two categories, the hererodyne type and the digital counter. For amateur use, the vhf/uhf counterparts of the

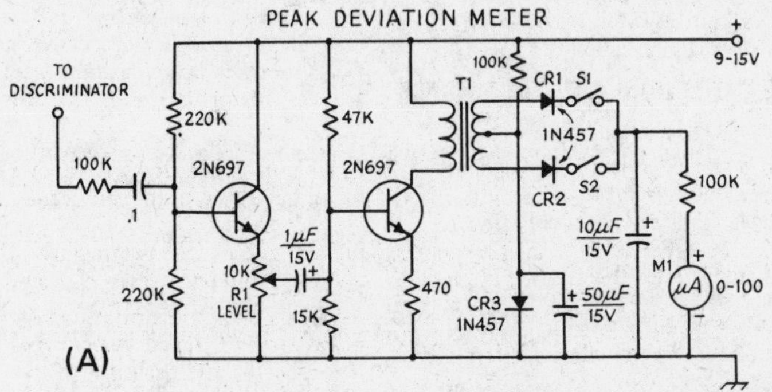

(B)

Audio Frequency	*Deviation Produced 1st Null*	*2nd Null*	*3rd Null*
905.8 Hz	±2.18 kHz	± 5.00 kHz	± 7.84 kHz
1000.0 Hz	±2.40 kHz	± 5.52 kHz	± 8.65 kHz
1500.0 Hz	±3.61 kHz	± 8.28 kHz	±12.98 kHz
1811.0 Hz	±4.35 kHz	±10.00 kHz	±15.67 kHz
2000.0 Hz	±4.81 kHz	±11.04 kHz	±17.31 kHz
2079.2 Hz	±5.00 kHz	±11.48 kHz	±17.99 kHz
2805.0 Hz	±6.75 kHz	±15.48 kHz	±24.27 kHz

Fig. 14-8 — (A) Schematic diagram of the deviation meter. Resistors are 1/2-watt composition and capacitors are ceramic, except those with polarity marked, which are electrolytic. CR1-CR3, incl. are high-speed silicon switching diodes. R1 is a linear-taper composition control, and S1, S2 are spst toggle switches. T1 is a miniature audio transformer with a 10,000-ohm primary and 20,000-ohm center-tapped secondary (Triad A31X). (B) Chart of audio frequencies which will produce a carrier null when the deviation of an fm transmitter is set for the values given.

popular BC-221 frequency meter, the TS-174 and TS-175, will provide sufficient accuracy. Frequency counters that will work directly up to 500 MHz and higher are available, but their cost is high. The less expensive low-frequency counters can be employed using a scaler, a device which divides an input frequency by a preset ratio, usually 10 or 100. The Heathkit IB-102 scaler may be used up to 175 MHz, using a counter with a 2-MHz (or more) upper frequency limit. If the counting system does not have a sufficient upper frequency limit to measure the output of an fm transmitter directly, one of the frequency-multiplier stages can be sampled to provide a signal in the range of the measurement device. Alternatively, a crystal-controlled converter feeding an hf receiver which has accurate frequency readout can be employed, if a secondary standard is available to calibrate the receiving system.

Deviation and Deviation Linearity

A simple deviation meter can be assembled following the diagram of Fig. 14-8A. This circuit was designed by K6VKZ. The output of a wide-band receiver discriminator (before any de-emphasis) is fed to two amplifier transistors. The output of the amplifier section is transformer coupled to a pair of rectifier diodes to develop a dc voltage for the meter, M1. There will be an indication on the meter with no signal input because of detected noise, so the accuracy of the instrument will be poor on weak signals.

To calibrate the unit, signals of known deviation will be required. If the meter is to be set to read 0-15 kHz, then a 7.5-kHz deviation test signal should be employed. R1 is then adjusted until M1 reads half scale, 50 μA. To check the peak deviation of an incoming signal, close both S1 and S2. Then, read the meter. Opening first one switch and then the other will indicate the amount of positive and negative deviation of the signal, a check of deviation linearity.

Measurement of Deviation Using Bessel Functions

Using a math. relationship known as the Bessel Function it is possible to predict the points at which, with certain audio-input frequencies and predetermined deviation settings, the carrier output of an fm transmitter will disappear completely. Thus, by monitoring the carrier frequency with a receiver, it will be possible by ear to identify the deviation at which the carrier is nulled. A heterodyne signal at either the input or receiver i-f is required so that the carrier will produce a beat note which can easily be identified. Other tones will be produced in the modulation process, so some concentration is required by the operator when making the test. With an audio tone selected from the chart (Fig. 14-8B), advance the deviation control slowly until the first null is heard. If a higher-order null is desired, continue advancing the control further until the second, and then the third, null is heard. Using a carrier null beyond the third is generally not practical.

For example, if a 905.8-Hz tone is used, the transmitter will be set for 5-kHz deviation when the second null is reached. The second null achieved with a 2805-Hz audio input will set the transmitter deviation at 15.48 kHz. The Bessel-function approach can be used to calibrate a deviation meter, such as the unit shown in Fig. 14-8A

RECEPTION OF FM SIGNALS

Receivers for fm signals differ from others principally in two features – there is no need for linearity preceding detection (it is, in fact, advantageous if amplitude variations in signal and background noise can be "washed out") and the detector must be capable of converting frequency variations in the incoming signal into amplitude variations.

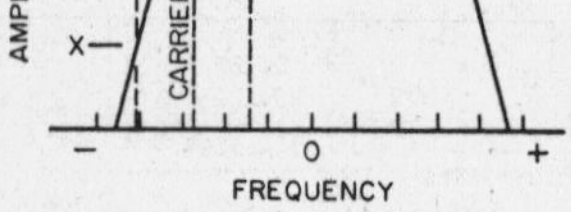

Frequency-modulated signals can be received after a fashion on any ordinary receiver. The receiver is tuned to put the carrier frequency partway down on one side of the selectivity curve. When the frequency of the signal varies with modulation it swings as indicated in Fig. 14-9, resulting in an a-m output varying between X and Y. This is then rectified as an a-m signal.

With receivers having steep-sided selectivity curves, the method is not very satisfactory because the distortion is quite severe unless the frequency deviation is small, since the frequency deviation and output amplitude is linear over only a small part of the selectivity curve.

Fig. 14-9 – Fm detector characteristics. Slope detection, using the sloping side of the receivers selectivity curve to convert fm to a-m for subsequent detection.

The FM Receiver

Block diagrams of an a-m/ssb and an fm receiver are shown in Fig. 14-10. Fundamentally, to achieve a sensitivity of less than one microvolt, an fm receiver requires a gain of several million – too much total gain to be accomplished with stability on a single frequency. Thus, the use of the

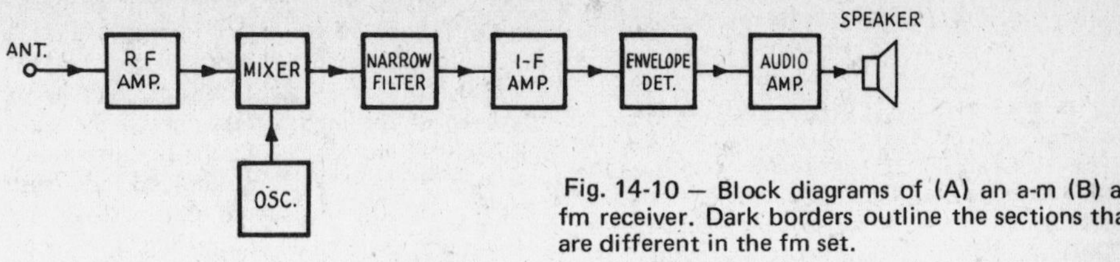

Fig. 14-10 — Block diagrams of (A) an a-m (B) an fm receiver. Dark borders outline the sections that are different in the fm set.

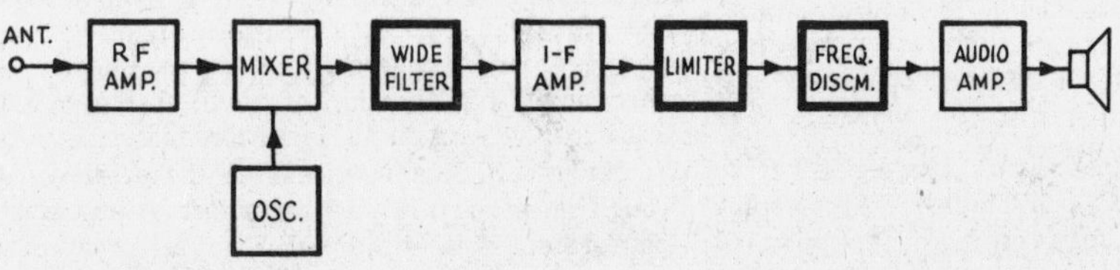

superheterodyne circuit has become standard practice. Three major differences will be apparent from a comparison of the two block diagrams. The fm receiver employs a wider-bandwidth filter, a different detector, and has a limiter stage added between the i-f amplifier and the detector. Otherwise the functions, and often the circuits, of the rf, oscillator, mixer and audio stages will be the same in either receiver.

In operation, the noticeable difference between the two receivers is the effect of noise and interference on an incoming signal. From the time of the first spark transmitters, "rotten QRM" has been a major problem for amateurs. The limiter and discriminator stages in an fm set can eliminate a good deal of impulse noise, except that noise which manages to acquire a frequency-modulation characteristic. Accurate alignment of the receiver i-f system and phase tuning of the detector are required to achieve good noise suppression. Fm receivers perform in an unusual manner when QRM is present, exhibiting a characteristic known as the *capture effect.* The loudest signal received, even if it is only two or three times stronger than other stations on the same frequency, will be the only transmission demodulated. By comparison, an S9 a-m or cw signal can suffer noticeable interference from an S2 carrier.

Bandwidth

Most fm sets that use tubes achieve i-f selectivity by using a number of overcoupled transformers. The wide bandwidth and phase-response characterisitic needed in the i-f system dictate careful design and alignment of all interstage transformers.

F M FILTERS

Manufacturer	Model	Center Frequency	Nonimal Bandwidth	Ultimate Rejection	Impedance (r) In	Out	Insertion Loss	Crystal Discriminator
KVG (1)	XF-9E	9.0 MHz	12 kHz	90 dB	1200	1200	3 dB	XD9-02
KVG (1)	XF-107A	10.7 MHz	12 kHz	90 dB	820	820	3.5 dB	XD107-01
KVG (1)	XF-107B	10.7 MHz	15 kHz	90 dB	910	910	3.5 dB	XD107-01
KVG (1)	XF-107C	10.7 MHz	30 kHz	90 dB	2000	2000	4.5 dB	XD107-01
Heath Dynamics (2)	–	21.5 MHz	15 kHz	90 dB	550	550	3 dB	–
Heath Dynamics (2)	–	21.5 MHz	30 kHz	90 dB	1100	1100	2 dB	–
E.S. (3)	FB-6D	10.7 MHz	15 kHz	80 dB	950	950	2 dB	AB-1C
E.S. (3)	10-MA	10.7 MHz	30 kHz	80 dB	2000	2000	4 dB	AB-1C
E.S. (3)	EL-3A	11.5 MHz	36 kHz	70 dB	50	50	4 dB	AL-1
E.S. (3)	DR-9	21.4 MHz	20 kHz	40 dB	750	750	5 dB	AR-10
Clevite (4)	TCF4-12D3CA	455 kHz	12 kHz	60 dB	40k	2200	6 dB	–
Clevite (4)	TCF4-18G45A	455 kHz	18 kHz	50 dB	40k	2200	6 dB	–
Clevite (4)	TCF6-30D55A	455 kHz	30 kHz	60 dB	20k	1000	5 dB	–

Fig. 14-11 — A list of fm-bandwidth filters that are available to amateurs. Manufacturer's addresses are as follows:

1) Spectrum International, P. O. Box 87, Topsfield, MA 01983.
2) Heath Dynamics, Inc., 6050 N. 52nd Avenue, Glendale, AZ 85301.
3) E. S. Electronic Labs, 301 Augustus, Excelsior Springs, MO 64024.
4) Semiconductor Specialists, Inc., P. O. Box 66125, O'Hare International Airport, Chicago, IL 60666. (Minimum order $5.00.)

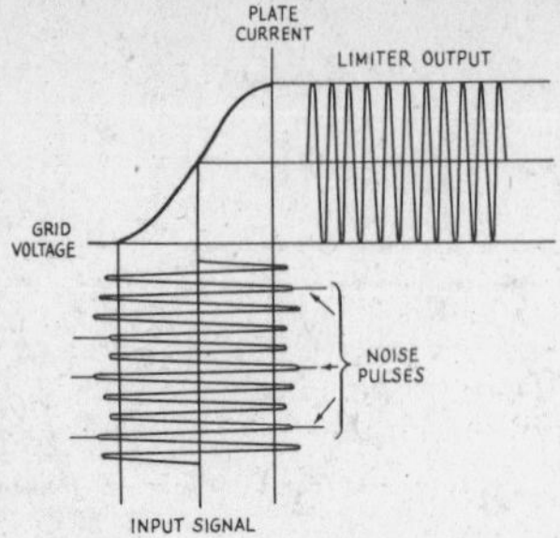

Fig. 14-12 — Representation of limiter action. Amplitude variations on the signal are removed by the diode action of the grid- and plate-current saturation.

For the average ham, the use of a high-selectivity filter in a homemade receiver offers some simplification of the alignment task. Following the techniques used in ssb receivers, a crystal or ceramic filter should be placed in the circuit as close as possible to the antenna connector – at the output of the first mixer, in most cases. Fig. 14-11 lists a number of suitable filters that are available to amateurs. Prices for these filters are in the range of $10 to $30. Experimenters who wish to "roll their own" can use surplus hf crystals, as outlined in ARRL's *Single Sideband for the Radio Amateur,* or ceramic resonators.

One item of concern to every amateur fm user is the choice of i-f bandwidth for his receiver, as both 15- and 5-kHz deviation are now in common use on the amateur bands. A wide-band receiver can receive narrow-band signals, suffering only some loss of audio in the detection process. However, a wideband signal will be badly distorted when received on a narrow-band rig. At this point it seems reasonable to assume that increasing fm activity and continued production of commercial narrow-band transceivers may gradually shift amateur operation to a 5-kHz deviation standard. But, as with the a-m operators, the wide-band enthusiasts will be around for some time to come, lured by inexpensive surplus wide-band gear.

Limiters

When fm was first introduced, the main selling point used for the new mode was the noise-free reception possibilities. The circuit in the fm receiver that has the task of chopping off noise and amplitude modulation from an incoming signal is the *limiter.* Most types of fm detectors respond to both frequency and amplitude variations of the signal. Thus, the limiter stages preceding the detector are included to "cleanse" the signal so that only the desired frequency modulation will be demodulated. This action can be seen in Fig. 14-13.

Limiter stages can be designed using tubes, transistors, or ICs. For a tube to act as a limiter, the applied B voltages are chosen so that the stage will overload easily, even with a small amount of signal input. A sharp-cutoff pentode such as the 6BH6 is usually employed with little or no bias applied. As shown in Fig. 14-12, the input signal limits when it is of sufficient amplitude so that diode action of the grid and plate-current saturation clip both sides of the input signal, producing a constant-amplitude output voltage.

Obviously, a signal of considerable strength is required at the input of the limiter to assure full clipping, typically several volts for tubes, one volt for transistors, and several hundred microvolts for ICs. Limiting action should start with an rf input of 0.2 μV or less, so a large amount of gain is required between the antenna terminal and the limiter stages. For example, the Motorola 80D has eight tubes before the limiter, and the solid-state MOTRAC receivers use nine transistor stages to get sufficient gain before the first limiter. The new ICs offer some simplification of the i-f system as they pack a lot of gain into a single package.

When sufficient signal arrives at the receiver to start limiting action, the set *quiets* – that is, the background noise disappears. The sensitivity of an fm receiver is rated in terms of the amount of input signal required to produce a given amount of quieting, usually 20 dB. Current practice using the new solid-state devices can produce receivers which achieve 20 dB quieting with 0.15 to 0.5 μV of input signal.

A single tube or transistor stage will not provide good limiting over a wide range of input signals. Two stages, with different input time constants, are a minimum requirement. The first stage is set to handle impulse noise satisfactorily while the second is designed to limit the range of signals passed on by the first. At frequencies below 1 MHz it is useful to employ untuned *RC*-coupled limiters which provide sufficient gain without a tendency toward oscillation.

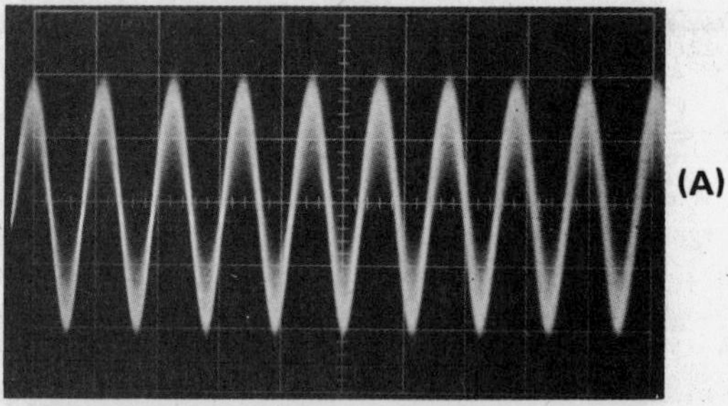
(A)

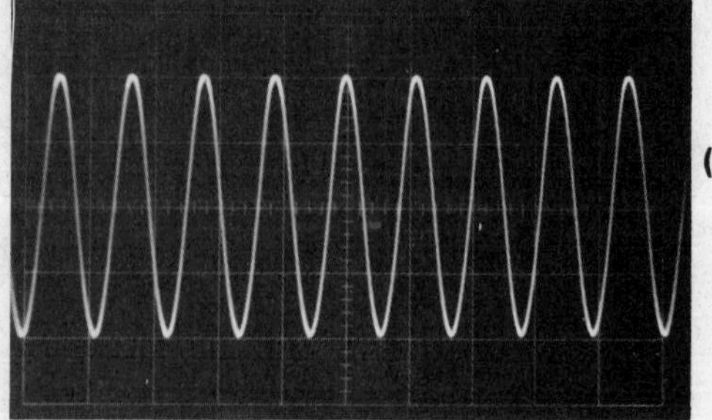
(B)

Fig. 14-13 — (A) Input wave form to a limiter stage shows a-m and noise. (B) The same signal, after passing through two limiter stages, is devoid of a-m components.

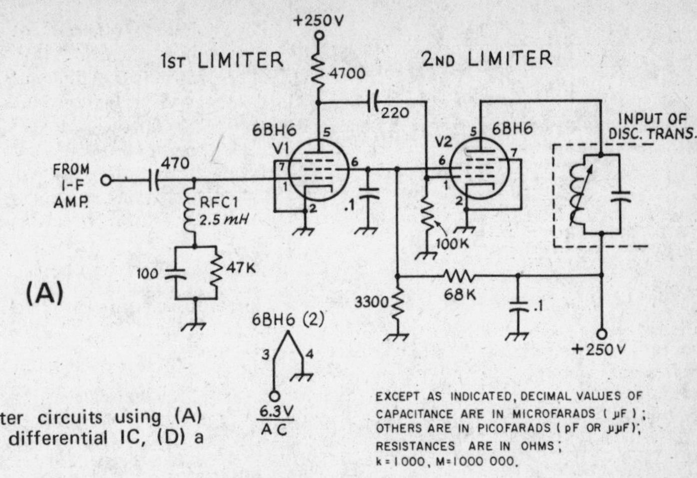

Fig. 14-14 — Typical limiter circuits using (A) tubes, (B) transistors, (C) a differential IC, (D) a high-gain linear IC.

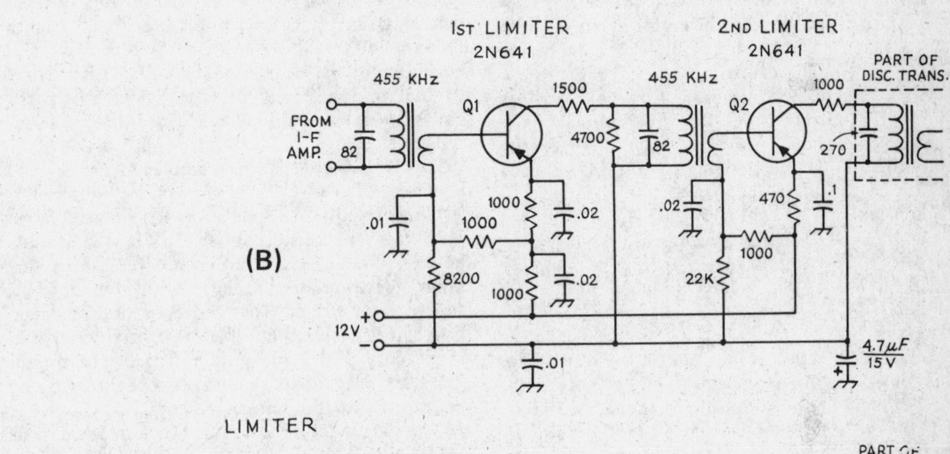

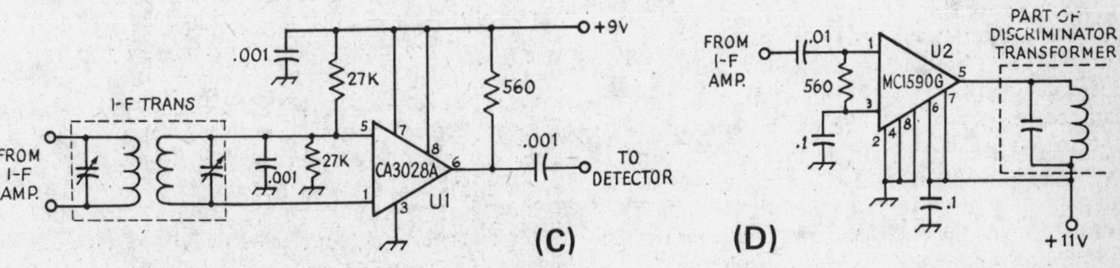

Fig. 14-14A shows a two-stage limiter using sharp-cutoff tubes, while 14-14B has transistors in two stages biased for limiter service. The base bias on either transistor may be varied to provide limiting at a desired level. The input-signal voltage required to start limiting action is called the *limiting knee*, referring to the point at which collector (or plate) current ceases to rise with increased input signal. Modern ICs have limiting knees of 100 mV for the circuit shown in Fig. 14-14C, using the CA3028A or MC1550G, or 200 μV for the Motorola MC1590G of Fig. 14-14D. Because the high-gain ICs such as the CA3076 and MC1590G contain as many as six or eight active stages which will saturate with sufficient input, one of these devices provides superior limiter performance compared to a pair of tubes or transistors.

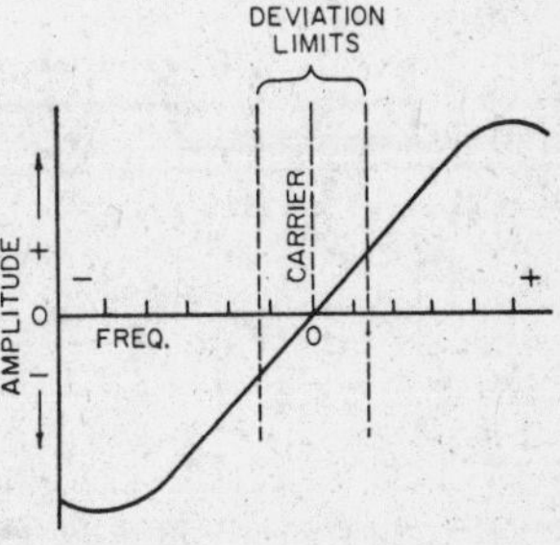

Fig. 14-15 — The characteristic of an fm discriminator.

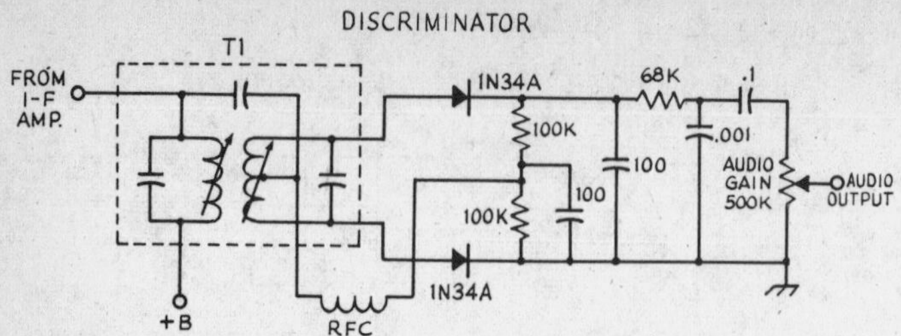

Fig. 14-16 – Typical frequency-discriminator circuit used for fm detection. T1 is a Miller 12-C45.

Detectors

The first type of fm detector to gain popularity was the frequency discriminator. The characteristic of such a detector is shown in Fig. 14-15. When the fm signal has no modulation, and the carrier is at point O, the detector has no output. When audio input to the fm transmitter swings the signal higher in frequency, the rectified output increases in the positive direction. When the frequency swings lower the output amplitude increases in the negative direction. Over a range where the discriminator is linear (shown as the straight portion of the line), the conversion of fm to a-m which is taking place will be linear.

A practical discriminator circuit is shown in Fig. 14-16. The fm signal is converted to a-m by transformer T1. The voltage induced in the T1 secondary is 90 degrees out of phase with the current in the primary. The primary signal is introduced through a center tap on the secondary, coupled through a capacitor. The secondary voltages combine on each side of the center tap so that the voltage on one side leads the primary signal while the other side lags by the same amount. When rectified, these two voltages are equal and of opposite polarity, resulting in zero-voltage output. A shift in input frequency causes a shift in the phase of the voltage components that results in an increase of output amplitude on one side of the secondary, and a corresponding decrease on the other side. The differences in the two changing voltages, after rectification, constitute the audio output.

In the search for a simplified fm detector, RCA developed a circuit that has now become standard in entertainment radios which eliminated the need for a preceding limiter stage. Known as the *ratio detector*, this circuit is based on the idea of dividing a dc voltage into a ratio which is equal to the ratio of the amplitudes from either side of a discriminator-transformer secondary. With a detector that responds only to ratios, the input signal may vary in strength over a wide range without causing a change in the level of output voltage – fm can be detected, but not a-m. In an actual ratio detector, Fig. 14-17, the dc voltage required is developed across two load resistors, shunted by an electrolytic capacitor. Other differences include the two diodes, which are wired in series aiding rather than series opposing, as in the standard discriminator circuit. The recovered audio is taken from a tertiary winding which is tightly coupled to the primary of the transformer. Diode-load resistor values are selected to be lower (5000 ohms or less) than for the discriminator.

The sensitivity of the ratio detector is one half that of the discriminator. In general, however, the transformer design values for *Q*, primary-secondary coupling, and load will vary greatly, so the actual performance differences between these two types of fm detectors are usually not significant. Either circuit can provide excellent results. In operation, the ratio detector will not provide sufficient limiting for communications service, so this detector also is usually preceded by at least a single limiting stage.

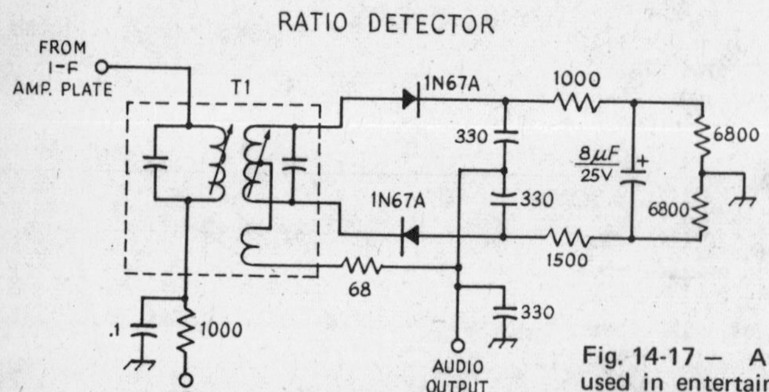

Fig. 14-17 – A ratio detector of the type often used in entertainment radio and TV sets. T1 is a ratio-detector transformer such as the Miller 1606.

Fig. 14-18 – Crystal discriminator, C1 and L1 are resonant at the intermediate frequency. C2 is equal in value to C3. C4 corrects any circuit imbalance so that equal amounts of signal are fed to the detector diodes.

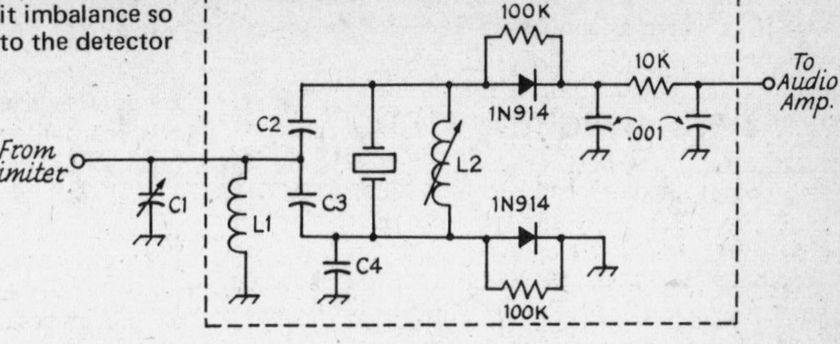

New Detector Designs

The difficulties often encountered in building and aligning *LC* discriminators have inspired research that has resulted in a number of adjustment-free fm detector designs. The *crystal discriminator* utilizes a quartz resonator, shunted by an inductor, in place of the tuned-circuit secondary used in a discriminator transformer. A typical circuit is shown in Fig. 14-18. Some commercially-made crystal discriminators have the input-circuit inductor, L1, built in (C1 must be added) while in other types both L1 and C1 must be supplied by the builder. Fig. 14-18 shows typical component values; unmarked parts are chosen to give the desired bandwidth. Sources for crystal discriminators are listed in Fig. 14-11.

The PLL

Now that the **phase-locked loop** (PLL) has been reduced to a single IC package, this circuit is destined to revolutionize some facets of receiver design. Introduction by Signetics of a PLL in a single flat-pack IC, followed by Motorola and Fairchild (who are making the PLL in separate building-block ICs), allows a builder to get to work with a minimum of bother.

A basic phase-locked loop (Fig. 14-19A) consists of a phase detector, a filter, a dc amplifier, and a voltage-controlled oscillator (VCO). The VCO runs at a frequency close to that of an incoming signal. The phase detector produces an error voltage if any difference in frequency exists between the VCO and the i-f signal. This error voltage is applied to the VCO. Any changes in the frequency of the incoming signal are sensed at the detector and the error voltage readjusts the VCO frequency so that it remains locked to the intermediate frequency. The bandwidth of the system is determined by a filter on the error-voltage line.

Because the error voltage is a copy of the audio variations originally used to shift the frequency of the transmitter, the PLL functions directly as an fm detector. The sensitivity achieved with the Signetics NE565 PLL is good – about 1 mV for the circuit shown in Fig. 14-19B. No transformers or tuned circuits are required. The PLL bandwidth is usually two to ten percent of the i-f for fm detection. Components R1-C1 set the VCO to near the desired frequency. C2 is the loop-filter capacitor which determines the capture range – that range of frequencies over which the loop will acquire lock with an input signal, initially starting

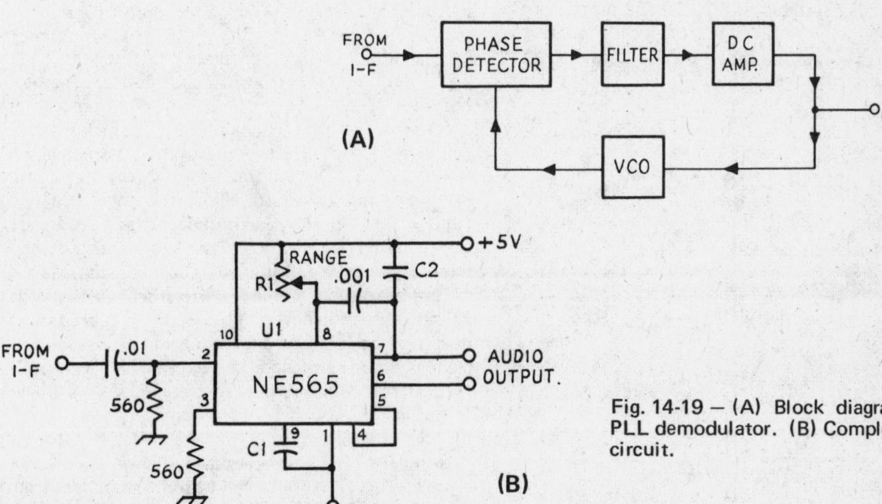

Fig. 14-19 – (A) Block diagram of a PLL demodulator. (B) Complete PLL circuit.

out of lock. The NE565 has an upper frequency limit of 500 kHz; for higher frequencies, the NE561, which is usable up to 30 MHz, can be employed.

FM RECEIVING ADAPTERS

To put the older tube receivers such as the 75A, HRO and Super Pro models into fm service, the receiving adapter shown in Fig. 14-21 was designed. Filament and plus B voltages are taken from the companion receiver. Obviously, the better the basic receiver, the better will be the performance of the fm receiving system. For this application sets with high-gain i-f amplifier sections and a broad-band selectivity position (such as the SP-400, SP-600, SX-73, and R-390) are excellent choices. Receivers that have only a 6-kHz or narrower bandwidth may need an extra i-f amplifier stage in the fm adapter in order to tap the receiver i-f at the output of the second mixer. Of course, a converter will also be required with the basic receiver if copy of vhf fm signals is desired.

A sample of the receiver i-f signal is passed to T1, a 455-kHz i-f transformer, which feeds amplifier/limiter V1. A low screen voltage and signal bias enhance the limiting characteristic of the tube. Further "hard" limiting action is provided by the two sections of V2, a 12AT7. A sample of the grid current of V2A is available at TP1, a test point used during alignment. A commercially made discriminator transformer converts the fm signal to a-m; the a-m is detected by CR1 and CR2. An *RC* de-emphasis network is included to match the standard pre-emphasis used on fm transmitters. Audio amplification is provided by V3 – in some receivers with high-gain audio systems this stage may not be necessary.

The adapter is constructed on an aluminum channel which is 11 inches long, 2 inches wide, and 1 3/4 inches high. A 1/4-inch lip is included on one side as a mounting foot. A Minibox or a standard chassis is also suitable as a base. The layout of the stages should be kept in a straight line so that rf feedback paths can be avoided. Point-to-point wiring is used throughout.

Fig. 14-20 – The fm adapter, wired for connection to a Collins 75A2.

Alignment

"Lining up" the adapter takes time and test equipment. A VTVM or microammeter plus a signal generator are required. Good alignment cannot be accomplished by ear; if the necessary test instruments aren't available, they should be borrowed.

To start, check the alignment of the communications receiver, following the manufacturer's instructions, to be sure that the rf and i-f stages are "peaked" before the fm adapter is installed. Two simple internal modifications are required in the receiver, as shown in Fig. 14-21 B and C. If the receiver has a wide i-f bandwidth, a sample of the i-f signal can be taken from the plate of the last i-f stage. Otherwise, the tap should be made at the plate of the first i-f amplifier, and an extra stage, a duplicate of V1, included in the adapter. Short lengths of shielded cable are used to carry the i-f signal to the adapter and to return audio to the receiver – see Fig. 14-21C. Some units (75A2, HRO-50) which have provision for fm adapters already have a front-panel switch wired for this purpose.

Connect the signal generator to the receiver, and set the generator to produce an S9 reading on the receiver signal-strength meter. The receiver crystal filter should be switched to its most selective position to insure that the incoming signal is being heterodyned to exactly 455 kHz. Then, with a voltmeter or microammeter connected to TP1, adjust both sections of T1, and L1, for maximum limiter current. The receiver i-f stage being "tapped" should also be realigned to compensate for the capacitance of the adapter cable.

To align the discriminator, set the receiver selectivity at the broad position, and connect the voltmeter to TP2. Voltage at this test point will swing both plus and minus, so a zero-center meter or VTVM with a lead-reversing switch should be employed. Set the secondary of the discriminator transformer for a zero-voltage indication on the meter. Then vary the signal-generator frequency plus or minus 15 kHz. Going off center frequency in one direction will produce positive voltage at TP2, while going in the other direction generates negative voltage. The primary of the transformer must be set so that, for example, if a shift down in frequency by 5 kHz produces plus 2 volts, then a change of 5 kHz in the other direction should produce minus 2 volts. Unfortunately, the two adjustments on the discriminator transformer are interlocking, so considerable experimentation is required. Also, the tuning of the preceding stages, if not centered on 455 kHz, will affect the discriminator linearity. The first time around, a half hour or more of alignment and realignment is usually required to achieve *equal* swings in output voltage for *equal* swings in frequency – a linear response.

One further check of the discriminator is required. An impulse-generating device, such as an electric shaver, should be switched on, and the receiver, set for a-m detection, tuned to a point in the spectrum where the noise is strong. Then,

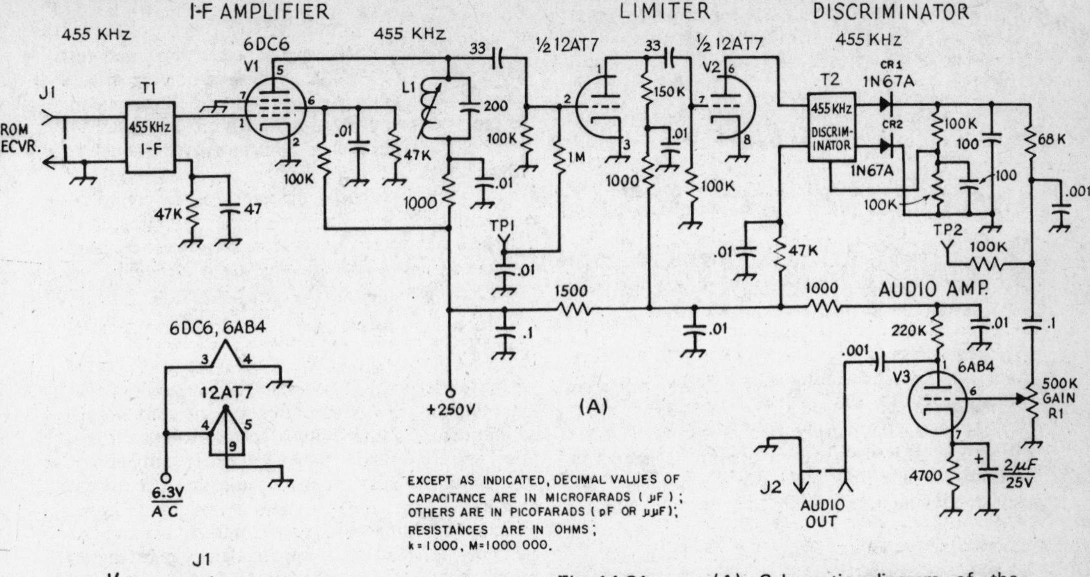

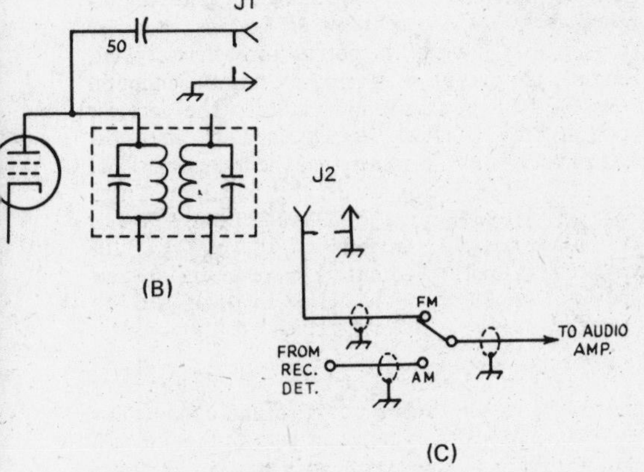

Fig. 14-21 — (A) Schematic diagram of the 455-kHz fm adapter. Resistors are 1/2-watt composition; capacitors are disk ceramic, except those with polarity marked, which are electrolytic.
J1, J2 — Phono jack, panel mount.
L1 — 430-850-µH slug-tuned variable inductor (Miller 42A684CBI).
R1 — Audio-taper composition control.
T1 — I-f transformer, 455 kHz (Miller 913-C1).
T2 — Discriminator transformer, 455 kHz (Miller 913-CD).
TP1, TP2 — Tip jack (Johnson 105-XX).
(B) Diagram of the connections to use the fm adapter with a communications receiver. The tap to the i-f stage is through a 50-pF disk-ceramic capacitor. If the receiver has a wide-band i-f system, the connection should be made to the last intermediate-frequency amplifier; for narrow i-fs, tap the first i-f stage. (C) Audio connections.

switch to the fm adapter and adjust the discriminator transformer for best suppression of the noise pulses. If the alignment with the signal generator has been completed properly, only a half a turn or so of the slugs will be needed to complete the phase tuning of the discriminator.

A SOLID-STATE ADAPTER

Tubes are seldom used in current designs. For those builders who prefer to be "up with the times," a solid-state version of the 455-kHz adapter was constructed. Using IC limiter/amplifier, and miniature i-f transformers, the unit requires only 25 mA at 12 V for power. See Fig. 14-24A. The Motorola MC1590G provides 70 dB gain, and hard limiting action superior to that obtained with the tube version.

The unit is built on a 2 X 6 1/2-inch circuit board; a template is given in Fig. 14-24B. Because of the high gain of the IC stage, a shield is required across pins 4 and 6 to isolate the input from the output. Alignment and installation are the same as for the tube version. The bandwidth of the miniature transformers restricts this adapter to narrow-band reception. However, builders wishing a wideband version can use the J. W. Miller 8811 miniature coils which are combined with a 12-pF coupling capacitor to form a wide-band transformer.

FM COMMUNICATIONS

Although information on fm theory and construction has been available to the amateur for a number of years, this mode has been largely neglected. But now large quantities of used commercial fm mobile equipment have become available for amateur use, creating new interest. Originally designed to cover frequency ranges adjacent to amateur bands, this equipment is easily retuned for amateur use.

One feature of fm is its noise-suppression capability. For signals above the receiver threshold, wideband fm has a signal-to-noise ratio advantage over a-m as a result of its greater "intelligence bandwidth." This same increased bandwidth, however, results in a much more abrupt signal threshold effect, causing weak signals to suddenly disappear. The generality can be made that a-m has

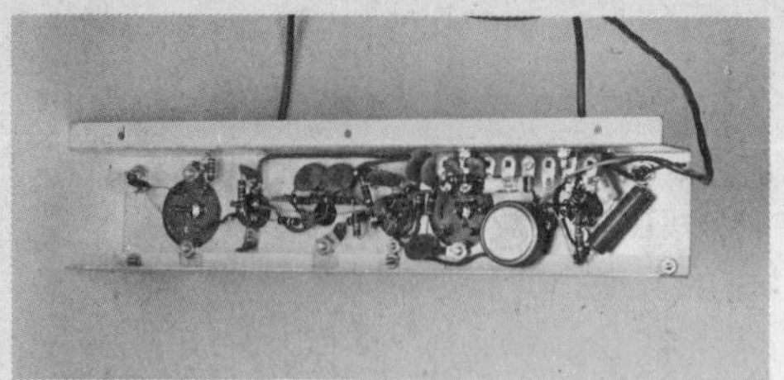

Fig. 14-22 – In this bottom view, the input transformer is to the left, followed by the i-f amplifier, limiter and detector. On the far right are the audio amplifier stage and gain control.

Fig. 14-23 – The solid-state fm adapter is constructed on a 6 X 2-inch etched-circuit board, mounted on a homemade chassis.

a greater range in weak signal work but that wideband fm will provide greater noise suppression in local work. However, in practice, vhf fm mobiles experience greater range than previously found on a-m due to the output powers employed which are considerably higher than those common on a-m.

Operating Practices

Amateur fm practice has been to retain the fixed-frequency channelized capability of the commercial equipment. VFOs and tunable receivers have not proven satisfactory because of the requirement for precise frequency netting. An off-frequency signal will be received with distortion and will not have full noise rejection. Channelized operation with squelched receivers permits continuous monitoring of the active frequencies. Long, time-consuming calls and CQs are not necessary (or appreciated) to establish communications, as all receivers on the channel "come alive" with the operator's first word. Natural, short transmissions are usually encour-

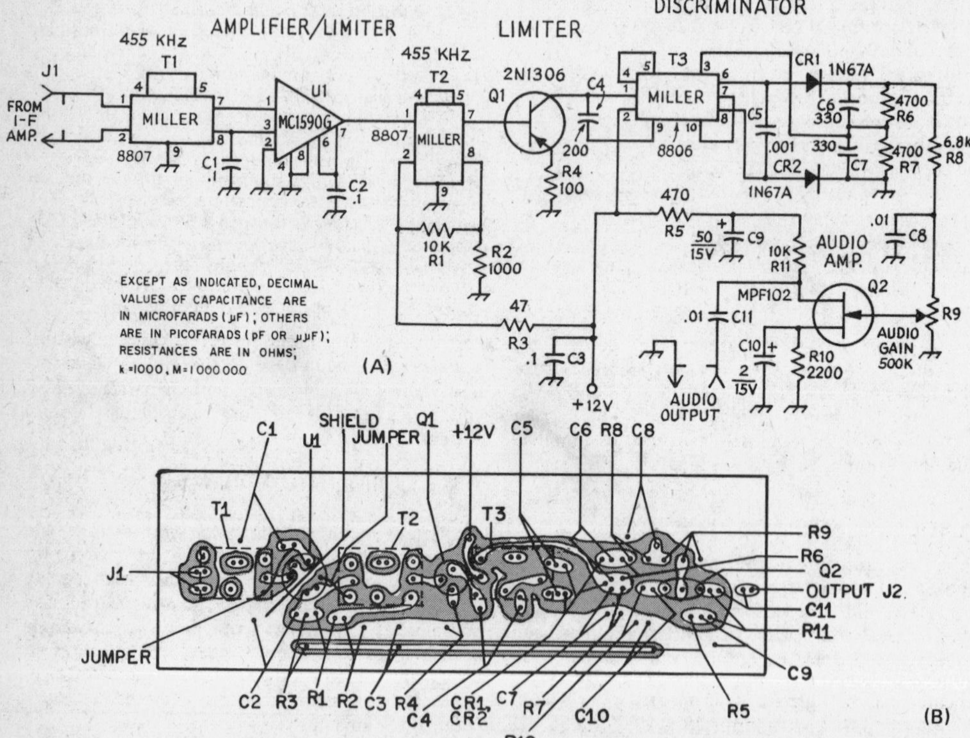

Fig. 14-24 – (A) Diagram of the 455-kHz narrow-band adapter. Resistors are 1/4- or 1/2-watt composition and capacitors are disk ceramic, except those with polarity marked, which are electrolytic. Components with reference numbers that are not listed below are noted for circuit-board location.

J1, J2 – Phono receptacle, panel mount.

R1 – Miniature 1/2-watt composition control.

T1 – Miniature 455-kHz i-f transformer (Miller 8807).

T2 – Miniature discriminator transformer, 455 kHz (Miller 8806).

U1 – Motorola MC1590G.

(B) Template for the solid-state adapter (not to scale).

aged. The old monopoly switch routine, where the operator gabs to himself for 10 minutes at a time, will get him invited off a busy fm channel. Some channels are calling channels on which extended ragchewing is discouraged, whereas other channels, or the same channel in another area, may be alive with chatter. This is a matter of local determination, influenced by the amount of activity, and should be respected by the new operators and the transient mobile operator alike. Some groups have adopted the use of the "10 code" which was originated for law enforcement communications. However, plain language in most cases is as fast and requires no clarification or explanation to anyone.

Standards

Standard channel frequencies have been agreed upon to permit orderly growth and to permit communications from one area to another. On two meters, it has been agreed that any frequency used will fall on increments of 60 kHz, beginning at 146.01 MHz. 146.94 MHz (or "nine-four") is the national calling frequency. On six meters, the national calling frequency is 52.525 MHz, with other channels having a 40-kHz spacing beginning at 52.56 MHz. Ten-meter fm activity can be found on 29.6 MHz. Recommendations for 10 meters and 220 MHz are for 40 kHz channel spacing starting at 29.04 and 220.02 MHz. Usage of the 420-MHz band varies from area to area, as it is used for control channels, repeaters, and remote bases, as will be discussed later. In the absence of any other local standard, usage should begin at 449.95 MHz and proceed downward in 50-kHz increments.

Two deviation standards are commonly found. The older standard, "wide band," calls for a maximum deviation of 15 kHz. The newer standard, "narrow band," imposed on commercial users by the splitting of their assigned channels, is 5 kHz. The deviation to be employed by amateurs on frequencies where fm is permitted is not limited to a specific value by the FCC, but it is limited by the bandpass filters in the fm receivers. In general, a receiver with a filter for 5-kHz deviation will not intelligibly copy a signal with 15-kHz deviation. In some areas, a compromise deviation of 7 or 8 kHz is used with some success with both wide and narrow receivers. When necessary, receiver filters can be exchanged to change the bandpass.

REPEATERS

A repeater is a device which retransmits received signals in order to provide improved communications range and coverage. This communications enhancement is possible because the repeater can be located at an elevated site which has coverage that is superior to that obtained by most stations. A major improvement is usually found when a repeater is used between vhf mobile stations, which normally are severely limited by their low antenna heights and resulting short communications range. This is especially true where rough terrain exists.

The simplest repeater consists of a receiver with its audio output directly connected to the audio

Fig. 14-25 — A homemade fm transceiver. The transmitter section uses the solid-state exciter and amplifier shown in Chapter 10.

input of an associated transmitter tuned to a second frequency. In this way, everything received on the first frequency is retransmitted on the second frequency. But, certain additional features are required to produce a workable repeater. These are shown in Fig. 14-28A. The "COR" or carrier-operated relay is a device connected to the receiver squelch circuit which provides a relay contact closure to key the transmitter when an input signal of adequate strength is present. As all amateur transmissions require a licensed operator to control the emissions, a "control" switch is provided in the keying path so that the operator may exercise his duties. This repeater, as shown, is

Fig. 14-26 — This typical 144-MHz amateur repeater uses GE Progress-Line transmitter and receiver decks. Power supplies and metering circuits have been added. The receiver located on the middle deck is a 440-MHz control receiver, also a surplus GE unit. A preamplifier, similar to that shown in Fig. 14-44, has been added to the 2-meter receiver to improve the sensitivity so that 0.2 μV of input signal will produce 20 dB quieting.

FM JARGON (Fig. 14-27)

Duplex – Simultaneous transmissions between two stations using two frequencies.
Simplex – Alternating transmission between two or more stations using one frequency.
Low band – 30 to 50 MHz. Also, the six-meter amateur band.
High band – 148 to 174 MHz. Also, the two-meter amateur band.
Remote base – A remotely controlled station, usually simplex (see text).
Machine – Either a repeater or a remote base. Also called a "box."
Vault – Building that houses the machine.
COR – Carrier-operated relay (see text).
CTCSS – Continuous tone-controlled squelch system. Continuous subaudible tone (250 Hz or lower) transmitted along with the audio to allow actuation of a repeater or receiver only by transmitters so equipped. More frequently referred to by various trade names such as Private Line, Channel Guard, and Quiet Channel.
Down channel – Communications circuit from the machine to the control point.
Up channel – Communications and/or control circuit from the control point to the machine.
Open repeater – A machine where transient Operators are welcome.
Closed repeater – A machine where use by non-members is not encouraged. (When heavy expenditures are involved, free-Loaders are not popular.)

suitable for installation where an operator is present, such as the home of a local amateur with a superior location, and would require no special licensing under existing rules.

In the case of a repeater located where no licensed operator is available, a special license for remote control operation must be obtained and provisions made to control the equipment over a telephone line or a radio circuit on 220 MHz or higher. The licensed operator must then be on hand at an authorized control point. Fig. 14-28B shows the simplest system of this type. The control decoder may be variously designed to respond to simple audio tones, dial pulsed tones, or even "Touch-Tone" signals. If a leased telephone line with dc continuity is used, control voltages may be sent directly, requiring no decoder. A 3-minute timer to disable the repeater transmitter is provided for fail-safe operation. This timer resets during pauses between transmissions and does not interfere with normal communications. The system just outlined is suitable where all operation is to be through the repeater and where the frequencies to be used have no other activity.

Remote Base Stations

The remote base, like the repeater, utilizes a superior location for transmission and reception, but is basically a simplex device. That is, it transmits and receives on a single frequency in order to communicate with other stations also operating on that frequency. The operator of the remote base listens to his hilltop receiver and keys his hilltop transmitter over his 220-MHz or higher control channels (or telephone line). Fig. 14-29A shows such a system. Control and keying features have been omitted for clarity. In some areas of high activity, repeaters have all but disappeared in favor of remote bases because of the interference to simplex activity caused by repeaters unable to minitor their output frequency from the transmitter location.

Complete System

Fig. 14-29B shows a repeater that combines the best features of the simple repeater and the remote base. Again, necessary control and keying features have not been shown in order to simplify the drawing, and make it easier to follow. This repeater is compatible with simplex operation on the output frequency because the operator in control monitors the output frequency from a receiver at the repeater site between transmissions. The control operator may also operate the system as a remote base. This type of system is almost mandatory for operation on one of the national calling frequencies, such as 146.94 MHz, because it minimizes interference to simplex operation and permits simplex communications through the system with passing mobiles who may not have facilities for the repeater-input frequency.

The audio interface between the repeater receivers and transmitters can, with some equipment, consist of a direct connection bridging the transmitter microphone inputs across the receiver speaker outputs. This is not recommended, however, because of the degradation of the audio quality in the receiver-output stages. A cathode

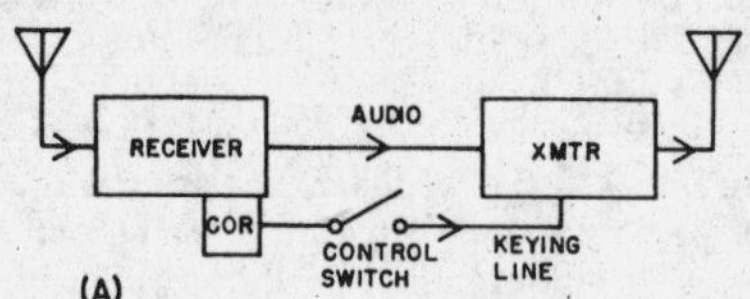

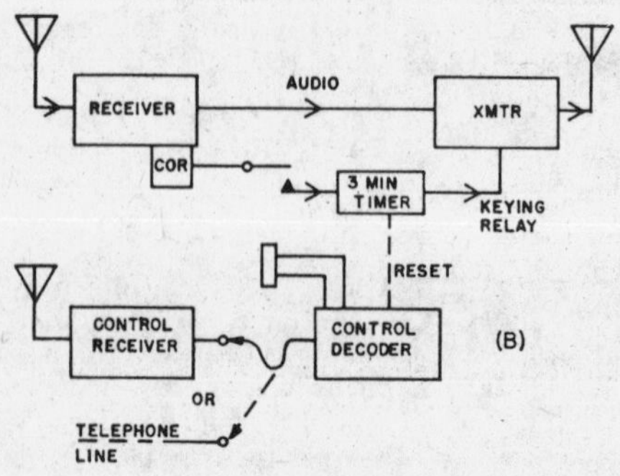

Fig. 14-28 – Simple repeaters. The system at A is for local control. Remote control is shown at B.

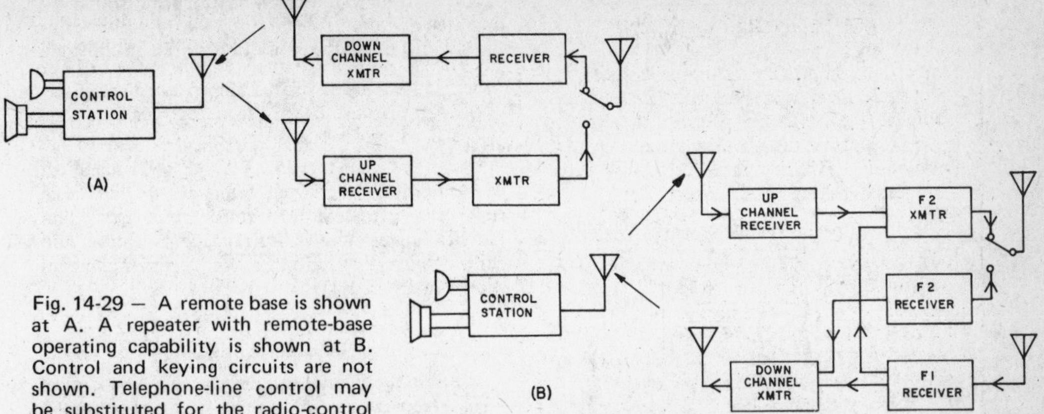

Fig. 14-29 – A remote base is shown at A. A repeater with remote-base operating capability is shown at B. Control and keying circuits are not shown. Telephone-line control may be substituted for the radio-control channels shown.

follower connected to each receiver's first squelch-controlled audio amplifier stage provides the best results. A repeater should maintain a flat response across its audio passband to maintain the repeater intelligibility at the same level as direct transmissions. There should be no noticeable difference between repeated and direct transmissions. The intelligibility of some repeaters suffers because of improper level settings which cause excessive clipping distortion. The clipper in the repeater transmitter should be set for the maximum system deviation, for example, 10 kHz. Then the receiver level driving the transmitter should be set by applying an input signal of known deviation below the maximum, such as 5 kHz, and adjusting the receiver audio gain to produce the same deviation at the repeater output. Signals will then be repeated linearly up to the maximum desired deviation. The only incoming signal that should be clipped in a properly adjusted repeater is an overdeviated signal.

The choice of repeater input and output frequencies must be carefully made. On two meters, 600-kHz spacing between the input and output frequencies is common. Closer spacing makes possible interference problems between the repeater transmitter and receiver more severe. Greater spacing is not recommended if the user's transmitters must be switched between the two frequencies, as happens when the output frequency is also used for simplex operation, either for short-range communications, or to maintain communications when the repeater is not functioning. A 5-MHz spacing is recommended on 440 MHz.

Careful consideration of other activity in the area should be made to prevent interference to or from the repeater. Many "open" or general-use repeaters have been installed on one of the national calling frequencies. On two meters, a 146.94 MHz output is usually paired with a 146.34-MHz input, and many travelers have made good use of this combination where it is found. Where 146.94-MHz simplex activity has not permitted a repeater on this frequency, 146.76 MHz has been used as an alternative. On six meters, several choices of input frequencies have been paired with 52.525 MHz. The choice and usage is a matter for local agreement.

In some cases where there is overlapping geographical coverage of repeaters using the same frequencies, special methods for selecting the desired repeater have been employed. One of the most common techniques requires the user to transmit automatically a 0.5-second burst of a specific audio tone at the start of each transmission. Different tones are used to select different repeaters. Standard tone frequencies are 1800, 1950, 2100, 2250, and 2400 Hz.

PRACTICAL REPEATER CIRCUITS

Because of their proven reliability, commercially made transmitter and receiver decks are generally used in repeater installations. Units designed for repeater or duplex service are preferred because they have the extra shielding and filtering necessary to hold mutual interference to a minimum when both the receiver and transmitter are operated simultaneously.

Wideband noise produced by the transmitter is a major factor in the design of any repeater. The use of high-*Q* tuned circuits between each stage of the transmitter, plus shielding and filtering throughout the repeater installation, will hold the wideband noise to approximately 80 dB below the output carrier. However, this is not sufficient to prevent **desensitization** – the reduction in sensitivity of the receiver caused by noise or rf overload from the nearby transmitter – if the antennas for the two units are placed physically close together.

Desensitization can easily be checked by monitoring the limiter current of the receiver with the transmitter switched off, then on. If the limiter current increases when the transmitter is turned on, then the problem is present. Only physical isolation of the antennas or the use of high-*Q* tuned cavities in the transmitter and receiver antenna feedline will improve the situation.

Antenna Considerations

The ultimate answer to the problem of receiver desensing is to locate the repeater transmitter a

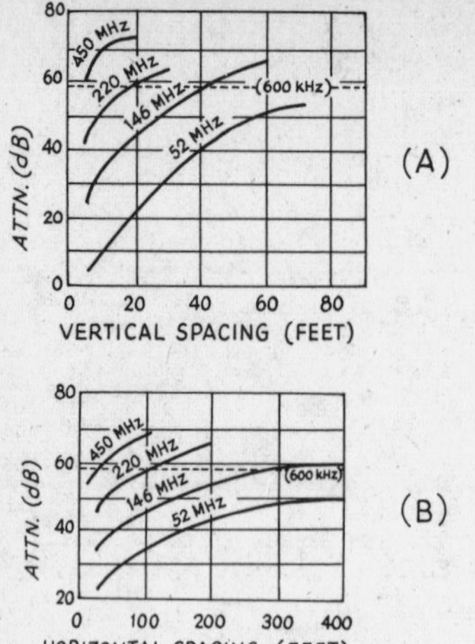

Fig. 14-30 – Charts to calculate the amount of isolation achieved by (A) vertical and (B) horizontal spacing of repeater antennas. If 600-kHz separation between the transmitted and received frequencies is used, approximately 58-dB attenuation (indicated by the dotted line) will be needed.

mile or more away from the receiver. The two can be interconnected by telephone line or uhf link. Another effective approach is to use a single antenna with a **duplexer**, a device that provides up to 120 dB of isolation between the transmitter and receiver. High-*Q* cavities in the duplexer prevent transmitted signal energy and wideband noise from degrading the sensitivity of the receiver, even though the transmitter and receiver are operating on a single antenna simultaneously. A commercially made duplexer is very expensive, and constructing a unit requires extensive metal-working equipment and test facilities.

If two antennas are used at a single site, there will be a minimum spacing of the two antennas required to prevent desensing. Fig. 14-30 indicates the spacing necessary for repeaters operating in the 50-, 144-, 220-, and 420-MHz bands. An examination of 14-30 will show that vertical spacing is far more effective than is horizontal separation. The chart assumes unity-gain antennas will be used. If some type of gain antenna is employed, the pattern of the antennas will be a modifying factor. A rugged repeater antenna was described in *QST* for January, 1970.

Control

Two connections are needed between the repeater receiver and transmitter, audio and transmitter control. The audio should be fed through an impedance-matching network to insure that the receiver output circuit has a constant load while the transmitter receives the proper input impedance. Filters limiting the audio response to the 300- to 3000-Hz band are desirable, and with some gear an audio-compensation network may be required. A typical COR (carrier-operated relay) circuit is shown in Fig. 14-31A. This unit may be operated by the grid current of a tube limiter or the dc output of the noise detector in a solid-state receiver.

Normally a repeater is given a "tail"; a timer holds the repeater transmitter on for a few seconds after the input signal disappears. This delay prevents the repeater from being keyed on and off by a rapidly fading signal. Other timers keep each transmission to less than three minutes duration (an FCC requirement), turn on identification, and control logging functions. A simple timer circuit is shown in Fig. 14-31B.

Logging and Identification

Current FCC rules require that a log be kept of repeater operations showing each time the repeater is placed in (or taken out of) service. Individual transmissions, however, need not be entered. Although regulations do not require logging of individual transmissions through a repeater, some repeater committees have tape recording equipment connected to the repeater system in order to record a small portion of each transmission. The tapes provide an "unofficial" record concerning repeater usage. A two track tape recorder may have one of the tracks connected to a receiver tuned to WWV or CHU if the repeater committee is interested in having time information.

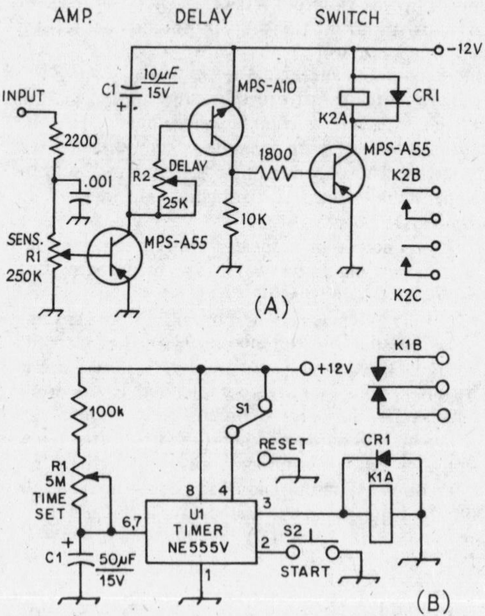

Fig. 14-31 – (A) COR circuit for repeater use. R2 sets the length of time that K1 will stay closed after the input voltage dissappears. K1 may be any relay with a 12-volt coil, although the long-life reed type is preferred. CR1 is a silicon diode. (B) Timer circuit using a Signetics NE555. R1, C1 sets the timers range. C1 should be a low-leakage type capacitor. S1, S2 could have their contacts paralleled by the receiver COR for automatic *START* and *RESET* controlled by an incoming signal.

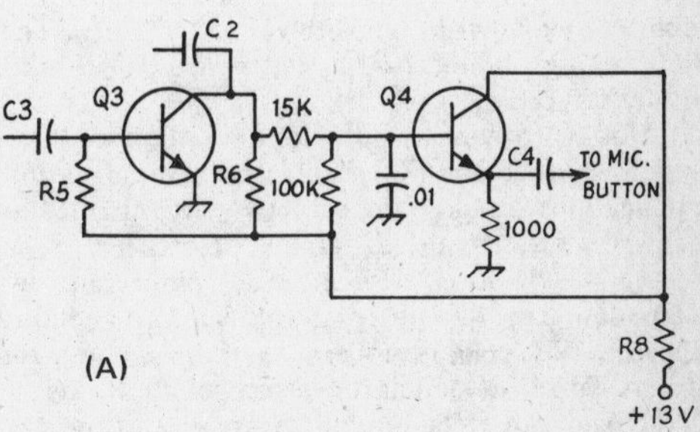

(A)

Fig. 14-32 – (A) Schematic diagram of the "electronic whistle." The main diagram is for high-impedance output. The lower portion has an emitter-follower added, for use with transmitters having low-impedance speech input circuits. All values of capacitance are in μF; polarity indicates electrolytic. (B) Tone-burst decoder. Resistors are 1/2-watt composition and capacitors are mylar. K1 is an spst reed relay with a 6-volt coil (C. P. Clare PRA-2010).

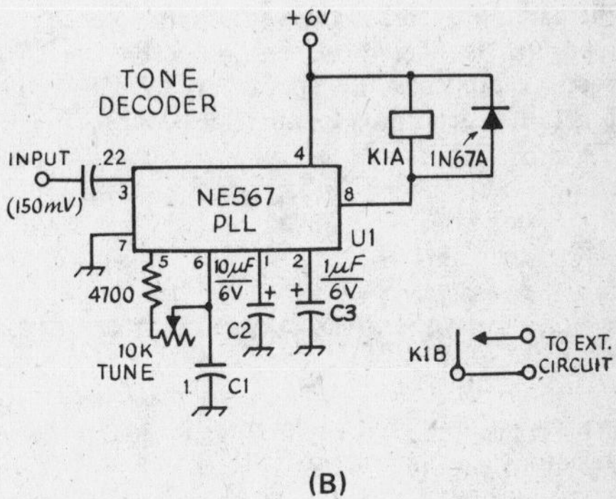

(B)

Identification of the repeater itself may be done by users, but lest a forgetful operator leave the repeater unknown, some form of automatic ID is preferred; A tape deck with a short loop tape for voice ID or a digital cw generator has proven to be effective. A suitable solid-state cw generator was described in *QST* for June, 1970.

Many repeaters use a form of tone control so that a carrier on the input frequency will not inadvertently key the transmitter. The most popular form of tone control is known as **tone burst**, often called **whistle on** because an operator with a good ear for frequency can use a short whistle instead of an electronically generated tone to key the repeater. A better approach, however, is a simple transistor tone generator, such as shown in Fig. 14-32A.

The whistle-on device was built for use with a Motorola 30-D transmitter, on a 1 1/2 X 2 1/2-inch piece of Vectorbord. It is nothing more than an astable multivibrator, triggered by a one-shot. When the push-to-talk switch is closed, actuating the transmitter relay, K1, Q1 goes from saturation to cutoff, and the multivibrator, Q2-Q3, begins oscillating with a period dependent on the values of R3, R5, C2 and C3. Values given result in a "whistle" of roughly 650 Hz.

Low Tone (Hz)	*High Tone* 1209 Hz	*1336 Hz*	*1477 Hz*	*1633 Hz*
697	1	2	3	cFO
770	4	5	6	F
852	7	8	9	I
941	*	0	#	P

Fig. 14-33 – Standard Touch-Tone frequencies for the 12-digit pad.

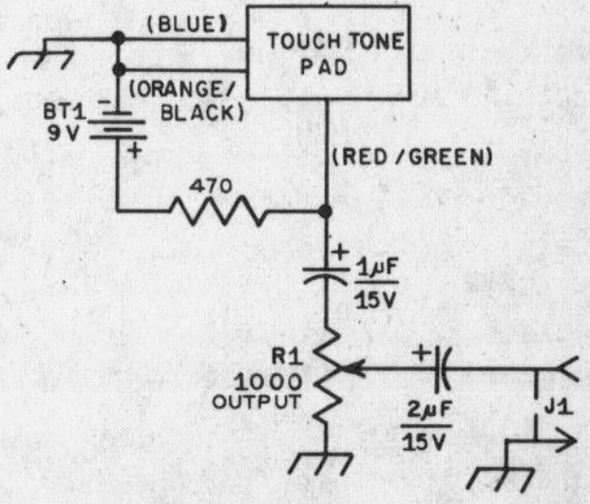

Fig. 14-34 – Typical connections to use a Touch-Tone pad for repeater control. Resistances are in ohms. R1 is a linear-taper composition control and J1 is a panel-mounted phono jack. Capacitors are electrolytic; color coding on the wire leads from the pad is shown in parentheses.

Oscillation ceases when Q1 turns on again. This is regulated by the values of R2 and C1, and is roughly 0.25 second with the values shown. The 470-ohm resistor, R1, protects the base of Q1 from current surges when the PTT is released.

The lower right portion of Fig. 14-32A shows an emitter-follower added, for use with transmitters employing carbon microphones. The value of C4 can be adjusted to give the appropriate output level.

Most of the component values are not critical, except the *RC* products which determine timing. Since the frequency is low, almost any bipolar transistors can be used. Npn types are shown, but pnp will work with opposite voltage polarity. The beta rating should be at least twice R3/R4, to insure saturation.

Most narrow-bandwidth tone decoders currently used in amateur repeater and remote-station applications employ several bulky *LC* circuits to achieve the required audio selectivity. The phase-locked loop (PLL) ICs, pioneered by Signetics, have simplified the design and reduced the size of tone decoders so that a complete Touch-Tone demodulator can be built on a 3 X 5 1/2-inch etched circuit board (about the size for a single-tone decoder using *LC* components).

A typical PLL single-tone decoder, such as might be employed for tone-burst entry control at a repeater, is shown in Fig. 14-32B. One *RC* network establishes the frequency to which the PLL is tuned, according to the relationship:

$$frequency = \frac{1}{R1C1}$$

The PLL, a Signetics NE567, may be operated from 0.1 Hz to 500 kHz. C2 establishes the bandwidth of the decoder, which can be set between one and fourteen percent of the operating frequency. C3 smooths the output signal, and, when this capacitor is made a high value, provides a delay in the turn-on function when a tone is received. Up to 100 mA may be drawn by the '567 output circuit, enough to key a relay directly or to drive TTL logic. The PLL contains 62 transistors.

Autopatch and Touch Tone

Some repeater groups have provided an interconnection to the public telephone network through a device called an **autopatch.** Details on all phases of phone patching are contained in Chapter 15. Such interconnection has led to the widespread use of the telephone company's Touch Tone system of tone signaling for repeater control functions, as well as telephone dialing. Because all of the Touch Tone frequencies are within the voice band, they can be transmitted by any amateur voice transmitter.

The Touch Tone control system consists of pairs of tones (see Fig. 14-33) for each of 10 numbers and the two special functions. One tone from the high-frequency group is generated simultaneously with one tone from the low-frequency group to represent each number or function. The Touch Tone generator pad from a standard telephone instrument is usually employed. See Fig. 14-34 for connections. A simple Touch Tone decoder using ICs throughout was described in July 1971 *QST*.

A LOW-POWER TRANSMITTER FOR 29.6 MHZ FM

The transmitter shown in Fig. 14-36 has been designed to produce wide- or narrow-band fm in the 10-meter band. Power output is about 6 watts, yet only three tubes are used. The unit is suitable for fixed-station or mobile use.

Circuits

Two section, V1A and V1B, of a triple-triode Compactron tube are used as audio voltage amplifiers. The high-impedance audio input circuit is suitable for dynamic, crystal or ceramic microphones. After voltage amplification the audio signal is passed through a full-wave clipper, which consists of CR1, CR2 and associated resistors. Use of the audio clipper will insure that peak fm deviation does not exceed a preset amount. The output of the clipper is filtered in a pi-section to remove high-order audio harmonics generated during the clipping process.

The audio signal is applied to a varactor diode, CR3, producing a capacitive change. This variation in capacitance shifts the frequency of the 7.4-MHz oscillator, V2A, in a manner proportional to the modulating signal. The frequency of the fm energy thus produced is doubled in the plate circuit of the oscillator, and then doubled again by the second section of V2, delivering output in the 10-meter band. V3, a 6GK6 tube, amplifies the signal,

Fig. 14-35 — The front view of the 10-meter fm transmitter reveals only the plate-current meter, microphone-gain control and microphone jack.

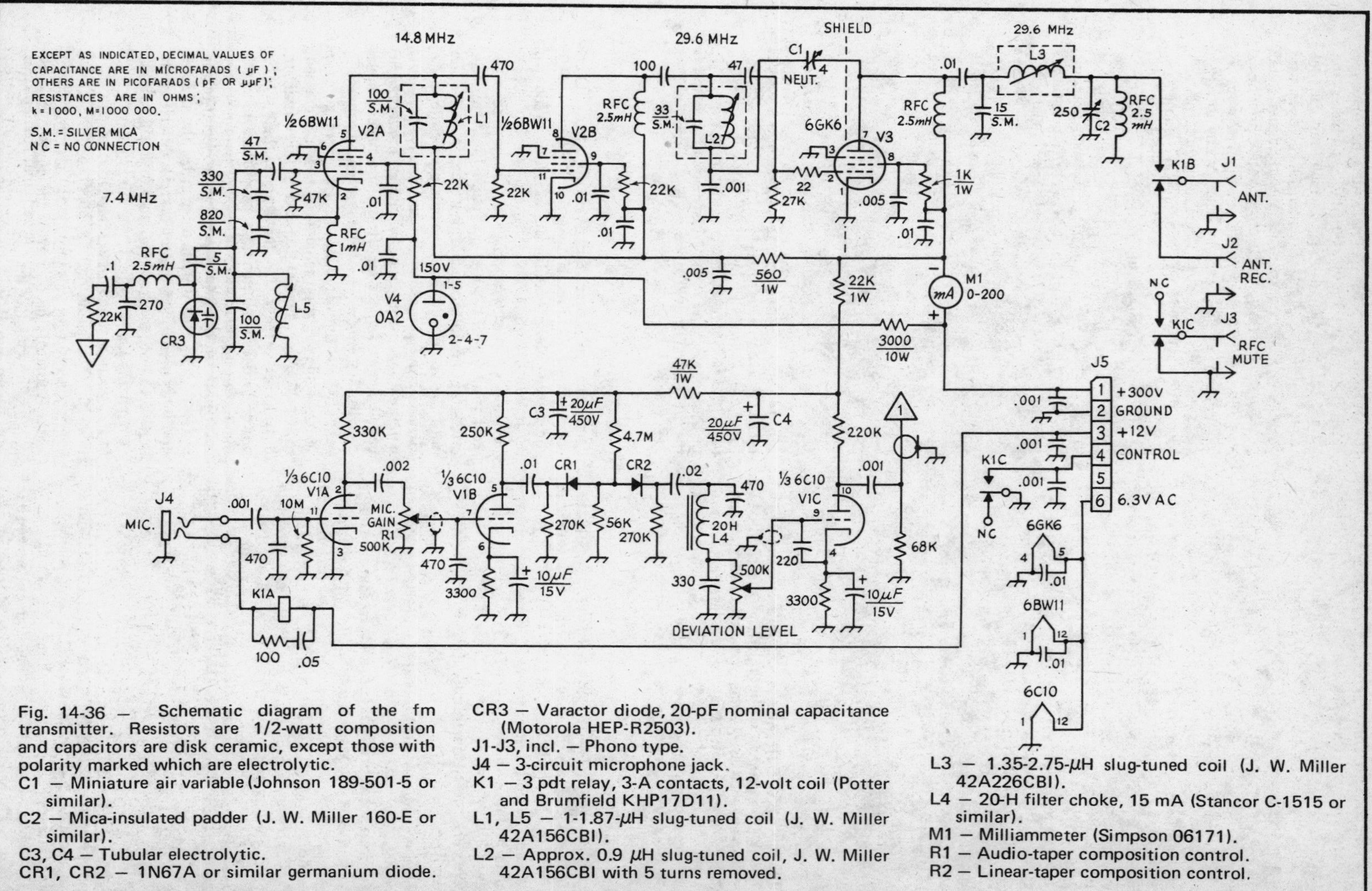

Fig. 14-36 — Schematic diagram of the fm transmitter. Resistors are 1/2-watt composition and capacitors are disk ceramic, except those with polarity marked which are electrolytic.

C1 — Miniature air variable (Johnson 189-501-5 or similar).

C2 — Mica-insulated padder (J. W. Miller 160-E or similar).

C3, C4 — Tubular electrolytic.

CR1, CR2 — 1N67A or similar germanium diode.

CR3 — Varactor diode, 20-pF nominal capacitance (Motorola HEP-R2503).

J1-J3, incl. — Phono type.

J4 — 3-circuit microphone jack.

K1 — 3 pdt relay, 3-A contacts, 12-volt coil (Potter and Brumfield KHP17D11).

L1, L5 — 1-1.87-μH slug-tuned coil (J. W. Miller 42A156CBI).

L2 — Approx. 0.9 μH slug-tuned coil, J. W. Miller 42A156CBI with 5 turns removed.

L3 — 1.35-2.75-μH slug-tuned coil (J. W. Miller 42A226CBI).

L4 — 20-H filter choke, 15 mA (Stancor C-1515 or similar).

M1 — Milliammeter (Simpson 06171).

R1 — Audio-taper composition control.

R2 — Linear-taper composition control.

Fig. 14-37 – Bottom view of the transmitter. The audio components are grouped on the right-hand side of the chassis, while the exciter section runs from top to bottom along the left-hand chassis wall. All external connections are brought out to the rear-deck jacks, with the exception of the microphone connector which is located on the front panel.

Fig. 14-38 – Either a single 0A2 or two 0A3 VR tubes may be used to regulate the screen voltage for the oscillator. In this model two regulators are used, the two tubes located at the lower-right side of the chassis. The control just below the meter is the DEVIATION adjustment.

running about 9-watts input power. A pi-section network couples the final amplifier to the antenna. Send-receive switching is accomplished by K1, which is activated by a PTT switch on the microphone.

Construction Details

The transmitter is built on a 7 X 7 X 2-inch chassis (Bud AC-405), using a 7 X 5-inch front panel. The plate-current meter, M1, is a useful tune-up accessory, but it may be replaced by a test jack in the interest of economy. After the initial adjustments have been accomplished, the rig will seldom need "touching up." The inexperienced builder should follow the general layout shown in the photographs. All tuned circuits except the oscillator are housed in shielded cans (J. W. Miller S-32). A shield isolating the input and output pins of the V3 socket is a good idea. Long audio leads should be run through shielded cable to prevent hum and rf pickup.

Tuning

The fm transmitter may be operated from an ac or mobile power supply. Suitable designs are given in Chapter 5. After checking the wiring for a second time for errors, apply filament power and allow the tubes to warm up. Then key K1 on, and check to see that the 0A2 (or two 0A3s) voltage-regulator tube is operating properly. Check the screen-voltage lead for the oscillator to see that it supplies 150 volts.

Use a 40-meter receiver to monitor the oscillator signal. With no audio applied, the oscillator should produce a clean carrier. Adjust L5 until the frequency of the oscillator is close to 7.4 MHz. A wavemeter, coupled to L1 and L2, should be employed to tune up the oscillator and doubler tank circuits, respectively. Insure that these tuned circuits are in fact resonated at the frequencies indicated on the diagram. Mistuning can result in spurious signals being radiated outside the amateur bands. Then, adjust L3 and C2 for maximum output power to a 50-ohm dummy load. An rf power bridge or Monimatch can be used to check the output level.

Erratic plate current readings usually indicate instability in the PA stage. If such a problem develops, disconnect the screen-voltage lead of the 6GK6. Couple a wavemeter to L3 and adjust the neutralizing capacitor, C1, for minimum rf energy at L3. Then, reconnect the screen lead.

With a test audio signal applied, the MIC. GAIN control should be advanced until clipping action starts (monitor the output of the clipper stage on an oscilloscope). Then, set the DEVIATION control for the desired amount of fm. Note: *FCC regulations require that the deviation of an amateur fm transmitter be held to 2.5 kHz or less below 29 MHz.* Above 29 MHz larger amounts of deviation may be employed; 5 and 15 kHz are the current standards for the operation around 29.6 MHz. Methods of setting deviation are discussed earlier in this chapter. With the microphone connected, the MIC. GAIN control should be advanced until about 10 dB of speech clipping is produced, when speaking in a normal voice.

A TONE-BURST GENERATOR FOR REPEATER ACCESS

This circuit was designed in an effort to side step some of the problems of tone-burst generators, such as instability, temperature effects, difficulty of adjustment, or hard-to-find components. Cost was also a consideration; the unit can be duplicated with all new parts (excluding the pc board) for $10 or less. Stability is such that drift is less than one hertz after an hour of operation. Potentiometers allow ease of adjustment to the desired frequencies of operation. The design is centered around a Signetics NE566V phase locked loop IC[1]. The tone frequencies are determined by C1 and R1 plus R2 through R7. The capacitance remains constant and the resistance is changed to set the various tones.

The formula $t = \frac{1}{3 \cdot R1 \cdot C1}$ is used to calculate the frequency of oscillation.

[1] *Phase-Locked Loops Applications,* Signetics Corporation, 811 East Arques Ave., Sunnyvale, CA 94086.

The total resistance needed is approximately 28 kΩ for 1800 Hz and 20 kΩ for 2400 Hz. Since the overall resistance, between the extremes, is only 8 kΩ, potentiometers of 10-kΩ value were used to adjust the frequency and a 50-kΩ unit was used to set the range. Shunting C1 with Q1 causes the tone to cease. The values of C2 and R8 determine the burst duration.

In operation Q1 has +12 V applied to the base and is in full conduction, shunting C1. When the PTT line is grounded, Q1 will cut off and allow the PLL to oscillate. C2 will begin charging through R8 and again force Q1 into conduction, shunting C1, and stopping the oscillation. The .05μF capacitor and the 1-MΩ resistor provide isolation and a high impedance to the audio line.

Construction

Since the NE566V is a voltage-controlled oscillator, it is very sensitive to voltage changes and a Zener-diode regulated supply is a necessity. The HEP724 (Q1) must be removed from the circuit in

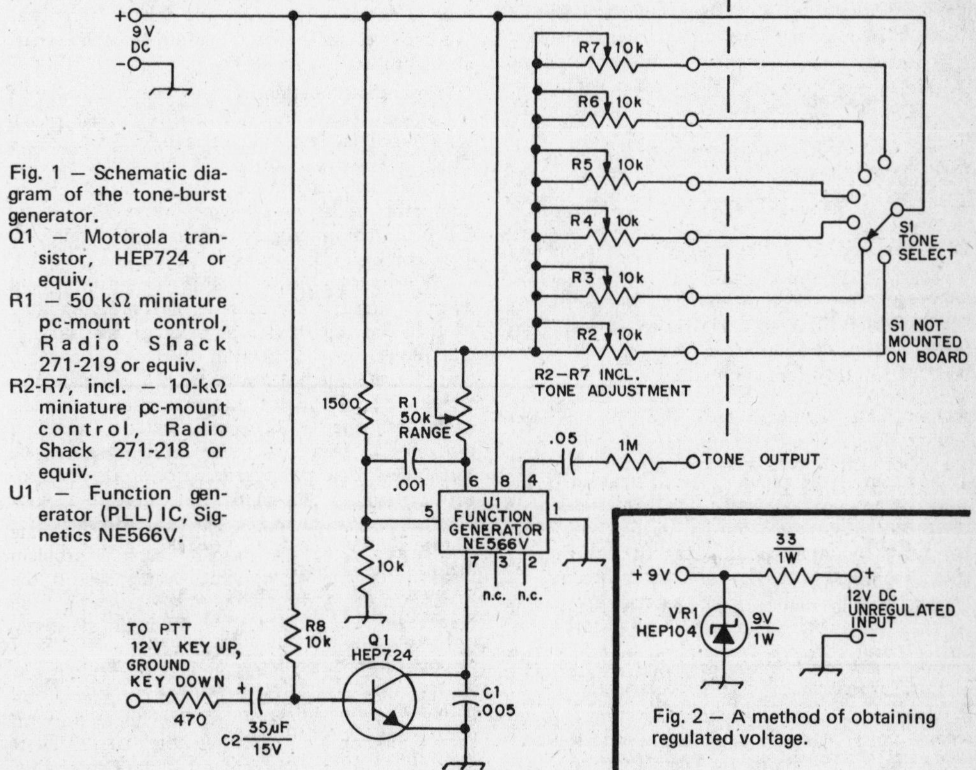

Fig. 1 — Schematic diagram of the tone-burst generator.
Q1 — Motorola transistor, HEP724 or equiv.
R1 — 50 kΩ miniature pc-mount control, Radio Shack 271-219 or equiv.
R2-R7, incl. — 10-kΩ miniature pc-mount control, Radio Shack 271-218 or equiv.
U1 — Function generator (PLL) IC, Signetics NE566V.

Fig. 2 — A method of obtaining regulated voltage.

Top view of the circuit board built by Glenn Dickson, WB5BAF. The unit was originally described in April, *QST*, 1974.

order to adjust the tones; therefore, a socket should be used for this transistor.

The circuit is constructed on a pc board measuring 1-1/4 × 2-7/8 inches (32 × 73 mm). A single-pole, 6-position switch is used to select the desired tone. Don't forget to provide an ON-OFF switch. Some people get upset if you are using tone-burst and the repeater doesn't require it.

Adjustment

Remove Q1 from the circuit. This will allow the oscillator to run continuously. Connect a counter to the junction of the .05μF capacitor and the 1-MΩ resistor.

Set R2 through R7 to minimum resistance, then adjust R1 for 2500 Hz. Set the selector switch to position 1 and adjust the corresponding control for the desired frequency. Repeat this with the rest of the potentiometers.

After setting all of the controls replace Q1 and check the burst duration. Using a value of 35 μF for C2 will give a burst duration of 0.4 second. If a different duration is desired change the value of C2. Do not change the value of R8.

A TONE BEEP KEYER FOR REPEATERS

This simple telemetry[1] circuit was designed for the WR6ABN repeater. Earlier uses of tones and tone bursts reminded users to allow time for breaking stations, and to indicate that the time-out timer had been reset. This latter indication was by means of transmitting two tones simultaneously.

This system is designed to inhibit one of the two tones, selectively, and allow either the high or low tone to indicate the position of the user's carrier in the receiver passband.

The sensors were adjusted to trip the relays at 1 kHz above or below the center frequency; this appears to be a practical value for narrow-band receivers. Thus, the "on-channel" slot is 2-kHz wide, centered about the receiver input frequency.

This system makes use of such nonexotic equipment as relays to perform the switching. Those readers who are well versed in solid-state logic systems will find it easy to apply the principles to their favorite machine.

Technical Description

The 741 op amp is set for a dc gain of 1000. The ac gain of the circuit is very low, as set by the 1 μF bypass capacitor across the 1-MΩ resistor in the feedback loop, and the 1 μF across the 50-kΩ control in the input circuit. The output of the 741 feeds two transistors and a zero-center meter.

The steering diodes, CR1 and CR2, allow the op amp to drive Q1 or Q2 into conduction and to charge C1 or C2 to the value of the op-amp output voltage. R1 and R2 allow capacitors C1 and C2 to charge above the base voltage of the transistors and to cause them to conduct for about 5 seconds after the drive voltage from the op amp is removed. This delay acts as a memory, so the delayed tone beep can indicate the frequency readout after the carrier of the user station goes off.

Note that the poor ac frequency response of the op-amp means that the input to it must remain for approximately 3 seconds in order for it to load C1 or C2 for the readout. This delay was intentional for two reasons: (1) to prevent noise or fluctuating signals from giving false readings, and (2) to prevent unscrupulous users from abusing the device by keying up several short bursts.

The input to the op amp is shorted to ground when a carrier is not present. This prevents noise from loading up the sensor prior to a reading. It also allows the adjustment of the dc offset control, R5. The calibrate potentiometer, R6, is adjusted to a point where signals 1 kHz above or below the center frequency of the receiver will just trip relays K4 or K5. (Note that the receiver should be adjusted so that the discriminator voltage is zero with no signal.) This adjustment of R6 to ±1 kHz determines the slot width. The center frequency is determined by the usual crystal-oscillator adjustments in the receiver.

K1 can be the normal COR or a separate relay keyed by the COR. This relay keys both the input to the op amp and the delay relay, K2. Because of the discharge time of C3, K2 will have a delayed release. When K2 releases, it keys K3 for a short period as determined by C4 and R8. The values needed for C3, C4, R7 and R8 will vary, depending upon the characteristics of K2 and K3.

[1] "Telemetering. Measurement with the aid of intermediate means that permit the measurement to be interpreted at a distance from the primary detector." – *IEEE Standard Dictionary of Electrical and Electronics Terms, 1972.*

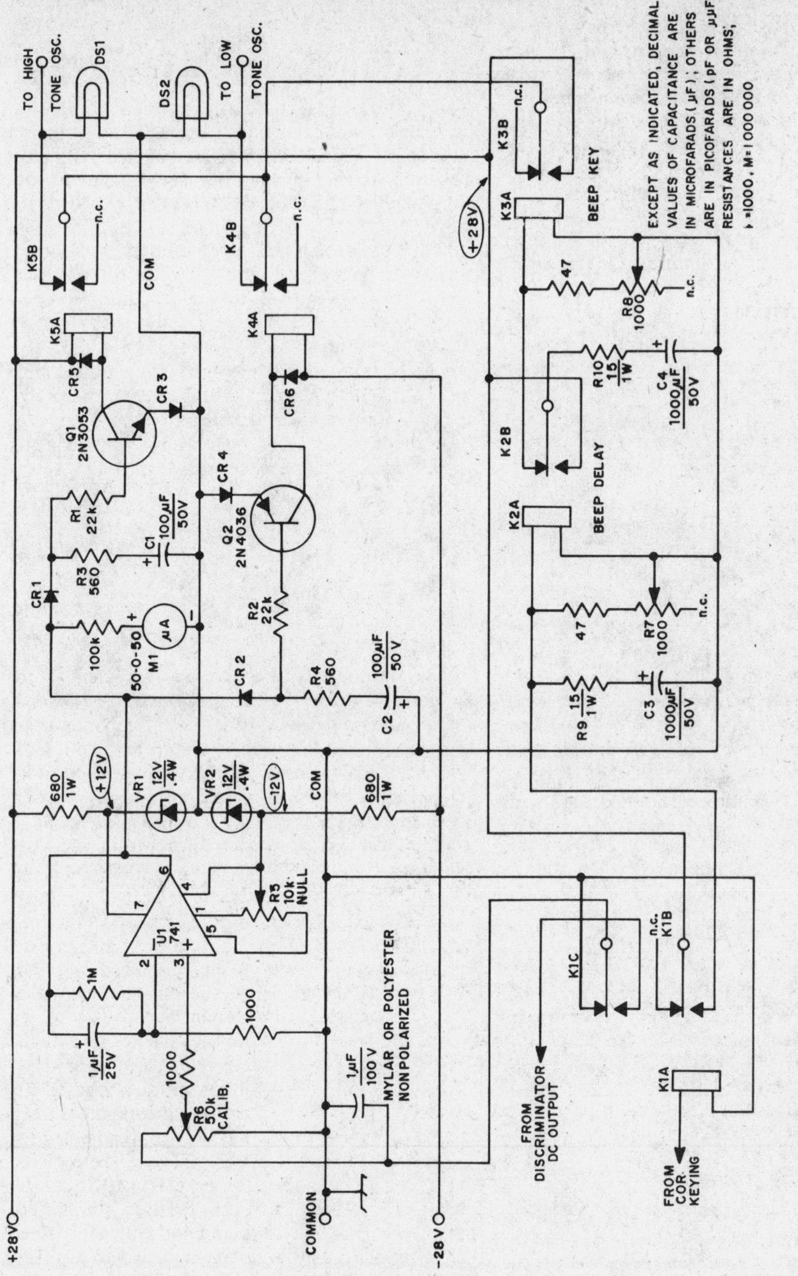

Fig. 1 — The schematic diagram of the tone-beep keyer. A dual 28-V supply is used in this system, but there should be no difficulty in revising values to make use of lower voltages. The charging current of C1 through C4 is limited to a safe value by means of the series resistor in each case. If the meter is omitted, tip jacks should be provided to aid in adjusting the circuit.

CR1-CR6, incl. — Silicon diodes, 1N2069 or equiv.

DS1, DS2 — 28-V pilot lamps. Lower-voltage units or LEDs with suitable dropping resistors may be used.

K1 — Dpdt relay. Coil voltage and current must be compatible with voltages available from receiver COR circuitry.

K2-K5, incl. — Spdt relays, 450- to 700-ohm coil for 24 V dc. Allied Control T154-2C or equiv.

U1 — Operational amplifier IC. Fairchild μA741 (U5B7741312), Signetics μA741T or μA741CV, Motorola MC1741G or MC1741P1 or equiv.

Operational Notes

1) K2 establishes length of delay between end of carrier and keying of tone beep.

2) K3 establishes length of tone beep.

3) K4 or K5 select the desired tone to be keyed.

4) Adjust R5, NULL control, for zero dc volts at the output of the 741 with K1 deenergized.

5) The trip point of K4 or K5 is adjusted by means of R6, the CALIBRATE control. It should be adjusted while monitoring a carrier set to the desired frequency offset value.

This unit was built by W6MEP and described originally in *QST* for May, 1974.

IMPROVING FM RECEIVER PERFORMANCE

Many older fm receivers, and some new models, do not have sufficient sensitivity or limiting capability. Also, the transceivers designed for the mobile telephone service do not have a squelch or audio power-amplifier circuit. Suitable accessory units can be easily constructed to improve the performance of a rig deficient in any of these areas.

A simple preamplifier, such as shown in Fig. 14-45 for 146 MHz and in Fig. 14-47 for 440 MHz, may be added to a receiver to increase its sensitivity and to improve limiting (as the overall gain before the limiter will be increased by 10-15 dB). The 2-meter version uses a dual-gate MOSFET while the 440-MHz unit employs two JFETs in a grounded-gate circuit. Both amplifiers are adjusted by peaking all tuned circuits for maximum limiter current while receiving a weak signal.

A receiver will have a poor limiting characteristic if the gain before the limiter circuit is insufficient, or if the limiter itself is of poor design. The circuit of Fig. 14-48 can be added to a receiver to replace an existing limiter stage. The new limiter uses an RCA CA3011 integrated circuit. Care must be used in the installation and layout of this high-gain IC to insure stability. The CA3011 will provide a "hard" limiting characteristic with about 100 mV of signal input.

Fig. 14-44 – The 2-meter preamp. may be mounted in a small Minibox or connected directly inside an fm receiver.

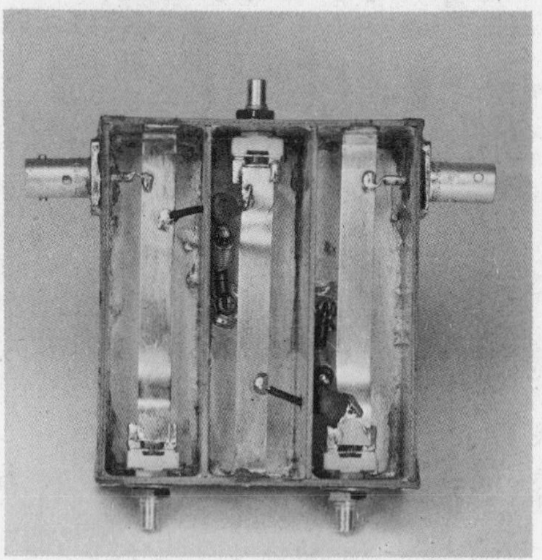

Fig. 14-46 – The 440-MHz preamplifier is constructed in a 3 X 3 1/2 X 1-inch box made of double-sided circuit board. All abutting edges are soldered to complete the enclosure. Two 3 X 15/16-inch shields separate the tuned lines.

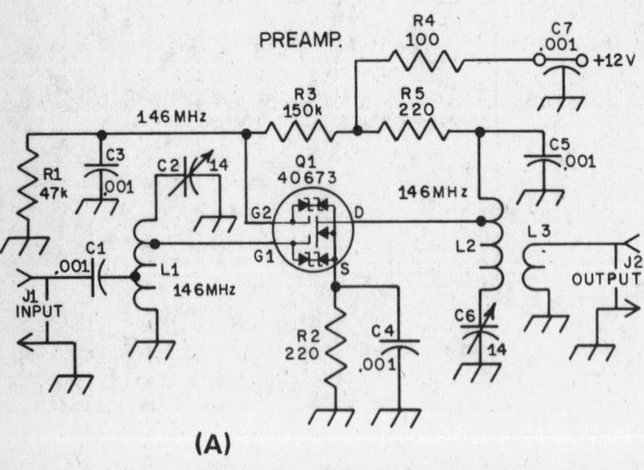

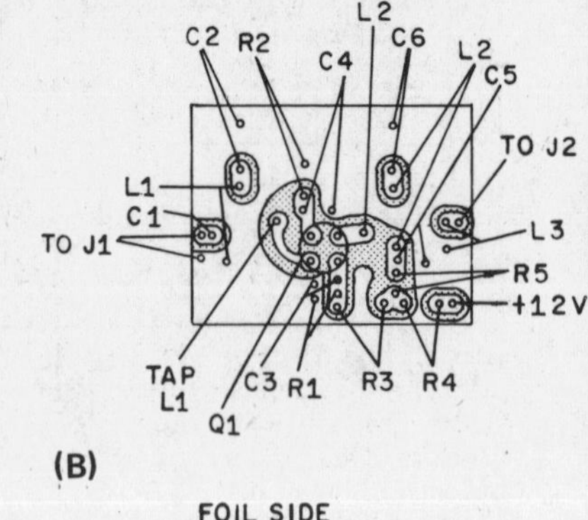

FOIL SIDE
(HALF SCALE)

Fig. 14-45 – Circuit diagram (A) and pc-board layout (B) for the 2-meter preamplifier. Resistors are 1/4-watt composition and capacitors are disk ceramic unless otherwise noted. Components not listed below are given designators for circuit-board location purposes.

C2, C6 – Air variable (Johnson 189-506-5).

J1, J2 – Phono type, panel mount

L1 – 5 turns, No. 16, 5/16 inch dia, 1/2 inch long. Tapped at 2 turns for the antenna connection, and 4 turns for G1.

L2 – 4 turns, No. 16, 5/16 inch dia, 3/8 inch long. Tapped at 2 turns.

L3 – 1 turn, plastic-covered hookup wire, 5/16 inch dia, placed between two turns of L2.

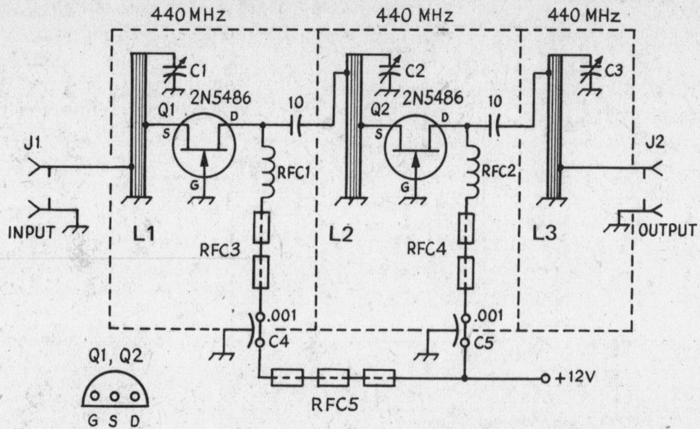

Fig. 14-47 – Schematic diagram of the uhf preamplifier. Capacitors are disk ceramic unless otherwise noted.
C1-C3, incl. – 1.4 to 9.2-pF miniature variable (Johnson 189-0563-001).
C4, C5 – Feedthrough type.
J1, J2 – BNC type, chassis mount.
L1-L3, incl. – 2 5/8 X 1/4-inch strip of brass, soldered to the enclosure on one end and to the capacitor at the other. Input and output taps (on L1 and L3) are 1/2-inch up from the ground end. Drain taps for Q1 and Q2 on L2 and L3, respectively, are made just below C2 and C3.
RFC1, RFC2 – 420-MHz choke (Miller 4584).
RFC3, RFC4 – Two ferrite beads on a short piece of No. 20 hookup wire. (Beads are available from Amidon Associates, 12033 Otsego St., N. Hollywood, CA 91607.)
RFC5 – Three ferrite beads on No. 20 hookup wire.
Q1, Q2 – Motorola JFET.

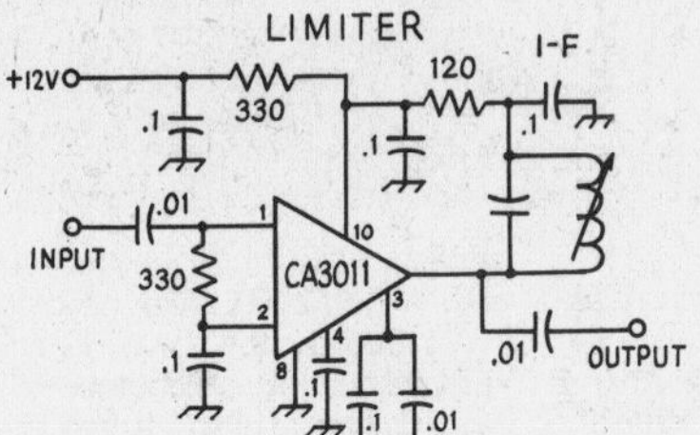

Fig. 14-48 – Diagram of a limiter which may be added between the last i-f stage and the detector of a receiver.

FM Bibliography

Goldsmith *et al, Frequency Modulation,* in two volumes, RCA Review, RCA, 1948.

Rider and Uslan, *FM Transmission and Reception,* John F. Rider Publisher, 1948.

Wolf, *FM Schematic Digest,* Two-Way Radio Engineers, 1970.

Pre-Progress Line Diagrams, in two volumes, Mobile Radio Department, General Electric Company, 1968.

Hund, *Frequency Modulation,* McGraw-Hill Book Company, 1942.

Lytel, *Two-Way Radio,* McGraw-Hill Book Company, 1959.

A SOLID-STATE FM TRANSMITTER FOR 146 MHz

In an effort to shrink the dimensions of the solid-state fm transmitter treated earlier in *QST*, and in the 1972 *ARRL Handbook*, it became necessary to eliminate one stage of the rf section, and to reduce the size of the speech amplifier and clipper. The product of that effort is shown schematically in Fig. 1.

A slightly different electrical approach was taken, wherein the oscillator was called upon to deliver a fair amount of power. The increased output from Q1 permitted the deletion of a driver stage ahead of the PA. The change made it necessary to pay particular attention to the design of all networks between stages, providing adequate selectivity to assure suppression of unwanted output frequencies. The criterion was met, as evidenced by a spectral display of the output energy. The MK-II version is as clean as was the MK-I model.

A logical approach to reducing the area occupied by the speech amplifier and clipper was the employment of a transistor-array IC as opposed to the use of discrete components. The latter technique was used in the MK-I example.

Circuit Highlights

Generally, the circuit of Fig. 1 follows the classic sonobuoy format given in RCA's *Power Circuits, DC to Microwaves.*[1] Some of the circuit changes made are radical; others are subtle. The

[1] Recommended for amateur libraries. Order from local radio store, or write RCA Electronic Components, Harrison, NJ 07029. Price: $2.

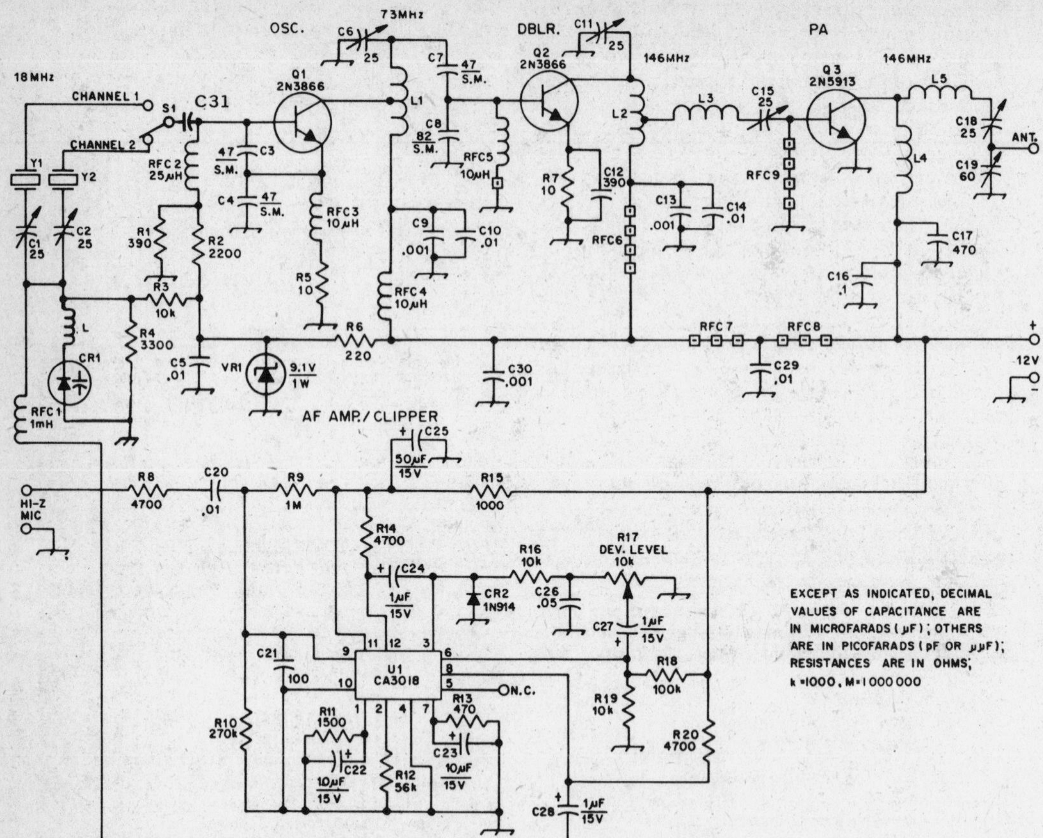

Fig. 1 – Schematic diagram of the 2-meter fm transmitter, Fixed-value capacitors are disk ceramic unless otherwise marked. Polarized capacitors are electrolytic. Fixed-value resistors are 1/2-watt composition. Numbered components not appearing in parts list are so numbered for pc-board layout purposes only. Use crown type heat sink on Q1, larger style on Q2 and Q3.

C1, C2, C6, C11, C15, C18 – 7- to 25-pF miniature ceramic trimmer (Erie 538-002B-7-25 or equiv. Avail. new from Newark Electronics. Avail. surplus from Reliance Merchandising Co., Phila. PA).

C19 – 15- to 60-pF miniature ceramic trimmer (Erie 538-002F-15-60 or equiv.).

C31 – 100-pF silver mica.

CR1 – Voltage-variable capacitor (Varicap) diode.

CR2 – High-speed silicon switching diode.

L – 1 to 2 μH inductor. 20 turns No. 30 enam. close-wound on 100,000 ohm, 1-watt resistor.

L1 – 5 turns No. 16 tinned bus wire, 1/4-inch ID × 5/8 inch long. Tap at 1-1/2 turns from 12-volt end.

L2 – 3 turns No. 16 tinned bus wire, 1/4-inch ID × 3/8 inch long. Tap at 1/2 turn from C13 end.

L3 – 4 turns No. 22 enam. wire, close-wound, 1/4-inch ID.

L4 – 25 turns No. 28 enam. wire, close-wound on body of 100,000-ohm, 1-watt resistor. Use resistor pigtails as anchor points for ends of winding.

L5 – 5 turns No. 16 tinned bus wire, 5/16 ID × 1/2 inch long.

Q1-Q3, incl. – RCA transistor.

R17 – 10,000-ohm pc-board carbon control linear taper (Mallory MTC 14L1 or equiv.).

RFC1 – 1-mH miniature rf choke (Millen J300-25).

RFC3, RFC4 – 10-μH miniature rf choke (Millen J300-10).

RFC5 – 10-μH miniature rf choke (Millen J300-10) with one Amidon ferrite bead over ground-end pigtail.

RFC6, RFC9 – 4 Amidon ferrite beads on 1/2-inch length of No. 24 wire (Amidon Associates, 12033 Otsego St., No. Hollywood, CA 91607).

RFC7, RFC8 – Same as RFC6 but with three beads on 3/8-inch length of wire.

S1 – Spdt slide or rotary switch.

U1 – RCA integrated circuit.

VR1 – 9.1 volt, 1-watt Zener diode.

Y1, Y2 – 18-MHz crystal (International Crystal Co. ground for 20-pF load capacitance. HC-25/U holder. Use International FM-2 pc-board crystal socket). High accuracy .002 percent temperature-tolerance crystal recommended.

boiled-down version is based on amateur-band performance criteria and the more commonly available supply voltage of 12. Emphasis has been placed on good frequency stability, narrow-band deviation (up to 6 kHz), and relative freedom from spurious output.

Low-cost transistors are used at Q1 and Q2. A ballasted transistor (mismatch protected) is used at Q3 to prevent burnout resulting from temporary open- or short-circuit conditions in the antenna system. The current OEM price (single lot) for the 2N5913 is $3.63. Over-the-counter prices will be slightly higher, but it is recommended that the builder use the '5913 if he wishes to have the circuit perform as specified here. Substitutes for any of the devices used in the circuit should be employed only by those who are experienced in semiconductor work. The wrong choice can lead to dismal results with the circuit – instability, low output, or destruction of one or more of the transistors.

Ferrite beads are used generously in the circuit, for decoupling of the dc bus and as rf chokes.[2] The beads provide low-*Q* impedances and are superior to solenoid-wound inductors in preventing circuit instability caused by tuned-base-tuned-collector conditions. A further aid to stability is provided through the use of high and low values of capacitance (combined) in various parts of the circuit. This standard technique helps to assure stability at hf and vhf, and is necessary because of the high f_T of the transistors used.[3]

Transistor sockets should not be used at Q1, Q2 or Q3. The additional lead lengths resulting from the use of sockets could lead to instability problems. Those wishing to use a socket at U1 may do so by redesigning the pc board to allow a socket to be installed (bringing the twelve holes for the IC closer together). Alternatively, one might employ an IC socket which has fairly long lugs, bending the lugs outward to mate with the holes in the pc-board.

Speech Amplifier

U1 consists of four bipolar transistors on a common substrate. Two of the transistors are connected for use as a Darlington pair. The remaining two are separate from one another. In the circuit of Fig. 1 the Darlington pair serves as a preamplifier for a high-impedance crystal, ceramic, or dynamic microphone. One of the separate transistors is used as a diode in the clipper circuit (an outboard silicon diode is used to clip the opposite side of the af sine wave), and the remaining transistor amplifies the clipped audio after it is filtered by an *R-C* network. Deviation is set by adjustment of a pc-board potentiometer, R17.

The processed audio is fed to CR1, the varactor diode modulator. Some reverse bias is used on CR1 to assure greater linearity of modulation (3 volts dc taken from the junction of R3 and R4). As the audio voltage is impressed across CR1, the junction capacitance of the diode shifts above the steady-state value which exists when no af voltage is present. The change in capacitance shifts the crystal frequency above and below its nominal value to provide fm.

Construction

There are no special instructions provided the builder follows the template pattern offered.[4] However, it is worth mentioning that the *QST*

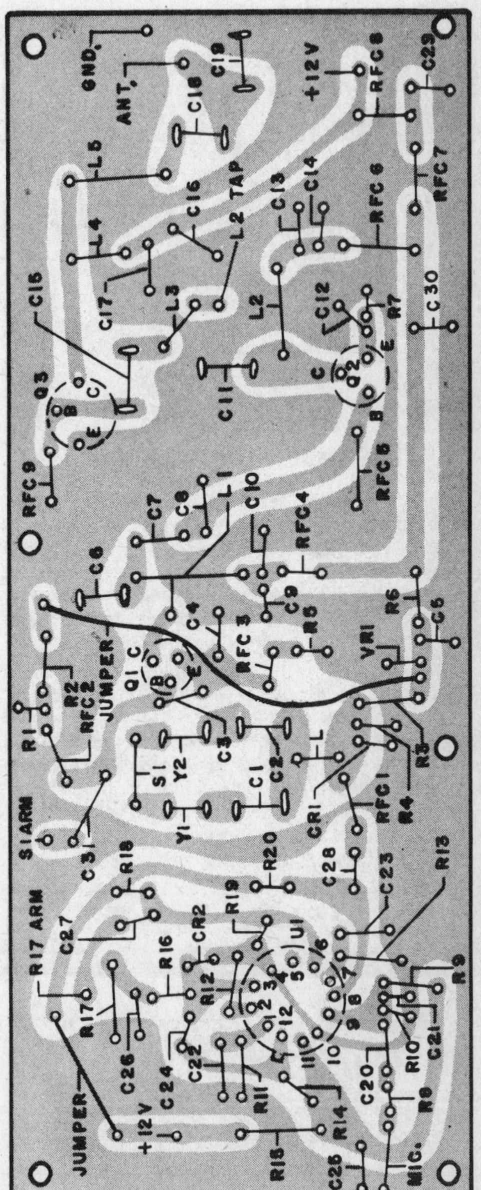

Fig. 2 — Template and parts layout for the transmitter drawn to full scale. Foil-side view.

[2] See parts list for ordering information.

[3] The higher the f_T (upper-frequency rating) of a transistor, the greater will be its gain capability at lower frequencies, thus giving rise to unwanted hf or lf oscillations.

model was built on glass-epoxy circuit board. Those attempting to use phenolic or other types of pc board may encounter difficulty in obtaining proper circuit performance. The dielectric properties of the various board materials are different, thereby causing different values of capacitance to exist between pc-board foil strips. The condition can cause instability, unwanted coupling, and tuned circuits that will not hit resonance. Some builders of the MK-I transmitter learned this the hard way!

Transistors Q2 and Q3 require fairly hefty heat sinks if good efficiency and longevity of the devices is to be realized. Homemade sinks are shown in the photo. Each consists of a piece of 1/16-inch thick aluminum (brass or copper is ok) formed over a drill bit slightly smaller in diameter than a TO-5 transistor case. The aluminum can be crimped in a bench vise until it fits snugly around the drill body. Silicone grease should be used to coat the transistor bodies prior to installation of the heat sinks. The height of the sinks is 1 inch. The ID is approximately 1/4 inch.

Lead lengths of the wires going from the pc board to S1 should be kept short – preferably less than 1-1/2 inches long. Coaxial cable (50-ohm impedance) should be used between the antenna terminals on the pc board and the antenna connector. The shield braid must be grounded at each end of the cable. Similarly, shielded cable should be employed between the microphone jack and the audio-input terminals on the pc board.

Checkout and Use

Initial checkout should be undertaken at reduced supply voltage. Apply a voltage of between 6 and 12, making certain that a dummy load of approximately 50 ohms is connected to the output of Q3. A 56-ohm 2-watt resistor or a No. 47 pilot lamp will suffice. Using a wavemeter tuned to 73 MHz, adjust the collector tank of Q1 for a peak reading on the wavemeter. Next, set the wavemeter for operation at 146 MHz and adjust the collector tuned circuit of Q2 for maximum meter indication. The tank circuit of Q3 should be adjusted for maximum power output as observed on an rf wattmeter or Monimatch-type SWR indicator. A rough check can be made by using a No. 47 lamp as a load, adjusting for maximum bulb brilliancy. The next step is to raise the supply voltage to 12 and repeat the tweaking procedure outlined above. If all stages are functioning normally, a No. 47 lamp should illuminate to slightly more than normal brilliance. Power output into a 50-ohm load should be between 1-1/2 and 2 watts Current drain will be between 200 and 250 mA, speech amplifier included.

Adjustment of the transmitter frequency and deviation can best be done while using a vhf frequency counter and deviation meter. Alternatively, one can put the transmitter in service and ask one of the other fm operators in the area to observe his receiver's discriminator meter while you adjust your crystal trimmer for a zero reading. Deviation can be set reasonably close to the desired amount by comparing your modulation against that of other local stations, having a third operator report the comparisons.

This transmitter is well suited as a companion unit to the fm receiver described in Chapter 3, and in *QST*.[5] The two units can be packaged to form a trans-receiver for portable, mobile, or fixed-station use. The transmitter can be used to drive a high-power solid-state 2-meter amplifier, described later in this chapter, if one wishes to put on a pair of "boots."[6]

---

[5] DeMaw, "A Single-Conversion 2-Meter FM Receiver," *QST*, August, 1972.

[6] Hejhall, "Some 2-Meter Solid-State RF Power-Amplifier Circuits," *QST*, May, 1972, p. 40.

[7] Write: Spectrum Research Laboratory, Box 5824, Tucson, AZ 85703.

2-METER SOLID-STATE RF POWER-AMPLIFIERS

The majority of the commercially made 2-meter fm transceivers available today have rf power-output levels of 1 to 15 watts. There are many occasions when an fm operator would like to have a little more power to be able to work over greater distances. Described here are two amplifiers, one for 25 watts and another for 50 watts output for the 2-meter band. Both amplifiers use a single transistor and operate directly from a 13.6-volt vehicular electrical system.

Circuit Description

The amplifier circuit shown in Fig. 14-53 utilizes a single 2N6084 transistor operated in a Class-C, zero-bias configuration. This mode of operation has the advantages of high collector efficiency at full output and zero dc current drain when no rf driving signal is applied. The reader should note that zero-bias operation yields an amplifier that is not a "linear." It is designed for

Fig. 14-52 – An end view of the breadboard version of the 50-watt 2-meter amplifier. The input circuit is at the lower right, and the output network is at the upper left.

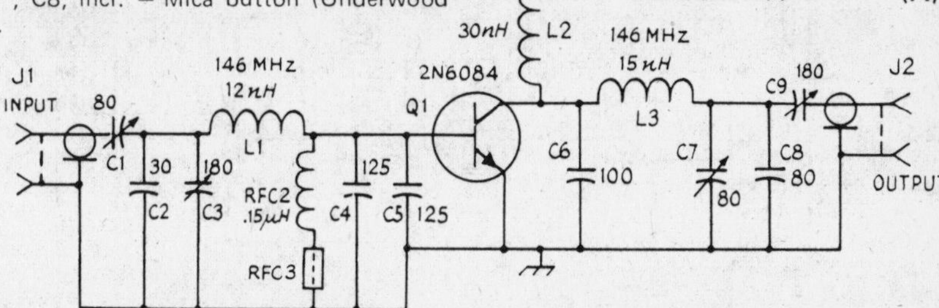

Fig. 14-53 (A) — Diagram of the amplifier which provides 40 to 50 watts output and its associated COR circuit. Capacitors are mica unless otherwise noted. The heat sink is a Thermalloy 6169B (Allied Electronics No. 957-2890).

C1, C7 — 5- to 80-pF compression trimmer (alco 462 or equiv.).
C2, C4-C , C8, incl. — Mica button (Underwood J-101).
C3, C9 — 9- to 180-pF compression trimmer (Arco 463 or equiv.).
C10 — Feedthrough type.
C11 — Tantalum.
C12, C15, C16 — Ceramic disk.
C13, C14 — 39-pF mica (Elmenco 6ED390J03 or equiv.).
CR1 — 100-PRV or more, 500-mA or more silicon diode (Motorola 1N4001 or equiv.).
CR2,CR3 — High-speed, low capacitance 100-PRV silicon diode (Motorola MSD7000 dual package used here).
J1,J2 — Coaxial connector, panel mount.
K1 — 4pdt open-frame relay, 12-V contacts (Comar CRD-1603-4S35 or equiv., Sigma 67R4-12D also suitable), modified as described below.
L1 — 12 nH, No. 10 tinned wire, 1 1/4-inch long straight conductor.
L2 — 30 nH, 1 3/4 turns, No. 10 tinned wire, 3/8 inch ID, 3/4 inch long.
L3 — 15 nH, No. 14 tinned wire, 3/4-inch long straight conductor.
L4 — 2 turns of No. 18 tinned wire 1/4-inch ID, 0.2 inch long (approximately 44 nH).
Q1 — Motorola silicon power transistor.
Q2 — Npn silicon Darlington transistor, h_{FE} of 5000 or more (Motorola MPS-A13 or equiv.).
R1 — 15 ohm, 1-watt composition.
R2 — 4700 ohm 1/2-watt composition
RFC1 — 17 turns, No. 16 enam. wire wound on Amidon T-80-2 toroid core.
RFC2 — Molded rf choke (J. W. Miller 9250-15).
RFC3 — Ferrite bead (Ferroxcube 56-590-65/3B or equiv.).

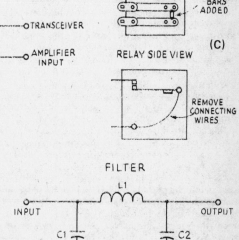

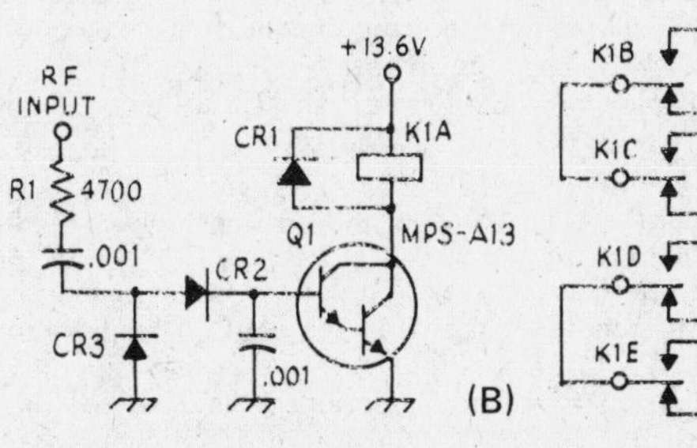

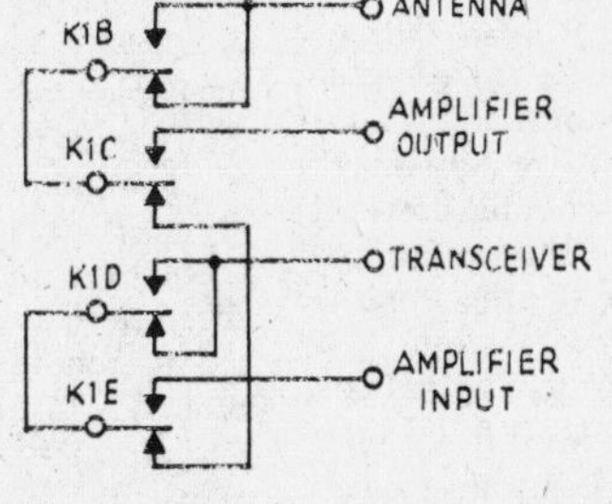

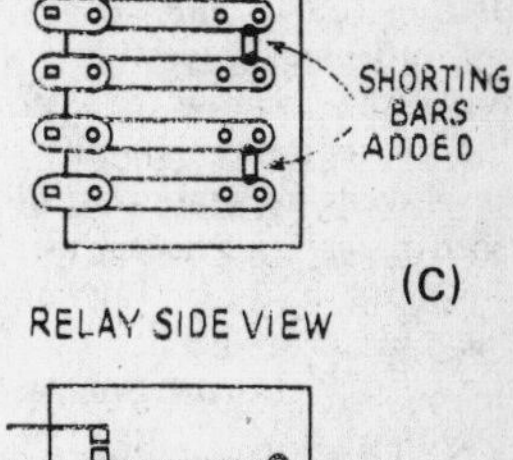

(B) COR circuit. Capacitors are disk ceramic.

The COR relay is modified by removing the connecting wires from all four wiper arms and adding two shorting bars, as shown. Only the stationary-contact connections are used.

CR1 — 100-PRV or more, 500-mA or more silicon diode (Motorola 1N4001 or equiv.).
CR2, CR3 — High-speed, low-capacitance 100-PRV silicon diode (Motorola MSD7000 dual package used here).
K1 — 4pdt open-frame relay, 12-V contacts (Comar CRD-1603-4S35 or equiv., Sigma 67R4-12D also suitable), modified as described below.
Q2 — Npn silicon Darlington transistor, h_{FE} of 5000 or more (Motorola MPS-A13 or equiv.).

(C) The COR relay is modified by removing the connecting wires from all four wiper arms and adding two shorting bars, as shown. Only the stationary-contact connections are used.

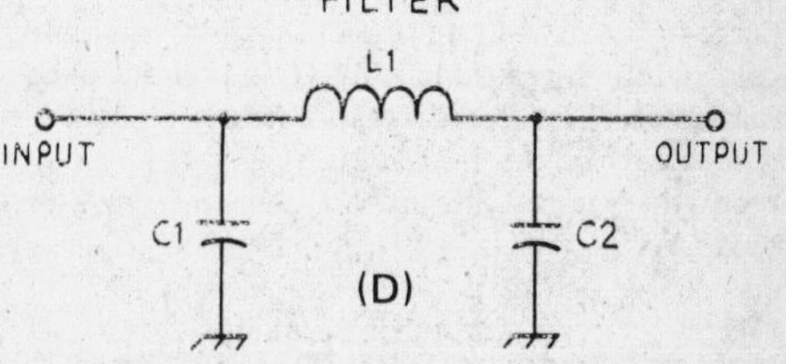

(D) Pi-section output filter, C1 and C2 are 39-pF mica capacitors (Elmenco 6ED390J03 or equiv.), and L1 consists of 2 turns of No. 18 tinned wire, 1/4 inch ID, 0.2 inch long (approximately 44 nH).

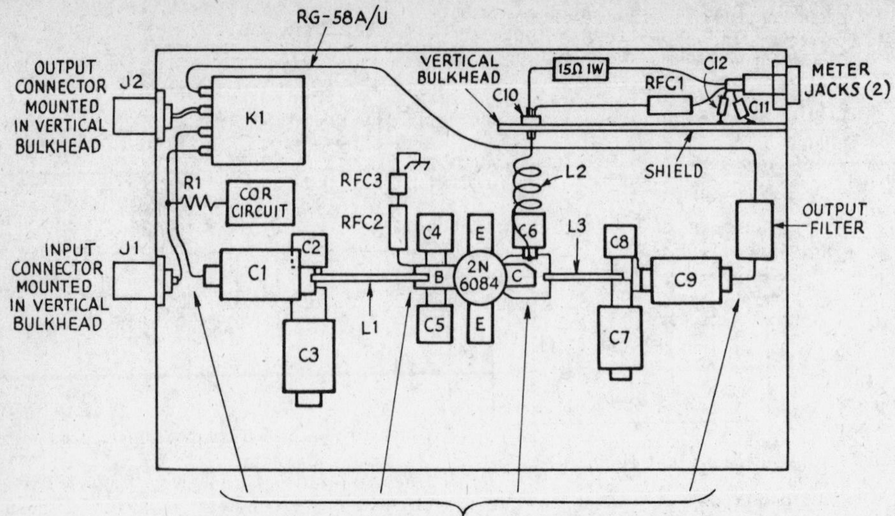

Fig. 14-54 – Parts-layout diagram for the 50-watt amplifier (not to scale). A 4 × 6-inch pc board is used as the base.

fm (or cw– operation only, and would produce objectional distortion and splatter if used to amplify either a-m or ssb signals.

The amplifier operates directly from an automobile electrical system, so no additional power supply is required for mobile operation. The input and output-tuned circuits are designed to match the impedances of the transistor to a 50-ohm driving source and to a 50-ohm antenna system, respectively. Since both the input and output impedances of the transistor are extremely low (in the 1- to 5-ohm region), the matching networks employed are somewhat different than those used with tubes. The networks chosen for the amplifier are optimized for low-impedance matching, and they perform their tasks efficiently. The network designs for this amplifier were done with the aid of a computer.

The elaborate decoupling network used in the collector dc feed is for the purpose of assuring amplifier stability with a wide variety of loads and tuning conditions. The 2N6084 transistor is conservatively rated at 40 watts output (approximately 60 watts dc input). The amplifier can readily be driven to power output levels considerably higher than 40 watts, but it is recommended that it be kept below 50 watts output. If your transmitter or transceiver has greater than 10 watts output, an attenuator should be used at the amplifier input to keep the output from the amplifier below 50 watts.

Construction Details

Construction of the amplifier is straightforward. The usual precautions that must be observed when building a solid-state final amplifier are followed. These precautions include proper mechanical mounting of the transistor, emitter grounding, heat sinking, and decoupling of the supply-voltage leads. Most of the components used are conventional items which are readily available, with two exceptions. The fixed mica capacitors, Underwood type J-101, are a special mica unit designed for high-frequency applications. The core for RFC1 and the rf bead used for RFC3 are available from Elna Ferrite Labs, Inc., 9 Pine Grove St., Woodstock, NY 12498.

The amplifier is constructed on a pc board which is bolted to a heat sink. A few islands can be etched on the board for tie points, at the builder's discretion; a complex foil pattern is not required. In the amplifier shown in the photo, islands were etched only for input and output tie points. Circuit-board islands may also be etched for the transistor base and collector leads. However, an interesting alternative method was used in the author's breadboard amplifier. The base and collector islands were formed by attaching small pieces of pc board to the top of the main board. This procedure added a few tenths of a pF of capacitance at the connection points, so if you choose to etch islands directly on the main board you may want to increase the value of C6 slightly. (The values of C4 and C5 are not critical.)

A word about the care of a stud-mount rf power transistor: Two of the most important mounting precautions are (1) to assure that there is no upward pressure (in the direction of the ceramic cap) applied to the leads, and (2) that the nut on the mounting stud is not over-tightened. The way to accomplish item 1 is to install the nuts *first* and solder the leads to the circuit later. For item 1, the recommended stud torque is 6 inch-pounds. For those who don't have a torque wrench in the

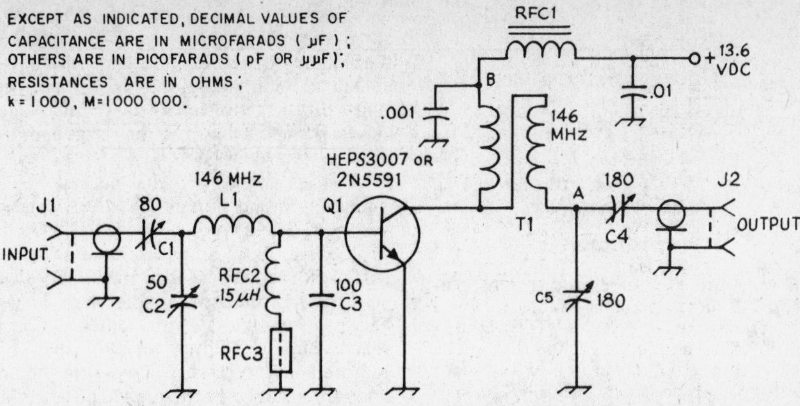

Fig. 14-55 — Circuit diagram of the 25-watt amplifier. Capacitors are disk ceramic unless otherwise noted.
C1 — 5- to 80-pF compression trimmer (Arco 462 or equiv.).
C2 — 2- to 50-pF compression trimmer (Arco 461 or equiv.).
C3 — Button mica (Underwood J-101).
C4, C5 — 9- to 180-]-pF compression trimmer (Arco 463 or equiv.).
J1, J2 — Coaxial connector, panel mount.
L1 — 1-inch length of No. 14 tinned wire.
Q1 — Motorola silicon power transistor (2N5591 or HEP S3007 for 25 W output, 2N5590 or HEP S3006 for 10 W output).
RFC1 — Ferroxcube VK200-19/4B ferrite choke.
RFC2 — Molded rf choke (J. W. Miller 9250-15).
RFC3 — Ferrite bead (Ferroxcube 56-590-65/3B or equiv.).
T1 — See Fig. 14-56.

shack, remember that it is better to under tighten than to over tighten the mounting nut.

The transistor stud is mounted through a hole drilled in the heat sink. A thermal compound, such as Dow Corning 340 heat-sink grease, should be used to decrease the thermal resistance from transistor case to heat sink. See the excellent article by White in *QST* for April, 1971, for details of heat-sink design.

Series impedance in the emitter circuit can drastically reduce the gain of the amplifier. Both transistor emitter leads should be grounded as close to the transistor body as is practical.

The wiring for the dc voltage feeder to the collector should have extremely low dc resistance. Even a drop of one volt can significantly reduce the power output of the amplifier. A good goal is less than 0.5 volt drop from the car battery to the transistor collector. With operating currents of several amperes, a total dc resistance of only a fraction of an ohm is needed. A standard commercially made heat sink is used for the 50-watt amplifier, and it is adequate for amateur communications. Forced-air cooling across the heat sink should be used for any appliation requiring long-term key-down operation at 40 watts or more of output.

Tune-Up Procedure

Generally, the best way to tune a transistor final is for maximum rf power output. If this approach results in exceeding the power ratings of the transistor, then the power output should be reduced by reducing the drive-level, not by detuning the final. In the case of an outboard PA stage, such as described here, both the input and output networks can be tuned for maximum rf output, if the driving source has an output impedance of approximately 50 ohms. However, a better procedure consists of tuning the output tank circuit for maximum rf output and tuning the input circuit for minimum SWR as measured between the exciter and the final amplifier. This tune-up procedure has the added advantage of assuring that the amplifier presents a 50-ohm load to the exciter. A dc ammeter to check collector current is a useful tune-up aid. Since tuning is for peak output, a Monimatch-type SWR bridge is adequate for the job. Also, the wattmeter described in Chapter 22 would be an excellent choice. The best tuning procedure is to monitor simultaneously both output power (absolute or relative) and the SWR between the exciter and amplifier.

First, apply dc voltage with no rf drive. No collector current should flow. Then apply a low level of rf drive – perhaps 25 percent or less of the rated 10 watts maximum drive – and tune the input network for maximum indicated collector current. The networks may not tune to resonance at this low drive level, but you should at least get an indication of proper operation by smooth tuning and lack of any erratic behavior in the collector-current reading. Gradually increase the drive, retuning as you go, until the rated 7-10 watts input and 40 to 50 watts output are obtained. As power input is increased, use the recommended tuning procedure of maximum output from the output tank and minimum input SWR for the input circuit.

There is danger of low-frequency oscillations with most transistor amplifiers. A scope of 5-MHz or more bandwidth connected to the dc feeder at point A makes an excellent indicator of any low-frequency oscillation. It is possible to have

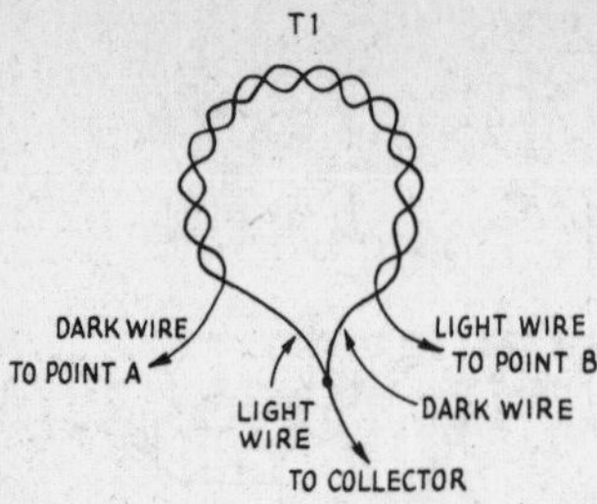

Fig. 14-56 – Transmission-line output transformer consisting of 2 4-inch long conductors, No. 20 enam. wire, twisted to 16 crests per inch, using an electric drill. The conductors should be color coded, one with one color and one with a second color. Form the twisted pair into a 1/2-inch dia circle. Unwind the leads so that only the portion of the pair forming the circle remains twisted. Connect the leads of each color as shown.

signal output on all hf and vhf amateur bands and all TV channels, simultaneously, when a bad case of parasitic oscillation occurs. For those who may have access to one, the best indicator of parasitic oscillation is a wide-band spectrum analyzer.

An Additional Design

For those who own a low-power fm transceiver, an intermediate amplifier stage or a final amplifier providing 10 to 25 watts may be desired. The circuit of Fig. 14-55 is suitable for the 2N5591 or HEP S3007 transistors (25 watts), and the 2N5590 or HEP 3006 transistors (10 watts). An unusual feature of this circuit is the use of a transmission-line transformer in the output network. The construction and tune-up procedures for the amplifiers of Fig. 14-55 is similar to that described earlier for the 50-watt amplifier.

Accessories

When an amplifier stage is used with an fm transceiver, a method of automatic transmit/receive switching is needed. A simple carrier-operated relay (COR), such as shown in Fig. 14-16 can be employed for the amplifiers described in this article. The level of input rf required to operate the COR is determined by the value of R1. One to two watts of 2-meter energy will operate K1 when a 4700-ohm resistor is employed. The rf signal is rectified by two high-speed switching diodes; the dc output from the rectifier is applied to Q1, a Darlington-connected transistor pair. When sufficient current is developed in the base circuit, Q1 will turn on, activating K1. A transient-suppression diode is included across the relay coil to prevent voltage-spike damage to Q1.

The switching circuits needed to take the amplifier in and out of the circuit- are somewhat complex. The cost of four coaxial relays would be prohibitive. But, an open-frame relay can cause sufficient loss at 146 MHz to severely degrade the sensitivity of the associated receiver. To get around this problem the author modified an inexpensive relay. The long leads to the wiper arms were removed and discarded. Two shorting bars were added, as shown in the drawing. External connections were made only to the stationary contacts. Received signal loss through the modified relay measured 0.4 dB – an insignificant amount.

Second-harmonic output from the 50-watt amplifier measured 34 dB down from the level of the 146-MHz energy. Thus, the computer-design output network compares favorably with the pi-section tank circuits often used in hf transmitters. To assure that harmonic energy didn't cause a problem to other services, a simple pi-section output filter was added. This filter is designed for 50-ohm input and output impedances; it can be used with any two-meter amplifier. The insertion loss of the filter at 146 MHz is 0.2 dB, while it provides 46 dB attenuation at 292 MHz and 25 dB at 438 MHz.

Appendix A

1) Amidon toriod cores are available from Amidon Associates, 12033 Otsego Street, No. Hollywood, CA 91607.

2) Ferroxcube components can be purchased from Elna Ferrite Laboratories, Inc., 9 Pine Grove Street, Woodstock, NY 12498.

3) J. W. Miller chokes are available from distributors, or directly from J. W. Miller, 19070 Reyes Ave., Compton, CA 90224.

4) Underwood mica capacitors must be ordered directly from the manufacturer, Underwood Electric and Manufacturing Company, Inc., P. O. Box 188, Maywood, IL 60153. Price for the J-101 units specified in this article is approximately $1.20 each (specify the value — in pF — desired).

5) A circuit board for the 50-watt amplifier will be available from Spectrum Research Labs, P. O. Box 5824, Tucson, AZ 85703.

2-METER FM RECEIVER

An fm purist is not likely to settle for second-rate receiver performance in this day of vhf-band saturation. A satisfactory fm receiver must be able to separate the various repeater output frequencies without being affected by IMD and overload problems. The sensitivity must be good, and so should the limiting characteristics. Few low-cost designs satisfy the foregoing criteria. The circuit of Fig. 14-58 represents a practical compromise between cost and circuit complexity, yet provides performance which is comparable to that of many commercial fm receivers in use by amateurs.

The single-conversion solid-state fm receiver described here is intended as a mate for the transmitter shown in Fig. 14-50. This design centers around a multifunction IC, the CA3089E. Circuit simplicity, good performance, and low cost are the keynotes in this project.

Circuit Highlights

A JFET was chosen for rf amplifier Q1, Fig. 14-58. Neutralization is unnecessary provided the gate and drain elements are tapped down on their

Fig. 14-57 – This photo shows the final breadboard version of the fm receiver. Some of the bypass capacitors are located on the foil side of the pc board in this example. The template and parts-layout sheet provides for topside mounting of the capacitors. The differences between the receiver shown here and the final model are quite minor.

respective tuned circuits. For simplicity's sake only two tuned circuits are used ahead of the mixer, which uses a dual-gate MOSFET. The combination of FETs Q1 and Q2 assures low IMD and provides good immunity to overloading. Output from the mixer is supplied to FL1. This is a four-pole 10.7-MHz i-f filter which is fed from a 900-ohm tap point on tuned circuit C9-C10-L3.

The oscillator/multiplier stage, Q3, is a carbon copy of that used by Pearce-Simpson in their Gladding 25 fm transceiver. It is one of the simplest circuits one can use, yet it performs well. Injection to the mixer is supplied at 157 MHz (10.7-MHz i-f plus the frequency of the received signal). The oscillator crystal frequency is one half the injection frequency – 78 MHz in this example. No netting trimmers are necessary if crystals for the Gladding circuit are ordered and used. Frequency doubling from 78 MHz is accomplished in the collector circuit of Q3.

I-f amplifier U1 is a CA3028A wired for cascode operation. FL1 connects to input terminal 2 through a .01-μF blocking capacitor. Terminating resistor R7 is selected for the characteristic impedance of the filter used. The KVG filter has a 910-ohm bilateral impedance, so if precise matching is desired one can use a 910-ohm unit at R7. Output from U1 is fed to multifunction chirp U2, across R11.

Audio output from U2 is amplified by Q4 before being routed to U3, a transformerless 1-watt output IC. Though the MC1454 is designed to work into a 16-ohm speaker, good results can be had when using an 8-ohm speaker.

Construction

How the receiver is packaged can best be decided by the builder. Two choices are offered: dividing the board in two parts and stacking one section above the other on standoff posts. If this is done it will be necessary to cut the board midway between U1 and U2. If compactness is not necessary the constructor can follow a one-piece assembly format, keeping the board its 8 × 2-11/16-inch size.

Those who desire additional crystal positions can make the board slightly longer. This will provide room for more crystal sockets, but will require that a switch with more positions be used for S1.

It is recommended that transistor and IC sockets be avoided except at Q4 and U3. Short leads between the bodies of the devices and the pc board must be maintained to prevent unstable operation. The use of sockets will cause instability unless low-profile receptacles are used. Similarly, the pigtails on the bypass capacitors should be kept as short as possible in all parts of the rf circuit.

The wiring which connects the audio and squelch controls to the circuit board should be of the shielded variety. If the board is cut into two sections, as mentioned earlier, use shielded cable between U1 and U2, routing the i-f signal from pin 6 of U1 to pin 1 of U2. *Don't leave out C16.*

The leads from S1 to the crystal sockets must be kept as short as possible – less than 1-1/2 inches each. As a further aid to circuit stability mount the pc board on a metal cabinet wall or chassis by means of four or six metal standoff posts. This technique is beneficial in preventing rf ground loops.

Checkout and Alignment

It should be stressed that there is no simple way to align an fm receiver. A stable signal generator will be required, preferably one with fm capability. Initial alignment cannot be properly effected by using off-the-air fm signals. A weak-signal source can be built by using the modulator and crystal oscillator stage of the low power transmitter described in Fig. 14-50. Whatever method is used, make certain that the test signal is no farther off frequency than 200 Hz from the desired frequency of reception. Ideally, the signal source should be *exactly* on the chosen input frequency of the receiver.

Connect the signal generator to J1. Attach a meter across J2 and J3. Make certain that a speaker is hooked to the output of U3. Assuming that an ohmmeter check shows no shorted or open circuits in the completed assembly, connect a 12-volt dc supply to the receiver. With the squelch turned off (maximum hiss noise) adjust C2, C4, and C44 for an upward deflection of the relative-signal-strength meter (at J2 and J3). Next, adjust C10 for maximum meter reading. Repeat these steps two more times. All tuning adjustments should provide fairly sharp peaks when the circuits are tuned to resonance.

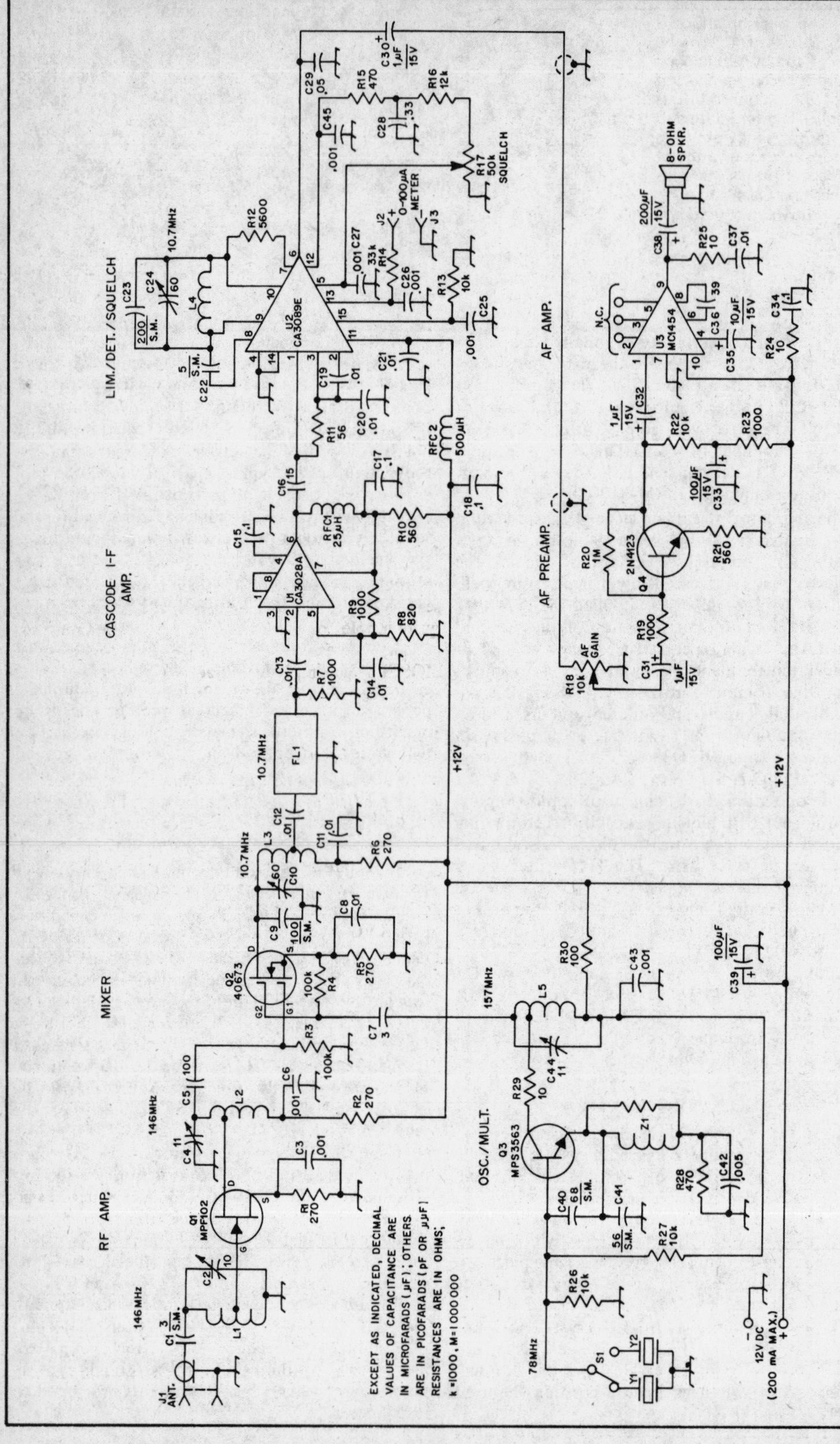
RF AMP.
MIXER
CASCODE I-F AMP.
LIM./DET./SQUELCH
AF PREAMP.
AF AMP.
OSC./MULT.
J1 ANT.
146MHz
10.7MHz
157MHz
78MHz
Q1 MPF102
Q2 40673
Q3 MPS3563
Q4 2N4123
U1 CA3028A
U2 CA3089E
U3 MC1454
FL1
R17 50k SQUELCH
0-100µA METER
R18 10k AF GAIN
8-OHM SPKR.
N.C.
+12V
12V DC (200 mA MAX.)
EXCEPT AS INDICATED, DECIMAL VALUES OF CAPACITANCE ARE IN MICROFARADS (µF); OTHERS ARE IN PICOFARADS (pF OR µµF) RESISTANCES ARE IN OHMS; k=1000, M=1 000 000

Fig. 14-58 — Schematic diagram of the fm receiver. Fixed-value capacitors are disk ceramic unless otherwise noted. Polarized capacitors are electrolytic. Fixed-value resistors are 1/2-watt composition types. Numbered components not in parts list are identified for pc-board layout purposes only. A template and parts layout diagram are available from ARRL Hq. for $0.50. A circuit board is available from Spectrum Research Labs., Box 5824, Tucson, AZ 85703.

C1 — 3-pF silver mica. For precise matching substitute a 10-pF trimmer for the fixed-value capacitor.
C2, C4, C44 — 11-pF pc-mount miniature air variable (E.F. Johnson 187-0106-005, avail. from Newark Electronics).
C10, C24 — Subminiature ceramic trimmer, 15 to 60 pF (Erie 538-011F-15-60, available from Newark Electronics, or surplus from Reliance Merchandising, 2223 Arch St., Phila., PA 19103).
FL1 — See text and footnotes.
J1 — Coax receptacle of builder's choice.
J2, J3 — Binding posts of pin jacks.
L1 — 5 turns No. 18 tinned bus wire, 1/4-inch ID × 1/2-inch long. Tap gate of Q1 at 2-1/2 turns from hi-Z end.
L2 — 4 turns tap at 1 turn from the top (high-impedance) end.
L3 — 16 turns No. 22 enam. wire to occupy entire circumference of Amidon T-50-2 toroid core. Tap at 6 turns from hi-Z end for FL1.
L4 — 1-μH high-Q inductor, unloaded Q 150 or greater. 18 turns No. 24 enam. wire to occupy entire circumference of Amidon T-37-2 toroid core (Amidon Assoc., 12033 Otsego St., N. Hollywood, CA 91607).
L5 — 5 turns No. 18 tinned bus wire, 1/4-inch ID × 1/2 inch long. Tap collector via R29 at 1 turn from hi-Z end.
Q1, Q3, Q4 — Motorola Transistor.
Q2 — RCA MOSFET
R17 — 50,000-ohm linear-taper carbon control.
R18 — 10,000-ohm audio-taper carbon control.
RFC1 — 25-μH choke (Millen J300-25 or equivalent).
RFC2 — 500-μH choke (Millen J300-500 or equivalent).
S1 — Spdt miniature slide or wafer switch, non-shorting.
U1, U2 — RCA integrated circuit.
U3 — Motorola integrated circuits.
Y1, Y2 — International Crystal Co. receiving crystal ground to Pearce-Simpson Gladding 25 specs. Nylon crystal sockets available from International Crystal Co.
Z1 — Rf choke consisting of 8 turns No. 24 enam. wire, close-wound on body of 1000-ohm 1/2-watt carbon resistor. Solder coil leads to resistor pigtails.

A frequency-modulated signal will be required for on-the-nose adjustment of the detector (L4 and C24). C24 should be adjusted slowly until the point is found where best audio quality occurs. Audio recovery will be the lowest at this point, creating the illusion of reduced receiver sensitivity. If no fm signal is available for this part of the alignment, tune the detector for minimum hiss noise as heard in the speaker. After the detector is aligned, readjust C10 for best audio quality of a received fm signal. It may be necessary to go back and forth between C10 and C24, carefully tweaking each capacitor for the best received-signal audio quality. The detector should be adjusted while a strong signal (100 μV or greater) is being supplied at J1.

Adjustment of the squelch control should provide complete muting of the hiss noise (no signal present) as approximately midrange in its rotation. If the audio channel is functioning properly one should find that plenty of volume occurs at less than a midrange setting of R18.

Performance

In two models built, both identical to the circuit of Fig. 14-58, sensitivity checked out at roughly 0.8 μV for 20 dB of quieting. This sensitivity figure is by no means spectacular, but is quite ample for work in the primary signal contour of any repeater. The addition of a dual-gate MOSFET preamplifier ahead of Q1 resulted in a sensitivity of 0.25 μV for 20 dB of quieting. The barefoot receiver requires approximately 0.5 μV of input signal to open the squelch. A more elaborate circuit would have provided greater sensitivity, but at increased cost and greater circuit complexity.

Hard limiting occurs at signal input levels in excess of 10 μV, with 3 dB of limiting exhibited at 1 μV. Addition of an outboard preamplifier will greatly improve the limiting characteristics, and this would benefit those who are dealing primarily with weak signals.

A KVG XM 107S04 i-f filter (FL1)[1] is used in the circuit of Fig. 14-58. However, any 10.7-MHz filter with suitable handwidth characteristics for amateur fm reception can be substituted for the unit specified. During the development period a Piezo Technology Comline filter was used at FL1.[2] The model tried was a PTI 2194F, which sells for $10 per unit in single lots. Club groups may wish to take advantage of the 5 to 9 price break . . $5.95 each. The PTI 2194F gave performance similar to that of the KVG unit.

Each brand of filter has its own characteristic impedance, so if substitutions are made it will be necessary to change the tap position on L3 to assure a proper match between Q2 and FL1. Similarly, the ohmic value of R7 will have to be changed.

1 A product review describing the filter's characteristics was given in *QST* for June,, 1972, p. 56. The filter sells for $15.95 and can be ordered from Spectrum International, Box 87, Topsfield, MA 01983. A drilled printed circuit board is available for $5 from: D.L. McClaren, W8URX, 19721 Maplewood Avenue, Cleveland, OH 44135.

2 Piezo Technology Inc., Box 7877, Orlando, FL 32804.

Specialized Communications Systems

The field of specialized amateur communications systems includes radioteletype, amateur television, amateur facsimile, phone patching, and space and satellite communications. Radio control of models is not a "communications" system in the amateur (two-way) sense. The specialized hobby of radio control does have a large following, but "citizen-band" provisions for frequency allocations and operator registrations divorce it from the strictly ham-radio field (unless one wishes to avoid the QRM).

By far the greatest activity in the specialized fields is to be found in radioteletype (RTTY). Operation using frequency-shift keying techniques is permitted on all amateur bands except 160 meters.

Activity in amateur TV (ATV) can be found primarily in a number of population centers around the country. Most of the work is based on converted entertainment receivers and manufacturer's-surplus camera tubes (vidicons). ATV is permitted on the amateur bands above 420 MHz, and this and the broadband nature of the transmissions precludes extensive DX work.

Slow-scan TV (SSTV) is a narrow-band system that is permitted in any of the phone bands except 160 meters. It is a completely electronic system, however; no photographic techniques are required. Pictures are transmitted in 8 seconds or less.

Amateur facsimile operation, under present U.S. regulations, is permitted only above 50.1 MHz. Operation in the 6- and 2-meter bands is restricted to the use of shifting audio tones with an amplitude-modulated carrier (A4 emission), so operation through an fm repeater on these bands is prohibited. Facsimile operation is undertaken primarily by groups in heavily populated areas.

Amateur satellites – called *Oscars* for Orbiting Satellites Carrying Amateur Radio – offer another way of extending the range of vhf and uhf stations. Satellites can also operate in the hf region to provide communication during times of poor ionospheric conditions.

Phone patches permit third parties to communicate via amateur radio, through an interconnection between the amateur's station equipment and his telephone line. With voice operation in use, phone patching may be conducted in any amateur voice band between domestic stations, or between stations of any two countries permitting third-party communications.

RADIOTELETYPE (RTTY)

Radioteletype (abbreviated **RTTY**) is a form of telegraphic communication employing typewriter-like machines for (1) generating a coded set of electrical impulses when a typewriter key corresponding to the desired letter or symbol is pressed, and (2) converting a received set of such impulses into the corresponding printed character. The message to be sent is typed out in much the same way that it would be written on a typewriter, but the printing is done at the distant receiving point. The teletypewriter at the sending point may also print the same material.

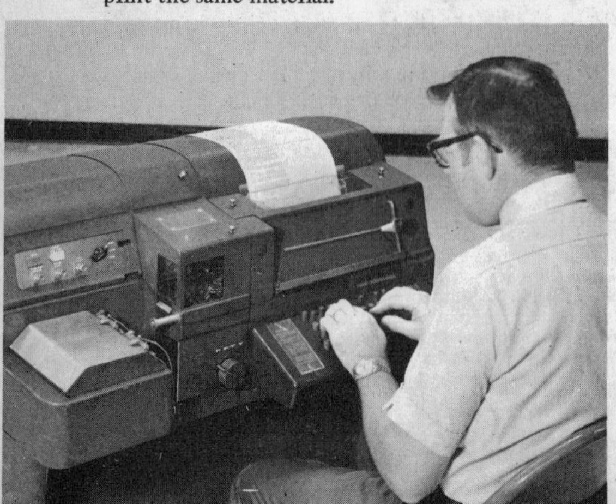

The teleprinter machines used for RTTY are far too complex mechanically for home construction, and if purchased new would be highly expensive. However, used teletypewriters in good mechanical condition are available at quite reasonable prices. These are machines retired from commercial service but capable of entirely satisfactory operation in amateur work. They may be obtained from several sources on condition that they will be used purely for amateur purposes and will not be resold for commercial use.

Some dealers and amateurs around the country make it known by advertising that they handle parts or may be a source for machines and accessory equipment. *QST*'s Ham-Ads and other publications often show good buys in equipment as amateurs move about, obtain newer equipment, or change interests.

Periodic publications are available which are devoted exclusively to amateur RTTY. Such publications carry timely technical articles and operating information, as well as classified ads.

The Teletype Corp. Model 28ASR teleprinter is used by many amateurs. In addition to the keyboard and page printer, this model contains facilities for making and sending perforated tapes.

Over the years *QST* has carried a number of articles on all aspects of RTTY, including a detailed series by Hoff in 1965 and 1966. For a list of surplus-equipment dealers, information on publishers of RTTY periodicals, and a bibliography of all articles on RTTY which have appeared in *QST*, write to RTTY T.I.S., ARRL Headquarters, 225 Main Street, Newington, CT 06111. U.S. residents should enclose a stamped business-size envelope bearing a return address with their request.

Types of Machines

There are two general types of machines, the **page printer** and the **tape printer.** The former prints on a paper roll about the same width as a business letterhead. The latter prints on paper tape, usually gummed on the reverse side so it may be cut to letter-size width and pasted on a sheet of paper in a series of lines. The page printer is the more common type in the equipment available to amateurs.

The operating speed of most machines is such that characters are sent at the rate of either 60, 67, 75 or 100 wpm depending on the gearing ratio of a particular machine. Current FCC regulations allow amateurs the use of any of these four speeds. Interchangeable gears permit most machines to operate at these speeds. Ordinary teletypewriters are of the **start-stop** variety, in which the pulse-forming mechanism (motor driven) is at rest until a typewriter key is depressed. At this time it begins operating, forms the proper pulse sequence, and then comes to rest again before the next key is depressed to form the succeeding character. The receiving mechanism operates in similar fashion, being set into operation by the first pulse of the sequence from the transmitter. Thus, although the actual transmission speed cannot exceed about 60 wpm (or whatever maximum speed the machine is geared for), it can be considerably slower, depending on the typing speed of the operator.

It is also possible to transmit by using perforated tape. This has the advantage that the complete message may be typed out in advance of actual transmission, at any convenient speed; when transmitted, however, it is sent at the machine's normal maximum speed. A special tape reader, called a **transmitter-distributor**, and tape perforator are required for this process. A **reperforator** is a device that may be connected to the conventional teletypewriter for punching tape when the machine is operated in the regular way. It may thus be used either for an original message or for "taping" an incoming message for later retransmission.

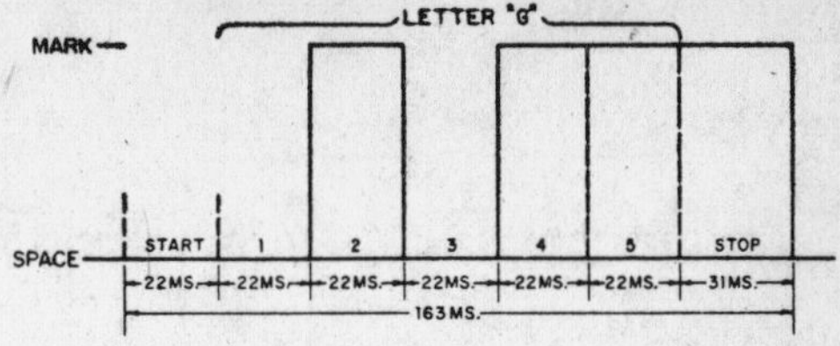

Fig. 15A-1 – Pulse sequence in the teleprinter code. Each character begins with a start pulse, always a "space," and ends with a "stop" pulse, always a "mark." The distribution of marks and spaces in the five elements between start and stop determines the particular character transmitted.

Teleprinter Code

In the special code used for teleprinter operation, every character has five "elements" sent in sequence. Each element has two possible states, either "mark" or "space," which are indicated by different types of electrical impulses (i.e., mark might be indicated by a negative voltage and space by a positive voltage). At 60 wpm each element occupies a time of 22 milliseconds. In addition, there is an intial "start" element (space), also 22 ms long, to set the sending and receiving mechanisms in operation, and a terminal "stop" element (mark) 31 ms long, to end the operation and ready the machine for the next character. This sequence is illustrated in Fig. 15A-1, which shows the letter G with its start and stop elements.

At maximum machine speed, it takes 163 ms to send each character. This is the equivalent of 368 operations per minute. At 75 wpm with this same code, 460 operations per minute result, and 600 for 100 wpm. The letter code as it appears on perforated tape is shown in Fig. 15A-2, where the black dots indicate marking pulses. Figures and arbitrary signs – punctuation, etc. – use the same set of code impulses as the alphabet, and are selected by shifting the carriage as in the case of an ordinary typewriter. The carriage shift is accomplished by transmitting either the "LTRS" or "FIGS" code symbol as required. There is also a "carriage return" code character to bring the carriage back to the starting position after the end of the line is reached on a page printer, and a "line feed" character to advance the page to the next line after a line is completed.

Additional System Requirements

To be used in radio communication, the pulses (dc) generated by the teletypewriter must be utilized in some way to key a radio transmitter so they may be sent in proper sequence and usable form to a distant point. At the receiving end the incoming signal must be converted into dc pulses suitable for operating the printer. These functions,

Fig. 15A-2 – Teleprinter letter code as it appears on perforated tape; start and stop elements do not appear. Elements are numbered from top to bottom; dots indicate marking pulses. Numerals, punctuation, and other arbitrary symbols are secured by carriage shift. There are no lower-case letters on a teletypewriter using this 5-unit code.

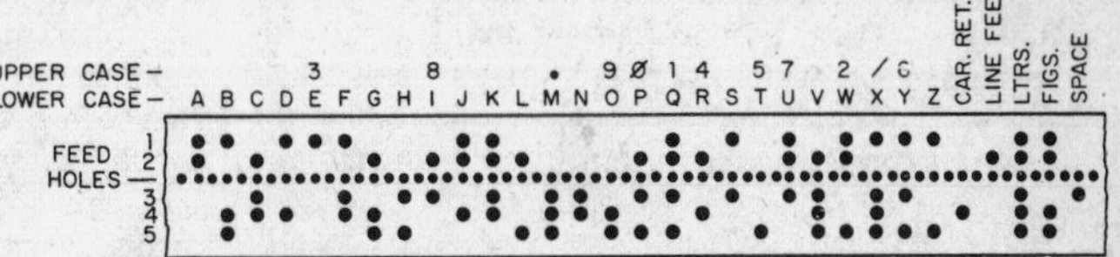

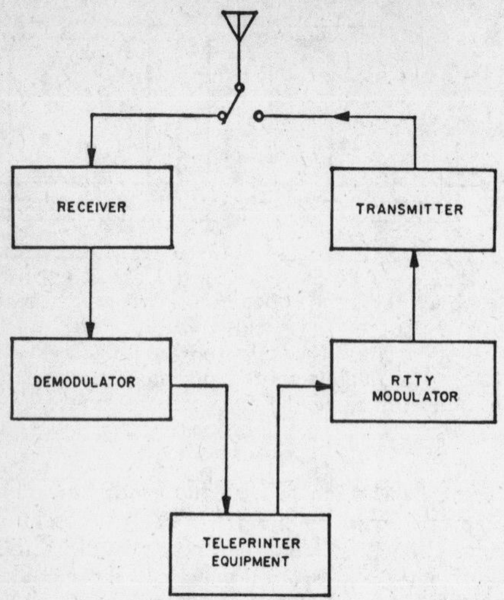

Fig. 15A-3 – Block diagram showing the basic equipment required for amateur RTTY operation.

shown in block form in Fig. 15A-3, are performed by electronic units known respectively as the **frequency-shift keyer** or RTTY modulator and **receiving converter** or RTTY **demodulator.**

The radio transmitter and receiver are quite conventional in design. Practically all the special features needed can be incorporated in the keyer and converter, so that most ordinary amateur equipment is suitable for RTTY with little or no modification.

Transmission Methods

It is quite possible to transmit teleprinter signals by ordinary "on-off" or "make-break" keying such as is used in regular hand-keyed cw transmission. In practice, however, **frequency-shift keying** is preferred because it gives definite pulses on both mark and space, which is an advantage in printer operation. Also, since fsk can be received by methods similar to those used for fm reception, there is considerable discrimination against noise, both natural and manmade, distributed uniformly across the receiver's passband, when the received signal is not too weak. Both factors make for increased reliability in printer operation.

Frequency-Shift Keying

On the vhf bands where A2 transmission is permitted, **audio frequency-shift keying (afsk)** is generally used. In this case the rf carrier is transmitted continuously, the pulses being transmitted by frequency-shifted tone modulation. The audio frequencies used have been more-or-less standardized at 2125 and 2975 Hz, the shift being 850 Hz. (These frequencies are the 5th and 7th harmonics, respectively, of 425 Hz, which is half the shift frequency, and thus are convenient for calibration and alignment purposes.) With afsk, the lower audio frequency is customarily used for mark and the higher for space.

Below 50 MHz, F1 or fsk emission must be used. The carrier is on continuously, but its frequency is shifted to represent marks and spaces. General practice with fsk is to use a frequency shift of 850 Hz, although FCC regulations permit the use of any value of frequency shift up to 900 Hz. The smaller values of shift have been shown to have a signal-to-noise-ratio advantage, and 170-Hz shift is currently being used by a number of amateurs. The nominal transmitter frequency is the mark condition and the frequency is shifted 850 Hz (or whatever shift may have been chosen) lower for the space signal.

RTTY with SSB Transmitters

A number of amateurs operating RTTY in the hf bands, below 30 MHz, are using audio tones fed into the microphone input of an ssb transmitter. With properly designed and constructed equipment which is correctly adjusted, this provides a satisfactory method of obtaining F1 emission. The user should make certain, however, that audio distortion, carrier, and unwanted sidebands are not present to the degree of causing interference in receiving equipment of good engineering design. The user should also make certain that *the equipment is capable of withstanding the higher-than-normal average power involved.* The RTTY signal is transmitted with a 100-percent duty cycle, i.e., the average-to-peak power ratio is 1, while ordinary speech waveforms generally have duty cycles in the order of 25 percent or less. Many ssb transmitters, such as those using sweep-tube final amplifiers, are designed only for low-duty-cycle use. Power-supply components, such as the plate-voltage transformer, may also be rated for light-duty use only. As a general rule when using ssb equipment for RTTY operation, the dc input power to the final PA stage should be no more than twice the plate dissipation rating of the PA tube or tubes.

FREQUENCY-SHIFT KEYERS

The keyboard contacts of the teletypewriter actuate a direct-current circuit that operates the printer magnets. In the "resting" condition the contacts are closed (mark). In operation the contacts open for "space." Because of the presence of dc voltage across the open keyboard contacts in such an arrangement, they cannot normally be used directly to frequency-shift-key another circuit. Isolation in the form of a keying relay or electronic switching is ordinarily used.

Saturated-Diode Keying

Perhaps the simplest satisfactory circuit for frequency-shift keying a VFO is the one shown in Fig. 1. This uses a diode to switch a capacitor in and out of the circuit, and is intended for use in a transmitter which heterodynes the VFO signal to the operating frequency. Because of the small number of parts required for the modification, they can often be mounted on a small homemade subchassis, which in turn is mounted alongside the VFO tube. Connection to the VFO circuit can be made by removing the tube from its socket,

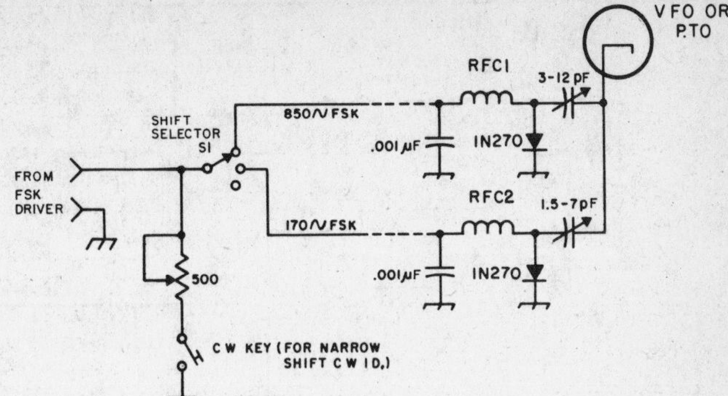

Fig. 1 — Frequency-shift keyer using saturated diodes

RFC1, RFC2 — 2.5 mH (National R-100 or equiv.).
S — Spdt rotary, toggle, or slide.

wrapping the connecting lead around the tube's cathode pin, and reinserting the tube in its socket. The variable capacitors are adjusted for the desired shifts. Once set, the shifts will remain constant for all bands of operation. With this circuit the VFO frequency will be lower on space when the fsk driver of the RTTY demodulator shown later is used. If VFO "sideband inversion" takes place in a mixer stage of the transmitter, it will be necessary to key from the afsk driver output of the demodulator to send a signal which is "right side up."

Be sure to use an NPO type miniature ceramic trimmer for best stability. Use only an rf choke wound on a ceramic form. Ferrite or iron-core types are not suitable because of excessive internal capacitance, so the National type R-100 is recommended. Use only the 1N270 diode specified. This diode is a special high-conductance computer type which provides maximum circuit *Q*, avoiding variations in oscillator output level.

"Shift-Pot" Keying Circuit

The circuit of Fig. 2 may be used with transmitters having a VFO followed by frequency-multiplying stages. The amount of frequency multiplication in such transmitters changes from one amateur band to another, and to maintain a constant transmitted frequency shift readjustment is necessary during band changes. In this circuit the natural VFO frequency is used for mark, and for space the frequency is lowered somewhat depending on the current flowing through CR1. R1 adjusts this current, and therefore controls the amount of frequency shift. As shown, the circuit may be keyed by the fsk driver stage of the RTTY demodulator shown later. If a keying relay is used, Q1 may be omitted and the keying contacts (closed on mark, open on space) connected directly from the junction of R1 and R2 to ground.

Leads inside the VFO compartment should be kept as short as possible. Lead length to the remainder of the circuit is not critical, but to avoid inducing rf or 60-Hz hum into the circuit, shielded wiring should be used for runs longer than a few inches. Positive voltages other than 150 may be used for the bias supply; the value and wattage of R3 should be chosen to supply a current of 2 mA or more to the 6.5-V Zener diode.

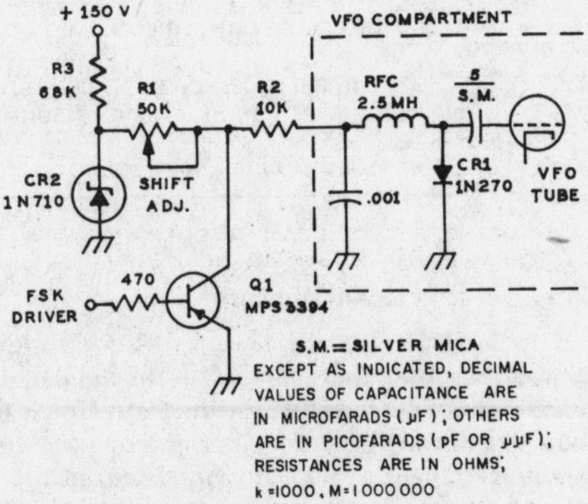

S.M.= SILVER MICA
EXCEPT AS INDICATED, DECIMAL VALUES OF CAPACITANCE ARE IN MICROFARADS (µF); OTHERS ARE IN PICOFARADS (pF OR µµF); RESISTANCES ARE IN OHMS; k=1000, M=1 000 000

Fig. 2 — "Shift-pot" frequency-shift keyer circuit. The shift-adjustment control may be remoted from the VFO circuit.
CR2 — Zener, 6.5-V 400 mW (1N710 or equiv.).
R1 — Linear-taper control, low wattage.
Q1 — Audio transistor, npn silicon (Motorola MPS3394 or equiv.).

AN RTTY DEMODULATOR

Fig. 1 on page 462 shows the diagram of a solid-state demodulator which can be built for approximately $50. Using surplus 88-mH toroidal inductors,[1] the discriminator filters operate with audio tones of 2125 and 2975 Hz for copying 850-Hz shift. The addition of C1 and S5 will permit one to switch-select 170-Hz-shift operation, using tones of 2125 and 2295 Hz.

The demodulator is intended to be operated from a 500-ohm source. If only a 4- or 8-ohm speaker output is available at the receiver, a small line-to-voice-coil transformer should be used between the receiver and the demodulator to provide the proper impedance match. An integrated-circuit operational amplifier, having very high gain capability, is used for the limiter. The discriminator filters and detectors convert the shifting audio tones into dc pulses which are amplified in the slicer section. The keyer transistor, Q5, controls the printer's selector magnets, which should be wired for 60-mA operation. The teleprinter keyboard is to be connected in series with the printer magnets, both being connected to the demodulator

[1] Toroids may be purchased from Typetronics, Box 8873, Ft. Lauderdale, FL 33310.

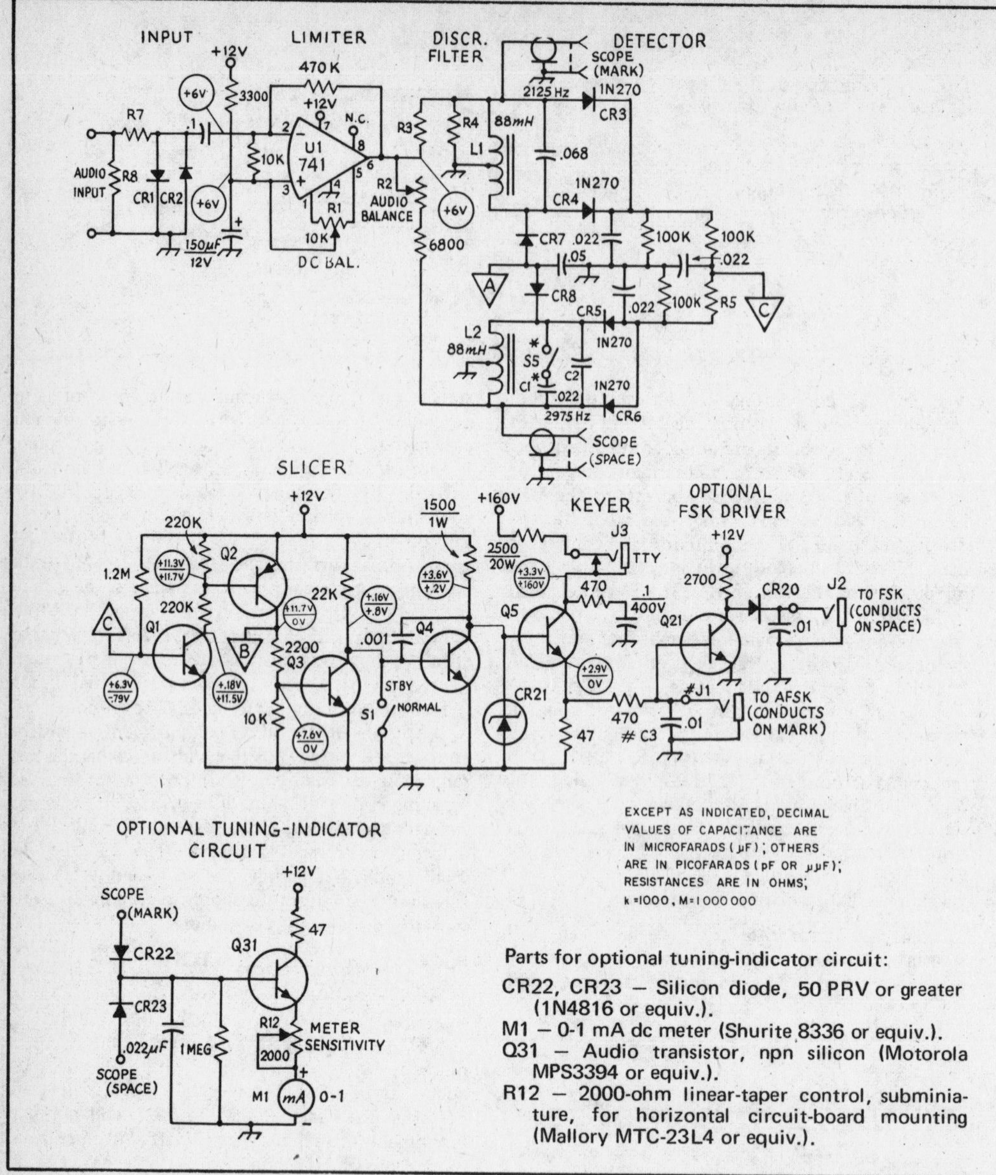

Parts for optional tuning-indicator circuit:

CR22, CR23 – Silicon diode, 50 PRV or greater (1N4816 or equiv.).
M1 – 0-1 mA dc meter (Shurite 8336 or equiv.).
Q31 – Audio transistor, npn silicon (Motorola MPS3394 or equiv.).
R12 – 2000-ohm linear-taper control, subminiature, for horizontal circuit-board mounting (Mallory MTC-23L4 or equiv.).

via J3. Typing at the keyboard will then produce local copy on the printer, and will also produce voltages at J1 and J2 for frequency-shift keying a transmitter or an audio oscillator.

The autoprint and motor-delay section provides optional features which are not necessary for basic operation. This section provides a simulated mark signal at the keyer when no RTTY signal is being received, preventing cw signals and random noise from printing "garble" at the printer. The motor-control circuit energizes the teleprinter motor in the presence of an RTTY signal, but turns off the motor should there be no RTTY signal present for approximately 30 seconds.

Adjustments

With a VTVM, measure the +12-V supply potential. Ground the audio input to the demodulator, and connect the VTVM to pin 3 of the IC. Adjust R1 through its total range, and note that the voltage changes from approximately 1.6 V at either extreme to about +6 V at the center setting of R1. Perform a coarse adjustment of R1 by setting it for a peak meter reading, approximately +6 V. Now move the VTVM lead to pin 6 of the IC. Slowly adjust R1 in either direction, and note that adjustment of just a *small fraction* of a turn causes the voltage to swing from approximately +1 V to +11 V. Carefully perform a fine

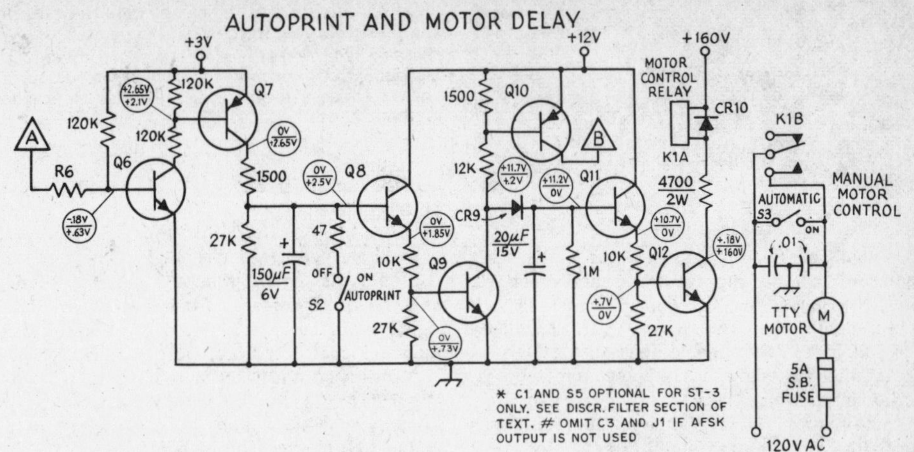

EXCEPT AS INDICATED, DECIMAL VALUES OF CAPACITANCE ARE IN MICROFARADS (μF); OTHERS ARE IN PICOFARADS (pF OR μμF); RESISTANCES ARE IN OHMS; k = 1000, M = 1 000 000

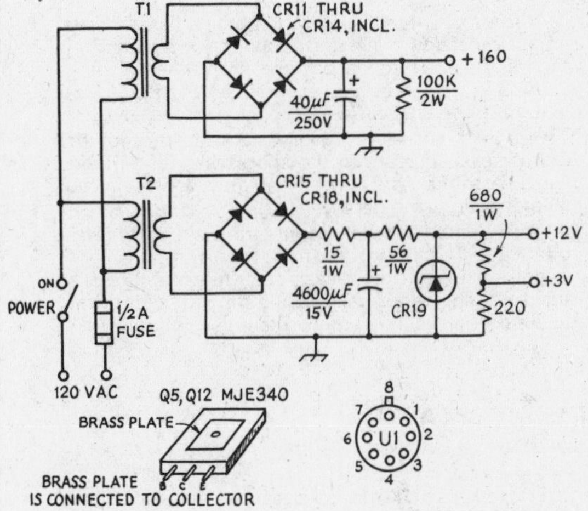

C1 – Optional
C2 – .033 μF, paper or Mylar, 75- or 100-volt rating.
C3 – .01 μF Mylar or disk, 600 volt. Omit if af keying output is not used.
CR1, CR2, CR7, CR8, CR9, CR15-CR18, incl., CR20 – Silicon diode, 50 PRV or greater (1N4816 or equiv.)
CR3-CR6, incl. – Germanium diode, type 1N270.
CR10-CR14, incl. – Silicon rectifier, 400 PRV or greater (1N4004 or equiv.).
CR19 – Zener diode, 12-V, 1-W (Sarkes-Tarzian VR-12 or equiv.).
CR21 – Zener diode, 4.3-V, 400-mW (1N4731 or equiv.).
J1, J2 – Phone jacks. Omit J1 if af keying output is not used.
J3 – Phone jack, single circuit, shorting.
K1 – 110-V dc relay, dpdt contacts with 10-A minimum rating (Potter and Brumfield type KA11DG or equiv.).
L1, L2 – 88 mH toroid.
Q1, Q6, Q8, Q9, Q11, Q21 – Audio transistor, npn silicon (Motorola MPS3394 or equiv.).
Q2, Q7, Q10 – Audio transistor, pnp silicon (Motorola MPS3702 or equiv.).
Q3, Q4 – General-purpose transistor, npn silicon (Motorola MPS2926 or equiv.).
Q5, Q12 – Audio transistor, npn silicon, 300-V collector-emitter rating (Motorola MJE340 or equiv.).
R1, R2 – 10,000-ohm linear taper control, subminiature, for horizontal circuit-board mounting (Mallory MTC-14L4 or equiv.).
R3 – 5600 ohms.
R4 – 18,000 ohms.
R5 – 82,000 ohms.
R6 – 0.1 megohm.
R7 – 1000 ohms.
R8 – 560 ohms.
S1-S5, incl. – Spst toggle. S5 optional.
T1 – Power; primary 120 V; secondary 125 V (Chicago-Stancor PA-8421 or Triad N51-X or equiv.).
T2 – Power; primary 120 V; secondary 12 V, 350 mA (Chicago-Stancor P8391 or equiv.).
U1 – Integrated-circuit operational amplifier, μA741, TO-5 package.

Fig. 1 – The ST-3 RTTY demodulator (by Hoff – from *QST*, April 1970). Unless otherwise indicated, resistors are 1/4-watt 10 percent tolerance. Capacitors with polarity indicated are electrolytic. Dc operating voltages are indicated in the limiter, slicer, keyer, and autoprint and motor delay circuits. All voltages are measured with respect to chassis ground with a VTVM. In the slicer and keyer stages, voltage values above the line should appear with a mark tone present at the demodulator input, while values below the line appear with a space tone present. In the autoprint and motor delay circuit, voltage values above the line occur with a mark or space tone present while those values below the line are present with only receiver noise applied at the demodulator input.

The RTTY demodulator may be constructed on a large circuit board which is mounted inside a standard aluminum chassis, as shown here. A decorative self-adhesive paper provides the grained-wood appearance. The meter is optional and provides a tuning indication for use in the hf amateur bands.

adjustment of R1 by setting it for a voltmeter reading of half the supply voltage, approximately +6 V. Next, again measure the voltage at pin 3. If the potential is approximately +6 V, R1 is properly set. If the potential is in the range of +2 V or less, R1 is misadjusted, and the procedure this far should be repeated.

Next connect the VTVM to point A, and open S5. With a mark-tone input, adjust the tone frequency for a maximum reading, around -2.5 volts. Then change the tone for maximum reading on the space frequency. Adjust R2 until the voltages are equal.

With afsk at vhf, audio tones modulating the carrier are fed from the receiver to the RTTY demodulator. At hf, the BFO must be energized and the signal tuned as if it were a lower-sideband signal for the proper pitches. If the tuning-indicator meter is used, the hf signal should be tuned for an unflickering indication. A VTVM connected at point A of Fig. 15A-7 will give the same type of indication. An oscilloscope may be connected to the points indicated in the filter section and used for a tuning indicator, as shown in the accompanying photographs.

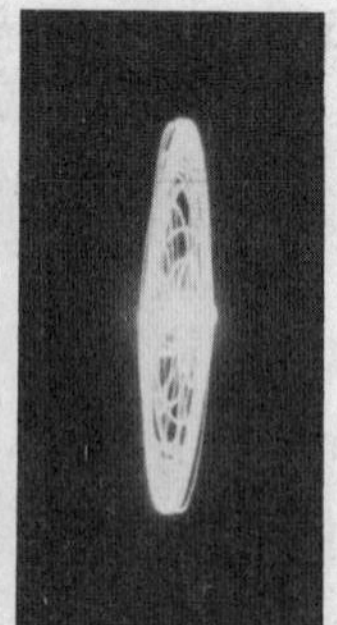

Oscilloscope presentations of the type obtained when the scope mark and scope space connections in the filter section are made. For these displays the mark frequency is displayed on the horizontal axis and the space frequency on the vertical axis. The signals appear as ellipses because some of the mark signal appears in the space channel and vice versa. Although only one frequency is present at a given instant, the persistence of the scope screen permits simultaneous observation of both frequencies. The photo at the left shows a received signal during normal reception, while the photo at the right shows a signal during unusual conditions of selective fading, where the mark frequency is momentarily absent.

AMATEUR TELEVISION (ATV)

Television is not exactly new to amateur radio. Enterprising amateurs have been playing with this branch of the electronics art for a matter of 45 years or more. Files of *QST* dating back to the '20s offer proof that there was amateur television before many of our present-day amateurs were born. The methods used then bore little resemblance to the techniques employed today, but hams were sending and receiving pictures (or trying to) two generations ago.

An actual 440-MHz TV picture transmitted with the equipment shown in Fig. 15B-2.

QST carried many articles on television from 1925 on, and there was plenty of interest. But the work was being done by the motor-driven scanning disk method, and it was doomed to failure. Though many dollars and man-hours were spent on the problem, nobody succeeded in developing mechanical systems that were completely practical. As early as 1928, a *QST* author was pointing out the possibilities of electronic television, using the then rare-and-expensive cathode-ray tube. The days of the scanning disk were numbered.

But predicting the coming of electronic television and bringing it about were two quite different matters. Though it had become fashionable, by 1931, to say that "Television is just around the corner," the cathode-ray tube was a laboratory curiosity, and it was to remain so for some years to come, as far as most amateurs were concerned. Not until 1937 was the subject of

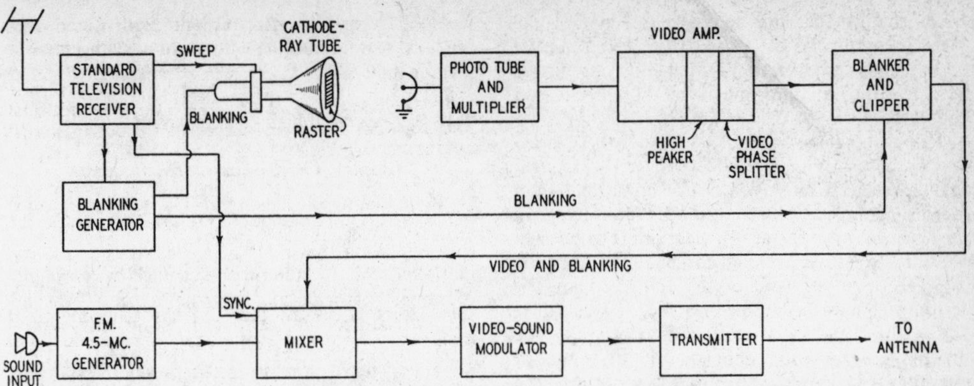

Fig. 15B-1 – Block diagram of the television system used by W2BK, formerly W2LNP. (From *QST*, June, 1950.)

television to appear again in *QST*. By then the problems involved in electronic television were gradually being solved. Usable components were beginning to appear, and television experimental work loomed as a possible field for the more advanced amateur. For more than two years almost every issue of *QST* carried something on television, but it was mostly concerned with the receiving end. The generation of a television picture for transmission was still considered to be beyond the radio amateur, until moderately priced iconoscope tubes were introduced for amateur use in 1940. Television transmitter and camera design were treated extensively in *QST* for 1940.

The highly involved and expensive process required in getting on the air for actual television communication was just too much for most amateurs, and progress in amateur television slowed to a standstill until well into the postwar period. At that time, availability of most of the needed components on the surplus market gave amateur television the push that it had always needed, and the period since 1948 has seen more amateur TV activity than existed in all previous years combined. By 1960, color-TV signals were being transmitted by amateurs.

From several cities in this country has come news of activity in amateur television. Much of the effort has been concerned with transmitting. The trend in this country has been to use transmitting systems that would tie in with those employed in commercial services, so that ordinary home television receivers could be used for amateur work by the addition of a simple converter. In this country amateur TV is limited to the frequencies from 420 MHz up, because of the bandwidth involved.

A Novel Way to Get Started

The cost and complexity of TV gear has so far left most amateurs convinced that television is not for them, but ways have been found to cut corners. There have been several ideas developed for bringing the transmission of television nearer to the abilities of the average experienced ham. One such simplified system was developed by J. R. Popkin-Clurman, W2LNP, later to become W2BK. This system simplifies matters for the ham who would like to transmit transparencies (film negatives or positives, movies, diagrams, visual messages) without going into the complexities of camera design and construction. It also lets a local TV station and a standard TV receiver do some of the work, as shown in block-diagram form in Fig. 15B-1. A standard TV receiver is tuned to a local station and the lead from the receiver video amplifier to the cathode-ray tube is disconnected and the output of the amplifier is fed to a blanking generator. The output of the blanking generator is applied to the receiver cathode-ray tube, the raster of which is used as a light source.

In the simplest form of picture transmission, a transparency is placed directly on the face of the cathode-ray tube, which for this purpose can be almost any type, including those with P-7 phosphor. Light from the raster, passing through the transparency, is picked up by a photo tube and multiplier and fed to a video-amplifier unit that includes a high-frequency peaker and possibly a video phase inverter. The latter is used only if it is desired to transmit negatives in positive form. After passing through a clipper and blanking inserter and a mixer, the signal is ready for the modulator and transmitter. Sound and video are

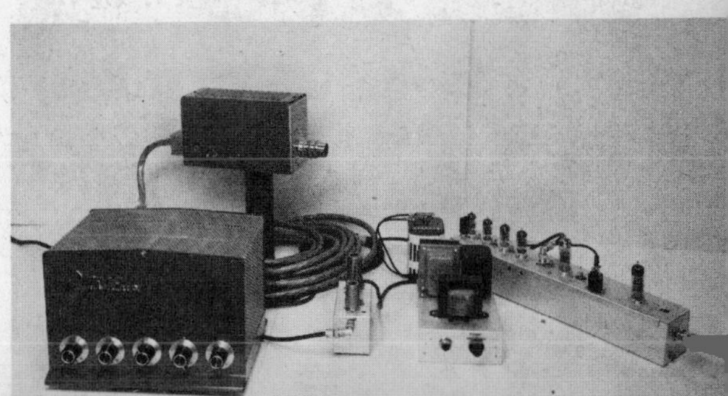

Fig. 15B-2 – The transmitting portion of a complete ATV station. The video system utilizes a modified RCA TV Eye closed-circuit camera and control unit, shown at the left. The 440-MHz TV signal comes out the BNC connector at the end of the mixer-amplifier chassis. The power supply and bias battery are also visible in the photograph. (From *QST*, November, 1962)

transmitted on the same channel, first by frequency modulating a 4.5-MHz oscillator. The 420-MHz transmitter is modulated simultaneously with this signal and the video, by means of the video-sound modulator.

The signal thus transmitted has all the characteristics of a commercial video transmission, and may be received on any standard home television receiver equipped with a 420-MHz converter. In the absence of a local TV station it is merely necessary to derive the sync and blanking from the receiver's own sweep circuits. In this case the picture will have only 262 lines, noninterlaced. It retains the same horizontal resolution, but the vertical resolution is reduced. In this type of operation it is desirable to sync the vertical to the 60-Hz power supply, to reduce hum effects.

The photo tube may be a 931-A multiplier type, available as surplus. The output of the photo tube is fed into a series of video amplifiers, one of which is a high-frequency peaker. This is necessary to compensate for the build-up and decay times of the cathode-ray tube's phosphor screen.

The rf section of the transmitter is crystal-controlled. The receiver has a crystal mixer and a 6J6 oscillator, followed by a cascode amplifier working into a home television receiver. The channel used for the i-f should be one that is not in use locally, and should be in the low-TV band for best results.

The system may be adapted for transmission of movies. A film-projector light source is removed, and the photo tube installed in its place. A 60-Hz synchronous motor is used to drive the film sprocket and the film is run at 30 frames per second instead of 16 or 24. It is necessary to blank the raster during the film pull-down time. Pictures of live subjects may also be transmitted by projecting the light from the raster on the subject and collecting the reflected light with a condensing-lens system for the photo tube. Considerably greater light is needed than for transparencies, and a 5TP4 or a 5WP15 projection cathode-ray tube, with its associated high voltage, is suitable.

Adapting Closed-Circuit TV Systems

By adapting closed-circuit TV systems, a number of amateurs have been able to get a picture on the air without having to struggle with cut-and-try methods, not to mention the mechanical problems of camera construction. A manufactured TV camera and control unit are used, along with home-built rf sections necessary for the ATV station. Such a system is not restricted to sending slides or stills. It is capable of transmitting a moving picture of professional quality. Such a station is shown in Fig. 15B-2.

Many closed-circuit TV cameras provide a picture signal on any regular TV channel from 2 to 6, inclusive. In a typical system, the camera contains a vidicon camera tube, a three-stage video amplifier, a video output stage, a 55- to 85-MHz tunable oscillator, and a modulator stage that combines the rf, video, and sync signals from a control unit. The control unit contains the horizontal and vertical deflection circuits for the vidicon tube, a protective circuit that prevents damage to the vidicon in the event of a sweep-circuit failure, a blanking and vertical sync stage, and the power supply. For use in an ATV station, most amateurs choose to modify the camera oscillator circuit to provide crystal-controlled operation on a locally unused low TV channel. In this way, a regular TV receiver can be used as a monitor. The video-modulated rf signal from the camera is fed through amplifier and mixer stages to derive the transmitted video signal. For reception, a converter is used ahead of a regular TV receiver.

SLOW-SCAN TELEVISION (SSTV)

Because of the required bandwidth, amateur TV transmissions in this country are limited to the frequencies above 420 MHz. With essentially line-of-sight propagation of signals at these frequencies, it has always been necessary for an amateur wishing to engage in ATV to interest another local amateur in this mode, or for him to work into a local group which may already be active if he did not wish to transmit pictures merely for his own amusement. For this reason, ATV has had little to offer to the amateur who lives in a sparsely populated area, perhaps hundreds of miles from any large city. Slow-scan TV, on the other hand, offers a great deal. By using voice-channel bandwidths, SSTV transmissions may be used in any amateur band except 160 meters. The amateur in the sparsely populated area can exchange pictures with the fellows in the big city, the next state, or even with fellows in other countries.

Fig. 51C-1 – A typical slow-scan TV picture.

Work in the area of SSTV was pioneered by a group of amateurs headed by Copthorne Macdonald, W4ZII (later to become in succession, WA2BCW, WAØNLQ, WA2FLJ, and W1GNQ). The first of Macdonald's several articles on the subject appeared in *QST* in 1958. Early on-the-air tests took place in the then-available 11-meter shared band, the only hf amateur band where "facsimile" transmissions were permitted. The video information was transmitted as amplitude modulation of a 2000-Hz subcarrier tone, which in turn was fed into the speech-amplifier circuits of a conventional transmitter.

The loss to U.S. amateurs of the 27-MHz band in September 1958 did much to dampen the enthusiasm of would-be slow scanners. However, special temporary authorizations were granted by the FCC to a few amateurs for the purpose of making experimental SSTV transmissions, first on 10 meters, and later on 20 meters. Tests by WA2BCW and others in 1959 and 1960 indicated that signal fading and interfering transmissions from other stations caused considerable degrading of pictures received from **subcarrier a-m (scam)** transmissions. This led to experiments with **subcarrier fm (scfm)** transmissions, and the superiority of this technique for average propagation conditions was immediately recognized. The resulting standards proposed by Macdonald in January 1961 have since been adapted and are in use today (see Table I). In the scfm system, the frequency of the audio tone conveys the video information, with 1500 Hz representing black and 2300 Hz representing white. Intermediate shades of gray are transmitted with intermediate-frequency tones. Tones of 1200 Hz (ultrablack) are used to transmit vertical and horizontal sync pulses. The success of experiments in the mid '60s on 20 meters with scfm, and especially the fact that SSTV occupies a normal voice-channel bandwidth with no side-frequency products to cause interference on adjacent channels, led to changes in the FCC rules.

SSTV Emissions

Since August 1968, narrow-band A5 and F5 emissions (SSTV) have been permitted in the Advanced and Extra Class portions of 75, 40, 20 and 15 meters, in all but the cw-only portions of 10, 6, and 2 meters, and the entire amateur range above 220 MHz. The regulations permit the transmission of independent sidebands, with picture information contained in one sideband and voice in the other. Few amateurs today are equipped for this type of operation, however. The usual practice is to intersperse picture transmissions with voice transmissions on single sideband.

A stipulation in the U.S. regulations limits the bandwidth of A5 or F5 emissions below 50 MHz; they must not exceed that of an A3 single-sideband emission, approximately 3000 Hz. This precludes the use of an a-m transmitter with the standard SSTV subcarrier tones. Most amateurs operating in the hf bands feed the video information as a varying-frequency tone into the microphone input of an ssb transmitter, and with carrier suppression, F5 emission results. A seldom-used but quite feasible alternative is to frequency modulate an rf oscillator with video signals from the camera.

Because of the narrow bandwidth used, tape recordings of SSTV video signals can be made with an ordinary *audio* tape recorder running at 3 3/4 inches per second. Nearly every slow scanner preserves some of his on-the-air contacts on tape, and most prepare an interesting program to be transmitted. A good number of amateurs begin making two-way picture transmissions while equipped with nothing more than a receiving monitor and a tape recorder, in addition to ordinary station equipment. In lieu of a camera, they enlist the aid of a friend having the proper equipment to prepare a taped program which is sent during transmissions. Because of the slow frame rate with SSTV (one picture every 7 or 8 seconds), live pictures of anything except still subjects are impractical. Viewing a series of SSTV frames has frequently been compared to viewing a series of projected photographic slides.

The SSTV Viewing Adapter with the top cover removed. The adapter may be constructed on Vectorbord, as shown. The transformer near the rear (left) is in the power supply circuit; the one near the front is in the video detector stage. On the front panel are the power switch and indicator, the manual vertical-sweep push button, and vertical sync control. Phono jacks on the rear panel are for connections to the oscilloscope and receiver. Two banana jacks are used for the CRT connections. (Originally described in *QST* for June, 1970, by W7ABW and W7FEN.)

Experiments are currently being made with the transmission of color pictures by SSTV. Various techniques are being used, but in essence the process involves the sending of three separate frames of the same picture, with a red, a blue, and

TABLE I

Amateur Slow-Scan Standards

	60-Hz Areas	*50-Hz Areas*
Sweep Rates:		
Horizontal	15 Hz (60 Hz/4)	16 2/3 Hz (50 Hz/3)
Vertical	8 sec.	7.2 sec.
No. of Scanning Lines	120	120
Aspect Ratio	1:1	1:1
Direction of Scan:		
Horizontal	Left to Right	Left to Right
Vertical	Top to Bottom	Top to Bottom
Sync Pulse Duration:		
Horizontal	5 millisec.	5 millisec.
Vertical	30 millisec.	30 millisec.
Subcarrier Freq.:		
Sync	1200 Hz	1200 Hz
Black	1500 Hz	1500 Hz
White	2300 Hz	2300 Hz
Req. Trans. Bandwidth	1.0 to 2.5 kHz	1.0 to 2.5 kHz

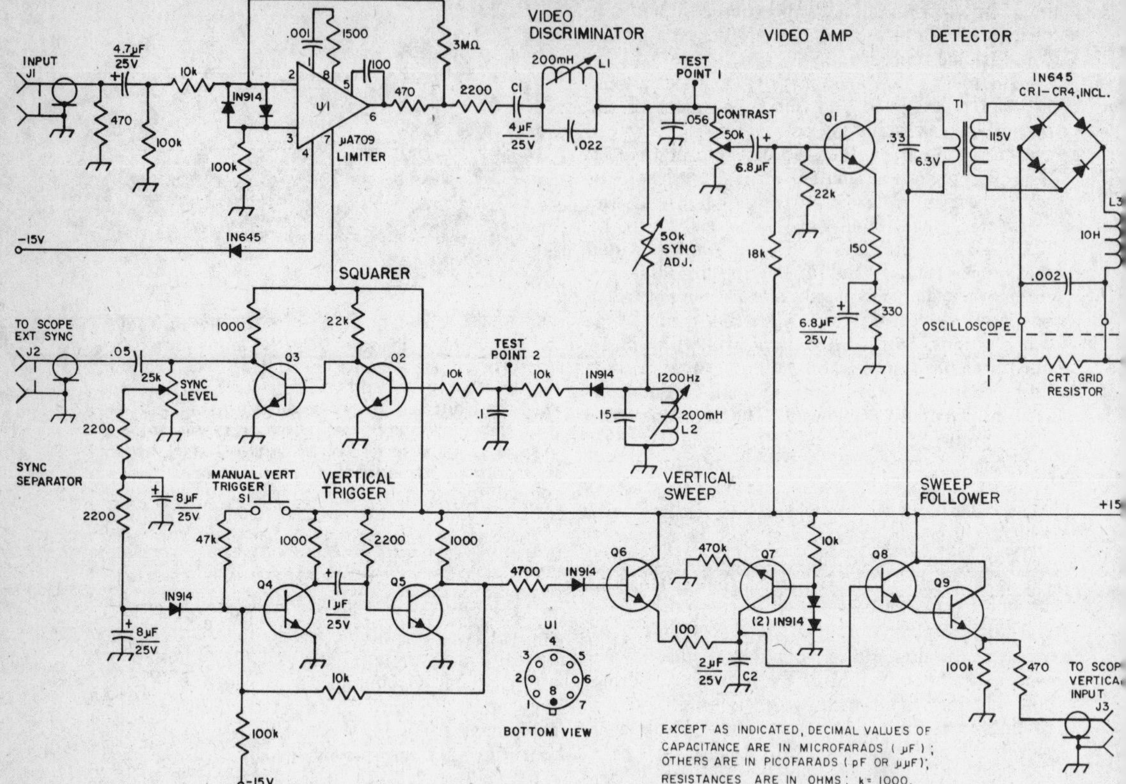

Fig. 1 — Schematic diagram of the slow-scan adapter. Capacitors with polarity indicated are electrolytic, others are ceramic or paper, except as indicated. Variable resistors are composition controls, linear taper. Resistors are 1/2-watt.

C1 — 4-μF, 25-volt, nonpolarized tantalum.
C2 — 2-μF, 25-volt, Mylar.
J1-J3, incl. — Phono jack.
L1, L2 — Variable inductor, approx. 200 mH (Miller 6330, UTC HVC-6, or Stancor WC-14).
L3 — 10-H, low-current choke, 3000-volt insulation from ground (Burstein-Applebee 18A959).
Q1-Q9, incl. — 2N718, 2N697, 2N2222, or 2N3641-3.
T1 — 6.3-volt, low current, 3000-volt insulation.
U1 — Operational amplifier (Fairchild μA709, Texas Instruments SN6715 or Motorola SC4070G).

a green filter successively placed in front of the camera lens for each of the three frames. At the receiving end of the circuit, corresponding filters are used and each frame is photographed on color film. After a tricolor exposure is made, the photograph is developed and printed in the normal manner. The use of Polaroid camera equipment with color film is popular in this work because it affords on-the-spot processing. Color reproduction by this technique can be quite good.

SLOW-SCAN TV VIEWING ADAPTER FOR OSCILLOSCOPES

The slow-scan TV adapter shown in Figs. 1-4, incl., permits the ham with an oscilloscope to view slow-scan TV with a minimum of investment and effort. The adapter has been used successfully with several oscilloscopes, including the Tektronix 514, Dumont 304, Heathkit IO-18, Heathkit IO-10, and a Navy surplus scope, OS-8B.

The oscilloscope's horizontal scan must be able to synchronize from an external trigger at 15 Hz. The scope should have a dc vertical input that will accept 10 volts. If the scope does not have a dc input, the vertical deflection amplifier may be able to be driven directly. The circuit shown in Fig. 3 was used with the Heath IO-18. This arrangement should be adaptable to other scopes not having a dc input, but R1 and R2 would have to be scaled to provide proper centering.

Most oscilloscopes have cathode-ray tubes with a P1 phosphor. The P1 phosphor is of short persistence, which is not suitable for slow-scan TV. Therefore, the P1 tube should be replaced with a P7-phosphor tube which has the long persistence required. The last two characters of the CRT type usually indicate the phosphor, and most types are available in several different phosphors. The Heath IO-18 uses a 5UP1 which was replaced with a 5UP7 at a cost of less than $15.00.[1] If a direct substitute cannot be found, it may be possible to find a

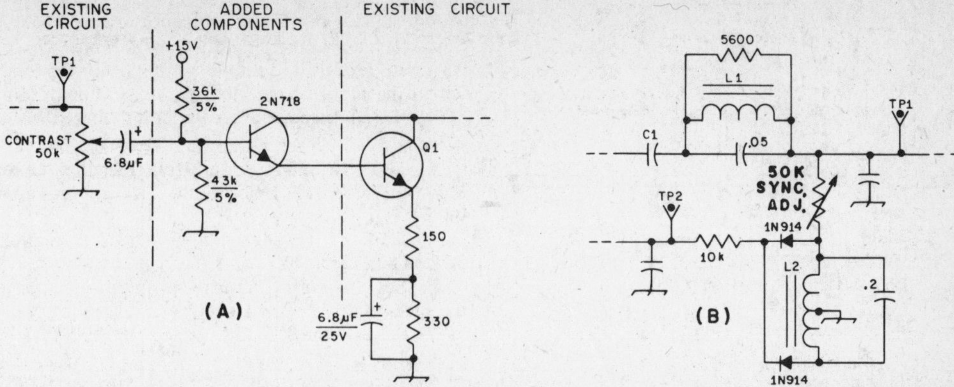

Fig. 2 – At A, a circuit which may be added to increase the contrast of the SSTV adapter, and at B, an alternative circuit using surplus 88-mH toroidal inductors for L1 and L2. If the circuit of A is used, the 18,000- and 22,000-ohm resistors shown connected to the base of Q1 in Fig. 1 are unnecessary.

surplus CRT of another type which will function. The Dumont 304 used a 5ABP1 CRT, which was replaced with a 5CP7. This CRT was obtained on the surplus market for less than $5.00.[2] If the purchase of a new oscilloscope is anticipated, a P7-phosphor cathode-ray tube should be requested.

Adapter Circuit Design

The schematic diagram of the slow-scan TV converter is shown in Fig. 1. The slow-scan signal from the audio output of a communications receiver, tape recorder, or other source is fed into the input of an integrated-circuit operational amplifier having a gain of 300. Therefore, a 0.1-volt ac peak-to-peak signal causes the amplifier to limit at the supply voltages, and the limited output will be approximately 28 volts ac peak-to-peak. The limited signal is then fed to a series video discriminator. The output of the video discriminator is fed to Q1, a video amplifier with a 6.3-volt ac filament transformer as a collector load. The transformer is used to provide voltage step-up. A transformer with 3000-volt insulation from ground is used, as the CRT grid circuit has a 1400-volt potential which must be insulated from ground. The video is then full-wave rectified and fed to a 1000-Hz filter. The output video dc is then connected across the scope CRT's series grid resistor to modulate the CRT intensity.

The output of the video discriminator is also fed to a 1200-Hz sync discriminator. This circuit passes only the 1200-Hz sync pulses. The 1200-Hz sync pulses are then rectified, filtered and fed to a two-stage amplifier, Q2 and Q3. The output of this squarer provides 15-volt sync pulses.

A 5-volt sawtooth voltage is required for vertical sweep on the oscilloscope. This voltage should have a very fast rise time and a linear decay. A sync separator circuit is used to separate the 30-ms vertical pulses from the 5-ms horizontal pulses. The vertical pulses are fed into the vertical trigger, a one-shot multivibrator. Provision is made for manually triggering the vertical sweep with a front-panel push button, S1, in case a vertical sync pulse is missed. The multivibrator triggers a transistor switch, Q6, that instantaneously charges C2 every time a vertical sync pulse is received. This capacitor is discharged at a linear rate through Q7. The base of Q7 is biased by two diodes at 1.2 volts. Thus, the current through the 0.47-megohm emitter resistor is held at a constant value, giving a linear voltage discharge across C2. This sawtooth voltage is sampled by a Darlington transistor follower, Q8 and Q9, whose output will sweep from 10 to 5 volts dc when receiving slow-scan TV. The value of 5 volts was chosen so that when a signal is not present, the dot on the scope CRT will be off the screen.

If the capability for high contrast is desired, the video signal level may be increased by adding a 2N718 transistor ahead of Q1, as shown in Fig. 2A. For those who wish to use 88-mH toroids in place of the variable inductors, L1 and L2, the circuit of Fig. 2B may be used.

Construction

The layout is relatively noncritical with the exception of the 6-volt ac filament transformer which will have high voltage on the secondary, so necessary precautions must be taken. It should be mounted away from the power transformer to minimize hum pickup. High-voltage wire is used to bring the CRT grid connection into the unit. Sockets were used for the IC amplifier and transistors; however, the components can be soldered directly into the circuit. The vertical-scan output lead should be shielded. Several types of transistors may be used; the circuit was designed for devices with a minimum beta of 50. A variety of integrated operational amplifiers may be used; however, the 709 was chosen because of its low cost and availability.

Scope Modification

The potential between the CRT's control grid and the cathode varies the intensity. The control

[1] Available from Barry Electronics, 512 Broadway, New York, NY 10012.
[2] Catalog SC2799P7, Fair Radio Sales, P. O. Box 1105, Lima, OH 45802.

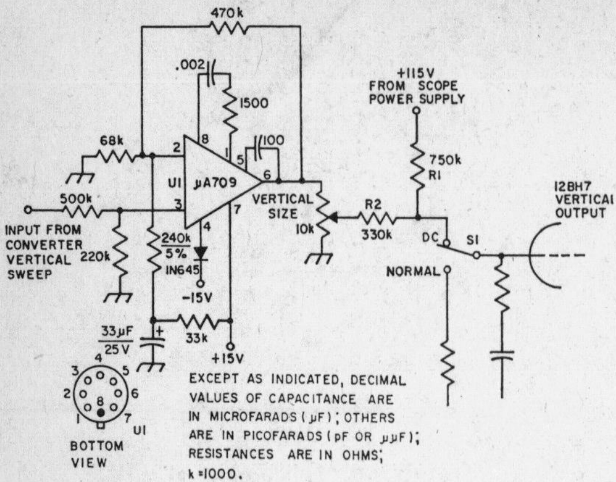

Fig. 3 — Amplifier circuit to provide a dc vertical input for ac-only oscilloscopes. Capacitors are ceramic, and resistors are 1/2-watt. The switch, S1, may be any convenient type. The operational amplifier, U1, is a Fairchild μA709. R1 and R2 should be adjusted in value to give proper centering, if necessary.

grid usually has an isolation resistor in series with the negative voltage lead. Video from the converter is connected across this resistor to vary the intensity of the CRT. This resistor should be at least 100 kΩ. If it is not this large in the existing scope circuit, it should be changed. This will have no effect on the scope's operation, since this control grid draws no current. There is usually ample room on most scopes to install two additional insulated jacks on the terminal board that has the direct deflection-plate connections.

Adjustment

1) Connect the scope's vertical input to test point 1.

2) Connect a 2350-Hz signal to the input and adjust the video discriminator coil L1 for minimum indication on the scope. This is usually with the slug fully inserted.

3) Connect the scope to test point 2. Change the input to 1200 Hz and peak the sync discriminator coil L2 for maximum indication on the scope. Connect a dc voltmeter between the collector of Q3 (sync level) and ground. With a 1300-Hz tone fed to the input of the adapter, adjust the 50,000 ohm sync adjust control to the point where the dc voltmeter just reads +15 volts.

4) Make the connections from the adpater to the oscilloscope's external sync, vertical input, and the CRT grid.

5) Connect the adapter's input to the receiver or tape recorder.

6) Set the contrast control at midposition and the sync control to maximum.

7) Adjust the scope's sweep to 15 Hz for trigger lock.

8) Adjust the size of the raster with the scope horizontal and vertical size controls until a square raster is obtained.

9) Adjust the adapter contrast and the scope intensity controls until a clear picture is obtained. If the picture is negative, the connections to the CRT grid should be reversed.

10) When a picture is obtained, the sync level should be adjusted to a point just before sync is lost. This will eliminate false triggering when copying weak signals and, if a vertical sync pulse is missed, the manual trigger can be used.

The finished adapter can be finally tested in several ways:

1) Tune to one of the SSTV frequencies listed below and look for a station transmitting SSTV. Tune the signal as you normally would for ssb. It is a good idea to tape-record a few pictures off the air — they then can be played back as often as necessary while adjusting the adapter.

2) Send a blank recording tape (with return postage) to any amateur who is equipped with an SSTV flying-spot scanner or camera. All amateurs in this field are happy to make a tape to get a newcomer going.

3) Listen to the SSTV frequencies. You may find a nearby amateur is on the air with SSTV. You can take your adapter to his shack to try it directly on a picture generator.

The slow-scan TV adapter has given good pictures on the scopes tried. A hood should be provided around the CRT face for direct viewing. Scopes with CRT tubes that have an accelerator will provide a brighter scan. The Heath IO-18 scope uses a CRT without the accelerator, and the brightness was noticeably less than others tried.

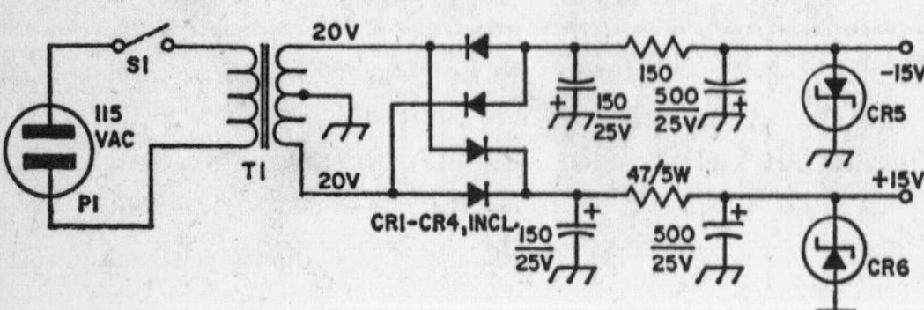

Fig. 4 — Power supply for the adapter. Capacitors are electrolytic. Resistors are 1/2-watt unless otherwise specified.
CR1-CR4, incl. — Silicon type, 200 PRV or greater (Motorola 1N4002, 1N4004 or 1N4007).
CR5, CR6 — 15-volt, 1-watt Zener (Centralab R4128-4, Unitriode Uz715).
P1 — Fused line plug.
S1 — Toggle.
T1 — 40-volt ct, 100 mA (Triad F90X).

At the present time, most SSTV operation takes place on 20 meters, on or above 14,230 kHz. Local nets operate on 3845 kHz. Other hf calling and working frequencies are 7171, 21,340, and 28,680 kHz. (In the U.S., SSTV emissions are authorized in the Advanced and Extra Class portions of all hf phone bands.) Stations from all continents are to be found on SSTV. The DX capability of SSTV is being demonstrated daily by picture exchanges between the U.S. and Canada and foreign amateurs.

FACSIMILE

Facsimile (FAX) is an electronic or electromechanical process by which graphic information is transmitted by wire or by radio to a distant receiving point, where it is recorded in a permanent printed form. Common uses of FAX include the transmission of maps, schematic diagrams, drawings, photographs, and other fixed images. At the present time, amplitude modulated facsimile (A4) is permitted in the U.S. on six meters between 50.1 and 54.0 MHz, on two meters between 144.1 and 148.0 MHz, and on all amateur frequencies above 220 MHz. Frequency modulated facsimile (F4) is permitted on all amateur frequencies above 220 MHz.

FAX TRANSMISSION

The most common method of converting written or printed images into the electrical signals used for modulating a transmitter involves photoelectric scanning. The material to be transmitted is wrapped around a cylinder or drum which is rotated about its longitudinal axis, while a tiny spot of light is projected on the surface of the material. The reflected light from the subject copy is focused on a photoconductive tube or photomultiplier. The amplified output of the phototube is an electrical analog of the varying light intensities reflected from the information being scanned. Each rotation of the drum provides one scanning line. As the drum turns, it is slowly moved laterally by a lead screw, causing slight separation of adjacent scanning lines. In this manner, the scanning beam strikes the subject copy in the form of a helix.

The band of frequencies that the output of the phototube occupies is called the baseband. The baseband ordinarily consists of varying dc levels (which represent the range of densities from white to black on the copy) and frequencies in the low audio and subaudio range (which arise from the rapid transitions between the various densities encountered by the scanning beam). On some systems, maximum output is interpreted as white, minimum output is interpreted as black, and intermediate values represent shades of grey. Other systems use the opposite scheme. The baseband signal may be used to vary the frequency of a voltage-controlled oscillator, in order to generate an fm subcarrier (not unlike an SSTV subcarrier) in which the highest frequency represents white, the lowest frequency represents black, and intermediate frequencies represent grey (or vice-versa). Alternatively, the baseband signal may be used to vary the amplitude of a constant-frequency subcarrier.

Another method sometimes used is to interrupt the reflected light from the subject copy by placing a chopper wheel between the light source and the phototube. If the light is interrupted 2400 times per second, the output of the phototube is an amplitude modulated 2400-Hz subcarrier. This system is used in the Western Union Telefax transceivers described later in this chapter.

The Telefax transceiver with cover removed. The shaft along which the drum traverses is visible at the left of the drum. The photo-optic assembly may be seen on the right-hand side of the chassis, just behind the drum.

RECEIVING FAX

Most FAX receiving systems available to the amateur operate on an electromechanical basis. Received a-m subcarrier signals may be demodulated with a diode or other envelope detector. Fm signals are first passed through a limiter to remove amplitude variations, and then through a discriminator and detector. The output from the detector in either case is a varying dc signal corresponding to the lightness and darkness variation in the subject material. There are several methods currently used to transfer the varying dc signal into a printed record of the original copy. Some of the more common processes include the use of electrolytic paper, electrothermal paper, and photosensitive paper.

The action of electrolytic paper is based on the change of color that results from the passage of an electric current through an iron stylus and paper treated with a special electrolyte. A sheet of paper is wrapped around a metal drum on the receiving machine, and the amplified signal voltage is applied between the pointed stylus and the drum. The variation in current caused by the signal voltage appears as variations in the darkness of the paper. The drum rotates, and simultaneously either the drum or the stylus moves laterally, in order to separate the adjacent lines. A drum and stylus are used with electrothermal paper, which has a coating that breaks down chemically when an electric current passes through it, and changes color according to the strength of the current. A lamp replaces the stylus when photosensitive paper is being used. The demodulated signal voltage is used to modulate the intensity of the light source, which exposes the paper. The paper is usually wrapped around a rotating cylinder (as in the previous cases). After exposure, the paper must be processed in a darkroom. Many modern facsimile recorders use a "flat paper" process whereby it is not necessary to place the sensitive recording material around a cylinder. Instead, the paper is continuously drawn from a roll across a flat "writing surface," and an electrode moves across this surface in synchronism with the drum revolution speed at the transmitter.

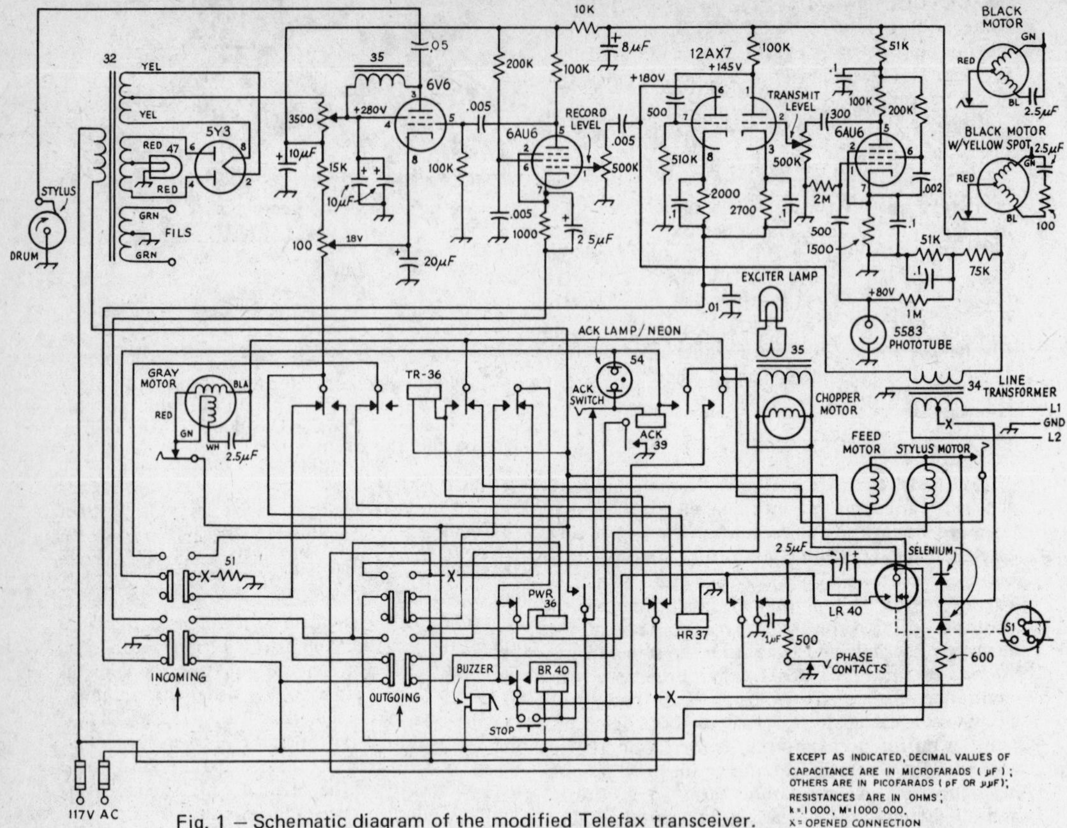

Fig. 1 – Schematic diagram of the modified Telefax transceiver.

Synchronization

It is important that the speeds of the FAX transmitter drum and FAX receiver drum be as close to identical as possible. Failure to match the speeds will result in diagonal tearing or skewing of the received copy. In practice, synchronous motors locked to the frequency of the 60-Hz ac line are used to drive both the drum and the lead screw on a machine.

Phasing

While synchronization ensures that the received FAX picture is spatially consistant with the subject copy being transmitted, it is also important that the start of each scan line coincide with the edge of the paper on the receiving end. If this is not done, the possibility exists (in fact it is probable) that the received image will run off the edge of the paper. Thus, it is necessary for the transmitting machine to send a series of phasing pulses prior to sending the actual picture.

CONVERSION OF TELEFAX TRANSCEIVERS TO AMATEUR SERVICE

Conversion of a telefax transceiver is easy to do. First, remove the cover and check the tubes in a tube tester. Check to see if you have a stylus. If necessary, replace the stylus with carbon-steel wire only. A wire brush is a common source of stylus wire.

Remove the exciter lamp, clean its opening, and set it aside in a safe place. These lamps are hard to obtain. Carefully remove the lamp telescope, then remove the lenses, and clean them. Be sure to replace the lenses in the same direction as they came out. Replace the telescope and exciter lamp. Plug in the 117-V line cord and push the white OUTGOING button to turn on the lamp. Focus the light spot on the drum by moving the telescope back and forth.

Remove the photo-tube telescope and clean both lenses, then reassemble. Turn on the lamp and focus the telescope image on the pinhole at the back of the telescope tube assembly. Put a paper with typed letters on the cylinder. Focus the edge of a letter on the pin hole. This is very important if you are to send sharp pictures.

Remove the bottom plate and solder a .01-μF disk capacitor from the junction of the 2000-ohm and 2700-ohm resistors in the cathode circuits of the 12AX7 tube to ground. This keeps rf out of the video amplifier. Clip one of the leads of the 51-ohm 2-watt resistor on the INCOMING pushbutton switch. The other two leads can also be clipped and the switch can be used to switch the line between your mic and the receiver's audio output.

Clip the wire coming from relay LR, the normally closed contact, and going to relay HR, the moving contact. Clip the wire on the rear of the OUTGOING push button, the normally open contact. Run a wire from this contact to the moving contact of relay HR just made available. See Fig. 1. These changes assure proper operation of the transmit-receive relay.

Remove the ACKNOWLEDGE push button, solder the leads together, and insulate them with spaghetti or tape. In the push-button hole, mount a spdt toggle switch. Disconnect the leads going to the contacts of relay LR (line relay). Run three wires from the spot switch to the three leads at relay LR, replacing the relay function with the switch. Now, when you close the switch, the carriage mechanism for the drum will feed. If your transmitter is keyed with a push-to-talk switch, you may use a dpdt switch, with the second pole to key the PTT line. This will key the transmitter automatically at the start of the scan.

Carefully remove the line transformer and remount it on the rear apron of the chassis in a vertical position behind relay LR. In the original position, the "gray motor" on the chassis above the line transformer will induce hum into the video signal. Solder the shield leads at the old line-transformer location, red to red and black to black. Run two shielded leads from the secondary of the line transformer through the nearby hole in the rear apron and to the LINE terminal strip. Hook a shielded lead to the LINE terminals of the line transformer for connection to your rig's mic jack and speaker leads.

It may be necessary to replace the stylus shielded lead. The old rubber-insulated shield may have become very leaky. Also it's a good idea to replace the lead from the 6V6 tube to the plate choke.

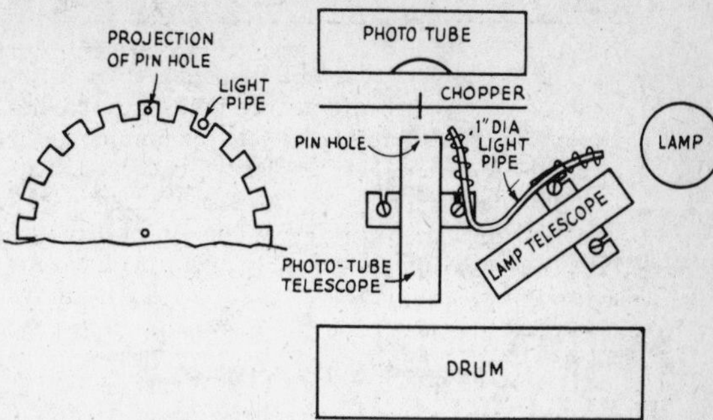

Fig. 2 – Addition of a fiber-optics light pipe for transmission of positive pictures.

Positive Pictures

Fig. 2 shows a modification for sending positive pictures. Mount a short piece of fiber-optics light pipe between the exciter lamp and the chopper wheel. The light pipe is easily held in place by wrapping it with No. 14 wire, placing the wire under the two telescope screws, as shown in Fig. 2. Carefully position the light pipe so it shines through a slot in the chopper wheel when the pin-hole light is cut off by the chopper. Connect an oscilloscope or ac voltmeter to the LINE leads and move the light pipe nearer to or farther from the exciter lamp until the scope or meter shows a null. Fig. 3 shows an experimentally derived circuit which will send sync pulses when in the OUTGOING mode before picture scanning begins. This circuit also receives sync pulses before scan begins to synchronize the drum angle.

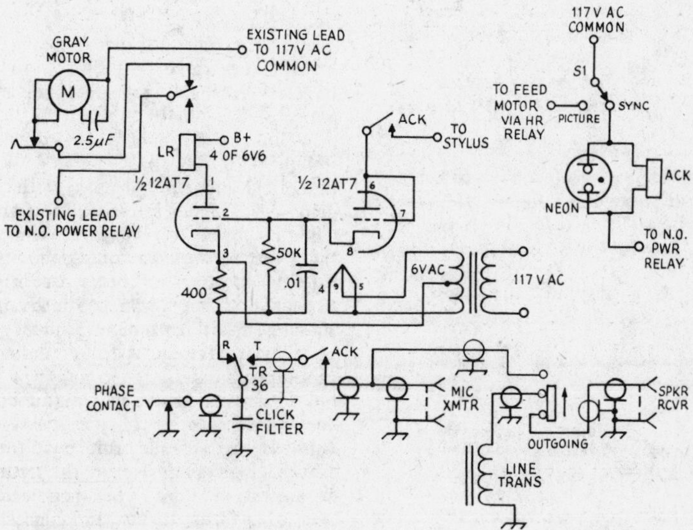

Fig. 3 – Circuit modification for sending or receiving sync information before picture scan begins. These modifications were originally described by W7QCV in *QST* for May, 1972.

EXCEPT AS INDICATED, DECIMAL VALUES OF CAPACITANCE ARE IN MICROFARADS (µF); OTHERS ARE IN PICOFARADS (pF OR µµF); RESISTANCES ARE IN OHMS; k=1000, M=1000 000.

SPACE COMMUNICATIONS

The use of vhf and uhf frequencies for intermediate and long distance communications has become possible through space communications techniques. There are basically two types of systems: passive and active. A passive system uses a celestial object such as the moon or an artificial reflecting satellite to return signals to earth. An active system consists of a space vehicle carrying an electronic repeater.

THE MOON AS A PASSIVE REFLECTOR

Communication by reflecting signals off the lunar surface has drawn the interest of an increasing number of amateurs in recent years, despite the considerable challenge such work represents. The requirements for earth-moon-earth (EME) communication are fairly well known. Overcoming the extremely high path loss of the EME circuit calls for close to the maximum transmitter power output obtainable with one kilowatt input, the best possible receiver, and very large high-gain antennas. The highest practical receiver selectivity is helpful, and visual signal-readout is often employed.

These requirements contribute their own problems. Narrow bandwidth demands exceptional frequency stability and calibration accuracy in both transmitter and receiver. High antenna gain means narrow beamwidth, in a system where a slowly moving target that is often invisible must be hit. And even when all demanding conditions are satisfied, the best one can expect is a signal barely distinguishable in the noise.

But the rewards are considerable, for the EME circuit provides vhf and uhf communications potential for any two points on earth where the moon is above the horizon. A surprising number of amateurs have accepted this supreme challenge, and before the end of 1970, all amateur bands from 144 to 2300 MHz had been employed successfully for lunar communications.

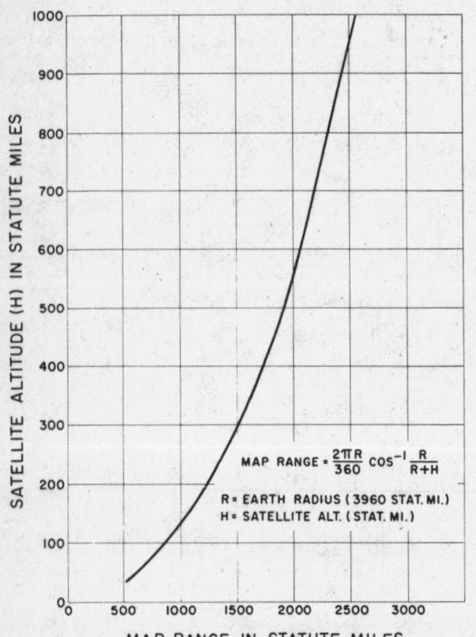

Fig. 15E-1 — Satellite altitude above earth versus ground station map range (statute miles).

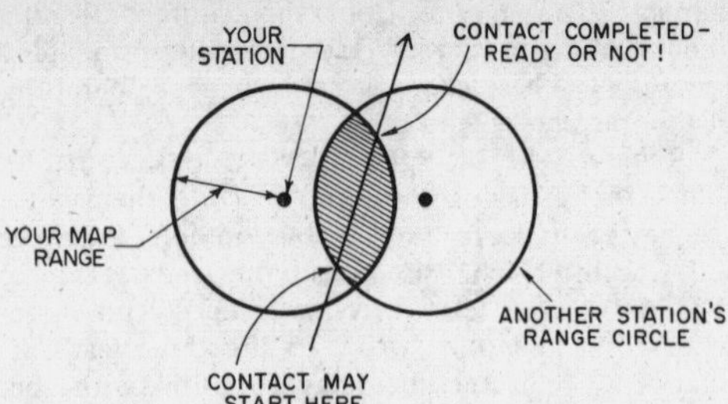

Fig. 15E-2 — Satellite passes through the range of two stations, enabling contact.

SATELLITES

Exciting communications possibilities are afforded through the use of amateur satellites. They function much in the same way as terrestrial repeaters, to relay signals over greater distances than normally feasible. (See chapter 14.) With satellites, the area is usually international in scope. Thus, DX communication on frequencies unable to support ionospheric propagation is possible.

Three amateur communications satellites have been orbited to date. Oscar 3, used in early 1965, was a 144-MHz in-band repeater; Oscar 4, launched in late 1965, repeated 144-MHz signals in the 420-MHz band; Oscar 6, launched in October, 1972, is a long-lifetime translator, repeating 144-MHz signals in the 28-MHz band. Oscars 1, 2, and 5 were beacon satellites for scientific and training purposes.

Current amateur plans for satellite systems involve the use of the 28-, 144-, and 420-MHz bands. Crossband repeaters are favored. Thus, expected combinations might be: 144 uplink, 28 downlink; 420 uplink, 144 downlink; or 144 uplink, 420 downlink. There is a trend toward designing amateur satellites with higher system gains (i.e., higher sensitivity and greater output). The objective is to permit the use of these satellites by average-sized amateur ground stations. Future satellite lifetimes of one year or more can be expected. Effort will be made for successive satellites to utilize similar frequency combinations to alleviate the need for equipment changes in ground stations.

A principal factor in determining how far one can communicate via a particular satellite is the orbit. Higher altitude orbits put the satellite within line-of-sight of greater areas of the earth. Fig. 15E-1 can be used to determine your map range for a satellite according to its altitude. For example, a satellite at 910 miles would give a map range of 2450 miles. For illustration, draw on a map a circle centered on your location with a radius equal to the map range. Each time the satellite is directly over any point

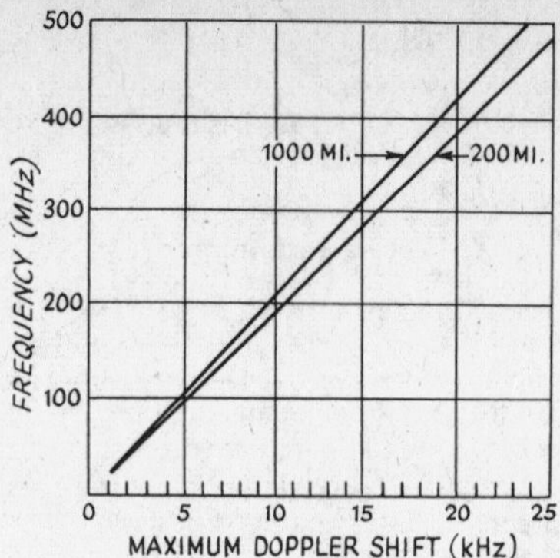

Fig. 15E-3 – Satellite transmitter frequency versus Doppler shift for satellite in 200- or 1000-statute-mile orbits. For a translator, use the difference between uplink and downlink frequencies as the "frequency."

within this circle, you will be able to use it for communication. Contact can be made with any other station having the satellite within its range at the same time. This is shown in Fig. 15E-2. Thus, the maximum map distance for communication would be about two times your map range.

The time duration for which a satellite will be within your range depends on two factors: the satellite's altitude and the distance between the subsatellite point (the point on the earth directly below the satellite) and your station. Higher altitude orbits increase the size of your range or acquisition circle, thus providing longer exposure to the satellite. Also, the longest duration for any given altitude will occur on orbits which pass directly over the station location. For example, a satellite in a 1000-mile orbit would be line-of-sight to a ground station for about 25 minutes on an overhead pass. At a map range of 1000 miles the duration would be 20 minutes, and at 2000 miles, availability would be about 10 minutes.

Conventional transceiver-type operation may offer some problems with satellites because of the Doppler phenomenon. Separate frequency control of the ground station's transmitter and receiver is desirable. (In some cases an "incremental tuning" feature on a transceiver will suffice.) Doppler is a frequency-shifting effect resulting from the motion of the satellite. It is a function of the transmitting frequency and the velocity of the satellite relative to the observing station. (Velocity is further a function of satellite's altitude.) Fig. 15E-3 compares Doppler shifts for frequencies up to 500 MHz for satellites in 200- and 1000-statute-mile orbits. The reason why Doppler shift requires a special consideration with transceiver operation is because two stations in contact would go through a series of frequency compensations, thus "walking" themselves across (and perhaps out of) the band! The frequency of a satellite moving toward a ground station appears higher than the actual satellite transmitter frequency. It drops as the satellite nears the ground station. At the exact point of closest approach, the observed frequency will be the same as the true frequency. Past this point, the satellite's signal will continue to drop lower in frequency as the satellite moves away.

There are two types of repeaters likely to be employed in future amateur satellites. A channelized repeater for fm would operate much like the ground-based fm repeaters used by amateurs; one station could use a channel at a time. Several contacts could be accommodated by a multichannel satellite. The other approach is called a frequency translator. It receives a segment of one band, say 100 kHz at 144 MHz, and retransmits the segment on another band, say 28 MHz. With a frequency translator, as many contacts as can be accommodated by the translator's bandwidth can take place simultaneously, and all modes can be used. Doppler shift from the fm repeater would be the same as expected for a transmitter on its downlink frequency. With a translator, however, the amount of Doppler shift is influenced by both the up- and downlinks. By employing a frequency inversion technique in the satellite's design, these amounts of Doppler will subtract; the resulting shift is then found from Fig. 15E-3 by using the frequency difference between up- and downlinks.

An aid to satellite communication is to monitor your own downlink signal coming from the satellite, while you are transmitting. This permits you to avoid interference from other stations, to compensate, where appropriate, for Doppler shift, and to adjust your transmitter power and antenna direction for maximum efficiency in sharing the satellite's output.

Best results in satellite communications are achieved when the ground-station antenna is pointed directly at the satellite. Movement of the antenna in elevation as well as azimuth is necessary. An easier alternative, providing adequate results, is also available. It is the use of a medium-gain antenna (about 10 dB) pointed at a fixed elevation of about 30 degrees and rotatable in azimuth. The beamwidth of such an antenna will

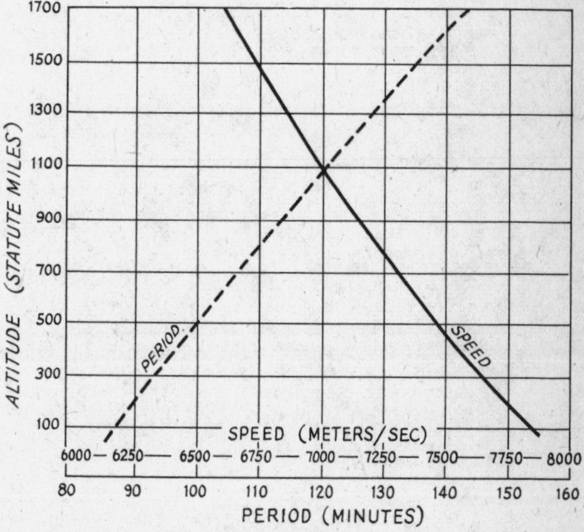

Fig. 15E-4 – Satellite altitude versus its period (time for one revolution) and speed.

allow satisfactory performance with most passes of the satellite. In the case of synchronous satellites, where the spacecraft maintains the same position relative to the observer, even the azimuth rotation can be eliminated – the antenna can be in a fixed position. However, greater antenna gain will most likely be needed in this case to compensate for the greater path loss from a satellite in such a high-altitude orbit.

Another antenna consideration for satellite communication is the use of circular polarization. Because the plane of a wave is rotated as it passes through the ionosphere, cross-polarization can occur between two linearly polarized (i.e., horizontal or vertical) antennas. This is called Faraday rotation. A circularly polarized antenna (such as a crossed-dipole, crossed-yagi, or a helix) at either the ground station or the satellite serves to minimize the effect.

Late Information

QST carries information about recent developments in Oscar. Since ground station requirements are dependent on the bands, modes, etc. used by the satellite, the amateur wishing to become equipped for space communication should consult ARRL headquarters to determine current amateur satellite plans.

PHONE PATCHING

A phone patch is an interconnection made between a radiotelephone system and a wire-line telephone. When the patch is made properly, the radio link and the wire line will effectively extend each other. Phone patches have provided vital communication when a natural disaster has caused disruption of normal communication facilities. More commonly, phone patches permit men in service or on scientific expeditions to talk with their families. Few activities can create a more favorable public image for amateurs than to bring people together in this way. Such public service is always appreciated. Amateurs are using phone patches for their own convenience, too. A phone patch might be used to talk with a friend in a distant city or to make a phone call from a car. In the latter case, a number of clubs are equipping their repeaters with unattended phone patch arrangements.

Occasionally, a phone patch will be used at both ends of a radio link. That is sometimes the case when the radio contact is made to overseas military bases. Some bases have a special phone booth or a small studio where the serviceman can have more privacy and be at ease while in conversation. The studio may be equipped with a regular telephone or it may have a microphone and earphones or a loudspeaker. It is common, too, for the participants to be asked to end each comment with the word "over" as a cue to radio operators (who may be using push-to-talk operation) to reverse the direction of transmission.

A few general considerations apply to phone patching. It constitutes the handling of third-party traffic. Agreements between governments specifically permitting such traffic must be in effect if the radio link is to a foreign country. Amateurs are responsible for conforming to regulations on station identification, prohibited language and the like while a phone patch is in progress. If a repeater is involved, the arrangement should meet all applicable rules regarding repeater-control facilities. Telephone companies, too, are concerned that the interconnection arrangements be made in the proper way and that the electrical signals meet certain standards.

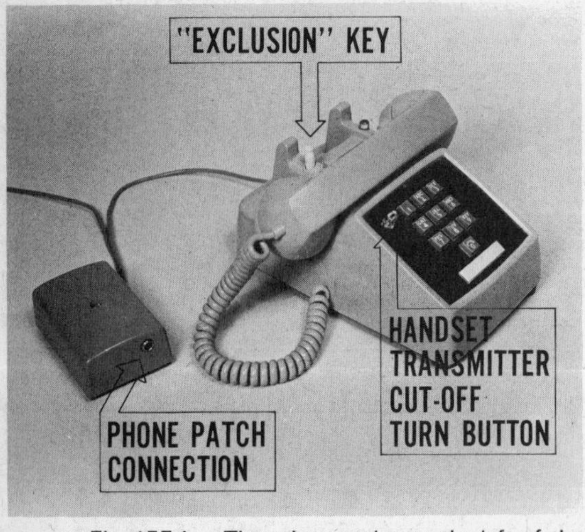

"EXCLUSION" KEY

HANDSET TRANSMITTER CUT-OFF TURN BUTTON

PHONE PATCH CONNECTION

Fig. 15F-1 – The voice coupler, to the left of the touch-tone telephone, is supplied by the telephone company. The coupler is normally fixed to a wall or desk, and contains a jack for connection of the amateur's phone patch.

THE TELEPHONE SYSTEM

Telephone company regulations are published in their tariffs, which in most states must be available in the company's business offices. In the tariffs, phone patches are included under "Interconnection Arrangements" or a similar designation. Telephone employees may not be familiar with the term, "phone patch" so it should be used with caution when talking with them. Patching is accomplished with the aid of devices called "couplers" or "voice connecting arrangements." These are provided by the telephone company and are important in several ways. They protect the amateur's telephone service from interruption that might result from a malfunction in his equipment; they protect other users, too. By isolating the amateur's equipment electrically from the telephone line, they give him a great deal of freedom in the design of his circuits. The protective device also permits proper adjustment of the circuit impedance, energy levels and other operating conditions to be met by the amateur's equipment.

Several different interconnection arrangements are listed in Table I.

A telephone line normally consists of a single pair of wires which is used for both directions of transmission. At the amateur's station it will be terminated in a telephone set. A voice coupler will be connected in parallel with the telephone set when the phone patch is in progress. For design purposes, the telephone set and line are each assumed to have an impedance of about 900 ohms (in the case of residence service) and the best impedance for the phone-patch circuit is also 900 ohms. In operation, the patch will see a load of about 450 ohms. This small mismatch should not be cause for concern, however, as it is the best possible compromise. The phone patch's basic function is to connect the radio receiver's audio output circuit and the radio transmitter's audio input circuit to the telephone voice coupler. It should do this in a way that results in correct circuit impedances and voice levels. Provision should be made, too, for measuring and adjusting the voice level that is transmitted to the telephone line and for electrical filtering to the extent needed to comply with telephone company limitations.

Fig. 15F-1 shows a typical voice coupler and a related telephone set. A simplified schematic diagram of this setup is given in Fig. 15F-2. The telephone is equipped with an exclusion key and a turn button. The telephone operates in the usual way when the two switches are in their normal positions. Lifting the exclusion key causes the voice coupler to be connected to the telephone line. If it is requested when the voice coupler is ordered, the turn button will be supplied and can be wired by the telephone company to cut off the handset transmitter, the receiver, or both of them. The *transmitter* cutoff feature is preferred, as it will eliminate the pickup of room noise by the telephone while permitting the patched communication to be monitored on the handset receiver. The operator can restore the turn button as required for station identification or to break in for other purposes.

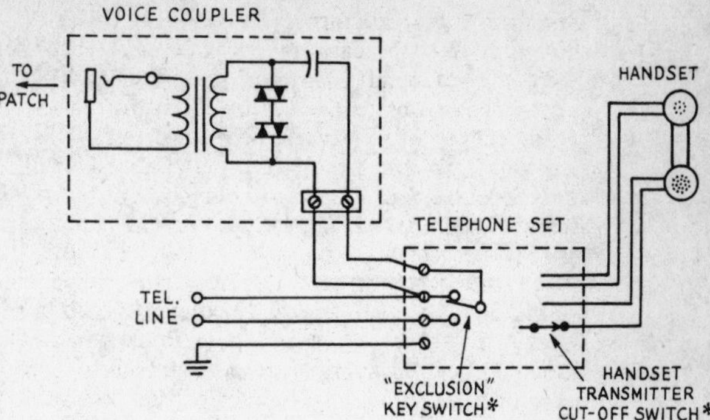

Fig. 15F-2 — Simplified diagram of voice coupler and telephone set. *Both the cutoff switch and the exclusion key switch are shown in their normal positions.

Supplemental information and pertinent telephone company technical specifications as they may apply to amateur radio are given in the appendix which appears at the end of this chapter.

PHONE PATCH CIRCUITS

Where push-to-talk operation is used, the phone patch can be as simple as a transfer switch (connecting the receiver and the transmitter, alternately, to the coupler) or it can be a resistive combining network of the kind shown in Fig. 15F-3. Included in the circuit is a 2600-Hz filter, the need for which is discussed later.

Hybrid Circuits

Where it is desirable to use voice-operated transmitter control (VOX), more elaborate arrangements are required. The VOX circuit must determine when the distant radio station is transmitting and inhibit the local transmitter. When the party

TABLE I

Voice Interconnection Arrangements of Interest to Amateurs

Applicable Bell System Publication	*Arrangement Service Code*	*Arrangement Description*
PUB42101	QKT	Provides manual connection of transmitting or receiving equipment to an exchange line by means of a telephone set; uses a 30A or L-7049A voice coupler. Telephone handset transmitter cutoff is optional. Connection to the coupler is made with a 1/4-inch tip-sleeve plug, provided by the user. Impedance, 900-ohms.
PUB 42208	STC (QX or VX)	Provides automatic (unattended) call origination and answering for one exchange line. Connection to the unit is made with a special plug to be supplied by the user. Required is a Cinch Co. No. 231-15-61-133 plug equipped with a hood, No. 239-13-99-069. Impedance, 600 ohms. Ac power is required.
PUB42402	CD8	Provides automatic (unattended) call origination for up to 14 trunks. Impedance, 600 ohms. Ac power is required.

NOTE: Publications are made available through the telephone company in local areas. Consult your telephone company about the use of these service arrangements.

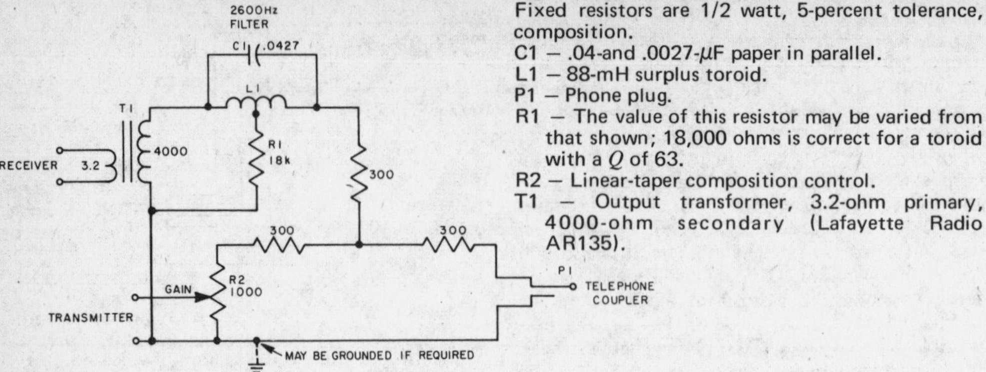

Fig. 15F-3 — Schematic of the simple phone patch. Fixed resistors are 1/2 watt, 5-percent tolerance, composition.
C1 — .04-and .0027-μF paper in parallel.
L1 — 88-mH surplus toroid.
P1 — Phone plug.
R1 — The value of this resistor may be varied from that shown; 18,000 ohms is correct for a toroid with a Q of 63.
R2 — Linear-taper composition control.
T1 — Output transformer, 3.2-ohm primary, 4000-ohm secondary (Lafayette Radio AR135).

on the land telephone is talking, the VOX circuit must activate the local transmitter. This function is made difficult by the difference in audio levels. The phone patch must transmit a voice level of approximately −5 VU toward the telephone line, whereas the level received from the distant land telephone may range from −45 VU to −10 VU.[1] The contrast in levels can be reduced considerably at the input to the local transmitter's VOX circuit by using a "hybrid" circuit. A hybrid circuit is an electrical network connecting together the transmitter, receiver and the voice coupler in such a way that the audio energy from the receiver is canceled at the input to the transmitter. Hybrids require a fourth circuit element, called a balancing network, in order to function.

Several kinds of hybrids can be constructed, the simplest of which is an adaptation of the Wheatstone bridge. Such a hybrid is shown in Fig. 15F-4.

1 Volume units (VU) are measured with an instrument which is basically an ac voltmeter of appropriate range and with dynamic characteristics which are carefully controlled to provide standardized measurement of complex wave forms. When sine-wave power is measured, a VU meter and one calibrated in dB relative to a milliwatt (dBm) should give the same numerical indication.

Fig. 15F-4 — Wheatstone-bridge hybrid phone-patch circuit. Resistances are in ohms. Half-watt resistors of 20-percent tolerance are adequate. Filters and level-measuring arrangements are not included in this simple circuit.
T1 — Line to voice coil; primary 1000 ohms, secondary 4 ohms, such as Allied 6W3HFL or equiv.
T2 — Audio; primary 1000 ohms, secondary as appropriate to match transmitter input impedance.
Z1 — Balancing network. See Fig. 15F-5 and text.

When the impedance of the balancing network is equal to the impedance at the input to the line filter, the bridge will be in a condition of balance. The amount of audio from the receiver that reaches the transmitter (or VOX circuit) will then be minimized.

The balancing network, shown schematically in Fig. 15F-5 is not complicated. In most cases it will consist only of a resistor and a capacitor in parallel. Typical values for a condition of balance when a voice coupler is used would be 470 ohms for R1 and .04 μF for C1. Other interface devices, such as might be used at repeaters for unattended operation, will require other values. The resistance might be between 500 and 1200 ohms and the shunt capacitance might range from .01 to 0.1 μF; in rare cases, a series capacitor in the order of 2 μF may be required. The values for a particular installation must be found by trial. The hybrid can be balanced by establishing a telephone call, and tuning in a clear voice signal on the receiver. With headphones connected to the transmitter audio circuit, adjust the hybrid balance network for minimum signal in the headset.

With the Wheatstone bridge hybrid circuit of Fig. 15F-4, losses between the receiver and the telephone line, and between the line and the transmitter, will be in the order of 6 to 10 dB. Transformer-type hybrid circuits exhibit lower losses, only 4.5 to 6 dB. A circuit for a single-transformer hybrid is shown in Fig. 15F-6. A two-transformer arrangement (giving better isola-

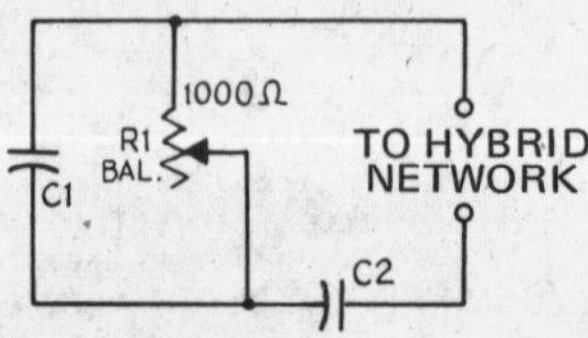

Fig. 15F-5 — Balancing network. R1 is a wire-wound control. C1 and R1 should balance a voice coupler; typical values are 470 ohms and .04 μF. C2 is ordinarily not used, but values in the order of 1 to 4 μF may be required with unattended interconnection devices.

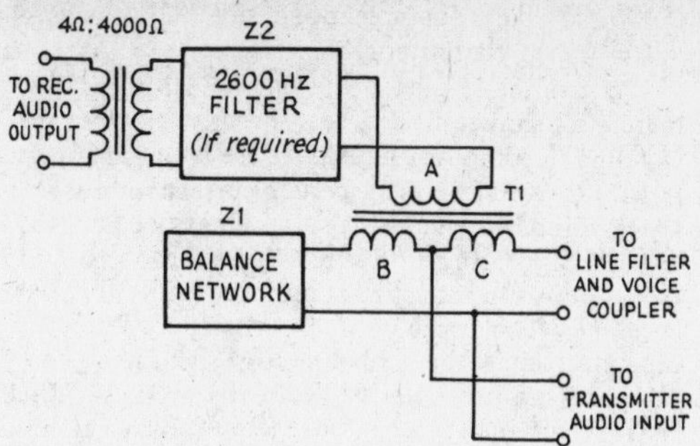

Fig. 15F-6 – Hybrid circuit made with a single audio transformer.
T1 – Windings designated "B" and "C" should be of about 900 ohms impedance each. Winding "A" may be of higher impedance if the 2600-Hz filter is used; a lower impedance may be used to match the receiver if a 2600-Hz filter is not needed.
Z1 – Balancing network. See Fig. 15F-5 and text.
Z2 – 2600-Hz filter (C1, L1, and R1 of Fig. 15F-3).

TABLE II

Maximum Permissible Energy Levels at the Input of a Voice Interconnection Arrangement

Freq. Band	Maximum Level
Direct current	0.5 milliampere
Voice range (nominally 300 to 3000 Hz)	Voice coupler: -3 dBm. Other arrangements: 9 dB below 1 mW (levels avaraged over 3 seconds, see note.)
2450 to 2750 Hz	Preferably no energy; in no case greater than the level present simultaneously in the 800- to 2450-Hz band.
3995 to 4005 Hz	18 dB below the voice-band level.
4.0 to 10.0 kHz	16 dB below one milliwatt (-16 dBm).
10.0 to 25.0 kHz	-24 dBm
25.0 to 40.0 kHz	-36 dBm
Above 40.0 kHz	-50 dBm

NOTE: The above limits should be met with amateur-provided equipment having an internal impedance of 900 ohms if it is to work into a voice coupler, or 600 ohms if other arrangements are to be used.

tion between elements) is shown later in this chapter.

Filters

Standards have been established for the maximum signal levels that can be connected to the input of a coupler or other interconnection device. They are listed in Table II. The limits of out-of-band energy are best met by using a low-pass line filter. Located between the coupler and the hybrid it will protect the line and also band-limit line signals to the transmitter. Filters of several types (image parameter, elliptic function, and so on) may be used. The filter should be of 600- or 900-ohm impedance (depending on the interface), passing frequencies below 3 kHz with losses rising rapidly above that point; a rejection notch should be provided at 4 kHz.

In the long distance network the telephone system uses 2600 Hz as a "disconnect" signal. If patched calls are made to telephone offices distant from your own, the need for filtering at that frequency can best be judged by experience. The filter can be made switchable, if desired. The best location for a 2600-Hz rejection filter is at the receiver output.

REPEATER PATCHES

Some interesting phone-patch possibilities exist at repeaters. Unattended interconnection devices are associated with the repeaters to provide a form of mobile telephone service for the clubs operating them. The connections to a typical unattended interface device are shown in Fig. 15F-7.

Suitable signals generated in mobile units work through a base station to activate the interconnection device, causing it to connect and pass dial pulses to the telephone line. The system may be arranged so that the base transmitter carries both sides of the conversation or only the voice of the distant telephone user. Switching of the patch's voice path between the transmitter and the receiver could be done under the control of tones or a carrier-operated relay. A simple combining circuit may be used if both sides of the conversation are to be put out over the air. To equalize audio levels, a wide-range agc amplifier might have to be provided, or an attenuator in the transmitter audio line would have to be switched in and out. A

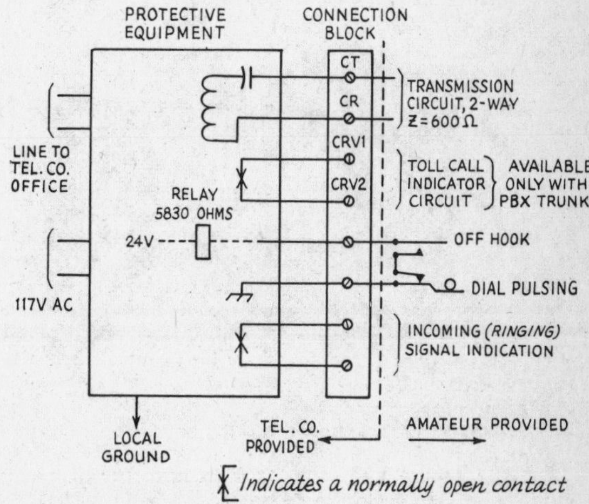

Fig. 15F-7 – Interconnection diagram for a Bell CD8 coupler, representative of connections to unattended interface devices.

hybrid circuit could be used in this case but the retransmitted audio from the mobile unit would not be as free from distortion as with the combining arrangement.

Some telephone lines and interface devices can be arranged to signal the fact that a toll call has been dialed. Such a signal might be used to disconnect the phone patch if the repeater owners do not want long distance calls to be made. Clubs would probably want to control access to the patch in any case, as they would be responsible for all telephone service charges, even if the calls were not made by their members.

A HYBRID PHONE PATCH

The photographs and Fig. 1 show a deluxe 2-transformer hybrid phone patch for home construction. Some form of hybrid circuit is necessary if VOX control of the transmitter is to be used. A third transformer matches the 3.2-ohm output of the receiver. A 2600-Hz filter is provided in the line from the receiver to reduce the possibility of unwanted disconnections resulting from heterodyning signals during use over long-distance telephone lines. The filter may be switched out for local calls for a slight improvement in voice fidelity from the received signal to the telephone line. A modified VU meter indicates the levels received from and applied to the telephone line entering the amateur station. This phone-patch unit can be duplicated for approximately $35 if all components are purchased new, but the use of surplus or "bargain" components, especially transformers, will greatly reduce the cost.

The circuit of the phone-patch unit is shown in Fig. 1. C1, L1, and R2 form the 2600-Hz receiver-line filter. Its insertion loss at 1000 Hz is negligible, but is in excess of 15 dB at 2600 Hz. T2 and T3 are the hybrid transformers, with C3 and R5 provided to balance the network. Independent level adjustments are provided for the signal

The phone patch unit is built into a homemade aluminum enclosure measuring 3 X 3 X 6 inches. A coating of spray-on enamel, rubber feet, and wet-transfer decal labels plus shiny knobs give the unit a professional appearance. This unit was constructed by W1NPG.

coupled from the receiver to the telephone line (R1) and from the telephone line to the transmitter speech amplifier (R3).

M1 is a modified Calectro model DI-930 "VU" meter, as shown in Fig. 2. In early models, the existing 7,000-ohm multiplier resistor must be replaced by a 365-ohm 1-percent precision resistor. Later models, which may be identified by the letter A appearing in a circle near the bottom of the meter-scale card, are supplied with a 300-ohm resistor which need not be changed. Damping capacitors must be added across the meter coil, observing proper polarity. For early models of the DI-930 meter, the correct capacitance value is 300 μF; for later models with the circled A appearing on the meter-scale card, the required value is 400 μF. These values apply only to this particular make and models of meter. The modified meter responds to speech signals of 3 kHz or less in a way that compares very closely with the measuring sets mentioned in the Bell interface specifications. Error should be less than 1 dB and should be found to be on the safe side. The meter, as modified, has a 1-kHz impedance of approximately 6500 ohms. It should be mounted only on a nonferrous panel.

Construction

The component layout for the phone patch is not critical, and any of several construction techniques is quite acceptable. In the model photographed all components except the modified meter, controls, and phono jacks were mounted on a piece of circuit-board material. The balance control was mounted on the front panel, but this is a "set once and forget" control so some builders may wish to include it inside the enclosure. An etched pattern in the copper foil provides a few of the circuit interconnections, but most connections, including all those to the two hybrid transformers, are made with point-to-point wiring. The UTC transformers specified have mounting studs affixed to the top of the case, and these are used to mount the transformers in an inverted position on the circuit board. This same construction idea can be used with perforated phenolic board and point-to-point wiring for all components, instead of an etched circuit board.

The only precaution to observe during construction is to keep J3 insulated from chassis ground, to reduce rf coupling into the telephone line. In the model photographed this was done by drilling a 1/2-inch hole in the rear panel where J3 was to be mounted, and then, with machine screws, fastening a small piece of phenolic board to cover the hole. Next J3 was mounted on the phenolic board, centered in the hole. Some types of phono jacks come supplied with phenolic mounting material, and if the clearance hole is large enough these types may be mounted directly on a metal panel without grounding the outer contact.

Adjustment

If one has access to an accurately calibrated audio signal generator or to an electronic fre-

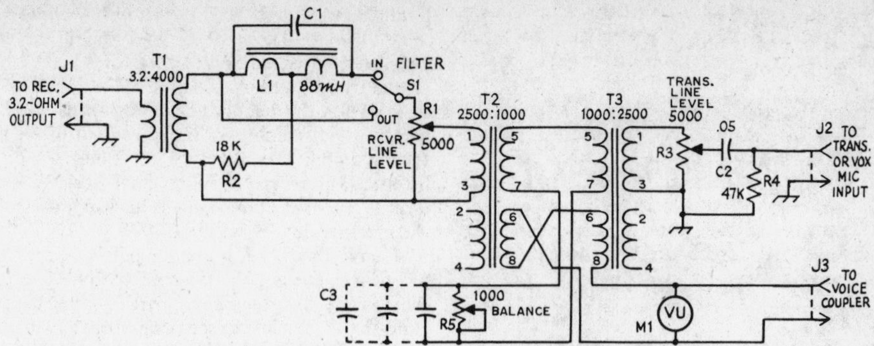

Fig. 1 — Schematic diagram of the phone-patch circuit. Resistances are in ohms, k = 1000. Fixed resistors may be 1/2 watt, 10 percent tolerance. Capacitance is in microfarads. Components not listed below are identified for text reference.

C1 — Capacitors in parallel to give required value of .0427 μF; low-voltage metallized paper or Mylar are suitable.

C3 — Typical value, .04 μF. See text and Fig. 15F-5 if hybrid network cannot be balanced.

J1, J2, J3 — Phono jack. J3 should be insulated from chassis.

L1 — Surplus 88-mH toroidal inductor, connected with half-windings in series aiding.

M1 — Calectro DI-930 VU meter, modified. See text and Fig. 2.

R1, R3 — 5000-ohm audio-taper control (Mallory U12 or equiv.).

R5 — 1000-ohm linear-taper control (Mallory U4 or equiv.).

T1 — Audio transformer, 4 or 8 ohms to 4000 ohms (UTC SO-10 or equiv.).

T2, T3 — Audio transformer, 2500-ohm split primary, 1000-ohm split secondary (UTC O-19 or equiv.).

quency counter he may wish to check the notch frequency of the 2600-Hz filter, although this step is not essential. The frequency may be adjusted by using various combinations of fixed-value capacitors for C1 until the notch appears at exactly 2600 Hz. In the model photographed stock-value capacitors, selected at random to provide the specified total capacitance for C1, resulted in a notch frequency of 2621 Hz, which is quite acceptable.

Correct adjustment of the balance control, R5, will facilitate the operation of the transmitter VOX circuit by the distant party on the land telephone. Connect all station equipment to place the patch into operation. Connect a pair of headphones or an ac voltmeter to the transmitter audio circuit. If a sensitive ac VTVM is available, one which will measure in the millivolt range, it may be connected directly to the output from J2, in parallel with the line connected to the transmitter. Establish a phone call and connect the phone patch to the voice coupler. Tune in a clear voice signal on the receiver, and adjust R5 for the best null of the received signal as monitored in the transmitter audio section. If the null does not occur within the range of R5, experimentally try different capacitance values for C3 and a larger value for R5 (connect a fixed-value resistor in series with R5 to obtain a higher equivalent value). With R5 properly adjusted, the distant party should be able to trip the transmitter VOX circuit satisfactorily even though no anti-trip connection is used from the receiver. With such a connection made, VOX operation will be quite reliable.

Installation and Operation

The receiver input to the phone-patch unit may be taken in parallel with the speaker leads from the receiver. Most operators prefer to disconnect or disable the speaker, however, and to connect the patch directly to the speaker-output terminals of the receiver. The switching to and from phone-patch station operation is generally done in suitable control circuits which may be included in the phone-patch enclosure itself, if desired. Operating with the speaker disconnected will result in a 3-dB-greater audio signal being fed to the hybrid circuit, and monitoring of the receiver audio by the amateur operator may be done through the telephone handset.

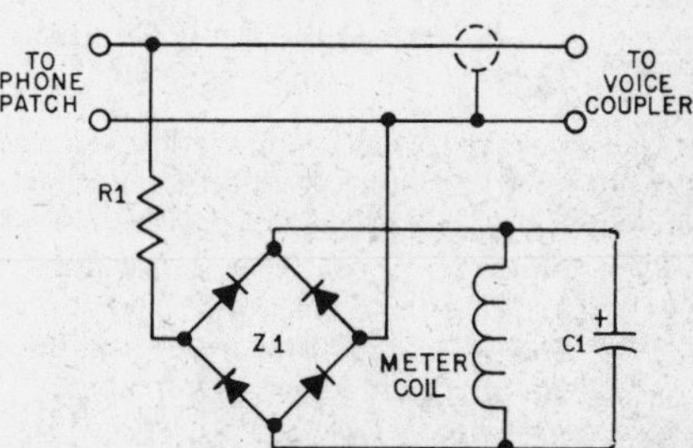

Fig. 2 — Schematic diagram of the modified Calectro DI-930 VU meter and its connections to a phone-patch circuit. Component values are different for early production models. See text for information on identifying a particular meter.

R1 — In DI-930, 365-ohm 1-percent tolerance precision wire-wound resistor to replace original 7000-ohm resistor. In DI-930A, original 300-ohm resistor.

C1 — Added capacitance; in DI-930, 300 μF, and in DI-930A, 400 μF. Consists of three or four 100-μF 6-V electrolytic capacitors connected in parallel.

Z1 — Part of original meter circuit.

The layout of the phone-patch components is not critical. The two hybrid-network transformers are visible to the right of center, and in the upper left corner of the circuit board the receiver matching transformer may be seen. Two damping capacitors added during modification of the Calectro DI-930A meter are visible atop the meter case; two more are hidden beneath the meter.

The level of signal being fed from the receiver to the telephone line during reception may be adjusted either with R1 or with the receiver audio gain control. Similarly, the level of audio being fed to the transmitter from the telephone line during transmission may be adjusted with R3 and with the transmitter microphone gain control. If the distant party on the telephone line is not talking loudly enough for proper operation of the transmitter, remember that often he can be made to speak louder *simply by reducing the level of audio being sent to him.* The speech level should never be permitted to exceed the ZERO or "100%" point on the DI-930 meter scale,or -2 VU on the DI-930A scale. When the telephone connection is made to a nearby point (such as a line served out of the same telephone building as the patched line), the distant listener will receive a more comfortable listening level if the maximum signal is held to about −7 on the meter scale (−9 on the DI-930A).

Many times when phone-patch operation is heard over the air, the transmitted voice quality of the distant land-telephone party seems to be as good as if he were speaking directly into the station microphone. Occasionally, however, signals will be heard with an undue amount of power-line-frequency hum present on the signal. Of course the quality and level of the voice signal coming in on the telephone line plays an important part in how that voice signal sounds over the air, but sometimes a hum problem can be traced directly to the installation of the phone-patch equipment. In particular, the phone patch (and the voice coupler) should be located away from power supply transformers in station equipment. Complete magnetic shielding may not exist even with steel enclosures for power supplies. If other equipment is mounted nearby, the 60-Hz field can induce hum into the transformers of the phone patch. Hum problems of this sort can usually be solved simply by relocating the position of the phone-patch unit.

During operation of a phone patch in the hf amateur bands it is considered good practice to avoid the transmission of operator chatter, dial tones, dial pulses, ringing and busy signals, as they are not essential to communications.

Appendix

Signals and Circuit Conditions Used in the Telephone System

1) The status of a local telephone line (idle or busy) is indicated by on-hook or off-hook signals as follows:

On-Hook	Minimum dc resistance between tip and ring conductors of 30,000 ohms.
Off-Hook	Maximum dc resistance between tip and ring conductors of 200 ohms.

Telephone sets give an off-hook condition at all times from the answer or origination of a call to its completion. The only exception to this is during dial pulsing.

2) Dial pulses consist of momentary opens in the loop; dial pulses should meet the following standards:

Pulsing rate	10 pulses/second ± 10%
Pulse Shape	58% to 64% break (open)
Interdigital time	600 milliseconds minimum

Note: Two pulses indicate the digit "2," three pulses indicate the digit "3," and so on, up to ten, indicating the digit "0."

3) The standards for tone "dialing" are as follows:

a) Each digit is represented by a unique pair of tones as shown below.

Digit	*Low tone High tone*
1	697 and 1209 Hz
2	697 and 1336 Hz
3	697 and 1477 Hz
4	770 and 1209 Hz
5	770 and 1336 Hz
6	770 and 1477 Hz
7	852 and 1209 Hz
8	852 and 1336 Hz
9	852 and 1477 Hz
0	941 and 1336 Hz
*	941 and 1209 Hz
#	941 and 1477 Hz

b) In order for the central-office receiver to register the digit properly, the tone-address signals must meet the following requirements:

(1) Signal levels:

Nominal level per frequency: −6 to −4

dBm. Minimum level per frequency: Low Group, −10 dBm; High Group, −8 dBm. Max, level per frequency pair: +2 dBm. Max, difference in levels between frequencies: 4 dB.

(2) Frequency deviation: ± 1.5 percent of the values given above.

(3) Extraneous frequency components: The total power of all extraneous frequencies accompanying the signal should be at least 20 dB below the signal power, in the voice band above 500 Hz.

(4) Voice Suppression: Voice energy from any source should be suppressed at least 45 dB during tone signal transmission. In the case of automatic dialing the suppression should be maintained continuously until pulsing is completed.

(5) Rise Time: Each of the two frequencies of the signal should attain at least 90 percent of full amplitude within 5 ms, and preferably within 3 ms for automatic dialers, from the time that the first frequency begins.

(6) Pulsing Rate: Minimum duration of two-frequency tone signal: 50 ms normally; 90 ms if transmitted by radio. Minimum interdigital time: 45 ms.

(7) Tone leak during signal off time should be less than −55 dBm.

(8) Transient Voltages: Peak transient voltages generated during tone signaling should be no greater than 12 dB above the zero-to-peak voltage of the composite two-frequency tone signal.

4) Audible tones will be used in the telephone system to indicate the progress or disposition of a call. These include:

a) Dial tone: 350 and 440 Hz.
b) Line busy: 480 and 620 Hz, interrupted at 60 interruptions per minute (I/min).
c) Reorder (all trunks busy): 480 and 620 Hz, interrupted at 120 I/min.
d) Audible ringing: 440 and 480 Hz, 2 seconds on, 4 seconds off.
e) Reserved high tone: 1633 Hz.
f) Invalid dialing code: Voice announcement.

Bibliography

Source material and more extended discussions of topics covered in this chapter can be found in the references given below. This listing does not include every article published in *QST* on the subjects of this chapter, however. A detailed bibliography of references in *QST* on any of the subjects amateur television, slow-scan television, radioteletype, phone patching, Oscar and moonbounce, will be sent on request to ARRL, Newington, CT 06111. Please enclose a business-size stamped self-addressed envelope.

RADIOTELETYPE

Antanaitis, "A Simple Two-Transistor A.F.S.K. Generator," *QST*, September, 1969.

Craig, "Teleprinter Selector Magnets," Technical Correspondence, *QST*, September, 1971.

Drake, "An Audio Synthesizer – A Device to Generate RTTY Tones with Crystal-Controlled Accuracy," *QST* April, 1972.

Hall, "Frequency Shift Keying the Johnson Ranger, Valiant, Navigator," *RTTY Journal*, Jan. 1968; "What is RTTY?," *QST*, Dec. 1968.

Hoff, "Transmitting Radioteletype," *QST*, May, 1965; "Audio Frequency-Shift Keying for RTTY," *QST*, June, 1965; "The Mainline TT/L F.S.K. Demodulator," *QST*, August, 1965; "The Mainline ST-3 RTTY Demodulator," *QST*, April, 1970.

Petersen, "The Mainline TT/L-2 F.S.K. Demodulator," Part I, "Construction and Adjustment," *QST*, May, 1969, and Part II, "Circuit Description, and the Mainline F.S.K. Keyer," *QST*, June, 1969.

Schecter, "First Steps in RTTY," *QST*, June, 1971.

AMATEUR TELEVISION

Campbell, "Amateur TV – The Easy Way," *QST*, November, 1962.

Keller, "An Amateur Television Camera," *QST*, November, 1953.

Tilton, "Amateur Television – A Progress Report," *QST*, June, 1950.

SLOW-SCAN TELEVISION

Briles and Gervenack, "Slow-Scan TV Viewing Adapter for Oscilloscopes," *QST*, June, 1970.

Macdonald, "S.C.F.M. – An Improved System for Slow-Scan Image Transmission," Part I, "Slow-Scan Modulation Tests and Proposed Standards," *QST*, Jan. 1961, and Part II, "Circuit Details," *QST*, Feb. 1961; "A New Narrow-Band Image Transmission System," Part I, "Principles of Slow Scan Picture Reproduction," *QST*, August 1958, and Part II, "Circuit and Construction Details," *QST*, Sept. 1958; "A Slow-Scan Vidicon Camera," in three parts, *QST*, June, July and Aug. 1965.

Tschannen, "A Solid-State SSTV Monitor," *QST*, March, 1971.

PHONE PATCHING

Berry, "Legalize Your Phone Patch," *QST*, May 1969; "An Improved Phone Patch," Hints and Kinks, *QST*, Nov. 1970.

Hoff, "Stopping Telephone Interference," *QST*, March, 1968.

Schleicher, "Phone Patching – Legitimately," *QST*, March, 1969; "Phone Patching – One Year Later," *QST*, Nov., 1970; "Measuring Phone-Patch Levels Accurately," *QST*, February, 1972.

Chapter 16

Interference with other Services

Every amateur has the obligation to make sure that the operation of his station does not, because of any shortcomings in equipment, cause interference with other radio and audio services. It is unfortunately true that much of the interference that amateurs cause to broadcast and television reception is directly the fault of bc, hi-fi, and TV receiver construction. Nevertheless, the amateur can and should help to alleviate interference even though the responsibility for it does not lie with him.

Successful handling of interference cases requires winning the listener's cooperation. Here are a few pointers on how to go about it.

Clean House First

The first step obviously is to make sure that the transmitter has no radiations outside the bands assigned for amateur use. The best check on this is your own a-m or TV receiver. It is always convincing if you can demonstrate that you do not interfere with reception in your own home.

Don't Hide Your Identity

Whenever you make equipment changes – or shift to a hitherto unused band or type of emission – that might be expected to change the interference situation, check with your neighbors. If no one is experiencing interference, so much the better; it does no harm to keep the neighborhood aware of the fact that you are operating without bothering anyone.

Should you change location, announce your presence and conduct occasional tests on the air, requesting anyone whose reception is being spoiled to let you know about it so steps may be taken to eliminate the trouble.

Act Promptly

The average person will tolerate a limited amount of interference, but the sooner you take steps to eliminate it, the more agreeable the listener will be; the longer he has to wait for you, the less willing he will be to cooperate.

Present Your Story Tactfully

When you interfere, it is natural for the complainant to assume that your transmitter is at fault. If you are certain that the trouble is not in your transmitter, explain to the listener that the reason lies in the receiver design, and that some modifications may have to be made in the receiver if he is to expect interference-free reception.

Arrange for Tests

Most listeners are not very competent observers of the various aspects of interference. If at all possible, enlist the help of another amateur and have him operate your transmitter while you see for yourself what happens at the affected receiver.

In General

In this "public relations" phase of the problem a great deal depends on your own attitude. Most people will be willing to meet you half way, particularly when the interference is not of long standing, if you as a person make a good impression. Your personal appearance is important. So is what you say about the receiver – no one takes kindly to hearing his possessions derided. If you discuss your interference problems on the air, do it in a constructive way – one calculated to increase listener cooperation, not destroy it.

INTERFERENCE WITH STANDARD BROADCASTING

Interference with a-m broadcasting usually falls into one or more rather well-defined categories. An understanding of the general types of interference will avoid much cut-and-try in finding a cure.

Transmitter Defects

Out-of-band radiation is something that must be cured at the transmitter. Parasitic oscillations are a frequently unsuspected source of such radiations, and no transmitter can be considered satisfactory until it has been thoroughly checked for both low- and high-frequency parasitics. Very often parasitics show up only as transients, causing key clicks in cw transmitters and "splashes" or "burps" on modulation peaks in a-m transmitters. Methods for detecting and eliminating parasitics are discussed in the transmitter chapter.

In cw transmitters the sharp make and break that occurs with unfiltered keying causes transients that, in theory, contain frequency components through the entire radio spectrum. Practically, they are often strong enough in the immediate vicinity of the transmitter to cause serious interference to broadcast reception. Key clicks can be eliminated by the methods detailed in the chapter on keying.

Non-linear operation of the final amplifier in an

ssb transmitter, or overmodulation in an a-m transmitter can cause transients similar to key clicks. It is important that either of these types of transmitters should be tuned up properly to avoid the generation of such spurious signals. In the case of ssb operation, the interference will not be intelligible at the bc set. A-m operation can produce readable interference. Methods for checking for correct operation of an ssb or a-m transmitter are described in Chapters 12 and 13, respectively.

BCI is frequently made worse by radiation from the power wiring or the rf transmission line. This is because the signal causing the interference, in such cases, is radiated from wiring that is nearer the broadcast receiver than the antenna itself. Much depends on the method used to couple the transmitter to the antenna, a subject that is discussed in the chapters on transmission lines and antennas. If it is at all possible the antenna itself should be placed so that it is not in close proximity to house wiring, telephone and power lines, and similar conductors.

The BC Set

Most present day receivers use solid-state active components, rather than tubes. A large number of the receivers in use are battery powered. This is to the amateur's advantage because much of the bc interference an amateur encounters is because of ac line pickup. In the case where the bc receiver is powered from the ac line, whether using tube or solid-stage components, the amount of rf pickup must be reduced or eliminated. A line filter such as is shown in Fig. 16-1 often will help accomplish this. The values used for the coils and capacitors are in general not critical. The effectiveness of the filter may depend considerably on the ground connection used, and it is advisable to use a short

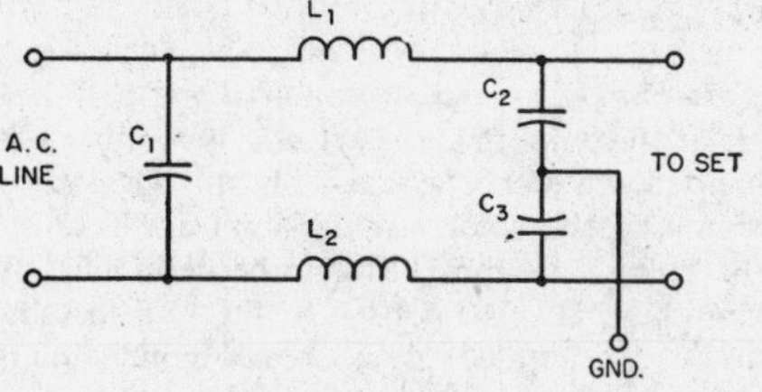

Fig. 16-1 – "Brute-force" ac line filter for receivers. The values of C1, C2 and C3 are not generally critical; capacitances from .001 to .01 μF can be used. L1 and L2 can be a 2-inch winding of No. 18 enameled wire on a half-inch diameter form. In making up such a unit for use external to the receiver, make sure that there are no exposed conductors to offer a shock hazard.

ground lead to a cold-water pipe if at all possible. The line cord from the set should be bunched up, to minimize the possibility of pick-up on the cord. It may be necessary to install the filter inside the receiver, so that the filter is connected between the line cord and the set wiring, in order to get satisfactory operation.

Cross-Modulation

With phone transmitters, there are occasionally cases where the voice is heard whenever the broadcast receiver is tuned to a bc station, but there is no interference when tuning between stations. This is cross-modulation, a result of rectification in one of the early stages of the receiver. Receivers that are susceptible to this trouble usually also get a similar type of interference from regular broadcasting if there is a strong local bc station and the receiver is tuned to some *other* station.

The remedy for cross modulation in the receiver is the same as for images and oscillator-harmonic response – reduce the strength of the amateur signal at the receiver by means of a line filter.

The trouble is not always in the receiver, since cross modulation can occur in any nearby rectifying circuit – such as a poor contact in water or steam piping, gutter pipes, and other conductors in the strong field of the transmitting antenna – external to both receiver and transmitter. Locating the cause may be difficult, and is best attempted with a battery-operated portable broadcast receiver used as a "probe" to find the spot where the interference is most intense. When such a spot is located, inspection of the metal structures in the vicinity should indicate the cause. The remedy is to make a good electrical bond between the two conductors having the poor contact.

Handling BCI Cases

Assuming that your transmitter has been checked and found to be free from spurious radiations, get another amateur to operate your station, if possible, while you make the actual check on the interference yourself. The following procedure should be used.

Tune the receiver through the broadcast band, to see whether the interference tunes like a regular bc station. If so, image or oscillator-harmonic response is the cause. If there is interference only when a bc station is tuned in, but not between stations, the cause is cross modulation. If the interference is heard at all settings of the tuning dial, the trouble is pickup in the audio circuits. In the latter case, the receiver's volume control may or may not affect the strength of the interference, depending on the means by which your signal is being rectified.

Having identified the cause, explain it to the set owner. It is a good idea to have a line filter with you, equipped with enough cord to replace the set's line cord, so it can be tried then and there. If it does not eliminate the interference, explain to the set owner that there is nothing further that can be done without modifying the receiver. Recommend that the work be done by a competent service technician, and offer to advise the service man on the cause and remedy. Don't offer to work on the set yourself, but if you are asked to do so use your own judgment about complying; set owners sometimes complain about the overall performance of the receiver afterward, often without justification. If you work on it, take it to your station so the effect of changes you make can be seen. Return the receiver promptly when you have finished.

HI-FI INTERFERENCE

Since the introduction of stereo and high-fidelity receivers, interference to this type of home-entertainment device has become a severe problem for amateurs. Aside from placing the amateur antenna as far as possible from any hi-fi installation, there is little else that can be done at the amateur's ham shack. Most of the hi-fi gear now being sold has little or no filtering to prevent rf interference. In other words, corrective measures must be done at hi-fi installation.

Hi-Fi Gear

Hi-fi gear can consist of a simple amplifier, with record or tape inputs, and speakers. The more elaborate installations may have a tape deck, record player, fm and a-m tuners, an amplifier, and two or more speakers. These units are usually connected together by means of shielded leads, and in most cases the speakers are positioned some distance from the amplifier, via long leads. When such a setup is operated near an amateur station, say within a few hundred feet, there are two important paths through which rf energy can reach the hi-fi installation to cause interference.

Step number one is to try and determine how the interference is getting into the hi-fi unit. If the volume control has no effect on the level of interference or very slight effect, the audio rectification of the amateur signal is taking place past the volume control, or on the output end of the amplifier. This is by far the most common type. It usually means that the amateur signal is being picked up on the speaker leads, or possibly on the ac line, and is then being fed back into the amplifier.

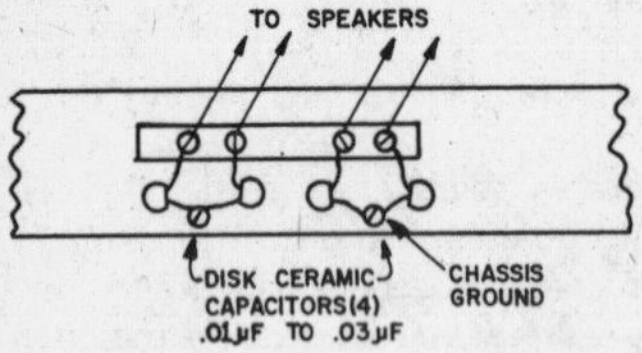

Fig. 16-2 – The disk capacitors should be mounted directly between the speaker terminals and chassis ground, keeping the leads as short as possible.

Experience has shown that most of the rf gets into the audio system via the speaker leads or the ac line, mostly the speaker leads. The amateur may find that on testing, the interference will only show up on one or two bands, or all of them. In hi-fi installations speakers are sometimes set up quite some distance from the amplifier. If the speaker leads happen to be resonant near an amateur band in use, there is likely to be an interference problem. The speaker lead will act as a resonant antenna and pick up the rf. One easy cure is to bypass the speaker terminals at the amplifier chassis. Use .01- to .03-µF disk capacitors from the speaker terminals directly to chassis ground; see Fig. 16-2. Try .01 µF and see if that does the job. In some amplifiers .03 µF are required to eliminate the rf. Be sure to install bypasses on *all* the speaker terminals. In some instances, it may appear that one of each of the individual speaker terminals are grounded to the chassis. However, some amplifiers have the speaker leads above ground on the low side, for feedback purposes. If you have a circuit diagram of the amplifier you can check, but in the absence of a diagram, bypass all the terminals. If

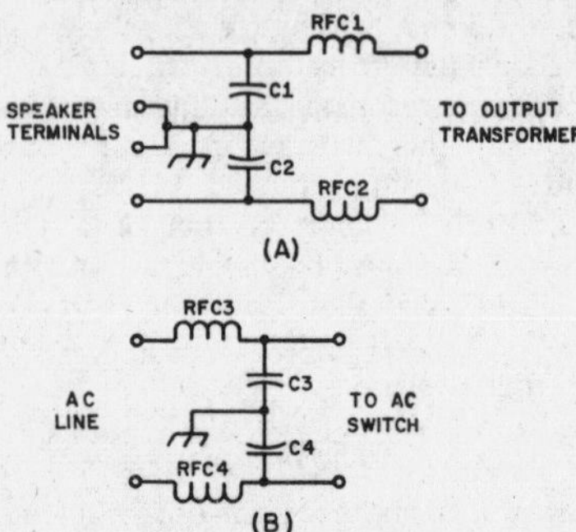

Fig. 16-3 – At A, the method for additional speaker filter, and at B, filtering the ac-line input. In both cases, these installations should be made directly inside the amplifier chassis, keeping the leads as short as possible.
C1,C2 – .01-to .03-µF disk ceramic.
C3, C4 – .01 disk ceramic, ac type.
RFC1 through RFC4 – 24 turns No. 18 enamel-covered wire, close-spaced and wound on a 1/4-inch diameter form (such as a pencil).

you can get into the amplifier, you can use the system shown in Fig. 16-3A.

In this system, two rf chokes are installed in series with the speaker leads from the output transformers, or amplifier output, to the speakers. These chokes are simple to make and help keep rf out of the amplifier. In particularly stubborn cases, shielded wire can be used for the speaker leads, grounding the shields at the amplifier chassis, and still using the bypasses on the terminals. When grounding, all chassis used in the hi-fi installation should be bonded together and connected to a good earth ground (such as a water pipe) if at all possible. It has been found that grounding sometimes eliminates the interference. On the other hand, don't be discouraged if grounding doesn't appear to help. Even with the bypassing and filtering grounding may make the difference.

Fig. 16-3B shows the method for filtering the ac line at the input of the amplifier chassis. The choke dimensions are the same as those given in Fig. 16-3A. Be sure that the bypasses are rated for ac because the dc types have been known to short out.

Antenna Pickup

If the hi-fi setup includes an fm installation, and many of them do, there is the possibility of rf getting into the audio equipment by way of the fm antenna. Chances for this method of entry are very good and precautions should be taken here to prevent the rf from getting to the equipment. A TV-type high-pass filter can prove effective in some cases.

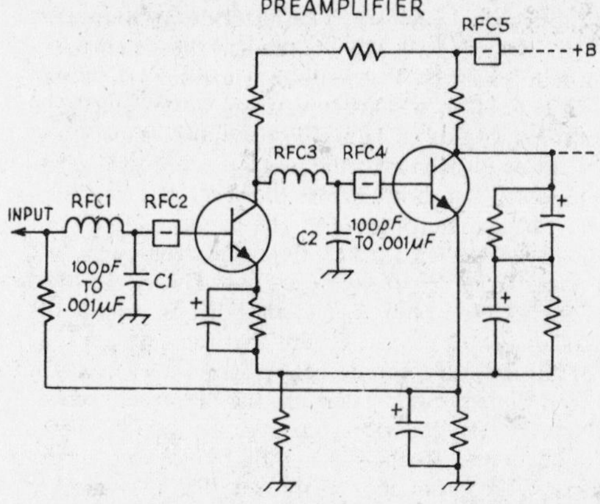

Fig. 16-4 – Typical circuit of a solid-state preamplifier.

Turntables and Tape Decks

In the more elaborate hi-fi setups, there may be several assemblies connected together by means of patch cords. It is a good idea when checking for RFI to disconnect the units, one at a time, observing any changes in the interference. Not only disconnect the patch cords connecting the pieces together, but also unplug the ac line cord for each item as you make the test. This will help you determine which section is the culprit.

Patch cords are usually, *but not always,* made of shielded cable. The lines *should* be shielded, which brings up another point. Many commercially available patch cords have poor shields. Some have wire spirally wrapped around the insulation, covering the main lead, rather than braid. This method provides poor shielding and could be the reason for RFI problems.

Record-player tone-arm connections to the cartridge are usually made with small clips. The existence of a loose clip, particularly if oxidation is present, offers an excellent invitation to RFI. Also, the leads from the cartridge and those to the amplifier are sometimes resonant at vhf, providing an excellent receiving antenna for rf. One cure for unwanted rf pickup is to install ferrite beads, one on each cartridge lead. Check all patch-cord connections for looseness or poor solder joints. Inferior connections can cause rectification and subsequent RFI.

Tape decks should be treated the same as turntables. Loose connections and bad solder joints all can cause trouble. Ferrite beads can be slipped over the leads to the recording and play-back pickup heads. Bypassing of the tone-arm or pickup-head leads is also effective, but sometimes it is difficult to install capacitors in the small area available. Disk capacitors (.001µF) should be used as close to the cartridge or pickup head as possible. Keep the capacitor leads as short as possible.

Preamplifiers

There are usually one or more preamplifiers used in a hi-fi amplifier. The inputs to these stages can be very susceptible to RFI. Fig. 16-4 illustrates a typical preamplifier circuit. In this case the leads to the bases of the transistors are treated for RFI with ferrite beads by the addition of RFC2 and RFC4. This is a very effective method for stopping RFI when vhf energy is the source of the trouble.

Within the circuit of a solid-state audio system, a common offender can be the emitter-base junction of a transistor. This junction operates as a forward-biased diode, with the bias set so that a change of base current with signal will produce a linear but amplified change in collector current. Should rf energy reach the junction, the bias could increase, causing nonlinear amplification and distortion as the result. If the rf level is high it can completely block (saturate) a transistor, causing a complete loss of gain. Therefore, it may be necessary to reduce the transmitter power output in order to pinpoint the particular transistor stage that is affected.

In addition to adding ferrite beads it may be necessary to bypass the base of the transistor to chassis ground, C1 and C2, Fig. 16-4. A suitable value is 100 pF, and keep the leads short! As a general rule, the capacitor value should be as large as possible without degrading the high-frequency response of the amplifier. Values up to .001µF can be used. In severe cases, a series inductor (RFC1 and RFC3) may be required, Ohmite Z-50 or Z-144, or their equivalents (7 and 1.8 µH respectively). Fig. 16-4 shows the correct placement for an inductor, bypass capacitor, and ferrite bead. Also, it might help to use a ferrite bead in the plus-B lead to the preamplifier stages (RFC5 in Fig. 16-4). Keep in mind that Fig. 16-4 represents only one preamplifier of a stereo set. *Both* channels may require treatment.

FM Tuners

There is often an fm tuner used in a hi-fi installation. Much of the interference to tuners is caused by fundamental overloading of the first stage (or stages) of the tuner, effected by the amateur's signal. The cure is the installation of a high-pass filter, the same type used for TVI. The filter should be installed as close as possible to the antenna input of the tuner. The high-pass filter will attenuate the amateur *fundamental* signal, thus preventing overloading of the front end.

Shielding

Lack of shielding on the various components in a hi-fi installation can permit rf to get into the equipment. Many units have no bottom plates, or are installed in plastic cases. One easy method of providing shielding is to use aluminum foil. Make sure the foil doesn't short circuit the components, and connect it to chassis ground.

MISCELLANEOUS TYPES OF INTERFERENCE

The operation of amateur phone transmitters occasionally results in interference on telephone lines and in audio amplifiers used in public-address work, plus other audio devices. The cause is rectification of the signal in an audio circuit.

Organs

An RFI problem area is the electronic organ. All of the techniques outlined for hi-fi gear hold true in getting rid of RFI in an organ. Two points should be checked – the speaker leads and the ac line. Many organ manufacturers have special servicemen's guides for taking care of RFI. However, to get this information you or the organ owner must contact the manufacturer, not the dealer or distributor. Don't accept the statement from a dealer or serviceman that there is nothing that can be done about the interference.

P-A Systems

The cure for RFI in p-a systems is almost the same as that for hi-fi gear. The one thing to watch for is rf on the leads that connect the various stations in a p-a system together. These leads should be treated the same as speaker *leads* and bypassing and filtering should be done at *both* ends of the lines. Also, watch for ac-line pickup of rf.

Telephone Interference

Telephone interference may be cured by connecting a bypass capacitor (about .001 μF) across the microphone unit in the telephone handset. The telephone companies have capacitors for this purpose. When such a case occurs, get in touch with the repair department of the phone company, giving the particulars. Section 500-150-100 of the Bell System Practices *Plant Series* gives detailed instructions. This section discusses causes and cures of telephone interference from radio signals. It points out that interference can come from corroded connections, unterminated loops, and other sources. It correctly points out that that rf can be picked up on the drop wire coming into the house, and also on the wiring within the house, but (usually) the detection of the rf occurs inside the phone. The detection usually takes place at the varistors in the compensation networks, and/or at the receiver noise suppressor and the carbon microphone. But interference suppression should be handled two ways: prevent the rf from getting to the phone, and prevent it from being rectified.

The telephone companies (Bell System) have two devices for this purpose. The first is a 40BA capacitor, which is installed at the service entrance protector, and the second is the 1542A inductor, which is installed at the connector block. According to the practices manual, the 40BA bypasses rf picked up on the drop wire coming into the house from the phone, and the 1542A suppresses rf picked up on the inside wiring. These are mentioned because in very stubborn cases they may be necessary. But first, it is suggested that the telephones be modified.

Since there are several different series of phones, they will be discussed separately:

500 series – These are the desk and wall phones most commonly in use. They come in several different configurations, but all use a 425-series compensation network. The letter designation can be A, B, C, D, E, F, G, or K, and all these networks contain varistors. The network should be replaced with a 425J, in which the varistors are replaced by resistors. Also, .01-μF disk-ceramic capacitors should be placedacross the receiver suppressor. The suppressor is a diode across the receiver terminals. The carbon microphone in the handset should be bypassed with a .01-μF ceramic capacitor.

Series 1500, 1600, 1700 – These are the "Touch-Tone" phones, and the cure is similar to that for the 500 series, except that the network is a 4010B or D, and should be replaced with a 4010E.

Trimline series – These are the "Princess" series phones. The practices manual says that these should be modified by installing bypass capacitors across *all* components in the set that may act as demodulators. This statement is rather vague, but evidently a solution is known to the telephone company for these sets.

At the end of section 500-150-100 is an ordering guide for special components and sets, as follows:

Ordering Guide:
Capacitor, 40BA
Inductor, 1542A
-49 Gray, -50 Ivory
Set, Telephone, -rf Modified
Set, Telephone Hand, 220A, -rf Modified
Set, Telephone Hand, 2220B, -rf Modified
Set, Hand G, -rf Modified
Dial – (Touch-Tone dial only) -rf Modified.

The type "G" Handset is the one used with the 500 and Touch-Tone series phones. Also, Mountain Bell has put out an "Addendum 500-150-100MS, Issue A, January 1971" to the practices manual, which states that items for rf modified phones should be ordered on nonstock Form 3218, as follows:

(Telephone Set type)
Modified for BSP 500-150-100
for Radio Signal Suppression

The FCC

The Field Engineering Bureau of the FCC has a bulletin that will be of help to the amateur in cases involving RFI to audio devices. These bulletins are available from any of the field offices. The bulletin is addressed to the users of hi-fi, record players, public-address systems, and telephones. It clearly spells out the problem and the obligation of the owner of such gear.

It is suggested that the amateur obtain copies of this bulletin, which is listed as *Attachment III, Bulletin, Interference to Audio Devices.* When the amateur receives a complaint he can provide the complainer with a copy of the bulletin. This approach will help put the problem in correct perspective.

TELEVISION INTERFERENCE

Interference with the reception of television signals usually presents a more difficult problem than interference with a-m broadcasting. In BCI cases the interference almost always can be attributed to deficient selectivity or spurious responses in the bc receiver. While similar deficiencies exist in many television receivers, it is also true that amateur transmitters generate harmonics that fall inside many or all television channels. These spurious radiations cause interference that ordinarily cannot be eliminated by anything that may be done at the receiver, so must be prevented at the transmitter itself.

The overall situation is further complicated by the fact that television broadcasting is in three distinct bands, two in the vhf region and one in the uhf.

VHF TELEVISION

For the amateur who does most of his transmitting on frequencies below 30 MHz, the TV band of principal interest is the low vhf band between 54 and 88 MHz. If harmonic radiation can be reduced to the point where no interference is caused to Channels 2 to 6, inclusive, it is almost certain that any harmonic troubles with channels above 174 MHz will disappear also.

The relationship between the vhf television channels and harmonics of amateur bands from 14 through 28 MHz is shown in Fig. 16-5. Harmonics of the 7- and 3.5-MHz bands are not shown because they fall in every television channel. However, the harmonics above 54 MHz from these bands are of such high order that they are usually rather low in amplitude, although they may be strong enough to interfere if the television receiver is quite close to the amateur transmitter. Low-order harmonics – up to about the sixth – are usually the most difficult to eliminate.

Of the amateur vhf bands, only 50 MHz will have harmonics falling in a vhf television channel (channels 11, 12 and 13). However, a transmitter for any amateur vhf band may cause interference if it has multiplier stages either operating in or having harmonics in one or more of the vhf TV channels. the rf energy on such frequencies can be radiated directly from the transmitting circuits or coupled by stray means to the transmitting antenna.

Frequency Effects

The degree to which transmitter harmonics or other undesired radiation actually in the TV channel must be suppressed depends principally on two factors, the strength of the TV signal on the channel or channels affected, and the relationship between the frequency of the spurious radiation and the frequencies of the TV picture and sound carriers within the channel. If the TV signal is very strong, interference can be eliminated by comparatively simple methods. However, if the TV signal is very weak, as in "fringe" areas where the received picture is visibly degraded by the appearance of set noise or "snow" on the screen, it may be necessary to go to extreme measures.

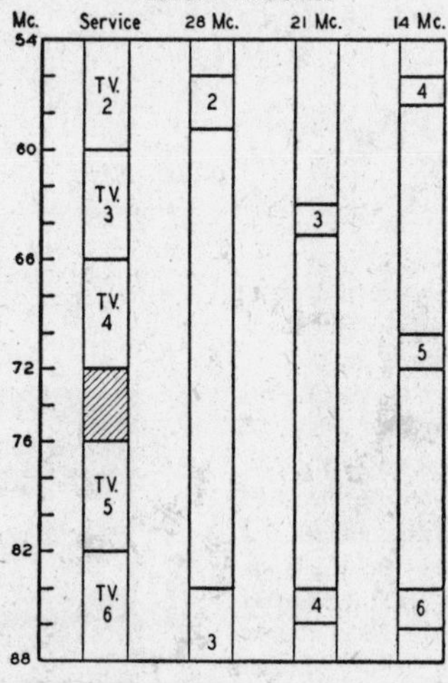

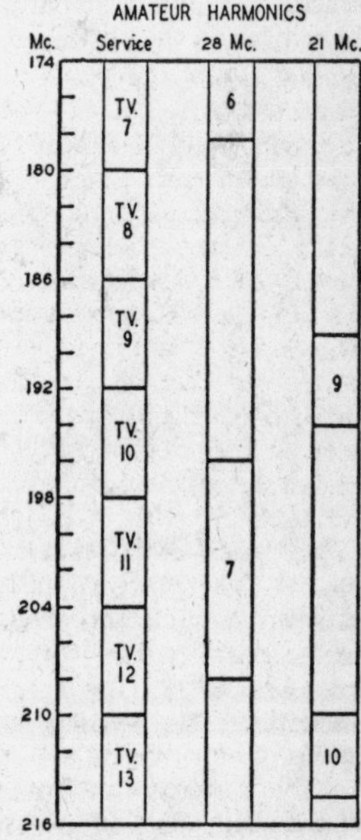

Fig. 16-5 – Relationship of amateur-band harmonics to vhf TV channels. Harmonic interference from transmitters operating below 30 MHz is likely to be serious in the low-channel group (54 to 88 MHz).

In either case the intensity of the interference depends very greatly on the exact frequency of the interfering signal. Fig. 16-6 shows the placement of the picture and sound carriers in the standard TV channel. In Channel 2, for example, the picture carrier frequency is 54 + 1.25 = 55.25 MHz and the sound carrier frequency is 60 – 0.25 = 59.75 MHz.

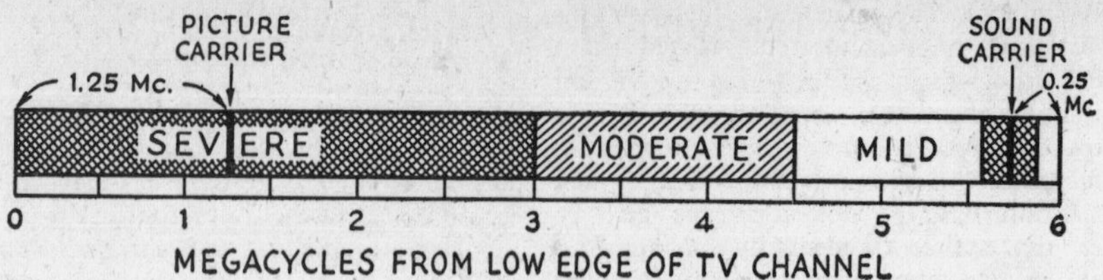

Fig. 16-6 – Location of picture and sound carriers in a monochrome television channel, and relative intensity of interference as the location of the interfering signal within the channels is varied without changing its strength. The three regions are not actually sharply defined as shown in this drawing, but merge into one another gradually.

The second harmonic of 28.010 kHz (56,020 kHz or 56.02 MHz) falls 56.02 – 54 = 2.02 MHz above the low edge of the channel and is in the region marked "Severe" in Fig. 16-6. On the other hand, the second harmonic of 29,500 kHz (59,000 kHz or 59 MHz) is 59 – 54 = 5 MHz from the low edge of the channel and falls in the region marked "Mild." Interference at this frequency has to be about 100 times as strong as at 56,020 kHz to cause effects of equal intensity. Thus an operating frequency that puts a harmonic near the picture carrier requires about 40 dB more harmonic suppression in order to avoid interference, as compared with an operating frequency that puts the harmonic near the upper edge of the channel.

For a region of 100 kHz or so either side of the sound carrier there is another "Severe" region where a spurious radiation will interfere with reception of the sound program and this region also should be avoided. In general, a signal of intensity equal to that of the picture carrier will not cause noticeable interference if its frequency is in the "Mild" region shown in Fig. 16-6, but the same intensity in the "Severe" region will utterly destroy the picture.

Fig. 16-7 – "Cross-hatching," caused by the beat between the picture carrier and an interfering signal inside the TV channel.

Interference Patterns

The visible effects of interference vary with the type and intensity of the interference. Complete "blackout," where the picture and sound disappear completely, leaving the screen dark, occurs only when the transmitter and receiver are quite close together. Strong interference ordinarily causes the picture to be broken up, leaving a jumble of light and dark lines, or turns the picture "negative" – the normally white parts of the picture turn black and the normally black parts turn white. "Cross-hatching" – diagonal bars or lines in the picture – accompanies the latter, usually, and also represents the most common type of less severe interference. The bars are the result of the beat between the harmonic frequency and the picture carrier frequency. They are broad and relatively few in number if the beat frequency is comparatively low – near the picture carrier – and are numerous and very fine if the beat frequency is very high – toward the upper end of the channel. Typical cross-hatching is shown in Fig. 16-7. If the frequency falls in the "Mild" region in Fig. 16-6 the cross-hatching may be so fine as to be visible only on close inspection of the picture, in which case it may simply cause the apparent brightness of the screen to change when the transmitter carrier is thrown on and off.

Whether or not cross-hatching is visible, an amplitude-modulated transmitter may cause "sound bars" in the picture. These look about as

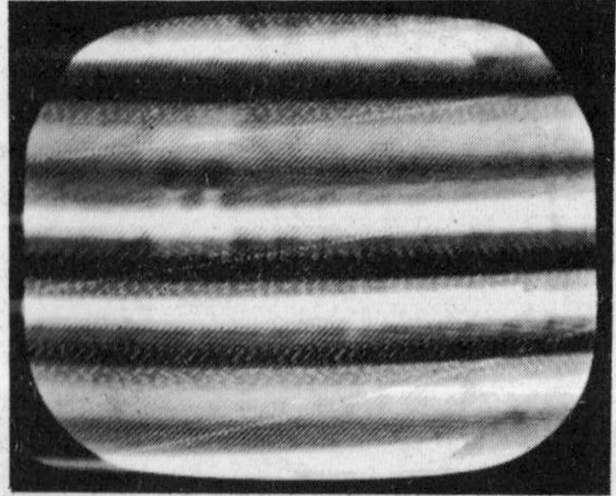

Fig. 16-8 – "Sound bars" or "modulation bars" accompanying amplitude modulation of an interfering signal. In this case the interfering carrier is strong enough to destroy the picture, but in mild cases the picture is visible through the horizontal bars. Sound bars may accompany modulation even though the unmodulated carrier gives no visible cross-hatching.

shown in Fig. 16-8. They result from the variations in the intensity of the interfering signal when modulated. Under most circumstances modulation bars will not occur if the amateur transmitter is frequency- or phase-modulated. With these types of modulation the cross-hatching will "wiggle" from side to side with the modulation.

Except in the more severe cases, there is seldom any effect on the sound reception when interference shows in the picture, unless the frequency is quite close to the sound carrier. In the latter event the sound may be interfered with even though the picture is clean.

Reference to Fig. 16-5 will show whether or not harmonics of the frequency in use will fall in any television channels that can be received in the locality. It should be kept in mind that not only harmonics of the final frequency may interfere, but also harmonics of any frequencies that may be present in buffer or frequency-multiplier stages. In the case of 144-MHz transmitters, frequency-multiplying combinations that require a doubler or tripler stage to operate on a frequency actually in a low-band vhf channel in use in the locality should be avoided.

Harmonic Suppression

Effective harmonic suppression has three separate phases:

1) Reducing the amplitude of harmonics generated in the transmitter. This is a matter of circuit design and operating conditions.

2) Preventing stray radiation from the transmitter and from associated wiring. This requires adequate shielding and filtering of all circuits and leads from which radiation can take place.

3) Preventing harmonics from being fed into the antenna.

It is impossible to build a transmitter that will not generate *some* harmonics, but it is obviously advantageous to reduce their strength, by circuit design and choice of operating conditions, by as large a factor as possible before attempting to prevent them from being radiated. Harmonic radiation from the transmitter itself or from its associated wiring obviously will cause interference just as readily as radiation from the antenna, so measures taken to prevent harmonics from reaching the antenna will not reduce TVI if the transmitter itself is radiating harmonics. But once it has been found that the transmitter itself is free from harmonic radiation, devices for preventing harmonics from reaching the antenna can be expected to produce results.

REDUCING HARMONIC GENERATION

Since reasonably efficient operation of rf power amplifiers always is accompanied by harmonic generation, good judgment calls for operating all frequency-multiplier stages at a very low power level. When the final output frequency is reached, it is desirable to use as few stages as possible in building up to the final output power level, and to use tubes that require a minimum of driving power.

Circuit Design and Layout

Harmonic currents of considerable amplitude flow in both the grid and plate circuits of rf power amplifiers, but they will do relatively little harm if they can be effectively bypassed to the cathode of the tube. Fig. 16-9 shows the paths followed by harmonic currents in an amplifier circuit; because of the high reactance of the tank coil there is little harmonic current in it, so the harmonic currents

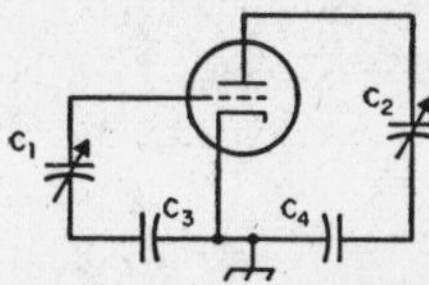

Fig. 16-9 – A vhf resonant circuit is formed by the tube capacitance and the leads through the tank and blocking capacitors. Regular tank coils are not shown, since they have little effect on such resonances. C1 is the grid tuning capacitor and C2 is the plate tuning capacitor. C3 and C4 are the grid and plate blocking or bypass capacitors, respectively.

simply flow through the tank capacitor, the plate (or grid) blocking capacitor, and the tube capacitances. The lengths of the leads forming these paths is of great importance, since the inductance in this circuit will resonate with the tube capacitance at some frequency in the vhf range (the tank and blocking capacitances usually are so large compared with the tube capacitance that they have little effect on the resonant frequency). If such a resonance happens to occur at or near the same frequency as one of the transmitter harmonics, the effect is just the same as though a harmonic tank circuit had been deliberately introduced; the harmonic at that frequency will be tremendously increased in amplitude.

Such resonances are unavoidable, but by keeping the path from plate to cathode and from grid to cathode as short as is physically possible, the resonant frequency usually can be raised above 100 MHz in amplifiers of medium power. This puts it between the two groups of television channels.

It is easier to place grid-circuit vhf resonances where they will do no harm when the amplifier is link-coupled to the driver stage, since this generally permits shorter leads and more favorable conditions for bypassing the harmonics than is the case with capacitive coupling. Link coupling also reduces the coupling between the driver and amplifier at harmonic frequencies, thus preventing driver harmonics from being amplified.

The inductance of leads from the tube to the tank capacitor can be reduced not only by shortening but by using flat strip instead of wire conductors. It is also better to use the chassis as the return from the blocking capacitor or tuned circuit to cathode, since a chassis path will have less inductance than almost any other form of connection.

The vhf resonance points in amplifier tank circuits can be found by coupling a grid-dip meter covering the 50-250 MHz range to the grid and plate leads. If a resonance is found in or near a TV channel, methods such as those described above should be used to move it well out of the TV range. The grid-dip meter also should be used to check for vhf resonances in the tank coils, because coils made for 14 MHz and below usually will show such resonances. In making the check, disconnect the coil entirely from the transmitter and move the grid-dip meter coil along it while exploring for a dip in the 54-88-MHz band. If a resonance falls in a TV channel that is in use in the locality, changing the number of turns will move it to a less-troublesome frequency.

Operating Conditions

Grid bias and grid current have an important effect on the harmonic content of the rf currents in both the grid and plate circuits. In general, harmonic output increases as the grid bias and grid current are increased, but this is not necessarily true of a *particular* harmonic. The third and higher harmonics, especially, will go through fluctuations in amplitude as the grid current is increased, and sometimes a rather high value of grid current will minimize one harmonic as compared with a low value. This characteristic can be used to advantage where a particular harmonic is causing interference, remembering that the operating conditions that minimize one harmonic may greatly increase another.

For equal operating conditions, there is little or no difference between single-ended and push-pull amplifiers in respect to harmonic generation. Push-pull amplifiers are frequently troublemakers on even-order harmonics because with such amplifiers the even-harmonic voltages are in phase at the ends of the tank circuit and hence appear with equal amplitude across the whole tank coil, if the center of the coil is not grounded. Under such circumstances the even harmonics can be coupled to the output circuit through stray capacitance between the tank and coupling coils. This does not occur in a single-ended amplifier having an inductively coupled tank, if the coupling coil is placed at the cold end, or with a pi-network tank.

Harmonic Traps

If a harmonic in only one TV channel is particularly bothersome – frequently the case when the transmitter operates on 28 MHz – a trap tuned to the harmonic frequency may be installed in the plate lead as shown in Fig. 16-10. At the harmonic frequency the trap represents a very high impedance and hence reduces the amplitude of the harmonic current flowing through the tank circuit. In the push-pull circuit both traps have the same constants. The L/C ratio is not critical but a high-C circuit usually will have least effect on the performance of the plate circuit at the normal operating frequency.

Since there is a considerable harmonic voltage across the trap, radiation may occur from the trap unless the transmitter is well shielded. Traps should be placed so that there is no coupling between them and the amplifier tank circuit.

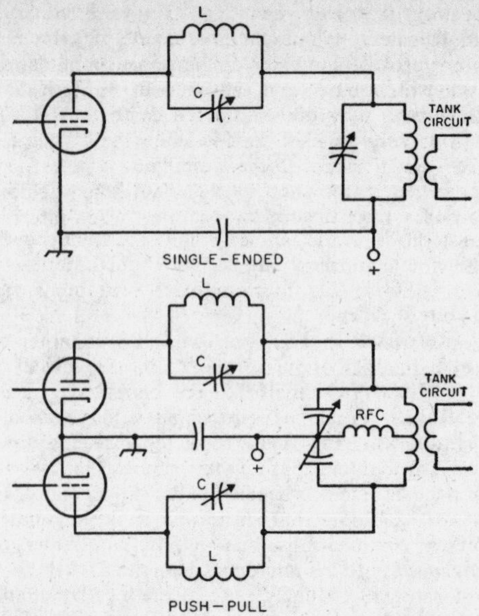

Fig. 16-10 – Harmonic traps in an amplifier plate circuit. L and C should resonate at the frequency of the harmonic to be suppressed. C may be a 25- to 50-pF midget, and L usually consists of 3 to 6 turns about 1/2 inch in diameter for Channels 2 through 6. The inductance should be adjusted so that the trap resonates at about half capacitance of C before being installed in the transmitter. The frequency may be checked with a grid-dip meter. When in place, the trap should be adjusted for minimum interference to the TV picture.

A trap is a highly selective device and so is useful only over a small range of frequencies. A second- or third-harmonic trap on a 28-MHz tank circuit usually will not be effective over more than 50 kHz or so at the fundamental frequency, depending on how serious the interference is without the trap. Because they are critical of adjustment, it is better to prevent TVI by other means, if possible, and use traps only as a last resort.

PREVENTING RADIATION FROM THE TRANSMITTER

The extent to which interference will be caused by direct radiation of spurious signals depends on the operating frequency, the transmitter power level, the strength of the television signal, and the distance between the transmitter and TV receiver. Transmitter radiation can be a very serious problem if the TV signal is weak, if the TV receiver and amateur transmitter are close together, and if the transmitter is operated with high power.

Shielding

Direct radiation from the transmitter circuits and components can be prevented by proper shielding. To be effective, a shield must completely enclose the circuits and parts and must have no openings that will permit rf energy to escape. Unfortunately, ordinary metal boxes and cabinets do not provide good shielding, since such openings as louvers, lids, and holes for running in connections allow far too much leakage.

A primary requisite for good shielding is that all joints must make a good electrical connection along their entire length. A small slit or crack will let out a surprising amount of rf energy; so will ventilating louvers and large holes such as those used for mounting meters. On the other hand, small holes do not impair the shielding very greatly, and a limited number of ventilating holes may be used if they are small – not over 1/4 inch in diameter. Also, wire screen makes quite effective shielding if the wires make good electrical connection at each crossover. Perforated aluminum such as the "do-it-yourself" sold at hardware stores also is good, although not very strong mechanically. If perforated material is used, choose the variety with the smallest openings. The leakage through large openings can be very much reduced by covering such openings with screening or perforated aluminum, well bonded to all edges of the opening.

The intensity of rf fields about coils, capacitors, tubes and wiring decreases very rapidly with distance, so shielding is more effective, from a practical standpoint, if the components and wiring are not too close to it. It is advisable to have a separation of several inches, if possible, between "hot" points in the circuit and the nearest shielding.

For a given thickness of metal, the greater the conductivity the better the shielding. Copper is best, with aluminum, brass and steel following in that order. However, if the thickness is adequate for structural purposes (over .02 inch) and the shield and a "hot" point in the circuit are not in close proximity, any of these metals will be satisfactory. Greater separation should be used with steel shielding than with the other materials not only because it is considerably poorer as a shield but also because it will cause greater losses in near-by circuits than would copper or aluminum at the same distance. Wire screen or perforated metal used as a shield should also be kept at some distance from high-voltage or high-current rf points, since there is considerably more leakage through the mesh than through solid metal.

Where two pieces of metal join, as in forming a corner, they should overlap at least a half inch and be fastened together firmly with screws or bolts spaced at close-enough intervals to maintain firm contact all along the joint. The contact surfaces should be clean before joining, and should be checked occasionally – especially steel, which is almost certain to rust after a period of time.

The leakage through a given size of aperture in shielding increases with frequency, so such points as good continuous contact, screening of large holes, and so on, become even more important when the radiation to be suppressed is in the high band – 174-216 MHz. Hence 50- and 144-MHz transmitters, which in general will have frequency-multiplier harmonics of relatively high intensity in this region, require special attention in this respect if the possibility of interfering with a channel received locally exists.

Lead Treatment

Even very good shielding can be made completely useless when connections are run to external power supplies and other equipment from the circuits inside the shield. Every such conductor leaving the shielding forms a path for the escape of rf, which is then radiated by the connecting wires. Hence a step that is essential in every case is to prevent harmonic currents from flowing on the leads leaving the shielded enclosure.

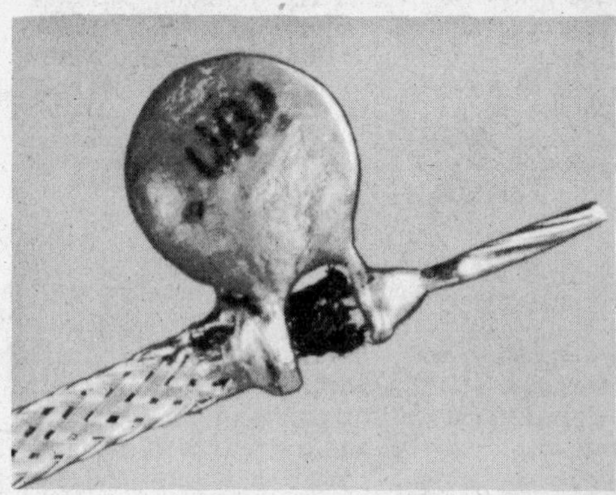

Fig. 16-11 – Proper method of bypassing the end of a shielded lead using disk ceramic capacitor. The .001-μF size should be used for 1600 volts or less; 500 pF at higher voltages. The leads are wrapped around the inner and outer conductors and soldered, so that the lead length is negligible. This photograph is about four times actual size.

Harmonic currents always flow on the dc or ac leads connecting to the tube circuits. A very effective means of preventing such currents from being coupled into other wiring, and one that provides desirable bypassing as well, is to use shielded wire for all such leads, maintaining the shielding from the point where the lead connects to the tube or rf circuit right through to the point where it leaves the chassis. The shield braid should be grounded to the chassis at both ends and at frequent intervals along the path.

Good bypassing of shielded leads also is essential. Bearing in mind that the shield braid about the conductor confines the harmonic currents to the *inside* of the shielded wire, the object of bypassing is to prevent their escape. Fig. 16-11 shows the proper way to bypass. The small .001-pF ceramic disk capacitor, when mounted on the end of the shielded wire as shown in Fig. 16-11, actually forms a series-resonant circuit in the 54-88-MHz range and thus represents practically a short circuit for low-band TV harmonics. The exposed wire to the connection terminal should be kept as short as is physically possible, to prevent any possible harmonic pickup exterior to the shielded wiring. Disk capacitors in the useful capacitance range of 500 to 1000 pF are available in several voltage ratings up to 6000 volts.

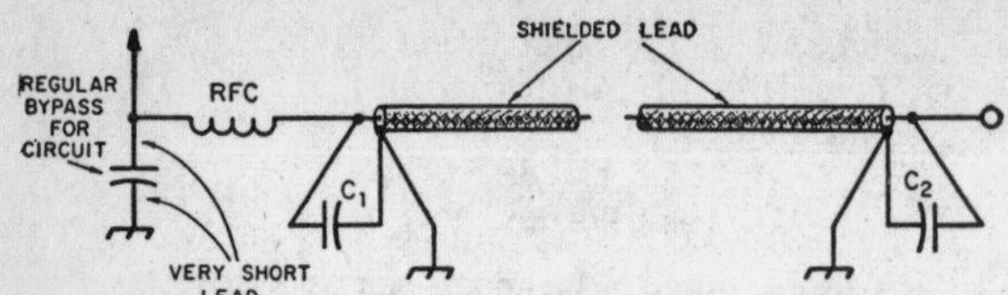

Fig. 16-12 – Additional rf filtering of supply leads may be required in regions where the TV signal is very weak. The rf choke should be physically small, and may consist of a 1-inch winding of No. 26 enameled wire on a 1/4-inch form, close-wound. Manufactured single-layer chokes having an inductance of a few microhenries also may be used.

These bypasses are essential at the connection-block terminals, and desirable at the tube ends of the leads also. Installed as shown with shielded wiring, they have been found to be so effective that there is usually no need for further harmonic filtering. However, if a test shows that additional filtering is required, the arrangement shown in Fig. 16-12 may be used. Such an rf filter should be installed at the tube end of the shielded lead, and if more than one circuit is filtered care should be taken to keep the rf chokes separated from each other and so oriented as to minimize coupling between them. This is necessary for preventing harmonics present in one circuit from being coupled into another.

In difficult cases involving Channels 7 to 13 – i.e., close proximity between the transmitter and receiver, and a weak TV signal – additional lead-filtering measures may be needed to prevent radiation of interfering signals by 50- and 144-MHz transmitters. A recommended method is shown in Fig. 16-13. It uses a shielded lead bypassed with a ceramic disk as described above, with the addition of a low-inductance feed-through type capacitor

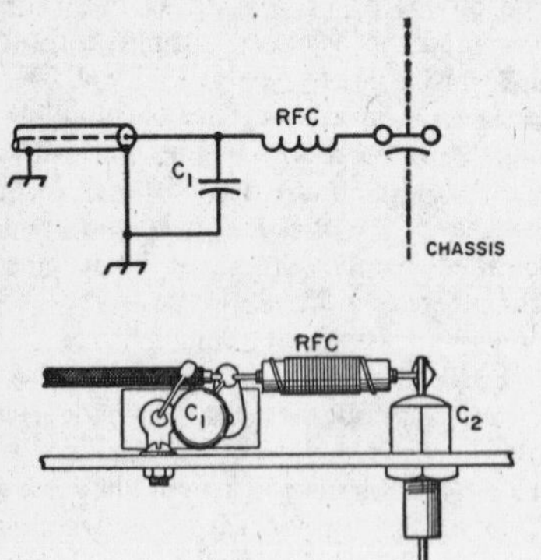

Fig. 16-13 – Additional lead filtering for harmonics or other spurious frequencies in the high vhf TV band (174-216 MHz).
C1 – .001-μF disk ceramic.
C2 – 500- or 1000-pF fed-through bypass (Centralab FT-1000. Above 500 volts, substitute Centralab 858S-500.).
RFC – 14 inches No. 26 enamel close-wound on 3/16-inch dia. form or composition resistor body.

and a small rf choke, the capacitor being used as a terminal for the external connection. For voltages above 400, a capacitor of compact construction (as indicated in the caption) should be used, mounted so that there is a very minimum of exposed lead. inside the chassis, from the capacitor to the connection terminal.

As an alternative to the series-resonant bypassing described above, feed-through type capacitors such as the Sprague "Hypass" type may be used as terminals for external connections. The ideal method of installation is to mount them so they protrude through the chassis, with thorough bonding to the chassis all around the hole in which the capacitor is mounted. The principle is illustrated in Fig. 16-14.

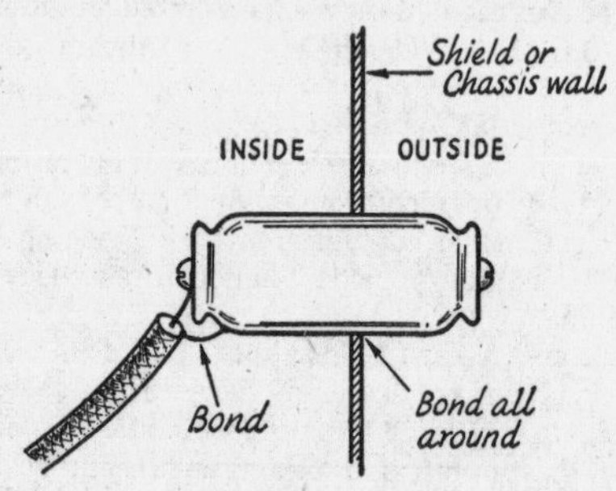

Fig. 16-14 – The best method of using the "Hypass" type feed-through capacitor. Capacitances of .01 to 0.1 μF are satisfactory. Capacitors of this type are useful for high-current circuits, such as filament and 117-volt leads, as a substitute for the rf choke shown in Fig. 16-12, in cases where additional lead filtering is needed.

Meters that are mounted in an rf unit should be enclosed in shielding covers, the connections being made with shielded wire with each lead bypassed as described above. The shield braid should be grounded to the panel or chassis immediately outside the meter shield, as indicated in Fig. 16-15. A bypass may also be connected across the meter terminals, principally to prevent any fundamental current that may be present from flowing through the meter itself. As an alternative to individual meter shielding the meters may be mounted entirely behind the panel, and the panel holes needed for observation may be covered with wire screen that is carefully bonded to the panel all around the hole.

Care should be used in the selection of shielded wire for transmitter use. Not only should the insulation be conservatively rated for the dc voltage in use, but the insulation should be of material that will not easily deteriorate in soldering. The rf characteristics of the wire are not especially important, except that the attenuation of harmonics in the wire itself will be greater if the insulating material has high losses at radio frequencies; in other words, wire intended for use at dc and low frequencies is preferable to cables designed expressly for carrying rf. The attenuation also will increase with the length of the wire; in general, it is better to make the leads as long as

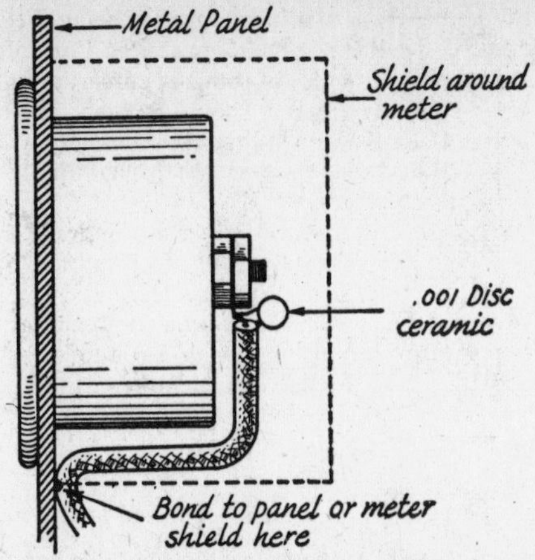

Fig. 16-15 – Meter shielding and bypassing. It is essential to shield the meter mounting hole since the meter will carry rf through it to be radiated. Suitable shields can be made from 2 1/2- or 3-inch diameter metal cans or small metal chassis boxes.

circumstances permit rather than to follow the more usual practice of using no more lead than is actually necessary. Where wires cross or run parallel, the shields should be spot-soldered together and connected to the chassis. For high voltages, automobile ignition cable covered with shielding braid is recommended.

Proper shielding of the transmitter requires that the rf circuits be shielded entirely from the external connecting leads. A situation such as is shown in Fig. 16-17, where the leads in the rf chassis have been shielded and properly filtered but the chassis is mounted in a large shield, simply invites the harmonic currents to travel over the chassis and on out over the leads *outside* the chassis. The shielding about the rf circuits should make complete contact with the chassis on which the parts are mounted.

Checking Transmitter Radiation

A check for transmitter radiation always should be made before attempting to use low-pass filters or other devices for preventing harmonics from

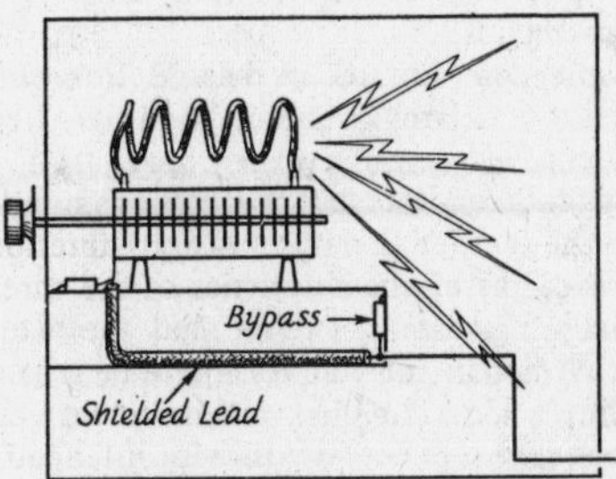

Fig. 16-17 – A metal cabinet can be an adequate shield, but there will still be radiation if the leads inside can pick up rf from the transmitting circuits.

reaching the antenna system. The only really satisfactory indicating instrument is a television receiver. In regions where the TV signal is strong an indicating wavemeter such as one having a crystal or tube detector may be useful; if it is possible to get any indication at all from harmonics either on supply leads or around the transmitter itself, the harmonics are probably strong enough to cause interference. However, the absence of any such indication does not mean that harmonic interference will not be caused. If the techniques of shielding and lead filtering described in the preceding section are followed, the harmonic intensity on any external leads should be far below what any such instruments can detect.

Radiation checks should be made with the transmitter delivering full power into a dummy antenna, such as an incandescent lamp of suitable power rating, preferably installed inside the shielded enclosure. If the dummy must be external, it is desirable to connect it through a coax-matching circuit such as is shown in Fig. 16-18. Shielding

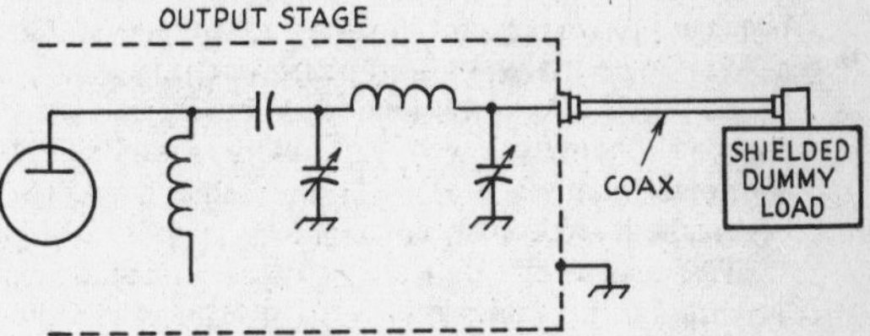

Fig. 16-18 – Dummy-antenna system for checking harmonic radiation from the transmitter and leads.

the dummy antenna circuit is also desirable, although it is not always necessary.

Make the radiation test on all frequencies that are to be used in transmitting, and note whether or not interference patterns show in the received picture. (These tests must be made while a TV signal is being received, since the beat patterns will not be formed if the TV picture carrier is not present.) If interference exists, its source can be detected by grasping the various external leads (by the insulation, not the live wire!) or bringing the hand near meter faces, louvers, and other possible points where harmonic energy might escape from the transmitter. If any of these tests cause a *change* – not necessarily an *increase* – in the intensity of the interference, the presence of harmonics at that point is indicated. The location of such "hot" spots usually will point the way to the remedy. If the TV receiver and the transmitter can be operated side-by-side, a length of wire connected to one antenna terminal on the receiver can be used as a probe to go over the transmitter enclosure and external leads. This device will very quickly expose the spots from which serious leakage is taking place.

As a final test, connect the transmitting antenna or its transmission line terminals to the outside of the transmitter shielding. Interference created when this test is applied indicates that weak currents are on the outside of the shield and can be conducted to the antenna when the normal antenna connections are used. Currents of this nature represent interference that is conducted *over* low-pass filters, and hence cannot be eliminated by such filters.

TRANSMITTING-ANTENNA CONSIDERATIONS

When a well-shielded transmitter is used in conjunction with an effective low-pass filter, and there is no incidental rectification in the area, it is impossible to have "harmonic-type" TVI, regardless of the type of transmitting antenna. However, the type of transmitting antenna in use can be responsible for "fundamental-overload" TVI.

To minimize the chances of TVI, the transmitting antenna should be located as far as possible from the receiving antenna. The chances of fundamental overload at the television receiver are reduced when a horizontal transmitting antenna or beam is mounted higher than the TV antenna. Other things being equal, fundamental overload is more likely to occur with a vertical transmitting antenna than with a horizontal one, because the vertical antenna has a stronger field at a low angle. If a ground-plane antenna can be located well above the height of the TV receiving antenna, there is less likelihood of fundamental overload than when it is at the same height or below the television antenna.

The SWR on the line to the transmitting antenna has no effect on TVI. However, when the line to the antenna passes near the TV antenna, radiation from the line can be a source of TVI. Methods for minimizing radiation from the line are discussed in the chapter on transmission lines.

PREVENTING HARMONICS FROM REACHING THE ANTENNA

The third and last step in reducing harmonic TVI is to keep the spurious energy generated in or passed through the final stage from traveling over the transmission line to the antenna. It is seldom worthwhile even to attempt this until the radiation from the transmitter and its connecting leads has been reduced to the point where, with the transmitter delivering full power into a dummy antenna, it has been determined by actual testing with a television receiver that the radiation is below the level that can cause interference. If the dummy antenna test shows enough radiation to be seen in a TV picture, it is a practical certainty that harmonics will be coupled to the antenna system no matter what preventive measures are taken. In inductively coupled output systems, some harmonic energy will be transferred from the final amplifier through the mutual inductance between the tank coil and the output coupling coil. Harmonics of the output frequency transferred in this way can be greatly reduced by providing sufficient selectivity between the final tank and the transmission line. A good deal of selectivity, amounting to 20 to 30 dB reduction of the second harmonic and much higher reduction of higher-order harmonics, is furnished by a matching circuit of the type described in the chapter on transmission lines. An "antenna coupler" is therefore a worthwhile addition to the transmitter.

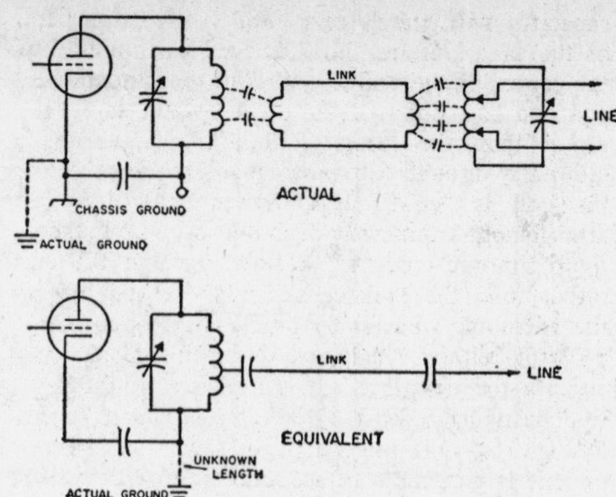

Fig. 16-19 – The stray capacitive coupling between coils in the upper circuit leads to the equivalent circuit shown below, for vhf harmonics.

In 50- and 144-MHz transmitters, particularly, harmonics not directly associated with the output frequency – such as those generated in low-frequency early stages of the transmitter – may get coupled to the antenna by stray means. For example, a 144-MHz transmitter might have an oscillator or frequency multiplier at 48 MHz, followed by a tripler to 144 MHz. Some of the 48-MHz energy will appear in the plate circuit of the tripler, and if passed on to the grid of the final amplifier will appear as a 48-MHz modulation on the 144-MHz signal. This will cause a spurious signal at 192 MHz, which is in the high TV band, and the selectivity of the tank circuits may not be sufficient to prevent its being coupled to the antenna. Spurious signals of this type can be reduced by using link coupling between the driver stage and final amplifier (and between earlier stages as well) in addition to the suppression afforded by using a Transmatch.

Capacitive Coupling

The upper drawing in Fig. 16-19 shows a parallel-conductor link as it might be used to couple into a parallel-conductor line through a matching circuit. Inasmuch as a coil is a sizable metallic object, there is capacitance between the final tank coil and its associated link coil, and between the matching-circuit coil and its link. Energy coupled through these capacitances travels over the link circuit and the transmission line as though these were merely single conductors. The tuned circuits simply act as masses of metal and offer no selectivity at all for capacitively-coupled energy. Although the actual capacitances are small, they offer a good coupling medium for frequencies in the vhf range.

Capacitive coupling can be reduced by coupling to a "cold" point on the tank coil – the end connected to ground or cathode in a single-ended stage. In push-pull circuits having a split-stator capacitor with the rotor grounded for rf, all parts of the tank coil are "hot" at even harmonics, but the center of the coil is "cold" at the fundamental and odd harmonics. If the center of the tank coil, rather than the rotor of the tank capacitor, is grounded through a bypass capacitor the center of the coil is "cold" at all frequencies, but this arrangement is not very desirable because it causes the harmonic currents to flow through the coil rather than the tank capacitor and this increases the harmonic transfer by pure inductive coupling.

With either single-ended or balanced tank circuits the coupling coil should be grounded to the chassis by a short, direct connection as shown in Fig. 16-20. If the coil feeds a balanced line or link, it is preferable to ground its center, but if it feeds a coax line or link one side may be grounded. Coaxial output is much preferable to balanced output, because the harmonics have to stay *inside* a properly installed coax system and tend to be attenuated by the cable before reaching the Transmatch.

At high frequencies – and possibly as low as 14 MHz – capacitive coupling can be greatly reduced by using a shielded coupling coil. The inner conductor of a length of coaxial cable is used to form a one-turn coupling coil. The outer conductor serves as an open-circuited shield around the turn, the shield being grounded to the chassis. The shielding has no effect on the inductive coupling. Because this construction is suitable only for one turn, the coil is not well adapted for use on the lower frequencies where many turns are required for good coupling.

A shielded coupling coil or coaxial output will not prevent stray capacitive coupling to the antenna if harmonic currents can flow over the *outside* of the coax line. In Fig. 16-21, the arrangement at either A or C will allow rf to flow over the outside of the cable to the antenna system. The proper way to use coaxial cable is to shield the transmitter completely, as shown at B, and make sure that the outer conductor of the cable is a continuation of the transmitter shielding. This prevents rf inside the transmitter from getting out by any path except the *inside* of the cable. Harmonics flowing *through* a coax line can be stopped by an antenna coupler or low-pass filter installed in the line.

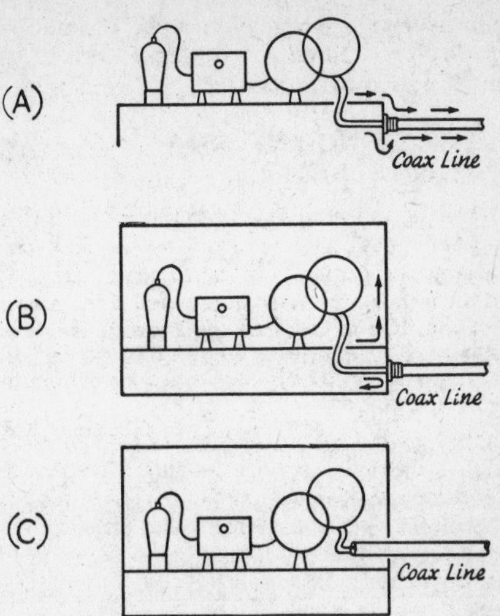

Fig. 16-21 – Right (B) and wrong (A and C) ways to connect a coaxial line to the transmitter. In A or C, harmonic energy coupled by stray capacitance to the outside of the cable will flow without hindrance to the antenna system. In B the energy cannot leave the shield and can flow out only through, not over, the cable.

Low-Pass Filters

A low-pass filter properly installed in a coaxial line, feeding either a matching circuit (antenna coupler) or feeding the antenna directly, will provide very great attenuation of harmonics. When

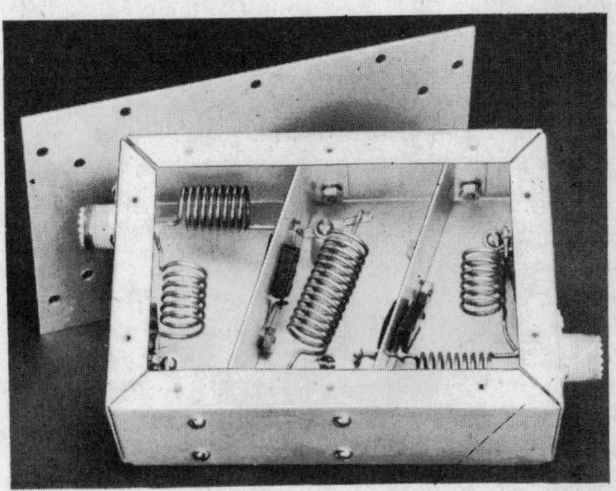

Fig. 16-22 – An inexpensive low-pass filter using silver-mica postage-stamp capacitors. The box is a 2 X 4 X 6 aluminum chassis. Aluminum shields, bent and folded at the sides and bottom for fastening to the chassis, form shields between the filter sections. The diagonal arrangement of the shields provides extra room for the coils and makes it easier to fit the shields in the box, since bending to exact dimensions is not essential. The bottom plate, made from sheet aluminum, extends a half inch beyond the ends of the chassis and is provided with mounting holes in the extensions. It is held on the chassis with sheet-metal screws.

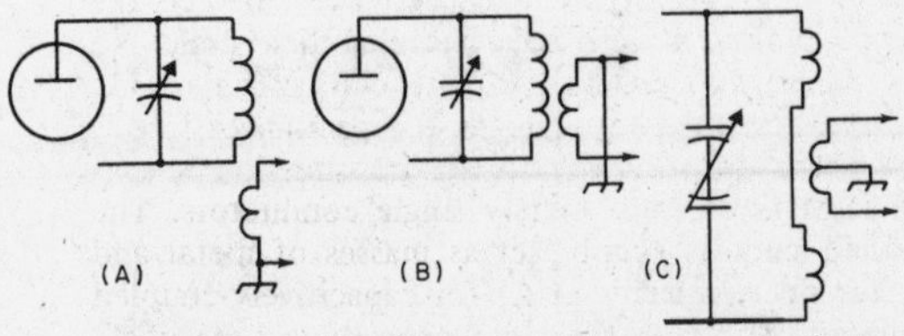

Fig. 16-20 – Methods of coupling and grounding link circuits to reduce capacitive coupling between the tank and link coils. Where the link is wound over one end of the tank coil the side toward the hot end of the tank should be grounded, as shown at B.

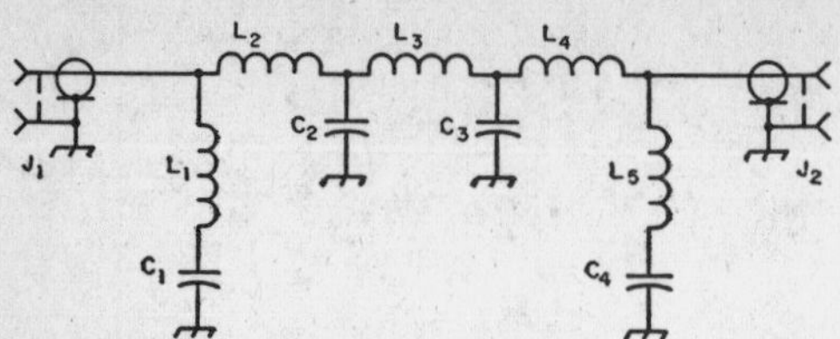

Fig. 16-23 – Low-pass filter circuit. In the table below the letters refer to the following:
A – Using 100- and 70-pF 500-volt silver mica capacitors in parallel for C2 and C3.
B – Using 70- and 50-pF silver mica capacitors in parallel for C2 and C3.
C – Using 100- and 50-pF mica capacitors, 1200-volt (case style CM-45) in parallel for C2 and C3.
D and E – Using variable air capacitors, 500- and 1000-volt rating, adjusted to values given.

	A	B	C	D	E	
Z_o	52	75	52	52	75	ohms
f_c	36	35.5	41	40	40	MHz
f_∞	44.4	47	54	50	50	MHz
f_1	25.5	25.2	29	28.3	28.3	MHz
f_2	32.5	31.8	37.5	36.1	36.1	MHz
C1, C4	50	40	50	46	32	pF
C2, C3	170	120	150	154	106	pF
L1, L5	5 1/2	6	4	5	6 1/2	turns*
L2, L4	8	11	7	7	9 1/2	turns*
L3	9	13	8	8 1/2	11 1/2	turns*

*No. 12 or 14 wire, 1/2-inch ID, 8 tpi.

the main transmission line is of the parallel-conductor type, the coax-coupled matching-circuit arrangement is highly recommended as a means for using a coax low-pass filter.

A low-pass filter will transmit power at the fundamental frequency without appreciable loss if the line in which it is inserted is properly terminated (has a low SWR).At the same time it has large attenuation for all frequencies above the "cutoff" frequency.

Low-pass filters of simple and inexpensive construction for use with transmitters operating below 30 MHz are shown in Fig. 16-22 and 16-24. The former is designed to use mica capacitors of readily available capacitance values, for compactness and low cost. Both use the same circuit, Fig. 16-23; the only difference being in the *L* and *C* values. Technically, they are three-section filters having two full constant-*k* sections and two *m*-derived terminating half-sections, and their attenuation in the 54-88-MHz range varies from over 50 to nearly 70 dB, depending on the frequency and the particular set of values used. At high frequencies the ultimate attenuation will depend somewhat on internal resonant conditions associated with component lead lengths. These leads should be kept as short as possible.

The power that filters using mica capacitors can handle safely is determined by the voltage and

Fig. 16-24 – Low-pass filter using variable capacitors. The unit is housed in two 2 1/4 X 2 1/4 X 5-inch Miniboxes, end to end. The cover should be secured to the box at several points.

current limitations of the capacitors. The power capacity is least at the highest frequency. The unit using postage-stamp silver mica capacitors is capable of handling approximately 50 watts in the 28-MHz band, when working into a properly-matched line, but is good for about 150 watts at 21 MHz and 300 watts at 14 MHz and lower frequencies. A filter with large mica capacitors (case type CM-45) will carry about 250 watts safely at 28 MHz, this rating increasing to 500 watts at 21 MHz and a kilowatt at 14 MHz and lower. If there is an appreciable mismatch between the filter and the line into which it works, these ratings will be considerably decreased, so, in order to avoid capacitor failure, it is highly essential that the line on the output side of the filter be carefully matched.

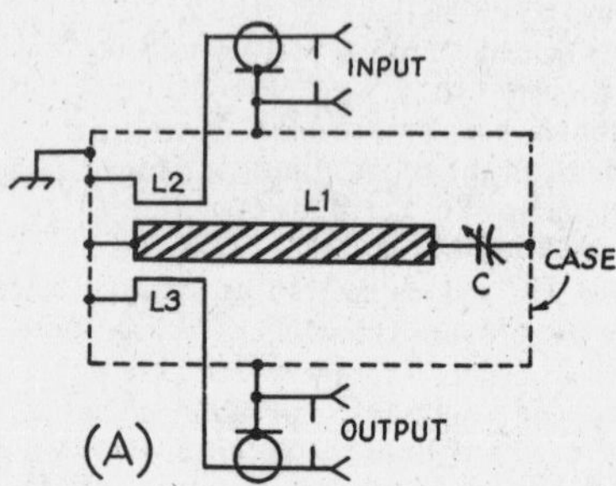

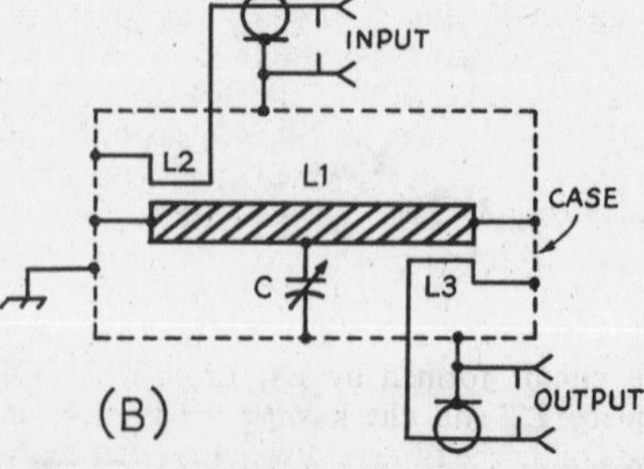

Fig. 16-25 – Equivalent circuits for the strip-line filters. At A, the circuit for the 6- and 2-meter filters are shown. L2 and L3 are the input and output links. These filters are bilaterial, permitting interchanging of the input and output terminals.

At B, the representative circuit for the 220- and 432-MHz filters. These filters are also bilaterial.

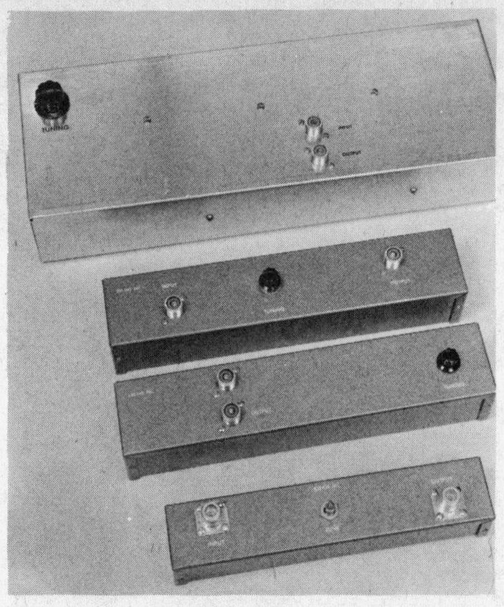

Fig. 16-26 – High-Q strip-line filters for 50 MHz (top), 220, 144 and 420 MHz. Those for the two highest bands are half-wave line circuits. All use standard chassis.

The power capacity of these filters can be increased considerably by substituting rf type fixed capacitors (such as the Centralab 850 series) or variable air capacitors, in which event the power capability will be such as to handle the maximum amateur power on any band. The construction can be modified to accommodate variable air capacitors as shown in Fig. 16-24.

Using fixed capacitors of standard tolerances, there should be little difficulty in getting proper filter operation. A grid-dip meter with an accurate calibration should be used for adjustment of the coils. First, wire up the filter without L2 and L4. Short-circuit J1 at its inside end with a screwdriver or similar conductor, couple the grid-dip meter to L1 and adjust the inductance of L1, by varying the turn spacing, until the circuit resonates at $f\infty$ as given in the table. Do the same thing at the other end of the filter with L5. Then couple the meter to the circuit formed by L3, C2 and C3, and adjust L3 to resonate at the frequency f_1 as given by the table. Then remove L3, install L2 and L4, and adjust L2 to make the circuit formed by L1, L2, C1 and C2 (without the short across J1) resonate at f_2 as given in the table. Do the same with L4 for the circuit formed by L4, L5, C3 and C4. Then replace L3 and check with the grid-dip meter at any coil in the filter; a distinct resonance should be found at or very close to the cutoff frequency, f_c.

FILTERS FOR VHF TRANSMITTERS

High rejection of unwanted frequencies is possible with the tuned-line filters of Fig. 16-25. Examples are shown for each band from 50 through 450 MHz. Construction is relatively simple, and the cost is low. Standard boxes are used, for ease of duplication.

The filter of Fig. 16-27 is selective enough to pass 50-MHz energy and attenuate the 7th harmonic of an 8-MHz oscillator that falls in TV Channel 2. With an insertion loss at 50 MHz of about 1 dB, it can provide up to 40 dB of attenuation to energy at 57 MHz in the same line. This should be more than enough attenuation to take care of the worst situations, provided that the radiation is by way of the transmitter output coax only. The filter will not eliminate interfering energy that gets out from power cables, the ac line, or from the transmitter circuits themselves. It also will do nothing for TVI that results from deficiencies in the TV receiver.

The 50-MHz filter, Fig. 16-27, uses a folded line in order to keep it within the confines of a standard chassis. The case is a 6 X 17 X 3-inch chassis (Bud AC-433) with a cover plate that fastens in place with self-tapping screws. An aluminum partition down the middle of the assembly is 14 inches long, and the full height of the chassis, 3 inches.

The inner conductor of the line is 32 inches long and 13/16 inch wide, of 1/16-inch brass, copper or aluminum. This was made from two pieces of aluminum spliced together to provide the 32-inch length. Splicing seemed to have no ill effect on the circuit Q. The side of the "U" are 2 7/8 inches apart, with the partition at the center. The line is supported on ceramic standoffs. These were shimmed up with sections of hard wood or bakelite rod, to give the required 1 1/2-inch height.

The tuning capacitor is a double-spaced variable (Hammarlund HF-30-X) mounted 1 1/2 inches from the right end of the chassis. Input and output coupling loops are of No. 10 or 12 wire, 10 inches long. Spacing away from the line is adjusted to about 1/4 inch.

The 144-MHz model is housed in a 2 1/4 X 2 1/2 X 12-inch Minibox (Bud CU-2114-A).

One end of the tubing is slotted 1/4 inch deep with a hacksaw. This slot takes a brass angle bracket 1 1/2 inches wide, 1/4 inch high, with a 1/2-inch mounting lip. This 1/4-inch lip is soldered into the tubing slot, and the bracket is then bolted to the end of the box, so as to be centered on the end plate.

The tuning capacitor (Hammarlund HF-15-X) is mounted 1 1/4 inches from the other end of the box, in such a position that the inner conductor can be soldered to the two stator bars.

The two coaxial fittings (SO-239) are 11/16 inch in from each side of the box, 3 1/2 inches from the left end. The coupling loops are No. 12 wire, bent so that each is parallel to the center line of the inner conductor, and about 1/8 inch from its surface. Their cold ends are soldered to the brass mounting bracket.

The 220-MHz filter uses the same size box as the 144-MHz model. The inner conductor is 1/16-inch brass or copper, 5/8 inch wide, just long enough to fold over at each end for bolting to the

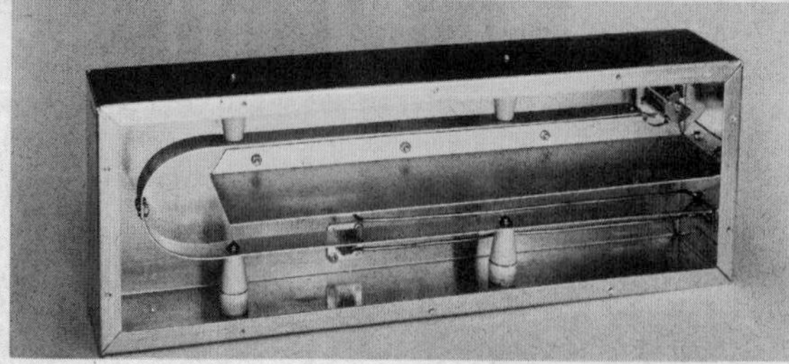

Fig. 16-27 – Interior of the 50-MHz strip line filter. Inner conductor of aluminum strip is bent into U shape, to fit inside a standard 17-inch chassis.

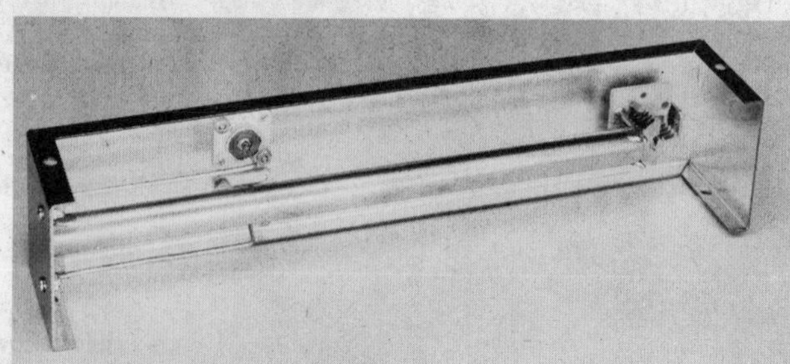

Fig. 16-28 – The 144-MHz filter has an inner conductor of 1/2-inch copper tubing 10 inches long, grounded to the left end of the case and supported at the right end by the tuning capacitor.

Fig. 16-29 – A half-wave strip line is used in the 220-MHz filter. It is grounded at both ends and tuned at the center.

box. It is positioned so that there will be 1/8 inch clearance between it and the rotor plates of the tuning capacitor. The latter is a Hammarlund HF-15-X, mounted slightly off-center in the box, so that its stator plates connect to the exact mid-point of the line. The 5/16-inch mounting hole in the case is 5 1/2 inches from one end. The SO-239 coaxial fittings are 1 inch in from opposite sides of the box, 2 inches from the ends. Their coupling links are No. 14 wire, 1/8 inch from the inner conductor of the line.

The 420-MHz filter is similar in design, using a 1 5/8 X 2 X 10-inch Minibox (Bud CU-2113-A). A half-wave line is used, with disk tuning at the center. The disks are 1/16-inch brass, 1 1/4-inch diameter. The fixed one is centered on the inner conductor, the other mounted on a No. 6 brass lead-screw. This passes through a threaded bushing, which can be taken from the end of a discarded slug-tuned form. An advantage of these is that usually a tension device is included. If there is none, use a lock nut.

Type N coaxial connectors were used on the 420-MHz model. They are 5/8 inch in from each side of the box, and 1 3/8 inches in from the ends. Their coupling links of No. 14 wire are 1/16 inch from the inner conductor.

Adjustment and Use

If you want the filter to work on both transmitting and receiving, connect the filter between antenna line and SWR indicator. With this arrangement you need merely adjust the filter for minimum reflected power reading on the SWR bridge. This should be zero, or close to it, if the antenna is well-matched. The bridge should be used, as there is no way to adjust the filter properly without it. If you insist on trying, adjust for best reception of signals on frequencies close to the ones you expect to transmit on. This works only if the antenna is well matched.

When the filter is properly adjusted (with the SWR bridge) you may find that reception can be improved by retuning the filter. Don't do it, if you want the filter to work best on the job it was intended to do; the rejection of unwanted energy, transmitting or receiving. If you want to improve reception with the filter in the circuit, work on the receiver input circuit. To get maximum power out of the transmitter and into the line, adjust the transmitter output coupling, not the filter. If the effect of the filter on reception bothers you, connect it in the line from the antenna relay to the transmitter only.

SUMMARY

The methods of harmonic elimination outlined in this chapter have been proved beyond doubt to be effective even under highly unfavorable conditions. It must be emphasized once more, however, that the problem must be solved one step at a time, and the procedure must be in logical order. It cannot be done properly without two items of simple equipment: a grid-dip meter and wavemeter covering the TV bands, and a dummy antenna.

To summarize:

1) Take a critical look at the transmitter on the basis of the design considerations outlined under "Reducing Harmonic Generation."

2) Check all circuits, particularly those connected with the final amplifier, with the grid-dip meter to determine whether there are any resonances in the TV bands. If so, rearrange the circuits so the resonances are moved out of the critical frequency region.

3) Connect the transmitter to the dummy antenna and check with the wavemeter for the presence of harmonics on leads and around the transmitter enclosure. Seal off the weak spots in the shielding and filter the leads until the wavemeter shows no indication at any harmonic frequency.

4) At this stage, check for interference with a TV receiver. If there is interference, determine the cause by the methods described previously and apply the recommended remedies until the interference disappears.

5) When the transmitter is completely clean on the dummy antenna, connect it to the regular antenna and check for interference on the TV receiver. If the interference is not bad, a Transmatch or matching circuit installed as previously described should clear it up. Alternatively, a low-pass filter may be used. If neither the Transmatch nor filter makes any difference in the interference, the evidence is strong that the interference, at least in part, is being caused by receiver overloading because of the strong fundamental-frequency field about the TV antenna and receiver. A Transmatch and/or filter, installed as described above, will invariably make a difference in the intensity of the interference if the interference is caused by transmitter harmonics alone.

6) If there is still interference after installing the Transmatch and/or filter, and the evidence shows that it is probably caused by a harmonic, more attenuation is needed. A more elaborate filter may be necessary. However, it is well at this stage to assume that part of the interference may be caused by receiver overloading, and take steps to alleviate such a condition before trying highly-elaborate filters and traps on the transmitter.

HARMONICS BY RECTIFICATION

Even though the transmitter is completely free from harmonic output it is still possible for interference to occur because of harmonics generated outside the transmitter. These result from rectification of fundamental-frequency currents induced in conductors in the vicinity of the transmitting antenna. Rectification can take place at any point where two conductors are in poor electrical contact, a condition that frequently exists in plumbing, downspouting, BX cables crossing each other, and numerous other places in the ordinary residence. It also can occur at any exposed vacuum tubes in the station, in power supplies, speech equipment, etc., that may not be enclosed in the shielding about the rf circuits. Poor joints anywhere in the antenna system are especially bad, and rectification also may take place in the contacts of antenna changeover relays. Another common cause is overloading the front end of the communications receiver when it is used with a separate antenna (which will radiate the harmonics generated in the first tube) for break-in.

Rectification of this sort will not only cause harmonic interference but also is frequently responsible for cross-modulation effects. It can be detected in greater or less degree in most locations, but fortunately the harmonics thus generated are not usually of high amplitude. However, they can cause considerable interference in the immediate vicinity in fringe areas, especially when operation is in the 28-MHz band. The amplitude decreases rapidly with the order of the harmonic, the second and third being the worst. It is ordinarily found that even in cases where destructive interference results from 28-MHz operation the interference is comparatively mild from 14 MHz, and is negligible at still lower frequencies.

Nothing can be done at either the transmitter or receiver when rectification occurs. The remedy is to find the source and eliminate the poor contact either by separating the conductors or bonding them together. A crystal wavemeter (tuned to the fundamental frequency) is useful for hunting the source, by showing which conductors are carrying rf and, comparatively, how much.

Interference of this kind is frequently intermittent since the rectification efficiency will vary with vibration, the weather, and so on. The possibility of corroded contacts in the TV receiving antenna should not be overlooked, especially if it has been up a year or more.

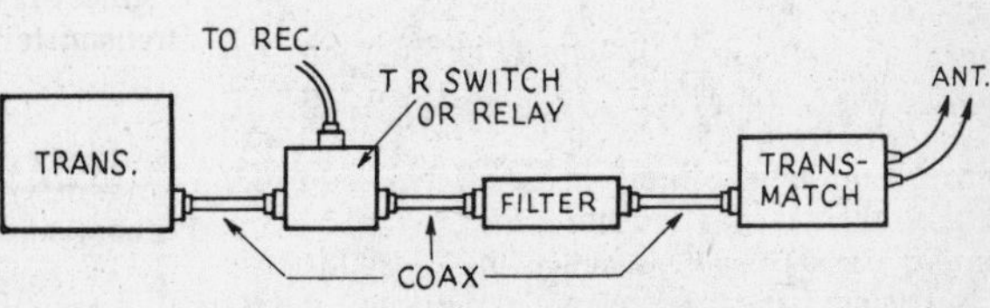

Fig. 16-30 – The proper method of installing a low-pass filter between the transmitter and a Transmatch. If the antenna is fed through coax, the Transmatch can be eliminated, but the transmitter and filter must be completely shielded. If a TR switch is used, it should be installed between the transmitter and low-pass filter. TR switches can generate harmonics themselves, so the low-pass filter should follow the TR switch.

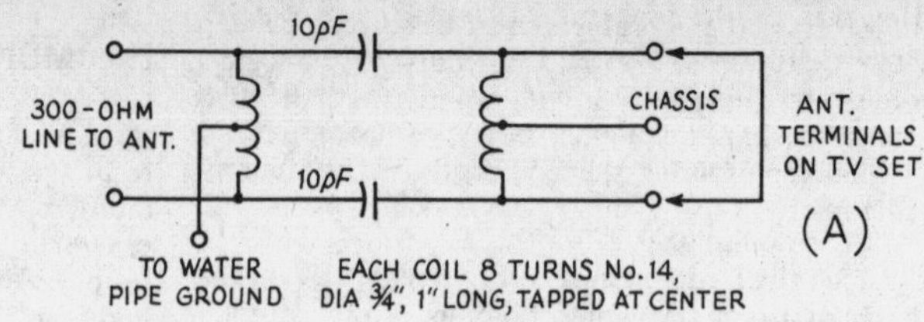

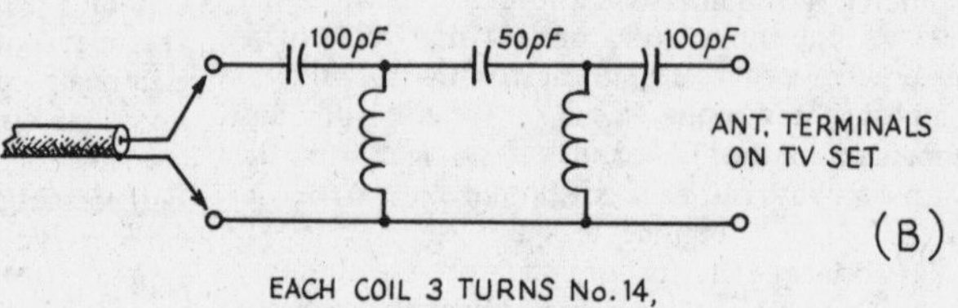

Fig. 16-31 – High-pass filters for installation at the TV receiver antenna terminals. A – balanced filter for 300-ohm line. B – for 75-ohm coaxial line. *Important:* Do not use a direct ground on the chassis of a transformerless receiver. Ground through a .001-μF mica capacitor.

TV RECEIVER DEFICIENCIES

When a television receiver is quite close to the transmitter, the intense rf signal from the transmitter's fundamental may overload one or more of the receiver circuits to produce spurious responses that cause interference.

If the overload is moderate, the interference is of the same nature as harmonic interference; it is caused by harmonics generated in the early stages of the receiver and, since it occurs only on channels harmonically related to the transmitting frequency, it is difficult to distinguish from harmonics actually radiated by the transmitter. In such cases additional harmonic suppression at the transmitter will do no good, but any means taken at the receiver to reduce the strength of the amateur signal reaching the first tube will effect an improvement. With very severe overloading, interference also will occur on channels *not* harmonically related to the transmitting frequency, so such cases are easily identified.

Cross-Modulation

Upon some circumstances overloading will result in cross-modulation or mixing of the amateur signal with that from a local fm or TV station. For example, a 14-MHz signal can mix with a 92-MHz fm station to produce a beat at 78 MHz and cause interference in Channel 5, or with a TV station on Channel 5 to cause interference in Channel 3. Neither of the channels interfered with is in harmonic relationship to 14 MHz. Both signals have to be on the air for the interference to occur, and eliminating either at the TV receiver will eliminate the interference.

There are many combinations of this type, depending on the band in use and the local frequency assignments to fm and TV stations. The interfering frequency is equal to the amateur fundamental frequency either added to or subtracted from the frequency of some local station, and when interference occurs in a TV channel that is not harmonically related to the amateur transmitting frequency the possibilities in such frequency combinations should be investigated.

I-f Interference

Some TV receivers do not have sufficient selectivity to prevent strong signals in the intermediate-frequency range from forcing their way through the front end and getting into the i-f amplifier. The once-standard intermediate frequency of, roughly, 21 to 27 MHz, is subject to interference from the fundamental-frequency output of transmitters operating in the 21-MHz band. Transmitters on 28 MHz sometimes will cause this type of interference as well.

A form of i-f interference peculiar to 50-MHz operation near the low edge of the band occurs with some receivers having the standard "41-MHz" i-f, which has the sound carrier at 41.25 MHz and the picture carrier at 45.75 MHz. A 50-MHz signal that forces its way into the i-f system of the receiver will beat with the i-f picture carrier to give a spurious signal on or near the i-f sound carrier, even though the interfering signal is not actually in the nominal passband of the i-f amplifier.

There is a type of i-f interference unique to the 144-MHz band in localities where certain uhf TV channels are in operation, affecting only those TV receivers in which double-conversion type plug-in uhf tuning strips are used. The design of these strips involves a first intermediate frequency that varies with the TV channel to be received and, depending on the particular strip design, this first i-f may be in or close to the 144-MHz amateur band. Since there is comparatively little selectivity in the TV signal-frequency circuits ahead of the first i-f, a signal from a 144-MHz transmitter will "ride into" the i-f, even when the receiver is at a considerable distance from the transmitter. The channels that can be affected by this type of i-f interference are:

Receivers with 21-MHz second i-f	*Receivers with 41-MHz second i-f*
Channels 14-18, incl.	Channels 20-25, incl.
Channels 41-48, incl.	Channels 51-58, incl.
Channels 69-77, incl.	Channels 82 and 83.

If the receiver is not close to the transmitter, a trap of the type shown in Fig. 16-33 will be effective.

However, if the separation is small the 144-MHz signal will be picked up directly on the receiver circuits and the best solution is to readjust the strip oscillator so that the first i-f is moved to a frequency not in the vicinity of the 144-MHz band. This has to be done by a competent technician.

I-f interference is easily identified since it occurs on all channels – although sometimes the intensity varies from channel to channel – and the cross-hatch pattern it causes will rotate when the receiver's fine-tuning control is varied. When the interference is caused by a harmonic, overloading, or cross modulation, the structure of the interference pattern does not change (its intensity may change) as the fine-tuning control is varied.

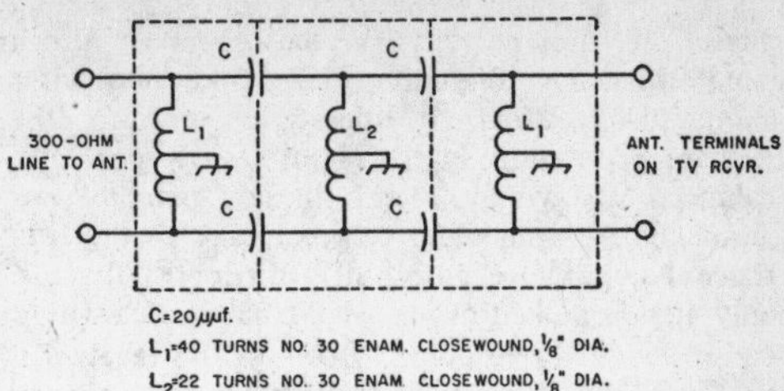

Fig. 16-32 – Another type of high-pass filter for 300-ohm line. The coils may be wound on 1/8-inch diameter plastic knitting needles. *Important:* Do not use a direct ground on the chassis of a transformerless receiver. Ground through a .001-μF mica capacitor.

High-Pass Filters

In all of the above cases the interference can be eliminated if the fundamental signal strength can be reduced to a level that the receiver can handle. To accomplish this with signals on bands below 30 MHz, the most satisfactory device is a high-pass filter having a cutoff frequency between 30 and 54 MHz, installed at the tuner input terminals of the receiver. Circuits that have proved effective are shown in Figs. 16-30 and 16-31. Fig. 16-30 has one more section than the filters of Fig. 16-31 and as a consequence has somewhat better cutoff characteristics. All the circuits given are designed to have little or no effect on the TV signals but will attenuate all signals lower in frequency than about 40 MHz. These filters preferably should be constructed in some sort of shielding container, although shielding is not always necessary. The dashed lines in Fig. 16-32 show how individual filter coils can be shielded from each other. The capacitors can be tubular ceramic units centered in holes in the partitions that separate the coils.

Simple high-pass filters cannot always be applied successfully in the case of 50-MHz transmissions, because they do not have sufficiently-sharp cutoff characteristics to give both good attenuation at 50-54 MHz and no attenuation above 54 MHz. A more elaborate design capable of giving the required sharp cutoff has been described (Ladd, "50-MHz TVI – Its Causes and Cures," *QST*, June and July, 1954). This article also contains other information useful in coping with the TVI problems peculiar to 50-MHz operation. As an alternative to such a filter, a high-*Q* wave trap tuned to the transmitting frequency may be used, suffering only the disadvantage that it is quite selective and therefore will protect a receiver from overloading over only a small range of transmitting frequencies in the 50-MHz band. A trap of this type is shown in Fig. 16-33. These "suck-out" traps, while absorbing energy at the frequency to which they are tuned, do not affect the receiver operation otherwise. The assembly should be mounted near the input terminals of the TV tuner and its case should be grounded to the TV set chassis. The traps should be tuned for minimum TVI at the transmitter operating frequency. An insulated tuning tool should be used for adjustment of the trimmer capacitors, since they are at a "hot" point and will show considerable body-capacitance effect.

High-pass filters are available commercially at moderate prices. In this connection, it should be understood by all parties concerned that while an amateur is responsible for *harmonic* radiation from his transmitter, it is no part of his responsibility to pay for or install filters, wave traps, etc. that may be required at the receiver to prevent interference caused by his *fundamental* frequency. Proper installation usually requires that the filter be installed right at the input terminals of the rf tuner of the TV set and not merely at the external antenna terminals, which may be at a considerable distance from the tuner. The question of cost is one to be settled between the set owner and the organization with which he deals.

Some of the larger manufacturers of TV receivers have instituted arrangements for cooperating with the set dealer in installing high-pass filters at no cost to the receiver owner. FCC-sponsored TVI Committees, now operating in many cities, have all the information necessary for effectuating such arrangements. To find out whether such a committee is functioning in your community, write to the FCC field office having jurisdiction over your location. A list of the field offices is contained in *The Radio Amateur's License Manual,* published by ARRL.

If the fundamental signal is getting into the receiver by way of the line cord a line filter such as that shown in Fig. 16-1 may help. To be most effective it should be installed inside the receiver chassis at the point where the cord enters, making the ground connections directly to chassis at this point. It may not be so helpful if placed between the line plug and the wall socket unless the rf is actually picked up on the house wiring rather than on the line cord itself.

Antenna Installation

Usually, the transmission line between the TV receiver and the actual TV antenna will pick up a great deal more energy from a nearby transmitter than the television receiving antenna itself. The currents induced on the TV transmission line in this case are of the "parallel" type, where the phase of the current is the same in both conductors. The line simply acts like two wires connected together to operate as one. If the receiver's antenna input circuit were perfectly balanced it would reject these "parallel" or "unbalance" signals and respond only to the true transmission-line ("push-pull") currents; that is, only signals picked up on the actual atenna would cause a receiver response. However, no receiver is perfect in this respect, and many TV receivers will respond strongly to such parallel currents. The result is that the signals from a nearby amateur transmitter are much more intense at the first stage in the TV receiver than they would be if the receiver response were confined entirely to energy picked up on the TV antenna alone. This situation can be improved by using shielded transmission line – coax or, in the balanced form, "twinax" – for the receiving installation. For best results the line should terminate in a coax fitting on the receiver chassis, but if this is not possible the shield should be grounded to the chassis right at the antenna terminals.

The use of shielded transmission line for the receiver also will be helpful in reducing response to harmonics actually being radiated from the transmitter or transmitting antenna. In most receiving installations the transmission line is very much longer than the antenna itself, and is consequently far more exposed to the harmonic fields from the transmitter. Much of the harmonic pickup, therefore, is on the receiving transmission line when the transmitter and receiver are quite close together. Shielded line, plus relocation of either the transmitting or receiving antenna to take advantage of directive effects, often will result in reducing overloading, as well as harmonic pickup, to a level that does not interfere with reception.

UHF TELEVISION

Harmonic TVI in the uhf TV band is far less troublesome than in the vhf band. Harmonics from transmitters operating below 30 MHz are of such high order that they would normally be expected to be quite weak; in addition, the components, circuit conditions and construction of low-frequency transmitters are such as to tend to prevent very strong harmonics from being generated in this region. However, this is not true of amateur vhf transmitters, particularly those working in the 144-MHz and higher bands. Here the problem is quite similar to that of the low vhf TV band with respect to transmitters operating below 30 MHz.

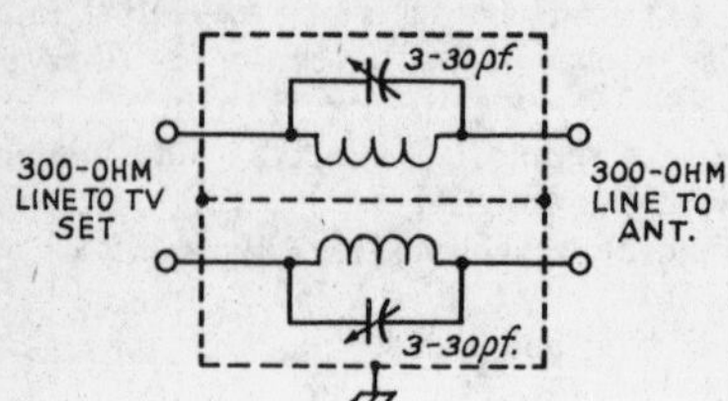

Fig. 16-33 – Parallel-tuned traps for installation in the 300-ohm line to the TV set. The traps should be mounted in an aluminum Minibox with a shield partition between them, as shown. For 50 MHz, the coils should have 9 turns of No. 16 enamel wire, close wound to a diameter of 1/2 inch. The 144-MHz traps should contain coils with a total of 6 turns of the same type wire, close-wound to a diameter of 1/4 inch. Traps of this type can be used to combat fundamental-overload TVI on the lower-frequency bands as well.

TABLE 16-I

Harmonic Relationship – Amateur VHF Bands and UHF TV Channels

Amateur Band	*Harmonic*	*Fundamental Freq. Range*	*Channel Affected*
144 MHz	4th	144.0–144.5	31
		144.5–146.0	32
		146.0–147.5	33
		147.5–148.0	34
	5th	144.0–144.4	55
		144.4–145.6	56
		145.6–146.8	57
		146.8–148.0	58
	6th	144.0–144.33	79
		144.33–145.33	80
		145.33–147.33	81
		147.33–148.0	82
220 MHz	3rd	220–220.67	45
		220.67–222.67	46
		222.67–224.67	47
		224.67–225	48
	4th	220–221	82
		221–222.5	83
420 MHz	2nd	420–421	75
		421–424	76
		424–427	77
		427–430	78
		430–433	79
		433–436	80

There is one highly favorable factor in uhf TV that does not exist in the most of the vhf TV band: If harmonics are radiated, it is possible to move the transmitter frequency sufficiently (within the amateur band being used) to avoid interfering with a channel that may be in use in the locality. By restricting operation to a portion of the amateur band that will not result in harmonic interference, it is possible to avoid the necessity for taking extraordinary precautions to prevent harmonic radiation.

The frequency assignment for uhf television consists of seventy 6-Megahertz channels (Nos. 14 to 83, inclusive) beginning at 470 MHz and ending at 890 MHz. The harmonics from amateur bands above 50-MHz span the uhf channels as shown in Table 16-1. Since the assignment plan calls for a minimum separation of six channels between any two stations in one locality, there is ample opportunity to choose a fundamental frequency that will move a harmonic out of range of a local TV frequency.

COLOR TELEVISION

The color TV signal includes a subcarrier spaced 3.58 MHz from the regular picture carrier (or 4.83 MHz from the low edge of the channel) for transmitting the color information. Harmonics which fall in the color subcarrier region can be epected to cause break-up of color in the received picture. This modifies the chart of Fig. 16-5 to introduce another "severe" region centering around 4.8 MHz measured from the low-frequency edge of the channel. Hence with color television reception there is less opportunity to avoid harmonic interference by choice of operating frequency. In other respects the problem of eliminating interference is the same as with black-and-white television.

INTERFERENCE FROM TV RECEIVERS

The TV picture tube is swept horizontally by the electron beam 15,750 times per second, using a wave shape that has very high harmonic content. The harmonics are of appreciable amplitude even at frequencies as high as 30 MHz, and when radiated from the receiver can cause considerable interference to reception in the amateur bands. While measures to suppress radiation of this nature are required by FCC in current receivers, many older sets have had no such treatment. The interference takes the form of rather unstable, ac-modulated signals spaced at intervals of 15.75 kHz.

Studies have shown that the radiation takes place principally in three ways, in order of their importance: (1) from the ac line, through stray coupling to sweep circuits; (2) from the antenna system, through similar coupling; (3) directly from the picture tube and sweep-circuit wiring. Line radiation often can be reduced by bypassing the ac line cord to the chassis at the point of entry, although this is not completely effective in all cases since the coupling may take place outside the chassis beyond the point where the bypassing is done. Radiation from the antenna is usually suppressed by installing a high-pass filter on the receiver. The direct radiation requires shielding of high-potential leads and, in some receivers, additional bypassing in the sweep circuit; in severe cases, it may be necessary to line the cabinet with screening or similar shielding material.

Incidental radiation of this type from TV and broadcast receivers, when of sufficient intensity to cause serious interference to other radio services (such as amateur), is covered by Part 15 of the FCC rules. When such interference is caused, the user of the receiver is obligated to take steps to eliminate it. The owner of an offending receiver should be advised to contact the source from which the receiver was purchased for appropriate modification of the receiving installation. TV receiver dealers can obtain the necessary information from the set manufacturer.

It is usually possible to reduce interference very considerably, without modifying the TV receiver, simply by having a good amateur-band receiving installation. The principles are the same as those used in reducing "hash" and other noise – use a good antenna, such as the transmitting antenna, for reception; install it as far as possible from ac circuits; use a good feeder system such as a properly balanced two-wire line or coax with the outer conductor grounded; use coax input to the receiver, with a matching circuit if necessary; and check the receiver to make sure that it does not pick up signals or noise with the antenna disconnected.

Chapter 17

Test Equipment and Measurements

Measurement and testing seemingly go hand in hand, but it is useful to make a distinction between "measuring" and "test" equipment. The former is commonly considered to be capable of giving a meaningful quantitative result. For the latter a simple indication of "satisfactory" or "unsatisfactory" may suffice; in any event, the accurate calibration associated with real measuring equipment is seldom necessary, for simple test apparatus.

Certain items of measuring equipment that are useful to amateurs are readily available in kit form, at prices that represent a genuine saving over the cost of identical parts. Included are volt-ohm-milliammeter combinations, vacuum-tube and transistor voltmeters, oscilloscopes, and the like. The coordination of electrical and mechanical design, components, and appearance make it far preferable to purchase such equipment than to attempt to build one's own.

However, some test gear is either not available or can easily be built. This chapter considers the principles of the more useful types of measuring equipment and concludes with the descriptions of several pieces that not only can be built satisfactorily at home but which will facilitate the operation of the amateur station.

THE DIRECT-CURRENT INSTRUMENT

In measuring instruments and test equipment suitable for amateur purposes the ultimate "readout" is generally based on a measurement of direct current. A meter for measuring dc uses electromagnetic means to deflect a pointer over a calibrated scale in proportion to the current flowing through the instrument.

In the **D'Arsonval** type a coil of wire, to which the pointer is attached, is pivoted between the poles of a permanent magnet, and when current flows through the coil it sets up a magnetic field that interacts with the field of the magnet to cause the coil to turn. The design of the instrument is usually such as to make the pointer deflection directly proportional to the current.

A less expensive type of instrument is the **moving-vane** type, in which a pivoted soft-iron vane is pulled into a coil of wire by the magnetic field set up when current flows through the coil. The farther the vane extends into the coil the greater the magnetic pull on it, for a given change in current, so this type of instrument does not have "linear" deflection – the intervals of equal current are crowded together at the low-current end and spread out at the high-current end of the scale.

Current Ranges

The **sensitivity** of an instrument is usually expressed in terms of the current required for full-scale deflection of the pointer. Although a very wide variety of ranges is available, the meters of interest in amateur work have basic "movements" that will give maximum deflection with currents measured in microamperes or milliamperes. They are called **microammeters** and **milliammeters**, respectively.

Thanks to the relationships between current, voltage, and resistance expressed by Ohm's Law, it becomes possible to use a single low-range instrument – e.g., 1 milliampere or less full-scale pointer deflection – for a variety of direct-current measurements. Through its ability to measure current, the instrument can also be used indirectly to measure voltage. Likewise, a measurement of *both* current and voltage will obviously yield a value of resistance. These measurement functions are often combined in a single instrument – the **volt-ohm-milliammeter** or "VOM", a multirange meter that is one of the most useful pieces of measuring and test equipment an amateur can possess.

Accuracy

The accuracy of a dc meter of the D'Arsonval type is specified by the manufacturer. A common specification is "2 percent of full scale," meaning that a 0-100 microammeter, for example, will be correct to within 2 microamperes at any part of the scale. There are very few cases in amateur work where accuracy greater than this is needed. However, when the instrument is part of a more complex measuring circuit, the design and components of which *all* can cause error, the *overall* accuracy of the complete device is always less.

EXTENDING THE CURRENT RANGE

Because of the way current divides between two resistances in parallel, it is possible to increase the range (more specifically, to decrease the sensitivity) of a dc micro- or milliammeter to any desired extent. The meter itself has an inherent resistance – its **internal resistance** – which determines the full-scale current through it when its rated voltage is applied. (This rated voltage is of the order of a few millivolts.) By connecting an

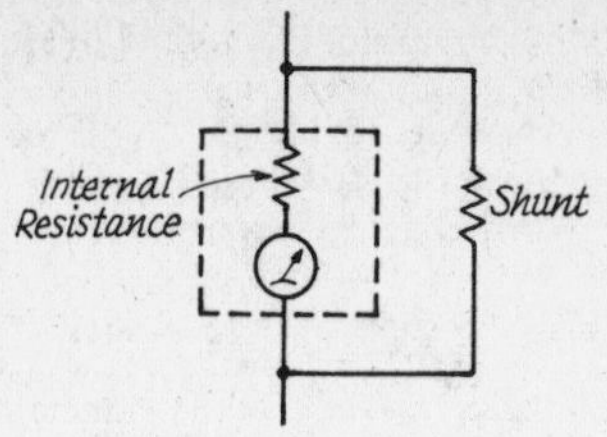

Fig. 17-1 – Use of a shunt to extend the calibration range of a current-reading instrument.

external resistance in parallel with the internal resistance, as in Fig. 17-1, the current will divide between the two, with the meter responding only to that part of the current which flows through the internal resistance of its movement. Thus it reads only part of the total current; the effect is to make more total current necessary for a full-scale meter reading. The added resistance is called a **shunt.**

It is necessary to know the meter's internal resistance before the required value for a shunt can be calculated. It may vary from a few ohms to a few hundred, with the higher resistance values associated with higher sensitivity. When known, it can be used in the formula below to determine the required shunt for a given current multiplication:

$$R = \frac{R_m}{n - 1}$$

where R is the shunt, R_m is the internal resistance of the meter, and n is the factor by which the original meter scale is to be multiplied.

Making Shunts

Homemade shunts can be constructed from any of various special kinds of resistance wire, or from ordinary copper wire if no resistance wire is available. The Copper Wire Table in this *Handbook* gives the resistance per 1000 feet for various sizes of copper wire. After computing the resistance required, determine the smallest wire size that will carry the full-scale current (250 circular mils per ampere is a satisfactory figure for this purpose). Measure off enough wire to provide the required resistance.

THE VOLTMETER

If a large resistance is connected in *series* with a current-reading meter, as in Fig. 17-2, the current

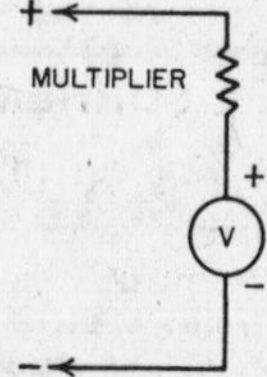

Fig. 17-2 – A voltmeter is a current-indicating instrument in series with a high resistance, the "multiplier."

multiplied by the resistance will be the voltage drop across the resistance, which is known as a **multiplier.** An instrument used in this way is calibrated in terms of the voltage drop across the multiplier resistor, and is called a **voltmeter.**

Sensitivity

Voltmeter sensitivity is usually expressed in **ohms per volt**, meaning that the meter's *full-scale* reading multiplied by the sensitivity will give the total resistance of the voltmeter. For example, the resistance of a 1000-ohms-per-volt voltmeter is 1000 times the full-scale calibration voltage, and by Ohm's Law the current required for full-scale deflection is 1 milliampere. A sensitivity of 20,000 ohms per volt, a commonly used value, means that the instrument is a 50-microampere meter.

The higher the resistance of the voltmeter the more accurate the measurements in high-resistance circuits. This is because in such a circuit the current flowing through the voltmeter will cause a change in the voltage between the points across which the meter is connected, compared with the voltage with the meter absent, as shown in Fig. 17-3.

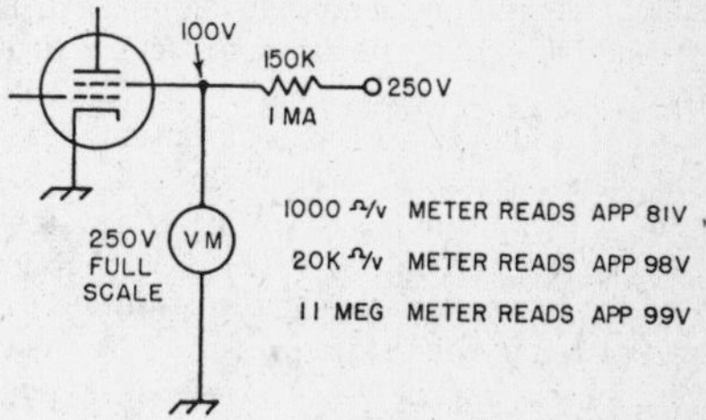

Fig. 17-3 – Effect of voltmeter resistance on accuracy of readings. It is assumed that the dc resistance of the screen circuit is constant at 100 kilohms. The actual current and voltage without the voltmeter connected are 1 mA and 100 volts. The voltmeter readings will differ because the different types of meters draw different amounts of current through the 150-kilohm resistor.

Multipliers

The required multiplier resistance is found by dividing the desired full-scale voltage by the current, in amperes, required for full-scale deflection of the meter alone. Strictly, the internal resistance of the meter should be subtracted from the value so found, but this is seldom necessary (except perhaps for very low ranges) because the meter resistance will be negligibly small compared with the multiplier resistance. An exception is when the instrument is already a voltmeter and is provided with an internal multiplier, in which case the multiplier resistance required to extend the range is

$$R = R_m(n - 1)$$

where R is the multiplier resistance, R_m is the total resistance of the instrument itself, and n is the factor by which the scale is to be multiplied. For example, if a 1000-ohms-per-volt voltmeter having a calibrated range of 0-10 volts is to be extended to 1000 volts, R_m is 1000 X 10 = 10,000 ohms, n is 1000/10 = 100, and R = 10,000 (100 − 1) = 990,000 ohms.

When extending the range of a voltmeter or converting a low-range meter into a voltmeter, the rated accuracy of the instrument is retained only when the multiplier resistance is precise. Precision wire-wound resistors are used in the multipliers of high-quality instruments. These are relatively expensive, but the home constructor can do quite well with 1-percent-tolerance composition resistors. They should be "derated" when used for this purpose – that is, the actual power dissipated in the resistor should not be more than 1/4 to 1/2 the rated dissipation – and care should be used to avoid overheating the body of the resistor when soldering to the leads. These precautions will help prevent permanent change in the resistance of the unit.

Ordinary composition resistors are generally furnished in 10- or 5-percent tolerance ratings. If possible errors of this order can be accepted, resistors of this type may be used as multipliers. They should be operated below the rated power dissipation figure, in the interests of long-time stability.

DC MEASUREMENT CIRCUITS

Current Measurement with a Voltmeter

A current-measuring instrument should have very low resistance compared with the resistance of the circuit being measured; otherwise, inserting the instrument will cause the current to differ from its value with the instrument out of the circuit. (This may not matter if the instrument is left permanently in the circuit.) However, the resistance of many circuits in radio equipment is quite high and the circuit operation is affected little, if at all, by adding as much as a few hundred ohms in series. In such cases the voltmeter method of measuring current, shown in Fig. 17-4, is frequently convenient. A voltmeter (or low-range milliammeter provided with a multiplier and operating as a voltmeter) having a full-scale voltage range of a few volts is used to measure the voltage drop across a suitable value of resistance acting as a shunt.

The value of shunt resistance must be calculated from the known or estimated maximum current expected in the circuit (allowing a safe margin) and the voltage required for full-scale deflection of the meter with its multiplier.

Power

Power in direct-current circuits is determined by measuring the current and voltage. When these are known, the power is equal to the voltage in volts multiplied by the current in amperes. If the current is measured with a milliammeter, the reading of the instrument must be divided by 1000 to convert it to amperes.

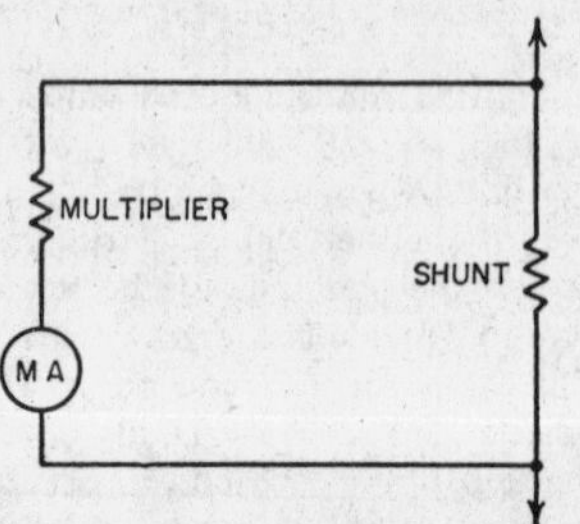

Fig. 17-4 – Voltmeter method of measuring current. This method permits using relatively large values of resistance in the shunt, standard values of fixed resistors frequently being usable. If the multiplier resistance is 20 (or more) times the shunt resistance, the error in assuming that all the current flows through the shunt will not be of consequence in most practical applications.

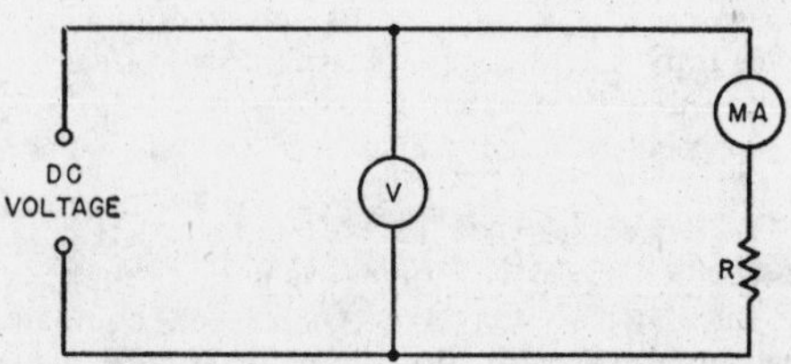

Fig. 17-5 – Measurement of power requires both current and voltage measurements; once these values are known the power is equal to the product – P = EI. The same circuit can be used for measurement of an unknown resistance.

The setup for measuring power is shown in Fig. 17-5, where R is any dc "load," not necessarily an actual resistor.

Resistance

Obviously, if both voltage and current are measured in a circuit such as that in Fig. 17-5 the value of resistance R (in case it is unknown) can be calculated from Ohm's Law. For accurate results, the internal resistance of the ammeter or milliammeter, MA, should be very low compared with the resistance, R, being measured, since the voltage read by the voltmeter, V, is the voltage across MA and R in series. The instruments and the dc voltage should be chosen so that the readings are in the upper half of the scale, if possible, since the percentage error is less in this region.

THE OHMMETER

Although Fig. 17-5 suffices for occasional resistance measurements, it is inconvenient when frequent measurements over a wide range of resistance are to be made. The device generally used for this purpose is the **ohmmeter.** This consists fundamentally of a voltmeter (or milliammeter, depending on the circuit used) and a small dry battery, the meter being calibrated so the value of an unknown resistance can be read

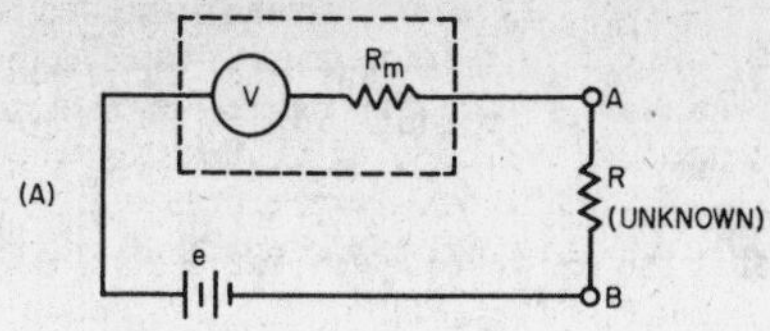

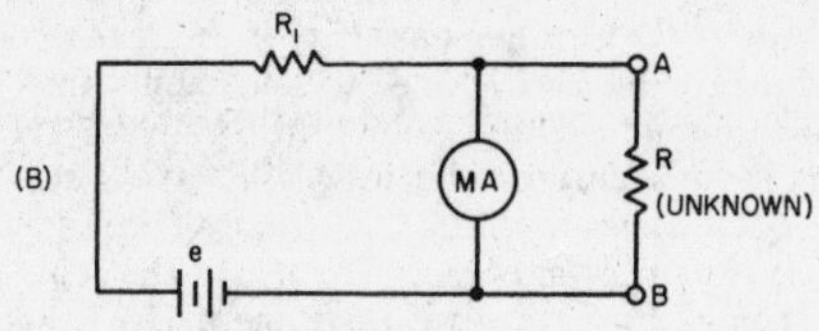

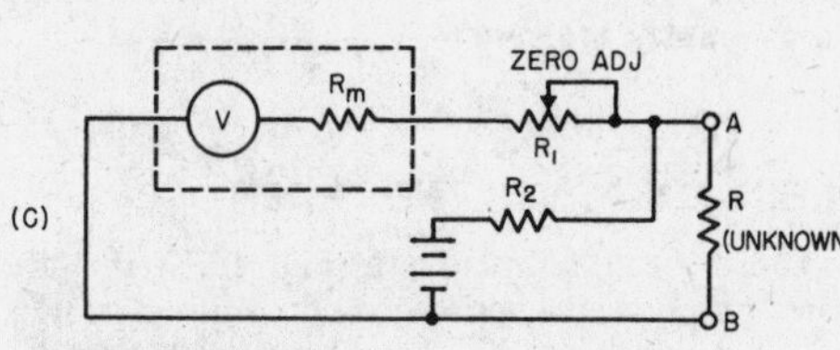

Fig. 17-6 – Ohmmeter circuits. Values are discussed in the text.

directly from the scale. Typical ohmmeter circuits are shown in Fig. 17-6. In the simplest type, shown in Fig. 17-6A, the meter and battery are connected in series with the unknown resistance. If a given deflection is obtained with terminals *A-B* shorted, inserting the resistance to be measured will cause the meter reading to decrease. When the resistance of the voltmeter is known, the following formula can be applied:

$$R = \frac{eR_m}{E} - R_m$$

where R is the resistance to be found,
e is the voltage applied (A-B shorted),
E is the voltmeter reading with R connected, and
R_m is the resistance of the voltmeter.

The circuit of Fig. 17-6A is not suited to measuring low values of resistance (below a hundred ohms or so) with a high-resistance voltmeter. For such measurements the circuit of Fig. 17-6B can be used. The unknown resistance is

$$R = \frac{I_2 R_m}{I_1 - I_2}$$

where R is the unknown,
R_m is the internal resistance of the milliammeter,
I_1 is the current with R disconnected from terminals A-B, and
I_2 is the current with R connected.

The formula is based on the assumption that the current in the complete circuit will be essentially constant whether or not the "unknown" terminals are short-circuited. This requires that R1 be very large compared with R_m – e.g., 3000 ohms for a 1-mA meter having an internal resistance of perhaps 50 ohms. A 3-volt battery would be necessary in this case in order to obtain a full-scale deflection with the "unknown" terminals open. R1 can be an adjustable resistor, to permit setting the open-terminals current to exact full scale.

A third circuit for measuring resistance is shown in Fig. 17-6C. In this case a high-resistance voltmeter is used to measure the voltage drop across a reference resistor, R2, when the unknown resistor is connected so that current flows through it, R2 and the battery in series. By suitable choice of R2 (low values for low-resistance, high values for high-resistance unknowns) this circuit will give equally good results on all resistance values in the range from one ohm to several megohms, provided that the voltmeter resistance, R_m, is always very high (50 times or more) compared with the resistance of R2. A 20,000-ohm-per-volt instrument (50-μA movement) is generally used. Assuming that the current through the voltmeter is negligible compared with the current through R2, the formula for the unknown is

$$R = \frac{eR2}{E} - R2$$

where R and $R2$ are as shown in Fig. 17-6C,
e is the voltmeter reading with A-B shorted, and
E is the voltmeter reading with R connected.

The "zero adjuster," R_1, is used to set the voltmeter reading exactly to full scale when the meter is calibrated in ohms. A 10,000-ohm variable resistor is suitable with a 20,000-ohms-per-volt meter. The battery voltage is usually 3 volts for ranges up to 100,000 ohms or so and 6 volts for higher ranges.

BRIDGE CIRCUITS

An important class of measurement circuits is the **bridge**, in which, essentially, a desired result is obtained by balancing the voltages at two different points in the circuit against each other so that there is zero potential difference between them. A voltmeter bridged between the two points will read zero (**null**) when this balance exists, but will indicate some definite value of voltage when the bridge is not balanced.

Bridge circuits are useful both on direct current and on ac of all frequencies. The majority of amateur applications is at radio frequencies, as shown later in this chapter. However, the principles of bridge operation are most easily introduced in terms of dc, where the bridge takes its simplest form.

The Wheatstone Bridge

The simple resistance bridge, known as the **Wheatstone** bridge, is shown in Fig. 17-7. All other bridge circuits – some of which are rather elaborate, especially those designed for ac – derive from this. The four resistors, R1, R2, R3, and R4 shown in A, are known as the bridge **arms**. For the

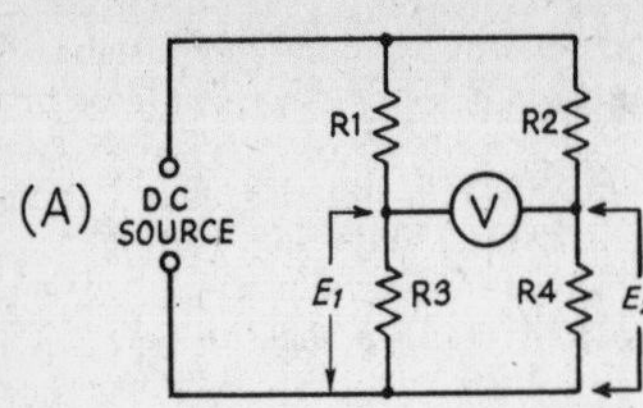

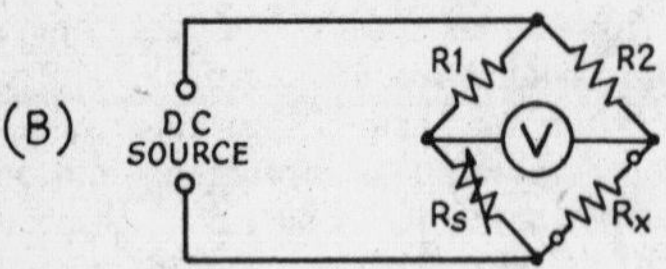

Fig. 17-7 – The Wheatstone bridge circuit. It is frequently drawn as at (B) for emphasizing its special function.

voltmeter reading to be zero, the voltages across R3 and R4 in series must add algebraically to zero; that is E1 must equal E2. R1R3 and R2R4 form voltage dividers across the dc source, so that if

$$\frac{R3}{R1 + R3} = \frac{R4}{R2 + R4}$$

E1 will equal E2.

The circuit is customarily drawn as shown at 17-7B when used for resistance measurement. The equation above can be rewritten

$$R_x = R_s \frac{R2}{R1}$$

to find R_x, the unknown resistance. R1 and R2 are frequently made equal; then the calibrated adjustable resistance (the **standard**), R_s, will have the same value as R_x when R_s is set to show a null on the voltmeter.

Note that the resistance *ratios*, rather than the actual resistance values, determine the voltage balance. However, the values do have important practical effects on the sensitivity and power consumption. The **bridge sensitivity** is the readiness with which the meter responds to small amounts of unbalance about the null point; the "sharper" the null the more accurate the setting of R_s at balance.

The Wheatstone bridge is rarely used by amateurs for resistance measurement, the ohmmeter being the favorite instrument for that purpose. However, it is worthwhile to understand its operation because it is the prototype of more complex bridges.

ELECTRONIC VOLTMETERS

It has been pointed out (Fig. 17-3) that for many purposes the resistance of a voltmeter must be extremely high in order to avoid "loading" errors caused by the current that necessarily flows through the meter. This tends to cause difficulty in measuring relatively low voltages (under perhaps 1000 volts) because a meter movement of given sensitivity takes a progressively smaller multiplier resistance as the voltage range is lowered.

The voltmeter resistance can be made independent of the voltage range by using vacuum tubes or field-effect transistors as electronic dc amplifiers between the circuit being measured and the actual indicator, which is usually a conventional meter movement. As the input resistance of the

Fig. 17-8 – Vacuum-tube voltmeter circuit.

C1, C3 – .002- to .005-μF mica.
C2 – .01 μF, 1000 to 2000 volts, paper or mica.
C4 – 16 μF electrolytic, 150 volts.
CR1 – 400 PRV rectifier.
M – 0-200 microammeter.
R1 – 1 megohm, 1/2 watt.
R2-R5, incl. – To give desired voltage ranges, totaling 10 megohms.
R6, R7 – 2 to 3 megohms.
R8 – 10,000-ohm variable (calibrate).
R9, R10 – 2000 to 3000 ohms.
R11 – 5000- to 10,000-ohm control (zero set).
R12 – 10,000 to 50,000 ohms.
R13, R14 – App. 25,000 ohms. A 50,000-ohm slider-type wire-wound can be used.
R15 – 10 megohms.
R16 – 3 megohms.
R17 – 10-megohm variable.
T1 – 130-volt 15-mA transformer (only secondary shown).
V1 – Dual triode, 12AU7A.
V2 – Dual diode, 6AL5.

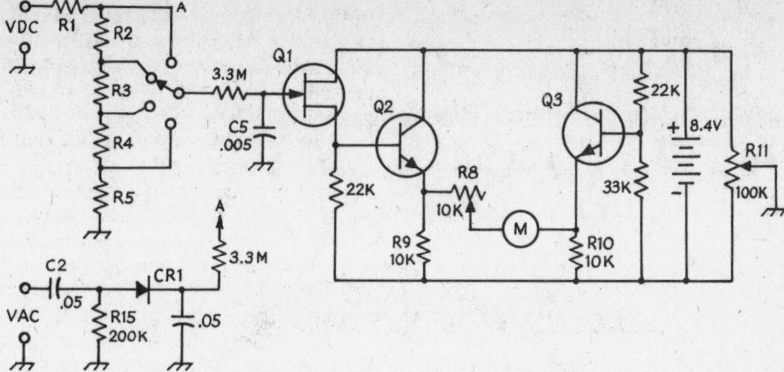

Fig. 17-9 – Electronic voltmeter using field-effect transistor for high input resistance. Components having the same functions as in the VTVM circuit of Fig. 17-8 carry the same designations. (Circuit is basic voltmeter circuit of the Heathkit IM-17.)
CR1 – Silicon diode.
Q1 – Field-effect transistor.
Q2, Q3 – Small-signal audio type.

electronic devices is extremely high – hundreds of megohms – they have essentially no loading effect on the circuit to which they are connected. They do, however, require a closed dc path in their input circuits (although this path can have very high resistance) and are limited in the amplitude of voltage that their input circuits can handle. Because of this, the device actually measures a small voltage across a portion of a high-resistance voltage divider connected to the circuit being measured. Various voltage ranges are obtained by appropriate taps on the voltage divider.

In the design of electronic voltmeters it has become practically standard to use a voltage divider having a resistance of 10 megohms, tapped as required, in series with a 1-megohm resistor incorporated in a **probe** that makes the actual contact with the "hot" side of the circuit under measurement. The total voltmeter resistance, including probe, is therefore 11 megohms. The 1-megohm probe resistor serves to isolate the voltmeter circuit from the "active" circuit.

The Vacuum-Tube Voltmeter

A typical vacuum-tube voltmeter (VTVM) circuit is given in Fig. 17-8. A dual triode, V1, is arranged so that, with no voltage applied to the left-hand grid, equal currents flow through both sections. Under this condition the two cathodes are at the same potential and no current flows through M. The currents can be adjusted to balance by potentiometer, R11, which takes care of variations in the tube sections and in the values of cathode resistors R9 and R10. When a positive dc voltage is applied to the left-hand grid the current through that tube section increases, so the current balance is upset and the meter indicates. The sensitivity of the meter is regulated by R8, which serves to adjust the calibration. R12, common to the cathodes of both tube sections, is a feedback resistor that stabilizes the system and makes the readings linear. R6 and C1 form a filter for any ac component that may be present, and R6 is balanced by R7 connected to the grid of the second tube section.

Values to be used in the circuit depend considerably on the supply voltage and the sensitivity of the meter, M. R12, and R13-R14, should be adjusted by trial so that the voltmeter circuit can be brought to balance, and to give full-scale deflection on M with about 3 volts applied to the left-hand grid (the voltage chosen for this determines the lowest voltage range of the instrument). The meter connections can be reversed to read voltages that are negative with respect to ground.

The small circuit associated with V2 is for ac measurements, as described in a later section.

As compared with conventional dc instruments, the VTVM has the disadvantages of requiring a source of power for its operation, and generally must have its "cold" terminal grounded in order to operate reliably. It is also somewhat susceptible to erratic readings from rf pickup when used in the vicinity of a transmitter, and in such cases may require shielding. However, its advantages outweigh these disadvantages in many applications.

The FET Voltmeter

The circuit of an electronic voltmeter using a field-effect transistor as an input device is shown in Fig. 17-9. Allowing for the differences between vacuum tubes and semiconductors, the operation of this circuit is analogous to that of Fig. 17-8. Transistors Q2 and Q3 correspond to the dual triode in the VTVM circuit, but since the input resistance of Q2 is fairly low, it is preceded by an FET, Q1, with source-coupled output. Note that in this circuit the "zero" or current-balance control, R11, varies the gate bias on Q1 by introducing an adjustable positive voltage in series with the source. This arrangement permits applying the adjustable bias to the gate through the voltmeter range divider, with no other provision needed for completing the dc gate-source path.

The small circuit associated with CR1 is for ac voltage measurement, to be discussed later.

As the power supply for the FET voltmeter is a self-contained battery, the grounding restrictions associated with a VTVM do not apply. The instrument can, however, be susceptible to rf fields if not shielded and grounded.

Electronic Ohmmeters

Most commercial electronic voltmeters include provision for measuring resistance and ac voltage, in addition to dc voltage. The basic ohmmeter circuit generally used is that of Fig. 17-6C. Since for practical purposes the input resistance of the vacuum tube or FET can be assumed to approach infinity, electronic ohmmeters are capable of measuring resistances in the hundreds of megohms – a much higher range than can be reached with an ordinary microammeter.

AC INSTRUMENTS AND CIRCUITS

Although purely electromagnetic instruments that operate directly from alternating current are available, they are seen infrequently in present-day amateur equipment. For one thing, their use is not feasible above power-line frequencies.

Practical instruments for audio and radio frequencies generally use a dc meter movement in conjunction with a rectifier. Voltage measurements suffice for nearly all test purposes. Current, as such, is seldom measured in the af range. When rf current is measured the instrument used is a thermocouple milliammeter or ammeter.

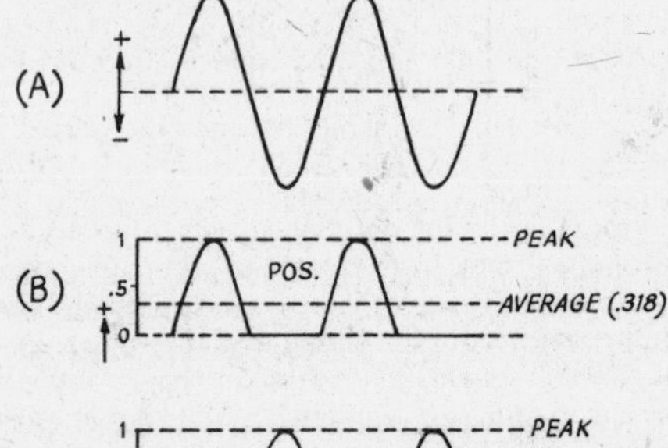

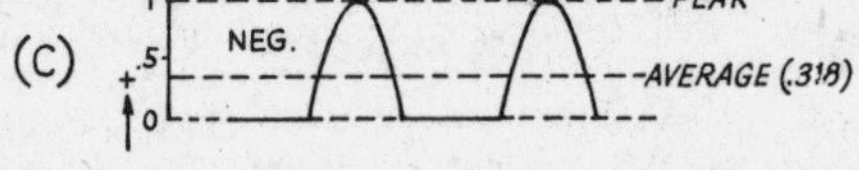

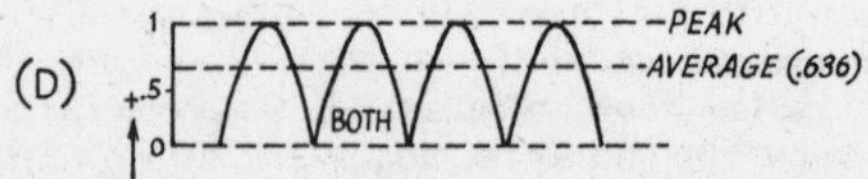

Fig. 17-11 – Sine-wave alternating current or voltage (A), with half-wave rectification of the positive half cycle (B) and negative half cycle (C). D – full-wave rectification. Average values are shown with relation to a peak value of 1.

The Thermocouple Meter

In a **thermocouple meter** the alternating current flows through a low-resistance heating element. The power lost in the resistance generates heat which warms a "thermocouple," a junction of certain dissimilar metals which has the property of developing a small dc voltage when heated. This voltage is applied to a dc milliammeter calibrated in suitable ac units. The heater-thermocouple-dc meter combination is usually housed in a regular meter case.

Fig. 17-10 – Rf ammeter mounted in a Minibox, with connectors for placing the meter in series with a coaxial line. A bakelite-case meter should be used to minimize shunt capacitance (which introduces error) although a metal-case meter can be used if mounted on bakelite sheet with a large cut-out in the case around the rim. The meter can be used for rf power measurements ($P = I^2R$) when connected between a transmitter and a nonreactive load of known resistance.

Thermocouple meters can be obtained in ranges from about 100 mA to many amperes. Their useful upper frequency limit is in the neighborhood of 100 MHz. Their principal value in amateur work is in measuring current into a known load resistance for calculating the rf power delivered to the load. A suitable mounting for this is shown in Fig. 17-10, for use in coaxial lines.

RECTIFIER INSTRUMENTS

The response of a rectifier-type meter is proportional (depending on the design) to either the peak amplitude or average amplitude of the rectified ac wave, and never directly responsive to the rms value. The meter therefore cannot be calibrated in rms without preknowledge of the relationship that happens to exist between the "real" reading and the rms value. This relationship, in general, is not known, except in the case of single-frequency ac (a sine wave). Very many practical measurements involve nonsinusoidal wave forms, so it is necessary to know what kind of instrument you have, and what it is actually

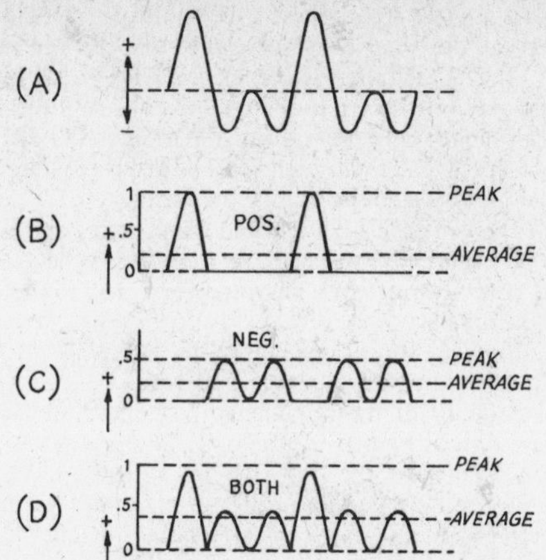

Fig. 17-12 — Same as Fig. 17-11 for an unsymmetrical waveform. The peak values are different with positive and negative half-cycle rectification.

reading, in order to make measurements intelligently.

Peak and Average with Sine-Wave Rectification

Fig. 17-11 shows the relative peak and average values in the outputs of half- and full-wave rectifiers (see power-supply chapter for further details). As the positive and negative half cycles of the sine wave have the same shape (A), half-wave rectification of either the positive half (B) or the negative half (C) gives exactly the same result. With full-wave rectification (D) the peak is still the same, but the average is doubled, since there are twice as many half cycles per unit of time.

Unsymmetrical Wave Forms

A nonsinusoidal waveform is shown in Fig. 17-12A. When the positive half cycles of this wave are rectified the peak and average values are as shown at B. If the polarity is reversed and the negative half cycles are rectified the peak value is different but the average value is unchanged. The fact that the average of the positive side is equal to the average of the negative side is true of *all* ac waveforms, but different waveforms have different averages. Full-wave rectification of such a "lop-sided" wave doubles the average value, but the peak reading is always the same as it is with the half cycle that produces the *highest* peak in half-wave rectification.

Effective-Value Calibration

The actual scale calibration of commercially-made rectifier-type voltmeters is very often (almost always, in fact) in terms of rms values. For sine waves this is satisfactory, and useful since rms is the standard measure at power-line frequency. It is also useful for many rf applications where the waveform is often closely sinusoidal. But in other cases, particularly in the af range, the error may be considerable when the waveform is not pure.

Turn-Over

From Fig. 17-12 it is apparent that the calibration of an average-reading meter will be the same whether the positive or negative sides are rectified. A half-wave *peak*-reading instrument, however, will indicate different values when its connections to the circuit are reversed (**turn-over effect**). Very often readings are taken both ways, in which case the sum of the two is the **peak-to-peak** value, a useful figure in much audio and video work.

Average- and Peak-Reading Circuits

The basic difference between average- and peak-reading rectifier circuits is that in the former the output is not filtered while in the latter a filter capacitor is charged up to the peak value of the output voltage. Fig. 17-13A shows typical average-reading circuits, one half-wave and the other full-wave. In the absence of dc filtering the meter responds to wave forms such as are shown at B, C and D in Figs. 17-11 and 17-12, and since the inertia of the pointer system makes it unable to follow the rapid variations in current, it averages them out mechanically.

In Fig. 17-13A CR1 actuates the meter; CR2 provides a low-resistance dc return in the meter circuit on the negative half cycles. R1 is the voltmeter multiplier resistance. R2 forms a voltage

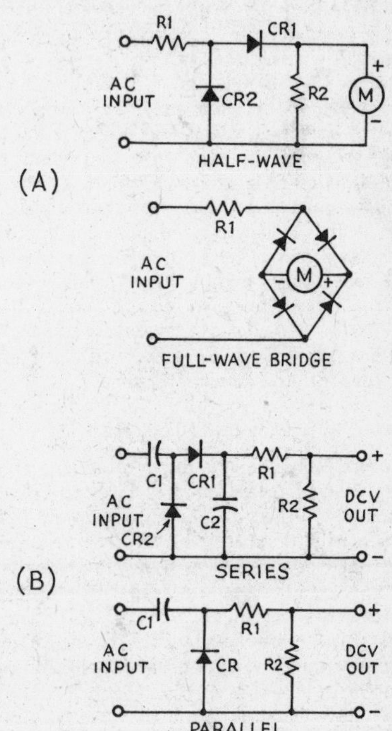

Fig. 17-13 — A — Half-wave and full-wave rectification for an instrument intended to operate on average values. B — half-wave circuits for a peak-reading meter.

divider with R1 (through CR1) which prevents more than a few ac volts from appearing across the rectifier-meter combination. A corresponding resistor can be used across the full-wave bridge circuit.

In these two circuits no provision is made for isolating the meter from any dc voltage that may be on the circuit under measurement. The error caused by this can be avoided by connecting a large capacitance in series with the "hot" lead. The reactance must be low compared with the meter impedance (see next section) in order for the full ac voltage to be applied to the meter circuit. As much as 1 μF may be required at line frequencies with some meters. The capacitor is not usually included in a VOM.

Series and shunt peak-reading circuits are shown in Fig. 17-13B. Capacitor C1 isolates the rectifier from dc voltage on the circuit under measurement. In the series circuit (which is seldom used) the time constant of the C2R1R2 combination must be very large compared with the period of the lowest ac frequency to be measured; similarly with C1R1R2 in the shunt circuit. The reason is that the capacitor is charged to the peak value of voltage when the ac wave reaches its maximum, and then must hold the charge (so it can register on a dc meter) until the next maximum of the same polarity. If the time constant is 20 times the ac period the charge will have decreased by about 5 percent by the time the next charge occurs. The *average* drop will be smaller, so the error is appreciably less. The error will decrease rapidly with increasing frequency, assuming no change in the circuit values, but will increase at lower frequencies.

In Fig. 17-13B R1 and R2 form a voltage divider which reduces the peak dc voltage to 71 percent of its actual value. This converts the peak reading to rms on sine-wave ac. Since the peak-reading circuits are incapable of delivering appreciable current without considerable error, R2 is usually the 11-megohm input resistance of an electronic voltmeter. R1 is therefore approximately 4.7 megohms, making the total resistance approach 16 megohms. A capacitance of .05 μF is sufficient for low audio frequencies under these conditions. Much smaller values of capacitance suffice for radio frequencies, obviously.

Voltmeter Impedance

The impedance of the voltmeter at the frequency being measured may have an effect on the accuracy similar to the error caused by the resistance of a dc voltmeter, as discussed earlier. The ac meter acts like a resistance in prallel with a capacitance, and since the capacitive reactance decreases with increasing frequency, the impedance also decreases with frequency. The resistance is subject to some variation with voltage level, particularly at very low voltages (of the order of 10 volts or less) depending upon the sensitivity of the meter movement and the kind of rectifier used.

The ac load resistance represented by a diode rectifier is approximately equal to one-half its dc load resistance. In Fig. 17-13A the dc load is essentially the meter resistance, which is generally quite low compared with the multiplier resistance R1, so the total resistance will be about the same as the multiplier resistance. The capacitance depends on the components and construction, test lead length and disposition, and such factors. In general, it has little or no effect at power-line and low audio frequencies, but the ordinary VOM loses accuracy at the higher audio frequencies and is of little use at rf. For radio frequencies it is necessary to use a rectifier having very low inherent capacitance.

Similar limitations apply to the peak-reading circuits. In the parallel circuit the resistive component of the impedance is smaller than in the series circuit, since the dc load resistance, R1R2, is directly across the circuit being measured, and is therefore in parallel with the diode ac load resistance. In both peak-reading circuits the effective capacitance may range from 1 or 2 to a few hundred pF. Values of the order of 100 pF are to be expected in electronic voltmeters of customary design and construction.

Linearity

Fig. 17-14, a typical current/voltage characteristic of a small semiconductor rectifier, indicates that the forward dynamic resistance of the diode is not constant, but rapidly decreases as the forward voltage is increased from zero. The transition from high to low resistance occurs at considerably less than 1 volt, but is in the range of voltage required by the associated dc meter. With an average-reading circuit the current tends to be proportional to the *square* of the applied voltage. This crowds the calibration points at the low end of the meter scale. For most measurement purposes, however, it is far more desirable for the output to be "linear;" that is, for the reading to be *directly* proportional to the applied voltage.

To achieve linearity it is necessary to use a relatively large load resistance for the diode – large enough so that this resistance, rather than the diode's own resistance, will govern the current flow. A linear or equally spaced scale is thus gained at the expense of sensitivity. The amount of resistance needed depends on the type of diode;

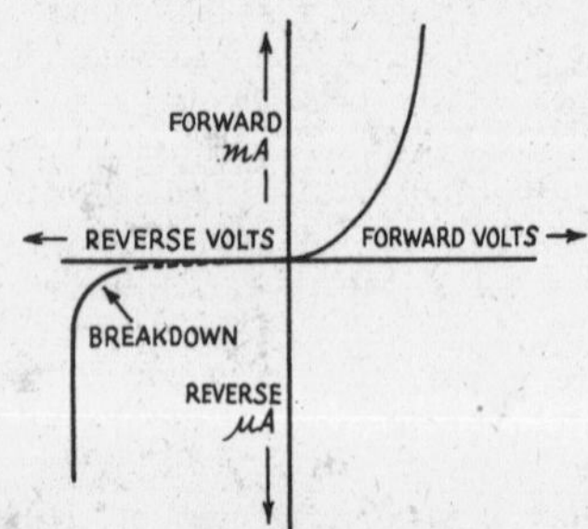

Fig. 17-14 – Typical semiconductor diode characteristic. Actual current and voltage values vary with the type of diode, but the forward-current curve would be in its steep part with only a volt or so applied. Note change in current scale for reverse current. Breakdown voltage, again depending on diode type, may range from 15 or 20 volts to several hundred.

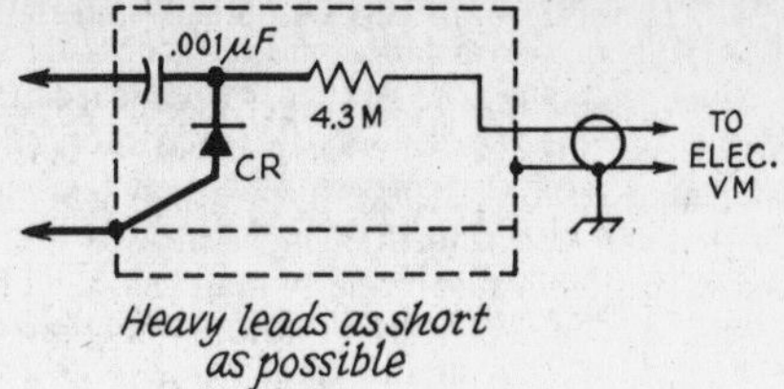

Fig. 17-15 – Rf probe circuit. CR is a small semiconductor rectifier, usually point-contact germanium. The resistor value, for exact voltage division to rms, should be 4.14 megohms, but standard values are generally used, including 4.7 megohms.

5000 to 50,000 ohms usually suffices for a germanium rectifier, depending on the dc meter sensitivity, but several times as much may be needed for silicon. The higher the resistance, the greater the meter sensitivity required; i.e., the basic meter must be a microammeter rather than a low-range milliammeter.

Reverse Current

When voltage is applied in the reverse direction there is a small leakage current in semiconductor diodes. This is equivalent to a resistance connected across the rectifier, allowing current to flow during the half cycle which should be completely nonconducting, and causing an error in the dc meter reading. This "back resistance" is so high as to be practically unimportant with silicon, but may be less than 100 kΩ with germanium.

The practical effect of back resistance is to limit the amount of resistance that can be used in the dc load resistance. This in turn affects the linearity of the meter scale.

The back resistance of vacuum-tube diodes is infinite, for practical purposes.

RF VOLTAGE

Special precautions must be taken to minimize the capacitive component of the voltmeter impedance at radio frequencies. If possible, the rectifier circuit should be installed permanently at the point where the rf voltage to be measured exists, using the shortest possible rf connections. The dc meter can be remotely located, however.

For general rf measurements an **rf probe** is used in conjunction with an electronic voltmeter, substituted for the dc probe mentioned earlier. The circuit of Fig. 17-15, essentially the peak-reading shunt circuit of Fig. 17-13B, is generally used. The series resistor, installed in the probe close to the rectifier, prevents rf from being fed through the probe cable to the electronic voltmeter, being helped in this by the cable capacitance. This resistor, in conjunction with the 10-megohm divider resistance of the electronic voltmeter, also reduces the peak rectified voltage to a dc value equivalent to the rms of the rf signal, to make the rf readings consistent with the regular ac calibration.

Of the diodes readily available to amateurs, the germanium point-contact type is preferred for rf applications. It has low capacitance (of the order of 1 pF) and in the high-back-resistance types the reverse current is not serious. The principal limitation is that its safe reverse voltage is only about 50-75 volts, which limits the rms applied voltage to 15 or 20 volts, approximately. Diodes can be connected in series to raise the overall rating.

Linearity at Radio Frequencies

The bypass or filter capacitance normally used in rf rectifier circuits is large enough, together with the resistance in the system, to have a time constant sufficient for peak readings. However, if the resistance is low (the load sometimes is just the microammeter or milliammeter alone) the *linearity* of the voltmeter will be affected as previously described, even if the time constant is fairly large. It is not safe to assume that the voltmeter is even approximately linear unless the load resistance is of the order of 10,000 ohms or greater.

Nonlinear voltmeters are useful as indicators, as where null indicators are called for, but should not be depended upon for actual measurement of voltage.

RF Power

Power at radio frequencies can be measured by means of an accurately-calibrated rf voltmeter connected across the load in which the power is being dissipated. If the load is a known pure resistance the power, by Ohm's Law, is equal to E^2/R, where E is the rms value of the voltage.

The method only indicates *apparent* power if the load is not a pure resistance. The load can be a terminated transmission line tuned, with the aid of bridge circuits such as are described in the next section, to act as a known resistance. An alternative load is a "dummy" antenna, a known pure resistance capable of dissipating the rf power safely.

AC BRIDGES

In its simplest form, the ac bridge is exactly the same as the Wheatstone bridge discussed earlier. However, complex impedances can be substituted for resistances, as suggested by Fig. 17-16A. The same bridge equation holds if Z is substituted for R in each arm. For the equation to be true, however, *the phase angles as well as the numerical values of the impedances must balance*; otherwise, a true null voltage is impossible to obtain. This means that a bridge with all "pure" arms (pure resistance or reactance) cannot measure complex impedances; a combination of R and X must be present in at least one arm besides the unknown.

The actual circuits of ac bridges take many forms, depending on the type of measurement intended and on the frequency range to be covered. As the frequency is raised stray effects (unwanted capacitances and inductances, principally) become more pronounced. At radio frequencies special attention must be paid to minimizing them.

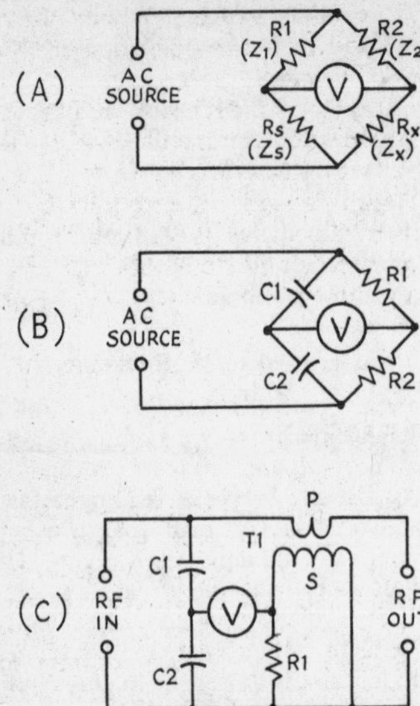

Fig. 17-16 – A – Generalized form of bridge circuit for either ac or dc. B – One form of ac bridge frequently used for rf measurements. C – SWR bridge for use in transmission lines. This circuit is often calibrated in power rather than voltage.

Most amateur-built bridges are used for rf measurements, especially SWR measurements on transmission lines. The circuits at B and C, Fig. 17-16, are favorites for this purpose. These basic forms are often modified considerably, as will be seen by the constructional examples later in the chapter.

Fig. 17-16B is useful for measuring both transmission lines and "lumped constant" components. Combinations of resistance and capacitance are often used in one or more arms; this may be required for eliminating the effects of stray capacitance.

Fig. 17-16C is used only on transmission lines, and only on those lines having the characteristic impedance for which the bridge is designed.

SWR Measurement – The Reflectometer

In measuring standing-wave ratio advantage is taken of the fact that the voltage on a transmission line consists of two components traveling in opposite directions. The power going from the transmitter to the load is represented by one voltage (designated "incident" or "forward") and the power reflected from the load is represented by the other. Because the relative amplitudes and phase relationships are definitely established by the line's characteristic impedance, its length and the load impedance in which it is terminated, a bridge circuit can separate the incident and reflected voltages for measurement. This is sufficient for determining the SWR. Bridges designed for this purpose are frequently called **reflectometers.**

Referring to Fig. 17-16A, if R1 and R2 are made equal, the bridge will be balanced when $R_X = R_S$. This is true whether R_X is an actual resistor or the input resistance of a perfectly matched transmission line, provided R_S is chosen to equal the characteristic impedance of the line. Even if the line is not properly matched, the bridge will still be balanced for power traveling *outward* on the line, since outward-going power sees only the Z_0 of the line until it reaches the load. However, power reflected back from the load does not "see" a bridge circuit, and the reflected voltage registers on the voltmeter. From the known relationship between the incident and reflected voltages the SWR is easily calculated:

$$SWR = \frac{V_0 + V_r}{V_0 - V_r}$$

where V_0 is the forward voltage and V_r is the reflected voltage. The forward voltage may be measured either by disconnecting R_X or shorting it.

The "Reflected Power Meter"

Fig. 17-16C makes use of mutual inductance between the primary and secondary of T1 to establish a balancing circuit. C1 and C2 form a voltage divider in which the voltage across C2 is in the same phase as the voltage at that point on the transmission line. The relative phase of the voltage across R1 is determined by the phase of the *current* in the line. If a pure resistance equal to the design impedance of the bridge is connected to the "RF Out" terminals, the voltages across R1 and C2 will be out of phase and the voltmeter reading will be minimum; if the *amplitudes* of the two voltages are also equal (they are made so by bridge adjustment) the voltmeter will read zero. Any other value of resistance or impedance connected to the "RF Out" terminals will result in a finite voltmeter reading. When used in a transmission line this reading is proportional to the reflected voltage. To measure the incident voltage the secondary terminals of T1 can be reversed. To function as described, the secondary leakage reactance of T1 must be very large compared to the resistance of R1.

Instruments of this type are usually designed for convenient switching between forward and reflected, and are often calibrated to read power in the specified characterisitic impedance. The net power transmission is equal to the incident power minus the reflected power.

Sensitivity vs. Frequency

In all of the circuits in Fig. 17-16 the sensitivity is independent of the applied frequency, within practical limits. Stray capacitances and couplings generally limit the performance of all three at the high-frequency end of the useful range. Fig. 17-16A will work right down to dc, but the low-frequency performance of Fig. 17-16B is degraded when the capacitive reactances become so large that voltmeter impedance becomes low in comparison (in all these bridge circuits, it is assumed that the voltmeter impedance is high compared with the impedance of the bridge arms). In Fig. 17-16C the performance is limited at low frequencies by the fact that the transformer reactance decreases with frequency, so that eventually the reactance is not very high in comparison with the resistance of R1.

The "Monimatch"

A type of bridge which is quite simple to make, but in which the sensitivity rises directly with frequency, is the **Monimatch** and its various offspring. The circuit cannot be described in terms of lumped constants, as it makes use of the distrbuted mutual inductance and capacitance between the center conductor of a transmission line and a wire placed parallel to it. The wire is terminated in a resistance approximating the characteristic impedance of the transmission line at one end and feeds a diode rectifier at the other. A practical example is shown later in this chapter.

FREQUENCY MEASUREMENT

The regulations governing amateur operation require that the transmitted signal be maintained inside the limits of certain bands of frequencies.* The exact frequency need not be known, so long as it is not outside the limits. On this last point there are no tolerances: It is up to the individual amateur to see that he stays safely "inside."

This is not difficult to do, but requires some simple apparatus and the exercise of some care. The apparatus commonly used is the **frequency-marker generator**, and the method involves use of the station receiver, as in Fig. 17-17.

THE FREQUENCY MARKER

The marker generator in its simplest form is a high-stability oscillator generating a series of signals which, when detected in the receiver, mark the exact edges of the amateur assignments. It does this by oscillating at a low frequency that has harmonics falling on the desired frequencies.

All U.S. amateur band limits are exact multiples of 25 kHz, whether at the extremes of a band or at points marking the subdivisions between types of emission, license privileges, and so on. A 25-kHz fundamental frequency therefore will produce the desired marker signals if its harmonics at the higher frequencies are strong enough. But since harmonics appear at 25-kHz intervals throughout the spectrum, along with the desired markers, the problem of identifying a *particular* marker arises. This is easily solved if the receiver has a reasonably good calibration. If not, most marker circuits provide for a choice of fundamental outputs of 100 and 50 kHz as well as 25 kHz, so the question can be narrowed down to initial identification of 100-kHz intervals. From these, the desired 25-kHz (or 50-kHz) points can easily be spotted. Coarser frequency intervals are rarely required; there are usually signals available from stations of known frequency, and the 100-kHz points can be counted off from them.

Transmitter Checking

In checking one's own transmitter frequency the signal from the transmitter is first tuned in on the receiver and the dial setting at which it is heard is noted. Then the *nearest* marker frequencies above and below the transmitter signal are turned in and identified. The transmitter frequency is obviously between these two known frequencies.

If the marker frequencies are accurate, this is all that needs to be known – except that the transmitter frequency must not be so close to a band (or subband) edge that sideband frequencies, especially in phone transmission, will extend over the edge.

If the transmitter signal is "inside" a marker at the edge of an assignment, to the extent that there is an audible beat note with the receiver's BFO turned off, normal cw sidebands are safely inside the edge. (This statement does not take into account *abnormal* sidebands such as are caused by clicks and chirps.) For phone the "safety" allowance is usually taken to be about 3 kHz, the nominal width of one sideband. A frequency difference of this order can be estimated by noting the receiver dial settings for the two 25-kHz markers which bracket the signal and dividing 25 by the number of dial divisions between them. This will give the number of kHz per dial division.

Transceivers

The method described above is applicable when the receiver and transmitter are separate pieces of equipment. When a transceiver is used and the

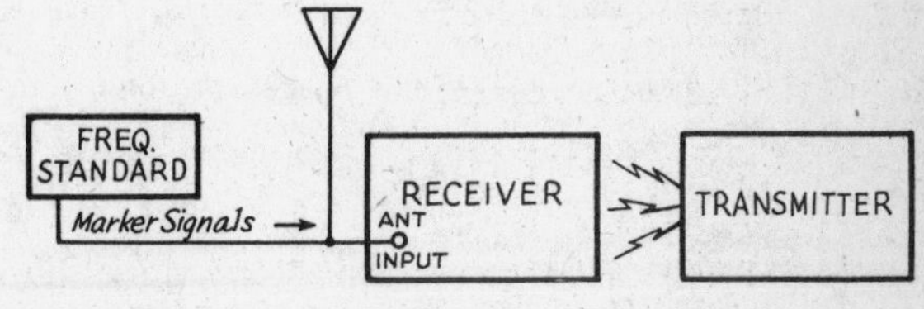

Fig. 17-17 – Setup for using a frequency standard. It is necessary that the transmitter signal be weak in the receiver – of the same order of strength as the marker signal from the standard. This requirement can usually be met by turning on just the transmitter oscillator, leaving all power off any succeeding stages. In some cases it may also be necessary to disconnect the antenna from the receiver.

* These limits depend on the type of emission and class of license held, as well as on international agreements. See the latest edition of *The Radio Amateur's License Manual* for current status.

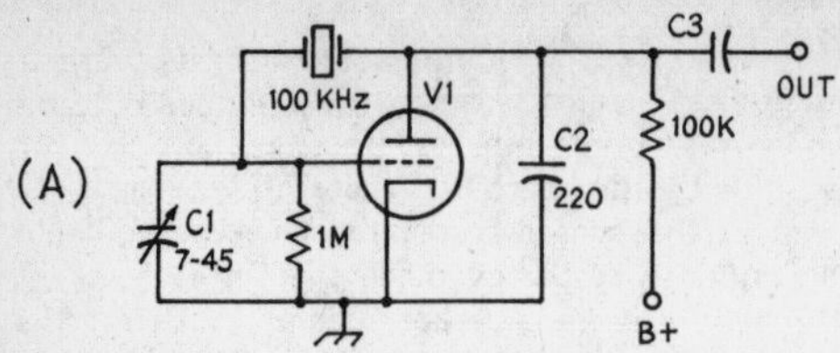

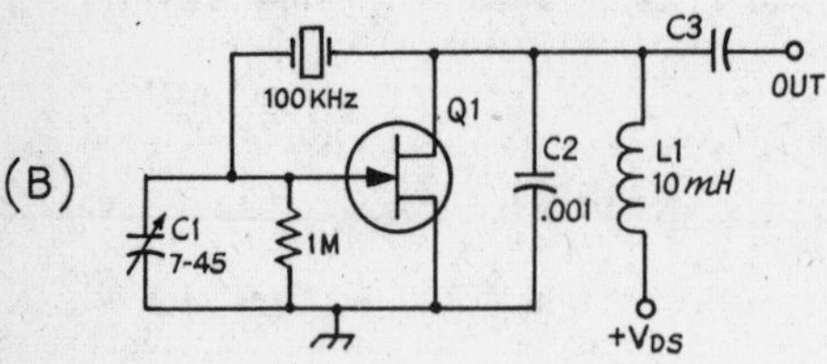

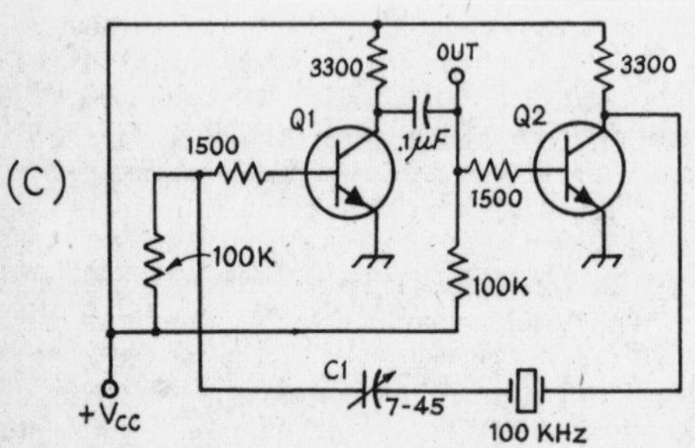

Fig. 17-18 – Three simple 100-kHz oscillator circuits. C is the most suitable of available transistor circuits (for marker generators) and is recommended where solid-state is to be used. In all three circuits C1 is for fine frequency adjustment. The output coupling capacitor, C3, is generally small – 20 to 50 pF – a compromise to avoid loading the oscillator by the receiver antenna input while maintaining adequate coupling for good harmonic strength.

transmitting frequency is automatically the same as that to which the receiver is tuned, setting the tuning dial to a spot between two known marker frequencies is all that is required.

The proper dial settings for the markers are those at which, with the BFO on, the signal is tuned to *zero* beat – the spot where the beat disappears as the tuning makes the beat tone progressively lower. Exact zero beat can be determined by a very slow rise and fall of background noise, caused by a beat of a cycle or less per second.

FREQUENCY-MARKER CIRCUITS

The basic frequency-determining element in most amateur frequency markers is a 100-kHz crystal. Although the marker generator should produce harmonics at 25-kHz and 50-kHz intervals, crystals (or other high-stability devices) for frequencies lower than 100 kHz are expensive and difficult to obtain. However, there is really no need for them, since it is easy to divide the basic frequency down to any figure one desires; 50 and 25 kHz require only two successive divisions, each by 2. In the division process, the harmonic output of the generator is greatly enhanced, making the generator useful at frequencies well into the vhf range.

Simple Crystal Oscillators

Fig. 17-18 illustrates a few of the simpler circuits. Fig. 17-18A is a long-time favorite where vacuum tubes are used and is often incorporated in receivers. C1 in this and the other circuits is used for exact adjustment of the oscillating frequency to 100 kHz, which is done by using the receiver for comparing one of the oscillator's harmonics with a standard frequency transmitted by WWV, WWVH, or a similar station.

Fig. 17-18B is a field-effect transistor analog of the vacuum-tube circuit. However, it requires a 10-mH coil to operate well, and since the harmonic output is not strong at the higher frequencies the circuit is given principally as an example of a simple transistor arrangement. A much better oscillator is shown at C. This is a cross-connected pair of transistors forming a **multivibrator** of the "free-running" or "astable" type, locked at 100 kHz by using the crystal as one of the coupling elements. While it can use two separate bipolar transistors as shown, it is much simpler to use an integrated-circuit **dual gate**, which will contain all the necessary parts except the crystal and capacitors and is considerably less expensive, as well as more compact, than the separate components. An example is shown later in the chapter.

Frequency Dividers

Electronic division is accomplished by a "bistable" **flip-flop** or cross-coupled circuit which produces one output change for every two impulses applied to its input circuit, thus dividing the applied frequency by 2. All division therefore must be in terms of some power of 2. In practice this is no handicap since with modern integrated-circuit flip-flops, circuit arrangements can be worked out for division by any desired number.

As flip-flops and gates in integrated circuits come in compatible series – meaning that they work at the same supply voltage and can be directly connected together – a combination of a dual-gate version of Fig. 17-18C and a dual flip-flop make an attractively simple combination for the marker generator.

There are several different basic types of flip-flops, the variations having to do with methods of driving (dc or pulse operation) and control of the counting function. Information on the operating principles and ratings of a specific type usually can be obtained from the manufacturer. The counting-control functions are not needed in using the flip-flop in a simple marker generator, although they come into play when dividing by some number other than a power of 2.

Frequency Standards

The difference between a marker generator and a **frequency standard** is that in the latter special pains are taken to make the oscillator frequency as stable as possible in the face of variations in temperature, humidity, line voltage, and other factors which could cause a small change in frequency.

While there are no definite criteria that distinguish the two in this respect, a circuit designated as a "standard" for amateur purposes should be capable of maintaining frequency within at least a few parts per million under normal variations in ambient conditions, without adjustment. A simple marker generator using a 100-kHz crystal can be expected to have frequency variations 10 times (or more) greater under similar conditions. It can of course be adjusted to exact frequency at any time the WWV (or equivalent) signal is available.

The design considerations of high-precision frequency standards are outside the scope of this chapter, but information is available from time to time in periodicals.

OTHER METHODS OF FREQUENCY CHECKING

The simplest possible frequency-measuring device is a parallel *LC* circuit, tunable over a desired frequency range and having its tuning dial calibrated in terms of frequency. It can be used only for checking circuits in which at least a small amount of rf power is present, because the energy required to give a detectable indication is not available in the *LC* circuit itself; it has to be extracted from the circuit being measured; hence the name **absorption frequency meter**. It will be observed that what is actually measured is the frequency of the rf *energy, not* the frequency to which the circuit in which the energy is present may be tuned.

The measurement accuracy of such an instrument is low, compared with the accuracy of a marker generator, because the Q of a practicable *LC* circuit is not high enough to make precise reading of the dial possible. Also, any two circuits coupled together react on each others' tuning. (This can be minimized by using the loosest coupling that will give an adequate indication.)

The absorption frequency meter has one useful advantage over the marker generator – it will respond *only* to the frequency to which it is tuned, or to a band of frequencies very close to it. Thus there is no harmonic ambiguity, as there sometimes is when using a marker generator.

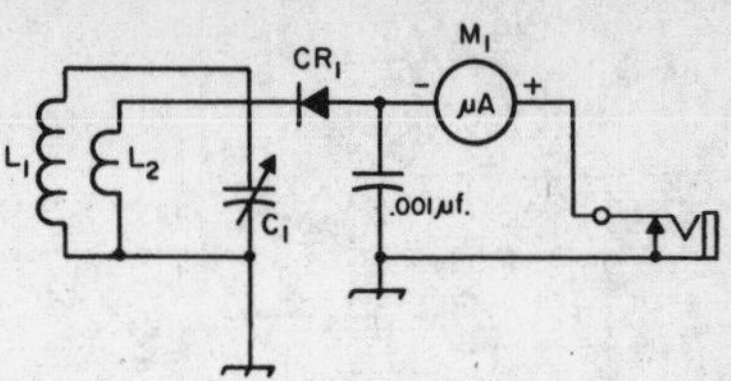

Fig. 17-19A – Absorption frequency-meter circuit. The closed-circuit phone jack may be omitted if listening is not wanted; in that case the positive terminal of M1 goes to common ground.

Absorption Circuit

A typical absorption frequency-meter circuit is shown in Fig. 17-19. In addition to the adjustable tuned circuit, L1C1, it includes a pickup coil, L2, wound over L1, a high-frequency semiconductor diode, CR1, and a microammeter or low-range (usually not more than 0-1 mA) milliammeter. A phone jack is included so the device can be used for listening to the signal.

The sensitivity of the frequency meter depends on the sensitivity of the dc meter movement and the size of L2 in relation to L1. There is an optimum size for this coil which has to be found by experiment. An alternative is to make the rectifier connection to an adjustable tap on L1, in which case there is an optimum tap point. In general, the rectifier coupling should be a little *below* (that is, less tight) the point that gives maximum response, since this will make the indications sharper.

Calibration

The absorption frequency meter must be calibrated by taking a series of readings on various frequencies from circuits carrying rf power, the frequency of the rf energy first being determined by some other means such as a marker generator and receiver. The setting of the dial that gives the highest meter indication is the calibration point for that frequency. This point should be determined by tuning through it with loose coupling to the circuit being measured.

OTHER INSTRUMENTS AND MEASUREMENTS

Many measurements require a source of ac power of adjustable frequency (and sometimes adjustable amplitude as well) in addition to what is already available from the transmitter or receiver. Rf and af test oscillators, for example, provide signals for purposes such as receiver alignment, testing of phone transmitters, and so on. Another valuable adjunct to the station is the oscilloscope, especially useful for checking phone modulation.

Rf Oscillators for Circuit Alignment

Receiver testing and alignment, covered in an earlier chapter, uses equipment common to ordinary radio service work. Inexpensive rf signal generators are available, both complete and in kit form. However, any source of signal that is weak enough to avoid overloading the receiver usually will serve for alignment work. The frequency marker generator is a satisfactory signal source. In addition, its frequencies, although not continuously adjustable, are known far more precisely, since the usual signal-generator calibration is not highly accurate. For rough work the dip meter described in the next section will serve.

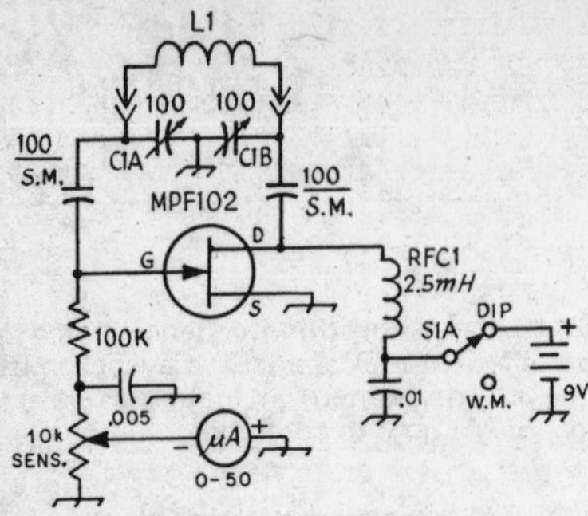

Fig. 17-19B – An FET source-dipper circuit suitable for use from 1.5 to 50 MHz. For operation at vhf and uhf the value of C1 should be made smaller, RFC1 would be a vhf type, and the bypass capacitors would be smaller in value. For uhf use Q1 would be changed to a uhf-type FET, a 2N4416 or similar.

THE DIP METER

The dip meter reverses the absorption-wavemeter procedure in that *it* supplies the rf power by incorporating a tunable oscillator from which the circuit being checked absorbs energy when this circuit and the oscillator are tuned to the same frequency and coupled together. In the vacuum-tube version the energy absorption causes a decrease or "dip" in the oscillator's rectified grid current, measured by a dc microammeter.

The same principle can be applied to solid-state oscillators. In some transistor versions the oscillator rf power is rectified by a diode to provide a meter indication. This technique can result in "dead spots" in the tuning range if the oscillator power is too low to enable the diode to conduct at all times. The circuit of Fig. 17-19B avoids the problem by measuring the changes in source current. In the W.M. (wavemeter) position of S1 the gate-source junction of Q1 serves as the detector diode.

Each tuning range of the dipper should overlap to provide sufficient coverage to check circuits of unknown resonant frequency. Plug-in coils are normally used to allow continuous coverage from 1.5 to at least 250 MHz.

Calibration

A dipper should have reasonably accurate calibration. Calibration of the dipper dial can be effected by monitoring the dipper output signal with a calibrated receiver. Make sure the *fundamental* frequency of the dipper is being used during calibration.

Operating the Dip Meter

The dip meter will check only resonant circuits, since nonresonant circuits or components will not absorb energy at a specific frequency. The circuit may be either lumped or linear (a transmission-line type circuit) provided only that it has enough Q to give sufficient coupling to the dip-meter coil for detectable absorption of rf energy. Generally the coupling is principally inductive, although at times there may be sufficient capacitive coupling between the meter and a circuit point that is at relatively high potential with respect to ground to permit a reading. For inductive coupling, maximum energy absorption will occur when the meter

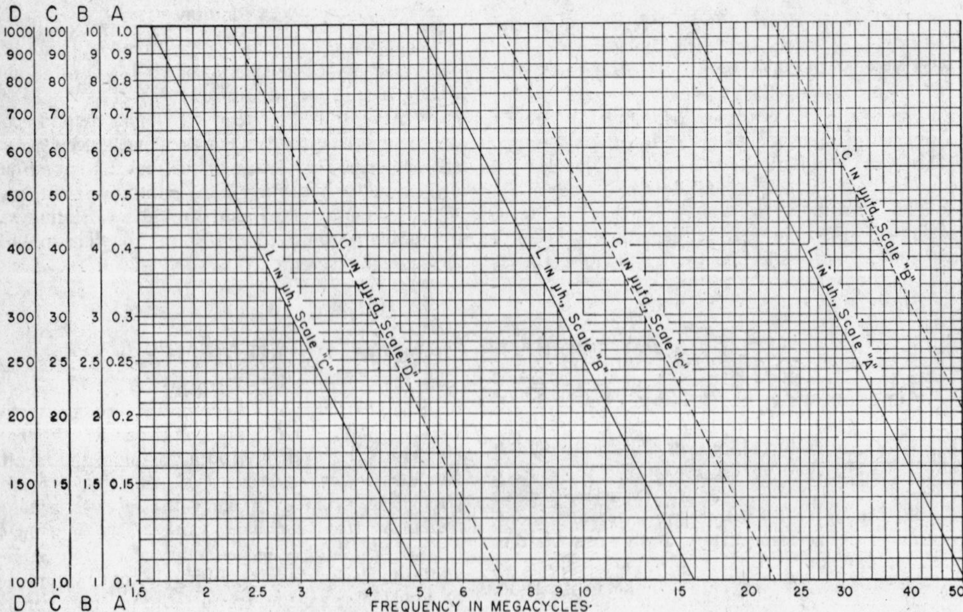

Fig. 17-20 – Chart for determining unknown values of L and C in the range of 0.1 to 100 μH and 2 to 1000 pF, using standards of 100 pF and 5 μH.

Fig. 17-21 – A convenient mounting, using binding-post plates, for L and C standards made from commercially available parts. The capacitor is a 100-pF silver mica unit, mounted so the lead length is as nearly zero as possible. The inductance standard, 5 μH, is 17 turns of coil stock, 1-inch diameter, 16 turns per inch.

is coupled to a coil (the same coupling rules that apply to any two coils are operative here) in the tuned circuit being checked, or to a high-current point in a linear circuit.

Because of distributed capacitance (and sometimes inductance) most circuits resonant at the lower amateur frequencies will show quasi-linear-type resonances at or close to the vhf region. A vhf dip meter will uncover these, often with beneficial results since such "parasitic" resonances can cause unwanted responses at harmonics of the intended frequency, or be responsible for parasitic oscillations in amplifiers. Caution must be used in checking transmission lines or antennas – and, especially, combinations of antenna and line – on this account, because these linear circuits have well-defined series of harmonic responses, based on the lowest resonant frequency, which may lead to false conclusions respecting the behavior of the system.

Measurements with the dip meter are essentially frequency measurements, and for best accuracy the coupling between the meter and circuit under checking must be as loose as will allow a perceptible dip. In this respect the dip meter is similar to the absorption wavemeter.

Measuring Inductance and Capacitance with the Dip Meter

With a carefully calibrated dip meter, properly operated, inductance and capacitance in the values ordinarily used for the 1.5-50 MHz range can be measured with ample accuracy for practical work. The method requires two accessories: an inductance "standard" of known value, and a capacitance standard also known with reasonable accuracy. Values of 100 pF for the capacitance and 5 μH for the inductance are convenient. The chart of Fig. 17-20 is based on these values.

The L and C standards can be quite ordinary components. A small silver-mica capacitor is satisfactory for the capacitance, since the customary tolerance is ±5 percent. The inductance standard can be cut from commercial machine-wound coil stock; if none is available, a homemade equivalent in diameter, turn spacing, and number of turns can be substituted. The inductance will be 5 μH within amply close tolerances if the specifications in Fig. 17-21 are followed closely. In any case, the inductance can easily be adjusted to the proper value; it should resonate with the 100-pF capacitor at 7100 kHz.

The setup for measuring an unknown is shown in Fig. 17-22. Inductance is measured with the unknown connected to the standard capacitance. Couple the dip meter to the coil and adjust the meter for the dip, using the loosest possible coupling that will give a usable indication. Similar procedure is followed for capacitance measurement, except that the unknown is connected to the standard inductance. Values are read off the chart for the frequency indicated by the dip meter.

Coefficient of Coupling

The same equipment can be used for measurement of the coefficient of coupling between two coils. This simply requires two measurements of inductance (of *one* of the coils) with the coupled coil first open-circuited and then short-circuited. Connect the 100-pF standard capacitor to one coil and measure the inductance with the terminals of the second coil open. Then short the terminals of the second coil and again measure the inductance of the first. The coefficient of coupling is given by

$$k = \sqrt{1 - \frac{L_2}{L_1}}$$

where k = coefficient of coupling

$L1$ = inductance of first coil with terminals of second coil open

$L2$ = inductance of first coil with terminals of second coil shorted.

AUDIO-FREQUENCY OSCILLATORS

Tests requiring an audio-frequency signal generally call for one that is a reasonably good sine wave, and the best oscillator circuits for this are RC-coupled, operating as nearly as possible as Class A amplifiers. Variable frequency covering the entire audio range is needed for determining frequency response of audio amplifiers, but this is

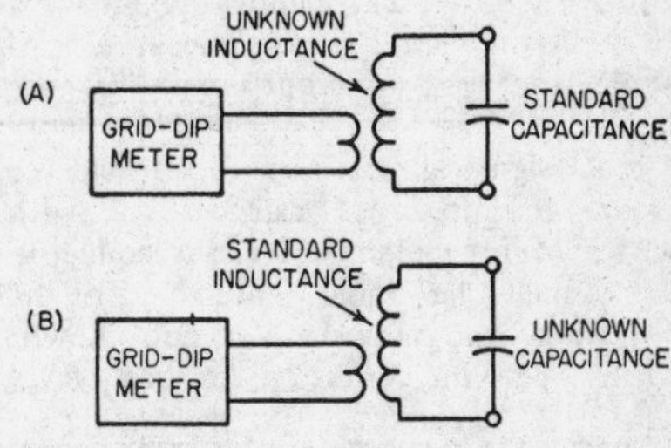

Fig. 17-22 – Setups for measuring inductance and capacitance with the dip meter.

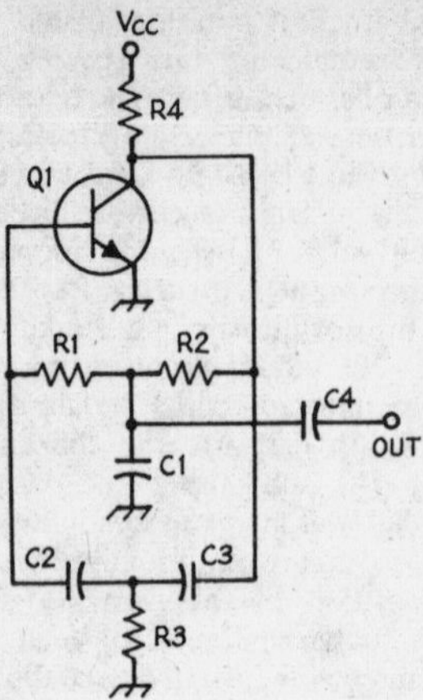

Fig. 17-23 – Twin-T audio oscillator circuit. Representative values for R1-R2 and C1 range from 18kΩ and .05 μF for 750 Hz to 15kΩ and .02 μF for 1800 Hz. For the same frequency range, R3 and C2-C3 vary from 1800 ohms and .02 μF to 1500 ohms and .01 μF. R4 should be approximately 3300 ohms. C4, the output coupling capacitor, can be .05 μF for high-impedance loads.

a relatively unimportant type of test in amateur equipment. The variable-frequency af signal generator is best purchased complete; kits are readily available at prices that compare very favorably with the cost of parts.

For most phone-transmitter testing, and for simple trouble shooting in af amplifiers, an oscillator generating one or two frequencies with good wave form is adequate. A "two-tone" (dual) oscillator is particularly useful for testing sideband transmitters, and a constructional example is found later in the chapter.

The circuit of a simple *RC* oscillator useful for general test purposes is given in Fig. 17-23. This "Twin-T" arrangement gives a wave form that is satisfactory for most purposes, and by choice of circuit constants the oscillator can be operated at any frequency in the usual audio range. R1, R2 and C1 form a low-pass type network, while C2C3R3 is high-pass. As the phase shifts are opposite, there is only one frequency at which the total phase shift from collector to base is 180 degrees, and oscillation will occur at this frequency. Optimum operation results when C1 is approximately twice the capacitance of C2 or C3, and R3 has a resistance about 0.1 that of R1 or R2 (C2 = C3 and R1 = R2). Output is taken across C1, where the harmonic distortion is least. A relatively high-impedance load should be used – 0.1 megohm or more.

A small-signal af transistor is suitable for Q1. Either npn or pnp types can be used, with due regard for supply polarity. R4, the collector load resistor, must be large enough for normal amplification, and may be varied somewhat to adjust the operating conditions for best waveform.

RESISTORS AT RADIO FREQUENCIES

Measuring equipment, in some part of its circuit, often requires essentially pure resistance – that is, resistance exhibiting only negligible reactive effects on the frequencies at which measurement is intended. Of the resistors available to amateurs, this requirement is met only by small composition (carbon) resistors. The inductance of wire-wound resistors makes them useless for amateur frequencies.

The reactances to be considered arise from the inherent inductance of the resistor itself and its leads, and from small stray capacitances from one part of the resistor to another and to surrounding conductors. Although both the inductance and capacitance are small, their reactances become increasingly important as the frequency is raised. Small composition resistors, properly mounted, show negligible capacitive reactance up to 100 MHz or so in resistance values up to a few hundred ohms; similarly, the inductive reactance is negligible in values *higher* than a few hundred ohms. The optimum resistance region in this respect is in the 50 to 200-ohm range, approximately.

Proper mounting includes reducing lead length as much as possible, and keeping the resistor separated from other resistors and conductors. Care must also be taken in some applications to ensure that the resistor, with its associated components, does not form a closed loop into which a voltage could be induced magnetically.

So installed, the resistance is essentially pure. In composition resistors the skin effect is very small, and the rf resistance up to vhf is very closely the same as the dc resistance.

Dummy Antennas

A **dummy antenna** is simply a resistor that, in impedance characteristics, can be substituted for an antenna or transmission line for test purposes. It permits leisurely transmitter testing without radiating a signal. (The amateur regulations strictly limit the amount of "on-the-air" testing that may be done.) It is also useful in testing receivers, in that electrically it resembles an antenna, but does not pick up external noise and signals, a desirable feature in some tests.

For transmitter tests the dummy antenna must be capable of dissipating safely the entire power output of the transmitter. Since for most testing it is desirable that the dummy simulate a perfectly-matched transmission line, it should be a pure resistance, usually of approximately 52 or 73

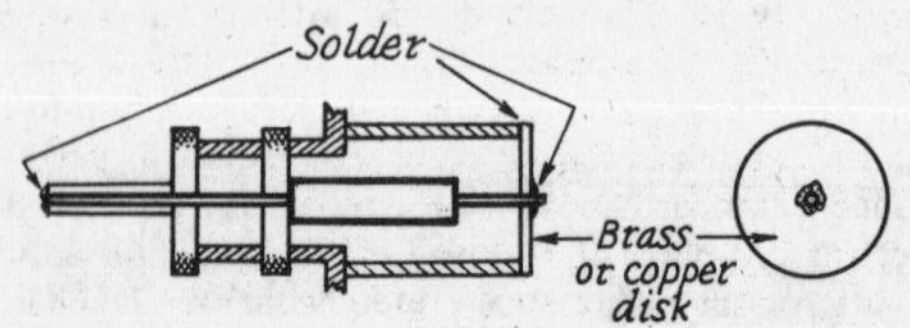

Fig. 17-24 – Dummy antenna made by mounting a composition resistor in a PL-259 coaxial plug. Only the inner portion of the plug is shown; the cap screws on after the assembly is completed.

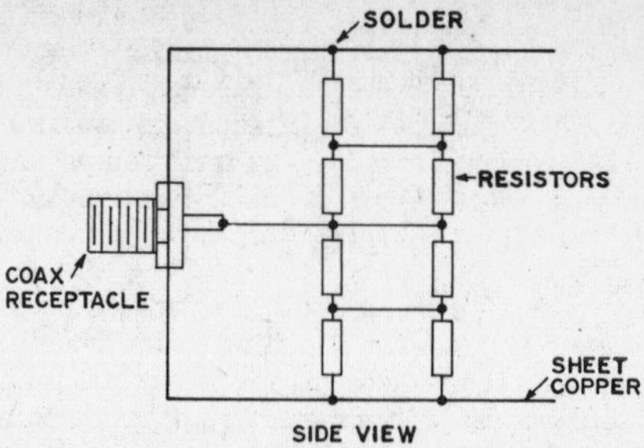

Fig. 17-25 – Using resistors in series-parallel to increase the power rating of a small dummy antenna. Mounted in this way on pieces of flat copper, inductance is reduced to a minimum. Eight 100-ohm 2-watt composition resistors in two groups, each four resistors in parallel, can be connected in series to form a 50-ohm dummy. The open construction shown permits free air circulation. Resistors drawn heavy are in one "deck"; light ones are in the other.

ohms. This is a severe limitation in home construction, because nonreactive resistors of more than a few watts rated safe dissipation are very difficult to obtain. (There are, however, dummy antenna kits available that can handle up to a kilowatt.)

For receiver and minipower transmitter testing an excellent dummy antenna can be made by installing a 51- or 75-ohm composition resistor in a PL-259 fitting as shown in Fig. 17-24. Sizes from one-half to two watts are satisfactory. The disk at the end helps reduce lead inductance and completes the shielding. Dummy antennas made in this way have good characteristics through the vhf bands as well as at all lower frequencies.

Increasing Power Ratings

More power can be handled by using a number of 2-watt resistors in parallel, or series-parallel, but at the expense of introducing some reactance. Nevertheless, if some departure from the ideal impedance characteristics can be tolerated this is a practical method for getting increased dissipations. The principal problem is stray inductance which can be minimized by mounting the resistors on flat copper strips or sheets, as suggested in Fig. 17-25.

The power rating on resistors is a *continuous* rating in free air. In practice, the maximum power dissipated can be increased in proportion to the reduction in duty cycle. Thus with keying, which has a duty cycle of about 1/2, the rating can be doubled. With sideband the duty cycle is usually not over about 1/3. The best way of judging is to feel the resistors occasionally; if too hot to touch, they may be dissipating more power than they are rated for.

THE OSCILLOSCOPE

The electrostatically deflected cathode-ray tube, with appropriate associated equipment, is capable of displaying both low- and radio-frequency signals on its fluorescent screen, in a form which lends itself to ready interpretation. (In contrast, the magnetically deflected television picture tube is not at all suitable for measurement purposes.) In the usual display presentation, the fluorescent spot moves across the screen horizontally at some known rate (**horizontal deflection** or **horizontal sweep**) and simultaneously is moved vertically by the signal voltage being examined (**vertical deflection**). Because of the retentivity of the screen and the eye, a rapidly deflected spot appears as a continuous line. Thus a varying signal voltage causes a **pattern** to appear on the screen.

Conventionally, oscilloscope circuits are designed so that in vertical deflection the spot moves upward as the signal voltage becomes more positive with respect to ground, and vice versa (there are exceptions, however). Also, the horizontal deflection is such that with an ac sweep voltage – the simplest form – positive is to the right; with a **linear sweep** – one which moves the spot at a uniform rate across the screen and then at the end of its travel snaps it back very quickly to the starting point – *time* progresses to the right.

Most cathode-ray tubes for oscilloscope work require a deflection amplitude of about 50 volts per inch. For displaying small signals, therefore, considerable amplification is needed. Also, special circuits have to be used for linear deflection. The design of amplifiers and linear deflection circuits is complicated, and extensive texts are available. For checking modulation of transmitters, a principal amateur use of the scope, quite simple circuits suffice. A 60-Hz voltage from the power line makes a satisfactory horizontal sweep, and the voltage required for vertical deflection can easily be obtained from transmitter rf circuits without amplification.

For general measurement purposes amplifiers and linear deflection circuits are needed. The most economical and satisfactory way to obtain a scope having these features is to assemble one of the many kits available.

Simple Oscilloscope Circuit

Fig. 17-26 is an oscilloscope circuit that has all the essentials for modulation monitoring: controls for centering, focusing, and adjusting the brightness of the fluorescent spot; voltage dividers to supply proper electrode potentials to the cathode-ray tube; and means for coupling the vertical and horizontal signals to the deflection plates.

The circuit can be used with electrostatic-deflection tubes from two to five inches in face diameter, with voltages up to 2500. Either set of deflecting electrodes (D1D2, or D3D4) may be used for either horizontal or vertical deflection, depending on how the tube is mounted.

In Fig. 17-26 the centering controls are not too high above electrical ground, so they do not need special insulation. However, the focusing and intensity controls are at a high voltage above ground and therefore should be carefully insulated. Insulated couplings or extension shafts should be used.

The tube should be protected from stray magnetic fields, either by enclosing it in an iron or steel box or by using one of the special CR tube

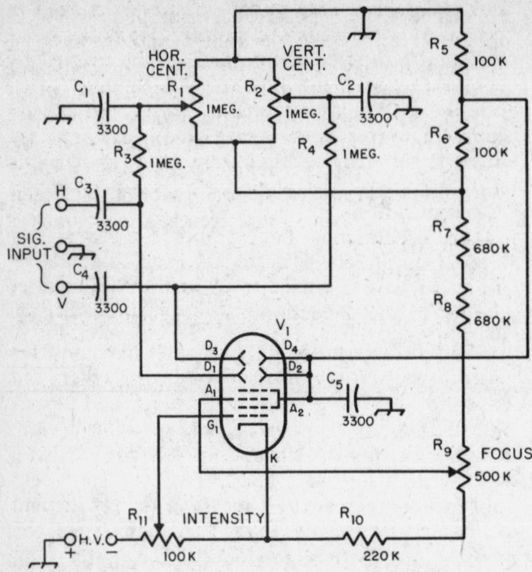

Fig. 17-26 – Oscilloscope circuit for modulation monitoring. Constants are for 1500- to 2500-volt high-voltage supply. For 1000 to 1500 volts, omit R8 and connect the bottom end of R7 to the top end of R9.
C1-C5, incl. – 1000-volt disk ceramic.
R1, R2, R9, R11 – Volume-control type, linear taper. R9 and R11 must be well insulated from chassis.
R3, R4, R5, R6, R10 – 1/2 watt.
R7, R8 – 1 watt.
V1 – Electrostatic-deflection cathode-ray tube, 2- to 5-inch. Base connections and heater ratings vary with type chosen.

shields available. If the heater transformer (or other transformer) is mounted in the same cabinet, care must be used to place it so the stray field around it does not deflect the spot. The spot cannot be focused to a fine point when influenced by a transformer field. The heater transformer must be well insulated, and one side of the heater should be connected to the cathode. The high-voltage dc can be taken from the transmitter plate supply; the current required is negligible.

Methods for connecting the oscilloscope to a transmitter for checking or monitoring modulation are given in earlier chapters.

Quasi-Linear Sweep

For wave-envelope patterns that require a fairly linear horizontal sweep, Fig. 17-27 shows a method of using the substantially linear portion of the 60-Hz sine wave – the "center" portion where the wave goes through zero and reverses polarity. A 60-Hz transformer with a center-tapped secondary winding is required. The voltage should be sufficient to deflect the spot well off the screen on both sides – 250 to 350 volts, usually. With such "over-deflection" the sweep is fairly linear, but it is as bright on retrace as on left-to-right. To blank it in one direction, it is necessary to couple the ac to the No. 1 grid of the CR tube as shown.

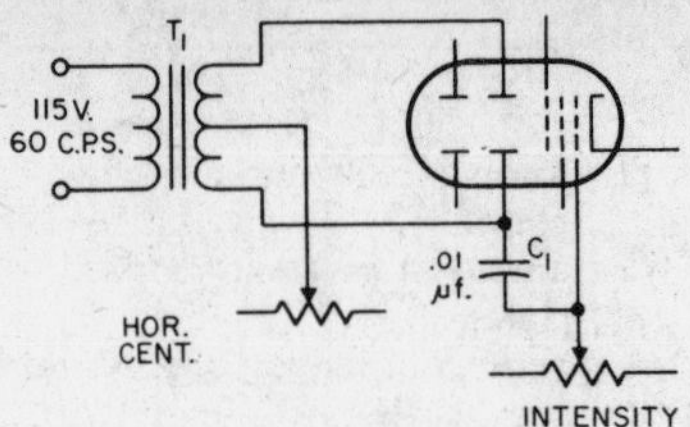

Fig. 17-27 – A quasi-linear time base for an oscilloscope can be obtained from the "center" portion of a sine wave. Coupling the ac to the grid gives intensity modulation that blanks the retrace.
C1 – Ceramic capacitor of adequate voltage rating.
T1 – 250- to 350-volt center-tapped secondary. If voltage is too high, use dropping resistor in primary side.

Lissajous Figures

When sinusoidal ac voltages are applied to both sets of deflecting plates in the oscilloscope the resultant pattern depends on the relative amplitudes, frequencies and phases of the two voltages. If the ratio between the two frequencies is constant and can be expressed in integers a stationary pattern will be produced.

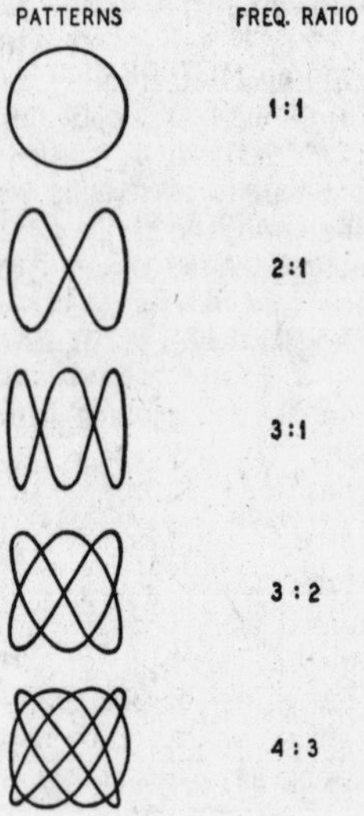

PATTERNS FREQ. RATIO
1:1
2:1
3:1
3 : 2
4 : 3

Fig. 17-28 – Lissajous figures and corresponding frequency ratios for a 90-degree phase relationship between the voltages applied to the two sets of deflecting plates.

The stationary patterns obtained in this way are called **Lissajous figures.** Examples of some of the simpler Lissajous figures are given in Fig. 17-28. The frequency ratio is found by counting the number of loops along two adjacent edges. Thus in the third figure from the top there are three loops along a horizontal edge and only one along the vertical, so the ratio of the vertical frequency to the horizontal frequency is 3 to 1. Similarly, in the fifth figure from the top there are four loops along the horizontal edge and three along the vertical edge, giving a ratio of 4 to 3. Assuming that the known frequency is applied to the horizontal plates, the unknown frequency is

$$f2 = \frac{n2}{n1}\ f1$$

where $f1$ = known frequency applied to horizontal plates,
$f2$ = unknown frequency applied to vertical plates,
$n1$ = number of loops along a vertical edge and,
$n2$ = number of loops along a horizontal edge

An important application of Lissajous figures is in the calibration of audio-frequency signal generators. For very low frequencies the 60-Hz power-line frequency is held accurately enough to be used as a standard in most localities. The medium audio-frequency range can be covered by comparison with the 440- and 600-Hz modulation on the WWV transmissions. It is possible to calibrate over a 10-to-1 range, both upwards and downwards, from each of the latter frequencies and thus cover the audio range useful for voice communication.

An oscilloscope having both horizontal and vertical amplifiers is desirable, since it is convenient to have a means for adjusting the voltages applied to the deflection plates to secure a suitable pattern size.

MARKER GENERATOR FOR 100, 50 AND 25 KHZ

The frequency generator in the accompanying illustrations will deliver marker signals of usable strength well into the vhf region when its output is connected to the antenna input terminals of a communications receiver. It uses a 100-kHz crystal in an integrated-circuit version of the solid-state multivibrator oscillator shown earlier. The oscillator is followed by a two-stage IC divider which produces 50- and 25-kHz marker intervals. Two inexpensive ICs are used, an MC-724P quad gate and an MC790P dual JK flip-flop. Two of the gates in the MC724P are used for the oscillator and a third serves as a following buffer amplifier and "squarer" for driving the first divide-by-2 circuit in the MC790P. This divider then drives the second divide-by-2 flip-flop. Outputs at the three frequencies are taken through a 3-position switch from taps as shown in the circuit diagram, Fig. 17-30.

Fig. 17-29 – Frequency marker generating 100-, 50-, or 25-kHz intervals. Battery power supply (two "D" cells) is inside the cabinet, a 3 X 4 X 6-inch aluminum chassis with bottom plate. The trimmer capacitor for fine adjustment of frequency is available through the hole in the top near the left front.

Two of the three poles of the 4-position switch are used for controlling the collector voltage for the ICs. Voltage is on the MC724P in all active positions of the switch, but is applied to the MC790P only when 50- and 25-kHz markers are required. This saves battery power, since the MC790P takes considerably more current than the MC724P.

The outputs on all three frequencies are good square waves. To assure reasonably constant harmonic strength through the hf spectrum the output is coupled to the receiver through a small capacitance which tends to attenuate the lower-frequency harmonics. This capacitance, C3, is not critical as to value and may be varied to suit individual preferences. The value shown, 22 pF, is satisfactory for working into a receiver having an input impedance of 50 ohms.

At 3 volts dc input the current taken in the 100-kHz position of S1 is 8 mA. In the 50- and 25-kHz positions the total current (both ICs) is 35 mA. The generator continues to work satisfactorily when the voltage drops as low as 1.5 volts. The oscillator frequency is subject to change as the voltage is lowered, the frequency shift amounting to approximately 30 Hz at 15 MHz on going from 3 to 2 volts. There is a slight frequency shift between the 100-kHz and 50/25-kHz positions, but this amounts to only 6 or 7 Hz at 15 MHz. Frequency changes resulting from temperature variations are larger; they may be as much as a few hundred Hz at 15 MHz in normal room-temperature variations. All such frequency changes can be compensated for by adjusting C2, and it is good practice to check the frequency occasionally against one of the WWV transmissions, readjusting C2 if necessary.

Layout and Construction

The physical layout of the circuit can be varied to suit the builder's tastes. The size of the box containing the generator shown in the photographs makes the batteries easily accessible for replacement. The method of mounting the crystal and C2 allows the latter to be reached through the top of the box for screwdriver adjustment, and makes possible the easy removal of the crystal since it plugs into a standard crystal socket. There is ample room for soldering the various wires that lead to the switch from the etched board on which the ICs, resistors, and C1 are mounted. The output

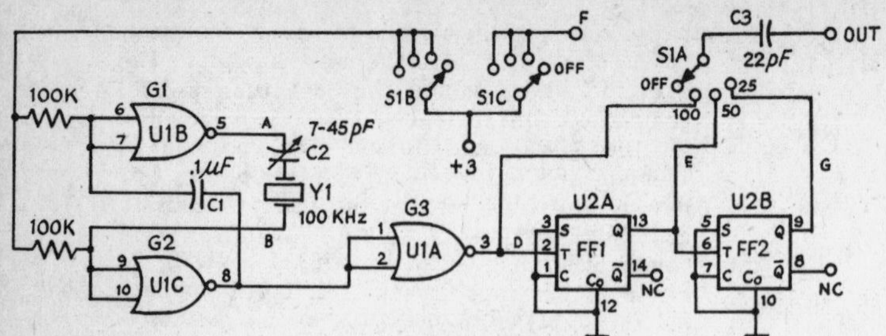

C1 – 0.1μF paper, low voltage.
C2 – 7-45-pF ceramic trimmer.
C3 – 22-pF dipped mica (ceramic also satisfactory).
S1 – 3-pole, 4-position rotary (Mallory 3134J).
U1 – Quad 2-input NOR gate, 1 section unused (Motorola MC724P).
U2 – Dual J-K flip-flop (Motorola MC790P).

Fig. 17-30 – Marker generator circuit. Pin 4 of both ICs is grounded. Connect pin 11 of U1 to point C, and pin 11 of U2 to point F.

jack is placed at the rear where it is convenient when the unit is alongside a receiver.

An etched board does not have to be used for wiring the ICs and associated parts, although it makes for neatness in construction. The wiring plan used in this one is shown in Fig. 17-32. Fig. 17-32 is not a conventional template, but is a scale drawing showing how the etched connections can run with a minimum number of cross-over points where jumpers are required (only one is needed in this layout). In following the wiring plan the resist can be put on as desired, so long as the separation between conductors is great enough to prevent short-circuits.

Fig. 17-32 shows the front or component side of the board. To get the reversed drawing that would be followed on the copper side, place a piece of paper under the figure, with a face-up piece of carbon paper under it. Then trace the wiring with a sharp pencil and the layout will be transferred to the back of the paper. The points where holes are to be drilled are shown by small dots and circles, the latter indicating the points at which external connections are to be made.

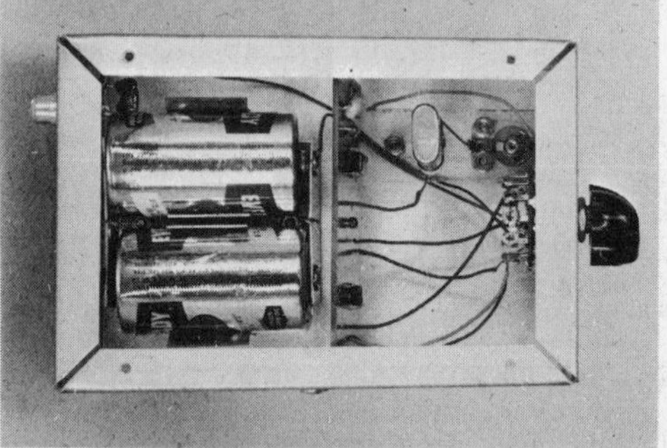

Fig. 17-31 – Integrated circuits and associated fixed capacitors and resistors are mounted on an etched broad measuring 3 3/4 X 2 1/2 inches, supported from one wall by an aluminum bracket. The 100-kHz crystal and trimmer capacitor are on a 1 X 2-inch plastic strip supported below the top on 1/2-inch spacers, with the capacitor facing upward so it can be adjusted from outside. The two dry cells are in a dual holder (available from electronics supply stores). The output connector is a phono jack, mounted on the rear wall (upper left in this view) with C3.

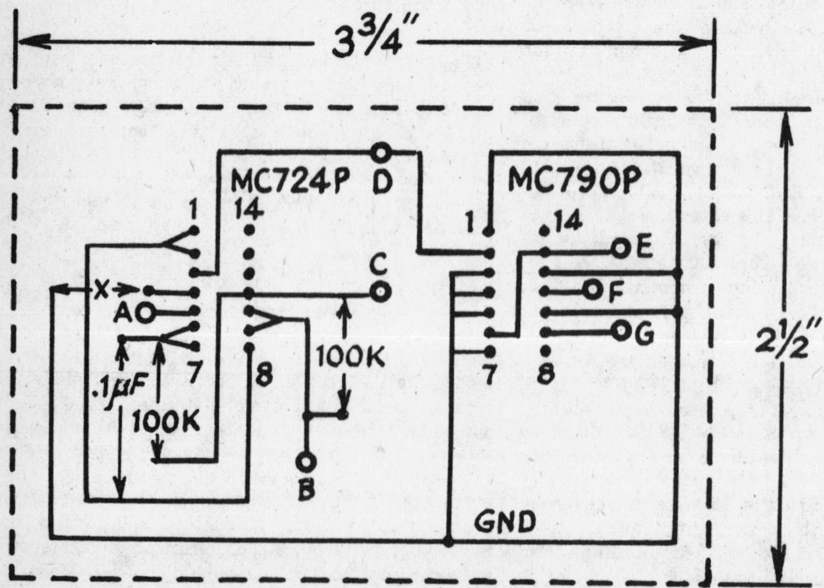

Fig. 17-32 – Wiring plan for the circuit board, component side. Dimensions for placement of parts are exact. X – jumper. Other letters indicate external connection points, corresponding to similarly lettered connections in Fig. 17-30.

TWO-TONE AUDIO TEST GENERATOR

The audio generator shown in the accompanying illustrations generates two audio frequencies which either can be combined to produce a two-tone signal for ssb transmitter testing or used independently for any test requiring a single audio-frequency voltage. Construction is easy and procurement of parts is simple because the generator makes use of RCA integrated-circuit kits. Only a few easy-to-get additional components are required.

A pair of RCA KC-4002 audio-oscillator modules are used as the tone generators. The output of these oscillators should be as free from harmonics as possible, and the tone frequencies used should not be harmonically related. A mixer combines the output of the two oscillators, and this mixing process must also be distortion free. One major objective of two-tone testing is to check the amount of distortion produced in the transmitter, so you need a clean signal from the generator to start with. Otherwise, harmonics from the generator will be indistinguishable from those produced in the transmitter. The circuit is shown in Fig. 17-34; parts not supplied with the kits are marked with an asterisk.

The capacitors supplied with the KC-4002 provide an output frequency of 2000 Hz. One oscillator is used on this frequency, and the other shifted down to 800 Hz by changing C1, C2 and C3. The capacitor values required are not standard so two capacitors are used in parallel in each case.

Fig. 17-33 – The two-tone audio test generator. Subminiature controls and switches are used on the front panel. The box is homemade; it consists of two U-shaped pieces of sheet aluminum, one forming the chassis, the other the cover. Overall size is 7 1/2 X 4 1/4 X 1 1/4 inches. For appearance's sake, the top cover overhangs the front panel by 1/4 inch. The controls adjust the output level and balance the relative tone levels.

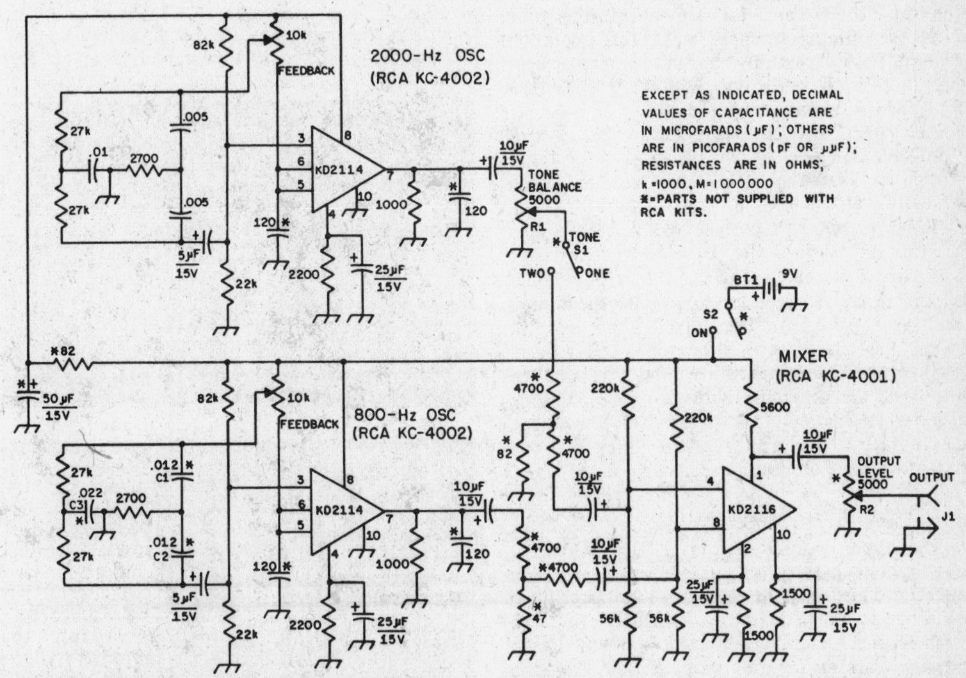

Fig. 17-34 – Circuit diagram of the integrated-circuit two-tone test generator (IC-TT). Resistors are 1/2-watt composition; capacitors with polarity marked are electrolytic, others are disk ceramic. All parts are supplied with the RCA kits, except those marked with an asterisk.

BT1 – 9-volt transistor-radio type.

C1, C2 – .01- and .002-μF disk ceramic (in parallel).

C3 – .02- and .002-μF disk ceramic (in parallel).

J1 – Phono type.

R1, R2 – Miniature control (Mallory MLC53L).

S1, S2 – Spdt miniature toggle (Radio Shack 275-376).

Fig. 17-35 — Interior view of the IC-TT. Interconnections carrying audio signals use subminiature coax to prevent hum pickup. A homemade clip holds the battery in place. Feedback adjustment of each oscillator is made with the controls on the KC-4002 boards.

While testing this system, both oscillators produced very healthy outputs on about 5 MHz in addition to the desired audio tones. A 120-pF capacitor across the input killed this oscillation, but then a weaker output at 50 MHz appeared. Another 120-pF capacitor was added, this time across the output terminals, and stable operation resulted. Both capacitors must have their leads cut very short to be effective. With these modifications, the ICs operate satisfactorily.

The mixer, a KC-2001 kit, showed no signs of rf oscillations. The output of the KC-4002s is far in excess of what the mixer can handle, so an attenuator was added on the output of each oscillator to reduce the level to a suitable value. Control R1 allows the output level of one oscillator to be matched to the other (both tones must be of equal amplitude to produce the desired oscillosope patterns). The mixer is an additive device, the output with two equal tones being twice that of either tone alone. Thus, checking the output of the generator with two- and one-tone output, alternately, for a 2 to 1 voltage relationship, is one way of determining that the BALANCE control is set correctly.

Alignment

The upper picture of Fig. 17-36 shows the proper scope pattern for single-tone output. The feedback adjustment in each oscillator is critical; too little feedback and the oscillator quits, too much feedback and the harmonic content of the outputs goes up. The best setting for the FEEDBACK control is at a point where oscillation just starts. Also, the oscillator modules are voltage-sensitive. If the battery voltages goes down during extended use, the oscillators may stop working, and the feedback must be increased to get them going again. A little experimentation will show the best point at which to set the FEEDBACK control. The oscillators should be set up and checked separately, and then connected to the mixer module.

The final alignment of the generator is as follows: Switch to two-tone output (S1 closed) and adjust the FEEDBACK control on the 2000-Hz oscillator until oscillation ceases. At this point you should have output from the 800-Hz oscillator alone. With the BALANCE control set at midrange, connect an oscilloscope to the output of the generator and note the height of the output pattern. S1 should then be set for single-tone output, and the FEEDBACK control reset so that the 2000-Hz oscillator starts. The FEEDBACK control should be adjusted so that the pattern height produced on the scope is close to that of the 800-Hz oscillator. Minor differences can be corrected with the BALANCE control.

Switching to two-tone output, you should get a pattern similar to the lower picture in Fig. 17-36. The two-tone pattern will be difficult to sync on an average oscilloscope because of the different frequency components in the signal. The pattern height of the two-tone output on the scope should be double that obtained with a single tone, as stated earlier.

Methods of using a two-tone generator in ssb transmitter testing are described in the chapter on single sideband principles and applications. (From May 1970 *QST*.)

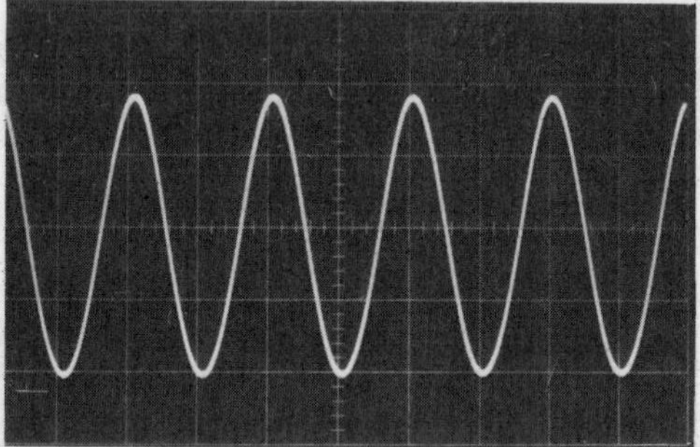

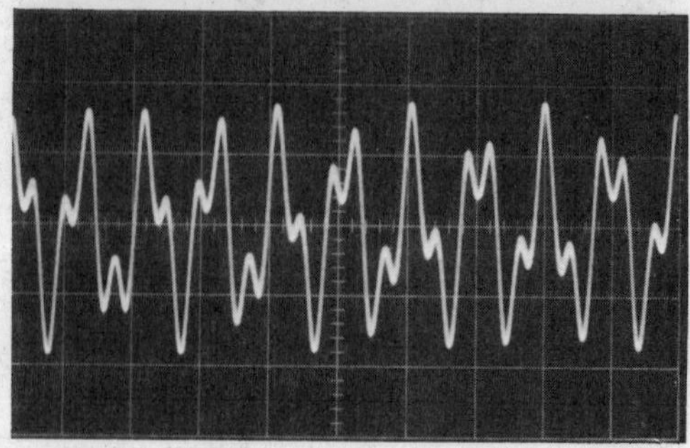

Fig. 17-36 — Proper output waveforms from the generator: (Upper) sine wave, indicating correct adjustment of the FEEDBACK control; (Lower) two-tone output.

DIP METERS FOR THE HF-VHF-UHF RANGE

Fig. 17-37 – Dip meter covering the range 1.7 to 275 MHz, with the 90- to 165-MHz coil in place.

Figs. 17-37 through 17-41 show representative construction of vacuum-tube dip meters for the frequencies of interest to amateurs. Two separate designs are required to cover the lower frequencies along with the vhf-uhf range. The same power supply/meter unit serves for both. The 6CW4 Nuvistor triode is used in both meters.

Referring to the circuit in Fig. 17-38, a resistor, R2, is plugged in with each coil (the resistor is mounted in the coil form). It forms a voltage divider with the normal grid leak, R1, and brings the metering circuit into the best range for the transistor dc amplifier.

A small aluminum bracket supports the Nuvistor socket within the 2 1/4 X 2 1/4 X 4-inch Minibox that is used as a housing. A 5-pin socket (Amphenol 78-S5S) is mounted at one end of the Minibox, and the variable capacitor stator leads are soldered directly to two of the pins. Coils in the low-frequency ranges are wound with enameled wire on 3/4-inch diameter forms. In the intermediate ranges coil stock (B&W Miniductor) is mounted inside the coil forms, with one end of the coil close to the open end of the form, for ease in coupling. The two highest-range coils are hairpin loops of No. 14 wire, covered with insulation as a safety precaution. In every case the associated R2 is mounted in the coil form. The highest range requires that only the base of the coil form be used, since the loop is shorter than the form.

The power supply may be included with the oscillator, but since this increases the bulk and weight a separate supply is often desirable. The power supply shown in Fig. 17-40 uses a miniature power transformer with a silicon rectifier and a simple filter to give approximately 120 volts for the oscillator plate. It is also built in a 2 1/4 X 2 1/4 X 4-inch Minibox. The two Miniboxes are connected by a length of 4-conductor cable.

Either meter may be used as an indicating-type absorption wavemeter by removing the plate voltage and using the grid and cathode of the tube as a diode.

UHF Grid-Dip Oscillator

The range of the grid-dip meter shown in Fig. 17-39 is from 275 to 725 MHz, a higher range than most of the inexpensive meters now available. It is able to cover these high frequencies by virtue of the 6CW4 tube and the series-tuned circuit.

The uhf grid-dip meter is built in a 2 1/4 X 2 1/4 X 4-inch Minibox. The "heart" of the meter is the oscillator section, which is built on a 1 3/4 X 1 7/8-inch piece of 1/8-inch thick polystyrene. The Nuvistor socket is mounted in one corner and the tuning capacitor is mounted a little above center. The coil socket, a National CS-6, is mounted on the end of the Minibox. The polystyrene sheet is supported by four 1-inch 6-32 screws, and the sockets and variable capacitor are positioned so that direct connections can be made between plate pin and coil socket, capacitor rotor and coil socket, and capacitor stator and grid pin. The various resistors and rf chokes are supported at one end by a multiple-terminal tie strip mounted on the polystyrene sheet and at the other end by the socket pins and other terminals.

The coils are made from No. 10 tinned copper wire; as a safety precaution they are covered except at the tips by clear plastic insulation. Details are given in Fig. 17-41.

Frequency calibration of the meter can be started by reference to uhf TV stations in the area, if any, or by reference to 420-MHz amateur gear.

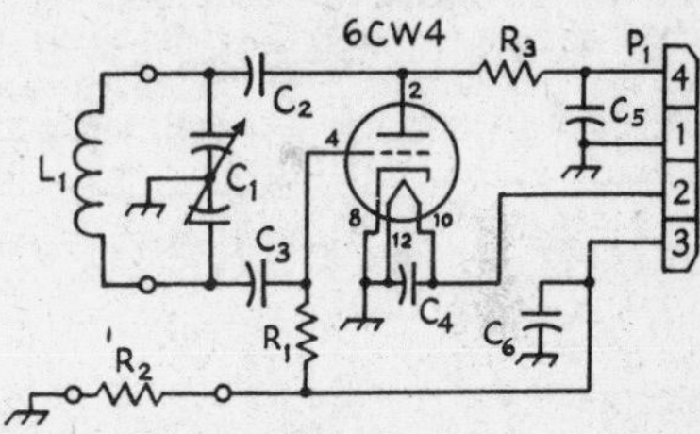

Fig. 17-38 – Circuit diagram of the hf-vhf dip meter.

C1 – 50 pF per section (Johnson 167-11 with stator bars sawed between 6th and 7th plates).
C2, C3 – 100-pF ceramic.
C4, C5, C6 – .001-μF disk ceramic.
P1 – 4-pin chassis plug (Amphenol 86-CP4).
R1 – 47,000 ohms, 1/2 watt.
R2 – See table below.
R3 – 10,000 ohms.

Range	*L1*	*R2*
1.7-3.2 MHz	195 turns No. 34 enam.*	680
2.7-5.0	110 turns No. 30 enam.*	470
4.4-7.8	51 1/2 turns No. 30 enam.*	470
7.5-13.2	24 1/2 turns No. 30 enam.*	470
12-22	31 t. No. 24 (B&W 3004)**	1000
20-36	14 t. No. 24 (B&W 3004)**	680
33-60	8 1/2 t. No. 20 (B&W 3003)***	680
54-99	3 3/4 t. No. 20 (B&W 3003)***	1000
90-165	3 3/8-inch loop No. 14 1/2-inch separation	1500
150-275	1 1/4-inch loop No. 14, 1/4-inch separation	3300

* Wound on 3/4-inch diameter polystyrene form.
**32 tpi ***16 tpi

Fig. 17-39 – Dip meter for the 300- to 700-MHz range. The oscillator section is at the left in its own case, and the power supply plus transistorized indicator is at the center and right. In the oscillator section, the 6CW4 (Nuvistor) socket is to the left of the tuning capacitor.

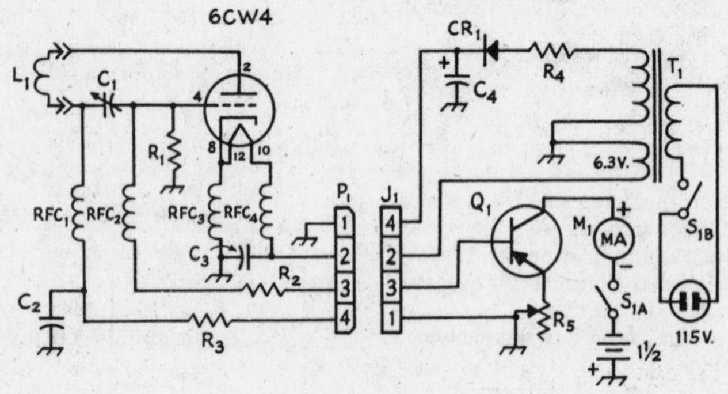

Fig. 17-40 – Circuit diagram of the uhf dip meter.

C1 – 8-pF midget variable (Hammarlund MAC-10 with one rotor plate removed).
C2 – 150-pF ceramic.
C3 – .001-μF ceramic.
C4 – 20μF at 450-V electrolytic.
CR1– 400 PRV rectifier (Sarkes Tarzian 2F4).
J1 – 4-pin tube socket.
M1 – 0-500 microammeter.
P1 – 4-pin plug (Amphenol 86-CP4).
Q1 – Motorola HEP253 transistor.
R1 – 330 ohms, 1 watt.
R2 – 47,000 ohms, 1/2 watt.
R3 – 10,000 ohms.
R4 – 22 ohms; 1/2 watt.
R5 – 10,000-ohm potentiometer.
RFC1, RFC2 – 22-μH rf choke (Millen 34300-22).
RFC3, RFC4 – 0.82-μH rf choke (Millen 34300-.82).
S1A, S1B – Dpst, part of R5. Switches should be open when R5 is at maximum resistance.
T1 – 6.3- and 125-V transformer (Knight 61 G 410).

Range	*Dimension "L"*	*"M"*
271-324 MHz	2 3/4	11/16
312-378	3 1/8	–
372-463	2	–
413-519	1 5/8	–
446-565	1 1/4	–
544-730	1/2*	–

* Shape closed end to be nearly square.

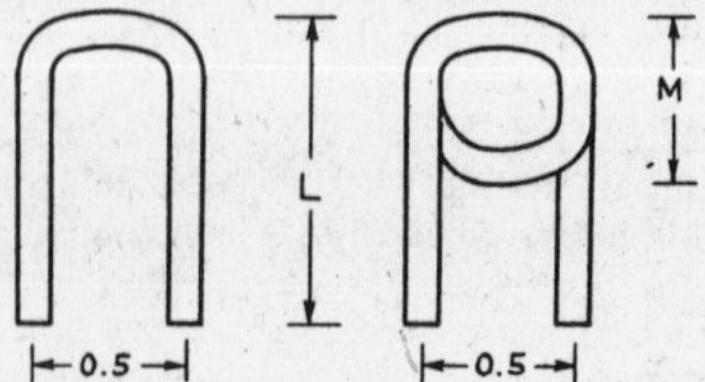

Fig. 17-41 – Details of the coils used in the uhf grid-dip meter. The material is No. 10 tinned-copper wire. One turn in end of low-frequency coil.

ABSORPTION FREQUENCY METER FOR 1.6-300 MHZ

The absorption frequency meter in the accompanying illustrations uses six plug-in coils (L1 in Fig. 17-43) to cover the frequency range 1.6-300 MHz. The indicator is a miniature 0-1 milliammeter. L1 is tapped appropriately for delivering maximum power to the meter, and the rf output is rectified by CR1, followed by an rf filter consisting of C2, C3 and RFC1. The circuit is built in a 2 1/8 X 3 X 5 1/4-inch Minibox, with C1 mounted so that the rotor tab and stator support bar can be soldered directly to the coil-socket terminals. The meter, M1, is mounted at the end opposite C1.

The coils are wound on Millen type 45004 four-prong coil forms. Taps are made by doubling the wire back on itself at the appropriate point, feeding the double portion through the hole in the side of the form, twisting, and inserting the twisted pair into the coil-form pin. Clean off the enamel where the tap goes into the pin so a good soldered connection can be made. The finished coils can be given several coats of clear spray lacquer for protection. Construction of the 95-300 MHz coil will be easier if 3/4 inch of the form is sawed off first.

Fig. 17-42 – Absorption frequency meter for 1.6-300 MHz.

FIELD-STRENGTH MEASUREMENTS

The radiation intensity from an antenna is measured with a device that is essentially a very simple receiver equipped with an indicator to give a visual representation of the comparative signal strength. Such a **field-strength meter** is used with a "pickup antenna," which should always have the same polarization as the antenna being checked – e.g., the pick-up antenna should be horizontal if the transmitting antenna is. Care should be taken to prevent stray pickup by the field-strength meter or by any transmission line that may connect it to the pickup antenna.

Field-strength measurements preferably should be made at a distance of several wavelengths from the transmitting antenna being tested. Measurements made within a wavelength of the antenna may be misleading, because of the possibility that the measuring equipment may be responding to the combined induction and radiation fields of the antenna, rather than to the radiation field alone. Also, if the pickup antenna has dimensions comparable with those of the antenna under test it is likely that with closer spacing the coupling between the two antennas will be great enough to cause the pickup antenna to tend to become part of the radiating system and thus result in misleading field-strength readings.

A desirable form of pickup antenna is a dipole installed at the same height as the antenna being

Coil Range	*A (inches)*	*B (inches)*	*Wire size*[1]	*Turns*	*Tap*[2]
1.6–4 MHz	3/8	7/8	No. 30	125	32 turns
3.2–7.4 MHz	1/8	1/4	No. 30	35	11
6–14 MHz	3/8	3/4	No. 20	27	8
12–29 MHz	1/8	1/4	No. 20	10	3
30–90 MHz	4 turns of No. 20, turns spaced to cover 1 inch; tap is 1 1/2 turns from ground end.				
95–300 MHz	Hairpin of No. 14 tinned wire, 1/2-inch spacing, 2 inches long including coil pins, tapped 1 1/2 inch from ground.				

Fig. 17-43 – Circuit diagram of the frequency meter.
C1 – 50-pF variable (Millen 20050).
C2, C3 – .001-μF disk ceramic.
CR1 – 1N34A germanium diode.
M1 – 0-1 milliammeter.
L1 – See coil table.
RFC1 – 2.5-mH rf choke (Millen 34000-2500).

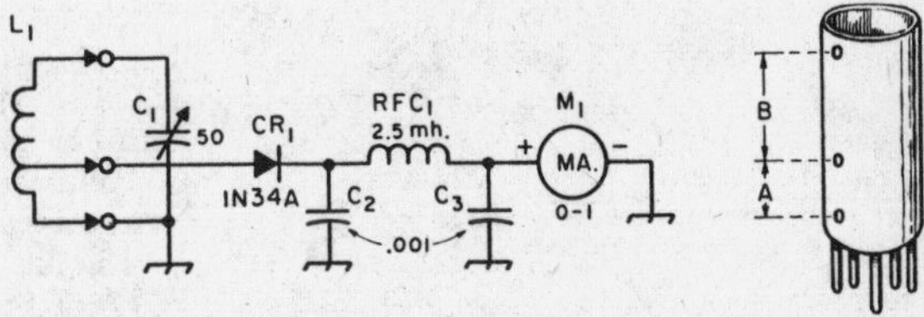

tested, with low-impedance balanced line connected at the center to transfer the rf signal to the field-strength meter. The length of the dipole need only be great enough to give adequate meter readings.

Field-Strength Meters

The absorption frequency meter just described may be used as a field-strength meter in conjunction with a pickup antenna. Coupling between the frequency-meter coil and the transmission line to the antenna may be a turn or two of wire wrapped around the coil at the ground end, with the ends of the wire loop connected to the ends of the line. The pickup antenna, installed in its selected position, should be adjusted in length for a suitable indication (about half scale) on the meter at the beginning of the tests. The meter of course should be tuned to the frequency being used.

The simple rectifier/milliammeter combination used in this frequency meter is not linear, so the indications tend to give an exaggerated picture of the results of changes in the antenna system under test. The readings can be made practically linear, and the sensitivity increased, by using the transistor dc amplifier circuit shown in Fig. 17-46. The 47,000-ohm resistor, R1, is substituted for M1 in Fig. 17-43. The FET amplifier with dc feedback through R2 is quite linear with respect to gate voltage. A bridge circuit, consisting of the drain-source resistance (with R2 in series), R3, R4 and R5, balances out the steady drain current, so that only the *change* in current is indicated by the 0-1 milliammeter. The meter current is balanced to zero with no signal input by means of R2.

The linear range of this amplifier is from 0.1 to 1 mA, representing a ratio of about 6.5 to 1 in applied voltage. This corresponds to a power ratio of about 40, or 16 dB.

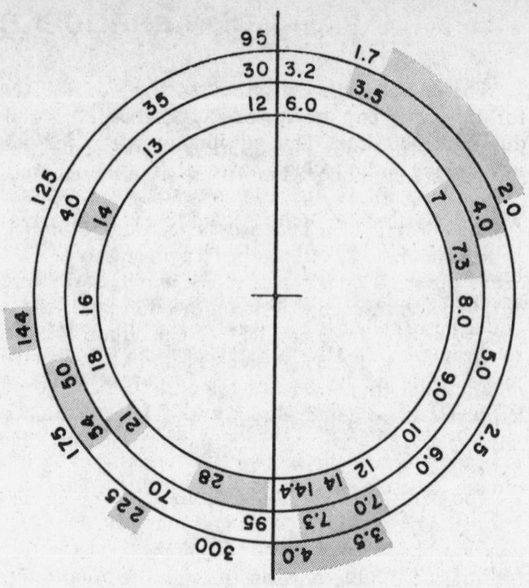

Fig. 17-45 – This dial chart may be copied full size and used as shown in Fig. 17-42 provided the tuned-circuit parts are exactly as specified in Fig. 17-43 and the construction duplicates Fig. 17-44.

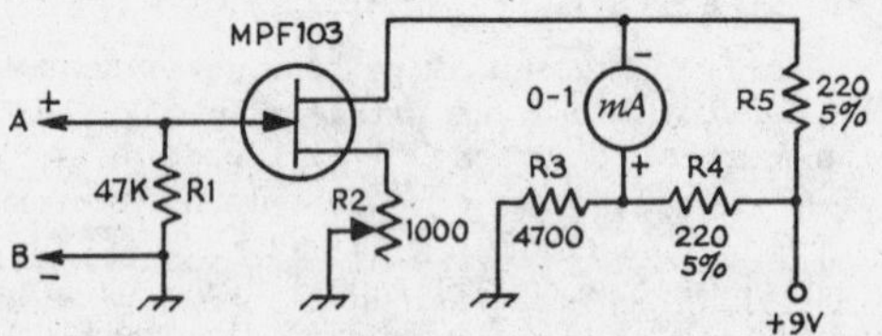

Fig. 17-46 – FET amplifier for absorption frequency meter. A and B replace the meter connections in Fig. 17-43. A 9-volt transistor radio battery may be used for drain voltage, as the total current is only 4-6 mA on the average.

Fig. 17-44 – Inside the absorption frequency meter, showing placement of tuning capacitor and coil socket.

A TESTER FOR FET AND BIPOLAR TRANSISTORS

The circuit shown is intended solely as a tester for npn and pnp transistors, junction FETs, and dual-gate MOSETs. This equipment is not for use in checking audio or high-power rf transistors.

The circuit of Fig. 1 is an oscillator which is wired so that it will test various small-signal transistors by switching the battery polarity and bias voltage. A crystal for the upper range of the hf spectrum is wired into the circuit permanently, but could be installed in a crystal socket if the builder so desires. A 20-MHz crystal was chosen for this model. Any hf crystal cut for fundamental mode operation can be used.

When testing FETs the bias switch, S3, is placed in the FET position, thus removing R2 from the circuit. However, when testing bipolar transistors the switch position must be changed to BIPOL so that forward bias can be applied to the base of the bipolar transistor under test. R1 is always in the circuit, and serves as a gate-leak resistor for FETs being evaluated. It becomes part of the bias network when bipolars are under test. C1 is used for feedback in combination with the internal capacitances of the transistors being checked. Its value may have to be changed experimentally if crystals for lower frequencies are utilized in the circuit. Generally speaking, the lower the crystal frequency, the greater the amount of capacitance needed to assure oscillation. Use only that amount necessary to provide quick starting of the oscillator.

Components R3 and R4 are used as a voltage divider to provide bias for dual-gate MOSFETs. C2 is kept small in value to minimize loading of the oscillator by the low-impedance voltage doubler, CR1 and CR2. Rectified rf from the oscillator is monitored on M1. Meter deflection is regulated manually by means of control R5. S1 is used to select the desired supply voltage polarity – negative ground for testing n-channel FETs and npn bipolars, and a positive ground when working with p-channel and pnp devices.

When testing MOSFETs that are not gate protected (3N140 for one), make certain that the transistor leads are shorted together until the device is seated in the test socket. Static charges on one's hands can be sufficiently great to damage the insulation within the transistor. Use a single strand of wire from some No. 22 or 24 stranded hookup wire, wrapping it two or three times around the pigtails of the FET as close to the transistor body as possible. After the FET is plugged into the

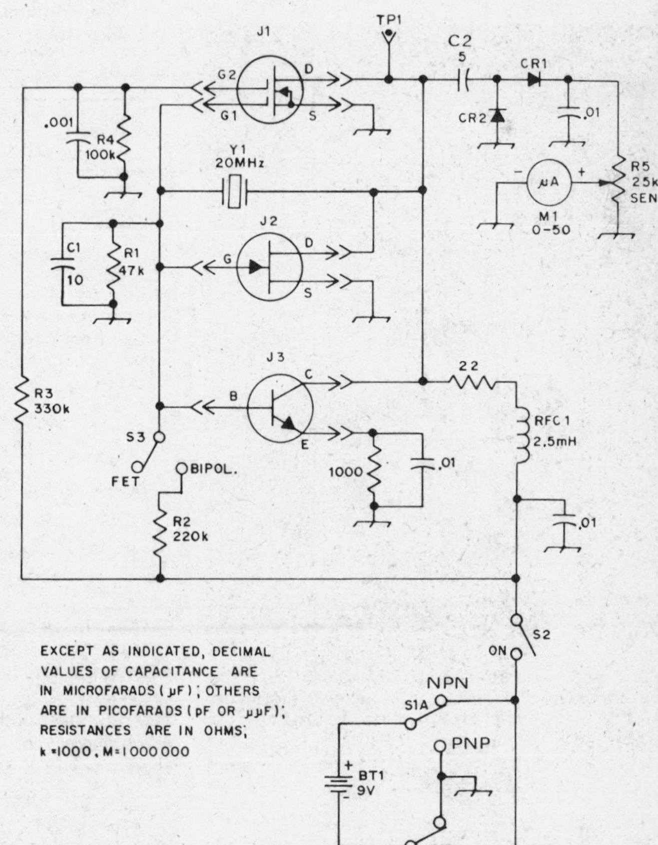

Fig. 1 – Schematic diagram of the transistor tester. Capacitors are disk ceramic or mica. Resistors are 1/2 or 1/4-watt composition execet for R5. Estimated cost for this tester (all parts new) is $15. Numbered components not appearing in parts list are so designated for text discussion.

BT1 – Small 9-V transistor-radio battery.
CR1, CR2 – 1N34A germanium diode or equiv.
J1 – Four-terminal transistor socket.
J2, J3 – Three-terminal transistor socket.
M1 – Microampere meter. Calectro D1-910 used here.
R5 – 25,000-ohm linear-taper composition control with switch.
RFC1 2.5-mH rf choke.
S1 – Two-pole double-throw miniature toggle.
S2 – Part of R5.
S3 – Spst miniature toggle.
Y1 – Surplus crystal (see tex).

socket, unwrap the wire and perform the tests. (It's not a bad idea to have an earth ground connected to the case of the tester when checking unprotected FETs.) Put the shorting wire back on the FET leads before removing the unit from the tester.

The meter indication is significant in checking any type of transistor. If the device is open, shorted, or extremely leaky, no oscillation will take place, and the meter will not deflect. The higher the meter reading, the greater the vigor of the transistor at the operating frequency. High meter readings suggest that the transistor is made for vhf or uhf service, and that its beta is medium to high. Lower readings may indicate that the transistor is designed for hf use, or that it has very low gain. Transistors that are known to be good but will not cause the circuit to oscillate are most likely made for low-frequency or audio applications.

A TESTER FOR CRYSTALS AND BIPOLAR TRANSISTORS

The circuit of Fig. 1 is intended primarily to test surplus crystals and bipolar transistors. It uses a Pierce oscillator. Battery polarity can be switched to allow testing of npn or pnp transistors. Crystal quality is indicated on M1. The greater the crystal activity, the higher the meter reading. A suitable transistor for use at Q1 (when testing crystals) is the 2N4124, MPS3563, or HEP53. All three have f_T ratings well into the vhf spectrum, and each has reasonably high beta. The two characteristics make the devices ideal as general-purpose oscillators.

This tester will work well from the upper hf range down to at least 455 kHz. S1 is used to change the value of feedback capacitance. The lower the frequency of operation, the greater the amount of capacitance required.

A transistor can be checked by plugging the unknown type into the panel socket while using a crystal of known frequency and condition. Both testers can be used as calibrators by inserting

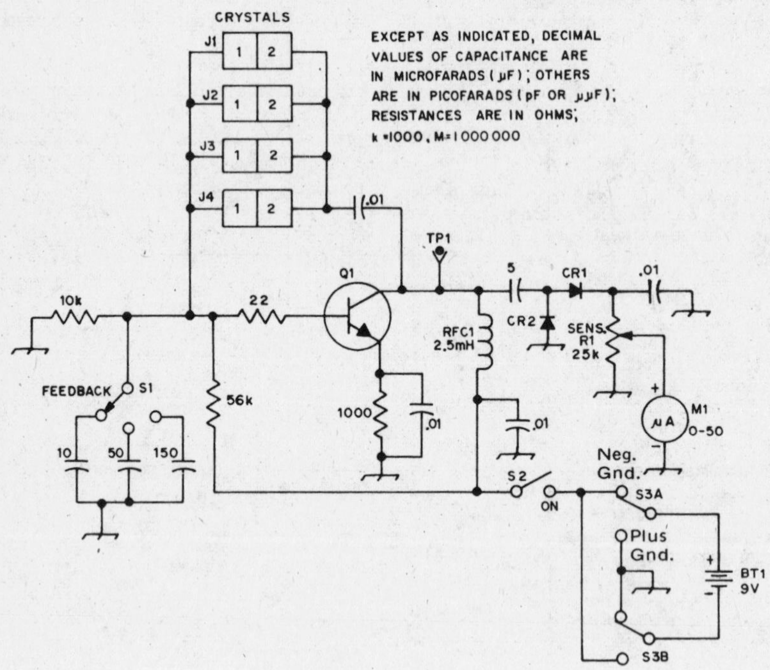

Fig. 1 — Schematic diagram of the No. 2 tester. Capacitors are disk ceramic. Fixed-value resistors are 1/2 or 1/4-watt composition. Estimated cost for this tester (all new parts) is $13.

BT1 — Small 9-V transistor-radio battery.
CR1, CR2 — 1N34A germanium diode or equiv.
J1-J4, incl. — Crystal socket of builder's choice.
M1 — Microampere meter. Calectro D1-910 used here.
R1 — 25,000-ohm linear-taper composition control with switch.
RFC1 — 2.5-mH rf choke.
S1 — Single-pole three-position phenolic rotary wafer type, miniature.
S2 — Part of R1.
S3 — Double-pole double-throw miniature toggle.
Q1 — Vhf npn bipolar, 2N4124, MPS3563, HEP53.

crystals for band-edge checking. The frequencies of unknown crystals can be checked by listening to the output from the test oscillators on a calibrated receiver or while using a frequency counter connected to the designated test point

Four crystal sockets are provided in the model shown here. J1 through J4 provide for testing of FT-243, HC-6/U, HC-17, and HC-25 crystals, the most popular holder styles in use today. Other types can be added by the builder if desired.

DIODE NOISE GENERATORS

A noise generator is a device for creating a controllable amount of rf noise ("hiss"-type noise) evenly distributed throughout the spectrum of interest. The simplest type of noise generator is a diode, either vacuum-tube or crystal, with dc flowing through it. The current is also made to flow through a load resistance which usually is chosen to equal the characteristic impedance of the transmission line to be connected to the receiver's input terminals. The resistance then substitutes for the line, and the amount of rf noise fed to receiver input is controlled by varying the dc through the diode.

The noise generator is useful for adjusting the "front-end" circuits of a receiver for best noise figure. A simple circuit using a crystal diode is shown in Fig. 17-51. The unit can be built into a small metal box; the main consideration is that the circuit from C1 through P1 be as compact as possible. A calibrated knob on R1 will permit resetting the generator to roughly the same spot each time, for making comparisons. If the leads are short, the generator can be used through the 144-MHz band for receiver comparisons.

To use the generator, screw the coaxial plug onto the receiver's input fitting, open S1, and measure the noise output of the receiver by connecting an audio-frequency voltmeter to the receiver's af output terminals. An average-reading voltmeter is preferable to the peak-reading type, since on this type of noise the average-reading meter will give a fair approximation of rms, and the object is to measure noise *power*, not voltage.

In using the generator for adjusting the input circuit of a receiver for optimum noise figure, first make sure that the receiver's rf and af gain controls are set well within the linear range of response, and turn off the automatic gain control. With the noise generator connected but S1 open, adjust the receiver gain controls for an output reading that is far enough below the maximum obtainable to

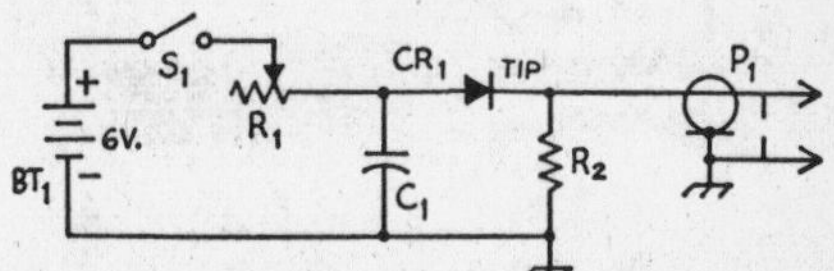

Fig. 17-51 – Circuit of a simple crystal-diode noise generator.
BT1 – Dry-cell battery, any convenient type.
C1 – 500-pF ceramic, disk or tubular.
CR1 – Silicon diode, 1N21 or 1N23. Diodes with "R" suffix have reversed polarity. (Do not use ordinary germanium diodes.)
P1 – Coaxial fitting, cable type.
R1 – 50,000-ohm control, ccw logarithmic taper.
R2 – 51 or 75 ohms, 1/2-watt composition.
S1 – Spst toggle (may be mounted on R1).

ensure that the receiver is operating linearly. This is your reference level of noise. Then close S1 and adjust R1 for a readily perceptible increase in output. Note the *ratio* of the two readings – i.e., the number of dB increase in noise when the generator is on. Then make experimental adjustments of the receiver input coupling, always with the object of obtaining the largest number of dB increase in output when the generator is switched on.

A simple crystal-diode noise generator is a useful device for the receiver adjustment, especially at vhf, and for comparing the performance of different receivers checked with the same instrument. It does not permit actual measurement of the noise figure, however, and therefore the results with one instrument cannot readily be compared with the readings obtained with another. In order to get a quantitative measure of noise figure it is necessary to use a temperature-saturated vacuum diode in place of the semiconductor diode. Suitable diodes are difficult to find.

RF PROBE FOR ELECTRONIC VOLTMETERS

The rf probe shown in Figs. 17-52 to 17-55, inclusive, uses the circuit discussed earlier in connection with Fig. 17-15.

The isolation capacitor, C1, crystal diode, and filter/divider resistor are mounted on a bakelite 5-lug terminal strip, as shown in Fig. 17-55. One end lug should be rotated 90 degrees so that it extends off the end of the strip. All other lugs should be cut off flush with the edge of the strip. Where the inner conductor connects to the terminal lug, unravel the shield three-quarters of an inch, slip a piece of spaghetti over it, and then solder the braid to the ground lug on the terminal strip. Remove the spring from the tube shield, slide it over the cable, and crimp it to the remaining quarter inch of shield braid. Solder both the spring and a 12-inch length of flexible copper braid to the shield.

Next, cut off the pins on a seven-pin miniature shield-base tube socket. Use a socket with a cylindrical center post. Crimp the terminal lug previously bent out at the end of the strip and insert it into the center post of the tube socket from the top. Insert the end of a phone tip or a

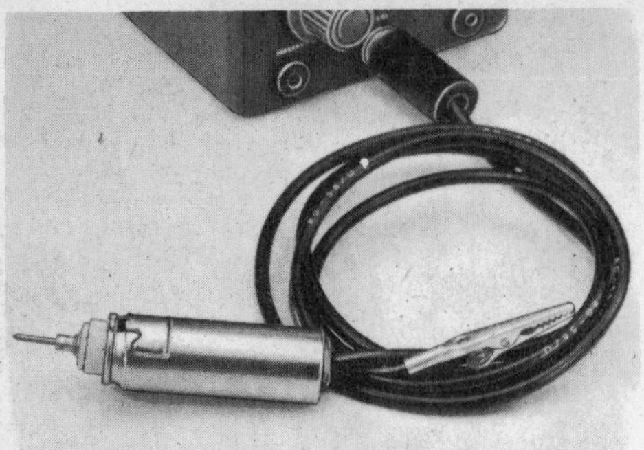

Fig. 17-52 – Rf probe for use with an electronic voltmeter. The case of the probe is constructed from a 7-pin ceramic tube socket and a 2 1/4-inch tube shield. A half-inch grommet at the top of the tube shield prevents the output lead from chafing. A flexible copper-braid grounding lead and alligator clip provide a low-inductance return path from the test circuit.

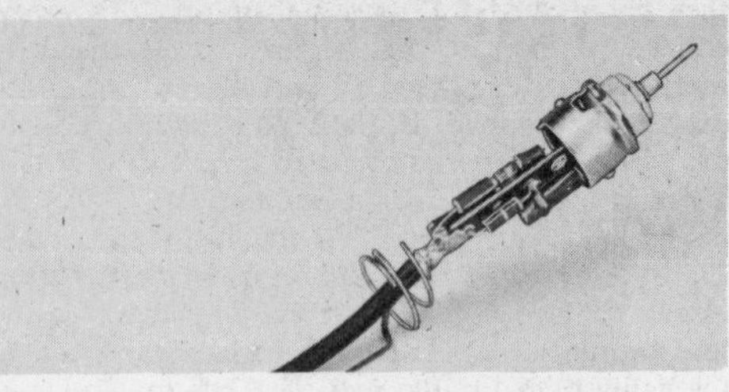

Fig. 17-54 – Inside the probe. The 1N34A diode, calibrating resistor, and input capacitor are mounted tight to the terminal strip with shortest leads possible. Spaghetti tubing is placed on the diode leads to prevent accidental short circuits. The tube-shield spring and flexible-copper grounding lead are soldered to the cable braid (the cable is RG-58/U coax). The tip can be either a phone tip or a short pointed piece of heavy wire.

pointed piece of heavy wire into the bottom of the tube socket center post, and solder the lug and tip to the center post. Insert a half-inch grommet at the top of the tube shield, and slide the shield over the cable and flexible braid down onto the tube socket. The spring should make good contact with the tube shield to insure that the tube shield (probe case) is grounded. Solder an alligator clip to the other end of the flexible braid and mount a phone plug on the free end of the shielded wire.

Mount components close to the terminal strip, to keep lead lengths as short as possible and minimize stray capacitance. Use spaghetti over all wires to prevent accidental shorts.

The phone plug on the probe cable plugs into the dc input jack of the electronic voltmeter and rms voltages are read on the voltmeter's negative dc scale.

The accuracy of the probe is within ±10 percent from 50 kHz to 250 MHz. The approximate input impedance is 6000 ohms shunted by 1.75 pF (at 200 MHz).

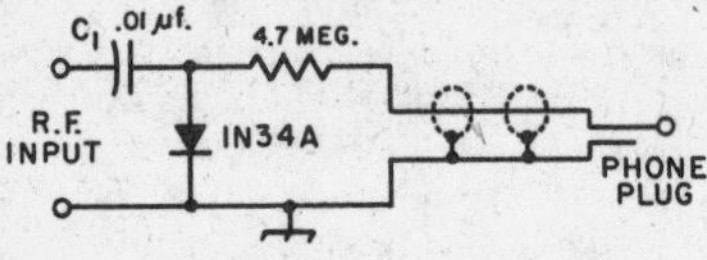

Fig. 17-53 – The rf probe circuit.

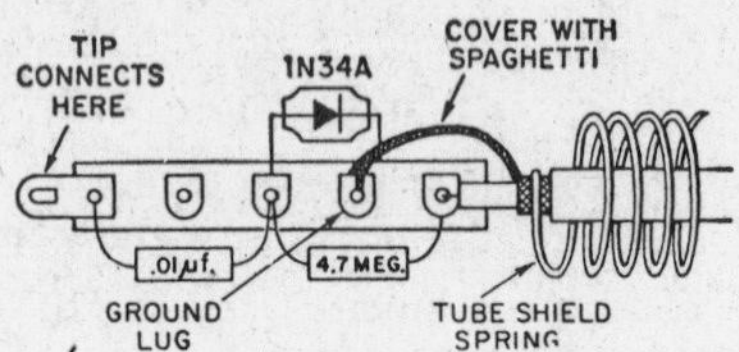

Fig. 17-55 – Component mounting details.

RF IMPEDANCE BRIDGE FOR COAX LINES

The bridge shown in Figs. 1 through 3 may be used to measure unknown complex impedances at frequencies below 30 MHz. Measured values are of equivalent series form, $R + jX$. The useful range of the instrument is from about 5 to 400 ohms if the unknown load is purely resistive, or 10 to 150 ohms resistive component in the presence of reactance. The reactance range is from 0 to approximately 100 ohms for either inductive or capacitive loads. Although the instrument cannot indicate impedances with the accuracy of a laboratory type of bridge, its readings are quite adequate for the measurement and adjustment of antenna systems for amateur use, including the taking of line lengths into account with a Smith chart or Smith transmission-line calculator.

The bridge incorporates a differential capacitor, C1, to obtain an adjustable ratio for measurement of the resistive component of the load. The capacitor consists of two identical sections on the same frame, arranged so that when the shaft is rotated to increase the capacitance of one section, the capacitance of the other section decreases. The capacitor is adjusted for a null reading on M1, and its settings are calibrated in terms of resistance at J3 so the unknown value can be read off the calibration. A coil-and-capacitor combination is used to determine the amount and type of reactance, inductive or capacitive. L1 and C2 in the bridge circuit are connected in series with the load. The instrument is initially balanced at the frequency of measurement with a purely resistive load connected at J3, so that the reactances of L1 and of C2 at its midsetting are equal. Thus, these reactances cancel each other in this arm of the bridge. With an unknown complex-impedance load then connected at J3, the setting of C2 is varied either to increase or decrease the capacitive reactance, as required, to cancel any reactance present in the load. If the load is inductive more capacitive reactance is required from C2 to obtain a balance, indicated by a null on M1, with less reactance needed from C2 if the load is capacitive. The settings of C2 are calibrated in terms of the value and type of reactance at J3. Because of the relationship of capacitive reactance to frequency, the calibration for the dial of C2 is valid at only one frequency. It is therefore convenient to calibrate this dial for equivalent reactances at 1 MHz, as shown in Fig. 4. Frequency corrections may then be made simply by dividing the reactance dial reading by the measurement frequency in megahertz.

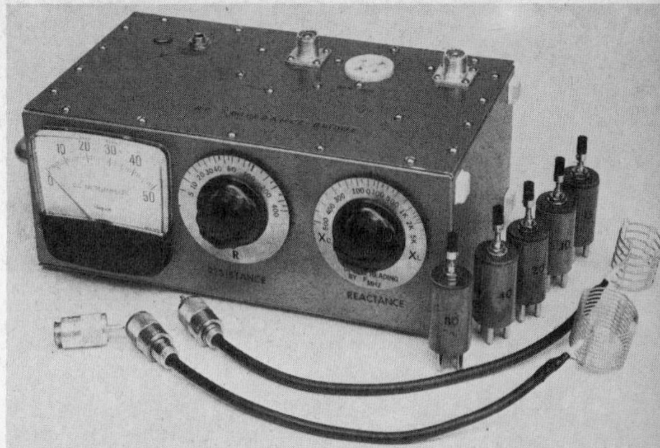

Fig. 1 — An *RCL* bridge for measuring unknown values of complex impedances. A plug-in coil is used for each frequency band. The bridge operates at an rf input level of about 5 volts; pickup-link assemblies for use with a grid-dip oscillator are shown. Before measurements are made, the bridge must be balanced with a nonreactive load connected at its measurement terminals. This load consists of a resistor mounted inside a coaxial plug, shown in front of the instrument at the left. The aluminum box measures 4 1/4 X 10 3/4 X 6 1/8 inches and is fitted with a carrying handle on the left end and self-sticking rubber feet on the right end and bottom. Dials are Millen No. 10009 with skirts reversed and calibrations added.

Construction

In any rf-bridge type of instrument, the leads must be kept as short as possible to reduce stray reactances. Placement of component parts, while not critical, must be such that lead lengths greater than about 1/2 inch (except in the dc metering circuit) are avoided. Shorter leads are desirable, especially for R1, the "standard" resistor for the bridge. In the unit photographed, the body of this resistor just fits between the terminals of C1 and J2 where it is connected. C1 should be enclosed in a shield and connections made with leads passing through holes drilled through the shield wall. The frames of both variable capacitors, C1 and C2, must be insulated from the chassis, with insulated couplings used on the shafts. The capacitor specified for C1 has provisions for insulated mounting. C2 is mounted on 1-inch ceramic insulating pillars.

Band-switching arrangements for L1 complicate the construction and contribute to stray reactances in the bridge circuit. For these reasons plug-in coils are used at L1, one coil for each band over which the instrument is used. The coils must be adjustable, to permit initial balancing of the bridge with C2 set at the zero-reactance calibration point. Coil data are given in Table I. Millen 45004 coil forms with the coils supported inside provide a convenient method of constructing these slug-tuned plug-in coils. A phenolic washer cut to the proper diameter is epoxied to the top or open end of each form, giving a rigid support for mounting of the coil by its bushing. Small knobs for 1/8-inch shafts, threaded with a No. 6-32 tap, are screwed onto the coil slug-tuning screws to permit ease of adjustment without a tuning tool. Knobs with setscrews should be used to prevent slipping. A ceramic socket to mate with the pins of the coil form is used for J2.

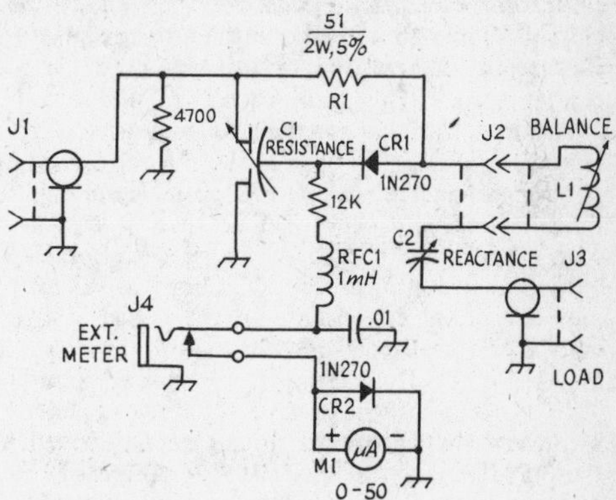

Fig. 2 — Schematic diagram of the impedance bridge. Capacitance is in microfarads; resistances are in ohms. Resistors are 1/2-W 10-percent tolerance unless otherwise indicated.

C1 — Differential capacitor, 11-161 pF per section (Millen 28801).

C2 — 17.5-327 pF with straight-line capacitance characteristic (Hammarlund RMC-325-S).

CR1, CR2 — Germanium diode, high back resistance.

J1, J3 — Coaxial connectors, chassis type.

J2 — To mate plug of L1, ceramic.

J4 — Phone jack, disconnecting type.

L1 — See text and Table I.

M1 — 0-50 μA dc (Simpson Model 1223 Bold-Vue, Cat. No. 15560 or equiv.).

R1 — For text reference.

RFC1 — Subminiature rf choke (Miller 70F103AI or equiv.).

Calibration

The resistance dial of the bridge may be calibrated by using a number of 1/2- or 1-watt 5-percent-tolerance composition resistors of different values in the 5- to 400-ohm range as loads. For this calibration, the appropriate frequency coil

TABLE 17-I

Coil Data for RF Impedance Bridge

Band	*Nominal Inductance Range, μH*	*Frequency Coverage, MHz*	*Coil Type or Data*
80	6.5–13.8	3.2–4.8	28 turns No. 30 enam. wire close-wound on Miller form 42A000CBI.
40	2.0–4.4	5.8–8.5	Miller 42A336CBI or 16 turns No. 22 enam. wire close-wound on Miller form 42A000CBI.
20	0.6–1.1	11.5–16.6	8 turns No. 18 enam. wire close-wound on Miller form 42A000CBI.
15	0.3–0.48	18.5–23.5	4 1/2 turns No. 18 enam. wire close-wound on Miller form 42A000CBI.
10	0.18–0.28	25.8–32.0	3 turns No. 16 or 18 enam. or tinned bus wire spaced over 1/4-inch winding length on Miller form 42A000CBI.

must be inserted at J2 and its inductance adjusted for the best null reading on the meter when C2 is set with its plates half meshed. For each test resistor, C1 is then adjusted for a null reading. Alternate adjustment of L1 and C1 should be made for a complete null. The leads between the test resistor and J3 should be as short as possible, and the calibration preferably should be done in the 3.5-MHz band where stray inductance and capacitance will have the least effect.

If the constructional layout of the bridge closely follows that shown in the photographs, the calibration scale of Fig. 4 may be used for the reactance dial. This calibration was obtained by connecting various reactances, measured on a laboratory bridge, in series with a 47-ohm 1-W resistor connected at J3. The scale is applied so that maximum capacitive reactance is indicated with C2 fully meshed. If it is desired to obtain an individual calibration for C2, known values of inductance and capacitance may be used in series with a fixed resistor of the same approximate value as R1. For this calibration it is *very important* to keep the leads to the test components as short as possible, and calibration should be performed in the 3.5-MHz range to minimize the effects of stray reactances. Begin the calibration by setting C2 at half mesh, marking this point as 0 ohms reactance. With a purely resistive load connected at J3, adjust L1 and C1 for the best null on M1. From this point on during calibration, do not adjust L1 except to rebalance the bridge for a new calibration frequency. The ohmic value of the known reactance for the frequency of calibration is multiplied by the frequency in MHz to obtain the calibration value for the dial.

Using the Impedance Bridge

This instrument is a low-input-power device, and is *not* of the type to be excited from a transmitter or left in the antenna line during station operation. Sufficient sensitivity for all measurements results when a 5-V rms rf signal is applied at J1. This amount of voltage can be delivered by most grid-dip oscillators. In no case should the power applied to J1 exceed 1 watt or calibration inaccuracy may result from a permanent change in the value of R1. The input impedance of the bridge at J1 is low, in the order of 50 to 100 ohms, so it is convenient to excite the bridge through a length of 52- or 75-ohm line such as RG-58/U or RG-59/U. If a grid-dip oscillator is used, a link coupling arrangement to the oscillator coil may be used. Fig. 1 shows two pick-up link assemblies. The larger coil, 10 turns of 1 1/4-inch-dia stock with turns spaced at 8 turns per inch, is used for the 80-, 40- and 20-meter bands. The smaller coil, 5 turns of 1-inch-dia stock with turns spaced at 4 turns per inch, is used for the 15- and 10-meter bands. Coupling to the oscillator should be as light as possible, while obtaining sufficient

Fig. 3 — All components except the meter are mounted on the top of the box. C1 is visible inside the shield at the left, with C2 at the right and J2 mounted between them. J1 is hidden beneath C1 in this view; a part of J3 may be seen in the lower right corner of the box. Components for the dc metering circuit are mounted on a tie-point strip which is affixed to the shield wall for C1; all other components are interconnected with very short leads. The 4700-ohm input resistor is connected across J1.

Fig. 4 — Calibration scale for the reactance dial associated with C2. See text.

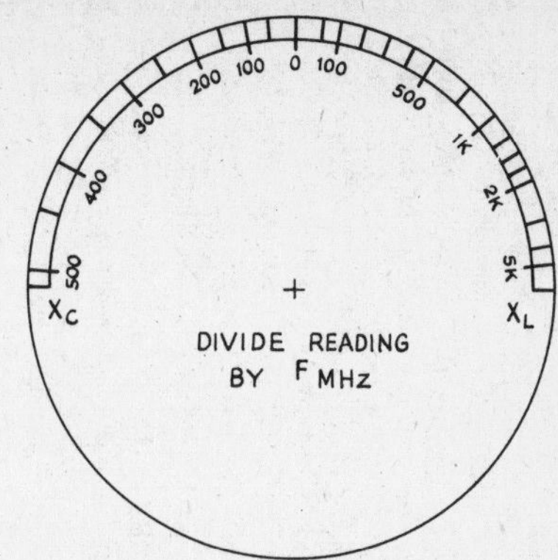

sensitivity, to prevent severe "pulling" of the oscillator frequency.

Before measurements are made, it is necessary to balance the bridge. Set the reactance dial at zero and adjust L1 and C1 for a null with a nonreactive load connected at J3. The bridge must be rebalanced after any appreciable change is made in the measurement frequency. A 51-ohm 1-W resistor mounted inside a PL-259 plug, as shown in Fig. 17-24, makes a load which is essentially nonreactive. After the bridge is balanced, connect the unknown load to J3, and alternately adjust C1 and C2 for the best null.

The calibration of the reactance dial is shown in Fig. 4. The measurement range for capacitive loads may be extended by "zeroing" the reactance dial at some value other than 0. For example, if the bridge is initially balanced with the reactance dial set at 500 in the X_L range, the 0 dial indication is now equivalent to an X_C reading of 500, and the total range of measurement for X_C has been extended to 1000.

A LOW-POWER RF WATTMETER

The wattmeter shown in Fig. 1 can be used with transmitters having power outputs from 1- to 25-watts within the frequency range of 1.8 to 30 MHz. For complete details, see *QST* for June, 1973. A bridge circuit based on a version of the one shown in Fig. 17-16C is used to measure the forward and reflected power on a transmission line.

The rf wattmeter.

It will be necessary to have a nonreactive 50-ohm dummy load for initial adjustment of the power meter. Connect the dummy load to one port of the instrument and apply rf power to the remaining port. S1 should now be thrown back and forth to determine which position gives the highest meter reading. This will be the FORWARD position. Adjust the sensitivity control for full-scale reading of the meter. Now, move the switch to the opposite (RELFECTED) position and adjust the trimmer nearest the transmitter input port for a null in the meter reading. The needle should drop to zero. It is recommended that these adjustments be made in the 10- or 15-meter band. Next, reverse the transmitter and load cables and repeat the nulling procedure while adjusting the trimmer on the opposite side of the pc board. Repeat these steps until a perfect null is obtained in both directions. The switch and the coax connectors can now be labeled, TRANSMITTER, LOAD, FORWARD, and REFLECTED, as appropriate.

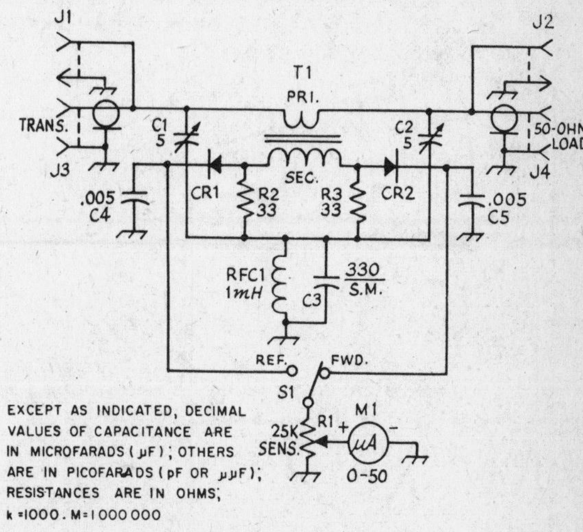

Fig. 1 — Schematic diagram of the wattmeter.
C1, C2 — 0.5- to 5-pF trimmer.
CR1, CR2 — 1N34A or equivalent.
M1 — 50-μA panel meter.
R1 — Linear-taper, 1/4 or 1/2 watt, 25,000 ohm.
R2, R3 — 33-ohm, 1/2-W composition resistor (matched pair recommended).
RFC1 — 1-mH rf choke.
S1 — Spdt toggle.
T1 — 60 turns No. 28 enam. wire, close wound on Amidon T-68-2 toroid core (secondary). Primary is 2 turns of small-diameter hookup wire over T1 secondary.

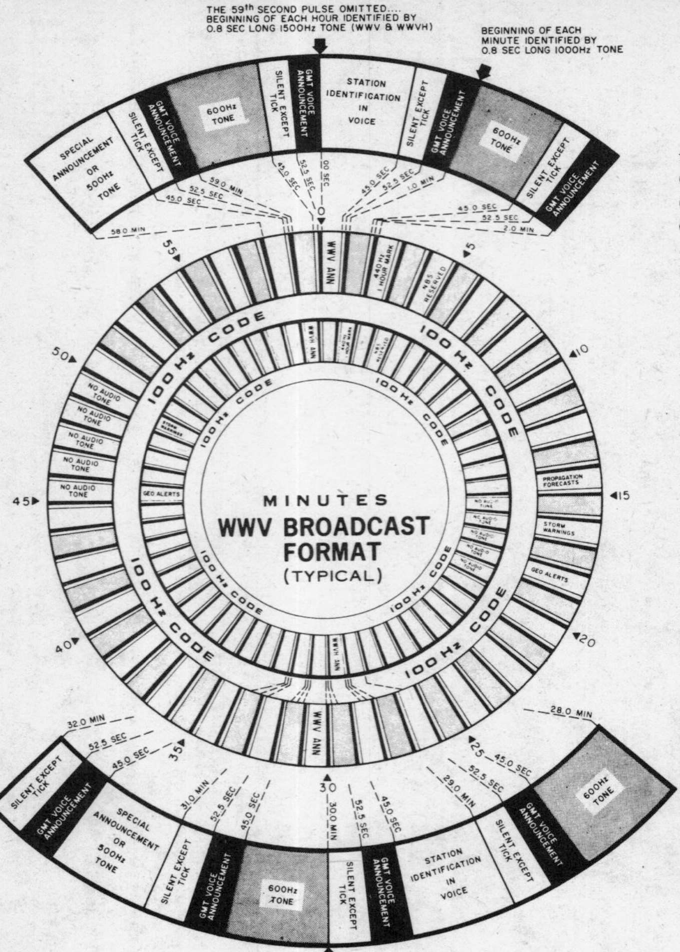

STANDARD FREQUENCIES AND TIME SIGNALS

The National Bureau of Standards maintains two radio transmitting stations, WWV at Ft. Collins, Co., and WWVH near Kekaha, Kauai (Hawaii), for broadcasting standard radio frequencies of high accuracy. WWV broadcasts are on 2.5, 5, 10, 15, 20, and 25 MHz, and those from WWVH are on 2.5, 5, 10, 15, and 20 MHz. The broadcasts of both stations are continuous, night and day. Standard audio frequencies of 440, 500, and 600 Hz on each radio-carrier frequency by WWV and WWVH. The duration of each tone is approximately 45 seconds. A 600-Hz tone is broadcast during odd minutes by WWV, and during even minutes by WWVH. A 500-Hz tone is broadcast during alternate minutes unless voice announcements or silent periods are scheduled. A 440-Hz tone is broadcast beginning one minute after the hour by WWVH and two minutes after the hour by WWV. The 440-Hz tone period is omitted during the first hour of the UT day.

Transmitted frequencies from the two stations are accurate to ± 2 parts in 10^{11}. Atomic frequency standards are used to maintain this accuracy.

Voice announcements of the time, in English, are given every minute. WWV utilizes a male voice, and WWVH features a female voice to distinguish between the two stations. WWV time and frequency broadcasts can be heard by telephone also. The number to call is (303) 499-7111, Boulder, CO.

All official announcements are made by voice. Time announcements are in GMT. One-second markers are transmitted throughout all programs except that the 29th and 59th markers of each minute are omitted. Detailed information on hourly broadcast schedules is given in the accompanying format chart. Complete information on the services can be found in NBS Special Publication 236, *NBS Frequency and Time Broadcast Services*, available for 25 cents from the Superintendent of Documents, U. S. Government Printing Office, Washington, D.C. 20402.

Geophysical Alerts

"Geoalerts" are broadcast in voice during the 19th minute of each hour from WWV and during the 46th minute of each hour from WWVH. The messages are changed each day at 0400 UT with provisions to schedule immediate alerts of outstanding occuring events. Geoalerts tell of geophysical events affecting radio propagation, stratospheric warming, etc.

Propagation Forecasts

Voice broadcasts of radio propagation conditions are given during part of every 15th minute of each hour from WWV. The announcements deal with short-term forecasts and refer to propagation along paths in the North Atlantic area, such as Washington, D.C. to London, or New York to Berlin.

CHU

CHU, the Canadian time-signal station, transmits on 3330.0, 7335.0 and 14,670.0 kHz. Voice announcements of the minute are made each minute; the 29th-second tick is omitted. Voice announcements are made in English and French.

A HETERODYNE DEVIATION METER

The instrument described here can be used to check the audio deviation of an fm transmitter, or to determine how far off frequency the transmitter carrier may be. It can also be used as a signal source to aid in setting a receiver on frequency, if a crystal of known accuracy is plugged into the oscillator.

The Circuit

As shown in Fig. 17-57 a transistor oscillator is used to feed energy to a mixer diode, CR1. A small pickup antenna is connected to the diode also, thereby coupling a signal from a transmitter to the mixer. The output from the diode, in the audio range, is amplified by U1, a 2747 operational amplifier. The 2747 amplifies and clips the audio, providing a square wave of nearly constant amplitude at the output. This square wave is applied to a rectifier circuit through variable coupling capacitors and a selector switch. A meter is connected to the rectifier circuit to read the average current. Since the amplitude of the input is constant, a change in frequency will produce a change of average current. Three ranges are selected by S1, with individual trimmers being placed in the circuit for calibration.

Fig. 17-56 – The deviation meter is constructed in a Calectro aluminum box. A four-position switch is at the lower right. The crystal plugs in on the left, with the frequency adjusting trimmer just below. A short whip or pickup wire can be plugged into the phono connector that is mounted on the back wall of the box.

Construction

An aluminum box is used for the enclosure, 6-1/4 × 3-1/2 × 2 inches. A meter switch, variable capacitor, and crystal socket are all mounted on the top panel. A small pc board is fastened to the

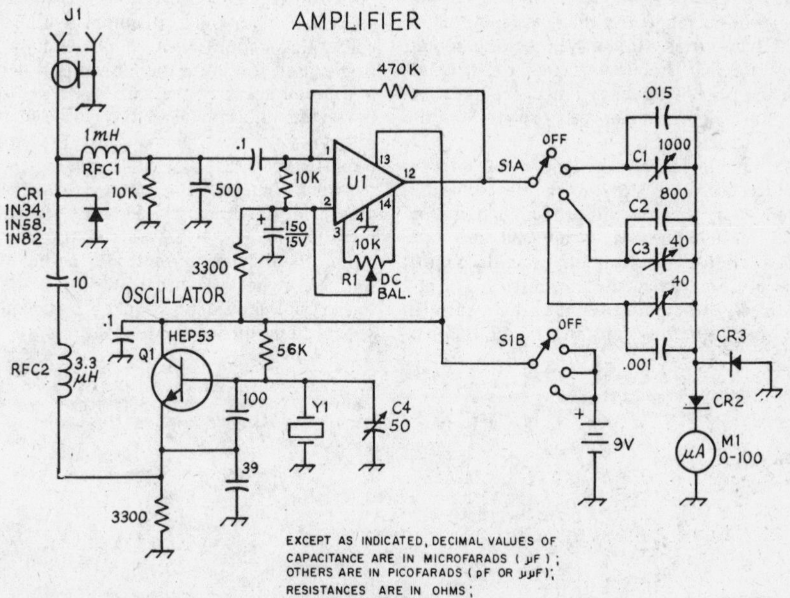

Fig. 17-57 – Circuit of the deviation meter. Connections shown are for a 2747 dual op amp. A 741 may be substituted with appropriate changes in pin numbers.

C1 – 360 to 1000 pF mica trimmer (J. W. Miller 160-A or equiv.).

C2, C3 – 3 to 30 pF mica trimmer (J. W. Miller 86 MA 2 or equiv.).

C4 – 50 pF miniature air variable (Hammarlund MAPC 50 or equiv.).

CR1 – Germanium diode, 1N34, 1N58, or 1N82 suitable.

CR2, CR3 – Silicon diode, 1N914 or equiv.

J1 – Coax connector, BNC or phono type suitable.

M1 – Microammeter, 0 to 1000 μA (Simpson Model 1212 Wide-Vue or equiv.).

Q1 – Motorola transistor.

R1 – 10,000-ohm miniature control, pc mount.

S1 – 2-pole, 4-position rotary switch, nonshorting.

U1 – Dual operational amplifier IC, Type 2747, one half not used.

Y1 – Crystal to produce harmonic on desired transmitter or receiver frequency. Fundamental range 6 to 20 MHz.

meter terminals as a convenient support. This board contains the IC and associated circuit components, as well as the rectifier diodes.

The oscillator is constructed on a separate pc board which mounts behind the crystal socket and variable capacitor. Metal spacers and 4-40 screws and nuts are used to fasten the oscillator board in place. A shield of pc board is placed between the oscillator and the amplifier to provide isolation. Power for the instrument is furnished by a 9-volt transistor radio battery that is held by a clip inside the box.

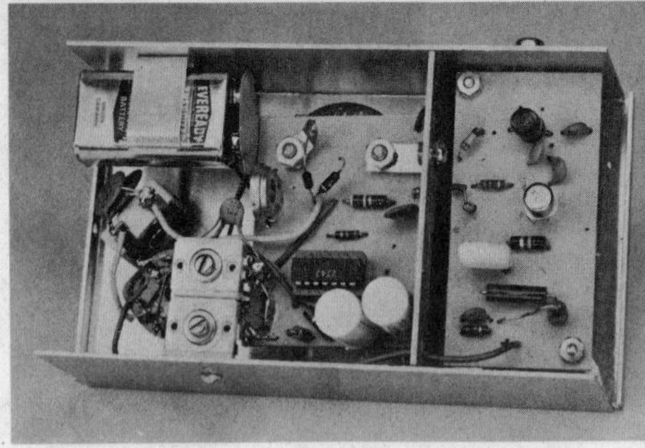

Fig. 17-58 – The dual op amp is located just below the center. Meter terminals are used as a convenient support for the amplifier pc board. The oscillator board is at the right, held in place by means of metal spacers.

Testing and Use.

Before calibrating the meter, the dc balance should be adjusted. A voltmeter should be connected to the output of U1, (pin 12) and R1 adjusted until the potential at this pin in one half of the supply voltage.

A low-level audio signal can be used to test the amplifier and meter circuit. As little as 10 mV, applied to pin 1, will produce a square wave at the output of the amplifier. Three ranges are provided in this meter; 0 - 1000Hz, 0 - 10 kHz, and 0 - 20 kHz. Each position can be calibrated by adjustment of the associated trimmer capacitor. The amount of capacitance needed may vary with different diodes, so fixed ceramic capacitors may be placed in parallel with the trimmers to bring the adjustment within range. As the frequency of the input to U1 is varied, the meter reading should correspond to that frequency over most of its range. On the upper frequency range, 0 - 20 kHz, a multiplication factor must be applied to the reading on the meter.

In use, a short whip or piece of wire is connected to J1, and the meter placed near a transmitter. A crystal that will produce a harmonic on the correct frequency is plugged into the socket. The selector switch should be in the first (0 - 1000 Hz) position. When the transmitter is turned on, the meter will indicate the difference in frequency between the transmitter and the harmonic from the oscillator. The trimmer, C4, should be adjusted for a minimum reading. Any hum, noise, or power-supply whine will cause a residual reading that could mask true zero beat. Modulation can be applied to the transmitter and the deviation control adjusted for the amount desired as indicated on the meter. Note that there is a difference between the indications obtained from a sine wave and those from voice. Readings will be lower with voice, the amount being dependent on the meter that is used and upon the individual voice.

Several transmitters can be netted to a system by setting the crystal in the device to the correct frequency at first, then adjust the frequency of each transmitter for an indication of zero beat.

Since there is some energy from the oscillator present at the input, J1, the same procedure can be used to align receivers to the correct frequency. When the deviation meter is acting as a signal source for checking either receivers or transmitters, the crystal should be checked for frequency drift several times during the test.

Chapter 18

Construction Practices and Data Tables

TOOLS AND MATERIALS

While an easier, and perhaps a better, job can be done with a greater variety of tools available, by taking a little thought and care it is possible to turn out a fine piece of equipment with only a few of the common hand tools. A list of tools which will be indispensable in the construction of radio equipment will be found on this page. With these tools it should be possible to perform any of the required operations in preparing panels and metal chassis for assembly and wiring. It is an excellent idea for the amateur who does constructional work to add to his supply of tools from time to time as finances permit.

RECOMMENDED TOOLS

Long-nose pliers, 6-inch and 4-inch
Diagonal cutters, 6-inch and 4-inch
Combination pliers, 6-inch
Screwdriver, 6- to 7-inch, 1/4-inch blade
Screwdriver, 4- to 5-inch, 1/8-inch blade
Phillips screwdriver, 6- to 7-inch
Phillips screwdriver, 3- to 4-inch
Long-shank screwdriver with holding clip on blade
Scratch awl or scriber for marking metal
Combination square, 12-inch, for layout work
Hand drill, 1/4-inch chuck or larger
Soldering pencil, 30-watt, 1/8-inch tip
Soldering iron, 200-watt, 5/8-inch tip
Hacksaw and 12-inch blades
Hand nibbling tool, for chassis-hole cutting
Hammer, ball-peen, 1-lb head
Heavy-duty jack knife
File set, flat, round, half-round, and triangular. Large and miniature types recommended
High-speed drill bits, No. 60 through 3/8-inch diameter
Set of "Spintite" socket wrenches for hex nuts
Crescent wrench, 6- and 10-inch
Machine-screw taps, 4-40 through 10-32 thread
Socket punches, 1/2", 5/8", 3/4", 1 1/8", 1 1/4", and 1 1/2"
Tapered reamer, T-handle, 1/2-inch maximum pitch
Bench vise, 4-inch jaws or larger
Medium-weight machine oil
Tin shears, 10-inch size
Motor-driven emery wheel for grinding
Solder, *rosin core only*
Contact cleaner, liquid or spray can
Duco cement or equivalent
Electrical tape, vinyl plastic

Radio-supply houses, mail-order retail stores and most hardware stores carry the various tools required when building or servicing amateur radio equipment. While power tools (electric drill or drill press, grinding wheel, etc.) are very useful and will save a lot of time, they are not essential.

Twist Drills

Twist drills are made of either high-speed steel or carbon steel. The latter type is more common and will usually be supplied unless specific request is made for high-speed drills. The carbon drill will suffice for most ordinary equipment construction work and costs less than the high-speed type.

While twist drills are available in a number of sizes, those listed in bold-faced type in Table 18-I will be most commonly used in construction of amateur equipment. It is usually desirable to purchase several of each of the commonly used sizes rather than a standard set, most of which will be used infrequently if at all.

Care of Tools

The proper care of tools is not alone a matter of pride to a good workman. He also realizes the energy which may be saved and the annoyance which may be avoided by the possession of a full kit of well-kept sharp-edged tools.

Drills should be sharpened at frequent intervals so that grinding is kept at a minimum each time. This makes it easier to maintain the rather critical surface angles required for best cutting with least wear. Occasional oilstoning of the cutting edges of a drill or reamer will extend the time between grindings.

The soldering iron can be kept in good condition by keeping the tip well tinned with solder and not allowing it to run at full voltage for long periods when it is not being used. After each period of use, the tip should be removed and cleaned of any scale which may have accumulated. An oxidized tip may be cleaned by dipping it in sal ammoniac while hot and then wiping it clean with a rag. If the tip becomes pitted it should be filed until smooth and bright, and then tinned immediately by dipping it in solder.

Useful Materials

Small stocks of various miscellaneous materials will be required in constructing radio apparatus, most of which are available from hardware or radio-supply stores. A representative list follows:

Fig. 1 – The SCR motor-speed control is housed in a small cabinet.

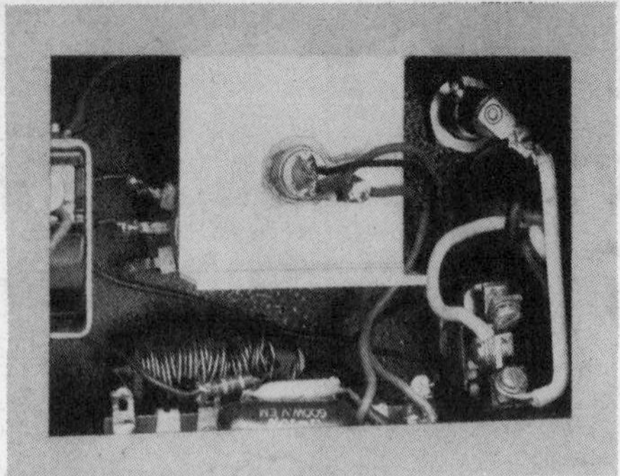

The working parts of the motor-speed control. The triac is centered on its aluminum heat sink, with the terminals of the speed-control resistor protruding from underneath. The rf-hash-suppression filter and components in the gate-triggering circuit are mounted on a tie-point strip, being visible at the bottom of the enclosure as shown in this view. The triac is barely discernable at the right end of the fixed resistor. Terminals of the strip which are associated with the mounting feet are unused, and are bent down to prevent accidental shorts to other parts of the circuit.

Sheet aluminum, solid and perforated, 16 or 18 gauge, for brackets and shielding.
1/2 X 1/2-inch aluminum angle stock.
1/ 4-inch diameter round brass or aluminum rod for shaft extensions. Machine screws: Round-head and flat-head, with nuts to fit. Most useful sizes: 4-40, 6-32 and 8-32, in lengths from 1/4 inch to 1 1/2 inches. (Nickel-plated iron will be found satisfactory except in strong rf fields, where brass should be used.)
Bakelite, lucite and polystyrene scraps.
Soldering lugs, panel bearings, rubber grommets, terminal-lug wiring strips, varnished-cambric insulating tubing.
Shielded and unshielded wire.
Tinned bare wire, Nos. 22, 14 and 12.

Machine screws, nuts, washers, soldering lugs, etc., are most reasonably purchased in quantities of a gross. Many of the radio-supply stores sell small quantities and assortments that come in handy.

TRIAC MOTOR-SPEED CONTROL

Most electric hand drills operate at a single high speed; however, from time to time, the need arises to utilize low or medium speeds. Low speeds are useful when drilling in tight spaces or on exposed surfaces where it is important that the drill bit doesn't slip, and when drilling bakelite, Plexiglas and similar materials. Medium speeds are useful for drilling non-ferrous metals such as aluminum and brass. One way to accomplish these ends with a single-speed electric drill is to use a silicon bidirectional thyristor (Triac) speed control.

The circuit for the Triac speed control is shown in Fig. 1. This type of circuit provides some degree of regulation with varying loads.

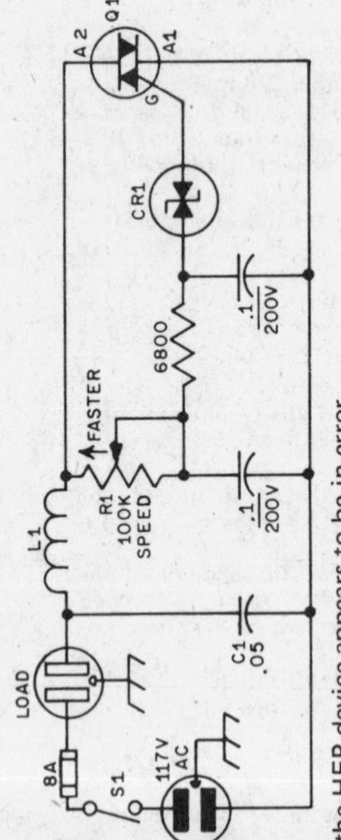

Fig. 1 — Schematic diagram of motor-speed control. Resistances are in ohms (k = 1000) and capacitances are in microfarads. **Important note**: The basing diagram for Q1 is correct as shown here. Some early literature accompanying the packaging of the HEP device appears to be in error.

C1 — .05-μF, 600-V paper.
CR1 — Diac (silicon bilateral trigger), 2-A, 300-mW (Motorola MPT28 or HEP311 or equiv.).
L1 — Approx. 70 μH; made with 18 ft. No. 18 enam. wire scramble-wound on body of C1, or on a 1-1/2-inch length of 1/2-inch dia. rod.
Q1 — Triac (silicon bidirectional thyristor), 8-A, 200-V (Motorola MAC2-4 or HEP340 or equiv.).
R1 — Linear-taper composition control, 2-W.
S1 — Spst toggle.

Construction

Because of the small complement of parts, the Triac speed control can be constructed inside a very small container. The model described was built in a 2-3/4 × 2-1/8 × 1-5/8-inch Minibox. Since the mounting stud and main body of the Triac are common with the anode, care should be used to mount the Triac clear from surrounding objects. In the unit shown, two soldering lugs were soldered together and the narrow ends connected to one side of the female output connector; the large ends were used as a fastening point for the Triac anode stud.

Operation

Although the circuit described is intended to be used to reduce the speed of electric hand drills that draw six amperes or less, it has many other applications. It can be used to regulate the temperature of a soldering iron, which is being used to wire a delicate circuit, or it may be used for dimming lamps or for controlling the cooking speed of a small hot plate. Note, however, if the circuit is used with a device drawing from three to six amperes for a continuous period of over ten minutes, it will be necessary to provide a heat sink (insulated from the chassis) for the Triac anode case.

CHASSIS WORKING

With a few essential tools and proper procedure, it will be found that building radio gear on a metal chassis is a relatively simple matter. Aluminum is to be preferred to steel, not only because it is a superior shielding material, but because it is much easier to work and provides good chassis contacts.

The placing of components on the chassis is shown quite clearly in the photographs in this *Handbook*. Aside from certain essential dimensions, which usually are given in the text, exact duplication is not necessary.

Much trouble and energy can be saved by spending sufficient time in planning the job. When all details are worked out beforehand the actual construction is greatly simplified.

Cover the top of the chassis with a piece of wrapping paper, or, preferably, cross-section paper, folding the edges down over the sides of the chassis

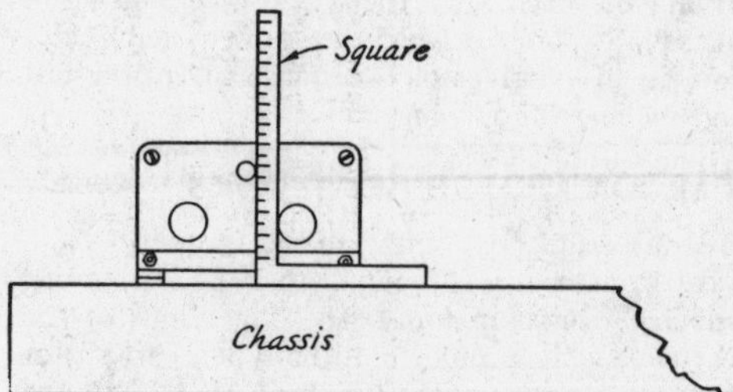

Fig. 18-3 – Method of measuring the heights of capacitor shafts. If the square is adjustable, the end of the scale should be set flush with the face of the head.

TABLE 18-I

Numbered Drill Sizes

Num.	Diameter (Mils)	Will Clear Screw	Drilled for Tapping from Steel or Brass*
1	228.0	–	–
2	221.0	12-24	–
3	213.0	–	14-24
4	209.0	12-20	–
5	205.0	–	–
6	204.0	–	–
7	201.0	–	–
8	199.0	–	–
9	196.0	–	–
10	193.5	10-32	–
11	191.0	10-24	–
12	189.0	–	–
13	185.0	–	–
14	182.0	–	–
15	180.0	–	–
16	177.0	–	12-24
17	173.0	–	–
18	169.5	8-32	–
19	166.0	–	12-20
20	161.0	–	–
21	159.0	–	10-32
22	157.0	–	–
23	154.0	–	–
24	152.0	–	–
25	149.5	–	10-24
26	147.0	–	–
27	144.0	–	–
28	140.0	6-32	–
29	136.0	–	8-32
30	128.5	–	–
31	120.0	–	–
32	116.0	–	–
33	113.0	4-40	–
34	111.0	–	–
35	110.0	–	6-32
36	106.5	–	–
37	104.0	–	–
38	101.5	–	–
39	099.5	3-48	–
40	098.0	–	–
41	096.0	–	–
42	093.5	–	4-40
43	089.0	2-56	–
44	086.0	–	–
45	082.0	–	3-48
46	081.0	–	–
47	078.5	–	–
48	076.0	–	–
49	073.0	–	2-56
50	070.0	–	–
51	067.0	–	–
52	063.5	–	–
53	059.5	–	–
54	055.0	–	–

***Use one size larger for tapping bakelite and phenolics.**

and fastening with adhesive tape. Then assemble the parts to be mounted on top of the chassis and move them about until a satisfactory arrangement has been found, keeping in mind any parts which are to be mounted underneath, so that interferences in mounting may be avoided. Place capacitors and other parts with shafts extending through the panel first, and arrange them so that

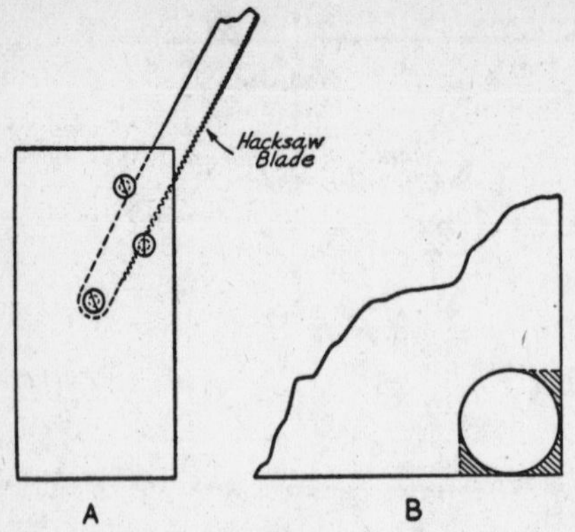

Fig. 18-4 – To cut rectangular holes in a chassis corner, holes may be filed out as shown in the shaded portion of B, making it possible to start the hack-saw blade along the cutting line. A shows how a single-ended handle may be constructed for a hack-saw blade.

the controls will form the desired pattern on the panel. Be sure to line up the shafts squarely with the chassis front. Locate any partition shields and panel brackets next, and then the tube sockets and any other parts, marking the mounting-hole centers of each accurately on the paper. Watch out for capacitors whose shafts are off center and do not line up with the mounting holes. Do not forget to mark the centers of socket holes and holes for leads under i-f transformers, etc., as well as holes for wiring leads. The small holes for socket-mounting screws are best located and center-punched, using the socket itself as a template, after the main center hole has been cut.

By means of the square, lines indicating accurately the centers of shafts should be extended to the front of the chassis and marked on the panel at the chassis line, the panel being fastened on temporarily. The hole centers may then be punched in the chassis with the center punch. After drilling, the parts which require mounting underneath may be located and the mounting holes drilled, marking sure by trial that no interferences exist with parts mounted on top. Mounting holes along the front edge of the chassis should be transferred to the panel, by once again fastening the panel to the chassis and marking it from the rear.

Next, mount on the chassis the capacitors and any other parts with shafts extending to the panel, and measure accurately the height of the center of each shaft above the chassis, as illustrated in Fig. 18-3. The horizontal displacement of shafts having already been marked on the chassis line on the panel, the vertical displacement can be measured from this line. The shaft centers may now be marked on the back of the panel, and the holes drilled. Holes for any other panel equipment coming above the chassis line may then be marked and drilled, and the remainder of the apparatus mounted. Holes for terminals etc., in the rear edge of the chassis should be marked and drilled at the same time that they are done for the top.

Drilling and Cutting Holes

When drilling holes in metal with a hand drill it is important that the centers first be located with a center punch, so that the drill point will not "walk" away from the center when starting the hole. When the drill starts to break through, special care must be used. Often it is an advantage to shift a two-speed drill to low gear at this point. Holes more than 1/4-inch in diameter should be started with a smaller drill and reamed out with the larger drill.

The check on the usual type of hand drill is limited to 1/4-inch drills. Although it is rather tedious, the 1/4-inch hole may be filed out to larger diameters with round files. Another method possible with limited tools is to drill a series of small holes with the hand drill along the inside of the circumference of the large hole, placing the holes as close together as possible. The center may then be knocked out with a cold chisel and the edges smoothed up with a file. Taper reamers which fit into the carpenter's brace will make the job easier. A large rat-tail file clamped in the brace makes a very good reamer for holes up to the diameter of the file.

For socket holes and other large holes in an aluminum chassis, socket-hole punches should be used. They require first drilling a guide hole to pass the bolt that is turned to squeeze the punch through the chassis. The threads of the bolt should be oiled occasionally.

Large holes in steel panels or chassis are best cut with an adjustable circle cutter. Occasional application of machine oil in the cutting groove will help. The cutter first should be tried out on a block of wood, to make sure that it is set for the right diameter.

The burrs or rough edges which usually result after drilling or cutting holes may be removed with a file, or sometimes more conveniently with a sharp knife or chisel. It is a good idea to keep an old wood chisel sharpened and available for this purpose.

Rectangular Holes

Square or rectangular holes may be cut out by making a row of small holes as previously described, but is more easily done by drilling a 1/2-inch hole inside each corner, as illustrated in Fig. 18-4, and using these holes for starting and turning the hack saw. The socket-hole punch and the square punches which are now available also may be of considerable assistance in cutting out large rectangular openings.

SEMICONDUCTOR HEAT SINKS

Homemade heat sinks can be fashioned from brass, copper or aluminum stock by employing ordinary workshop tools. The dimensions of the heat sink will depend upon the type of transistor used, and the amount of heat that must be conducted away from the body of the semiconductor.

Fig. 18-5 shows the order of progression for forming a large heat sink from aluminum or brass

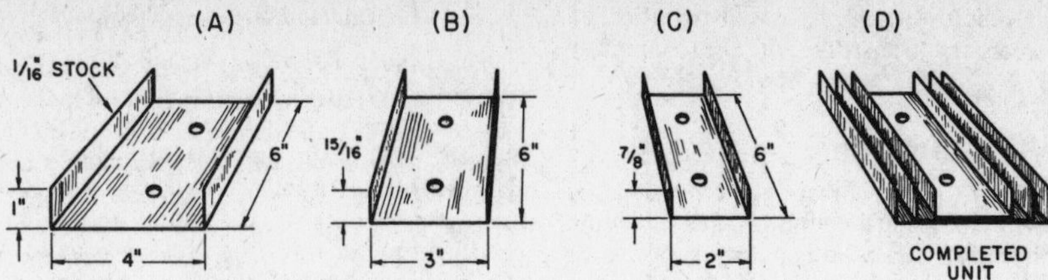

Fig. 18-5 – Details for forming channel type heat sinks.

channels of near-equal height and depth. The width is lessened in parts (B) and (C) so that each channel will fit into the preceding one as shown in the completed model at (D). The three pieces are bolted together with 8-32 screws and nuts. Dimensions given are for illustrative purposes only.

Heat sinks for smaller transistors can be fabricated as shown in Fig. 18-7. Select a drill bit that is one size smaller than the diameter of the transistor case and form the heat sink from 1/16 inch thick brass, copper or aluminum stock as shown in steps (A), (B), and (C). Form the stock around the drill bit by compressing it in a vise (A). The completed heat sink is press-fitted over the body of the semiconductor as illustrated at (D). The larger the area of the heat sink, the greater will be the amount of heat conducted away from the transistor body. In some applications, the heat sinks shown in Fig. 18-7 may be two or three inches in height (power transistor stages).

Another technique for making heat sinks for TO-5 type transistors (1) and larger models (1) is shown in Fig. 18-6. This style of heat sink will dissipate considerably more heat than will the type shown in Fig. 18-5. The main body of the sink is fashioned from a piece of 1/8-inch thick aluminum angle bracket – available from most hardware stores. A hole is bored in the angle stock to allow the transistor case to fit *snugly* into it. The

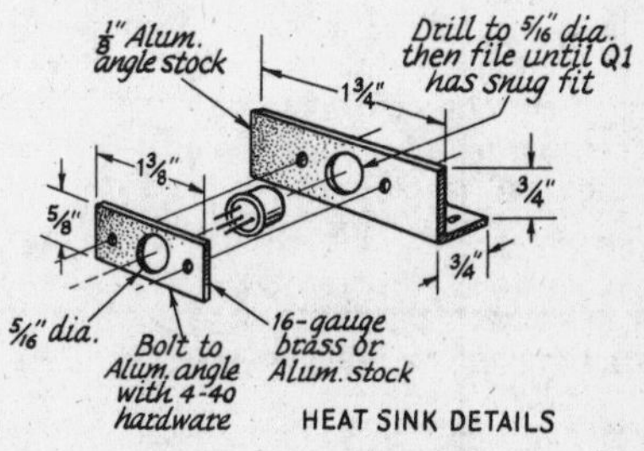

Fig. 18-6 – Layout and assembly details of another homemade heat sink. The completed assembly can be insulated from the main chassis of the transmitter by using insulating washers.

transistor is held in place by a small metal plate whose center hole is slightly smaller in diameter than the case of the transistor. Details are given in Fig. 18-6.

A thin coating of silicone grease, available from most electronics supply houses, can be applied between the case of the transistor and the part of the heat sink with which it comes in contact. The silicone grease will aid the transfer of heat from the transistor to the sink. This practice can be applied to all models shown here. In the example given in Fig. 18-5, the grease should be applied between the

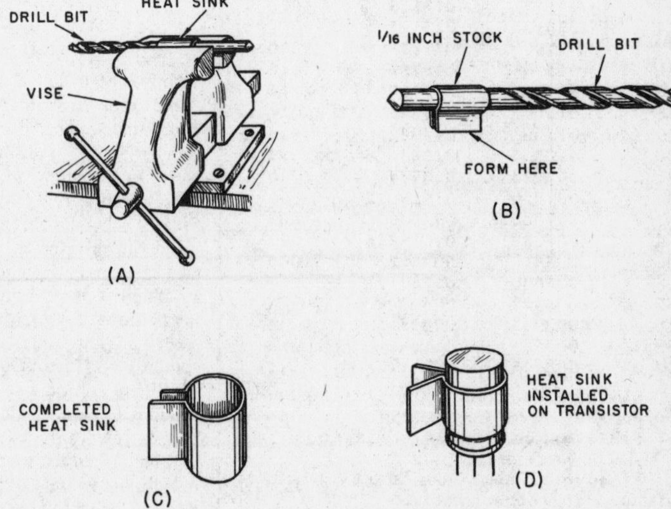

Fig. 18-7 – Steps used in constructing heat sinks for small transistors.

three channels before they are bolted together, as well as between the transistor and the channel it contacts.

CONSTRUCTION NOTES

If a control shaft must be extended or insulated, a flexible shaft coupling with adequate insulation should be used. Satisfactory support for the shaft extension, as well as electrical contact for safety, can be provided by means of a metal panel bearing made for the purpose. These can be obtained singly for use with existing shafts, or they can be bought with a captive extension shaft included. In either case the panel bearing gives a "solid" feel to the control.

The use of fiber washers between ceramic insulation and metal brackets, screws or nuts will prevent the ceramic parts from breaking.

STANDARD METAL GAUGES

Gauge No.	*American or B&S*[1]	*U.S. Standard*[2]	*Birmingham or Stubs*[3]
1	.2893	.28125	.300
2	.2576	.265625	.284
3	.2294	.25	.259
4	.2043	.234375	.238
5	.1819	.21875	.220
6	.1620	.203125	.203
7	.1443	.1875	.180
8	.1285	.171875	.165
9	.1144	.15625	.148
10	.1019	.140625	.134
11	.09074	.125	.120
12	.08081	.109375	.109
13	.07196	.09375	.095
14	.06408	.078125	.083
15	.05707	.0703125	.072
16	.05082	.0625	.065
17	.04526	.05625	.058
18	.04030	.05	.049
19	.03589	.04375	.042
20	.03196	.0375	.035
21	.02846	.034375	.032
22	.02535	.03125	.028
23	.02257	.028125	.025
24	.02010	.025	.022
25	.01790	.021875	.020
26	.01594	.01875	.018
27	.01420	.0171875	.016
28	.01264	.015625	.014
29	.01126	.0140625	.013
30	.01003	.0125	.012
31	.008928	.0109375	.010
32	.007950	.01015625	.009
33	.007080	.009375	.008
34	.006350	.00859375	.007
35	.005615	.0078125	.005
36	.005000	.00703125	.004
37	.004453	.006640626	....
38	.003965	.00625	....
39	.003531	....	....
40	.003145	....	....

[1] Used for aluminum, copper, brass and non-ferrous alloy sheets, wire and rods.
[2] Used for iron, steel, nickel and ferrous alloy sheets, wire and rods.
[3] Used for seamless tubes; also by some manufacturers for copper and brass.

Cutting and Bending Sheet Metal

If a sheet of metal is too large to be cut conveniently with a hack saw, it may be marked with scratches as deep as possible along the line of the cut on both sides of the sheet and then clamped in a vise and worked back and forth until the sheet breaks at the line. Do not carry the bending too far until the break begins to weaken; otherwise the edge of the sheet may become bent. A pair of iron bars or pieces of heavy angle stock, as long or longer than the width of the sheet, to hold it in the vise, will make the job easier. "C" clamps may be used to keep the bars from spreading at the ends. The rough edges may be smoothed with a file or by placing a large piece of emery cloth or sandpaper on a flat surface and running the edge of the metal back and forth over the sheet. Bends may be made similarly.

Finishing Aluminum

Aluminum chassis, panels and parts may be given a sheen finish by treating them in a caustic bath. An enamelled or plastic container, such as a dishpan or infant's bathtub, should be used for the solution. Dissolve ordinary household lye in cold water in a proportion of 1/4 to 1/2 can of lye per gallon of water. The stronger solution will do the job more rapidly. Stir the solution with a stick of wood until the lye crystals are completely dissolved. Be very careful to avoid any skin contact with the solution. It is also harmful to clothing. Sufficient solution should be prepared to cover the piece completely. When the aluminum is immersed, a very pronounced bubbling takes place and ventilation should be provided to disperse the escaping gas. A half hour to two hours in the solution should be sufficient, depending upon the strength of the solution and the desired surface.

Remove the aluminum from the solution with sticks and rinse thoroughly in cold water while swabbing with a rag to remove the black deposit. When dry, finish by spraying on a light coat of clear lacquer.

Soldering

The secret of good soldering is to use the right amount of heat. Too little heat will produce a "cold-soldered joint"; too much may injure a component. The iron and the solder should be applied simultaneously to the joint. Keep the iron clean by brushing the hot tip with a paper towel. Always use rosin-core solder, never acid-core. Solders have different melting points, depending upon the ratio of tin to lead. A 50-50 solder melts at 425 degrees F, while 60-40 melts at 371 degrees F. When it is desirable to protect from excessive heat the components being soldered, the 60-40 solder is preferable to the 50-50. (A less-common solder, 63-37, melts at 361 degrees F.)

When soldering transistors, crystal diodes or small resistors, the lead should be gripped with a pair of pliers up close to the unit so that the heat will be conducted away. Overheating of a transistor or diode while soldering can cause permanent damage. Also, mechanical stress will have a similar effect, so that a small unit should be mounted so that there is no appreciable mechanical strain on the leads.

Trouble is sometimes experienced in soldering to the pins of coil forms or male cable plugs. It helps if the pins are first cleaned on the inside with a suitable twist drill and then tinned by flowing rosin-core solder into them. Immediately clear the surplus solder from each hot pin by a whipping motion or by blowing through the pin from the inside of the form or plug. Before inserting the wire in the pin, file the nickel plate from the tip. After soldering, round the solder tip off with a file.

When soldering to the pins of polystyrene coil forms, hold the pin to be soldered with a pair of heavy pliers, to form a "heat sink" and insure that the pin does not heat enough in the coil form to loosen and become misaligned.

Wiring

The wire used in connecting amateur equipment should be selected considering both the maximum current it will be called upon to handle and the voltage its insulation must stand without breakdown. Also, from the consideration to TVI, the power wiring of all transmitters should be done with wire that has a braided shielding cover. Receiver and audio circuits may also require the use of shielded wire at some points for stability, or the elimination of hum.

No. 20 stranded wire is commonly used for most receiver wiring (except for the high-frequency circuits) where the current does not exceed 2 or 3 amperes. For higher-current heater circuits, No. 18 is available. Wire with cellulose acetate insulation is good for voltages up to about 500. For higher voltages, themoplastic-insulated wire should be used. Inexpensive wire strippers that make the removal of insulation from hookup wire an easy job are available on the market.

When power leads have several branches in the chassis, it is convenient to use fiber-insulated multiple tie points as anchorages or junction points. Strips of this type are also useful as insulated supports for resistors, rf chokes and capacitors. High-voltage wiring should have exposed points held to a minimum; those which cannot be avoided should be made as inaccessible as possible to accidental contact or short-circuit.

Where shielded wire is called for and capacitance to ground is not a factor, Belden type 8885 shielded grid wire may be used. If capacitance must be minimized, it may be necessary to use a piece of car-radio low-capacitance lead-in wire, or coaxial cable.

For wiring high-frequency circuits, rigid wire is often used. Bare soft-drawn tinned wire, size 22 to 12 (depending on mechanical requirements) is suitable. Kinks can be removed by stretching a piece of 10 or 15 feet long and then cutting into short lengths that can be handled conveniently. Rf wiring should be run directly from point to point with a minimum of sharp bends and the wire kept well spaced from the chassis or other grounded metal surfaces. Where the wiring must pass through the chassis or a partition, a clearance hole should

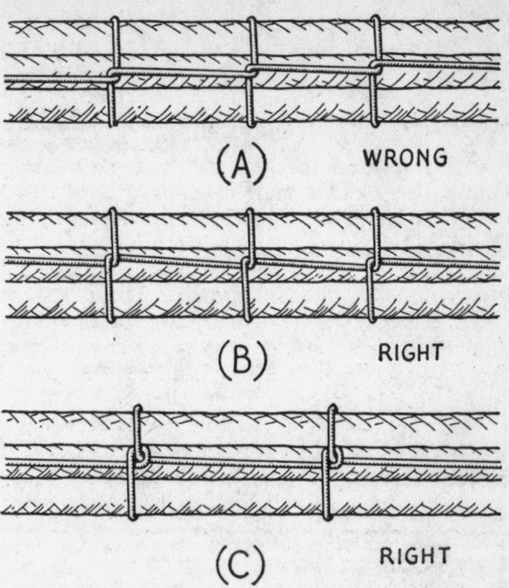

Fig. 18-8 – Methods of lacing cables. The method shown at C is more secure, but takes more time than the method of B. The latter is usually adequate for most amateur requirements.

be cut and lined with a rubber grommet. In case insulation becomes necessary, varnished cambric tubing (spaghetti) can be slipped over the wire.

In transmitters where the peak voltage does not exceed 2500 volts, the shielded grid wire mentioned above should be satisfactory for power circuits. For higher voltages, Belden type 8656, Birnbach type 1820, or shielded ignition cable can be used. In the case of filament circuits carrying heavy current, it may be necessary to use No. 10 or 12 bare or enameled wire, slipped through spaghetti, and then covered with copper braid pulled tightly over the spaghetti. The chapter on TVI shows the manner in which shielded wire should be applied. If the shielding is simply slid back over the insulation and solder flowed into the end of the braid, the braid usually will stay in place without the necessity for cutting it back or binding it in place. The braid should be cleaned first so that solder will take with a minimum of heat.

Rf wiring in transmitters usually follows the method described above for receivers with due respect to the voltages involved.

Where power or control leads run together for more than a few inches, they will present a better appearance when bound together in a single cable. The correct technique is illustrated in Fig. 18-8; both plastic and waxed-linen lacing cords are available. Plastic cable clamps are available to hold the laced cable.

To give a "commercial look" to the wiring of any unit, run any cabled leads along the edge of the chassis. If this isn't possible, the cabled leads should then run parallel to an edge of the chassis. Further, the generous use of tie points (mounted parallel to an edge of the chassis), for the support of one or both ends of a resistor or fixed capacitor,

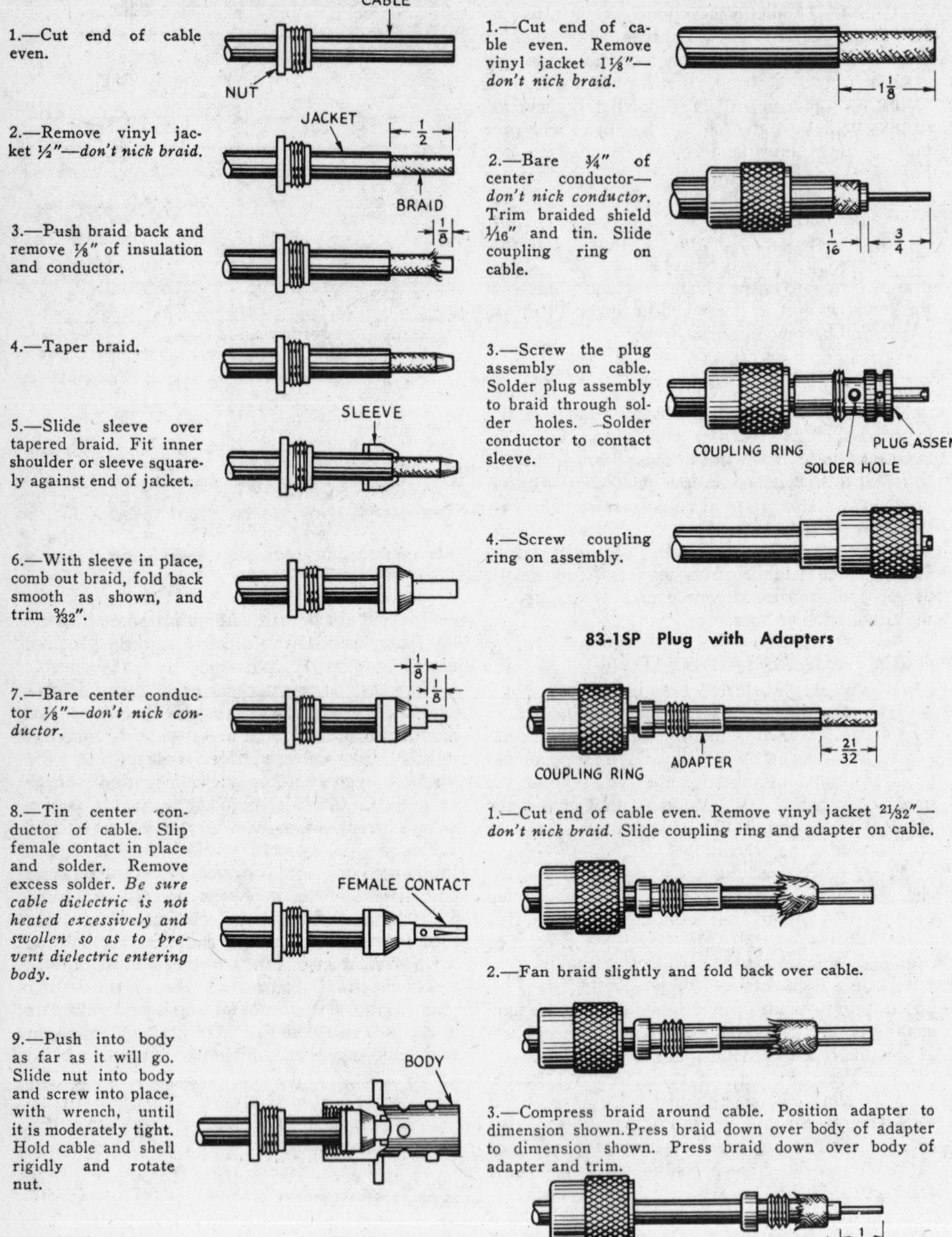

BNC Connectors

1.—Cut end of cable even.

2.—Remove vinyl jacket $\frac{1}{2}$"—*don't nick braid.*

3.—Push braid back and remove $\frac{1}{8}$" of insulation and conductor.

4.—Taper braid.

5.—Slide sleeve over tapered braid. Fit inner shoulder or sleeve squarely against end of jacket.

6.—With sleeve in place, comb out braid, fold back smooth as shown, and trim $\frac{3}{32}$".

7.—Bare center conductor $\frac{1}{8}$"—*don't nick conductor.*

8.—Tin center conductor of cable. Slip female contact in place and solder. Remove excess solder. *Be sure cable dielectric is not heated excessively and swollen so as to prevent dielectric entering body.*

9.—Push into body as far as it will go. Slide nut into body and screw into place, with wrench, until it is moderately tight. Hold cable and shell rigidly and rotate nut.

10.—This assembly procedure applies to BNC jacks. The assembly for plugs is the same except for the use of male contacts and a plug body.

83-1SP Plug

1.—Cut end of cable even. Remove vinyl jacket $1\frac{1}{8}$"—*don't nick braid.*

2.—Bare $\frac{3}{4}$" of center conductor—*don't nick conductor.* Trim braided shield $\frac{1}{16}$" and tin. Slide coupling ring on cable.

3.—Screw the plug assembly on cable. Solder plug assembly to braid through solder holes. Solder conductor to contact sleeve.

4.—Screw coupling ring on assembly.

83-1SP Plug with Adapters

1.—Cut end of cable even. Remove vinyl jacket $\frac{21}{32}$"—*don't nick braid.* Slide coupling ring and adapter on cable.

2.—Fan braid slightly and fold back over cable.

3.—Compress braid around cable. Position adapter to dimension shown. Press braid down over body of adapter to dimension shown. Press braid down over body of adapter and trim.

4.—Bare $\frac{1}{2}$" of center conductor—*don't nick conductor.* Pre-tin exposed center conductor.

5, 6.—Same as 3 and 4 under 83-1SP Plug.

Fig. 18-9 — Cable-stripping dimensions and assembly instructions for several popular coaxial-cable plugs. This material courtesy Amphenol Connector Division, Amphenol-Borg Electronics Corp.

will add to the appearance of the finished unit. In a similar manner, "dress" the small components so that they are parallel to the panel or sides of the chassis.

Winding Coils

Close-wound coils are readily wound on the specified form by anchoring one end of a length of wire (in a vise or to a doorknob) and the other end to the coil form. Straighten any kinks in the wire and then pull to keep the wire under slight tension. Wind the coil to the required number of turns while walking toward the anchor, always maintaining a slight tension on the wire.

To space-wind the coil, wind the coil simultaneously with a suitable spacing medium (heavy thread, string or wire) in the manner described above. When the winding is complete, secure the end of the coil to the coil-form terminal and then carefully unwind the spacing material. If the coil is wound under suitable tension, the spacing material can be easily removed without disturbing the winding. Finish the space-wound coil by judicious applications of Duco cement, to hold the turns in place.

The "cold" end of a coil is the end at or close to chassis or ground potential. Coupling links should be wound on the cold end of a coil, to minimize capacitive coupling.

CIRCUIT-BOARD FABRICATION

Many modern-day builders prefer the neatness and miniaturization made possible by the use of etched or printed circuit boards. There are additional benefits to be realized from the use of circuit boards: Low lead inductances, excellent physical stability of the components and interconnecting leads, and good repeatability of the basic layout of a given project. The latter attribute makes the use of circuit boards ideal for group projects.

Methods

Perhaps the least complicated approach to circuit-board fabrication is the use of unclad perforated board into which a number of push-in terminals have been installed. The perforated board can be obtained with one of many hole patterns, dependent upon the needs of the builder. Perforated terminal boards are manufactured by such firms as Vector, Kepro, and Triad. Their products are available from the large mail-order houses.

Once the builder plots the layout of his circuit on paper, push-in terminals can be installed in the "perf" board to match the layout which was done on paper. The terminals serve as tie points and provide secure mounting-post anchors for the various components. Selected terminals can be wired together to provide ground and B-plus lines. Although this technique is the most basic of the methods, it is entirely practical.

An approach to etched-circuit board assembly can be realized by cutting strips of flashing copper, hobby copper, or brass shim stock into the desired shapes and lengths, then gluing them to a piece of unclad circuit board. Epoxy cement is useful for the latter. Alternatively, the strips can be held in place by means of brass eyelets which have been installed with a hand eyelet tool. If standard unclad circuit board is not handy, linoleum or Formica sheeting can be made to serve as a base for the circuit board. If this technique is used, the metal strips should be soldered together at each point where they join, assuring good electrical contact.

Etched-circuit boards provide the most professional end result of the three systems described here. They are the most stable, physically and electrically, and can be easily repeated from a single template. Etched-circuits can be formed on copper-clad perforated board, or on unpunched copper-clad board. There is no advantage in using the perforated board as a base unless push-in terminals are to be used.

Planning and Layout

The constructor should first plan the physical layout of the circuit by sketching a pictorial diagram on paper, drawing it to scale. Once this has been done, the interconnecting leads can be inked in to represent the copper strips that will remain on the etched board. The Vector Company sells layout paper for this purpose. It is marked with the same patterns that are used on their perforated boards.

After the basic etched-circuit design has been completed the designer should go over the proposed layout several times to insure against errors. When the foregoing has been done, the pattern can be painted on the copper surface of the board to be etched. Etch-resistant solutions are available from commercial suppliers and can be selected from their catalogs. Some builders prefer to use India ink for this purpose. Perhaps the most readily-available material for use in etch-resist applications is ordinary exterior enamel paint. The portions of the board to be retained are covered with a layer of paint, applied with an artist's brush, duplicating the pattern that was drawn on the layout paper. The job can be made a bit easier by tracing over the original layout with a ballpoint pen and carbon paper while the pattern is taped to the copper side of the unetched circuit board. The carbon paper is placed between the pattern and the circuit board. After the paint has been applied, it should be allowed to dry for at least 24 hours prior to the etching process. The Vector Company produces a rub-on transfer material that can also be used as etch-resist when laying out circuit-board patterns. Thin strips of ordinary masking tape, cut to size and firmly applied, serve nicely as etch-resist material too.

The Etching Process

Almost any strong acid bath will serve as an etchant, but the two chemical preparations recommended here are the safest to use. A bath can be prepared by mixing 1 part ammonium persulphate crystals with 2 parts clear water. A

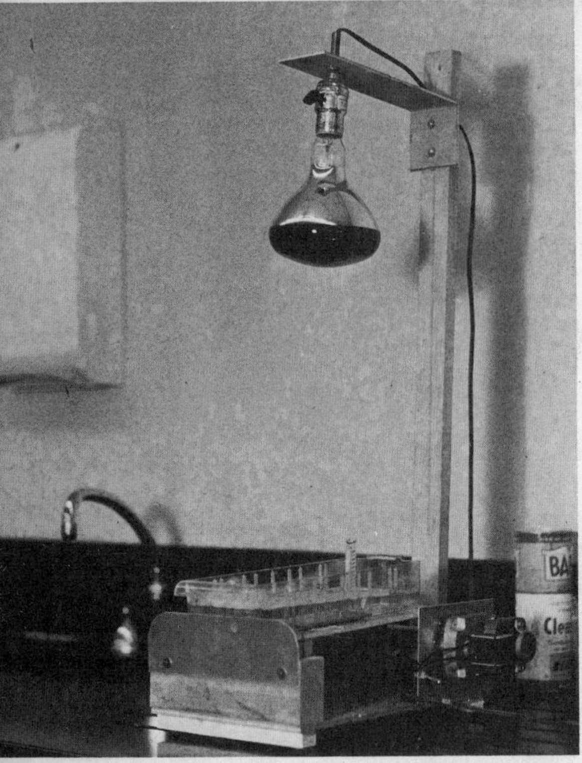

Fig. 18-10 — A homemade stand for processing etched-circuit boards. The heat lamp maintains the etchant-bath temperature between 90 and 115 degrees, F. and is mounted on an adjustable arm. The tray for the bath is raised and lowered at one end by the action of a motor-driven eccentric disk, providing the necessary agitation of the chemical solution. A darkroom thermometer monitors the temperature of the bath.

normal quantity of working solution for most amateur radio applications is composed of 1 cup of crystals and 2 cups of water. To this mixture add 1/4 teaspoon of mercuric chloride crystals. The latter serves as an activator for the bath. Ready-made etchant kits which use these chemicals are available from Vector. A two-bag kit is sold as item 2594 and costs just over $1. Complete kits which contain circuit boards, etchant powders, etch-resist transfers, layout paper, and plastic etchant bags are also available from Vector at moderate prices.

Another chemical bath that works satisfactorily for copper etching is made up from one part ferric chloride crystals and 2 parts water. No activator is required with this bath. Ready-made solutions (one-pint and one-gallon sizes) are available through some mail-order houses at low cost. They are manufactured by Kepro Co. and carry a stock number of E-1PT and E-1G, respectively. One pint costs less than a dollar.

Etchant solutions become exhausted after a certain amount of copper has been processed, therefore it is wise to keep a quantity of the bath on hand if frequent use is anticipated. With either chemical bath, the working solution should be maintained at a temperature between 90 and 115 degrees F. A heat lamp can be directed toward the bath during the etching period, its distance set to maintain the required temperature. A darkroom thermometer is handy for monitoring the temperature of the bath.

While the circuit board is immersed in the solution, it should be agitated continuously to permit uniform reaction to the chemicals. This action will also speed up the etching process somewhat. Normally, the circuit board should be placed in the bath with the copper side facing down, toward the bottom of the tray. The tray should be non-metallic, preferably a Pyrex dish or a photographic darkroom tray.

The photograph, Fig. 18-10, shows a homemade etching stand made up from a heat lamp, some lumber, and an 8 rpm motor. An eccentric disk has been mounted on the motor shaft and butts against the bottom of the etchant tray. As the motor turns, the eccentric disk raises and lowers one end of the try, thus providing continuous agitation of the solution. The heat lamp is mounted on an adjustable, slotted wooden arm. Its height above the solution tray is adjusted to provide the desired bath temperature. Because the etching process takes between 15 minutes and one hour –dependent upon the strength and temperature of the bath – such an accessory is convenient.

After the etching process is completed, the board is removed from the tray and washed thoroughly with fresh, clear water. The etch-resist material can then be rubbed off by applying a few brisk strokes with medium-grade steel wool. **WARNING:** *Always use rubber gloves when working with etchant powders and solutions. Should the acid bath come in contact with the body, immediately wash the affected area with clear water. Protect the eyes when using acid baths.*

COMPONENT VALUES

Values of composition resistors and small capacitors (mica and ceramic) are specified throughout this *Handbook* in terms of "preferred values." In the preferred-number system, all values represent (approximately) a constant-percentage increase over the next lower value. The base of the system is the number 10. Only two significant figures are used.

"Tolerance" means that a variation of plus or minus the percentage given is considered satisfactory. For example, the actual resistance of a "4700-ohm" 20-percent resistor can lie anywhere between 3700 and 5600 ohms, approximately. The permissible variation in the same resistance value with 5-percent tolerance would be in the range from 4500 to 4900 ohms, approximately.

In the component specifications in this *Handbook*, it is to be understood that when no tolerance is specified the *largest* tolerance available in that value will be satisfactory.

Values that do not fit into the preferred-number system (such as 500, 25,000) easily can be substituted. It is obvious, for example, that a 5000-ohm resistor falls well within the tolerance range of the 4700-ohm 20-percent resistor used in the example above. It would not, however, be usable if the tolerance were specified as 5 percent.

TABLE 18-II

Approximate Series-Resonance Frequencies of Disc Ceramic Bypass Capacitors

Capacitance	*Freq.*[1]	*Freq.*[2]
.01 μF	13 MHz	15 MHz
.0047	18	22
.002	31	38
.001	46	55
.0005	65	80
.0001	135	165

[1] Total lead length of 1 inch
[2] Total lead length of 1/2-inch

COLOR CODES

Standardized color codes are used to mark values on small components such as composition resistors and mica capacitors, and to identify leads from transformers, etc. The resistor-capacitor number color code is given in Table 18-III.

Fixed Capacitors

The methods of marking "postage-stamp" mica capacitors, molded paper capacitors and tubular ceramic capacitors are shown in Fig. 18-11.

Capacitors made to American War Standards or Joint Army-Navy specifications are marked with the 6-dot code shown at the top. Practically all surplus capacitors are in this category.

The 3-dot EIA code is used for capacitors having a rating of 500 volts and ±20 percent tolerance only; other ratings and tolerances are covered by the 6-dot EIA code.

Example: A capacitor with a 6-dot code has the following markings: Top row, left to right, black, yellow, violet; bottom row, right to left, brown, silver, red. Since the first color in the top row is black (significant figure zero) this is the AWS code and the capacitor has mica dielectric. The significant figures are 4 and 7, the decimal multiplier 10 (brown, at right of second row), so the capacitance is 470 pF. The tolerance is ±0%. The final color, the characteristic, deals with temperature coefficients and methods of testing (see Table 18-V).

A capacitor with a 3-dot code has the following colors, left to right: brown, black, red. The significant figures are 1, 0 (10) and the multiplier is 100. The capacitance is therefore 100 pF.

A capacitor with a 6-dot code has the following markings: Top row, left to right, brown, black, black; bottom row, right to left, black, gold, blue. Since the first color in the top row is neither black nor silver, this is the EIA code. The significant figures are 1, 0, 0 (100) and the decimal multiplier is 1 (black). The capacitance is therefore 100 pF. The gold dot shows that the tolerance is ±5% and the blue dot indicates 600-volt rating.

Ceramic Capacitors

Conventional markings for ceramic capacitors are shown in the lower drawing of Fig.18-11.The colors have the meanings indicated in Table 18-III. In practice, dots may be used instead of the *narrow* bands indicated in Fig. 18-11.

Example: A ceramic capacitor has the following markings: Broad band, violet; narrow bands or dots, green, brown, black, green. The significant figures are 5, 1 (51) and the decimal multiplier is 1, so the capacitance is 51 pF. The temperature coefficient is −750 parts per million per degree C., as given by the broad band, the capacitance tolerance is ±5%.

Fixed Composition Resistors

Composition resistors (including small wire-wound units molded in cases identical with the composition type) are color-coded as shown in Fig. 18-12. Colored bands are used on resistors having axial leads; on radial-lead resistors the colors are placed as shown in the drawing. When bands are used for color coding the body color has no significance.

Examples: A resistor of the type shown in the lower drawing of Fig. 18-12 has the following color bands: A, red; B, red; C, orange; D, no color. The significant figures are 2, 2 (22) and the decimal multiplier is 1000. The value of resistance is therefore 22,000 ohms and the tolerance is ±20%.

A resistor of the type shown in the upper drawing has the following colors: body (A), blue; end (B), gray; dot, red; end (D), gold. The significant figures are 6, 8 (68) and the decimal multiplier is 100, so the resistance is 6800 ohms. The tolerance is ± 5%.

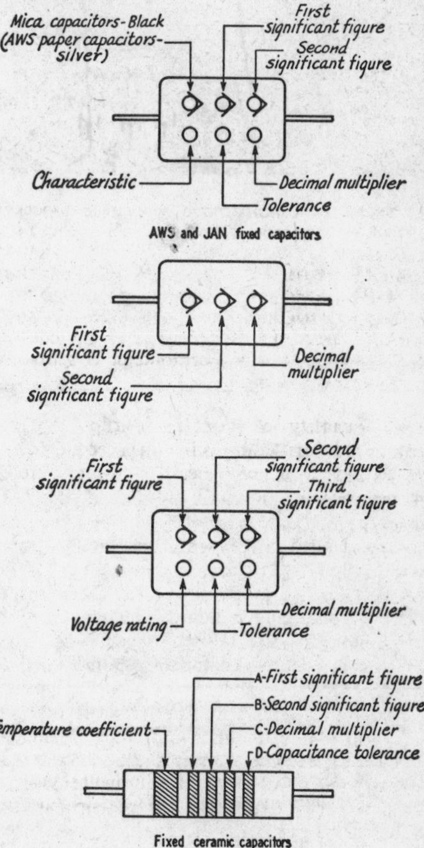

Fig. 18-11 — Color coding of fixed mica, molded paper and tubular ceramic capacitors. The color code for mica and molded paper capacitors is given in Table 18-III. Table 18-IV gives the color code for tubular ceramic capacitors.

TABLE 18-III

Resistor-Capacitor Color Code

Color	*Significant Figure*	*Decimal Multiplier*	*Tolerance (%)*	*Voltage Rating**
Black	0	1	–	–
Brown	1	10	1*	100
Red	2	100	2*	200
Orange	3	1,000	3*	300
Yellow	4	10,000	4*	400
Green	5	100,000	5*	500
Blue	6	1,000,000	6*	600
Violet	7	10,000,000	7*	700
Gray	8	100,000,000	8*	800
White	9	1,000,000,000	9*	900
Gold	–	0.1	5	1000
Silver	–	0.01	10	2000
No color	–		20	500

* Applies to capacitors only.

TABLE 18-IV

Color Code for Ceramic Capacitors

Color	*Significant Figure*	*Decimal Multiplier*	Capacitance Tolerance *More than 10 pF (in %)*	Capacitance Tolerance *Less than 10 pF (in pF)*	*Temp. Coeff. ppm /deg. C.*
Black	0	1	±20	2.0	0
Brown	1	10	± 1		– 30
Red	2	100	± 2		– 80
Orange	3	1000			–150
Yellow	4				–220
Green	5				–330
Blue	6		± 5	0.5	–470
Violet	7				–750
Gray	8	0.01		0.25	30
White	9	0.1	±10	1.0	500

TABLE 18-V

Capacitor Characteristic Code

Color Sixth Dot	*Temperature Coefficient ppm/deg. C.*	*Capacitance Drift*
Black	±1000	±5% +1 pF
Brown	±500	±3% +1 pF
Red	±200	±0.5%
Orange	±100	±0.3%
Yellow	–20 to +100	±0.1% +0.1 pF
Green	0 to +70	±0.05% +0.1 pF

I-f Transformers

Blue – plate lead.
Red – "B" + lead.
Green – grid (or diode) lead.
Black – grid (or diode) return.

NOTE: If the secondary of the i-f transformer is center-tapped, the second diode plate lead is green-and-black striped, and black is used for the center-tap lead.

Audio Transformers

Blue – plate (finish) lead of primary.
Red – "B" + lead (this applies whether the primary is plain or center-tapped).
Brown – plate (start) lead on center-tapped primaries. (Blue may be used for this lead if polarity is not important.)
Green – grid (finish) lead to secondary.
Black – grid return (this applies whether the secondary is plain or center-tapped).
Yellow – grid (start) lead on center-tapped secondaries. (Green may be used for this lead if polarity is not important.)

NOTE: These markings apply also to line-to-grid and tube-to-line transformers.

Power Transformers

1) Primary Leads .... *Black*
   If tapped:
   Common .... *Black*
   Tap .... *Black and Yellow Striped*
   Finish .... *Black and Red Striped*
2) High-Voltage Place Winding .... *Red*
   Center-Tap .... *Red and Yellow Striped*
3) Rectifier Filament Winding .... *Yellow*
   Center-Tap .... *Yellow and Blue Striped*
4) Filament Winding No. 1 .... *Green*
   Center-Tap ..... *Green and Yellow Striped*
5) Filament Winding No. 2 .... *Brown*
   Center-Tap ..... *Brown and Yellow Striped*
6) Filament Winding No. 3 .... *Slate*
   Center-Tap ..... *Slate and Yellow Striped*

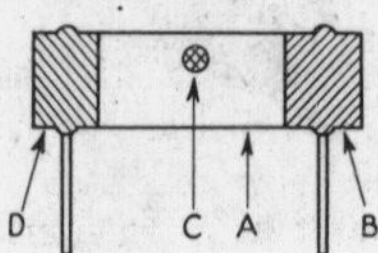

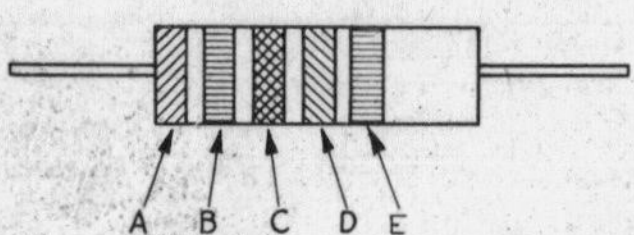

Fixed composition resistors

Fig. 18-12 – Color coding of fixed composition resistors. The color code is given in Table 18-III. The colored areas have the following significance:
A – First significant figure of resistance in ohms.
B – Second significant figure.
C – Decimal multiplier.
D – Resistance tolerance in percent. If no color is shown the tolerance is ±20 percent.
E – Relative percent change in value per 1000 hours of operation; Brown, 1 percent; Red, 0.1 percent; Orange, .01 percent; Yellow, .001 percent.

TABLE 18-VI

Color Code for Hookup Wire

Wire Color	*Type of Circuit*
Black	Grounds, grounded elements, and returns
Brown	Heaters or filaments, off ground
Red	Power supply B plus
Orange	Screen grids and Base 2 of transistors
Yellow	Cathodes and transistor emitters
Green	Control grids, diode plates, and Base 1 of transistors
Blue	Plates and transistor collectors
Violet	Power supply, minus leads
Gray	Ac power line leads
White	Bias supply, B or C minus, agc

Wires with tracers are coded in the same manner as solid-color wires, allowing additional circuit identification over solid-color wiring. The body of the wire is white and the color band spirals around the wire lead. When more than one color band is used, the widest band represents the 1st color.

TABLE 18-VII

Metric Multiplier Prefixes

Multiples and submultiples of fundamental units (e.g., ampere, farad, gram, meter, watt)) may be indicated by the following prefixes.

Prefix	*Abbreviation*	*Multiplier*
tera	T	10^{12}
giga	G	10^{9}
mega	M	10^{6}
kilo	k	10^{3}
hecto	h	10^{2}
deci	d	10^{-1}
centi	c	10^{-2}
milli	m	10^{-3}
micro	μ	10^{-6}
nano	n	10^{-9}
pico	p	10^{-12}

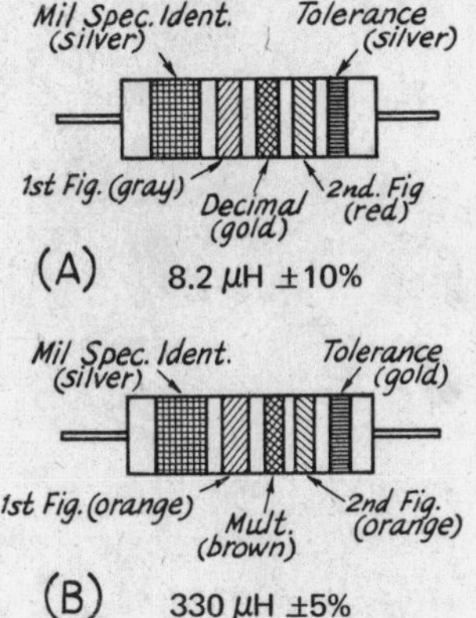

Fig. 18-13 – Color coding for tubular encapsulated rf chokes. At A, an example of the coding for an 8.2-μH choke is given. At B, the color bands for a 330-μH inductor are illustrated.

Color	*Figure*	*Multiplier*	*Tolerance*
Black	0	1	
Brown	1	10	
Red	2	100	
Orange	3	1000	
Yellow	4		
Green	5		
Blue	6		
Violet	7		
Gray	8		
White	9		
None			20%
Silver			10%
Gold			5%

Multiplier is the factor by which the two color figures are multiplied to obtain the inductance value of the choke coil.

PILOT-LAMP DATA

Lamp No.	*Bead Color*	*Base (Miniature)*	*Bulb Type*	RATING *Volts*	RATING *Amp.*
40	Brown	Screw	T-3 1/4	6–8	0.15
40A[1]	Brown	Bayonet	T-3 1/4	6–8	0.15
41	White	Screw	T-3 1/4	2.5	0.5
42	Green	Screw	T-3 1/4	3.2	**
43	White	Bayonet	T-3 1/4	2.5	0.5
44	Blue	Bayonet	T-3 1/4	6–8	0.25
45	*	Bayonet	T-3 1/4	3.2	**
46[2]	Blue	Screw	T-3 1/4	6–8	0.25
47[1]	Brown	Bayonet	T-3 1/4	6–9	0.15
48	Pink	Screw	T-3 1/4	2.0	0.06
49[3]	Pink	Bayonet	T-3 1/4	2.0	0.06
49A[3]	White	Bayonet	T-3 1/4	2.1	0.12
50	White	Screw	G-3 1/2	6–8	0.2
51[2]	White	Bayonet	G-3 1/2	6–8	0.2
53	–	Bayonet	G-3 1/2	14.4	0.12
55	White	Bayonet	G-4 1/2	6–8	0.4
292[5]	White	Screw	T-3 1/4	2.9	0.17
292A[5]	White	Bayonet	T-3 1/4	2.9	0.17
1455	Brown	Screw	G-5	18.0	0.25
1455A	Brown	Bayonet	G-5	18.0	0.25
1487	–	Screw	T-3 1/4	12–16	0.20
1488	–	Bayonet	T-3 1/4	14	0.15
1813	–	Bayonet	T-3 1/4	14.4	0.10
1815	–	Bayonet	T-3 1/4	12–16	0.20

1 40A and 47 are interchangeable.
2 Have frosted bulbs.
3 49 and 49A are interchangeable.
4 Replace with No. 48.
5 Use in 2.5-volt sets where regular bulb burns out too frequently.
* White in G.E. and Sylvania; green in National Union, Raytheon and Tung-Sol.
** 0.35 in G.E. and Sylvania; 0.5 in National Union, Raytheon and Tung-Sol.

Finding Parts

No chapter on construction would be complete without information on where to buy parts. Amateurs, on a dwarfed scale, must function as purchasing agents in these perplexing times. A properly equipped buyer maintains as complete a catalog file as possible. Many of the companies listed in Chart I will provide free catalogs upon written request. Others may charge a small fee for catalogs. Mail ordering, especially for those distant from metropolitan areas, is today's means to the desired end when collecting component parts for an amateur project. Prices are, to some extent, competitive. A wise buyer will study the catalogs and select his merchandise accordingly.

Delays in shipment can be lessened by avoiding the use of personal checks when ordering. Bank or postal money orders are preferred by most distributors. Personal checks often take a week to clear, thereby causing frustrating delays in the order reaching you.

FRACTIONS OF AN INCH WITH METRIC EQUIVALENTS

Fractions of an inch	*Decimals of an inch*	*Millimeters*	*Fractions of an inch*	*Decimals of an inch*	*Millimeters*
1/64	0.0156	0.397	33/64	0.5156	13.097
1/32	0.0313	0.794	17/32	0.5313	13.494
3/64	0.0469	1.191	35/64	0.5469	13.891
1/16	0.0625	1.588	9/16	0.5625	14.288
5/64	0.0781	1.984	37/64	0.5781	14.684
3/32	0.0938	2.381	19/32	0.5938	15.081
7/64	0.1094	2.778	39/64	0.6094	15.478
1/8	0.1250	3.175	5/8	0.6250	15.875
9/64	0.1406	3.572	41/64	0.6406	16.272
5/32	0.1563	3.969	21/32	0.6563	16.669
11/64	0.1719	4.366	43/64	0.6719	17.066
3/16	0.1875	4.763	11/16	0.6875	17.463
13/64	0.2031	5.159	45/64	0.7031	17.859
7/32	0.2188	5.556	23/32	0.7188	18.256
15/64	0.2344	5.953	47/64	0.7344	18.653
1/4	0.2500	6.350	3/4	0.7500	19.050
17/64	0.2656	6.747	49/64	0.7656	19.447
9/32	0.2813	7.144	25/32	0.7813	19.844
19/64	0.2969	7.541	51/64	0.7969	20.241
5/16	0.3125	7.938	13/16	0.8125	20.638
21/64	0.3281	8.334	53/64	0.8281	21.034
11/32	0.3438	8.731	27/32	0.8438	21.431
23/64	0.3594	9.128	55/64	0.8594	21.828
3/8	0.3750	9.525	7/8	0.8750	22.225
25/64	0.3906	9.922	57/64	0.8906	22.622
13/32	0.4063	10.319	29/32	0.9063	23.019
27/64	0.4219	10.716	59/64	0.9219	23.416
7/16	0.4375	11.113	15/16	0.9375	23.813
29/64	0.4531	11.509	61/64	0.9531	24.209
15/32	0.4688	11.906	31/32	0.9688	24.606
31/64	0.4844	12.303	63/64	0.9844	25.003
1/2	0.5000	12.700	—	1.0000	25.400

Chart 1

Code	Supplier
L * $1 ** $10	Allied Electronics 2400 W. Washington Blvd. Chicago, IL 60612
A *	Allied/Radio Shack Stores (See local phone directory)
L * free **	Amateur Electronic Supply 4828 W. Fond du Lac Ave. Milwaukee, WI 53216
B * free ** none	Amidon Associates 12033 Otsego Street N. Hollywood, CA 91607
L * free **	AM Tech PO Box 624 Marion, OH 52302
M, N * free ** f	Andy Electronics 6427 Springer Houston, TX 77017
M, N * sase ** none L	Associated Comtronics PO Box 200 Port Jefferson Station L.I. NY 11776
O * free ** none	Atlantic Surplus Sales 580 Third Avenue Brooklyn, NY 11215
B * free ** none	Barken Electronics 274 Mt. Pleasant Ave. Livingston, NJ 07039
A * free **	Barker & Williamson, Inc. Canal St. Bristol, PA 19007
L, M, N ** 50¢ * $5	Barry Electronics 512 Broadway New York, NY 10012
M, N * free ** $10	Budget Electronics 2704 West North Avenue Chicago, IL 60647
L, M, N * free ** $5	Burstein-Applebee 3199 Mercier Street Kansas City, MO 64111
L,A * free **	Cambridge Thermionic Corp. 445 Concord Ave. Cambridge, MA 02138
C, P * free ** none	Circuit Board Specialists 3011 Norwich Ave. Pueblo, CO 81008
A, E * free ** none	Circuit Specialists Co. PO Box 3047 Scottsdale, AZ 85257
J,M * free **	Theodore E. Dames Co. 308 Hickory St. Arlington, NJ 07032
I, M, N * free ** $3	Delta Electronics Co. PO Box 1 Lynn, MA 01903
L * free ** none	Dominion Radio & Elect. Co. 535 Yonge St. Toronto, Ontario, CANADA
L * free **	Electronics Distributors, Inc. 1960 Peck Street Muskegon, MI 49441
L * free ** $5	Electro-Sonic Supply 543 Yonge St. Toronto, Ontario, CANADA
A, C, E * free ** $5	Environmental Products Box 1014 Glenwood Springs CO 81601
B, J * free ** none	E. S. Electronic Labs Box 434 Excelsior Springs, MO 64024
M, N * free **	Fair Radio Sales Box 1105 Lima, OH 45902
P * free **	Gregory Electronics Corp. 249 Rte. 46 Saddle Brook, NJ 07662
A,H,O * free ** none	HAL Devices Box 365 Urbana, IL 61801
L * free **	Ham Radio Center 8342 Olive Blvd. St. Louis, MO 63132
I, K * free ** $10	Hammond Transformer 394 Edinburgh Rd. N. Guelph, Ontario CANADA
	U.S. Distributor for Hammond: Genesee Radio Co. 2550 Delaware Ave. Buffalo, NY 14216
L * none **	Harrison Radio 20 Smith Street Farmingdale, L.I., NY 11735
M, N * free ** none	Hazelton Scientific Co. Box 163 Hazel Park, MI 48030
A * free **	Heath Co. Benton Harbor, MI 49022
L * none **	Henry Radio 11240 W. Olympic Blvd. Los Angeles, CA 92801
L * free **	Hobby Industries Box 864 Council Bluffs, IA 51501
D * free ** $5	International Crystal Co. 10 N. Lee Street Oklahoma City, OK 73102
D * free **	JAN Crystals 2400 Crystal Drive Ft. Myers, FL 33901
A, M, N * 25¢ ** $2	Jeff-Tronics 4252 Pearl Road Cleveland, OH 44109
C * free ** none	Kepro Circuit Systems; 3630 Scarlet Oak St. St. Louis, MO 63122
F * free ** $10	Kirk Electronics Division Electrotec Corp. 400 Town St. East Haddam, CT 06423
L * free ** none	Lafayette Radio Elect 111Jericho Tpk. Syosset, L.I. NY 11791 (See local phone directory)
M, N * free ** $5	John Meshna, Jr. Box 62 E. Lynn, MA 01904
J * free **	MFJ Enterprises PO Box 494 Mississippi State, MS 39762
A, G, H * free ** $5	James Millen Mfg. Co. 150 Exchange Street Malden, MA 02148
A, G, L * free **	J. W. Miller Company 19070 Reyes Avenue Compton, CA 90224
A, F, B * free ** none	N.E.E.E. P. O. Box 145 Wethersfield CT 06109
N * free ** $5	Nurmi Electronic Supply 1727 Donna Rd. West Palm Beach, FL 33401
L * free **	Olsen Electronics 260 S. Forge St Akron, OH 44327
F * free **	Payette Radio 730 ST-Jacques O. Montreal 101, Quebec, CANADA
A * free ** none	C. M. Peterson Co. Ltd. 575 Dundas St London, Ontario CANADA
J * free **	Piezo Technology, Inc. Box 7877 Orlando, FL 32804
E, M * 15¢ ** none	Poly Paks Box 942 Lynnfield, MA 01940
M, N * free ** $2	Precision Systems PO Box 6, Murray Hill NJ 07974
D * free ** none	Savoy Electronics, Inc Box 7127 Ft Lauderdale FL 33304
D * free ** none	Sentry Mfg. Co. Crystal Park Chickasha, OK 73108
F * free ** $10	Skylane Products 406 Bon Air Avenue Temple, Terrace, FL 33617
A, P * free ** none	Spectronics, Inc. 1009 Garfield Street Oak Park, IL 60304
J * free ** none	Spectrum International PO Box 1084 Concord, MA 01742
M, N * free ** $4	Star Tronics Box 17127 Portland, OR 97217
M, N * free ** $5	Surplus Electronics 10518 Connecticut Ave. Kensington, MD 20795
A * free ** none	Solid State Systems, Inc. 800 N. Providence Rd. Columbia, MO 65201
O	Teletype Corp., 5555 Touhy A. Skokie, IL 60076
K, A	Ten-Tec Inc. Highway 411, E. Sevierville, TN 37862
A, C, E * free ** none	Trigger Electronics 7361 North Ave. River Forest IL 60305
O * sase ** none	Typetronics Box 8873 Ft. Lauderdale, FL 33310
E, M * free ** none	Weinschenker, K3DPJ Box 353 Irwin, PA 15642

Chart I Coding

A – New Components
B – Toroids and Ferrites
C – Etched-circuit board materials
D – Transmitting and receiving crystals
E – Solid-state devices
F – Antenna hardware
G – Dials and knobs
H – Variable capacitors
I – Transformers
J – I-f filters
K – Cabinet and boxes
L – All of above, general distributor
M – Surplus parts
N – Surplus assemblies
O – RTTY equipment and parts
P – Surplus fm gear and parts

* Catalog price
** Minimum billing

To the best of our knowledge, the suppliers shown in Chart I are willing to sell components to amateurs in small quantities by mail. This listing does not necessarily indicate that these firms have the approval of ARRL.

COPPER-WIRE TABLE

Wire Size A.W.G. (B&S)	Diam. in Mils[1]	Circular Mil Area	Turns per Linear Inch[2]			Cont.-duty current[3] single wire in open air	Cont.-duty current[3] wires or cables in conduits or bundles	Feet per Pound, Bare	Ohms per 1000 ft. 25° C.	Current Carrying Capacity[4] at 700 C.M. per Amp.	Diam. in mm.	Nearest British S.W.G. No.
			Enamel	S.C.E.	D.C.C.							
1	289.3	83690	—	—	—	—	—	3.947	.1264	119.6	7.348	1
2	257.6	66370	—	—	—	—	—	4.977	.1593	94.8	6.544	3
3	229.4	52640	—	—	—	—	—	6.276	.2009	75.2	5.827	4
4	204.3	41740	—	—	—	—	—	7.914	.2533	59.6	5.189	5
5	181.9	33100	—	—	—	—	—	9.980	.3195	47.3	4.621	7
6	162.0	26250	—	—	—	—	—	12.58	.4028	37.5	4.115	8
7	144.3	20820	—	—	—	—	—	15.87	.5080	29.7	3.665	9
8	128.5	16510	7.6	—	7.1	73	46	20.01	.6405	23.6	3.264	10
9	114.4	13090	8.6	—	7.8	—	—	25.23	.8077	18.7	2.906	11
10	101.9	10380	9.6	9.1	8.9	55	33	**31.82**	**1.018**	14.8	2.588	12
11	90.7	8234	10.7	—	9.8	—	—	40.12	1.284	11.8	2.305	13
12	80.8	6530	12.0	11.3	10.9	41	23	50.59	1.619	9.33	2.053	14
13	72.0	5178	13.5	—	12.8	—	—	63.80	2.042	7.40	1.828	15
14	64.1	4107	15.0	14.0	13.8	32	17	80.44	2.575	5.87	1.628	16
15	57.1	3257	16.8	—	14.7	—	—	101.4	3.247	4.65	1.450	17
16	50.8	2583	18.9	17.3	16.4	22	13	127.9	4.094	3.69	1.291	18
17	45.3	2048	21.2	—	18.1	—	—	161.3	5.163	2.93	1.150	18
18	40.3	1624	23.6	21.2	19.8	16	10	203.4	6.510	2.32	1.024	19
19	35.9	1288	26.4	—	21.8	—	—	256.5	8.210	1.84	.912	20
20	32.0	1022	29.4	25.8	23.8	11	7.5	323.4	10.35	1.46	.812	21
21	28.5	810	33.1	—	26.0	—	—	407.8	13.05	1.16	.723	22
22	25.3	642	37.0	31.3	30.0	—	5	514.2	16.46	.918	.644	23
23	22.6	510	41.3	—	37.6	—	—	648.4	20.76	.728	.573	24
24	20.1	404	46.3	37.6	35.6	—	—	817.7	26.17	.577	.511	25
25	17.9	320	51.7	—	38.6	—	—	1031	33.00	.458	.455	26
26	15.9	254	58.0	46.1	41.8	—	—	1300	41.62	.363	.405	27
27	14.2	202	64.9	—	45.0	—	—	1639	52.48	.288	.361	29
28	12.6	160	72.7	54.6	48.5	—	—	2067	66.17	.228	.321	30
29	11.3	127	81.6	—	51.8	—	—	2607	83.44	.181	.286	31
30	10.0	101	90.5	64.1	55.5	—	—	3287	105.2	.144	.255	33
31	8.9	80	101	—	59.2	—	—	4145	132.7	.114	.227	34
32	8.0	63	113	74.1	62.6	—	—	5227	167.3	.090	.202	36
33	7.1	50	127	—	66.3	—	—	6591	211.0	.072	.180	37
34	6.3	40	143	86.2	70.0	—	—	8310	266.0	.057	.160	38
35	5.6	32	158	—	73.5	—	—	10480	335	.045	.143	38-39
36	5.0	25	175	103.1	77.0	—	—	13210	423	.036	.127	39-40
37	4.5	20	198	—	80.3	—	—	16660	533	.028	.113	41
38	4.0	16	224	116.3	83.6	—	—	21010	673	.022	.101	42
39	3.5	12	248	—	86.6	—	—	26500	848	.018	.090	43
40	3.1	10	282	131.6	89.7	—	—	33410	1070	.014	.080	44

[1] A mil is .001 inch. [2] Figures given are approximate only; insulation thickness varies with manufacturer. [3] Max. wire temp. of 212° F and max. ambient temp. of 135° F. [4] 700 circular mils per ampere is a satisfactory design figure for small transformers, but values from 500 to 1000 c.m. are commonly used.

SEMICONDUCTOR DIODE COLOR CODE

The "1N" prefix is omitted. A double-width band, which also identifies the cathode terminal end of the diode, is usually used as the first band. (An alternative method uses equal band widths with the set clearly grouped toward the cathode end.) The code is read starting at the cathode end.

Diodes having two-digit numbers are coded with a black band followed by second and third bands. A suffix letter is indicated by a fourth band.

Diodes with three-digit numbers are coded with the sequence numbers in the first, second and third bands. Any suffix letter is indicated by a fourth band.

Diodes with four-digit numbers are coded by four bands followed by a black band. A suffix letter is indicated by a fifth band replacing the black band.

The color code (numbers) is the same as the resistor-capacitor code. The suffix-letter code is A—brown, B—re[illegible], C—orange, D—yellow, E—green, and F—blue.

Chapter 19

Wave Propagation

Much of the appeal of amateur communication lies in the fact that the results are not always predictable. Transmission conditions on the same frequency vary with the year, season and with the time of day. Although these variations usually follow certain established patterns, many peculiar effects can be observed from time to time. Every radio amateur should have some understanding of the known facts about radio wave propagation so that he will stand some chance of interpreting the unusual conditions when they occur. The observant amateur is in an excellent position to make worthwhile contributions to the science, provided he has sufficient background to understand his results. He may discover new facts about propagation at the very-high frequencies or in the microwave region, as amateurs have in the past. In fact, it is through amateur efforts that most of the extended-range possibilities of various radio frequencies have been discovered, both by accident and by long and careful investigation.

CHARACTERISTICS OF RADIO WAVES

Radio waves, like other forms of electromagnetic radiation such as light, travel at a speed of 300,000,000 meters per second in free space, and can be reflected, refracted, and diffracted.

An electromagnetic wave is composed of moving fields of electric and magnetic force. The lines of force in the electric and magnetic fields are at right angles, and are mutually perpendicular to the direction of travel. A simple representation of a wave is shown in Fig. 19-1. In this drawing the electric lines are perpendicular to the earth and the magnetic lines are horizontal. They could, however, have any position with respect to earth so long as they remain perpendicular to each other.

The plane containing the continuous lines of electric and magnetic force shown by the grid- or mesh-like drawing in Fig. 19-1 is called the wave **front.**

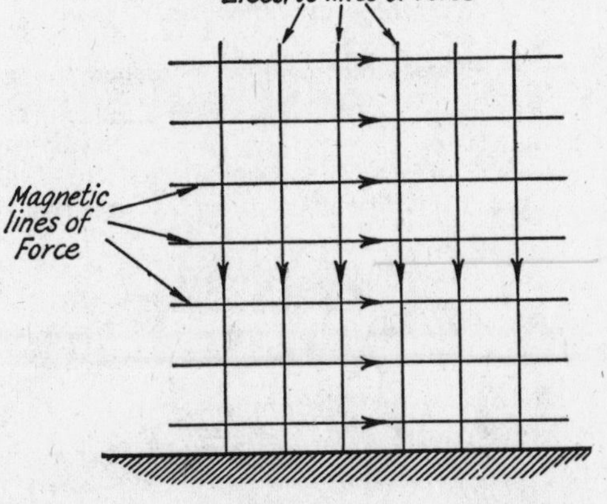

Fig. 19-1 – Representation of electric and magnetic lines of force in a radio wave. Arrows indicate instantaneous directions of the fields for a wave traveling toward the reader. Reversing the direction of one set of lines would reverse the direction of travel.

The **medium** in which electromagnetic waves travel has a marked influence on the speed with which they move. When the medium is empty space the speed, as stated above, is 300,000,000 meters per second. It is almost, but not quite, that great in air, and is much less in some other substances. In dielectrics, for example, the speed is inversely proportional to the square root of the dielectric constant of the material.

When a wave meets a good conductor it cannot penetrate it to any extent (although it will travel through a dielectric with ease) because the electric lines of force are practically short circuited.

Polarization

The **polarization** of a radio wave is taken as the direction of the lines of force in the electric field. If the electric lines are perpendicular to the earth, the wave is said to be **vertically polarized**; if parallel with the earth, the wave is **horizontally polarized**. The longer waves, when traveling along the ground, usually maintain their polarization in the same plane as was generated at the antenna. The polarization of shorter waves may be altered during travel, however, and sometimes will vary quite rapidly.

Spreading

The field intensity of a wave is inversely proportional to the distance from the source. Thus if in a uniform medium one receiving point is twice as far from the transmitter as another, the field strength at the more distant point will be just half the field strength at the nearer point. This results from the fact that the energy in the wave front must be distributed over a greater area as the wave moves away from the source. This **inverse-distance law** is based on the assumption that there is nothing in the medium to absorb energy from the wave as it travels. This is not the case in practical communication along the ground and through the atmosphere.

Fig. 19-2 – Showing how both direct and reflected waves may be received simultaneously.

Types of Propagation

According to the altitudes of the paths along which they are propagated, radio waves may be classified as **ionospheric waves, tropospheric waves** or **ground waves.**

The ionospheric or **sky wave** is that part of the total radiation that is directed toward the ionosphere. Depending upon variable conditions in that region, as well as upon transmitting wave length, the ionospheric wave may or may not be returned to earth by the effects of refraction and reflection.

The tropospheric wave is that part of the total radiation that undergoes refraction and reflection in regions of abrupt change of dielectric constant in the troposphere, such as may occur at the boundaries between air masses of differing temperature and moisture content.

The ground wave is that part of the total radiation that is directly affected by the presence of the earth and its surface features. The ground wave has two components. One is the **surface wave,** which is an earth-guided wave, and the other is the **space wave** (not to be confused with the ionospheric or sky wave). The space wave is itself the resultant of two components – the **direct wave** and the **ground-reflected wave,** as shown in Fig. 19-2.

IONOSPHERIC PROPAGATION

PROPERTIES OF THE IONOSPHERE

Except for distances of a few miles, nearly all amateur communication on frequencies below 30 MHz is by means of the sky wave. Upon leaving the transmitting antenna, this wave travels upward from the earth's surface at such an angle that it would continue out into space were its path not bent sufficiently to bring it back to earth. The medium that causes such bending is the **ionosphere**, a region in the upper atmosphere, above a height of about 60 miles, where free ions and electrons exist in sufficient quantity to have an appreciable effect on wave travel.

The ionization in the upper atmosphere is believed to be caused by ultraviolet radiation from the sun. The ionosphere is not a single region but is composed of a series of layers of varying densities of ionization occurring at different heights. Each layer consists of a central region of relatively dense ionization that tapers off in intensity both above and below.

Refraction

The greater the intensity of ionization in a layer, the more the path of the wave is bent. The bending, or refraction (often also called reflection), also depends on the wavelength; the longer the wave, the more the path is bent for a given degree of ionization. Thus low-frequency waves are more readily bent those those of high frequency. For this reason the lower frequencies – 3.5 and 7 MHz – are more "reliable" than the higher frequencies – 14 to 28 MHz; there are times when the ionization is of such low value that waves of the latter frequency range are not bent enough to return to earth.

Absorption

In traveling through the ionosphere the wave gives up some of its energy by setting the ionized particles into motion. When the moving ionized particles collide with others this energy is lost. The **absorption** from this cause is greater at lower frequencies. It also increases with the intensity of ionization, and with the density of the atmosphere in the ionized region.

Virtual Height

Although an ionospheric layer is a region of considerable depth, it is convenient to assign to it a definite height, called the **virtual height.** This is the height from which a simple reflection would give the same effect as the gradual bending that actually takes place, as illustrated in Fig. 19-3. The wave traveling upward is bent back over a path having an appreciable radius of turning, and a measurable inteval of time is consumed in the turning process. The virtual height is the height of a triangle having equal sides of a total length proportional to the time taken for the wave to travel from *T* to *R*.

Normal Structure of the Ionosphere

The lowest useful ionized layer is called the ***E* layer.** The average height of the region of maximum ionization is about 70 miles. The air at this height is sufficiently dense so that the ions and

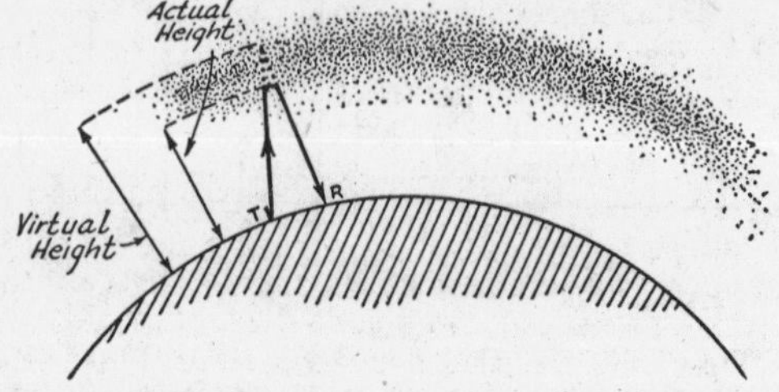

Fig. 19-3 – Bending in the ionosphere, and the echo or reflection method of determining virtual height.

electrons set free by the sun's radiation do not travel far before they meet and recombine to form neutral particles, so the layer can maintain its normal intensity of ionization only in the presence of continuing radiation from the sun. Hence the ionization is greatest around local noon and practically disappears after sundown.

In the daytime there is a still lower ionized area, the ***D* region**. *D*-region ionization is proportional to the height of the sun and is greatest at noon. The lower amateur-band frequencies (1.8 and 3.5 MHz) are almost completely absorbed by this layer, and only the high-angle radiation is reflected by the *E* layer. (Lower-angle radiation travels farther through the *D* region and is absorbed.)

The second principal layer is the ***F* layer**, which has a height of about 175 miles at night. At this altitude the air is so thin that recombination of ions and electrons takes place very slowly. The ionization decreases after sundown, reaching a minimum just before sunrise. In the daytime the *F* layer splits into two parts, the F_1 and F_2 **layers**, with average virtual heights of, respectively, 140 miles and 200 miles. These layers are most highly ionized at about local noon, and merge again at sunset into the *F* layer.

SKY-WAVE PROPAGATION

Wave Angle

The smaller the angle at which a wave leaves the earth, the less the bending required in the ionosphere to bring it back. Also, the smaller the angle the greater the distance between the point where the wave leaves the earth and that at which it returns. This is shown in Fig. 19-4. The vertical angle that the wave makes with a tangent to the earth is called the **wave angle** or **angle of radiation.**

Skip Distance

More bending is required to return the wave to earth when the wave angle is high, and at times the bending will not be sufficient unless the wave angle is smaller than some critical value. This is illustrated in Fig. 19-4, where *A* and smaller angles give useful signals while waves sent at higher angles penetrate the layer and are not returned. The distance between *T* and R_1 is, therefore, the shortest possible distance, at that particular frequency, over which communication by ionospheric refraction can be accomplished.

The area between the end of the useful ground wave and the beginning of ionospheric-wave reception is called the **skip zone**, and the distance from the transmitter to the nearest point where the sky wave returns to earth is called the **skip distance**. The extent of the skip zone depends upon the frequency and the state of the ionosphere, and also upon the height of the layer in which the refraction takes place. The higher layers give longer skip distances for the same wave angle. Wave angles at the transmitting and receiving points are usually, although not always, approximately the same for any given wave path.

Critical and Maximum Usable Frequencies

If the frequency is low enough, a wave sent vertically to the ionosphere will be reflected back down to the transmitting point. If the frequency is then gradually increased, enventually a frequency will be reached where this vertical reflection just fails to occur. This is the **critical frequency** for the layer under consideration. When the operating frequency is below the critical value there is no skip zone.

The critical frequency is a useful index to the highest frequency that can be used to transmit over a specified distance – the **maximum usable frequency (muf).** If the wave leaving the transmitting point at angle *A* in Fig. 19-4 is, for example, at a frequency of 14 MHz, and if a higher frequency would skip over the receiving point R_1, then 14 MHz is the muf for the distance from *T* to R_1.

The greatest possible distance is covered when the wave leaves along the tangent to the earth; that is, at zero wave angle. Under average conditions this distance is about 4000 kilometers or 2500 miles for the F_2 layer, and 2000 km or 1250 miles for the *E* layer. The distances vary with the layer height. Frequencies above these limiting muf's will not be returned to earth at any distance. The 4000-km muf for the F_2 layer is approximately 3 times the critical frequency for that layer, and for the *E* layer the 2000-km muf is about 5 times the critical frequency.

Absorption in the ionosphere is least at the maximum usable frequency, and increases very rapidly as the frequency is lowered below the muf. Consequently, the best results with low power always are secured when the frequency is as close to the muf as possible.

It is readily possible for the ionospheric wave to pass through the *E* layer and be refracted back to earth from the *F*, F_1 or F_2 layers. This is because the critical frequencies are higher in the latter layers, so that a signal too high in frequency to be returned by the *E* layer can still come back from one of the others, depending upon the time of day and the existing conditions.

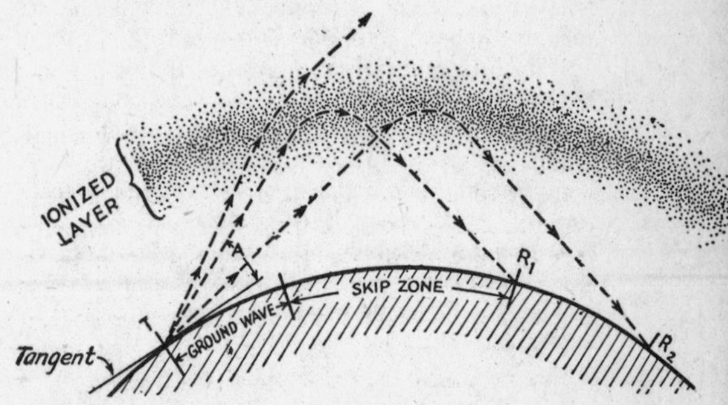

Fig. 19-4 – Refraction of sky waves, showing the critical wave angle and the skip zone. Waves leaving the transmitter at angles above the critical (greater than A) are not bent enough to be returned to earth. As the angle is decreased, the waves return to earth at increasingly greater distances.

Multihop Transmission

On returning to the earth the wave can be reflected upward and travel again to the ionosphere. There it may once more be refracted, and again bent back to earth. This process may be repeated several times. **Multihop** propagation of this nature is necessary for transmission over great distances because of the limited heights of the layers and the curvature of the earth, which restrict the maximum one-hop distance to the values mentioned in the preceding section. However, ground losses absorb some of the energy from the wave on each reflection (the amount of the loss varying with the type of ground and being least for reflection from sea water), and there is also absorption in the ionosphere at each reflection. Hence the smaller the number of hops the greater the signal strength at the receiver, other things being equal.

Fading

Two or more parts of the wave may follow slightly different paths in traveling to the receiving point, in which case the difference in path lengths will cause a phase difference to exist between the wave components at the receiving antenna. The total field strength will be the sum of the components and may be larger or smaller than one component alone, since the phases may be such as either to aid or oppose. Since the paths change from time to time, this causes a variation in signal strength called **fading.** Fading can also result from the combination of single-hop and multihop waves, or the combination of a ground wave with an ionospheric or tropospheric wave.

Fading may be either rapid or slow, the former type usually resulting from rapidly-changing conditions in the ionosphere, the latter occurring when transmission conditions are relatively stable. Severe changes in signal strength of 10 to 20 dB or more are called "deep" fades, in contrast to the more normal "shallow" fades of a few dB.

It frequently happens that transmission conditions are different for waves of slightly different frequencies, so that in the case of voice-modulated transmission, involving sidebands differing slightly from the carrier in frequency, the carrier and various sideband components may not be propagated in the same relative amplitudes and phases they had at the transmitter. This effect, known as **selective fading,** causes severe distortion of the signal. The distortion is most marked on amplitude-modulated signals and at high percentages of modulation; it is possible to reduce the effects considerably by using "exalted-carrier reception" and "single-sideband" techniques that, in effect, reduce the modulation percentage at the receiver.

BackScatter

Even though the operating frequency is above the muf for a given distance, it is usually possible to hear signals from within the skip zone. This phenomenon, called **backscatter,** is caused by reflections from distances beyond the skip zone. Such reflections can occur when the transmitted energy strikes the earth at a distance and some of it is reflected back into the skip zone to the receiver. Such scatter signals are weaker than those normally propagated, and also have a rapid fade or "flutter" that makes them easily recognizable.

A certain amount of scattering of the wave also takes place in the ionosphere because the ionized region is not completely uniform. Scattering in the normal propagation direction is called **forward scatter,** and is responsible for extending the range of transmission beyond the distance of a regular hop, and for making communication possible on frequencies greater than the actual muf.

OTHER FEATURES OF IONOSPHERIC PROPAGATION

Cyclic Variations in the Ionosphere

Since ionization depends upon ultraviolet radiation, conditions in the ionosphere vary with changes in the sun's radiation. In addition to the daily variation, seasonal changes result in higher critical frequencies in the E layer in summer, averaging about 4 MHz as against a winter average of 3 MHz. The F layer critical frequency is of the order of 4 to 5 MHz in the evening. The F_1 layer, which has a critical frequency near 5 MHz in summer, usually disappears entirely in winter. The daytime maximum critical frequencies for the F_2 are highest in winter (10 to 12 MHz) and lowest in summer (around 7 MHz). The virtual height of the F_2 layer, which is about 185 miles in winter, averages 250 miles in summer. These values are representative of latitude 40 deg. North in the Western hemisphere, and are subject to considerable variation in other parts of the world.

Very marked changes in ionization also occur in step with the **11-year sunspot cycle.** Although there is no apparent direct correlation between sunspot activity and critical frequencies on a given day, there is a definite correlation between *average* sunspot activity and critical frequencies. The critical frequencies are highest during sunspot maxima and lowest during sunspot minima. During the period of minimum sunspot activity, the lower frequencies – 7 and 3.5 MHz – frequently are the only usable bands at night. At such times the 28-MHz band is seldom useful for long-distance work, while the 14-MHz band performs well in the daytime but is not ordinarily useful at night.

Ionosphere Storms

Certain types of sunspot activity cause considerable disturbances in the ionosphere (**ionospheric storms**) and are accompanied by disturbances in the earth's magnetic field (**magnetic storms**). Ionosphere storms are characterized by a marked increase in absorption, so that radio conditions become poor. The critical frequencies also drop to relatively low values during a storm, so that only the lower frequencies are useful for communication. Ionosphere storms may last from a few hours to several days. Since the sun rotates on its axis once every 28 days, disturbances tend to recur at such intervals, if the sunspots responsible do not become inactive in the meantime. Absorption is usually low, and radio conditions good, just preceding a storm.

Sporadic-*E* Ionization

Scattered patches or clouds of relatively dense ionization occasionally appear at heights approximately the same as that of the *E* layer, for reasons not yet known. This **sporadic-*E*** ionization is most prevalent in the equatorial regions, where it is substantially continuous. In northern latitudes it is most frequent in the spring and early summer, but is present in some degree a fair percentage of the time the year 'round. It accounts for much of the night-time short distance work on the lower frequencies (3.5 to 7 MHz) and, when more intense, for similar work on 14 to 28 MHz. Exceptionally intense sporadic-*E* ionization permits work over distances exceeding 400 or 500 miles on the 50-MHz band.

There are indications of a relationship between sporadic-*E* ionization and average sunspot activity, but it does not appear to be directly related to daylight and darkness since it may occur at any time of the day. However, there is an apparent tendency for the ionization to peak at mid-morning and in the early evening.

Troposheric Propagation

Changes in temperature and humidity of air masses in the lower atmosphere often permit work over greater than normal ground-wave distances on 28 MHz and higher frequencies. The effect can be observed on 28 MHz but it is generally more marked on 50 and 144 MHz. The subject is treated in detail later.

PREDICTION MAPS

The Institute for Telecommunication Sciences offers ionospheric prediction maps with which it is possible to predict with considerable accuracy the maximum usable frequency that will hold over any path on the earth. The maps and instructions for their use are contained in four volumes, which can be obtained from the Superintendent of Documents, U. S. Government Printing Office, Washington, DC 20402, for $9.30. They are called *Telecommunications Research and Engineering Report 13, Ionospheric Predictions,* OT-TRER 13. The use of the maps is explained in Vol. 1, available separately for 30 cents. Vols. 2, 3, and 4, available individually for $3.00 each, contain maps for predicted Zurich smoothed relative sunspot numbers of 10, 110 and 160, respectively. Linear interpolation of data from two volumes must be made for periods of solar activity at intermediate levels. Information on predicted relative sunspot numbers is contained periodically in Propagation Forecast Bulletins, transmitted by W1AW and many Official Bulletin Stations.

Predictions on *E*-layer propagation may be obtained from information included in the above volumes.

PROPAGATION IN THE BANDS BELOW 30 MHZ

The 1.8-MHz or "160-meter" band offers reliable working over ranges up to 25 miles or so during daylight. On winter nights, ranges up to several thousand miles are not impossible. Only small sections of the band are currently available to amateurs, because of the loran (navigation) service in that part of the spectrum.

The 3.5-MHz or "80-meter" band is a more useful band during the night than during the daylight hours. In the daytime, one can seldom hear signals from a distance of greater than 200 miles or so, but during the darkness hours distances up to several thousand miles are not unusual, and transoceanic contacts are regularly made during the winter months. During the summer, the static level is high.

The 7-MHz or "40-meter" band has many of the same characteristics as 3.5, except that the distances that can be covered during the day and night hours are increased. During daylight, distances up to a thousand miles can be covered under good conditions, and during the dawn and dusk periods in winter it is possible to work stations as far as the other side of the world, the signals following the darkness path. The winter months are somewhat better than the summer ones. In general, summer static is much less of a problem than on 80 meters, although it can be series in the simitropical zones.

The 14-MHz or "20-meter" band is probably the best one for long-distance work. During the high portion of the sunspot cycle it is open to some parts of the world during practically all of the 24 hours, while during a sunspot minimum it is generally useful only during daylight hours and the dawn and dusk periods. There is practically always a skip zone on this band.

The 21-MHz or "15-meter" band shows highly variable characteristics depending on the sunspot cycle. During sunspot maxima it is useful for long-distance work during a large part of the 24 hours, but in years of low sunspot activity it is almost wholly a daytime band, and sometimes unusable even in daytime. However, it is often possible to maintain communication over distances up to 1500 miles or more by sporadic-*E* ionization which may occur either day or night at any time in the sunspot cycle.

The 28-MHz or "10-meter" band is generally considered to be a DX band during the daylight hours (except in summer) and good for local work during the hours of darkness, for about half the sunspot cycle. At the very peak of the sunspot cycle, it may be "open" into the late evening hours for DX communication. At the sunspot minimum the band is usually "dead" for long-distance communications, by means of the F_2 layer, in the northern latitudes. Nevertheless, sporadic-*E* propagation is likely to occur at any time, just as in the case of the 21-MHz band.

There will often be exceptions to the general conditions described above, and their observation is a very interesting facet of amateur radio.

THE WORLD ABOVE 50 MHZ

Familiarity with propagation modes is vital to the vhf enthusiast, and exploiting DX opportunities that nature affords has been a challenge since the earliest days of communication on the frequencies above 50 MHz. Much of what is known about long-distance vhf propagation was turned up by amateur pioneering, and more may yet be, for some aspects of vhf DX are still far from completely explained.

NATURE OF THE VHF BANDS

A valuable feature of this vast territory is its usefulness for consistent communication within an essentially local service area. Lower frequencies are subject to varying conditions that impair local communication at least part of the time. Our hf bands are narrow, and often seriously overcrowded. The vhf bands are far wider and capable of much greater occupancy, and their characteristics are ideal for local work.

It was once though that these frequencies would be useful only locally, but increased occupancy and improved techniques demonstrated that there are many forms of long-distance vhf propagation. As a result, vhf activity has developed in isolated areas, as well as those of high population density, until, depending on the skill and resourcefulness of the individual, there are few areas of the world left where interesting and productive vhf work is impossible.

What follows supplements information given earlier in this chapter. First, let us consider the nature of our bands above 50 MHz.

50 to 54 MHz This borderline region has some of the characteristics of adjacent frequencies, both higher and lower. Just about every form of wave propagation is found occasionally in the 50-MHz band, which has contributed greatly to its popularity. However, its utility for service-area communication should not be overlooked. In the absence of any favorable condition, the well-equipped 50-MHz station should be able to work regularly over a radius of 75 to 100 miles or more, depending on terrain, antenna size and height, and operator skill.

Changing weather patterns extend coverage to 300 miles or more at times, mainly in the warmer months. Sporadic-*E* skip provides seasonal openings for work over 400 to 2500 miles, in seasons centered on the longest and shortest days of the year. Auroral effects afford vhf men in the temperate latitudes an intriguing form of DX up to about 1300 miles. During the peak of "11-year" sunspot cycle 50-MHz DX of worldwide proportions may be workable by reflections of waves by the ionospheric F_2 layer. Various weak-signal scatter modes round out the exciting propagation fare available to the 50-MHz operator.

144 to 148 MHz Ionospheric effects are greatly reduced at 144 MHz. *F*-layer propagation is unknown. Sporadic-*E* skip is rare, and much more limited in duration and coverage than on 50 MHz. Auroral propagation is quite similar to that on 50 MHz, except that signals tend to be somewhat weaker and more distorted at 144. Tropospheric propagation improves with increasing frequency. It has been responsible for 144-MHz work over distances up to 2500 miles, and 500-mile contacts are fairly common in the warmer months. Reliable range on 144 is slightly less than on 50, under minimum conditions.

220 MHz and Higher Ionospheric propagation of the sorts discussed above is virtually unknown above about 200 MHz. Auroral communication is possible on 220 and 420 MHz, but probably not on higher frequencies, with amateur power levels. Tropospheric bending is very marked, and may be better on 432 than on 144 MHz, for example. Communication has been carried on over paths far beyond line of sight, on all amateur frequencies up through 10,000 MHz. Under minimum conditions, signal levels drop off slightly with each higher band.

PROPAGATION MODES

Known means by which vhf signals are propagated beyond the horizon are described below.

F_2-Layer Reflection Most communication on lower frequencies is by reflection of the wave in the *F* region, highest of the ionized layers. Its density varies with solar activity, the maximum usable frequency (muf) being highest in peak years of the sunspot cycle. These cycles vary, and indications are that we are now in a down trend. Cycle 19 (in the recorded history of sunspot activity) hit an all-time high in the fall of 1958, which may never be equalled within the lifetime of most of us. Cycle 20 produced some 50-MHz F_2 DX in 1968 to 1970, but less than Cycle 18 (1946 to 1949), and far less than Cycle 19.

The muf for F_2-layer propagation follows other well-defined cycles: daily, monthly and seasonal, all related to conditions on the sun and its position with respect to the earth. The F_2 muf is quite easily determined if one has a continuous-tuning receiver for about 14 to 50 MHz. These frequencies are in almost continuous worldwide use, so signals are likely to be heard up to the highest frequency being propagated at the time of observation. Frequent checks will show if the muf is rising or falling, and the times and directions for which it is highest. Monthly peaks follow a 27-day cycle, coinciding with the turning of the sun on its axis. Spring and fall show the highest muf, with a slight drop in winter and a major one in summer.[1]

Communications range via the F_2 layer on 50 MHz is comparable to that on 28, but the minimum distance is greater. Two-way work has been done over about 1800 to 12,500 miles; even greater, if daylight routes around the earth the long way are included. The muf is believed to have reached about 70 MHz in 1958.

The TE Mode Also associated with high solar activity is a transequatorial mode, having an muf

---

[1] **For this and following references, see bibliography at the end of this chapter.**

somewhat higher than the F_2. This is observed most often between points up to 2500 miles north and south of the *geomagnetic* equator, mainly in late afternoon or early evening. A classic amateur discovery, pioneering of the TE mode is a fascinating story.[2]

Sporadic-E Skip Patchy ionization of the E region of the ionosphere often propagates 28- and 50-MHz signals over 400 to 1300 miles or more. Often called "short skip," this is most common in May, June and July, with a shorter season around year end. Seasons are reversed in the southern hemisphere. E skip can occur at any time or season, but is most likely in mid-morning or early evening. Multiple-hop effects may extend the range to 2500 miles or more.

The upper frequency limit for E_s propagation is unknown, but it has been observed in the 144-MHz band, and on TV channels up to about 200 MHz. Minimum skip distance is greater, and duration of openings much shorter, on 144 MHz than on 50. Reception of strong E_s signals from under 300 miles on 50 MHz indicates some possibility of skip propagation on 144, probably to 800 miles or more.[3]

Aurora Effect High-frequency communication may be wiped out or seriously impaired by absorption in the ionosphere, during disturbances associated with high solar activity and variations in the earth's magnetic field. If this occurs at night in clear weather, there may be a visible aurora, but the condition also develops in daylight, usually in late afternoon. Weak wavery signals in the 3.5-MHz band, or from the 5-MHz WWV, are good indicators.

Vhf waves can be returned to earth from the auroral region, but the varying intensity of the aurora and its porosity as a propagation medium impart a multipath distortion to the signal, which garbles or even destroys any modulation. Distortion increases with signal frequency and varies, often quite quickly, with the nature of the aurora. In general, 50-MHz signals have less auroral distortion than those on higher frequencies, and voice is usable more often on 50 than on 144 MHz. Single-sideband is preferred to modes requiring more bandwidth. The most effective mode is cw, which may be the only reliable communications method at 144 MHz and higher, during most auroras.

Propagation is generally from the north, regardless of the direct path between communicating stations, but probing with a directional array is recommended. Maximum range is about 1300 miles, though 50-MHz signals are heard occasionally over greater distances, usually with little or no auroral distortion.

How often auroral communication is possible is related to the *geomagnetic* latitude of participating stations, auroras being most frequent in northeastern USA and adjacent areas of Canada. They are rare below about latitude 32 in the Southeast and about latitude 38 to 40 in the Southwest. The highest frequency for auroral returns depends on equipment and antennas, but auroral communication has been achieved by amateurs up to at least 432 MHz.[4]

Tropospheric Bending An easily-anticipated extension of normal vhf coverage results from abrupt changes in the refractive index of the atmosphere, at boundaries between air masses of differing temperature and humidity characteristics. Such warm-dry over cool-moist boundaries often lie along the southern and western edges of stable slow-moving areas of fair weather and high barometric pressure. Troposheric bending can increase signal levels from within the normal working range, or bring in more distant stations, not normally heard.

A condition known as *ducting* or *trapping* may simulate propagation within a waveguide, causing vhf waves to follow earth curvature for hundreds or even thousands of miles. Ducting incidence increases with frequency. It is rare on 50 MHz, fairly common on 144, and more so on higher frequencies. It occurs most often in temperate or low latitudes. It was the medium for such memorable vhf DX as the W6NLZ-KH6UK work on 144, 220 and 432 MHz, over a 2540-mile path.[5] Gulf-Coast states see it often, the Atlantic Seaboard, Great Lakes and Mississippi Valley areas occasionally, usually in September and October.

Many local conditions contribute to tropospheric bending. Convection in coastal areas in warm weather; rapid cooling of the earth after a hot day, with upper air cooling more slowly; warming of air aloft with the summer sunrise; subsidence of cool moist air into valleys on calm summer evenings – these familiar situations create upper-air conditions similar to those shown in Fig. 19-5, which can extend normal vhf coverage.

The alert vhf enthusiast soon learns to correlate various weather signs and propagation patterns. Temperature and barometric-pressure trends, changing cloud formations, wind direction, visibility and other natural indicators can give him clues as to what is in store in the way of tropospheric propagation. Radio and TV weather programs may help in this.[6]

The 50-MHz band is more responsive to weather effects than 28, and 144 MHz is much more active than 50. This trend continues into the microwave region, as evidenced by tropospheric records on all our bands, up to and including work over a 275-mile path on 10,000 MHz.

The Scatter Modes Though they provide signal levels too low for routine communication, several marginal modes attract the advanced vhf operator. They are lumped under the term "scatter," implying an incidental by-product of some stronger-signal mode, but they are of real interest on their own.

Tropospheric scatter offers marginal communication up to 500 miles or so, almost regardless of conditions and frequency, when optimum equipment and methods are used.[7]

Ionospheric scatter is useful mainly on 50 MHz, where it usually is a composite of meteor bursts and a weak residual scatter signal. The latter may be heard only when optimum conditions prevail. The best distances are 600 to 1200 miles.[8]

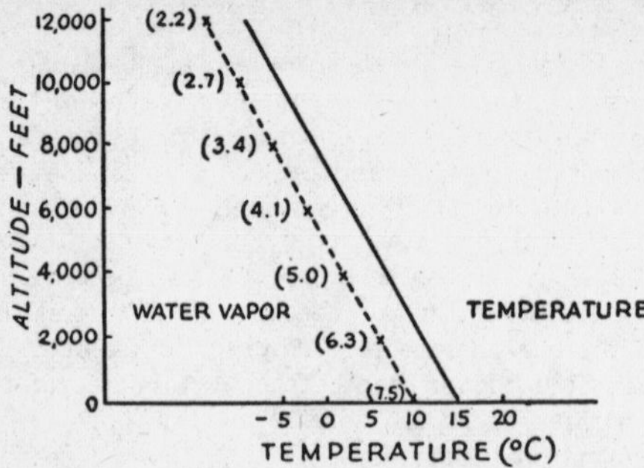

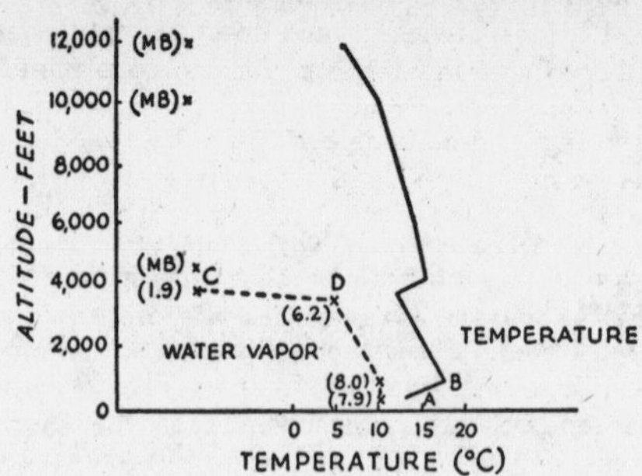

Fig. 19-5 — Upper-air conditions that produce extended-range vhf propagation. In the U.S. Standard Atmosphere curve, left, the humidity curve (dotted) is that which would result if the relative humidity were 70 percent from the ground level to 12,000 feet, resulting in only slight refraction. At the right is shown a sounding that is typical of marked refraction of vhf waves. Figures in parentheses are the "mixing ratio" — grams of water vapor per kilogram of dry air. Note the sharp break in both curves at about 4000 feet. From Collier, "Upper-air conditions for 2-Meter DX," *QST*, September, 1955.

Back scatter, common on lower frequencies, is observed on 50 MHz during ionospheric propagation, mainly of the F_2 variety. Signals are usually weak, with a fast flutter. Distance may be anything up to normal for mode in use. Because it peaks in directions of highest ionization density, F_2 back scatter is helpful in determining when, and in what directions, the band is open, especially in aiming toward areas of the world where 50-MHz activity is low or nonexistent.

Scatter from meteor trails in the *E* region can cause signal enhancement, or isolated bursts of signal from a station not otherwise heard. Exploitation of this medium for quick information exchanges poses an exciting challenge to the skilled vhf operator. Strength and duration of meteor bursts decrease with increasing signal frequency, but the mode is popular for marginal communication in the 50- and 144-MHz bands. It has been used on 220 MHz, and optimum equipment and large antennas have yielded bursts long enough for identification at 432 MHz.

Random meteor bursts can be heard by cooperating vhf stations at any time or season, but early-morning hours are preferred. Major meteor showers (August Perseids and December Geminids) provide frequent bursts. Some other showers have various periods, and may show phenomenal burst counts in peak years.[9]

Few meteor bursts on 144 MHz are more than a few seconds long, and some are mere "pings" of signal. Long bursts, or several superimposed, may yield continuous signal for a minute or more, but these are rare, except during major showers. A "shower of the century," such as the Leonids of November 1966 and 1967, may provide almost continuous propagation on 50 or 144 MHz for several hours. Otherwise, brief precisely-timed transmitting sequences and agreed-upon reporting methods are necessary for information exchange. Distances are similar to other *E*-layer communication.

All scatter communication requires good equipment and optimum operating methods. The narrow-band modes are superior to wide-band systems. Single sideband is being used more effectively all the time, but cw remains supreme for all weak-signal vhf work. Some redundance is nearly always helpful, regardless of mode.

Communication Via the Moon Though amateurs first bounced signals off the moon in the early 1950s,[10] real communication via the earth-moon-earth (eme) route is a fairly recent accomplishment. Requirements are maximum legal power, optimum receiving equipment, very large high-gain antennas, and precise aiming. Sophisticated tracking systems, narrow bandwidth (with attendant requirements for receiver and transmitter stability) and visual signal-resolution methods are desirable. Lunar work has been done on all amateur frequencies from 144 to 2300 MHz, over distances limited only by the ability of the stations to "see" the moon simultaneously.

VHF Propagation Footnotes

Propagation modes are discussed in more detail in Chapter 2 of *The Radio Amateur's VHF Manual*, and in *QST* references given below.

1 Heightman, "Any DX Today?" January,1948.

2 Cracknell "Transequatorial Propagation of VHF Signals," December, 1959. "More on TE Propagation," August 1947, p. 47. Whiting, "How TE Works" April, 1963.

3 Ennis, "Working 2-Meter *E*-Layer DX," June, 1957. Also, "World Above 50 MHz," August, 1968, p. 84.

4 Moore, "Aurora and Magnetic Storms," June, 1951. Dyce, "More About Auroral Propagation," January, 1955. Mellen, Milner and Williams, "Hams on Ice," January, 1960.

5 September, 1957, p. 68, August, 1959, p. 68, September, 1960, p. 78.

6 Botts "A Night To Remember," January, 1970.

7 Moore, "Over The Hills and Far Away," February, 1951.

8 Moynahan, "VHF Scatter Propagation," March, 1956.

9 Bain, "VHF Meteor Scatter Propagation," April, 1957. Table of meteor showers, *VHF Manual*, p. 23.

10 "Lunar DX on 144 MHz," March, 1953.

Chapter 20

Transmission Lines

The place where rf power is generated is very frequently not the place where it is to be utilized. A transmitter and its antenna are a good example: The antenna, to radiate well, should be high above the ground and should be kept clear of trees, buildings and other objects that might absorb energy, but the transmitter itself is most conveniently installed indoors where it is readily accessible.

The means by which power is transported from point to point is the rf transmission line. At radio frequencies a transmission line exhibits entirely different characterisitcs than it does at commercial power frequencies. This is because the speed at which electrical energy travels, while tremendously high as compared with mechanical motion, is not infinite. The peculiarities of rf transmission lines result from the fact that a time interval comparable with an rf cycle must elapse before energy leaving one point in the circuit can reach another just a short distance away.

OPERATING PRINCIPLES

If a source of emf – a battery, for example – is connected to the ends of a pair of insulated parallel wires that extend outward for an infinite distance, electric currents will immediately become detectable in the wires near the battery terminals. The electric field of the battery will cause free electrons in the wire connected to the positive terminal to be attracted to the battery, and an equal number of free electrons in the wire connected to the negative terminal will be repelled from the battery. These currents do not flow instantaneously throughout the length of the wires; the electric field that causes the electron movement cannot travel faster than the speed of light, so a measurable interval of time elapses before the currents become evident even a relatively short distance away.

For example, the currents would not become detectable 300 meters (nearly 1000 feet) from the battery until at least a microsecond (one millionth of a second) after the connection was made. By ordinary standards this is a very short length of time, but in terms of radio frequency it represents the time one complete cycle of a 1000-kilohertz current – a frequency considerably lower than those with which amateurs communicate.

The current flows to charge the capacitance between the two wires. However, the conductors of this "linear" capacitor also have appreciable inductance. The line may be thought of as being composed of a whole series of small inductances and capacitances connected as shown in Fig. 20-1, where each coil is the inductance of a very short section of one wire and each capacitor is the capacitance between two such short sections.

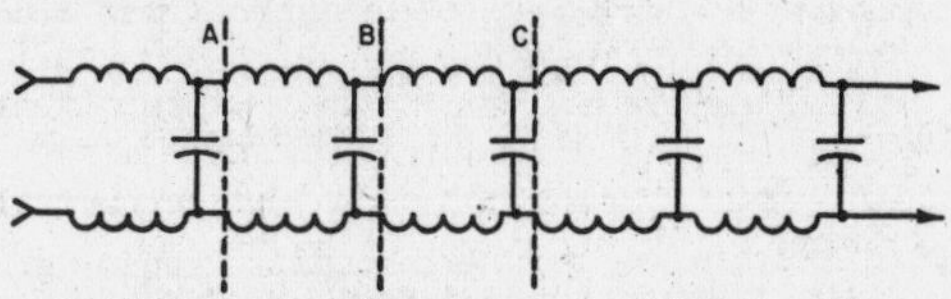

Fig. 20-1 – Equivalent of a transmission line in lumped circuit constants.

Characteristic Impedance

An infinitely long chain of coils and capacitors connected as in Fig. 20-1, where the small inductances and capacitances all have the same values, respectively, has an important property. To an electrical impulse applied at one end, the combination appears to have an impedance – called the **characteristic impedance** or **surge impedance** – approximately equal to $\sqrt{L/C}$ where L and C are the inductance and capacitance per unit length. This impedance is purely resistive.

In defining the characteristic impedance as $\sqrt{L/C}$, it is assumed that the conductors have no inherent resistance – that is, there is no I^2R loss in them – and that there is no power loss in the dielectric surrounding the conductors. There is thus no power loss in or from the line no matter how great its length. This may not seem consistent with calling the characteristic impedance a pure resistance, which implies that the power supplied is all dissipated in the line. But in an infinitely long line the effect, so far as the source of power is concerned, is exactly the same as though the power were dissipated in a resistance, because the power leaves the source and travels outward forever along the line.

The characteristic impedance determines the amount of current that can flow when a given voltage is applied to an infinitely long line, in exactly the same way that a definite value of actual resistance limits current flow when a voltage is applied.

The inductance and capacitance per unit length of line depend upon the size of the conductors and the spacing between them. The closer the two conductors and the greater their diameter, the higher the capacitance and the lower the inductance. A line with large conductors closely spaced will have low impedance, while one with small conductors widely spaced will have relatively high impedance.

"Matched" Lines

Actual transmission lines do not extend to infinity but have a definite length and are connected to, or **terminate** in, a load at the "output" end, or end to which the power is delivered. If the load is a pure resistance of a value equal to the characteristic impedance of the line, the line is said to be **matched.** To current traveling along the line such a load just looks like still more transmission line of the same characteristic impedance.

In other words, a short line terminated in a purely resistive load equal to the characteristic impedance of the line acts just as though it were infinitely long. In a matched transmission line, power travels outward along the line from the source until it reaches the load, where it is completely absorbed.

RF on Lines

The principles discussed above, although based on direct-current flow from a battery, also hold when an rf voltage is applied to the line. The difference is that the alternating voltage causes the amplitude of the current at the input terminals of the line to vary with the voltage, and the direction of current flow also periodically reverses when the polarity of the applied voltage reverses. The current at a given instant at any point along the line is the result of a voltage that was applied at some *earlier* instant at the input terminals. Since the distance traveled by the electromagnetic fields in the time of one cycle is equal to one wavelength, the instantaneous amplitude of the current is different at all points in a one-wavelength section of line. In fact, the current flows in opposite directions in the same wire in successive half-wavelength sections. However, at any given point along the line the current goes through similar variations with time that the current at the input terminals did.

Thus the current (and voltage) travels along the wire as a series of waves having a length equal to the speed of travel divided by the frequency of the ac voltage. On an infinitely long line, or one properly matched by its load, an ammeter inserted anywhere in the line will show the same current, because the ammeter averages out the variations in current during a cycle. It is only when the line is not properly matched that the wave motion becomes apparent through observations made with ordinary instruments.

STANDING WAVES

In the infinitely long line (or its matched counterpart) the impedance is the same at any point on the line because the ratio of voltage to current is always the same. However, the impedance at the end of the line in Fig. 20-2 is zero – or at least extremely small – because the line is short-circuited at the end. The outgoing power, on meeting the short-circuit, reverses its direction of flow and goes back along the transmission line toward the input end. There is a large current in the short-circuit, but substantially no voltage across the line at this point. We now have a voltage and current representing the power going outward (**incident power**) toward the short-circuit, and a second voltage and current representing the **reflected power** traveling back toward the source.

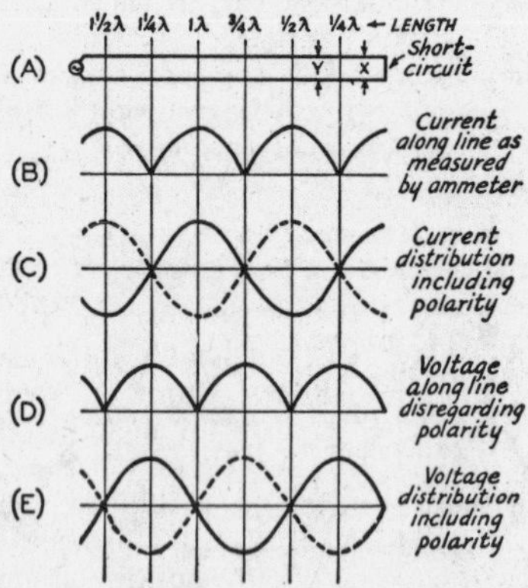

Fig. 20-2 – Standing waves of voltage and current along a short-circuited transmission line.

The reflected current travels at the same speed as the outgoing current, so its instantaneous value will be different at every point along the line, in the distance represented by the time of one cycle. At some points along the line the phase of the incident and reflected currents will be such that the currents cancel each other while at others the amplitude will be doubled. At in-between points the amplitude is between these two extremes. The points at which the currents are in and out of phase depend only on the *time* required for them to travel and so depend only on the *distance* along the line from the point of reflection.

In the short-circuit at the end of the line the two current components are in phase and the total current is large. At a distance of one-half wavelength back along the line from the short-circuit the outgoing and reflected components will again be in phase and the resultant current will again have its maximum value. This is also true at any point that is a multiple of a half wavelength from the short-circuited end of the line.

The outgoing and reflected currents will cancel at a point one-quarter wavelength, along the line, from the short-circuit. At this point, then, the current will be zero. It will also be zero at all points that are an *odd* multiple of one-quarter wavelength from the short-circuit.

If the current along the line is measured at successive points with an ammeter, it will be found to vary about as shown in Fig. 20-2B. The same result would be obtained by measuring the current in either wire, since the ammeter cannot measure phase. However, if the phase could be checked, it would be found that in each successive half-wavelength section of the line the currents at any given instant are flowing in opposite directions, as indicated by the solid line in Fig. 20-2C. Furthermore, the current in the second wire is flowing in the opposite direction to the current in the adjacent section of the first wire. This is indicated by the broken curve in Fig. 20-2C. The variations in current intensity along the transmission line are referred to as **standing waves.** The point of maximum line current is called a **current loop** or **current antinode** and the point of minimum line current is called a **current node.**

Voltage Relationships

Since the end of the line is short-circuited, the voltage at that point has to be zero. This can only be so if the voltage in the outgoing wave is met, at the end of the line, by a reflected voltage of equal amplitude and opposite polarity. In other words, the phase of the voltage wave is *reversed* when reflection takes place from the short-circuit. This reversal is equivalent to an extra half cycle or half wavelength of travel. As a result, the outgoing and returning voltages are in phase a quarter wavelength from the end of the line, and again out of phase a half wavelength from the end. The standing waves of voltage, shown at D in Fig. 20-2, are therefore displaced by one-quarter wavelength from the standing waves of current. The drawing at E shows the voltage on both wires when phase is taken into account. The polarity of the voltage on each wire reverses in each half wavelength section of transmission line. A voltage maximum is called a **voltage loop** or **antinode** and a voltage minimum is called a **voltage node.**

Open-Circuited Line

If the end of the line is open-circuited instead of short-circuited, there can be no current at the end of the line but a large voltage can exist. Again the incident power is reflected back toward the source. The incident and reflected components of current must be equal and opposite in phase at the open circuit in order for the total current at the end of the line to be zero. The incident and reflected components of voltage are in phase and add together. The result is again that there are standing waves, but the conditions are reversed as compared with a short-circuited line. Fig. 20-3 shows the open-circuited line case.

Lines Terminated in Resistive Load

Fig. 20-4 shows a line terminated in a resistive load. In this case at least part of the incident power is absorbed in the load, and so is not available to be reflected back toward the source. Because only part of the power is reflected, the reflected components of voltage and current do not have the same magnitude as the incident components. Therefore neither voltage nor current cancel completely at any point along the line. However, the *speed* at which the incident and reflected components travel is not affected by their amplitude, so the phase relationships are similar to those in open- or short-circuited lines.

It was pointed out earlier that if the load resistance, Z_R, is equal to the characteristic impedance, Z_0, of the line all the power is absorbed in the load. In such a case there is no reflected power and therefore no standing waves of current and voltage. This is a special case that represents the change-over point between "short-circuited" and "open-circuited" lines. If Z_R is less than Z_0, the current is largest at the load, while if Z_R is greater than Z_0 the voltage is largest at the load. The two conditions are shown at B and C, respectively, in Fig. 20-4.

The resistive termination is an important practical case. The termination is seldom an actual resistor, the most common terminations being resonant circuits or resonant antenna systems, both of which have essentially resistive impedances. If the load is reactive as well as resistive, the operation of the line resembles that shown in Fig.

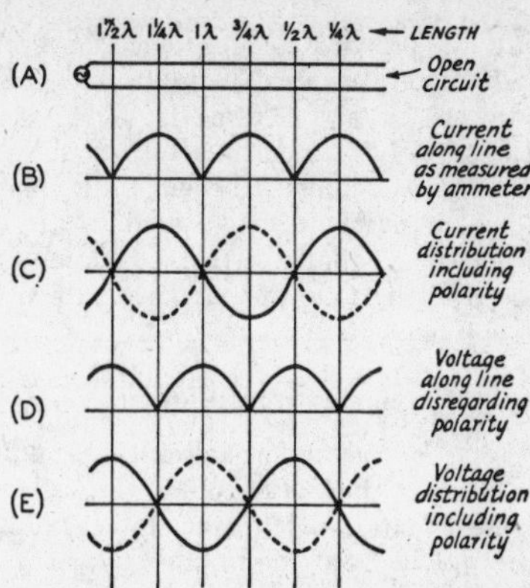

Fig. 20-3 — Standing waves of current and voltage along an open-circuited transmission line.

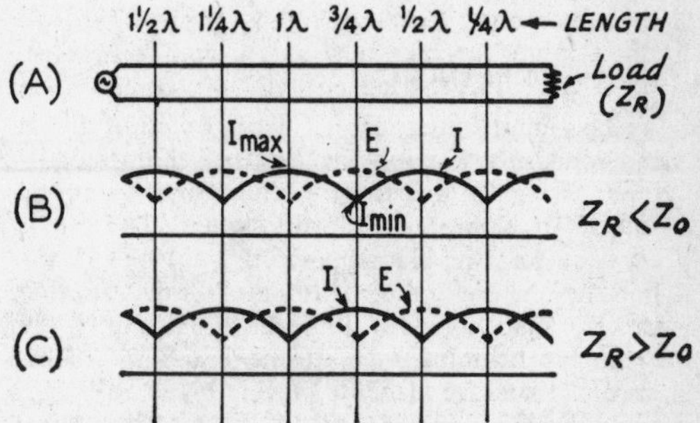

Fig. 20-4 — Standing waves on a transmission line terminated in a resistive load.

20-4, but the presence of reactance in the load causes two modifications: The loops and nulls are shifted toward or away from the load; and the amount of power reflected back toward the source is increased, as compared with the amount reflected by a purely resistive load of the same total impedance. Both effects become more pronounced as the ratio of reactance to resistance in the load is made larger.

Standing-Wave Ratio

The ratio of maximum current to minimum current along a line, Fig. 20-5, is called the **standing-wave ratio.** The same ratio holds for maximum voltage and minimum voltage. It is a measure of the mismatch between the load and the line, and is equal to 1 when the line is perfectly matched. (In that case the "maximum" and "minimum" are the same, since the current and voltage do not vary along the line.) When the line is terminated in a purely resistive load, the standing-wave ratio is

$$SWR = \frac{Z_R}{Z_0} \text{ or } \frac{Z_0}{Z_R} \qquad (20\text{-A})$$

where SWR = Stand-wave ratio
Z_R = Impedance of load (pure resistance)
Z_0 = Characteristic impedance of line

Example: A line having a characteristic impedance of 300 ohms is terminated in a resistive load of 25 ohms. The SWR is

$$SWR = \frac{Z_0}{Z_R} = \frac{300}{25} = 12 \text{ to } 1$$

It is customary to put the larger of the two quantities, Z_R or Z_0, in the numerator of the fraction so that the SWR will be expressed by a number larger than 1.

It is easier to measure the standing-wave ratio than some of the other quantities (such as the impedance of an antenna) that enter into transmission-line computations. Consequently, the SWR is a convenient basis for work with lines. The higher the SWR the greater the mismatch between line and load. In practical lines, the power loss in the line itself increases with the SWR as shown later.

INPUT IMPEDANCE

The input impedance of a transmission line is the impedance seen looking into the sending-end or input terminals; it is the impedance into which the source of power must work when the line is connected. If the load is perfectly matched to the line the line appears to be infinitely long, as stated earlier, and the input impedance is simply the characteristic impedance of the line itself. However, if there are standing waves this is no longer true; the input impedance may have a wide range of values.

This can be understood by referring to Figs. 20-2, 20-3, or 20-4. If the line length is such that standing waves cause the voltage at the input terminals to be high and the current low, then the input impedance is higher than the Z_0 of the line, since impedance is simply the ratio of voltage to current. Conversely, low voltage and high current at the input terminals mean that the input impedance is lower than the line Z_0. Comparison of the three drawings also shows that the range of input impedance values that may be encountered is greater when the far end of the line is open- or short-circuited than it is when the line has a resistive load. In other words, the higher the SWR the greater the range of input impedance values when the line length is varied.

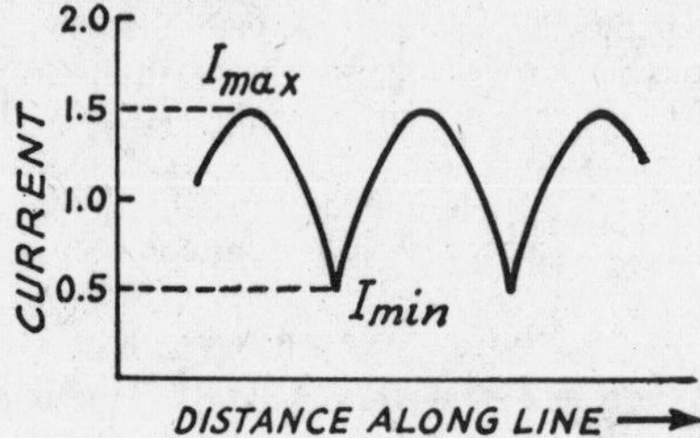

Fig. 20-5 – Measurement of standing-wave ratio. In this drawing, I_{max} is 1.5 and I_{min} is 0.5, so the SWR = Imax/Imin = 1.5/0.5 = 3 to 1.

In addition to the variation in the absolute value of the input impedance with line length, the presence of standing waves also causes the input impedance to contain both reactance and resistance, even though the load itself may be a pure resistance. The only exceptions to this occur at the exact current loops or nodes, at which points the input impedance is a pure resistance. These are the only points at which the outgoing and reflected voltages and currents are exactly in phase: At all other distances along the line the current either leads or lags the voltage and the effect is exactly the same as though a capacitance or inductance were part of the input impedance.

The input impedance can be represented either by a resistance and a capacitance or by a resistance and an inductance. Whether the impedance is inductive or capacitive depends on the characteristics of the load and the length of the line. It is possible to represent the input impedance by an equivalent circuit having resistance and reactance either in series or parallel, so long as the total impedance and phase angle are the same in either case.

The magnitude and character of the input impedance are quite important, since they determine the method by which the power source must be coupled to the line. The calculation of input impedance is rather complicated and its measurement is not feasible without special equipment. Fortunately, in amateur work it is unnecessary either to calculate or measure it. The proper coupling can be achieved by relatively simple methods described later in this chapter.

Lines Without Load

The input impedance of a short-circuited or open-circuited line not an extact multiple of one-quarter wavelength long is practically a pure reactance. This is because there is very little power lost in the line. Such lines are frequently used as "linear" inductances and capacitances.

If a shorted line is less than a quarter-wave long, as at *X* in Fig. 20-2, it will have inductive reactance. The reactance increases with the line length up to the quarter-wave point. Beyond that, as at *Y*, the reactance is capacitive, high near the quarter-wave point and becoming lower as the half-wave point is approached. It then alternates between inductive and capacitive in successive quarter-wave sections. Just the reverse is true of the open-circuited line.

At exact multiples of a quarter wavelength the impedance is purely resistive. It is apparent, from examination of B and D in Fig. 20-2, that at points that are a multiple of a half wavelength – i.e., 1/2, 1, 1 1/2 wavelengths, etc. – from the short-circuited end of the line that the current and voltage have the same values that they do at the short circuit. In other words, if the line were an exact multiple of a half wavelength long the generator or source of power would "look into" a short circuit. On the other hand, at points that are an odd multiple of a quarter wavelength – i.e., 1/4, 3/4, 1 1/4, etc. – from the short circuit the voltage is maximum and the current is zero. Since $Z = E/I$, the impedance at these points is theoretically infinite. (Actually it is very high, but not infinite.) This is because the current does not actually go to zero when there are losses in the line. Losses are always present, but usually are small.)

Impedance Transformation

The fact that the input impedance of a line depends on the SWR and line length can be used to advantage when it is necessary to transform a given impedance into another value.

Study of Fig. 20-4 will show that, just as in the open- and short-circuited cases, if the line is one-half wavelength long the voltage and current are exactly the same at the input terminals as they are at the load. This is also true of lengths that are integral multiples of a half wavelength. It is also true for all values of SWR. Hence the input impedance of any line, no matter what its Z_0, that is a multiple of a half wavelength long is exactly the same as the load impedance. Such a line can be used to transfer the impedance to a new location without changing its value.

When the line is a quarter wavelength long, or an odd multiple of a quarter wavelength, the load impedance is "inverted." That is, if the current is low and the voltage is high at the load, the input impedance will be such as to require high current and low voltage. The relationship between the load impedance and input impedance is given by

$$Z_S = \frac{Z_0^2}{Z_R} \qquad \text{(20-B)}$$

where Z_S = Impedance looking into line (line length and odd multiple of one-quarter wavelength
Z_R = Impedance of load (pure resistance)
Z_0 = Characteristic impedance of line

Example: A quarter-wavelength line having a characteristic impedance of 500 ohms is terminated in a resistive load of 75 ohms. The impedance looking into the input or sending end of the line is

$$Z_S = \frac{Z_0^2}{Z_R} = \frac{(500)^2}{75} = \frac{250{,}000}{75} = 3333 \text{ ohms}$$

If the formula above is rearranged, we have

$$Z_0 = \sqrt{Z_S Z_R} \qquad \text{(20-C)}$$

This means that if we have two values of impedance that we wish to "match," we can do so if we connect them together by a quarter-wave transmission line having a characteristic impedance equal to the square root of their product. A quarter-wave line, in other words, has the characteristics of a transformer.

Resonant and Nonresonant Lines

The input impedance of a line operating with a high SWR is critically dependent on the line length, and resistive only when the length is some integral multiple of one-quarter wavelength. Lines cut to such a length and operated with a high SWR are called "tuned" or "resonant" lines. On the other hand, if the SWR is low the input impedance is close to the Z_0 of the line and does not vary a great deal with the line length. Such lines are called "flat," or "untuned," or "nonresonant."

There is no sharp line of demarcation between tuned and untuned lines. If the SWR is below 1.5 to 1 the line is essentially flat, and the same input coupling method will work with all line lengths. If the SWR is above 3 or 4 to 1, the type of coupling system, and its adjustment, will depend on the line length and such lines fall into the "tuned" category.

It is usually advantageous to make the SWR as low as possible. A resonant line becomes necessary only when a considerable mismatch between the load and the line has to be tolerated. The most important practical example of this is when a single antenna is operated on several harmonically related frequencies, in which case the antenna impedance will have widely different values on different harmonics.

RADIATION

Whenever a wire carries alternating current the electromagnetic fields travel away into space with the velocity of light. At power-line frequencies the field that "grows" when the current is increasing has plenty of time to return or "collapse" about the conductor when the current is decreasing, because the alternations are so slow. But at radio frequencies fields that travel only a relatively short distance do not have time to get back to the conductor before the next cycle commences. The consequence is that some of the electromagnetic energy is prevented from being restored to the conductor; in other words, energy is radiated into space in the form of electromagnetic waves.

The lines previously considered have consisted of two parallel conductors of the same diameter. Provided there is nothing in the system to destroy symmetry, at every point along the line the current in one conductor has the same intensity as the current in the other conductor at that point, but the currents flow in opposite directions. This was shown in Figs. 20-2C and 20-3C. It means that the fields set up about the two wires have the same intensity, but *opposite directions.* The consequence is that the total field set up about such a transmission line is zero; the two fields "cancel out." Hence no energy is radiated.

Practically, the fields do not quite cancel out because for them to do so the two conductors would have to occupy the same space, whereas they are actually slightly separated. However, the cancellation is substantially complete if the distance between the conductors is very small compared to the wavelength. Transmission line radiation will be negligible if the distance between the conductors is .01 wavelength or less, provided the currents in the two wires are balanced.

The amount of radiation also is proportional to the current flowing in the line. Because of the way in which the current varies along the line when there are standing waves, the effective current, for purposes of radiation, becomes greater as the SWR is increased. For this reason the radiation is least when the line is flat. However, if the conductor spacing is small and the currents are balanced, the radiation from a line with even a high SWR is inconsequential. A small unbalance in the line currents is far more serious – and is just as serious when the line is flat as when the SWR is high.

PRACTICAL LINE CHARACTERISTICS

The foregoing discussion of transmission lines has been based on a line consisting of two parallel conductors. The **parallel-conductor** line is but one of two general types, the other being the **coaxial** or **concentric** line. The coaxial line consists of a conductor placed in the center of a tube. The inside surface of the tube and the outside surface of the smaller inner conductor form the two conducting surfaces of the line.

In the coaxial line the fields are entirely inside the tube, because the tube acts as a shield to prevent them for appearing outside. This reduces radiation to the vanishing point. So far as the electrical behavior of coaxial lines is concerned, all that has previously been said about the operation of parallel-conductor lines applies. There are, however, practical differences in the construction and use of parallel and coaxial lines.

PARALLEL-CONDUCTOR LINES

A type of parallel-conductor line sometimes used in amateur installations is one in which two wires (ordinarily No. 12 or No. 14) are supported a fixed distance apart by means of insulating rods called "spacers." The spacings used vary from two to six inches, the smaller spacings being necessary at frequencies of the order of 28 MHz and higher so that radiation will be minimized. The construction is shown in Fig. 20-6. Such a line is said to be **air insulated**. The characteristic impedance of such "open-wire" lines is between 400 and 600 ohms, depending on the wire size and spacing.

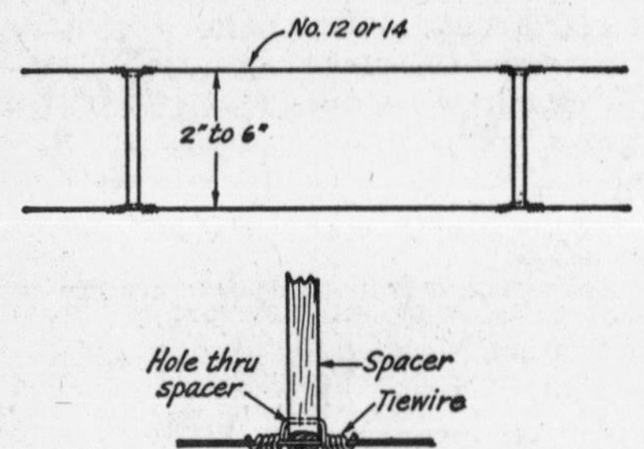

Fig. 20-6 – Typical construction of open-wire line. The line conductor fits in a groove in the end of the spacer, and is held in place by a tie-wire anchored in a hole near the groove.

Parallel-conductor lines also are occasionally constructed of metal tubing of a diameter of 1/4 to 1/2 inch. This reduces the characteristic impedance of the line. Such lines are mostly used as quarter-wave transformers, when different values of impedance are to be matched.

Prefabricated parallel-conductor line with air insulation, developed for television reception, can be used in transmitting applications. This line consists of two conductors separated one-half to one inch by molded-on spacers. The characterstic impedance is 300 to 450 ohms, depending on the wire size and spacing.

A convenient type of manufactured line is one in which the parallel conductors are imbedded in low-loss insulating material (polyethylene). It is commonly used as a TV lead-in and has a characteristic impedance of about 300 ohms. It is sold under various names, the most common of which is "Twin-Lead." This type of line has the advantages of light weight, close and uniform conductor spacing, flexibility and neat appearance. However, the losses in the solid dielectric are higher than in air, and dirt or moisture on the line tends to change the characteristic impedance. Moisture effects can be reduced by coating the line with silicone grease. A special form of 300-ohm Twin-Lead for transmitting uses a polyethylene tube with the conductors molded diametrically

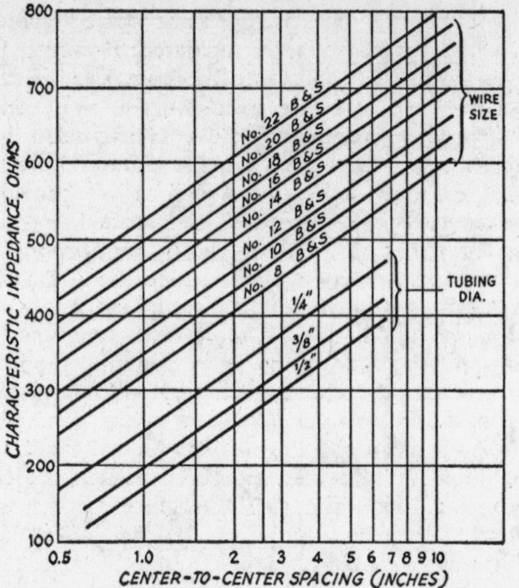

Fig. 20-7 — Chart showing the characteristic impedance of spaced-conductor parallel transmission lines with air dielectric. Tubing sizes given are for outside diameters.

opposite; the longer dielectric path in such line reduces moisture troubles.

In addition to 300-ohm line, Twin-Lead is obtainable with a characteristic impedance of 75 ohms for transmitting purposes. Light-weight 75- and 150-ohm Twin-Lead also is available.

Characteristic Impedance

The characteristic impedance of an air-insulated parallel-conductor line is given by:

$$Z_0 = 276 \log \frac{b}{a} \qquad \textbf{(20-D)}$$

where Z_0 = Characteristic impedance
b = Center-to-center distance between conductors
a = Radius of conductor (in same units as b)

It does not matter what units are used for a and b so long as they are the *same* units. Both quantities may be measured in centimeters, inches, etc. Since it is necessary to have a table of common logarithms to solve practical problems, the solution is given in graphical form in Fig. 20-7 for a number of common conductor sizes.

In solid-dielectric parallel-conductor lines such as Twin-Lead the characteristic impedance cannot be calculated readily, because part of the electric field is in air as well as in the dielectric.

Unbalance in Parallel-Conductor Lines

When installing parallel-conductor lines care should be taken to avoid introducing electrical unbalance into the system. If for some reason the current in one conductor is higher than in the other, or if the currents in the two wires are not exactly out of phase with each other, the electromagnetic fields will not cancel completely and a considerable amount of power may be radiated by the line.

Maintaining good line balance requires, first of all, a balanced load at its end. For this reason the antenna should be fed, whenever possible, at a point where each conductor "sees" exactly the same thing. Usually this means that the antenna system should be fed at its electrical center. However, even though the antenna appears to be symmetrical physically, it can be unbalanced electrically if the part connected to one of the line conductors is coupled to something (such as house wiring or a metal pole or roof) that is not duplicated on the other part of the antenna. Every effort should be made to keep the antenna as far as possible from other wiring or sizable metallic objects. The transmission line itself will cause some unbalance if it is not brought away from the antenna at right angles to it for a distance of at least a quarter wavelength.

In installing the line conductors take care to see that they are kept away from metal. The minimum separation between either conductor and all other wiring should be at least four or five times the conductor spacing. The shunt capacitance introduced by close proximity to metallic objects can drain off enough current (to ground) to unbalance the line currents, resulting in increased radiation. A shunt capacitance of this sort also constitutes a reactive load on the line, causing an impedance "bump" that will prevent making the line actually flat.

COAXIAL LINES

The most common form of coaxial line consists of either a solid or stranded-wire inner conductor surrounded by polyethylene dielectric. Copper braid is woven over the dielectric to form the outer conductor, and a waterproof vinyl covering is placed on top of the braid. This cable is made in a number of different diameters. It is moderately flexible, and so is convenient to install. This solid coaxial cable is commonly available in impedances approximating 50 and 70 ohms.

Air-insulated coaxial lines have lower losses than the solid-dielectric type, but are rarely used in amateur work because they are expensive and difficult to install as compared with the flexible cable. The common type of air-insulated coaxial line uses a sold-wire conductor inside a copper tube, with the wire held in the center of the tube by means of insulating "beads" placed at regular intervals.

Characteristic Impedance

The characteristic impedance of an air-insulated coaxial line is given by the formula

$$Z_0 = 138 \log \frac{b}{a} \qquad \textbf{(20-E)}$$

where Z_0 = Characteristic impedance
b = Inside diameter of outer conductor
a = Outside diameter of inner conductor (in same units as b)

The formula for coaxial lines is approximately correct for lines in which bead spacers are used, provided the beads are not too closely spaced. When the line is filled with a solid dielectric, the characteristic impedance as given by the formula should be multiplied by $1/\sqrt{K}$, where K is the dielectric constant of the material.

ELECTRICAL LENGTH

In the discussion of line operation earlier in this chapter it was assumed that currents traveled along the conductors at the speed of light. Actually, the velocity is somewhat less, the reason being that electromagnetic fields travel more slowly in material dielectrics than they do in free space. In air the velocity is practically the same as in empty space, but a practical line always has to be supported in some fashion by solid insulating materials. The result is that the fields are slowed down; the currents travel a shorter distance in the time of one cycle than they do in space, and so the wavelength along the line is less than the wavelength would be in free space at the same frequency.

Whenever reference is made to a line as being so many wavelengths (such as a "half wavelength" or "quarter wavelength") long, it is to be understood that the *electrical* length of the line is meant. Its actual physical length as measured by a tape always will be somewhat less. The physical length corresponding to an electrical wavelength is given by

$$\textit{Length in feet} = \frac{984V}{f} \qquad \textbf{(20-F)}$$

where f = Frequency in megahertz
V = Velocity factor

The **velocity factor** is the ratio of the actual velocity along the line to the velocity in free space. Values of V for several common types of line are given in Table 20-I.

Example: A 75-foot length of 300-ohm Twin-Lead is used to carry power to an antenna at a frequency of 7150 kHz. From Table 20-I, V is 0.82. At this frequency (7.15 MHz) a wavelength is

$$\textit{Length}\text{ (feet)} = \frac{984V}{f} = \frac{984}{7.15} \times 0.82$$

$$= 137.6 \times 0.82 = 112.8 \text{ feet}$$

The line length is therefore 75/112.8 = 0.665 wavelength.

Because a quarter-wavelength line is frequently used as a linear transformer, it is convenient to calculate the length of a quarter-wave line directly. The formula is

$$\textit{Length}\text{ (feet)} = \frac{246V}{f} \qquad \textbf{(20-G)}$$

where the symbols have the same meaning as above.

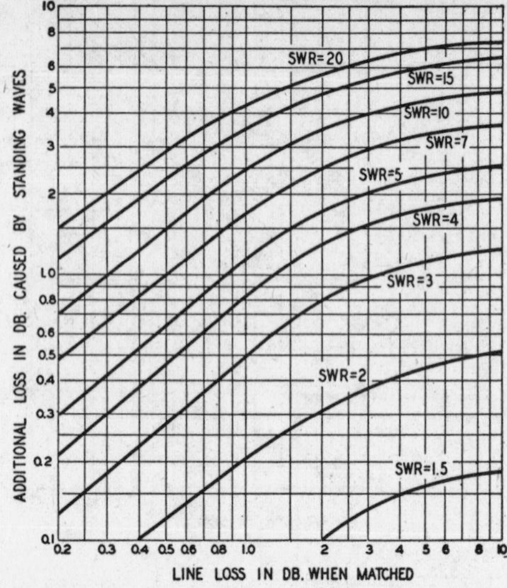

Fig. 20-8 – Effect of standing-wave ratio on line loss. The ordinates give the *additional* loss in decibels for the loss, under perfectly matched conditions, shown on horizontal scale.

LOSSES IN TRANSMISSION LINES

There are three ways by which power may be lost in a transmission line: by radiation, by heating of the conductors (I^2R), and by heating of the dielectric, if any. Radiation losses are in general the result from undesired coupling to the radiating antenna. They cannot readily be estimated or measured, so the following discussion is based only on conductor and dielectric losses.

Heat losses in both the conductor and the dielectric increase with frequency. Conductor losses also are greater the lower the characteristic impedance of the line, because a higher current flows in a low-impedance line for a given power input. The converse is true of dielectric losses because these increase with the voltage, which is greater on high-impedance lines. The dielectric loss in air-insulated lines is negligible (the only loss is in the insulating spacers) and such lines operate at high efficiency when radiation losses are low.

It is convenient to express the loss in a transmission line in decibels per unit length, since the loss in dB is directly proportional to the line length. Losses in various types of lines operated without standing waves (that is, terminated in a resistive load equal to the characteristic impedance of the line) are given in Table 20-I.

When there are standing waves on the line the power loss increases as shown in Fig. 20-8. Whether or not the increase in loss is serious depends on what the original loss would have been if the line were perfectly matched. If the loss with perfect matching is very low, a large SWR will not greatly affect the *efficiency* of the line – i.e., the ratio of the power delivered to the load to the power put into the line.

TABLE 20-I

Characteristics of Commonly-Used Transmission Lines

Type of Line	Z_0 *Ohms*	*Vel. %*	*pF per ft.*	*OD*	*Attenuation in dB per 100 feet* 3.5	7	14	21	28	50	144	420
RG58/A-AU	53	66	28.5	0.195	0.68	1.0	1.5	1.9	2.2	3.1	5.7	10.4
RG58 Foam Diel.	50	79	25.4	0.195	0.52	0.8	1.1	1.4	1.7	2.2	4.1	7.1
RG59/A-AU	73	66	21.0	0.242	0.64	0.90	1.3	1.6	1.8	2.4	4.2	7.2
RG59 Foam Diel.	75	79	16.9	0.242	0.48	0.70	1.0	1.2	1.4	2.0	3.4	6.1
RG8/A-AU	52	66	29.5	0.405	0.30	0.45	0.66	0.83	0.98	1.35	2.5	4.8
RG8 Foam Diel.	50	80	25.4	0.405	0.27	0.44	0.62	0.76	0.90	1.2	2.2	3.9
RG11/A-AU	75	66	20.5	0.405	0.38	0.55	0.80	0.98	1.15	1.55	2.8	4.9
Aluminum Jacket, Foam Diel.[1]												
3/8 inch	50	81	25.0	–	–	–	0.36	0.48	0.54	0.75	1.3	2.5
1/2 inch	50	81	25.0	–	–	–	0.27	0.35	0.40	0.55	1.0	1.8
3/8 inch	75	81	16.7	–	–	–	0.43	0.51	0.60	0.80	1.4	2.6
1/2 inch	75	81	16.7	–	–	–	0.34	0.40	0.48	0.60	1.2	1.9
Open-wire[2]	–	97	–		0.03	0.05	0.07	0.08	0.10	0.13	0.25	–
300-ohm Twin-lead	300	82	5.8		0.18	0.28	0.41	0.52	0.60	0.85	1.55	2.8
300-ohm tubular	300	80	4.6		0.07	0.25	0.39	0.48	0.53	0.75	1.3	1.9
Open-wire, TV type												
1/2 inch	400	95			0.028	0.05	0.09	0.13	0.17	0.30	0.75	–
1 inch	450	95			0.028	0.05	0.09	0.13	0.17	0.30	0.75	–

[1] Polyfoam dielectric type line information courtesy of Times Wire and Cable Co.

[2] Attenuation of open-wire line based on No. 12 conductors, neglecting radiation.

TABLE 20-II

Type of Line	*Power Rating in Watts* 20-MHz	30-	60-	200-
RG58/A-AU	550	430	290	14
RG58 Foam Diel.[1]				
RG59/A-AU	860	680	440	208
RG8/A-AU	2000	1720	1250	680
RG11/A-AU	1800	1400	900	400

[1] Power handling capabilities of foam-type coaxial lines is approximately 30 percent greater than the polyethylene dielectric types.

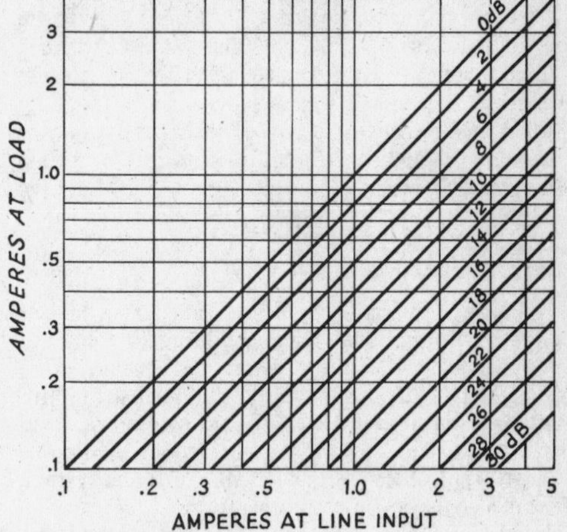

Fig. 20-9 — Graph for calculating losses in transmission lines with an SWR of 1.

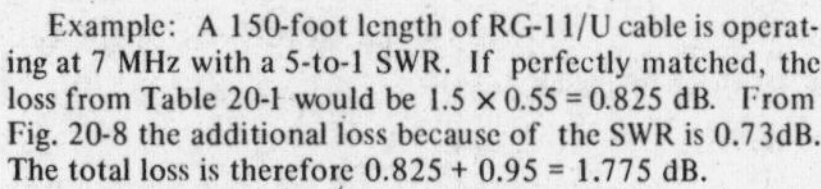

Example: A 150-foot length of RG-11/U cable is operating at 7 MHz with a 5-to-1 SWR. If perfectly matched, the loss from Table 20-1 would be 1.5 × 0.55 = 0.825 dB. From Fig. 20-8 the additional loss because of the SWR is 0.73dB. The total loss is therefore 0.825 + 0.95 = 1.775 dB.

TESTING OLD COAXIAL CABLE

Unknown coaxial cable or cable that has been exposed to the weather may have losses above the published figures for the cable type. A simple method for checking the losses in a cable is to use an rf ammeter (mounted in a Minibox with coax fittings). Connect one end of the cable to a nonreactive dummy load of the *same* impedance as the coax. At the other end of the line insert the rf ammeter and connect it to a transmitter. Tune up the rig and make a note of the exact amount of current. Without touching the transmitter tuning, move the ammeter to the other end of the line, at the dummy load, and note the meter reading. Compare the readings to Fig. 20-9 and this will give you the decibel loss that is present in the line. Keep in mind that the cable must be terminated in its characteristic impedance (SWR of 1); otherwise, the figures in Fig. 20-9 will not be accurate.

MATCHING THE ANTENNA TO THE LINE

The load for a transmission line may be any device capable of dissipating rf power. When lines are used for transmitting applications the most common type of load is an antenna. When a transmission line is connected between an antenna and a receiver, the receiver input circuit (not the antenna) is the load, because the power taken from a passing wave is delivered to the receiver.

Whatever the application, the conditions existing at the load, and *only* the load, determine the standing-wave ratio on the line. If the load is purely resistive and equal in value to the characteristic impedance of the line, there will be no standing waves. In case the load is not purely resistive, and/or is not equal to the line Z_0, there will be standing waves. No adjustments that can be made at the input end of the line can change the SWR, nor is it affected by changing the line length.

Only in a few special cases is the load inherently of the proper value to match a practicable transmission line. In all other cases it is necessary either to operate with a mismatch and accept the SWR that results, or else to take steps to bring about a proper match between the line and load by means of transformers or similar devices. Impedance-matching transformers may take a variety of physical forms, depending on the circumstances.

Note that it is essential, if the SWR is to be made as low as possible, that the load at the point of connection to the transmission line be purely resistive. In general, this requires that the load be tuned to resonance. If the load itself is not resonant at the operating frequency the tuning sometimes can be accomplished in the matching system.

THE ANTENNA AS A LOAD

Every antenna system, no matter what its physical form, will have a definite value of impedance at the point where the line is to be connected. The problem is to transform this **antenna input impedance** to the proper value to match the line. In this respect there is no one "best" type of line for a particular antenna system, because it is possible to transform impedances in any desired ratio. Consequently, any type of line may be used with any type of antenna. There are frequently reasons other than impedance matching that dictate the use of one type of line in preference to another, such as ease of installation, inherent loss in the line, and so on, but these are not considered in this section.

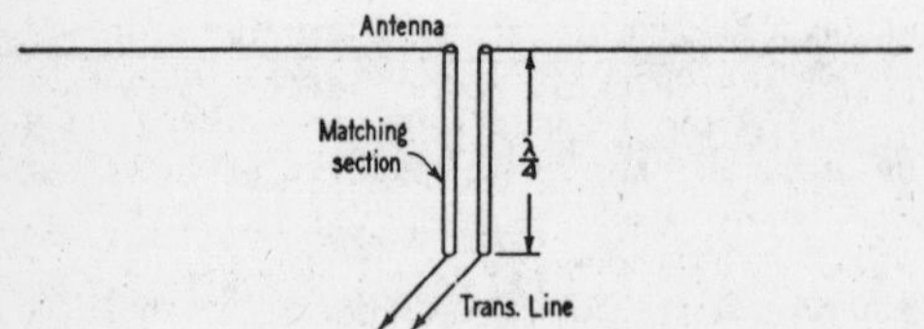

Fig. 20-10A – "Q" matching section, a quarter-wave impedance transformer.

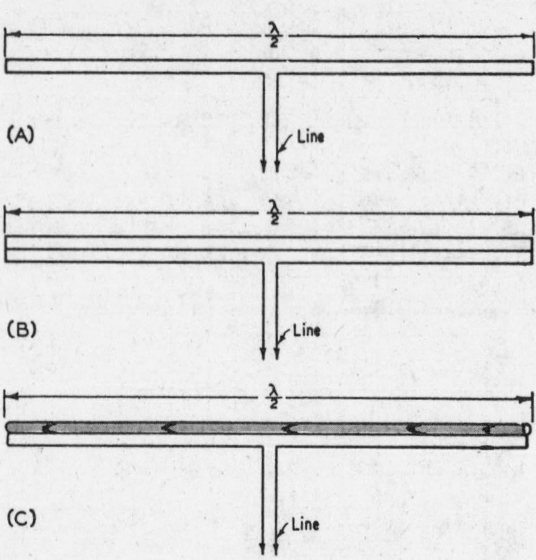

Fig. 20-10B – The folded dipole, a method for using the antenna element itself to provide an impedance transformation.

Although the input impedance of an antenna system is seldom known very accurately, it is often possible to make a reasonably close estimate of its value.

Matching circuits can be built using ordinary coils and capacitors, but are not used very extensively because they must be supported at the antenna and must be weatherproofed. The systems to be described use **linear transformers.**

The Quarter-Wave Transformer or "Q" Section

As mentioned previously, a quarter-wave transmission line may be used as an impedance transformer. Knowing the antenna impedance and the characteristic impedance of the transmission line to be matched, the required characteristic impedance of a matching section such as is shown in Fig. 20-10A is:

$$Z = \sqrt{Z1\,ZO} \qquad \text{(20-H)}$$

Where Zl is the antenna impedance and ZO is the characteristic impedance of the line to which it is to be matched.

Example: To match a 600-ohm line to an antenna presenting a 72-ohm load, the quarter-wave matching section would require a characteristic impedance of

$$\sqrt{72 \times 600} = \sqrt{43{,}200} = 208 \text{ ohms}$$

The spacings between conductors of various sizes of tubing and wire for different surge impedances

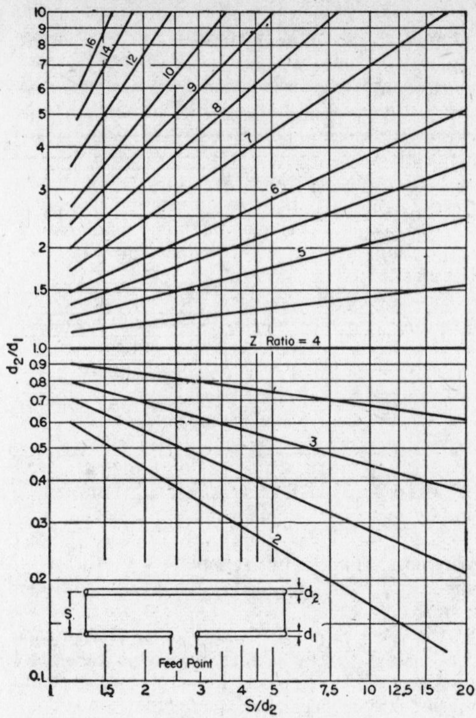

Fig. 20-11 – Impedance transformation ratio, two-conductor folded dipole. The dimensions d1, d2 and s are shown on the inset drawing. Curves show the ratio of the impedance (resistive) seen by the transmission line to the radiation resistance of the resonant antenna system.

are given in graphical form in the chapter on "Transmission Lines." (With 1/2-inch tubing, the spacing in the example above should be 1.5 inches for an impedance of 208 ohms.)

The length of the quarter-wave matching section may be calculated from

$$\textit{Length}\text{ (feet)} = \frac{246V}{f} \qquad \text{(20-I)}$$

where V = Velocity factor
f = Frequency in MHz

Example: A quarter-wave transformer of RG-11/U is to be used at 28.7 MHz. From the table 20-1, $V = 0.66$.

$$\textit{Length} = \frac{246 \times 0.66}{28.7} = 5.65 \text{ feet}$$

$$= 5 \text{ feet } 8 \text{ inches}$$

The antenna must be resonant at the operating frequency. Setting the antenna length by formula is amply accurate with single-wire antennas, but in other systems, particularly close-spaced arrays, the antenna should be adjusted to resonance before the matching section is connected.

When the antenna input impedance is not known accurately, it is advisable to construct the matching section so that the spacing between conductors can be changed. The spacing then may be adjusted to give the lowest possible SWR on the transmission line.

Folded Dipoles

A half-wave antenna element can be made to match various line impedances if it is split into two or more parallel conductors with the transmission line attached at the center of only one of them. Various forms of such "folded dipoles" are shown in Fig. 20-10B. Currents in all conductors are in phase in a folded dipole, and since the conductor spacing is small the folded dipole is equivalent in radiating properties to an ordinary single-conductor dipole. However, the current flowing into the input terminals of the antenna from the line is the current in one conductor only, and the entire power from the line is delivered at this value of current. This is equivalent to saying that the input impedance of the antenna has been raised by splitting it up into two or more conductors.

The ratio by which the input impedance of the antenna is stepped up depends not only on the number of conductors in the folded dipole but also on their relative diameters, since the distribution of current between conductors is a function of their diameters. (When one conductor is larger than the other, as in Fig. 20-10B, the larger one carries the greater current.) The ratio also depends, in general, on the spacing between the conductors, as shown by the graphs of Figs. 20-11 and 20-12. An important special case is the 2-conductor dipole with conductors of equal diameter; as a simple antenna, not a part of a directive array, it has an

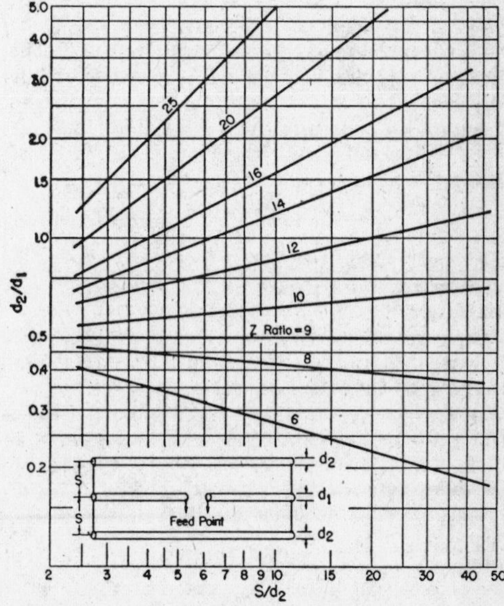

Fig. 20-12 – Impedance transformation ratio, three-conductor folded dipole. The dimensions d1, d2 and s are shown on the inset drawing. Curves show the ratio of the impedance (resistive) seen by the transmission line to the radiation resistance of the resonant antenna system.

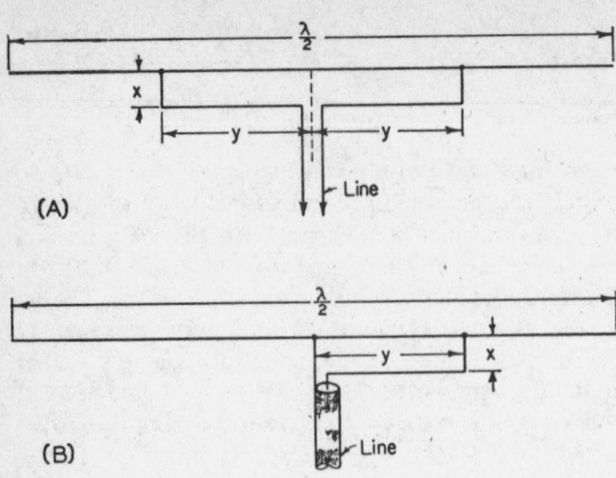

Fig. 20-13 – The "T" match and "gamma" match.

input impedance close enough to 300 ohms to afford a good match to 300-ohm Twin-Lead.

The required ratio of conductor diameters to give a desired impedance ratio using two conductors may be obtained from Fig. 20-11. Similar information for a 3-conductor dipole is given in Fig. 20-12. This graph applies where all three conductors are in the same plane. The two conductors not connected to the transmission line must be equally spaced from the fed conductor, and must have equal diameters. The fed conductor may have a different diameter, however. The unequal-conductor method has been found particularly useful in matching to low-impedance antennas such as directive arrays using close-spaced parasitic elements.

The length of the antenna element should be such as to be approximately self-resonant at the median operating frequency. The length is usually not highly critical, because a folded dipole tends to have the characteristics of a "thick" antenna and thus has a relatively broad frequency-response curve.

"T" and "Gamma" Matching Sections

The method of matching shown in Fig. 20-13A is based on the fact that the impedance between any two points along a resonant antenna is resistive, and has a value which depends on the spacing between the two points. It is therefore possible to choose a pair of points between which the impedance will have the right value to match a transmission line. In practice, the line cannot be connected directly at these points because the distance between them is much greater than the conductor spacing of a practicable transmission line. The "T" arrangement in Fig. 20-13A overcomes this difficulty by using a second conductor paralleling the antenna to form a matching section to which the line may be connected.

The "T" is particularly suited to use with a parallel-conductor line, in which case the two points along the antenna should be equidistant from the center so that electrical balance is maintained.

The operation of this system is somewhat complex. Each "T" conductor (y in the drawing) forms with the antenna conductor opposite it a short section of transmission line. Each of these transmission-line sections can be considered to be terminated in the impedance that exists at the point of connection to the antenna. Thus the part of the antenna between the two points carries a transmission-line current in addition to the normal antenna current. The two transmission-line matching sections are in series, as seen by the main transmission line.

If the antenna by itself is resonant at the operating frequency its impedance will be purely resistive, and in such case the matching-section lines are terminated in a resistive load. However, since these sections are shorter than a quarter wavelength their input impedance – i.e., the impedance seen by the main transmission line looking into the matching-section terminals – will be reactive as well as resistive. This prevents a perfect match to the main transmission line, since its load must be a pure resistance for perfect matching. The reactive component of the input impedance must be tuned out before a proper match can be secured.

One way to do this is to detune the antenna just enough, by changing its length, to cause reactance of the opposite kind to be reflected to the input terminals of the matching section, thus cancelling the reactance introduced by the latter. Another method, which is considerably easier to adjust, is to insert a variable capacitor in series with the matching section where it connects to the transmission line, as shown in Fig. 21-39. The capacitor must be protected from the weather.

The method of adjustment commonly used is to cut the antenna for approximate resonance and then make the spacing x some value that is convenient constructionally. The distance y is then adjusted, while maintaining symmetry with respect to the center, until the SWR on the transmission line is as low as possible. If the SWR is not below 2 to 1 after this adjusment, the antenna length should be changed slightly and the matching section taps adjusted again. This procedure may be continued until the SWR is as close to 1 to 1 as possible.

When the series-capacitor method of reactance compensation is used (Fig. 21-32), the antenna should be the proper length to be resonant at the operating frequency. Trial positions of the matching-section taps are then taken, each time adjusting the capacitor for minimum SWR, until the standing waves on the transmission line are brought down to the lowest possible value.

The unbalanced ("gamma") arrangement in Fig. 20-13B is similar in principle to the "T," but is adapted for use with single coax line. The method of adjustment is the same.

BALANCING DEVICES

An antenna with open ends, of which the half-wave type is an example, is inherently a balanced radiator. When opened at the center and fed with a parallel-conductor line this balance is maintained throughout the system, so long as the causes of unbalance discussed in the transmission-line chapter are avoided.

If the antenna is fed at the center through a coaxial line, as indicated in Fig. 20-14A, this balance is upset because one side of the radiator is connected to the shield while the other is connected to the inner conductor. On the side connected to the shield, a current can flow down over the *outside* of the coaxial line, and the fields thus set up cannot be canceled by the fields from the inner conductor because the fields *inside* the line cannot escape through the shielding afforded by the outer conductor. Hence these "antenna" currents flowing on the outside of the line will be responsible for radiation.

Linear Baluns

Line radiation can be prevented by a number of devices whose purpose is to detune or decouple the line for "antenna" currents and thus greatly reduce their amplitude. Such devices generally are known as **baluns** (a contraction for "balanced to unbalanced"). Fig. 20-14B shows one such arrangement, known as a **bazooka**, which uses a sleeve over the transmission line to form, with the outside of the outer line conductor, a shorted quarter-wave line section. As described earlier in this chapter, the impedance looking into the open end of such a section is very high, so that the end of the outer conductor of the coaxial line is effectively insulated from the part of the line below the sleeve. The length is an *electrical* quarter wave, and may be physically shorter if the insulation between the sleeve and the line is other than air. The bazooka has no effect on the impedance relationships between the antenna and the coaxial line.

Another method that gives an equivalent effect is shown at C. Since the voltages at the antenna terminals are equal and opposite (with reference to ground), equal and opposite currents flow on the surfaces of the line and second conductor. Beyond the shorting point, in the direction of the transmitter, these currents combine to cancel out. The balancing section "looks like" an open circuit to the antenna, since it is a quarter-wave parallel-conductor line shorted at the far end, and thus has no effect on the normal antenna operation. However, this is not essential to the line-balancing function of the device, and baluns of this type are sometimes made shorter than a quarter wavelength in order to provide the shunt inductive reactance required in certain types of matching systems.

Fig. 20-14D shows a third balun, in which equal and opposite voltages, balanced to ground, are taken from the inner conductors of the main transmission line and half-wave phasing section. Since the voltages at the balanced end are in series while the voltages at the unbalanced end are in parallel, there is a 4-to-1 step-down in impedance from the balanced to the unbalanced side. This arrangement is useful for coupling between a balanced 300-ohm line and a 75-ohm coaxial line, for example.

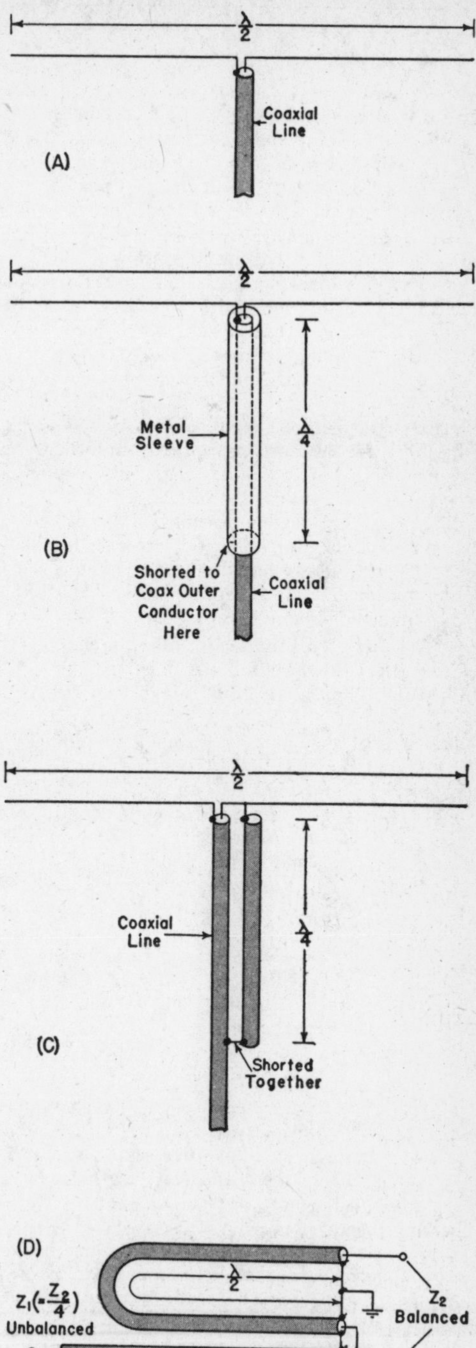

Fig. 20-14 — Radiator with coaxial feed (A) and methods of preventing unbalanced currents from flowing on the outside of the transmission line (B and C). The half-wave phasing section shown at D is used for coupling between an unbalanced and a balanced circuit when a 4-to-1 impedance ratio is desired or can be accepted.

OTHER LOADS AND BALANCING DEVICES

The most important practical load for a transmission line is an antenna which, in most cases, will be "balanced" – that is, symmetrically constructed with respect to the feed point. Aside from considerations of matching the actual impedance of the antenna at the feed point to the characteristic impedance of the line (if such matching is attempted) a balanced antenna should be fed through a balanced transmission line in order to preserve symmetry with respect to ground and thus avoid difficulties with unbalanced currents on the line and consequent undesirable radiation from the transmission line itself.

If, as is often the case, the antenna is to be fed through coaxial line (which is inherently unbalanced) some method should be used for connecting the line to the antenna without upsetting the symmetry of the antenna itself. This requires a circuit that will isolate the balanced load from the unbalanced line while providing effecient power transfer. Devices for doing this are called **baluns.** The types used between the antenna and transmission line are generally "linear," consisting of transmission-line sections.

The need for baluns also arises in coupling a transmitter to a balanced transmission line, since the output circuits of most transmitters have one side grounded. (This type of output circuit is desirable for a number of reasons, including TVI reduction.) The most flexible type of balun for this purpose is the inductively coupled matching network described in a subsequent section in this chapter. This combines impedance matching with balanced-to-unbalanced operation, but has the disadvantage that it uses resonant circuits and thus can work over only a limited band of frequencies without readjustment. However, if a fixed impedance ratio in the balun can be tolerated, the coil balun described below can be used without adjustment over a frequency range of about 10 to 1 – 3 to 30 MHz, for example.

Coil Baluns

The type of balun known as the "coil balun" is based on the principles of linear-transmission-line balun as shown in the upper drawing of Fig. 20-15. Two transmission lines of equal length having a characteristic impedance (Z_0) are connected in series at one end and in parallel at the other. At the series-connected end the lines are balanced to ground and will match an impedance equal to $2Z_0$. At the parallel-connected end the lines will be matched by an impedance equal to $Z_0/2$. One side may be connected to ground at the parallel-connected end, provided the two lines have a length such that, considering each line as a single wire, the balanced end is effectively decoupled from the parallel-connected end. This requires a length that is an odd multiple of 1/4 wavelength.

A definite line length is required only for decoupling purposes, and so long as there is adequate decoupling the system will act as a 4-to-1 impedance transformer regardless of line length. If

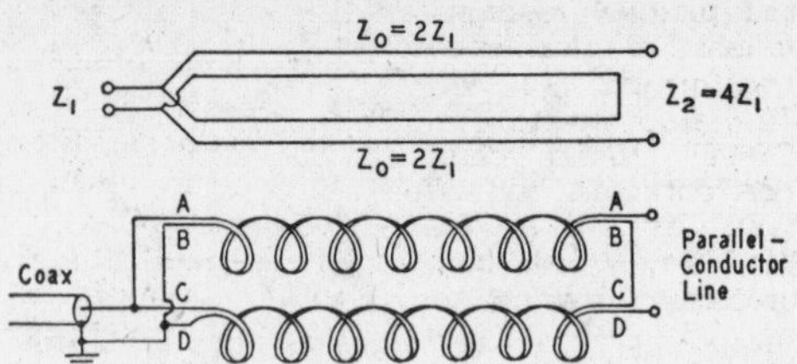

Fig. 20-15 – Baluns for matching between push-pull and single-ended circuits. The impedance ratio is 4 to 1 from the push-pull side to the unbalanced side. Coiling the lines (lower drawing) increases the frequency range over which satisfactory operation is obtained.

each line is wound into a coil, as in the lower drawing, the inductances so formed will act as choke coils and will tend to isolate the series-connected end from any ground connection that may be placed on the parallel-connected end. Balun coils made in this way will operate over a wide frequency range, since the choke inductance is not critical. The lower frequency limit is where the coils are no longer effective in isolating one end from the other; the length of line in each coil should be about equal to a quarter wave-length at the lowest frequency to be used.

The principal application of such coils is in going from a 300-ohm balanced line to a 75-ohm coaxial line. This requires that the Z_0 of the lines forming the coils be 150 ohms.

A balun of this type is simply a fixed-ratio transformer, when matched. It cannot compensate for inaccurate matching elsewhere in the system. With a "300-ohm" line on the balanced end, for example, a 75-ohm coax cable will not be matched unless the 300-ohm line actually is terminated in a 300-ohm load.

TWO BROAD-BAND TOROIDAL BALUNS

Air-wound balun transformers are somewhat bulky when designed for operation in the 1.8- to 30-MHz range. A more compact broad-band transformer can be realized by using toroidal ferrite core material as the foundation for bifilar-wound coil balun transformers. Two such baluns are described here.

In Fig. 20-16 at A, a 1:1 ratio balanced-to-unbalanced-line transformer is shown. This transformer is useful in converting a 50-ohm balanced line condition to one that is 50 ohms, unbalanced. Similarly, the transformer will work between balanced and unbalanced 75-ohm impedances. A 4:1 ratio transformer is illustrated in Fig. 20-16 at B. This balun is useful for converting a 200-ohm balanced condition to one that is 50 ohms, unbalanced. In a like manner, the transformer can be used between a balanced 300-ohm point and a 75-ohm unbalanced line. Both balun transformers will handle 1000 watts of rf power and are designed to operate from 1.8 through 60 MHz.

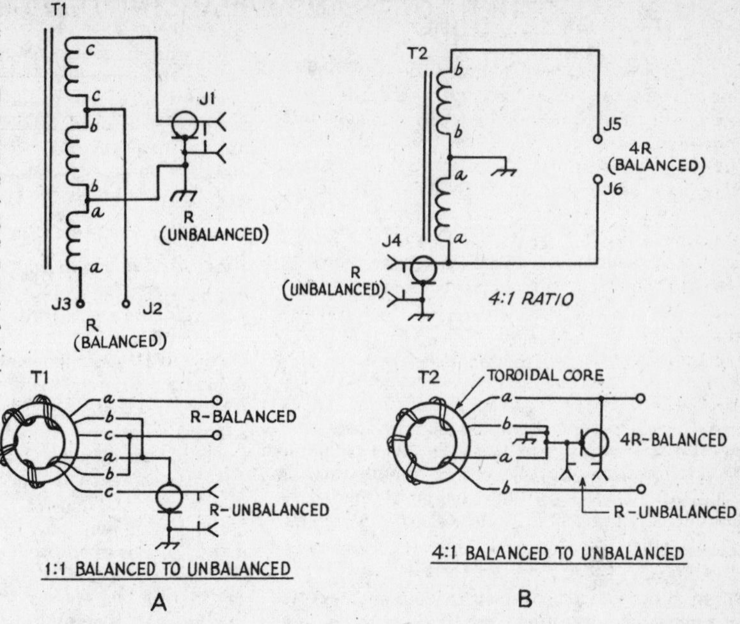

Fig. 20-16— Schematic and pictorial representations of the balun transformers. T1 and T2 are wound on CF-123 toroid cores (see footnote 1, and the text). J1 and J4 are SO-239-type coax connectors, or similar. J2, J3, J5, and J6 are steatite feedthrough bushings. The windings are labeled a, b, and c to show the relationship between the pictorial and schematic illustrations.

Low-loss high-frequency ferrite core material is used for T1 and T2.[1,3] The cores are made from Q-2 material and cost approximately $5.50 in single-lot quantity. They are 0.5 inches thick, have an OD of 2.4 inches, and the ID is 1.4 inches. The permeability rating of the cores is 40. A packaged one-kilowatt balun kit, with winding instructions for 1:1 or 4:1 impedance transformation ratios, is available, but uses a core of slightly different dimensions.[2]

Winding Information

The transformer shown in Fig. 20-16 at A has a trifilar winding consisting of 10 turns of No. 14 formvar-insulated copper wire. A 10-turn bifilar winding of the same type of wire is used for the balun of Fig. 20-16 at B. If the cores have rough edges, they should be carefully sanded until smooth enough to prevent damage to the wire's formvar insulation. The windings should be spaced around the entire core as shown in Fig. 20-17. Insulation can be used between the core material and the windings to increase the power handling capabilities of the core.

Using the Baluns

For indoor applications, the transformers can be assembled open style, without benefit of a protective enclosure. For outdoor installations, such as at the antenna feed point, the balun should be encapsulated in epoxy resin or mounted in a suitable weather-proof enclosure. A Minibox, sealed against moisture, works nicely for the latter.

[1] Available in single-lot quantity from Permag Corp, 88-06 Van Wyck Expy, Jamaica, NY 11418.

[2] Amidon Associates, 12033 Otsego Street, North Hollywood, CA 91601.

[3] Toroid cores are also available from Ferroxcube Corp. of America, Saugerties, NY 12477.

NONRADIATING LOADS

Typical examples of nonradiating loads for a transmission line are the grid circuit of a power amplifier (considered in the chapter on transmitters), the input circuit of a receiver, and another transmission line. This last case includes the "antenna tuner" – a misnomer because it is

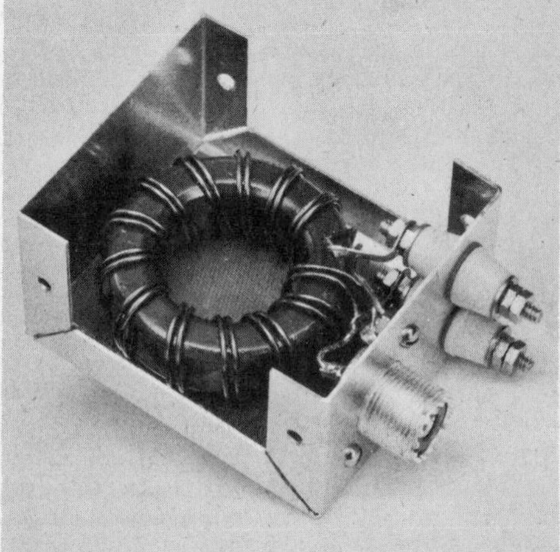

Fig. 20-17 – Layout of a kilowatt 4:1 toroidal balun transformer. Phenolic insulating board is mounted between the transformer and the Minibox wall to prevent short-circuiting. The board is held in place with epoxy cement. Cement is also used to secure the transformer to the board. For outdoor use, the Minibox cover can be installed, then sealed against the weather by applying epoxy cement along the seams of the box.

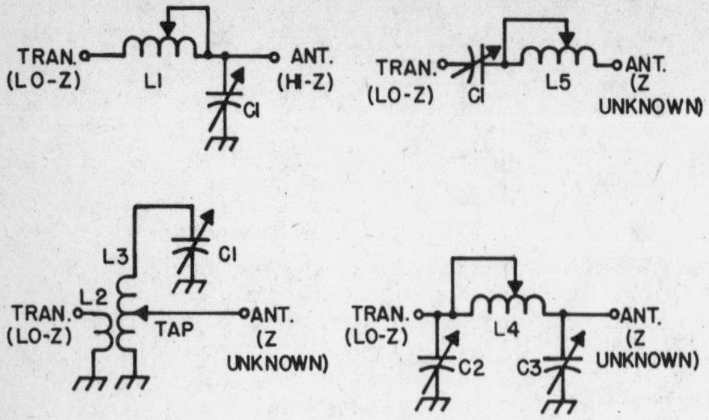

Fig. 20-18 – Networks for matching a low-Z transmitter output to random-length end-fed wire antennas.

actually a device for coupling a transmission line to the transmitter. Because of its importance in amateur installations, the antenna coupler is considered separately in a later part of this chapter.

Coupling to a Receiver

A good match between an antenna and its transmission line does not guarantee a low standing-wave ratio on the line when the antenna system is used for receiving. The SWR is determined wholly by what the line "sees" at the receiver's antenna-input terminals. For minimum SWR the receiver input circuit must be matched to the line. The rated input impedance of a receiver is a nominal value that varies over a considerable range with frequency. Most hf receivers are sensitive enough that exact matching is not necessary. The most desirable condition is that in which the receiver is matched to the line Z_0 and the line in turn is matched to the antenna. This transfers maximum power from the antenna to the receiver with the least loss in the transmission line.

COUPLING TO RANDOM-LENGTH ANTENNAS

Several impedance-matching schemes are shown in Fig. 20-18, permitting random-length wires to be matched to normal low-Z transmitter outputs. The circuit used will depend upon the length of the antenna wire and its impedance at the desired operating frequency. Ordinarily, one of the four methods shown will provide a suitable impedance match to an end-fed random wire, but the configuration will have to be determined experimentally. For operation between 3.5 and 30 MHz, C1 can be a 200-pF type with suitable plate spacing for the power level in use. C2 and C3 should be 500-pF units to allow for flexibility in matching. L1, L4, and L5 should be tapped or rotary inductors with sufficient L for the operating frequency. L3 can be a tapped Miniductor coil with ample turns for the band being used. An SWR bridge should be used as a match indicator.

COUPLING THE TRANSMITTER TO THE LINE

The type of coupling system that will be needed to transfer power adequately from the final rf amplifier to the transmission line depends almost entirely on the input impedance of the line. As shown earlier in this chapter, the input impedance is determined by the standing-wave ratio and the line length. The simplest case is that where the line is terminated in its characteristic impedance so that the SWR is 1 to 1 and the imput impedance is equal to the Z_0 of the line, regardless of line length.

Coupling systems that will deliver power into a flat line are readily designed. For all practical purposes the line can be considered to be flat if the SWR is no greater than about 1.5 to 1. That is, a coupling system designed to work into a pure resistance equal to the line Z_0 will have enough leeway to take care of the small variations in input impedance that will occur when the line length is changed, if the SWR is higher than 1 to 1 but no greater than 1.5 to 1.

Current practice in transmitter design is to

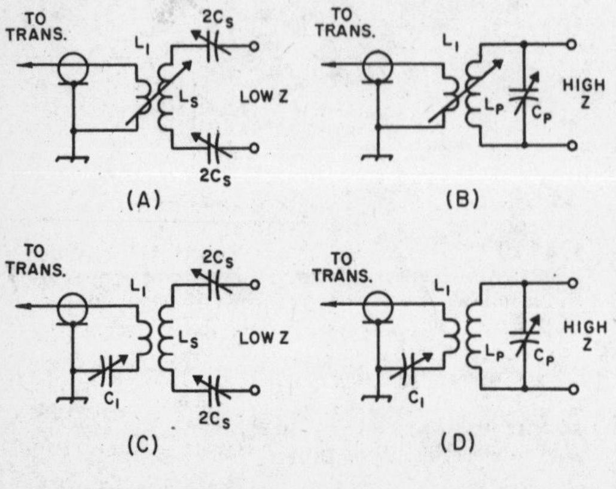

Fig. 20-19 – Simple circuits for coupling a transmitter to a balanced line that presents a load different than the transmitter output impedance. (A) and (B) are respectively series- and parallel-tuned circuits using variable inductive coupling between coils, and (C) and (D) are similar but use fixed inductive coupling and a variable series capacitor, C1. A series-tuned circuit works well with a low-impedance load; the parallel circuit is better with high-impedance loads (several hundred ohms or more).

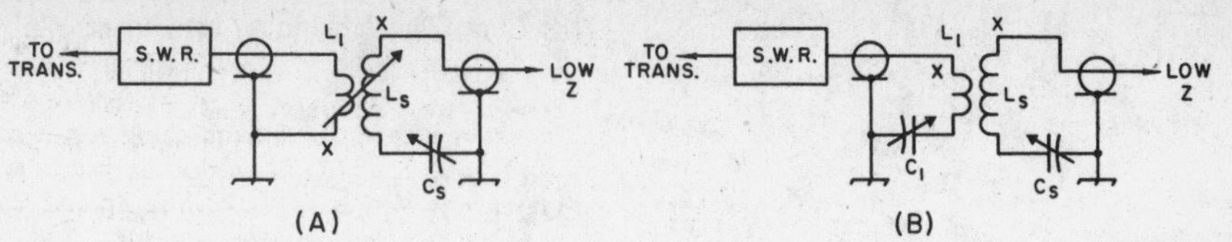

Fig. 20-20 — Coupling from a transmitter designed for 50- to 75-ohm output to a coaxial line with a 3- or 4-to-1 SWR is readily accomplished with these circuits. Essential difference between the circuits is (A) adjustable inductive coupling and (B) fixed inductive coupling with variable series capacitor.

In either case the circuit can be adjusted to give a 1-to-1 SWR on the meter in the line to the transmitter. The coil ends marked "x" should be adjacent, for minimum capacitive coupling.

provide an output circuit that will work into such a line, usually a coaxial line of 50 to 75 ohms characteristic impedance. The design of such output circuits is discussed in the chapter on high-frequency transmitters. If the input impedance of the transmission line that is to be connected to the transmitter differs appreciably from the value of impedance into which the transmitter output circuit is designed to operate, an impedance-matching network must be inserted between the transmitter and the line input terminals.

IMPEDANCE-MATCHING CIRCUITS FOR TRANSMISSION LINES

As shown earlier in this chapter, the input impedance of a line that is operating with a high standing-wave ratio can vary over quite wide limits. The simplest type of circuit that will match such a range of impedances to 50 to 75 ohms is a simple series- or parallel-tuned circuit, approximately resonant at the operating frequency. If the load presented by the line at the operating frequency is low (below a few hundred ohms), a series-tuned circuit should be used. When the load is higher than this, the parallel-tuned circuit is easier to use.

Typical simple circuits for coupling between the transmitter with 50- to 75-ohm coaxial-line output and a balanced transmission line are shown in Fig. 20-19. The inductor L1 should have a reactance of about 60 ohms when adjustable inductive coupling is used (Figs. 20-19A and 20-19B). When a variable series capacitor is used, L1 should have a reactance of about 120 ohms. The variable capacitor, C1, should have a reactance at maximum capacitance of about 100 ohms.

On the secondary side, L_s and C_s should be capable of being tuned to resonance at about 80 percent of the operating frequency. In the series-tuned circuits, for a given low-impedance load looser coupling can be used between L1 and L_s as the L_s-to-C_s ratio is increased. In the parallel-tuned circuits, for a given high-impedance load looser coupling can be used between L1 and L_p as the C_p-to-L_p ratio is increased. The constants are not critical; the rules of thumb are mentioned to assist in correcting a marginal condition where sufficient transmitter loading cannot be obtained.

Coupling to coaxial lines that have a high SWR, and consequently may present a transmitter with a load it cannot couple to, is done with an unbalanced version of the series-tuned circuit, as shown in Fig. 20-20. The rule given above for coupling ease and L_s-to-C_s ratio applies to these circuits as well.

The most satisfactory way to set up initially any of the circuits of Fig. 20-19 or 20-20 is to connect a coaxial SWR bridge in the line to the transmitter, as shown in Fig. 20-20. The "Monimatch" type of bridge, which can handle the full transmitter power and may be left in the line for continuous monitoring, is excellent for this purpose. However, a simple resistance bridge such as is described in the chapter on measurements is perfectly adequate, requiring only that the transmitter output be reduced to a very low value so that the bridge will not be overloaded. To adjust the circuit, make a trial setting of the coupling (coil spacing in Figs. 20-19A and B and 20-20A, C1 setting in others) and adjust C_s or C_p for minimum SWR as indicated by the bridge. If the SWR is not close to practically 1 to 1, readjust the coupling and return C_s or C_p, continuing this procedure until the SWR is practically 1 to 1. The settings may then be logged for future reference.

In the series-tuned circuits of Figs. 20-20A and 20-20C, the two capacitors should be set at similar settings. The "$2C_s$" indicates that a balanced series-tuned coupler requires twice the capacitance in each of two capacitors as does an unbalanced series-tuned circuit, all other things being equal.

It is possible to use circuits of this type without initially setting them up with an SWR bridge. In such a case it is a matter of cut-and-try until adequate power transfer between the amplifier and main transmission line is secured. However, this method frequently results in a high SWR in the link, with consequent power loss, "hot spots" in the coaxial cable, and tuning that is critical with frequency. The bridge method is simple and gives the optimum operating conditions quickly and with certainty.

A TRANSMATCH FOR BALANCED OR UNBALANCED LINES

Nearly all commercially made transmitters are designed to work into a 50- to 70-ohm load, and they are not usually equipped to handle loads that depart far from these values. However, many antenna systems (the antenna plus its feed line) have complex impedances that make it difficult, if not impossible, to load and tune a transmitter

Fig. 20-21 — The universal Transmatch shown here will couple a transmitter to almost any antenna system. If the amateur already has a matching indicator, the Monimatch section of the circuit can be eliminated. The counter dial and knobs are James Millen & Co. components.

properly. What is required is a coupling method to convert the reactive/resistive load to a non-reactive 50-ohm load. This task can be accomplished with a **Transmatch**, a device that consists of one or more *LC* circuits. It can be adjusted to tune out any load reactance plus, when necessary, transforming the load impedance to 50 or 70 ohms.

As has been discussed earlier in this chapter, losses in transmission lines depend on several factors: the size of the conductors, the spacing between conductors, the dielectric material used in the construction of the feed line, and the frequency at which the line is used. Coaxial lines can be classed as lossy lines when compared to a low-loss line such as open-wire feeders, at least below 100 MHz. Because losses increase as the SWR increases, the type of line used to feed an antenna should be chosen carefully. If the transmission line has very low-loss characteristics, high standing wave ratios can be tolerated with no practical loss of power in the line.

A wire antenna, fed at the center with open-wire line, is the most efficient multiband antenna devised to date. For all practical purposes, the feed line is lossless, so extremely high SWRs can be tolerated. This should not be construed to mean that coaxial feed lines cannot be used because of a high SWR, but only the very expensive types are really suitable in this application.

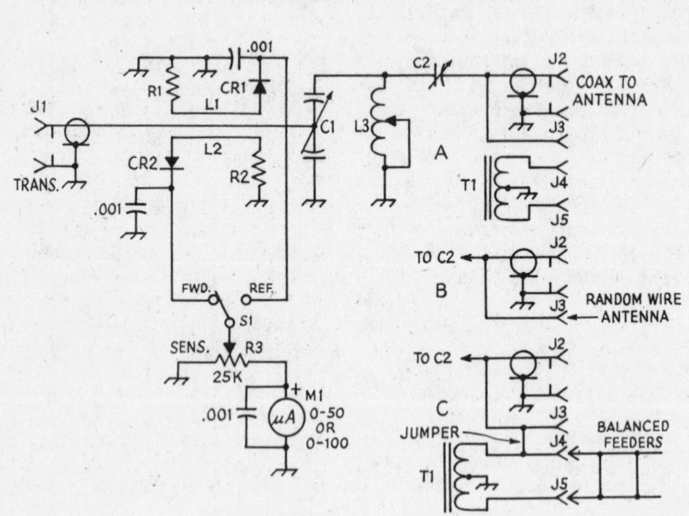

Fig. 20-22 — Circuit diagram of the Transmatch. The .001-μF capacitors used are disk ceramic.

C1 — Dual-section or air variable, 200 pF per section (E. F. Johnson 154-507 or Millen 16250).
C2 — Air variable 350 pF, (E. F. Johnson 154-10 or Millen 16520A).
CR1, CR2 — 1N34A germanium diode.
J1, J2 — Coax chassis connector, type SO-239.
J3, J4, J5 — Isolantite feedthrough insulators.
L1, L2 — See Fig. 20-25.
L3 — Roller inductor, 28 μH (E. F. Johnson 229-203).
M1 — 50 or 100 μA.
R1, R2 — 68-ohm, 1/2-watt carbon or composition.
R3 — 25,000-ohm control, linear taper.
S1 — Spst toggle.
T1 — Balun transformer, see text and Fig. 20-23.

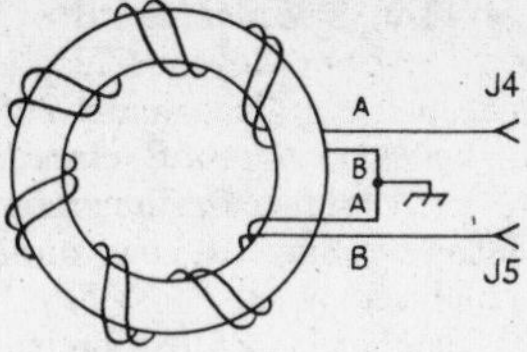

Fig. 20-23 – Details of the balun bifilar windings. The drawing shows the connections required. In the actual balun, the turns should be closed spaced on the inside of the core and spread evenly on the outside.

The Transmatch shown in Fig. 20-22 is designed to handle practically any mismatch that an amateur is likely to encounter. The unit can be used with either open-wire feeders, balanced lines, coaxial lines, or even an end-fed single wire. Frequency range of the unit is from 3 to 30 MHz, accomplished without the use of bandswitching. Basically, the circuit is designed for use with unbalanced lines, such as "coax." For balanced lines, a 1:4 (unbalanced-to-balanced) balun is connected to the output of the Transmatch.

The chassis used for the Transmatch is made of a 16 X 25-inch sheet of aluminum. When bent to form a U, the completed chassis measures 16 X 13 X 6 inches. When mounting the variable capacitors, the roller inductor and the balun, allow at least 1/2-inch clearance to the chassis and adjoining components. The capacitors should be mounted on insulated standoff insulators. The balun can be mounted on a cone insulator or piece of Plexiglas.

The balun requires three ferrite cores stacked for 2-kW or two cores for 1-kW power levels. Amidon type T-200-2 cores are used in making the balun.[1] Each core should be covered with two layers of 3M No. 27 glass-cloth insulating tape. Next, the cores are stacked and covered with another layer of the tape. The winding consists of 15 bifilar turns of No. 14, Teflon-covered wire. Approximately 20 feet of wire (two 10-foot lengths) are required.

A template for the etched-circuit Monimatch is shown in Fig. 20-25. Details for making etched circuits are given in the Construction Practices chapter. If the builder desires, a power-type bridge can be substituted. Such a unit is described in the Measurements chapter. In addition to providing standing-wave indications for Transmatch adjustment purposes, the power bridge will accurately measure transmitter output power.

For coax-to-coax feeder matching, the antenna feed line should be connected to J2 of Fig. 20-22. C1 and C2 should be set at maximum capacitance and power applied to the transmitter. The SWR indicator should be switched to read reflected power. Then, adjust L3 until there is a drop in the reflected reading. C1 and C2 should then be reset, along with L3, until a perfect match is obtained. It will be found that with many antenna systems, several different matching combinations can be obtained. Always use the matching setting that uses the most capacitance from C1 and C2, as maximum *C* provides the best harmonic attenuation.

Fig. 20-24 – Interior view of the Transmatch. The etched-circuit Monimatch is mounted 1/2 inch above the chassis. Both C1 and C2 must be mounted on insulated stand-offs and insulated shaft couplers used between the capacitors and the panel knobs. Likewise, T1 should be installed on an insulated mounting. An isolantite cone is used in the unit shown (the balun could be mounted on a piece of Plexiglas). Feedthrough isolantite insulators, mounted through the rear deck, are used for the antenna connectors.

End-fed wires should be connected to J3. Use the same adjustment procedures for setting up the Transmatch as outlined above. For balanced feeders, the feed line should be connected to J4 and J5, and a jumper must be connected between J3 and J4 (see Fig. 20-22 at C).

A slight modification will permit this Transmatch to be used on the 160-meter band. Fixed capacitors, 100 pF each (Centralab type 850S-100N), can be installed across each of the stator sections of C1, providing sufficient *C* to tune to 1.8 MHz. But, the fixed capacitors must be removed when using the Transmatch on the other hf bands.

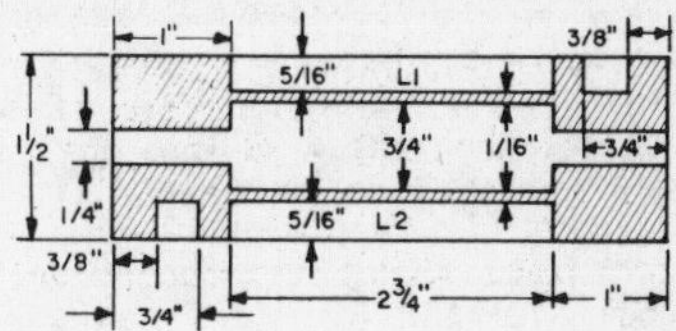

Fig. 20-25 – Template for the etched-circuit Monimatch, foil side shown, etched portion shaded.

[1] Amidon Associates, 12033 Otsego Street, North Hollywood, CA 91601.

A SIMPLE COUPLER FOR BALANCED LINES

Generally speaking, antenna balance can be neglected with many of the systems commonly used by amateurs. Such closed-loop configurations as the quad and the folded dipole tend to cancel out the effects of imbalance even though they are inherently balanced antennas in nature. Other antennas have only a limited vulnerability (the ordinary half-wave dipole for example) to imbalance effects and often can be operated with no balancing networks being necessary. However, some antennas require a balanced source and the best approach is to tailor the coupler design accordingly. These systems usually have a high input impedance also.

The coupler shown in Fig. 1 can be used to match the transmitter to a balanced load with a high input impedance. Typical examples would be short dipoles fed with short lengths of open-wire line or a half-wave dipole fed with a quarter-wave section of high-impedance line. For instance, the coupler was used with an 80-meter dipole fed with 67-feet of 450-ohm line on both 80 and 160 meters with the values given for L1 and C1.

In most instances, values for this type of coupler are not critical and any number of combinations could be used. If desired, a link could be substituted for the phase-reversing transformer. However, the latter provides a simple means for getting a voltage with the necessary 180-degree phase shift for the opposite half of a balanced load. This allows tap adjustment over a wide range of values eliminating the need for changing coils (usually necessary with such couplers). Recommended power limit with the components given would be approximately 100 watts which means the coupler should handle any transmitter in the 150-watt, PEP class without any difficulty on either phone or cw.

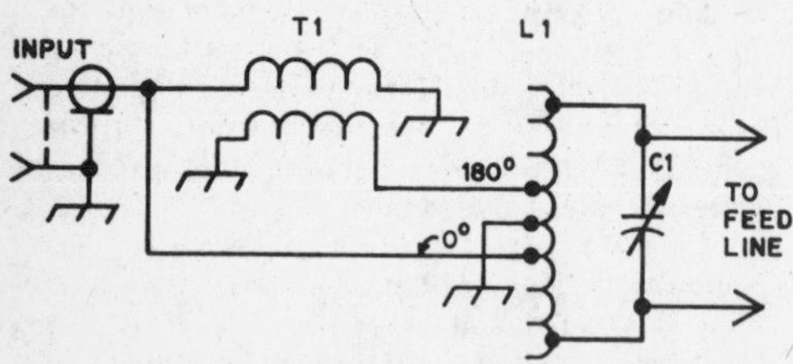

Fig. 1 – Schematic diagram for the coupler.

C1 – Air variable, 325 pF (Millen 19335 or equiv.).

L1 – Air-wound inductor, 2-1/2-inch dia., 6 tpi (B&W 3029 or equiv.), 7 inches long.

T1 – Phase-reversal transformer, stack two Amidon FT-61-601 ferrite cores and wrap with glass tape. Wind 18 turns of twisted pair made from two strands of No. 20 enam. wire twisted such that there are approximately 34 "bumps" or notches per foot as the pair is pulled between the thumb and forefinger.

To construct the twisted pair, bend a four-foot piece of wire in the middle and clamp this end in a vice. Pull the wires taut and twist slightly so that the wires come together over the entire length. Roll the free ends into a ball large enough to be clamped in the chuck of a small hand-powered drill. Twist slowly until the desired pitch is obtained.

Construction of the coupler. Note method of mounting T1 (seen to the left of the coil L1).

Adjustment of the coupler should proceed as follows. First, tune the receiver to the band segment of interest. Next, adjust the taps and tune C1 until signals begin to peak up (the taps should be adjusted equally with the same number of turns from ground to the outer taps on each side and likewise with the inner ones). If a high-impedance load is suspected, start with the inner taps close to the ground connection and adjust the outer taps. With medium-impedance levels, the inner taps will be farther out. Finally, turn the transmitter on and adjust for minimum SWR with the meter connected *between the transmitter and the coupler.* With the antenna mentioned earlier, only minor retuning of C1 was required to cover the 75-meter phone band.

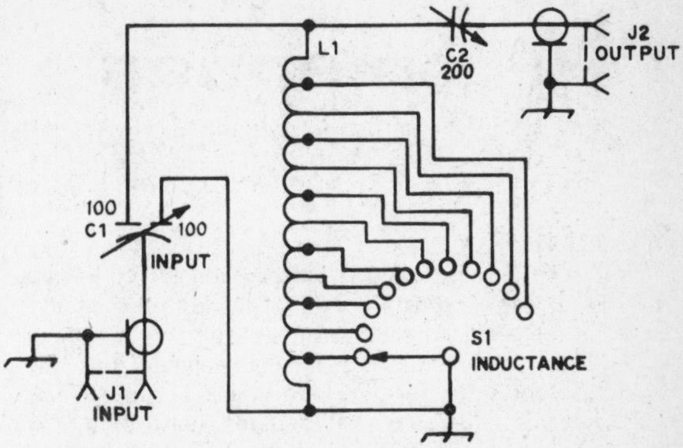

Fig. 1 – Circuit diagram for the Unimatch. C1 is a dual 100 pF variable (E. F. Johnson 167-53). C2 is 200 pF (E. F. Johnson 167-0012-001). S1 is 12 positions.

THE UNIMATCH

Transmatches have appeared in almost every issue of the *Handbook* over the years. The style and circuitry vary considerably but the end purpose is generally the same – to match the antenna feed line to the transmitter output impedance. Most of the transmatches described for hf-band operation have as a feature the ability to handle high power (usually a kilowatt) while transforming impedances. Presented here is a device which will couple energy from a 50-ohm transmitter to any *low-impedance* load. Power handling capability of the unit is typically about 500 watts but will handle a kilowatt under some conditions (matching a very low-impedance load). The purpose is to allow the operator to properly load his triband beam, for instance, on the end of a band for which it is not tuned. Another purpose for the Unimatch is to provide a proper termination for the station low-pass filter (very important for proper filter operation). One of the difficult tasks for an 80-meter operator to accomplish is to set up one antenna which will load correctly on both ends of the band. While open-wire balanced transmission line can be used in conjunction with a conventional coupler, it is sometimes inconvenient to use "open feeders." In such a case, a coaxial-fed dipole, cut for operation at the center of the band, may be used at either end by coupling the line to the transmitter via the Unimatch circuit. The mismatch on the feed line will *not* introduce any noticeable amount of loss in power or cause TVI.

Construction and Tuning

The Unimatch is built in a homemade enclosure of lightweight aluminum. Since both capacitors are operated above ground potential, insulated shaft couplings or insulated shaft material is needed. A 12-position switch is used to select the proper amount of inductance. Both input and output connectors are placed on the rear panel.

Adjustment of the Unimatch is simple especially if a wattmeter or SWR indicator is normally used as a part of the station equipment. The wattmeter should be interconnected between the transmitter output connector and the Unimatch input. If a low-pass filter is included, it should be positioned between the wattmeter input and the transmitter. An antenna should be attached to the Unimatch. Apply a small amount of power to the system (a sufficient level to get a meaningful display on the SWR indicator) and adjust C1 and C2 until a reduction in reflected power is observed. If a perfect match is not possible with a particular setting of S1, rotate S1 a step and attempt to obtain a match by adjustment of C1 and C2. S1 settings which provide the larger amounts of inductance should be used on the lower-frequency bands. The higher-frequency bands (20, 15 and 10 meters) will normally require only a few turns of L1 for typical operation.

Inside view of the Unimatch. The cabinet is homemade and measures 4 × 8 × 6 inches (HWD).

HF Antennas

HF ANTENNAS

An *antenna system* can be considered to include the antenna proper (the portion that radiates the rf energy), the feed line, and any coupling devices used for transferring power from the transmitter to the line and from the line to the antenna. Some simple systems may omit the transmission line or one or both of the coupling devices. This chapter will describe the antenna proper, and in many cases will show popular types of lines, as well as line-to-antenna couplings where they are required. However, it should be kept in mind that *any* antenna proper can be used with *any* type of feedline if a suitable impedance matching is used between the antenna and the line.

ANTENNA SELECTION AND CONSIDERATIONS

In choosing an antenna one must base his selection upon available space, the number of bands to be operated, and the type of propagation he will most often make use of. Frequently, because of limitations in available antenna space, the hf operator must settle for relatively simple antenna systems. It is wise to choose an antenna that will offer the best performance for its size. The "compromise antenna" – those offering multi-band possibilities, and those using physically shortened elements – cannot perform as efficiently as full-size antennas cut for a single band of operation. However, many of the so-called compromise antennas are suitable for DX work even though they have less gain than other types. Ideally, one should attempt to have separate antennas – full size – for the bands to be operated. Also, erecting the antennas as high as possible, and away from trees and man-made objects, will greatly enhance their operational effectiveness.

In general, antenna construction and location become more critical and important on the higher frequencies. On the lower frequencies (1.8, 3.5, and 7 MHz) the vertical angle of radiation and the plane of polarization may be of relatively little importance; at 28 MHz they may be all-important.

Definitions

The **polarization** of a straight-wire antenna is determined by its position with respect to the earth. Thus a vertical antenna radiates vertically polarized waves, while a horizontal antenna radiates horizontally polarized waves in a direction broadside to the wire and vertically polarized waves at high vertical angles off the ends of the wire. The wave from an antenna in a slanting position, or from the horizontal antenna in directions other than mentioned above, contains components of both horizontal and vertical polarization.

The **vertical angle of maximum radiation** of an antenna is determined by the free-space pattern of the antenna, its height above ground, and the nature of the ground. The angle is measured in a vertical plane with respect to a tangent to the earth at that point, and it will usually vary with the horizontal angle, except in the case of a simple vertical antenna. The **horizontal angle of maximum radiation** of an antenna is determined by the free-space pattern of the antenna.

The **impedance** of the antenna at any point is the ratio of the voltage to the current at that point. It is important in connection with feeding power to the antenna, since it constitutes the load to the line offered by the antenna. It can be either resistive or complex, depending upon whether or not the antenna is resonant.

The **field strength** produced by an antenna is proportional to the current flowing in it. When there are standing waves on an antenna, the parts of the wire carrying the higher current have the greater radiating effect. All resonant antennas have standing waves – only terminated types, like the terminated rhombic and terminated "V" have substantially uniform current along their length.

The ratio of power required to produce a given field strength with a "comparison" antenna to the power required to produce the same field strength with a specified type of antenna is called the **power gain** of the latter antenna. The field is measured in the optimum direction of the antenna under test. The comparison antenna is generally a half-wave antenna at the same height and having the same polarization as the antenna under consideration. Gain usually is expressed in decibels.

In unidirectional beams (antennas with most of the radiation in only one direction) the **front-to-back** ratio is the ratio of power radiated in the maximum direction to power radiated in the opposite direction. It is also a measure of the reduction in received signal when the beam direction is changed from that for maximum response to the opposite direction. Front-to-back ratio is usually expressed in decibels.

The **bandwidth** of an antenna refers to the frequency range over which a property falls within acceptable limits. The **gain bandwidth**, the **front-to-back-ratio bandwidth** and the **standing-wave-ratio bandwidth** are of prime interest in amateur work. The gain bandwidth is of interest because, generally, the higher the antenna gain is the narrower the gain bandwidth will be. The SWR bandwidth is of interest because it is an indication of the transmission-line efficiency over the useful frequency range of the antenna.

The radiation pattern of any antenna that is many wavelengths distant from the ground and all other objects is called the **free-space pattern** of the antenna. The free-space pattern of an antenna is almost impossible to obtain in practice, except in the vhf and uhf ranges. Below 30 MHz, the height of the antenna above ground is a major factor in determining the radiation pattern of the antenna.

When any antenna is near the ground the free-space pattern is modified by reflection of radiated waves from the ground, so that the actual pattern is the resultant of the free-space pattern and ground reflections. This resultant is dependent upon the height of the antenna, its position or orientation with respect to the surface of the ground, and the electrical characteristics of the ground. The effect of a perfectly reflecting ground is such that the original free-space field strength may be multiplied by a factor which has a maximum value of 2, for complete reinforcement, and having all intermediate values to zero, for complete cancellation. These reflections only affect the radiation pattern in the vertical plane – that is, in directions upward from the earth's surface – and not in the horizontal plane, or the usual geographical directions.

Fig. 21-1 shows how the multiplying factor varies with the vertical angle for several representative heights for horizontal antennas. As the height is increased the angle at which complete reinforcement takes place is lowered, until for a height equal to one wavelength it occurs at a vertical angle of 15 degrees. At still greater heights, not shown on the chart, the first maximum will occur at still smaller angles.

Radiation Angle

The vertical angle of maximum radiation is of primary importance, especially at the higher frequencies. It is advantageous, therefore, to erect the antenna at a height that will take advantage of ground reflection in such a way as to reinforce the space radiation at the most desirable angle. Since low angles usually are most effective, this generally means that the antenna should be high – at least one-half wavelength at 14 MHz, and preferably three-quarters or one wavelength, and at least one wavelength, and preferably higher, at 28 MHz. The physical height required for a given height in wavelengths decreases as the frequency is increased, so that good heights are not impracticable; a half wavelength at 14 MHz is only 35 feet, approximately, while the same height represents a full wavelength at 28 MHz. At 7 MHz and lower frequencies the higher radiation angles are effective, so that again a useful antenna height is not difficult to attain. Heights between 35 and 70 feet are suitable for all bands, the higher figures being preferable. It is well to remember that most simple horizontally polarized antennas do not exhibit the directivity they are capable of unless they are one half wavelength above ground, or greater, at their operating frequency. Therefore, with dipole-type antennas it is not important to choose a favored broadside direction unless the antenna is at least one-half wavelength above ground.

Imperfect Ground

Fig. 21-1 is based on ground having perfect conductivity, whereas the actual earth is not a perfect conductor. The principal effect of actual ground is to make the curves inaccurate at the lowest angles; appreciable high-frequency radiation at angles smaller than a few degrees is practically impossible to obtain over horizontal ground. Above 15 degrees, however, the curves are accurate enough for all practical purposes, and may be taken as indicative of the result to be expected at angles between 5 and 15 degrees.

The effective ground plane – that is, the plane from which ground reflections can be considered to take place – seldom is the actual surface of the ground but is a few feet below it, depending upon the characteristics of the soil.

Impedance

Waves that are reflected directly upward from the ground induce a current in the antenna in passing, and, depending on the antenna height, the phase relationship of this induced current to the original current may be such as either to increase or decrease the total current in the antenna. For the same power input to the antenna, an increase in current is equivalent to a decrease in impedance, and vice versa. Hence, the impedance of the antenna varies with height. The theoretical curve of variation of radiation resistance for a very thin half-wave antenna above perfectly reflecting ground is shown in Fig. 21-2. The impedance approaches the free-space value as the height becomes large, but at low heights may differ considerably from it.

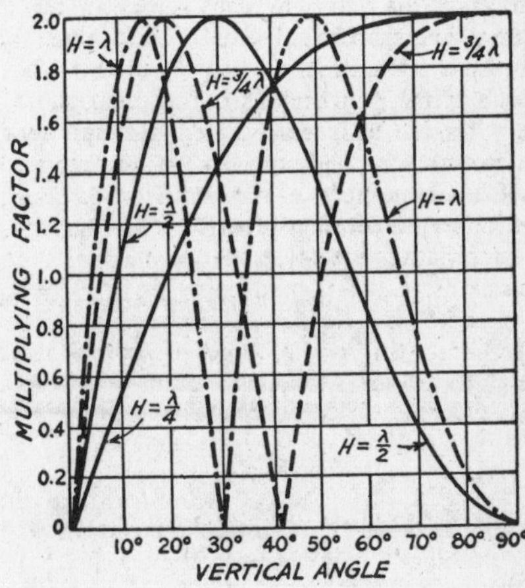

Fig. 21-1 – Effect of ground on radiation of horizontal antennas at vertical angles for four antenna heights. This chart is based on perfectly conducting ground.

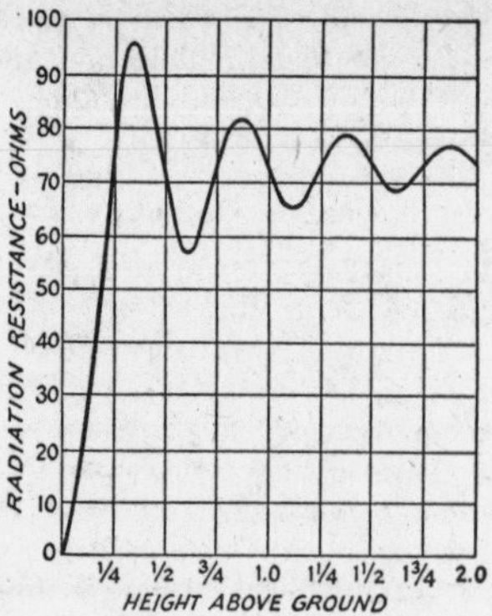

Fig. 21-2 — Theoretical curve of variation of radiation resistance for a very thin half-wave horizontal antenna as a function of height in wavelength above perfectly reflecting ground.

Choice of Polarization

Polarization of the transmitting antenna is generally unimportant on frequencies between 3.5 and 30 MHz, when considering sky-wave communications. However, the question of whether the antenna should be installed in a horizontal or vertical position deserves consideration for other reasons. A vertical half-wave or quarter-wave antenna will radiate equally well in all *horizontal* directions, so that it is substantially nondirectional, in the usual sense of the word. If installed horizontally, however, the antenna will tend to show directional effects, and will radiate best in the direction at right angles, or broadside, to the wire. The radiation in such a case will be *least* in the direction toward which the wire points.

The vertical angle of radiation also will be affected by the position of the antenna. If it were not for ground losses at high frequencies, the vertical antenna would be preferred because it would concentrate the radiation horizontally, and this low-angle radiation is preferable for practically all work. Another advantage to the use of a vertically polarized antenna, especially at 1.8, 3.5, and 7 MHz, is that local communications during night-time hours are improved. The vertical antenna is not as subject to signal fading as is the horizontal antenna.

THE HALF-WAVE ANTENNA

A fundamental form of antenna is a single wire whose length is approximately equal to half the transmitting wavelength. It is the unit from which many more-complex forms of antennas are constructed. It is known as a **dipole antenna.**

The length of a half-wave in space is:

$$\textit{Length}\text{ (feet)} = \frac{492}{\textit{Freq.}\text{ (MHz)}} \qquad \textbf{21-A}$$

The actual length of a half-wave antenna will not be exactly equal to the half-wave in space, but depends upon the thickness of the conductor in relation to the wavelength as shown in Fig. 21-3, where K is a factor that must be multiplied by the half wavelength in free space to obtain the resonant antenna length. An additional shortening effect occurs with wire antennas supported by insulators at the ends because of the capacitance added to the system by the insulators **(end effect).** The following formula is sufficiently accurate for wire antennas for frequencies up to 30 MHz:

$$\textit{Length of half-wave antenna}\text{ (feet)} = \frac{492 \times 0.95}{\textit{Freq.}\text{ (MHz)}} = \frac{468}{\textit{Freq.}\text{ MHz)}} \qquad \textbf{21-B}$$

Example: A half-wave antenna for 7150 kHz (7.15 MHz) is $\frac{468}{7.15} = 65.45$ feet, or 65 feet 5 inches.

Above 30 MHz the following formulas should be used, particularly for antennas constructed from rod or tubing. K is taken from Fig. 21-3.

$$\textit{Length of half-wave antenna}\text{ (feet)} = \frac{492 \times K}{\textit{Freq.}\text{ (MHz)}} \qquad \textbf{21-C}$$

$$\textit{or length}\text{ (inches)} = \frac{5905 \times K}{\textit{Freq.}\text{ (MHz)}} \qquad \textbf{21-D}$$

Example: Find the length of a half wavelength antenna at 28.7 MHz, if the antenna is made of 1/2-inch diameter tubing. At 28.7 MHz, a half wavelength in space is

$$\frac{492}{28.7} = 17.14 \text{ feet}$$

from Equation **21-A**. Ratio of half wavelength to conductor diameter (changing wavelength to inches) is

$$\frac{(17.14 \times 12)}{0.5} = 411$$

From Fig. 21-3, K = 0.97 for this ratio. The length of the antenna, from Equation **21-C**, is

$$\frac{(492 \times 0.97)}{28.7} = 16.63 \text{ feet}$$

or 16 feet 7 1/2 inches. The answer is obtained directly in inches by substitution of Equation **21-D**:

$$\frac{(5905 \times 0.97)}{28.7} = 199.6 \text{ inches.}$$

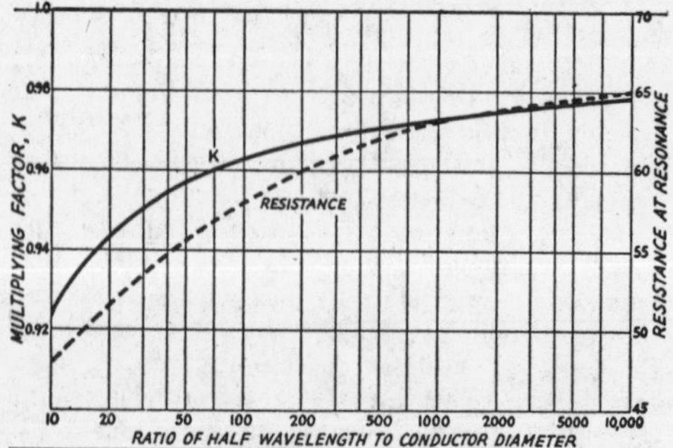

Fig. 21-3 — Effect of antenna diameter on length for half-wave resonance, shown as a multiplying factor, K, to be applied to the free-space half wavelength (Equation 21-A). The effect of conductor diameter on the center impedance also is shown.

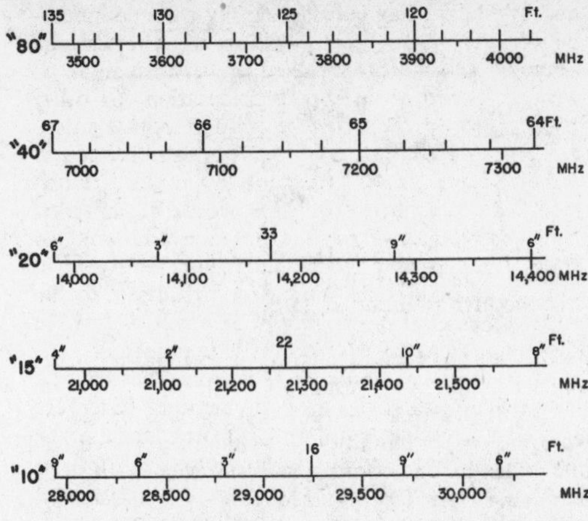

Fig. 21-4 — The above scales, based on Eq. 21-B, can be used to determine the length of a half-wave antenna of wire.

Current and Voltage Distribution

When power is fed to an antenna, the current and voltage vary along its length. The current is maximum **(loop)** at the center and nearly zero **(node)** at the ends, while the opposite is true of the rf voltage. The current does not actually reach zero at the current nodes, because of the end effect; similarly, the voltage is not zero at its node because of the resistance of the antenna, which consists of both the rf resistance of the wire (*ohmic resistance*) and the **radiation resistance.** The radiation resistance is an *equivalent* resistance, a convenient conception to indicate the radiation properties of an antenna. The radiation resistance is the equivalent resistance that would dissipate the power the antenna radiates, with a current flowing in it equal to the antenna current at a current loop (maximum). The ohmic resistance of a half-wavelength antenna is ordinarily small enough, compared with the radiation resistance, to be neglected for all practical purposes.

Impedance

The radiation resistance of an infinitely-thin half-wave antenna in free-space is about 73 ohms.

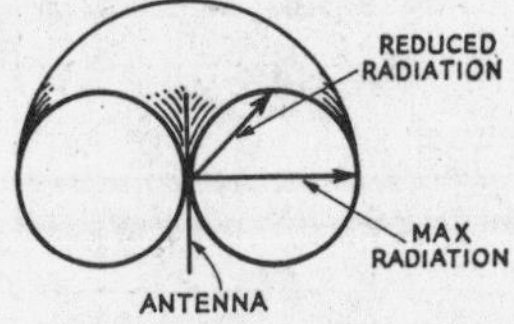

Fig. 21-5 — The free-space radiation pattern of a half-wave antenna. The antenna is shown in the vertical position, and the actual "doughnut" pattern is cut in half to show how the line from the center of the antenna to the surface of the pattern varies. In practice this pattern is modified by the height above ground and if the antenna is vertical or horizontal. Fig. 21-1 shows some of the effects of height on the vertical angele of radiation.

The value under practical conditions is commonly taken to be in the neighborhood of 60 to 70 ohms, although it varies with height in the manner of Fig. 21-2. It increases toward the ends. The actual value at the ends will depend on a number of factors, such as the height, the physical construction, the insulators at the ends, and the position with respect to ground.

Conductor Size

The impedance of the antenna also depends upon the diameter of the conductor in relation to the wavelength, as indicated in Fig. 21-3. If the diameter of the conductor is increased the capacitance per unit length increases and the inductance per unit length decreases. Since the radiation resistance is affected relatively little, the decreased L/C ratio causes the Q of the antenna to decrease, so that the resonance curve becomes less sharp. Hence, the antenna is capable of working over a wide frequency range. This effect is greater as the diameter is increased, and is a property of some importance at the very high frequencies where the wavelength is small.

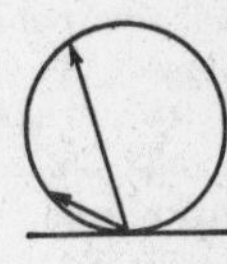

Fig. 21-6 — Illustrating the importance of vertical angle of radiation in determining antenna directional effects. Off the end, the radiation is greater at higher angles. Ground reflection is neglected in this drawing of the free-space pattern of a horizontal antenna.

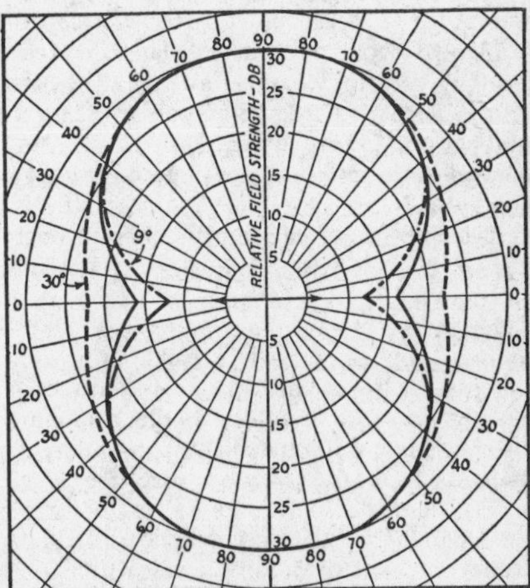

Fig. 21-7 — Horizontal pattern of a horizontal half-wave antenna at three vertical radiation angles. The solid line is relative radiation at 15 degrees. Dotted lines show deviation from the 15-degree pattern for angles of 9 and 30 degrees. The patterns are useful for shape only, since the amplitude will depend upon the height of the antenna above ground and the vertical angle considered. The patterns for all three angles have been proportioned to the same scale, but this does not mean that the maximum amplitudes necessarily will be the same. The arrow indicates the direction of the horizontal antenna wire.

Radiation Characteristics

The radiation from a dipole antenna is not uniform in all directions but varies with the angle with respect to the axis of the wire. It is most intense in directions perpendicular to the wire and zero along the direction of the wire, with intermediate values at intermediate angles. This is shown by the sketch of Fig. 21-5, which represents the radiation pattern in free space. The relative intensity of radiation is proportional to the length of a line drawn from the center of the figure to the perimeter. If the antenna is vertical, as shown, then the field strength will be uniform in all horizontal directions; if the antenna is horizontal, the relative field strength will depend upon the direction of the receiving point with respect to the direction of the antenna wire. The variation in radiation at various vertical angles from a half-wavelength horizontal antenna is indicated in Figs. 21-6 and 21-7.

FEEDING A DIPOLE ANTENNA

Since the impedance at the center of a dipole is in the vicinity of 70 ohms, it offers a good match for 75-ohm transmission lines. Several types are available on the market, with different power-handling capabilities. They can be connected in the center of the antenna, across a small strain insulator to provide a convenient connection point. Coaxial line should be used with a 1:1 balun transformer to assure symmetry. Direct feed (without a balun) is also acceptable, but may cause a slight skew in the radiation pattern. The transmission line should be run away at right angles to the antenna for at least one-quarter wavelength, if possible, to avoid current unbalance in the line caused by pickup from the antenna. The antenna length is calculated from Equation 21-B, for a half wavelength antenna. When No. 12 or No. 14 enameled wire is used for the antenna, as is generally the case, the length of the wire is the overall length measured from the loop through the insulator at each end. This is illustrated in Fig. 21-8.

The use of 75-ohm line results in a "flat" line over most of any amateur band. However, by making the half-wave antenna in a special manner, called the **two-wire** or **folded dipole**, a good match is offered for a 300-ohm line. Such an antenna is shown in Fig. 21-9. The open-wire line shown in Fig. 21-9 is made of No. 12 or No. 14 enameled wire, separated by lightweight spacers of Plexiglas or other material (it doesn't have to be a *low-loss* insulating material), and the spacing can be on the order of from 4 to 8 inches, depending upon what is convenient, and what the operating frequency is.

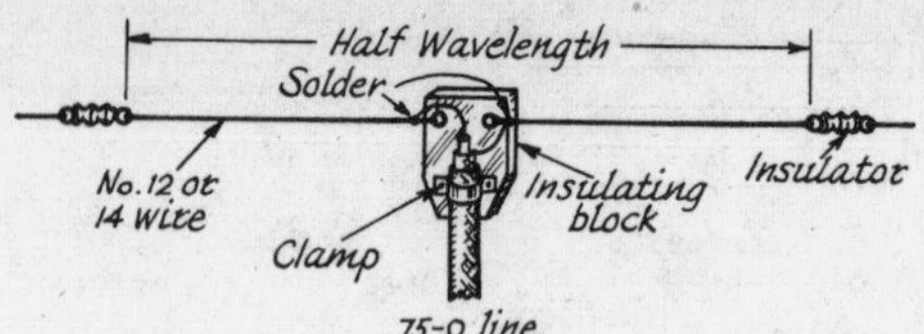

Fig. 21-8 — Construction of a dipole fed with 75-ohm line. The length of the antenna is calculated from Equation 21-B or Fig. 21-4.

At 14 MHz, 4-inch separation is satisfactory, and 8-inch spacing can be used at 3.5 MHz.

The half-wavelength antenna can also be made from the proper length of 300-ohm line, opened on one side in the center and connected to the feedline. After the wires have been soldered together, the joint can be strengthened by molding some of the excess insulating material (polyethylene) around the joint with a hot iron, or a suitable lightweight clamp of two pieces of Plexiglas can be devised.

Similar in some respects to the two-wire folded dipole, the three-wire folded dipole of Fig. 21-10 offers a good match for a 600-ohm line. It is favored by amateurs who prefer to use an open-wire line instead of the 300-ohm insulated line. The three wires of the antenna proper should all be of the same diameter.

Another method for offering a match to a 600-ohm open-wire line with a half wavelength antenna is shown in Fig. 21-11. The system is called a **delta match**. The line is "fanned" as it approaches the antenna, to have a gradually increasing impedance that equals the antenna impedance at the point of connection. The dimensions are fairly critical, but careful measurement before installing the antenna and matching section is generally all that is necessary. The length of the antenna, L, is calculated from Equation **21-B** or Fig. 21-4. The length of section C is computed from:

$$C\ (\text{feet}) = \frac{118}{\textit{Freq.}\ (\text{MHz})} \qquad \text{21-E}$$

The feeder clearance, E, is found from

$$E\ (\text{feet}) = \frac{148}{\textit{Freq.}\ (\text{MHz})} \qquad \text{21-F}$$

Example: For a frequency of 7.1 MHz, the length

$L = \frac{468}{7.1} = 65.91$ feet, or 65 feet 11 inches.

$C = \frac{118}{7.1} = 16.62$ feet, or 16 feet 7 inches.

$E = \frac{148}{7.1} = 20.84$ feet, or 20 feet 10 inches.

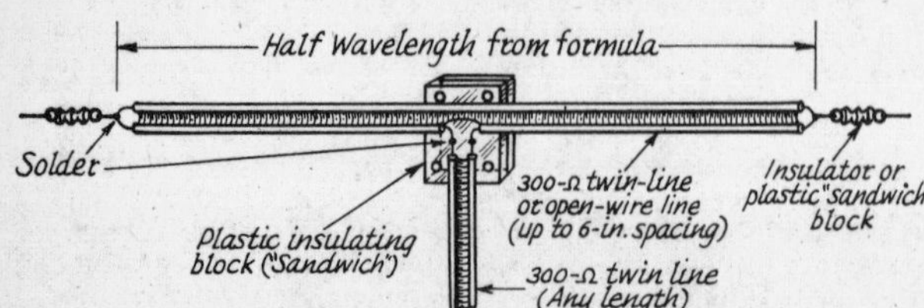

Fig. 21-9 — The construction of an open-wire or twin-line folded dipole fed with 300-ohm line. The length of the antenna is calculated from Equation 21-B or Fig. 21-4.

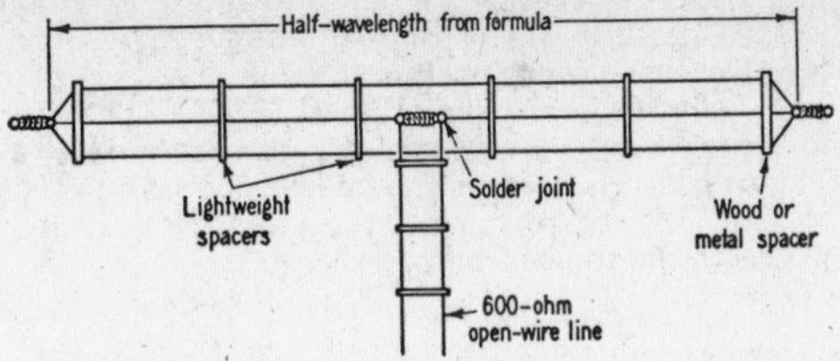

Fig. 21-10 – The construction of a 3-wire folded dipole is similar to that of the 2-wire folded dipole. The end spacers may have to be slightly stronger than the others because of the greater compression force on them. The length of the antenna is obtained from Equation 21-B or Fig. 21-4. A suitable line can be made from No. 14 wire spaced 5 inches, or from No. 12 wire spaced 6 inches.

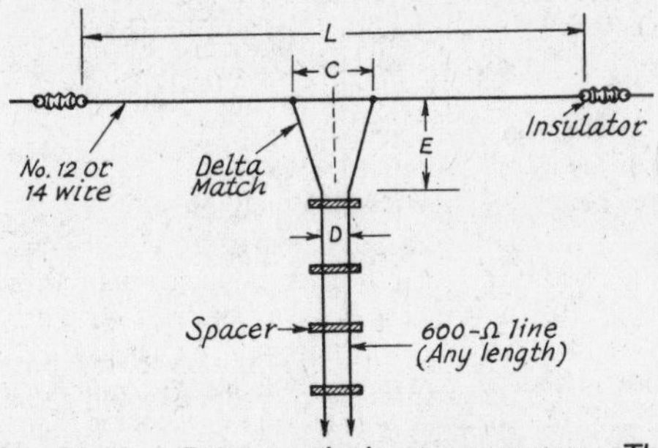

Fig. 21-11 – Delta-matched antenna systems. The dimensions, C, D, and E are found by formulas given in the text. It is important that the matching section, E, come straight away from the antenna.

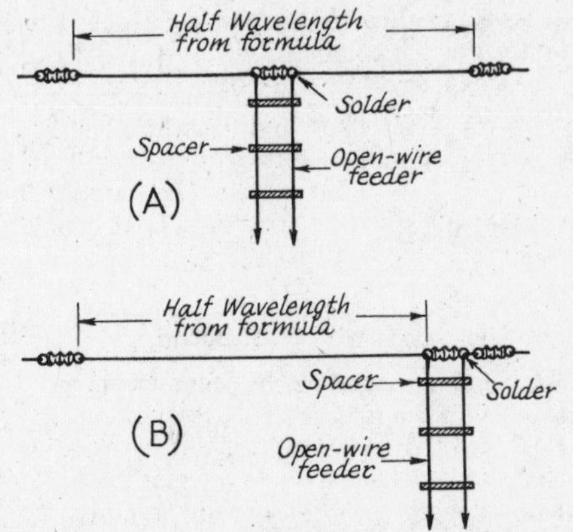

Fig. 21-12 – The half-wave antennas can be fed at the center or at one end with open-wire feeders. The length of the antennas can be computed from Equation 21-B or Fig. 21-4.

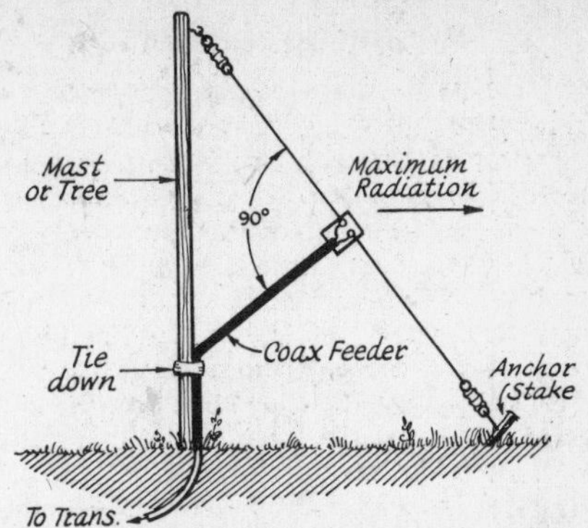

Fig. 21-13 – Method of supporting a half-wave dipole from a single upright such as a tree or wooden mast. Maximum directivity will be in the direction of the arrow, and the signal will be vertically polarized at a fairly low radiation angle. By having anchor stakes at different compass points, the directivity can be changed to favor different DX regions.

Since the equations hold only for 600-ohm line, it is important that the line be close to this value. This requires 5-inch spaced No. 14 wire, 6-inch spaced No. 12 wire, or 3 3/4-inch spaced No. 16 wire.

If a half-wavelength antenna is fed at the center with other than 75-ohm line, or if a two-wire dipole is fed with other than 300-ohm line, standing waves will appear on the line and coupling to the transmitter may become awkward for some line lengths, as described in Chapter 20. However, in many cases it is not convenient to feed the half-wave antenna with the correct line (as is the case where multiband operation of the same antenna is desired), and sometimes it is not convenient to feed the antenna at the center. Where multiband operation is desired (to be discussed later) or when the antenna must be fed at one end by a transmission line, an open-wire line of from 450 to 600 ohms impedance is generally used. The impedance at the end of a half-wavelength antenna is in the vicinity of several thousand ohms, and hence a standing-wave ratio of 4 or 5 is not unusual when the line is connected to the end of the antenna. It is advisable, therefore, to keep the losses in the line as low as possible. This requires the use of ceramic or Micalex feeder spacers, if any appreciable power is used. For low-power installations in dry climates, dry wood spacers boiled in paraffin are satisfactory. Mechanical details of half wavelength antennas fed with open-wire lines are given in Fig. 21-12.

THE "INVERTED V" ANTENNA

A popular nondirectional antenna is the so-called "inverted V" or "drooping doublet." Its principal advantages are that it requires but one supporting structure, and that it exhibits more or less omnidirectional radiation characteristics when cut for a single band. The multiband version of Fig. 21-14 is somewhat directional above 7 MHz, off the ends (not broadside) of the antenna. This is because the legs of the "V" are long in terms of wavelength at 14, 21 and 28 MHz. The antenna offers a good compromise between vertical and horizontal polarization, thus making it effective for local as well as DX communications. Its low-angle radiation compares favorably with that of a full-

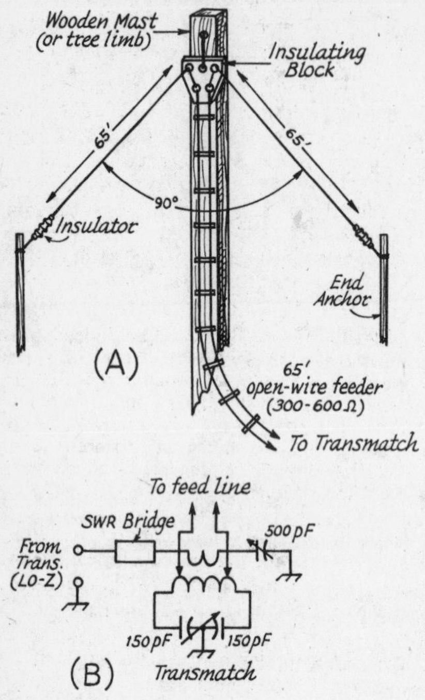

Fig. 21-14 — Details for an Inverted-V antenna (sometimes called a "drooping doublet"). At A, a wooden mast supports the antenna at its center. Open-wire feeders permit the antenna to be used for multiband operation. If this is done, a Transmatch of the type shown at B should be used to tune the system to resonance, and to match the feeder to the transmitter and receiver.

size one quarter wavelength vertical worked against ground. When fed as shown in Fig. 21-14 it serves as an excellent multiband antenna.

For single-band operation the "V" is cut to the same length as a half-wavelength doublet, and is fed with 52-ohm coaxial line. Its center (feed point) should be as high above ground as possible, preferably one-quarter wavelength or more at the operating frequency. The apex angle should be as close to 90 degrees as possible, but in practice any angle between 90 and 120 degrees provides good results. Less than a 90-degree angle causes excessive cancellation of the signal, and should be avoided.

Though some operators have reported satisfactory results when supporting the "V" from a metal mast or tower, it is best to use a wooden mast to keep the field of the antenna unobstructed. Good results can be had by supporting the center of the antenna from a limb on a tall tree, provided the area below the limb is completely open.

Single-band, coax-fed inverted Vs will normally require some pruning to make them resonant at the desired frequency. The standard doublet formula is recommended for a starting point, but because the ends of the "V" are normally in close proximity to ground this antenna will be slightly shorter than a horizontal dipole. No formula can be given because of the variations in the ground properties in different areas. Also, the actual height above ground in a particular installation, plus the proximity of the ends of the antenna to nearby objects, will have a marked effect upon resonance. The best way to tune the antenna is to insert an SWR bridge in the coax feed line and prune an inch at a time off each end of the "V" until the lowest SWR is obtained.

LONG-WIRE ANTENNAS

An antenna is a long wire only when it is long *in terms of wavelength.* An antenna, simply because it is a long piece of wire is not a long-wire antenna. Space permitting, these antennas are effective for DX work, and when erected high above ground offer considerable power gain over a dipole. The longer the antenna, the greater the gain. Maximum directivity occurs off the ends of the antenna, and not off the broad side of it. A long-wire antenna, unless terminated at the far end in its characteristic impedance by a noninductive resistance, is bidirectional. A terminated long wire is directional only off the terminated end. This antenna radiates minor lobes at many wave angles in the vertical and horizontal planes. The longer the wire, the greater and more complex the lobes become. It is not uncommon to find a long-wire antenna outperforming a beam antenna on DX contacts under certain propagation conditions. This is because it can respond to a variety of incoming wave angles (and can radiate a signal in a like manner), which is not the case with a well-designed beam-type antenna.

Long-Wire Characteristics

An antenna will be resonant so long as an integral number of standing waves of current and voltage can exist along its length; in other words, so long as its length is some integral multiple of a half wavelength.

Current and Voltage Distribution

Fig. 21-15 shows the current and voltage distribution along a wire operating at its fundamental frequency (where its length is equal to a half wavelength) and at its second, third, and fourth harmonics. For example, if the fundamental frequency of the antenna is 7 MHz, the current and voltage distribution will be as shown at A. The same antenna excited at 14 MHz would have current and voltage distribution as shown at B. At 21 MHz, the third harmonic of 7 MHz, the current and voltage distribution would be as in C; and at 28 MHz, the fourth harmonic, as in D. The number of the harmonic is the number of half waves

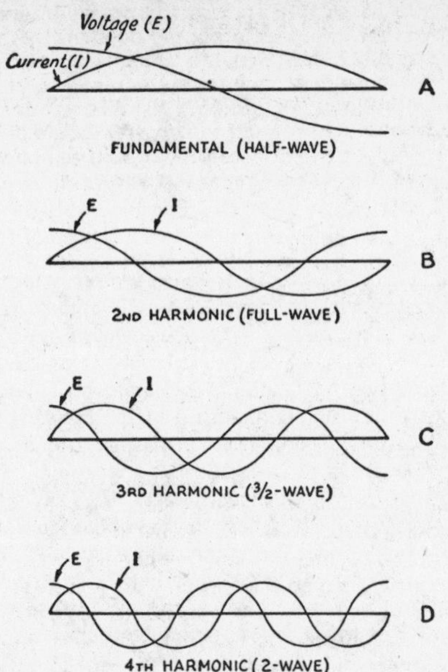

Fig. 21-15 – Standing-wave current and voltage distribution along an antenna when it is operated at various harmonics of its fundamental resonant frequency.

contained in the antenna at the particular operating frequency.

The polarity of current or voltage in each standing wave is opposite to that in the adjacent standing waves. This is shown in the figure by drawing the current and voltage curves successively above and below the antenna (taken as a zero reference line), to indicate that the polarity reverses when the current or voltage goes through zero. Currents flowing in the same direction are *in phase*; in opposite directions, *out of phase.*

Physical Lengths

The length of a long-wire antenna is not an exact multiple of that of a half-wave antenna because the end effects operate only on the end sections of the antenna; in other parts of the wire these effects are absent, and the wire length is approximately that of an equivalent portion of the wave in space. The formula for the length of a long-wire antenna, therefore, is

$$Length\ (\text{feet}) = \frac{492\,(N-0.05)}{Freq.\ (\text{MHz})} \qquad \text{21-G}$$

where N is the number of *half*-waves on the antenna.

Example: An antenna 4 half-waves long at 14.2 MHz would be

$$\frac{492\,(4-0.05)}{14.2} = \frac{492 \times 3.95}{14.2}$$

= 136.7 feet, or 136 feet 8 inches

It is apparent that an antenna cut as a half wave for a given frequency will be slightly off resonance at exactly twice that frequency (the second harmonc), because of the decreased influence of the end effects when the antenna is more than one-half wavelength long. The effect is not very important, except for a possible unbalance in the feeder system and consequent radiation from the feed line. If the antenna is fed in the exact center, no unbalance will occur at any frequency, but end-fed systems will show an unbalance on all but one frequency in each harmonic range.

Impedance and Power Gain

The radiation resistance as measured at a current loop becomes higher as the antenna length is increased. Also, a long-wire antenna radiates more power in its most favorable direction than does a half-wave antenna in its most favorable direction. This power gain is secured at the expense of radiation in other directions. Fig. 21-16 shows how the radiation resistance and the power in the lobe of maximum radiation vary with the antenna length.

Directional Characteristics

As the wire is made longer in terms of the number of half wavelengths, the directional effects change. Instead of the "doughnut" pattern of the half-wave antenna, the directional characteristic splits up into "lobes" which make various angles with the wire. In general, as the length of the wire is increased the direction in which maximum radiation occurs tends to approach the line of the antenna itself.

Methods of Feeding

In a long-wire antenna, the currents in adjacent half-wave sections must be out of phase, as shown in Fig. 21-15. The feeder system must not upset this phase relationship. This is satisfied by feeding the antenna at either end or at any current loop. A two-wire feeder cannot be inserted at a current node, however, because this invariably brings the currents in two adjacent half-wave sections in phase. A long-wire antenna is usually made a half wavelength at the lowest frequency and fed at the end.

MULTIBAND ANTENNAS

One of the most simple antenna systems for multiband use is one which is a half wavelength long at the lowest operating frequency, and which is fed either at the center, or at one end with open-wire tuned feeders, Fig. 21-12. The center-fed system is superior to the end-fed type in that it will have less feeder radiation, but the end-fed variety is often more practical from an installation viewpoint. The center-fed antenna will not have the same radiation pattern as an end-fed one of the same length, except on frequencies where the length of the antenna is a half wavelength. The end-fed antenna acts like a long-wire antenna on all bands (for which it is longer than a half wavelength), but the center-fed one acts like two antennas of half that length fed in phase. For

TABLE 21-I

Multiband Tuned-Line-Fed Antennas

Antenna Length (Ft.)	*Feeder Length (Ft.)*	*Band*	*Type of Coupling Circuit*
With end feed:			
135	45	3.5–21	Series
		28	Parallel
67	45	7–21	Series
		28	Parallel
With center feed:			
135	42	3.5–21	Parallel
		28	Series
135	77 1/2	3.5–28	Parallel
67	42 1/2	3.5	Series
		7–28	Parallel
67	65 1/2	3.5,14,28	Parallel
		7,21	Series

Antenna lengths for end-fed antennas are approximate and should be cut to formula length at favorite operating frequency.

Where parallel tuning is specified, it will be necessary in some cases to tap in from the ends of the coil for proper loading – see Chapter 20 for examples of antenna couplers.

example, if a full-wavelength antenna is fed at one end, it will have a radiation pattern somewhat like a four-leaf clover. With either of these multiband antennas the SWR will never be 1, but these antennas will be efficient provided low-loss tuned feeders are used.

Since multiband operation of an antenna does not permit matching of the feed line, some attention should be paid to the length of the feed line if convenient transmitter-coupling arrangements are to be obtained. Table 21-I gives some suggested antenna and feeder length for multiband operation. In general, the length of the feed line can be other than that indicated, but the type of coupling circuit may change.

Since open-wire line is recommended for this antenna, TV-type (open-wire) 300- or 450-ohm feeders are satisfactory. Home made open-wire line can be made up from lengths of No. 14 or 12 soft-drawn copper wire. The spacers can be made from Plexiglas strips or similar low-loss material. Some amateurs have had success using plastic hair curlers or plastic clothespins. Any line spacing from 1 to 6 inches will give satisfactory results since the line impedance is not an important consideration with this antenna.

If antenna space is at a premium, a shortened version of the multiband antenna can be erected. The feeders are lengthened, and the flat-top portion is shortened as shown in Fig. 21-17. The antenna can be as short as a quarter wavelength long, but will still radiate fairly well if tuned to resonance. This method will not give as good results as the full-size version, but will still be useful. A Transmatch tuner of the type described in Chapter 20 can be used with this system.

MULTIBAND OPERATION WITH COAXIAL LINE FEED

The proper use of coaxial line requires that the standing-wave ratio be held to a low value, preferably below 3:1. Since the impedance of an ordinary antenna changes widely from band to band, it is not possible to feed a simple antenna with coaxial line and use it on a number of bands without tricks of some kind. One exception to this is the use of 75-ohm coaxial line to feed a 7-MHz half-wave antenna, as in Fig. 21-18; this antenna can also be used on 21 MHz and the SWR in the line will not run too high.

However, the diagram shows a separate dipole element for 21-MHz use. Though the 7-MHz element will operate as a 1 1/2 wavelength doublet on 21 MHz, and will present a low impedance feed point at its center, some may wish to add a separate dipole for 21-MHz operation. This antenna is capable of radiating harmonics from the transmitter, so it is important to make sure the transmitter output is clean. A coax-to-coax type antenna coupler can also be installed at the transmitter end to help reduce harmonic radiation from the antenna.

A MULTIBAND "TRAP" ANTENNA

Another method of obtaining multiband operation from a single antenna, with a single feed line, is the use of parallel-tuned traps in each leg of a two-wire doublet. If the traps are installed in the right points of the antenna they "divorce" the remainder of the antenna from the center portion as the transmitter is changed to operate a higher

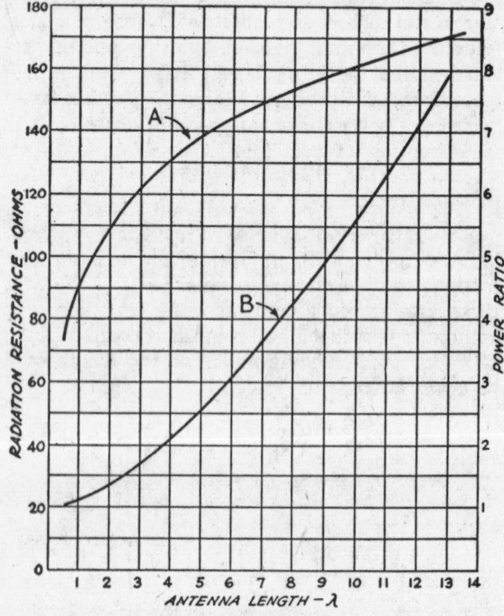

Fig. 21-16 – Curve A shows variation in radiation resistance with antenna length. Curve B shows power in lobes of maximum radiation for long-wire antennas as a ratio to the maximum radiation for a half-wave antenna.

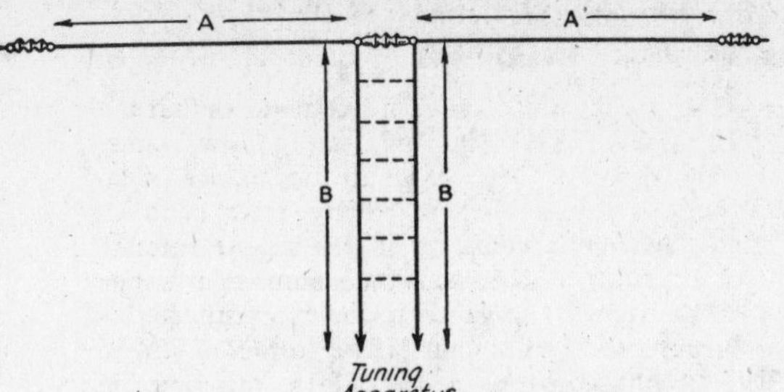

Fig. 21-17 – Practical arrangements of a shortened antenna. When the total length, A + B + B + A, is the same as the antenna length plus twice the feeder length of the center-fed antennas of Table 21-I, the same type of coupling circuit will be used. When the feeder length or antenna length, or both, makes the sum different, the type of coupling circuit may be different but the effectiveness of the antenna is not changed, unless A + A is less than a quarter wavelength.

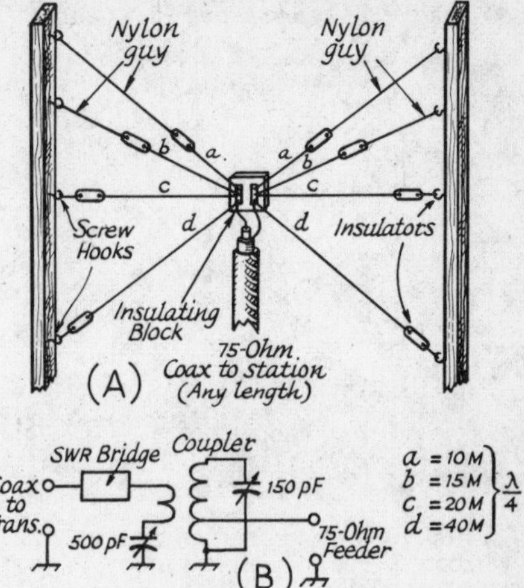

Fig. 21-18 – Illustration of a multiband coax-fed antenna. Wooden support poles are recommended so that they will not interfere with the radiation pattern of the antenna. At B, a representative diagram of a coax-to-coax coupler that will reduce harmonic radiation from the system. It should be installed in the operating room, near the transmitter, and adjusted for a 1:1 SWR.

band. On the lowest operating band the traps act as loading inductors, thus allowing a shorter overall length for the doublet than would be possible if it were cut for use without the traps.

The trap-antenna concept has been adopted by several manufacturers who produce multiband beam antennas, multiband doublets, and vertical antennas for several bands of operation.

The antenna of Fig. 21-19 may be of interest to those amateurs not having sufficient room to erect a full-size 80-meter doublet. The overall length of this system is 106 feet. If need be, the ends can be bent slightly downward so that the horizontal portion will occupy even less space. It is best, however, to keep the entire antenna horizontal if possible. The antenna is fed with 75-ohm coax, or balanced line of the same impedance. The latter is recommended, or system balance can be enhanced by using a 1:1 balun transformer at the feed point if coaxial line is used. This antenna is an adaptation of the W3DZZ design described in the *ARRL Antenna Book.*

As shown in Fig. 21-20, each trap is literally built around a "strain" insulator. With this insulator, the hole at one end is at right angles to the hole at the opposite end, and the wires are fastened as illustrated in Fig. 21-21. This style of insulator has greater compressive strength than tensile strength and will not permit the antenna to fall should the insulator break. There is plenty of space inside the inductor to install the insulator and the trap capacitor. The plastic protective covers are not essential, but are used to protect the traps from ice, snow, and soot which could cause a deterioration in performance.

Electrically, each trap consists of a 50-pF capacitor which is shunted by a 10-μH inductor. A Centralab 850S-50Z capacitor is used. It is rated at 7500 volts, and should safely handle a kilowatt. Miniductor coil stock is used for the inductor. Those wishing to optimize the antenna for a specific portion of the 40-meter band can experimentally adjust the number of turns in the trap coil for resonance in the desired segment. Similarly, the end sections of the dipole can be adjusted for lowest SWR in the portion of the 80-meter band most favored. With the dimensions given in Fig. 21-19, the antenna performs well from 3.5 to 30 MHz. The lowest SWR on 80

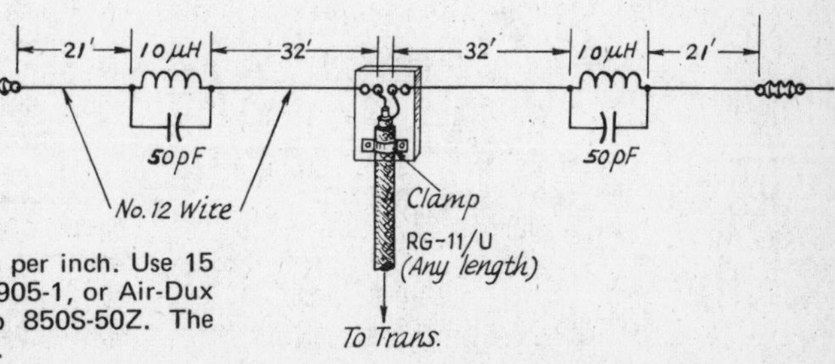

Fig. 21-19 – Sketch of a trap dipole for use on 80 through 10 meters. SWR on all of the bands is less than 2.5:1. With the dimensions given here the SWR rises at each end of the 80-meter band, but is approximately 1.5:1 at the center of the band. The 10-μH trap coils consist of 15 turns No. 12 wire, 2 1/2 inches in diameter, 6 turns per inch. Use 15 turns from Polycoils No. 1774, B&W 3905-1, or Air-Dux 2006T. Trap capacitors are Centralab 850S-50Z. The traps are tuned to resonance at 7.1 MHz.

Fig. 21-20 – Photo of a typical trap. The unit shown here is cut for resonance at 14 MHz, but construction techniques are the same as for the traps used in the antenna of Fig. 21-19. A weatherproof cover can be made from plastic tubing, sheeting which is heated and formed, or from a plastic refrigerator container. The capacitor and strain insulator are inside the coil.

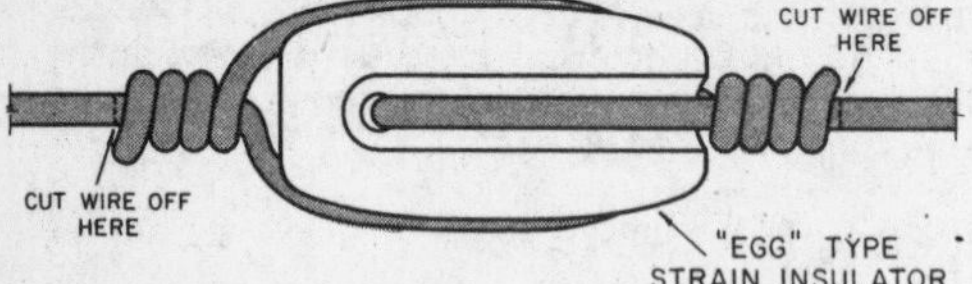

Fig. 21-21 – Method of connecting the antenna wire to the strain insulator. The antenna wire is cut off close to the wrap.

meters occurs at midband. SWR on all other bands is less than 2.5 to 1, an acceptable figure for all but the most critical operator. Most modern-day transmitters will load into this antenna without difficulty.

Trap Adjustment

As a preliminary step, loops of No. 12 wire are fitted to one of the egg insulators in the normal manner (see Fig. 21-21), except that after the wraps are made, the end leads are snipped off close to the wraps. A capacitor is then placed in position and bridged with short leads across the insulator and soldered sufficiently to provide temporary support. The combination is then slipped inside about 10 turns of the inductor, one end of which should be soldered to an insulator-capacitor lead. Adjustment to the resonant frequency can now proceed, using a grid-dip meter.

Coupling between the GDO and the trap should be very loose. To assure accuracy, the station receiver should be used to check the GDO frequency. The inductance should be reduced 1/4 turn at a time. If one is careful, the resonant frequency can easily be set to within a few kilohertz of the chosen figure.

The reason for snipping the end leads close to the wraps and the inclusion of the loops through the egg insulator soon becomes apparent. The resonant frequency of the capacitor and inductor alone is reduced about 10 kHz per inch of end lead length and about 150 kHz by the insulator loops. The latter add approximately 2 pF to the fixed capacitor value.

Assembly

Having determined the exact number of inductor turns, the trap is taken apart and reassembled with leads of any convenient length. One may, of course, connect the entire lengths of the antenna sections to the trap at this time, if desired. But, if more convenient, a foot or two of wire can be fastened and the remaining lengths soldered on just before the antenna is raised.

The protective covers are most readily formed by wrapping two turns (plus an overlap of 1/2 inch) of 0.020-inch polystyrene or Lucite sheeting around a 3-inch plastic disk held at the center of the cylinder so formed. The length of the cover should be about 4 inches. A very small amount of plastic solvent (a cohesive cement that actually softens the plastic surfaces) should then be applied under the edge of the overlap and the joint held firmly for about two minutes to insure a strong, tight seal. The disk is pushed out and the inner seam of the sheeting sealed.

The trap is then placed in the plastic cylinder and the end disks marked where the antenna wires are to pass through. After drilling these holes, the disks are slipped over the leads, pressed into the ends of the cylinder and a small amount of solvent applied to the periphery to obtain a good seal.

Some air can flow in and out of the trap through the antenna-wire holes, and this will prevent the accumulation of condensation.

AN END-FED HERTZ

One of the more simple multiband antennas is the end-fed Hertz of Fig. 21-22. It consists of an end-fed length of No. 12 wire, 130 feet long. This type of antenna performs in the same manner as the end-fed half-wave system of Fig. 21-12B, but has no feeder. One end of the wire connects directly into an L-network impedance matcher, as shown in the diagram. This type of antenna is very convenient for those who have their stations on the top floor of the house, thus enabling the user to bring one end of the antenna in through a window and to the coupler. Ideally, the entire antenna should be in a horizontal plane for best results. However, either end can be bent to make the system fit into whatever space is available. First-floor dwellers can drop the fed end of the wire to the window of the radio room, as shown in Fig. 21-22A. Or, the wire can be kept straight and rise diagonally to the support at the far end. Height is important with antennas of this type, so an effort should be made to get the system as high above ground as possible, and clear of power lines and other structures.

This antenna is intended for operation from 3.5 to 28 MHz. A coupler of the kind shown in Fig. 21-43 (L-Network Coupler) will match the antenna on all of the hf amateur bands mentioned. It will also perform well as an end-fed quarter wavelength on 1.8 MHz if the reactance is tuned out by means

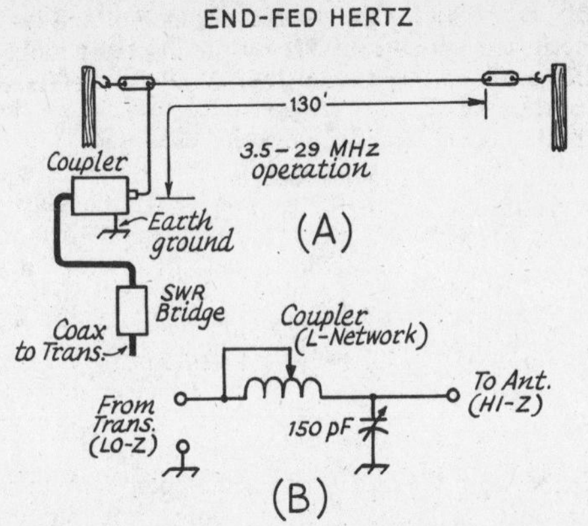

END-FED HERTZ

Fig. 21-22 – Diagram of an end-fed Hertz. It is cut for the lowest desired operating frequency (1/2 wavelength), and is operated on its harmonic frequencies on the remaining bands above. An L-network is used to match it to 50- or 75-ohm unbalanced transmitter terminals. At B, schematic representation of an L-network tuner. The value of L and C is adjusted until a 1:1 match is obtained.

of a 1500-pF series variable capacitor. A good earth ground will be needed for proper operation on 1.8 MHz. For hf-band use, a good earth ground is also important in order to keep unwanted rf voltages from appearing on the transmitter and receiver chassis. No one wants (or needs) a "hot" key or microphone. Sometimes a good water-pipe ground is sufficient for preventing rf potentials on the equipment.

It must be remembered that the ends of this antenna are voltage points (high impedance), and bringing the end of the antenna into the "shack" can often introduce rf into the equipment as mentioned. During phone operation the rf can get into the microphone circuit and cause howling and hum if the ground system is not used. Similarly, the operation of some electronic keyers can be made erratic by the introduction of rf chassis currents. The operator, therefore, may wish to locate the tuner at the window and have the ham station across the room at some distant point. If this is done, coaxial cable can be used to connect the station to the tuner. Operation with this antenna at W1CKK has been without problems for nearly three years, operating all bands with a kilowatt of power. The fed end of the wire is three feet from the station equipment. A water pipe and an earth ground are used. The L network provides a 1:1 match on all of the bands, and DX operation has been quite successful on the 20-, 15- and 10-meter bands. While using a parallel-tuned antenna coupler, successful 6- and 2-meter operation has been realized.

It should be remembered that the antenna will perform as a long wire on those bands above 3.5 MHz. At the higher end of the hf range – particularly 15 and 10 meters – the antenna will tend to be directional off its ends (bidirectional), and will begin to have some gain. It exhibits more or less omnidirectional characteristics on 7 and 14 MHz, the pattern being somewhat like the shape of a four-leaf clover. There will not be much directivity on 3.5 MHz unless the antenna is at least a half wavelength above ground at that frequency.

A BROAD-BAND DIPOLE

Most untuned doublet antennas are not broad enough to provide a low SWR across an entire amateur band. This is a particularly troublesome situation on the 80- and 40-meter bands. The antenna of Fig. 21-23, sometimes called a "double-bazooka" antenna, was developed by the staff of M.I.T. for radar use, and was later popularized by W8TV for amateur use (*QST*, July 1968). An 80-meter version of this system, cut for

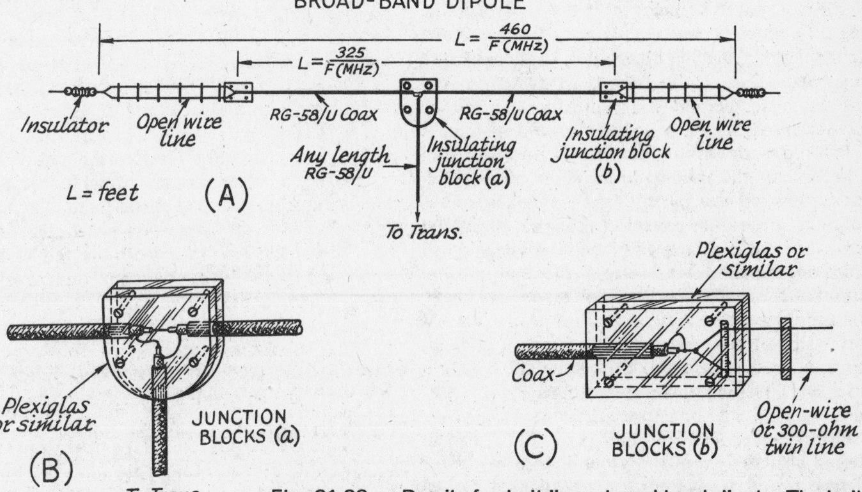

Fig. 21-23 – Details for building a broad-band dipole. The builder may choose to employ other methods for joining the sections, but the illustrations at B and C represent one of the better, more secure techniques.

3.7 MHz, provides an SWR of less than 2:1 across the entire band, and shows a 1:1 reading at 3.7 MHz. SWR at 3.5 MHz is 1.7:1, and is 1.9:1 at 4 MHz.

The antenna consists of a half-wavelength section of coax line with the sheath opened at the center and the feed line attached to the open ends of the sheath. The *outside* conductor of the coax thus acts as a half-wave dipole, in combination with the open-wire end sections of the antenna. The inside sections, which *do not* radiate, are quarter-wave shorted stubs which present a very high resistive impedance to the feed point at resonance. At frequencies off resonance the stub reactance changes in such a way as to tend to cancel the antenna reactance, thus increasing its bandwidth. This antenna can be cut for any operating frequency, including that of the 160-meter band. Formulas are given in Fig. 21-23. RG-58/U coax line is capable of handling a full kilowatt from the transmitter with the SWR figures given earlier. Details are given for making up the junction blocks where connections are made. Other construction techniques are possible, and this will be pretty much up to the builder. If the plastic blocks of Fig. 21-23 are used, their inner surfaces can be grooved to provide a snug fit for the coax cables when the two halves are bolted together. After assembly, the mating outer surfaces of the junction blocks can be sealed with epoxy cement to assure a weatherproof bond. This antenna can be mounted from a single center support and used as an "inverted V" if desired. Single-wire end sections can be substituted for the open-wire stubs, but the open-wire sections contribute to the antenna's broadband characteristics.

VERTICAL ANTENNAS

A vertical quarter-wavelength antenna is often used in the lower-frequency amateur bands to obtain low-angle radiation. It is also used when there isn't enough room for the supports for a horizontal antenna. For maximum effectiveness it should be located free of nearby objects and it should be operated in conjunction with a good ground system, but it is still worth trying where these ideal conditions cannot be obtained.

Four typical examples and suggested methods for feeding a vertical antenna are shown in Fig. 21-24. The antenna may be wire or tubing supported by wood or insulated guy wires. When tubing is used for the antenna, or when guy wires (broken up by insulators) are used to reinforce the structure, the length given by the formula is likely to be long by a few percent. A check of the standing-wave ratio on the line will indicate the frequency at which the SWR is minimum, and the antenna length can be adjusted accordingly.

A good ground connection is necessary for the most effective operation of a vertical antenna (other than the ground-plane type). In some cases a short connection to the cold-water system of the house will be adequate. But maximum performance usually demands a separate ground system. A single 4- to 6-foot ground rod driven into the earth at the base of the antenna is usually not sufficient, unless the soil has exceptional conductivity. A minimum ground system that can be depended upon is 6 to 12 quarter-wavelength radials laid out as the spokes of a wheel from the base of the antenna. These radials can be made of heavy aluminum wire, of the type used for grounding TV antennas, buried at least 6 inches in the ground. This is normally done by slitting the earth with a spade and pushing the wire into the slot, after which the earth can be tamped down.

The examples shown in Fig. 21-24 all require an antenna insulated from the ground, to provide for the feed point. A *grounded* tower or pipe can be used as a radiator by employing "shunt feed," which consists of tapping the inner conductor of the coaxial-line feed up on the tower until the best match is obtained, in much the same manner as the "gamma match" (described later) is used on a horizontal element. If the antenna is not an electrical quarter wavelength long, it is necessary to tune out the reactance by adding capacitance or inductance between the coaxial line and the shunting conductor. A metal tower supporting a TV antenna or rotary beam can be shunt fed only if all of the wires and leads from the supported antenna run down the center of the tower and underground away from the tower.

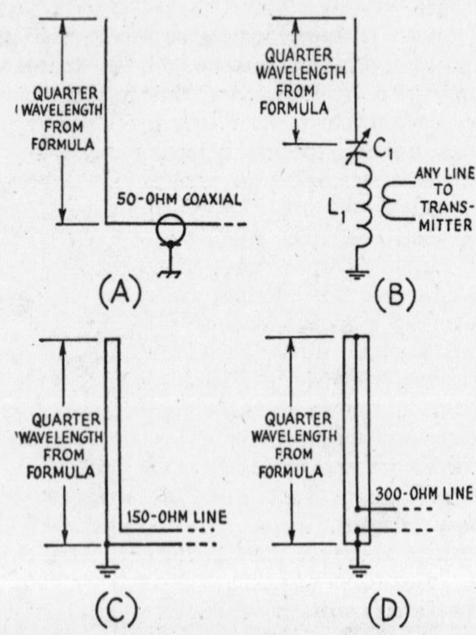

Fig. 21-24 — A quarter-wavelength antenna can be fed directly with 50-ohm coaxial line (A), with a low standing-wave ratio, or a coupling network can be used (B) that will permit a line of any impedance to be used. In (B), L1 and C1 should resonate to the operating frequency and L1 should be larger than is normally used in a plate tank circuit at the same frequency. By using multiwire antennas, the quarter-wave vertical can be fed with (C) 150- or (D) 300-ohm line.

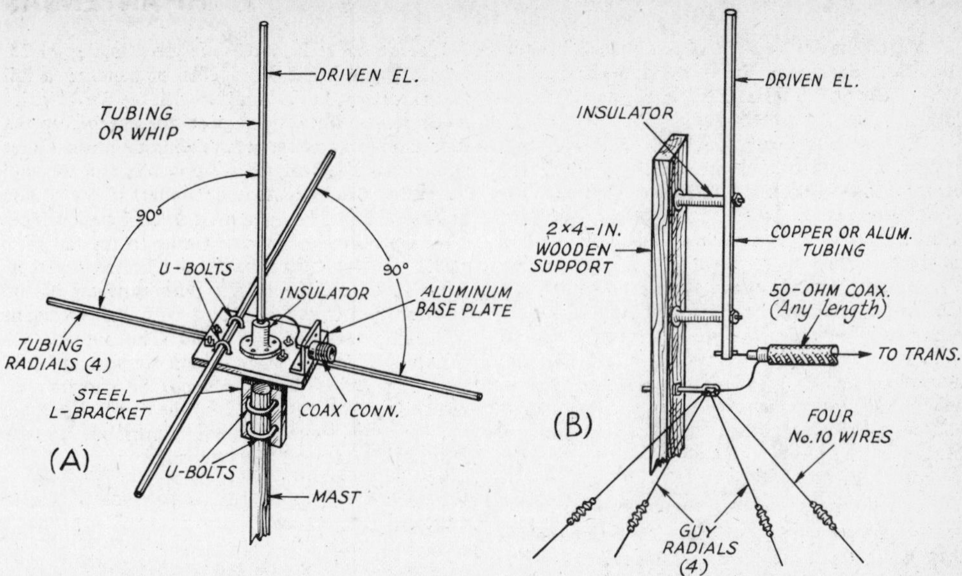

Fig. 21-25 — All-metal construction of a vertical ground-plane antenna can be effected as shown at A. The driven element is insulated from the remainder of the system, but the tubing radials are common to the mounting plate, and to one another. The outer conductor of the coax connects to the base plate and radials. The center conductor of the feed line attaches to the base of the driven element with as short a lead as possible. If a metal mast is used, it, too, can be common to the base plate and radials. At B, the radials are made of No. 10 wire (approximately 5 percent longer than the resonant vertical element) and are used as guy wires. Drooping the wires at a 45-degree angle raises the feed-point impedance to approximately 50 ohms for direct connection to RG-8/U.

THE GROUND-PLANE ANTENNA

A ground-plane antenna is a vertical quarter-wavelength antenna using an artificial metallic ground, usually consisting of four rods or wires perpendicular to the antenna and extending radially from its base, Fig. 21-25. Unlike the quarter-wavelength vertical antennas without an artificial ground, the ground-plane antenna will give low-angle radiation regardless of the height above actual ground. However, to be a true ground-plane antenna, the plane of the radials should be at least a quarter-wavelength above ground. Despite this one limitation, the antenna is useful for DX work in any band below 30 MHz.

The vertical portion of the ground-plane antenna can be made of self-supported aluminum tubing, or a top-supported wire, depending upon the necessary length and the available supports. The radials are also made of tubing or heavy wire depending upon the available supports and necessary lengths. They need not be exactly symmetrical about the base of the vertical portion.

The radiation resistance of a ground-plane antenna varies with the diameter of the vertical element. The radiation resistance is usually in the vicinity of 30 ohms, and the antenna can be fed with 75-ohm coaxial line with a quarter-wavelength section of 50-ohm line between line and antenna. For multiband operation, a ground-plane antenna can be fed with tuned open-wire line, or the vertical section can be quarter-wavelength pieces for each band. The radials should be a quarter wavelength at the lowest frequency.

Matching by Length Adjustment

The radiation resistance as measured at the base of a ground-plane antenna also changes as a function of the length of the radiating element. It is possible to choose a length such that the base radiation resistance will equal the characteristic impedance (Zo) of the transmission line to be used. The lengths of most interest are a little over 100 degrees (0.28 wavelength), where the resistance is approximately 52 ohms, and about 113 degrees (0.31 wavelength), where the resistance is 75 ohms, to match the two common types of coaxial line. These lengths are quite practicable for ground-plane antennas for 14 MHz and higher frequencies. The lengths in degrees as given above do not require any correction for length/diameter ratio; i.e., they are free-space lengths.

Since the antenna is not resonant at these lengths, its input impedance will be reactive as well as resistive. The reactance must be tuned out in order to make the line see a purely resistive load equal to its characteristic impedance. This can be done with a *series capacitor* of the proper value, when the lengths given above are used. The approximate value of capacitive reactance required, for antennas of typical length/diameter ratio, is about 100 ohms for the 52-ohm case and about 175 ohms for the 75-ohm case. The corresponding capacitance values for the frequency in question can be determined from appropriate charts or by equation. Variable capacitors of sufficient range may be used and adjustment made for the lowest SWR.

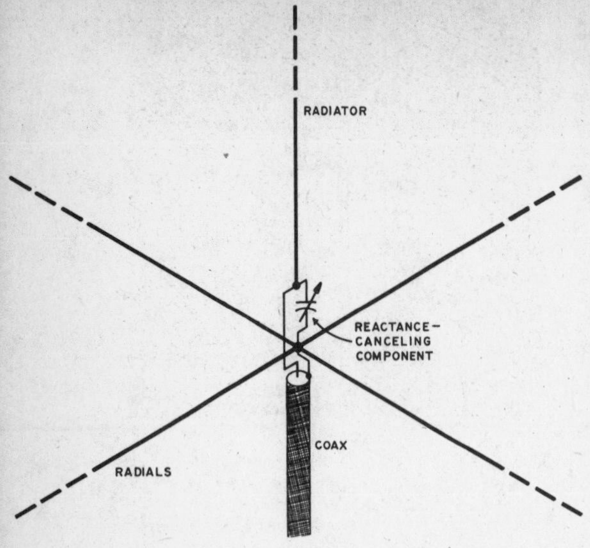

Fig. 21-26 — Matching to ground-plane antenna with shunt reactance. If the length of the radiator (but not the radials) is slightly more than that required for resonance, a capacitive shunt will provide a match to either 52- or 75-ohm line, depending on the exact radiator length. Similarly, a shorter-than-resonant radiator length may be used with a shunt inductor to offer a 52- or 75-ohm match.

From a practical construction standpoint it may be preferable to connect the reactance-canceling component in parallel or shunt with the base feed point, rather than in series with the radiating element. If a capacitor is used, for example, this would eliminate the requirement for insulating its frame from the supporting structure, as may be seen from Fig. 21-26. To obtain a match to 52- or 75-ohm line, radiator lengths must be different than those given above when the reactance-canceling component is shunt connected, however. As a matter of fact, there are *two* lengths where a match may be obtained for 52-ohm line, and *two* lengths for matching 75-ohm line. One of these two lengths for either impedance is somewhat less than that required for resonance. This results in the base feed point being capacitive, therefore requiring a shunt inductor for a resistive line termination. The other length is somewhat longer than that for resonance, requiring a shunt capacitor. So far as radiation is concerned, one is as good as the other, and the choice becomes the one of the simpler mechanical approach, or perhaps one of economy. The following information applies to conductor half-wavelength/diameter ratios in the order of 1000, but will not be greatly different for other length/diameter ratios. Radiator lengths are free-space lengths, requiring no correction for length/diameter ratios.

Feed-Line Zo, Ohms	*Radiator Length*	*Shunt-Canceling Component*
52	82.5 degrees 0.229 wavelength	Inductor, 57.1 ohms
52	93.6 degrees 0.260 wavelength	Capacitor, 78.1 ohms
75	84.0 degrees 0.233 wavelength	Inductor, 58.1 ohms
75	92.0 degrees 0.256 wavelength	Capacitor, 80.6 ohms

It may be seen from the above that, for an inductive shunt-canceling component, the radiator lengths are not much different for a 52-ohm or for a 75-ohm termination. The same is true for a capacitive shunt for the two impedances. This indicates that the radiator length for a proper match is somewhat critical. This causes no problems, however, as the final length can merely be adjusted for the lowest SWR in the feed line. Similarly, it may be seen that there is little difference in the required reactance values for 52 versus 75 ohms terminating impedance. If matching by final length adjustment is performed, this means that the reactance value is not critical. In other words, a shunt inductor having a reactance in the order of 57 ohms will afford a close match to either 52 or 75 ohms.

Construction and Adjustment

From an economy standpoint, inductors are generally more satisfactory than capacitors as shunt elements, if one considers that the component will be required to handle rf currents in the order of 1 ampere or more, even at modest power levels. Suitable inductors may be made from heavy bus wire or from available coil stock.

The photographs of Fig. 21-27 show the construction of a sturdy ground-plane system. As pictured, the antenna is constructed for 6-meter operation, but provisions for telescoping additional lengths of aluminum tubing to extend the radials and radiator make it readily adaptable to 10, 15, or even 20 meters. The base-plate assembly is made from 1/4-inch thick aluminum stock, obtained at a modest price as salvaged scrap from a local machine shop. Two pieces of this material are joined at right angles with short lengths of 3/4-inch angle aluminum and No. 8 nickel-plated brass hardware. A length of angle stock is attached to either side of the vertical plate, which is drilled to accept U bolts for attachment to the mast. A 2-inch circular hole is cut in the 9-inch-square horizontal plate to clear the hardware which supports the radiator. A 4-inch square piece of 1/4-inch thick phenolic material is used as the insulator for the radiator, the insulator being mounted atop the base plate with No. 10 hardware at each corner. A 1/2- by 6-inch hex-head cap screw (with head removed) serves to support the radiator, and electrical connection is made by means of a solder lug which is attached by drilling and tapping the wrought-iron flat washer underneath the insulating phenolic. Flat washers and nuts are used above and below the phenolic insulator, and lock washers are used on all hardware. The radials are attached directly to the base plate by drilling through them, but the method shown in Fig. 21-25 with U bolts would avoid weakening the tubing material by drilling. The radiator, consisting of 1/2-inch ID aluminum tubing for the lower portion, is slipped over the cap

Fig. 21-27 – The ground-plane antenna partially assembled (left) and completely assembled, ready for installation (right). Both views are looking down on the base plate, which is in an inverted position in these photos. In the view at the right may be seen an added bracket which supports a coaxial chassis connector, type SO-239, and the shunt inductor. A right-angle connector is used at the chassis connector to avoid a bend in the coax, which is secured to the mast during installation.

TABLE I – Coil and dimension data for ground-plane antennas.

Freq., MHz	*Impedance, ohms*	*Each Radial Length*	*Approx. Radiator Length*	*Coil Value, μH*	*Coil Data*
14.2	52	17'7"	15'5"	0.64	6-1/3 turns, 1"dia, 6 tpi
14.2	75	17'7"	15'8"	0.65	6-1/2 turns, 1"dia, 6 tpi
21.25	52	11'9"	10'3"	0.43	4-1/2 turns, 1"dia, 6 tpi
21.25	75	11'9"	10'6"	0.44	4-3/4 turns, 1"dia, 6 tpi
28.5	52	8'9"	7'8"	0.32	4-1/2 turns, 1"dia, 4 tpi
28.5	75	8'9"	7'10"	0.32	4-1/2 turns, 1"dia, 4 tpi
29.5	52	8'6"	7'5"	0.31	4-1/3 turns, 1"dia, 4 tpi
29.5	75	8'6"	7'7"	0.31	4-1/3 turns, 1"dia, 4 tpi
51	52	4'11"	4'3"	0.18	3 turns, 1"dia, 4 tpi
51	75	4'11"	4'4"	0.18	3 turns, 1"dia, 4 tpi
53	52	4'9"	4'1"	0.17	2-3/4 turns, 1"dia, 4 tpi
53	75	4'9"	4'2"	0.17	2-3/4 turns, 1"dia, 4 tpi

screw and secured with a No. 6 screw which passes through both the tubing and the cap screw. A "weep" hole, 1/16-inch or so diameter, is drilled through one wall of the tubing just above the top of the cap screw, to permit an escape point for condensed moisture. The length of the radiator is adjusted during final pruning by varying the amount of telescoping of the tubing at the top of the element. Table I gives dimensions and coil data for the construction of ground-plane antennas for which this construction technique is suitable.

ANTENNAS FOR 160 METERS

Results on 1.8 MHz will depend to a large extent on the type of antenna used and the time of day or night that operations will take place. Almost any random length of wire that is tuned to resonance and matched to the transmitter will give fair results at night. During daylight hours the absorption is high, and such high-angle radiators become ineffective. For this reason a vertically polarized, low-radiation-angle antenna is best for use on the 160-meter band, day and night. Fig. 21-29 shows three effective 160-meter antennas. At A, a shortened inverted V is made resonant by means of *L*, a loading coil in each leg of the doublet. This antenna will give vertical polarization, and will perform well for day and night use. A full-size inverted V with tuned feeders would be better, even if the voltage ends were but a few inches off the ground. However, when antenna space is at a premium, a 75-meter doublet can be equipped with loading inductors as shown, and the antenna will perform on 1.8 MHz. Two-band operation can be had by merely shorting the loading coils with clip leads during 75-meter use. For use on 1.8 MHz the coils are experimentally pruned, a half turn at a time, until the lowest SWR is obtained.

As a starting point, the coils should be 70 μH each, 16 feet, 5 inches for the length between the coil and antenna center (one side), and 46 feet from the coil to the end insulator. Resonate the antenna on the desired 80-meter frequency by shorting out turns on the coil, looking for the lowest SWR. Note that point and follow the same

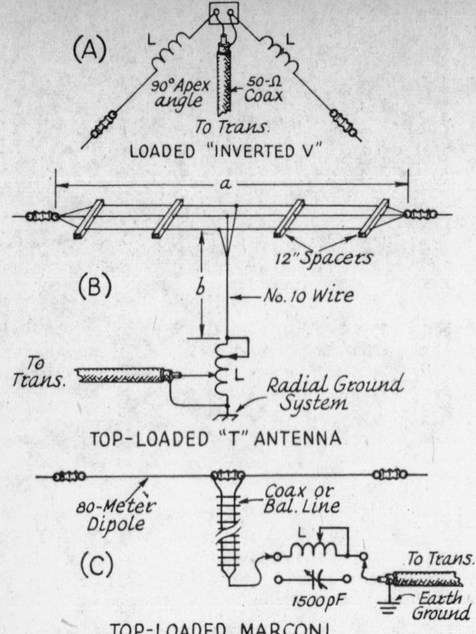

Fig. 21-29 – Illustrations of three vertically polarized short antennas for use on 1.8 to 2 MHz. They are described in the text.

procedure for 160. Of course, the shorting taps must be changed each time one changes bands.

The antenna at B is nothing more than a top-loaded quarter-wavelength Marconi. The flat-top section, *a*, can be any convenient length – 25 to 50 feet – and should be as high in the air as possible. Its three wires are joined at the ends and center, and a single vertical wire drops down to the loading/matching inductor, *L*. The flat-top section serves as a capacitance hat for the vertical member, *b*. The larger that *a* is made, the less coil will be needed at *L*. A good earth ground is essential to proper performance. A buried radial system is recommended, but if the soil has good conductivity it may be possible to get by with six or eight ground rods driven into the earth, 4 feet apart, and bonded together by means of No. 10 wire. They should be centered around the bottom end of section *b*. There are two taps on *L*. The bottom one is adjusted for a match to the coax feeder. The top tap is adjusted for antenna resonance. There will be some interaction between the adjustments, so several attempts may be necessary before the system is tuned up. Section *b* should be made as long as possible – 30 feet or more – for best results.

An adaptation of the antenna just described is shown at C in Fig. 21-29. Here an 80-meter doublet is used as a quarter-wavelength top-loaded Marconi. The feeders, whether coax or balanced line, are twisted together at the transmitter end and tuned with series *L* or *C*. The method used will depend upon the length of the feed line. Ordinarily, an 80-meter dipole with a quarter wavelength feeder will require the series *C* to tune out reactance. If the feed line is much less than one quarter wavelength, the series *L* will be needed. An SWR bridge should be used during these adjustments. A good earth ground is necessary with this antenna.

Other Antennas

Most of the full-size horizontal and vertical antennas described earlier in this chapter are suitable for 1.8 MHz, too. When space is available for a large antenna one should try to make use of this advantage on "160." The helically-wound short vertical described in the section on "limited-space antennas" should be of interest to the 160-meter operator, too.

LIMITED-SPACE ANTENNAS

Reducing losses which detract from the radiated power is the key to success in any limited-space antenna system. In fact, if there were no losses present, the radiating efficiency of a shortened antenna would be as good as its full-sized counterpart. The only difference between the two is that the bandwidth over which the input impedance remains relatively constant is less for the former than it is for the latter. As the length of a radiator becomes shorter in comparison to the wavelength of operation, less rf energy is radiated during each rf cycle and most of the energy is stored in the electric field surrounding the antenna. This means the *Q* of the antenna is very high and consequently the bandwidth becomes very narrow. From a circuit point of view, the radiator looks like a small-value capacitor (large capacitive reactance) in series with a small resistance or in parallel with large resistance value. The problem reduces to one of tuning out the reactance and matching the transmitter or feed line to the antenna radiation resistance. While this sounds relatively simple to do in theory, the effects of losses complicate the problem considerably. It is the unwanted losses which set practical limits on how small an antenna can be made and still be useful for communication purposes.

Electrical length, and not physical size, determine whether or not an antenna is "small." For instance, a 20-meter dipole is approximately 34 feet long and could easily be installed in an attic or other area. The same length antenna would be quite short on 75 meters and would present formidable matching and loss problems. Antenna height is subject to the same considerations in regards to physical versus electrical size and the effects of height are covered elsewhere in this *Handbook.* Since the high-current parts of an antenna are responsible for most of the radiation, they should be kept as high as possible. This will improve the angle of radiation somewhat.

A Multiple-Tuned Short Dipole

The use of limited-space antennas is becoming more of a necessity than formerly. Therefore, any possibilities for new or different designs should be explored. Shown in Fig. 21-30 is an antenna

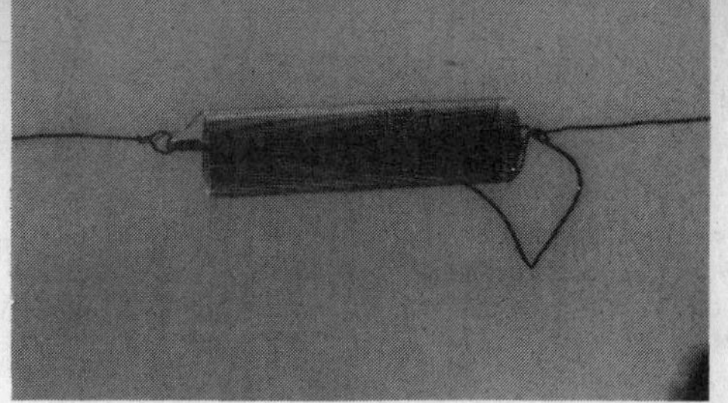

Fig. 21-30 – At left, construction of the dipole. Heavier spreaders with insulators were used at the ends with a lighter one in the middle. The weight of the feed line is distributed on both sides of the spreader by means of a cord, forming the Y-shaped object in the middle. Also shown are the four loading coils. At right, close-up view of a loading coil showing tap connection and polypropylene insulator.

utilizing a technique seldom found in amateur antennas with the exception of the folded dipole. The method is called multiple tuning and has been used extensively in vlf antenna installations.

Some advantages to the technique are as follows: if two or more resonant radiators are paralleled in folded-dipole fashion then the impedance ($R_a + R_o/N$) is stepped up by a factor of N^2 (where N is the number of radiators and R_a is the radiation resistance of each radiator). The loss resistance is R_o which is associated with loading-coil losses, wire conductivity, and other sources. R_o is decreased by a factor of $1/N$. Antenna efficiency is equal to $100\%/(1 + R_o/NR_a)$ and improves as N is increased. These effects are of less importance when the electrical length of the resonant radiator is large since efficiency is high to begin with. Also, reasonable input impedances make matching to the feed line or transmitter relatively simple. However, the advantages become pronounced when the efficiency is poor (R_o/R_a large) and $R_a + R_o$ is small making matching difficult. This is the case when the length of the resonant radiator becomes short compared to the wavelength being used.

While space is usually available for full-size dipoles on the higher amateur frequencies, the idea of using multiple tuning for a high-efficiency short dipole for one of the lower bands seemed attractive. Some experimental antennas for the 75-meter band were constructed and one is shown in Fig. 21-31. Even though only 30 feet long, performance on both receiving and transmitting of this antenna seemed to compare favorably with much larger ones. Using a 180-watt transceiver in a temporary setup, a number of contacts were made and the reports were generally good in comparison with stations running higher power and with larger antennas.

If the value of $R_a + R_o/N$ is on the order of 13 ohms, an impedance step up of four will give 52 ohms. This would allow matching to a transmitter or 52-ohm feed line without additional networks. While not an advantage in particular (since other values could be used with an appropriate matching network), it turned out that this occured with the length and antenna height used. The latter would be realistic ones for many limited-space installations, however.

Bandwidth of the antenna was quite narrow (20 kHz) indicating an antenna Q of approximately 190. However, this is as it should be (as pointed out previously) and a broad bandwidth would be suspect with an antenna this short. In many applications, the narrow bandwidth would not prove to be a great objection. Since nets and round tables tend to operate on a fixed-frequency basis, the inconvenience of retuning would not pose a problem. Improved performance because of the increased efficiency may offset this disadvantage in some instances. Tuning was accomplished by lowering the antenna and changing the taps on the loading coils. The SWR was then checked until a point where a minimum occured was found.

Initial values for the loading-coil inductance were calculated for a single dipole from curves in *The ARRL Antenna Book*, 13th edition. The chart in Fig. 10-2 was used to determine these starting values and good agreement with the actual value needed was observed. Antennas for other lengths and frequencies could be designed with these curves. Keeping the coils approximately midway between the center and the outer end of the antenna is advisable, however. It is also a good idea to make the L of coils somewhat larger than calculated and then tap down to get the correct value. Tap connections should be soldered for highest conductivity. In order to avoid disappointment, it is advisable to reduce *all* the losses as much as possible. This philosophy holds for other types of limited-space antennas as well. Compromises made for convenience or other reasons will normally result in poorer efficiency.

Construction of the dipole can follow the

Fig. 21-31 – Dipole dimensions and coil data.
L1-L4, incl. – 82 μH for 3.86 MHz. Air wound preferable, 57 turns, 2-1/2-inch dia., 10 tpi of No. 16 solid wire (B&W 3031).

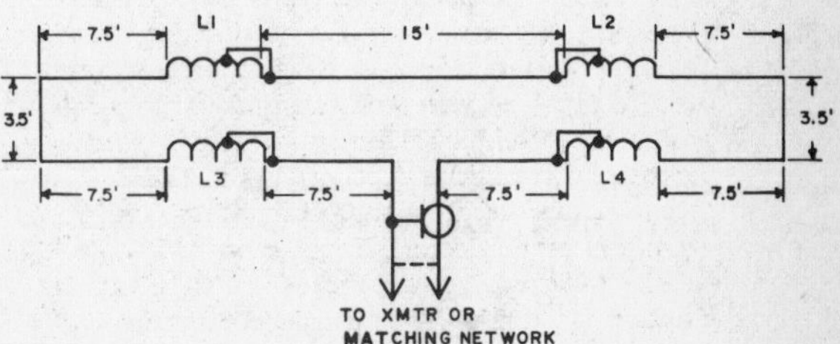

builder's requirements but the factors mentioned previously should be kept in mind. Using the antenna in an attic installation might be attractive since it could be strung from the rafters by means of standoff insulators. Caution should be taken that no contact with metallic or flammable objects occurs. When used in outdoor setups, construction of the loading-coil supports may be improved by using fiberglass rods instead of the polypropylene rope insulators shown in the experimental dipole. However, polypropylene has very low-loss dielectric properties which makes it adequate for insulating applications. Generally speaking, weatherproofing is unadvisable since a poor job tends to keep moisture in once it gets there while an open-type construction quickly dries out once inclement weather clears up. If air-wound coil stock is used for the loading coils, alternate windings near the tap points should be pushed in slightly to ease the task of soldering connections and insure that no unwanted shorts between turns occur. While many types of homemade coils are possible, it should be pointed out that PVC plastics have relatively poor dielectric-loss properties. This may or may not be an important factor in loading-coil operation and will depend upon the voltage across the coil.

Other types of limited-space antennas may be of interest and *The ARRL Antenna Book*, 13th edition, contains additional designs. The particular type selected will depend upon factors such as ground conductivity, ability to install ground planes, height available, and proximity to surrounding objects.

HELICALLY-WOUND SHORT VERTICAL ANTENNAS

An effective physically-short radiator can be built by helically-winding a length of wire on a long insulating rod or pole as shown in the sketch. Supporting poles such as bamboo rods, fiber glass tubing, or treated dowel rod, serve as practical foundation material for such an antenna. This type of antenna is most often used as a vertical radiator and is worked against ground as a quarter-wavelength system. The voltage and current distribution is more linear than when a lumped-inductance (loading coil and whip) is employed, a possible reason for its effective performance.

This type of antenna is particularly useful for limited-space applications in the lower part of the hf spectrum – 1.8, 3.5 and 7.0 MHz. It can be used for 14 MHz and higher, but is desirable only if an antenna shorter than a natural quarter wavelength is required.

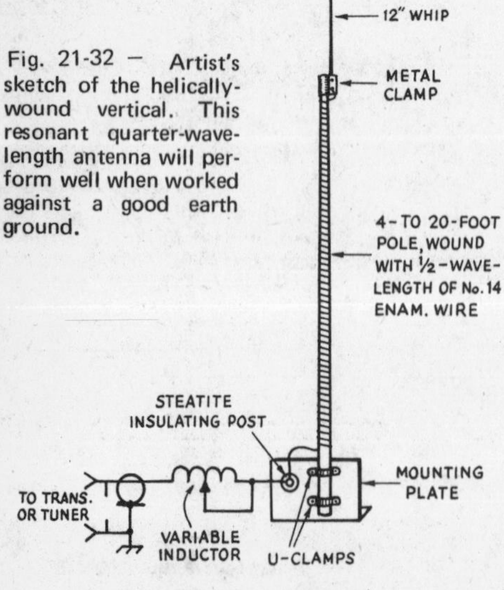

Fig. 21-32 – Artist's sketch of the helically-wound vertical. This resonant quarter-wavelength antenna will perform well when worked against a good earth ground.

12" WHIP
METAL CLAMP
4-TO 20-FOOT POLE, WOUND WITH ½-WAVE-LENGTH OF No. 14 ENAM. WIRE
STEATITE INSULATING POST
MOUNTING PLATE
TO TRANS. OR TUNER
VARIABLE INDUCTOR
U-CLAMPS

Construction

The length of the supporting pole can be anything between 4 feet and 20 feet in length. The longer the rod, the better the performance. Fiber glass spreader poles for cubical-quad antennas are ideal for this application. Alternatively, bamboo fishing poles, covered with fiber glass, work well. Some lumber yards carry 16-foot long hand-rail stock (wooden) which can be coated with fiber glass or several coats of exterior spar varnish and used as a coil form. The main consideration is that the antenna pole be of good dielectric properties and that it be weatherproofed.

So that the antenna will be approximately 1/4-wavelength long *electrically*, a 1/2-wavelength piece of insulated wire is needed for the radiating element. When helically-wound as shown, the antenna becomes approximately one-quarter wavelength long, electrically. No. 14 or No. 12 Formvar-insulated copper wire is recommended for the antenna winding. It should be space-wound in as linear a manner as possible. The far end of the vertical should have a 6-inch diameter metal disk, or 12-inch spike, to add sufficient capacitance to lower the impedance at the far end of the radiator sufficiently to prevent corona effects which can burn the far end of the element during medium- and high-power operation. An aluminum base-mounting plate and two U clamps can serve as a support for the antenna.

Operation

To build the antenna for use on 160 meters, for example, wind approximately 248 feet of wire on the pole as shown. Since this will fall just short of natural resonance at one-quarter wavelength, some type of variable inductor will be needed at the base of the antenna. A rotary inductor from an old Command Set transmitter will do the job. It should be enclosed in a weatherproof box of plastic or metal. The inductor is adjusted by means of an SWR indicator for the best match obtainable at the operating frequency. An earth ground is required for proper operation, and a buried radial system is recommended. Alternatively, several ground rods can be driven into the earth near the base of the antenna and bonded together with heavy wire.

It may not be possible to secure a 1:1 SWR without using some form of impedance-matching system. After the antenna is made resonant at the operating frequency, a tuning network such as that

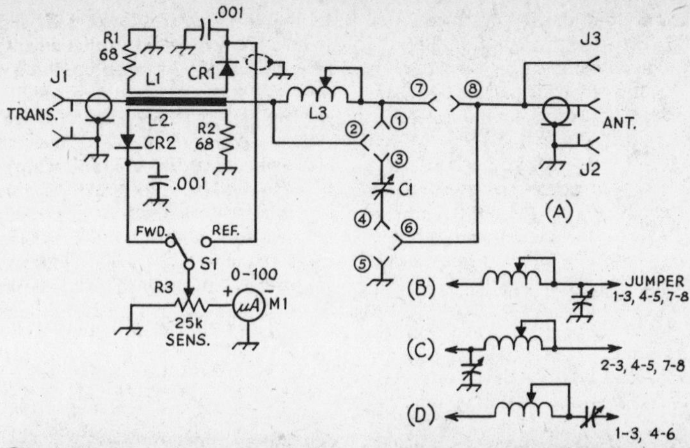

Fig. 21-33 – Circuit diagram of the L-network Transmatch. The eight banana jacks are E. F. Johnson type 108-900, and three dual banana plugs are required, E. F. Johnson type 108-200.

C1 – Variable capacitor, 350 pF (E. F. Johnson 154-10).

CR1, CR2 – 1N34A germanium diode.

J1, J2 – Chassis connector, type SO-239.

J3 – Feedthrough terminal, isolantite.

L1, L2 – See Fig. 21-34, part of etched-circuit assembly.

L3 – Variable inductor 28 μH (E. F. Johnson 229-203).

M1 – 100-μA meter.

R1, R2 – 68-ohm, 1/2-watt carbon or composition, *not wirewound*.

R3 – 25,000-ohm carbon control, linear taper.

S1 – Spst toggle.

of Fig. 21-33 can be employed to provide the desired 1:1 SWR. Since antennas of this type are relatively "frequency conscious," it will be necessary to retune the matching network when moving from one part of the band to another. The completed antenna should be given a coating of fiber glass or spar varnish to seal it against the weather, and to secure the coil turns. It has been observed that this antenna has exceptional immunity to man-made electrical noises. It also cuts down the response to broadcast-band signals which sometimes tend to overload the station receiver. The foregoing attributes result from the fact that it is a narrow-band antenna.

INDOOR ANTENNAS

Amateurs residing in apartment buildings may not be able to put up outdoor antennas or to use limited-space antennas such as shown in Fig. 21-30. The answer to the problem is to use a window-mounted mobile antenna, or random-length wire fed at one end.

Some General Considerations

There are exceptions to the following rules but, in general, they can be depended upon.

1) An outdoor antenna will work better than an indoor one.

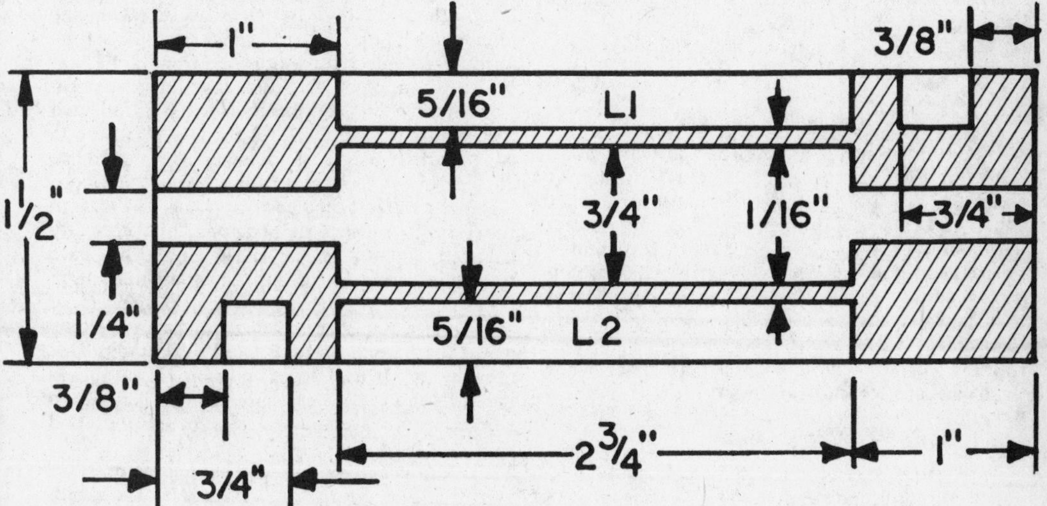

Fig. 21-34 – Etched circuit-board template. The foil side is shown, the etched portion is shaded.

Fig. 21-35 – The Monimatch is at the upper left, covered by a metal enclosure. Connections from the roller inductor and the variable capacitor to the terminals on the jacks are made with thin strips of copper, although No. 12 or 14 wire can be used instead. The two antenna terminals are at the rear right. The top terminal is for use with a coax-fed antenna, if desired.

2) An antenna inside a frame building with wood exteriors is better than the same antenna in a steel-and-concrete building.

3) The higher above ground, inside or out, the better the antenna will work.

4) The bigger (or longer) you can make an indoor antenna, the better – even if it means running wire around corners.

5) Even a poor antenna *should* produce some contacts.

The Coupling Problem

Most transmitters are designed to work into a 50-ohm load, and contain little or no provision for adjusting the transmitter when the load is other than 50 ohms. Unfortunately, there is no random-length wire antenna that will present a 50-ohm load on all bands. What is required is a Transmatch. A Transmatch is simply an adjustable *LC* network that converts the unknown antenna impedance to 50 ohms. The unit, shown in Fig. 21-35, will cover the 80- through 10-meter bands and can handle 1 kW of rf power.

Circuit Details

The unit shown in Fig. 21-33 is designed to be used in three configurations. They are shown at B, C, and D. With one of the three hookups, it should be possible to match practically any antenna to the transmitter.

In order to get complete band coverage and avoid the complexities of band-switching, banana and jack plugs are used to change the circuit to the configuration needed. For example, if the setup shown at B is desired, jumper terminals 7 and 8, 1 and 3, and 4 and 5 should be used. Using the banana plugs makes for easy changing of the circuit.

Whenever a Transmatch is used, the operator should have a way of knowing when the unit is adjusted correctly. The answer to this need is a Monimatch or other SWR indicator.

Construction Details

The chassis for mounting the Transmatch is made from a piece of aluminum measuring 10 X 19 inches. The ends of the 19-inch length of aluminum are bent up to form a U-shaped chassis, the ends being 4 1/2 inches high to form a chassis 10 X 10 X 4 1/2 inches. The back side of the U has an opening cut out, 3 1/4 inches high by 4 1/2 inches long. A piece of Plexiglas is mounted over this opening. The jack-plug sockets are installed directly on the plastic. Connections from the roller inductor, L3, and variable capacitor, C1, are made to the banana jacks. Be careful when drilling the holes for the jacks to insure that they will mate with the plugs. Fig. 21-34 shows the details for a pc-board Monimatch. Methods for making etched circuit boards are given in detail in the Construction Practices chapter.

How to Tune Up

Using the Transmatch is not complicated. Although it takes some time to find the correct combination of settings, once determined, they can be logged for later reference. Use a short length of 50-ohm coax to connect the Transmatch to the transmitter. Attach the antenna to the Transmatch. Tune up the transmitter on the desired band, making sure that the final amplifier is resonated, but with the power output reduced. With the Monimatch in the forward-reading position, set the sensitivity control for a full-scale reading. Be sure to keep the final amplifier tank in resonance. Switch the meter to the reflected position, and then adjust L1 and C1, until the lowest indication of reflected power is obtained. It should be possible to get the meter to read zero, With a zero reading in the reflected position, versus full scale in the forward setting, the Transmatch is correctly adjusted, and the SWR is 1. The circuit may have to be changed to one of the other configurations in order to get a match, but one combination *should* work. Once the Transmatch is set properly, then adjust the transmitter to its rated power input. One other point: It isn't always possible to get a good ground connection in an apartment. Therefore, a connection to a cold-water pipe or earth ground should be used.

Try to make the antenna as long as possible, even if it must be run around corners. The length that will work best is from 120 to 130 feet. The end of the wire can be terminated at a window screen, which will get *part* of the antenna outside.

DIRECTIVE ARRAYS WITH PARASITIC ELEMENTS

With few exceptions, the antennas described so far in Chapter 21 have unity gain or less, and are either omnidirectional or bidirectional. In order for antennas to have gain and take on directional characteristics they must employ additional elements. Antennas with these properties are commonly referred to as "beam" antennas. This section will deal with the design and characteristics of directional antennas with gain.

Parasitic Excitation

In most of these arrangements the additional elements receive power by induction or radiation from the driven element generally called the "antenna," and reradiate it in the proper phase relationship to achieve the desired effect. These elements are called *parasitic* elements, as contrasted to the driven elements which receive power directly from the transmitter through the transmission line.

The parasitic element is called a **director** when it reinforces radiation on a line pointing to it from the antenna, and a **reflector** when the reverse is the case. Whether the parasitic element is a director or reflector depends upon the parasitic-element tuning, which usually is adjusted by changing its length.

Gain vs. Spacing

The gain of an antenna with parasitic elements varies with the spacing and tuning of the elements and thus for any given spacing there is a tuning condition that will give maximum gain at this spacing. The maximum front-to-back ratio seldom, if ever, occurs at the same condition that gives maximum forward gain. The impedance of the driven element also varies with the tuning and spacing, and thus the antenna system must be tuned to its final condition before the match between the line and the antenna can be completed. However, the tuning and matching may interlock to some extent, and it is usually necessary to run through the adjustments several times to insure that the best possible tuning has been obtained.

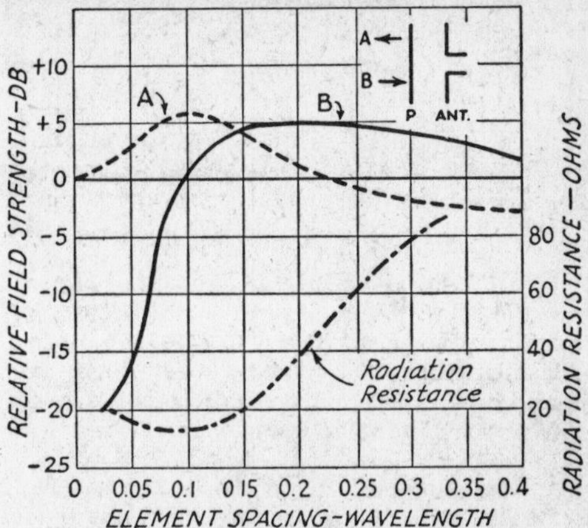

Fig. 21-36 -Gain vs. element spacing for an antenna and one parasitic element. The reference point, 0 dB, is the field strength from a half-wave antenna alone. The greatest gain is in the direction A at spacings of less than 0.14 wavelength, and in direction B at greater spacings. The front-to-back ratio is the difference in dB between curves A and B. Variation in radiation resistance of the driven element is also shown. These curves are for a self-resonant parasitic element. At most spacings the gain as a reflector can be increased by slight lengthening of the parasitic element; the gain as a director can be increased by shortening. This also improves the front-to-back ratio.

Two-Element Beams

A 2-element beam is useful where space or other considerations prevent the use of the larger structure required for a 3-element beam. The general practice is to tune the parasitic element as a reflector and space it about 0.15 wavelength from the driven element, although some successful antennas have been built with 0.1-wavelength spacing and director tuning. Gain *vs.* element spacing for a 2-element antenna is given in Fig. 21-36, for the special case where the parasitic element is resonant. It is indicative of the performance to be expected under maximum-gain tuning conditions.

TABLE 21-II

Freq.	*Driven Element*		*Reflector*		*1st Director*		*2nd Director*	
	A	*B*	*A*	*B*	*A*	*B*	*A*	*B*
14050	33' 5 3/8"	33' 8"	35' 2 1/2"	35' 5 1/4"	31' 9 3/8"	31' 11 5/8"	31' 1 1/4"	31' 3 5/8"
14250	32' 11 3/4"	33' 2 1/4"	34' 8 1/2"	34' 11 1/4"	31' 4"	31' 6 3/8"	30' 8"	30' 10 1/2"
21050	22' 4"	22' 5 5/8"	23' 6"	23' 7 3/4"	21' 2 1/2"	21' 4"	20' 9 1/8"	20' 10 7/8"
21300	22' 3/4"	22' 2 3/8"	23' 2 5/8"	23' 4 1/2"	20' 11 1/2"	21' 1"	20' 6 1/4"	20' 7 3/4"
28050	16' 9"	16' 10 1/4"	17' 7 5/8"	17' 8 7/8"	15' 11"	16'	15' 7"	15' 9 1/2"
28600	16' 5 1/4"	16' 6 3/8"	17' 3 1/2"	17' 4 3/4"	15' 7 1/4"	15' 8 1/2"	15' 3 3/8"	15' 4 1/2"

A: .2 .2 .2

B: .15 .15 .15

Element lengths for 20, 15 and 10 meters, phone and cw. These lengths are for 0.2 or .15 wavelength element spacing.

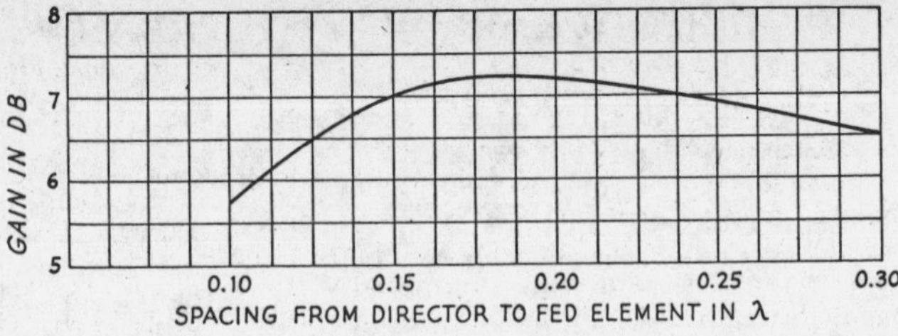

Fig. 21-37 – Gain of 3-element Yagi versus director spacing, the reflector spacing being fixed at 0.2 wavelength.

Three-Element Beams

A theoretical investigation of the 3-element case (director, driven element and reflector) has indicated a maximum gain of slightly more than 7 dB. A number of experimental investigations have shown that the optimum spacing between the driven element and reflector is in the region of 0.15 to 0.25 wavelength, with 0.2 wavelength representing probably the best overall choice. With 0.2-wavelength reflector spacing, Fig. 21-37 shows the gain variation with director spacing. It is obvious that the director spacing is not especially critical, and that the overall length of the array (boom length in the case of a rotatable antenna) can be anywhere between 0.35 and 0.45 wavelength with no appreciable difference in gain.

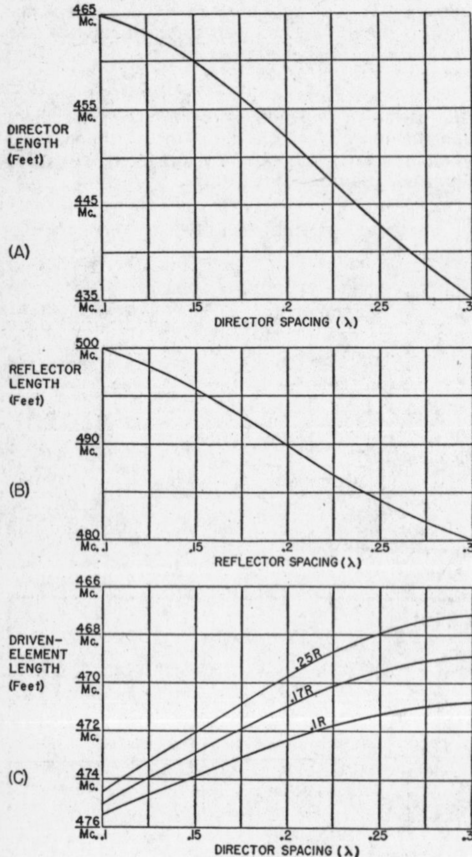

Fig. 21-38 – Element lengths for a 3-element beam. These lengths will hold closely for tubing elements supported at or near the center.

Wide spacing of both elements is desirable not only because it results in high gain but also because adjustment of tuning or element length is less critical and the input resistance of the driven element is higher than with close spacing. The latter feature improves the efficiency of the antenna and makes a greater bandwidth possible. However, a total antenna length, director to reflector, of more than 0.3 wavelength at frequencies of the order of 14 MHz introduces considerable difficulty from a constructional standpoint, so lengths of 0.25 to 0.3 wavelength are frequently used for this band, even though they are less than optimum.

In general, the gain of the antenna drops off less rapidly when the reflector length is increased beyond the optimum value than it does for a corresponding decrease below the optimum value. The opposite is true of a director. It is therefore advisable to err, if necessary, on the long side for a reflector and on the short side for a director. This also tends to make the antenna performance less dependent on the exact frequency at which it is operated, because an increase above the design frequency has the same effect as increasing the length of both parasitic elements, while a decrease in frequency has the same effect as shortening both elements. By making the director slightly short and the reflector slightly long, there will be a greater spread between the upper and lower frequencies at which the gain starts to show a rapid decrease.

When the over-all length has been decided upon, the element lengths can be found by referring to Fig. 21-38. The lengths determined by these charts will vary slightly in actual practice with the element diameter and the method of supporting the elements, and the tuning of a beam should always be checked after installation. However, the lengths obtained by the use of the charts will be close to correct in practically all cases, and they can be used without checking if the beam is difficult of access.

In order to make it even easier for the Yagi builder, Table 21-II can be used to determine the element lengths needed. Both cw and phone lengths are included for the three bands, 20, 15, and 10 meters. The 0.2 wavelength spacing will provide greater bandwidth than the 0.15 spacing. Antenna gain is essentially the same with either spacing. The element lengths given will be the same whether the beam has 2, 3 or 4 elements. It is recommended that "Plumber's Delight" type construction be used where all the elements are

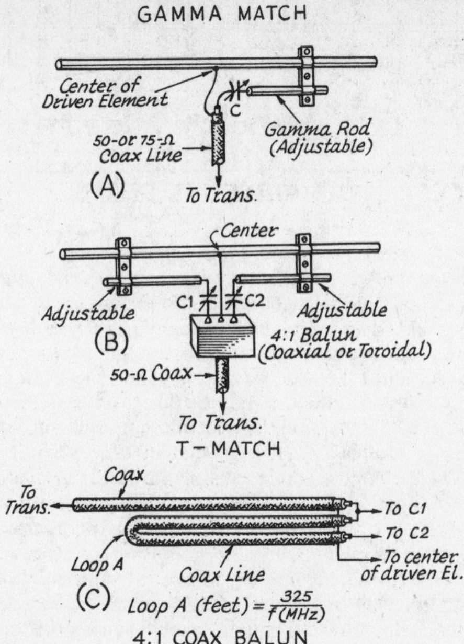

Fig. 21-39 — Illustrations of gamma and T-matching systems. At A, the gamma rod is adjusted along with C until the lowest possible SWR is obtained. A T-match is shown at B. It is the same as two gamma-match rods. The rods and C1 and C2 are alternately adjusted for a 1:1 SWR. A coaxial 4:1 balun transformer is shown at C. A toroidal balun can be used in place of the coax model shown. Details for the toroidal version are given in Chapter 20, and it has a broader frequency range than the coaxial version. The T-match is adjusted for 200 ohms and the balun steps this *balanced* value down to 50 ohms, *unbalanced*. Or, the T-match can be set for 300 ohms, and the balun used to step this down to 75 ohms, unbalanced. Dimensions for the gamma and T-match rods cannot be given by formula. Their lengths and spacing will depend upon the tubing size used, and the spacing of the parasitic elements of the beam. Capacitors C, C1 and C2 can be 140 pF for 14-MHz beams. Somewhat less capacitance will be needed at 21 and 28 MHz.

mounted directly on and grounded to the boom. This puts the entire array at dc ground potential, affording better lightning protection. A gamma section can be used for matching the feed line to the array.

Tuning Adjustments

The preferable method for checking the beam is by means of a field-strength meter or the S meter of a communications receiver, used in conjunction with a dipole antenna located at least 10 wavelengths away and as high as or higher than the beam that is being checked. A few watts of power fed into the antenna will give a useful signal at the observation point, and the power input to the transmitter (and hence the antenna) should be held constant for all of the readings.

Preliminary matching adjustments can be done on the ground. The beam should be set up so that the reflector element rests on earth with the remaining elements in a vertical configuration. In other words, the beam should be aimed straight up. The matching system is then adjusted for 1:1 SWR between the feed line and driven element. When the antenna is raised into its operating height, only slight touch-up of the matching network will be required.

A great deal has been printed about the need for tuning the elements of a Yagi-type beam. However, experience has shown that lengths given in Fig. 21-38 and Table II are close enough to the desired length that no further tuning should be required. This is true for Yagi arrays made from metal tubing. However, in the case of quad antennas, made from wire, the reflectors and directors *should* be tuned with the antenna in its operating location. The reason is that it is practically impossible to cut and install wire to the *exact* dimensions required for maximum gain or front-to-back.

Simple Systems: The Rotary Beam

Two- and three-element systems are popular for rotary-beam antennas, where the entire antenna system is rotated, to permit its gain and directivity to be utilized for any compass direction. They may be mounted either horizontally (with the plane containing the elements parallel to the earth) or vertically.

A four-element beam will give still more gain than a three-element one, provided the support is sufficient for about 0.2 wavelength spacing between elements. The tuning for maximum gain involves many variables, and complete gain and tuning data are not available.

The elements in close-spaced (less than one-quarter wavelength element spacing) arrays preferably should be made of tubing of one-half to one-inch diameter. A conductor of large diameter not only has less ohmic resistance but also has lower Q; both these factors are important in close-spaced arrays because the impedance of the driven element usually is quite low compared to that of a simple dipole antenna. With three- and four-element close-spaced arrays the radiation resistance of the driven element may be so low that ohmic losses in the conductor can consume an appreciable fraction of the power.

Feeding the Rotary Beam

Any of the usual methods of feed (described later under "Matching the Antenna to the Line") can be applied to the driven element of a rotary beam. The popular choices for feeding a beam are the gamma match with series capacitor and the T match with series capacitors and a half-wavelength phasing section, as shown in Fig. 21-39. These methods are preferred over any others because they permit adjustment of the matching and the use of coaxial line feed. The variable capacitors can be housed in small plastic cups for weatherproofing; receiving types with close spacing can be used at powers up to a few hundred watts. Maximum

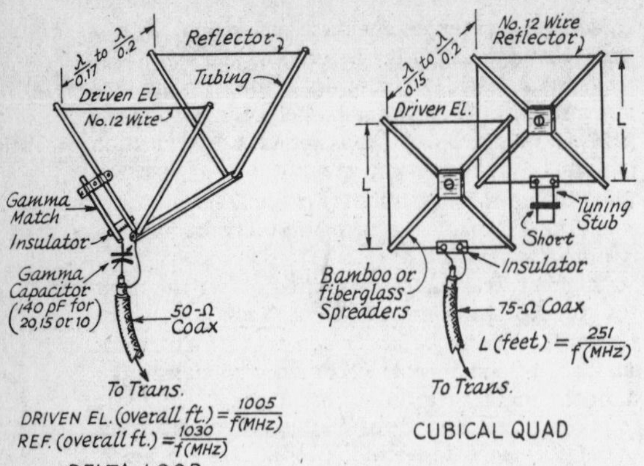

Fig. 21-40 – Information on building a quad or a Delta-Loop antenna. The antennas are electrically similar, but the Delta-Loop uses "plumber's delight" construction. Additional information is given in the text.

capacitance required is usually 140 pF at 14 MHz and proportionately less at the higher frequencies.

If physcially possible, it is better to adjust the matching device after the antenna has been installed at its ultimate height, since a match made with the antenna near the ground may not hold for the same antenna in the air.

Sharpness of Resonance

Peak performance of a multielement parasitic array depends upon proper phasing or tuning of the elements, which can be exact for one frequency only. In the case of close-spaced arrays, which because of the low radiation resistance usually are quite sharp-tuning, the frequency range over which optimum results can be secured is only of the order of 1 or 2 percent of the resonant frequency, or up to about 500 kHz at 28 MHz. However, the antenna can be made to work satisfactorily over a wider frequency range by adjusting the director or directors to give maximum gain at the *highest* frequency to be covered, and by adjusting the reflector to give optimum gain at the *lowest* frequency. This sacrifices some gain at all frequencies, but maintains more uniform gain over a wider frequency range.

The use of large-diameter conductors will broaden the response curve of an array because the larger diameter lowers the *Q*. This causes the reactances of the elements to change rather slowly with frequency, with the result that the tuning stays near the optimum over a considerably wider frequency range than is the case with wire conductors.

Combination Arrays

It is possible to combine parasitic elements with driven elements to form arrays composed of collinear driven and parasitic elements and combination broad-side-collinear-parasitic elements. Thus two or more collinear elements might be provided with a collinear reflector or director set, one parasitic element to each driven element. Or both directors and reflectors might be used. A broadside-collinear array can be treated in the same fashion.

DELTA LOOPS AND QUAD BEAMS

One of the more effective DX arrays is called the "cubical quad" or, simply, "quad" antenna. It consists of two or more square loops of wire supported by a bamboo or fiberglass cross-arm assembly. The loops are a quarter wavelength per side (full wavelength overall) one loop being driven, and the other serving as a parasitic element – usually a reflector. A variation of the quad is called the Delta Loop. The electrical properties of both antennas are the same, generally speaking, though some operators report better DX results with the Delta Loop. Both antennas are shown in Fig. 21-40. They differ mainly in their physical properties, one being of "Plumber's Delight" construction, while the other uses insulating support members. One or more directors can be added to either antenna if additional gain and directivity is desired, though most operators use the two-element arrangement.

It is possible to interlace quads or "deltas" for two or more bands, but if this is done the formulas given in Fig. 21-40 may have to be changed slightly to compensate for the proximity effect of the second antenna. For quads the length of the full-wave loop can be computed from

$$\textit{Full-wave loop}\ (\text{ft}) = \frac{1005}{f\,(\text{MHz})} \qquad \textbf{21-H}$$

If multiple arrays are used, each antenna should be tuned up separately for maximum forward gain as noted on a field-strength meter. The reflector stub on the quad should be adjusted for the foregoing condition. The Delta-Loop gamma match should be adjusted for a 1:1 SWR. No reflector tuning is needed. The Delta-Loop antenna has a broader frequency response than the quad, and holds at an SWR of 1.5:1 or better across the band it is cut for.

TABLE 21-III

Quantity	*Length (ft.)*	*Diameter (in.)*	*Reynolds No.*
2	8	1	9A
4	8	3/4	8A
1	8	1 1/4	10A
1	6	7/8	4231

2 U-bolts, TV antenna to mast type, 1 variable capacitor, 150 pF maximum, any type, 1 plastic freezer container, approximately 5 X 5 X 5 inches, to house gamma capacitor.

Gamma rod, 3/8- to 1/2-inch diameter aluminum tubing, 36 inches long. (Aluminum curtain rod or similar.)

The resonance of the quad antenna can be found by checking the frequency at which the lowest SWR occurs. The element length (driven element) can be adjusted for resonance in the most-used portion of the band by lengthening or shortening it.

It is believed that a two-element quad or Delta-Loop antenna compares favorably with a three-element Yagi array in terms of gain (see *QST*, May, 1963, and *QST*, January 1969 for additional information). The quad and Delta-Loop antennas perform very well at 50 and 144 MHz. A discussion of radiation patterns and gain, quads vs. Yagis, was presented by Lindsay in *QST*, May, 1968.

A SHORT 20-METER YAGI

Described here is a small, yet effective, three-element 20-meter Yagi that offers gain and good directivity. This system exhibits a front-to-back ratio in excess of 18 dB as measured with a good quality communications receiver.

Construction

The boom and all the elements are made from 1-1/4-inch diameter aluminum tubing available at most hardware stores. The two boom sections and the two pieces which make up the center portion of the driven element are coupled together using 15-inch sleeves of 1-3/8-inch OD aluminum tubing. Sheet metal screws should be used to secure the sections within the coupling sleeves.

The loading coils are wound on 1-1/8-inch diameter Plexiglas rod. Details are shown in Fig. 1. Be sure to slit the ends of the aluminum tubing where the compression clamps are placed. The coils are made from No. 14 enameled copper wire. The specified number of turns are equally spaced to cover the entire nine inches of Plexiglas.

The capacitance hats are constructed from 3/4-inch angle aluminum. Two pieces two feet in length are required for each hat. The model shown in the diagrams has the angle aluminum fastened to the element using aluminum strips however No. 8 sheet metal screws provide a suitable substitute. Solder lugs are fastened to the ends of the angle aluminum and No. 12 or 14 wire connects the ends of the aluminum resulting in a square loop. The wires should be soldered at each of the solder lugs.

All of the elements are secured to the boom with TV U-bolt hardware. Plated bolts are desirable to prevent rust from forming. An aluminum plate nine inches square by 1/4-inch thick was used as the boom-to-mast plate.

TABLE I

Complete parts list for the short beam.

QTY	*MATERIAL*
2	10-foot lengths of 1-1/4-inch dia. aluminum tubing (one for the reflector center section, one for the reflector end sections).
3	Eight-foot lengths of 1-1/4-inch dia. aluminum tubing (two lengths for the boom, one length for the director element center).
4	Six-foot lengths of 1-1/4-inch dia. aluminum tubing (two lengths for the driven element center, two lengths for the director and driven element ends).
2	15-inch lengths of 1-5/8-inch dia. aluminum tubing.
1	40-inch length of 3/8-inch dia. aluminum tubing.
4	Six-foot lengths of 3/4-inch angle aluminum.
6	12-inch lengths of 1-1/8-inch dia. Plexiglas rod.
1	Nine-inch square, 1/4-inch thick aluminum plate.
8	U-bolts.
12	Compression hose clamps.
8	Crutch caps.
38'	No. 12 enameled copper wire.
60'	No. 14 enameled copper wire.

A boom strut is recommended because the weight of the elements is sufficient to cause the boom to sag. A 1/8-inch diameter nylon line is plenty strong. A U-bolt clamp is placed on the mast several feet above the antenna and provides

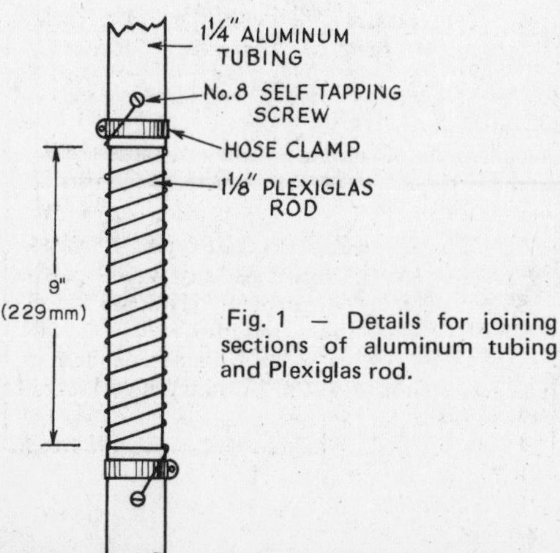

Fig. 1 — Details for joining sections of aluminum tubing and Plexiglas rod.

Shown here is WA1LNQ standing near the twenty-meter beam mounted atop the tower. Keep in mind the longest element is only 20 feet.

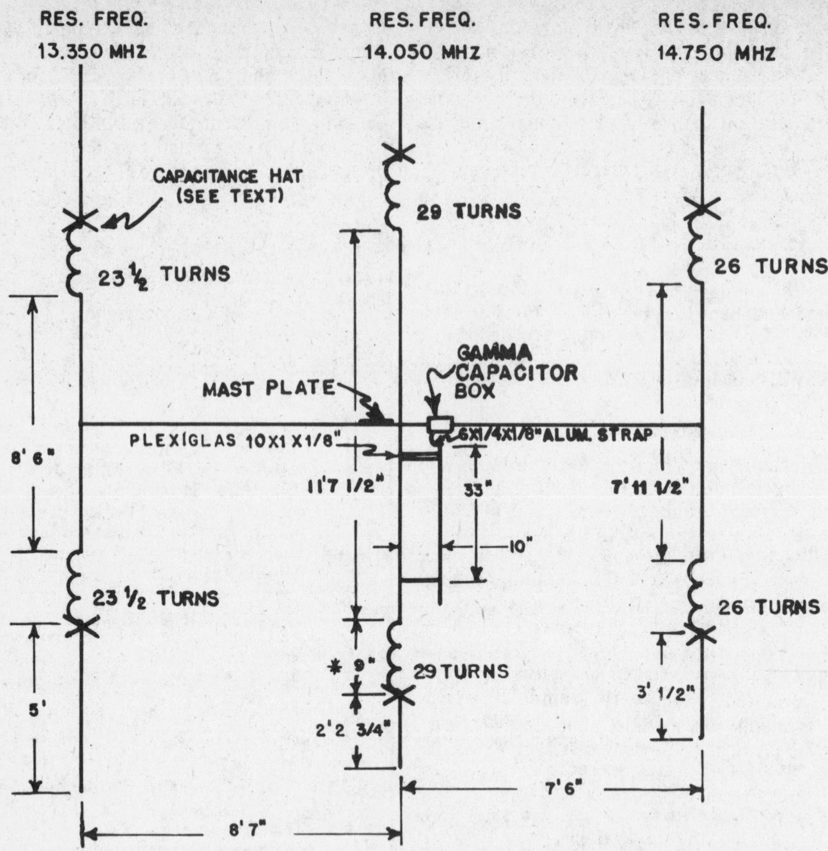

Fig. 2 – Constructional details for the 20-meter beam. The coils on each side of the element are identical. The gamma capacitor is a 140-pF variable unit manufactured by E. F. Johnson Co.

the attachment point for the center of the truss line. To reduce the possibility of water accumulating in the element tubing and subsequently freezing, crutch caps are placed over the ends. Rubber feet suitable for keeping furniture from scratching hardwood floors would serve the same purpose.

A piece of Plexiglas was mounted inside an aluminum Minibox to provide support and insulation for the gamma capacitor. A plastic refrigerator box would serve the purpose just as well. The capacitor housing is mounted to the boom by means of a U-bolt. The gamma rod is made of 3/8-inch aluminum 40-inches long and is connected to the gamma capacitor by a 6-inch length of strap aluminum.

Tune-Up and Operation

The builder is encouraged to follow the dimensions given in Fig. 1 as a starting point for the position of the gamma rod shorting strap. Connect the coaxial cable and install the antenna near or at the top of the tower. The gamma capacitor should be adjusted for minimum SWR at 14.100 MHz as indicated by an SWR meter (or power meter) connected in the feedline at the gamma capacitor box. If a perfect match cannot be obtained a slight repositioning of the gamma short might be required. The dimensions given favor the cw portion of the band. At 14.050 MHz the SWR is 1.1:1 and at 14.350 MHz the SWR is less than 2:1 making this antenna useful for phone as well as cw.

AN OPTIMUM-GAIN TWO-BAND ARRAY

If optimum performance is desired from a Yagi, the dual-4-element array shown in Fig. 21-43 will be of interest. This antenna consists of four elements on 15 meters interlaced with the same number for 10. Wide spacing is used, providing excellent gain and good bandwidth on both bands. Each driven element is fed separately with 50-ohm coax; gamma-matching systems are employed. If desired, a single feed line can be run to the array and then switched by a remotely controlled relay.

The element lengths shown in Fig. 21-44 are for the phone portions of the band, centered at 21,300 and 28,600 kHz. If desired, the element lengths can be changed for cw operation, using the dimensions given in Table 21-II. The spacing of the

Fig. 21-43 – Ready for erection, this is the completed dual-band beam.

elements will remain the same for both phone and cw.

Construction Details

The elements are supported by commercially made U-bolt assemblies. Or, muffler clamps make excellent element supports. The boom-to-mast support is also a manufactured item that is designed to hold a 2-inch diameter boom and that can be used with mast sizes up to 2 1/2 inches in diameter. Another feature of this device is that it permits the beam to be tilted after it is mounted in place on the tower, providing access to the elements if they need to be adjusted once the beam has been mounted on the tower.

The elements are made from 6061-T6 aluminum tubing, which is available from metal suppliers. The tubing comes in 12-foot lengths and can be purchased in telescoping sizes. The center sections of the 15-meter beam elements are 1-inch outside diameter and the 10-meter sections are 3/4-inch. The ends of the tubing are slit with a hack saw, and hose clamps are used to hold the telescoping portions.

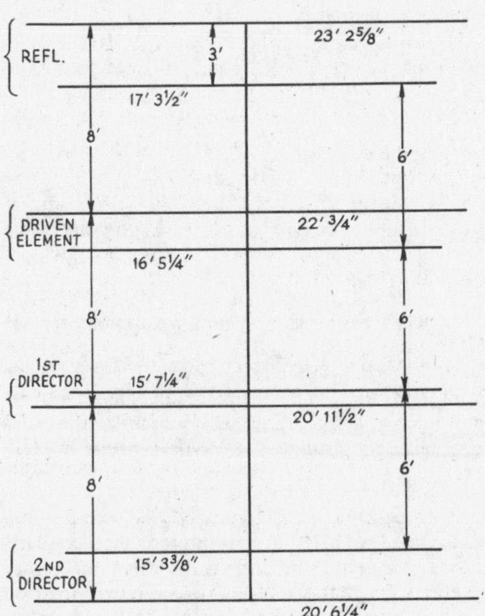

Fig. 21-44 – The element lengths shown are for the phone sections of the bands. Table 21-II provides the dimensions for cw frequencies.

Fig. 21-45 – This is the boom-to-mast fixture that holds the two 12-foot boom sections together. The unit is made by Hy-Gain Electronics, P. O. Box 5407-HE, Lincoln, NE 68505.

A THREE-BAND QUAD ANTENNA SYSTEM

Quads have been popular with amateurs during the past few decades because of their light weight, relatively small turning radius, and their unique ability to provide good DX performance when mounted close to the earth. A two-element three-band quad, for instance, with the elements

The three-band quad antenna.

mounted only 35 feet above the ground, will give good performance in situations where a triband Yagi will not. Fig. 1 shows a large quad antenna which can be used as a basis for design for either smaller or larger arrays.

Five sets of element spreaders are used to support the three-element 20-meter, four-element 15-meter, and five-element 10-meter wire-loop system. The spacing between elements has been chosen to prcvide optimum performance con-

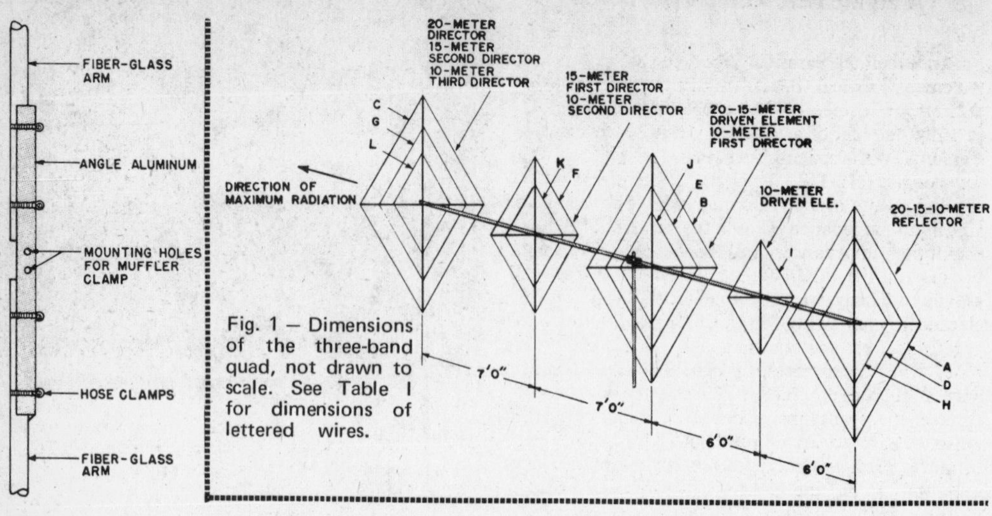

Fig. 1 — Dimensions of the three-band quad, not drawn to scale. See Table I for dimensions of lettered wires.

Fig. 2 — Details of one of two assemblies for a spreader frame. The two assemblies are jointed to form an X with a muffler clamp mounted at the position shown.

TABLE I

Three-Band Quad Loop Dimensions

Band	*Reflector*	*Driven Element*	*First Director*	*Second Director*	*Third Director*
20 Meters	(A) 72' 8"	(B) 71' 3"	(C) 69' 6"	–	–
15 Meters	(D) 48' 6½"	(E) 47' 7½"	(F) 46' 5"	(G) 46' 5"	–
10 Meters	(H) 36' 2½"	(I) 35' 6"	(J) 34' 7"	(K) 34' 7"	(L) 34' 7"

Letters indicate loops identified in Fig. 1

sistent with boom length and mechanical construction. Each of the parasitic loops is closed (ends soldered together) and requires no tuning. All of the loop sizes are listed in Table I and are designed for a center frequency of 14.1, 21.1, and 28.3 MHz. Since quad antennas are rather broad-tuning devices excellent performance is achieved in both cw and ssb band segments of each band (with the possible exception of the very high end of 10 meters). Changing the dimensions to favor a frequency 200 kHz higher in each band to create a "phone" antenna is not necessary.

One question which comes up quite often is whether to mount the loops in a diamond or a square configuration. In other words, should one spreader be horizontal to the earth, or should the wire be horizontal to the ground (spreaders mounted in the fashion of an X)? From the electrical point of view, it is probably a trade-off. While the square configuration has its lowest point higher above ground than a diamond version (which may lower the angle of radiation slightly), the top is also lower than that of a diamond shaped array. Some authorities indicate that separation of the current points in the diamond system gives slightly more gain than is possible with a square layout. It should be pointed out, however, that there never has been any substantial proof in favor of one or the other, electrically.

Spreader supports (sometimes called spiders) are available from many different manufacturers. If the builder is keeping the cost at a minimum, he should consider building his own. The expense is about half that of a commercially manufactured equivalent and, according to some authorities, the homemade arm supports described below are less likely to rotate on the boom as a result of wind pressure.

A three-foot long section of one-inch-per-side steel angle stock is used to interconnect the pairs of spreader arms. The steel is drilled at the center to accept a muffler clamp of sufficient size to clamp the assembly to the boom. The fiber glass is attached to the steel angle stock with automotive hose clamps, two per pole. Each quad-loop spreader frame consists of two assemblies of the type shown in Fig. 2.

A 20-METER VERTICAL BEAM

An excellent parasitic array for 20 meters is a 3-element vertical beam originally described by W2FMI in June, 1972, *QST*. The antenna is actually one-half of a Yagi array using quarter-wave elements with spacing between elements of 0.2 wavelength (12-1/2 feet on 20 meters). This spacing results in a good compromise between gain and input impedance. Closer spacing would reduce the input impedance, and hence the efficiency, because of the inherent earth losses with vertical antennas. This vertical symmetrical Yagi allows for electrical beam switching (changing a director into a reflector by switching in a loading coil at the base) while maintaining a constant input impedance at the driven element. The dimensions of the three-element antenna, when used as a fixed or a switched array, are shown in Table 21-IV. The elements are constructed using 1/16-inch-wall aluminum tubing and consist of three telescoping sections with one-inch OD tubing used for the bottom portions. This results in a self-supporting structure. Actually, many choices are available, including No. 14 or 12 wire taped to bamboo poles.

The three-element array with the full image plane presents an input impedance of 15 ohms. Matching is accomplished with the step-down transformer, a 4:1 unbalanced-to-unbalenced toroidal balun. This transformer is also shown in Fig. 21-52 connected to the driven element.

Fig. 21-53 shows the geometry of the image plane. The inner square has a diagonal of 4/10 wavelength (25 feet). The outer wires of these sections are No. 14 wire and the inner wires are No. 18. All cross-connected wires were wire-wrapped and soldered. The pattern was chosen to give an easy path for the surface currents of a five-element array (parasitic elements at the four corners). The outer radials were all 0.4 wavelength long and also of No. 18 wire. Twenty-five wires emanated from each corner and nine from the sides.

TABLE 21-IV

Dimensions of 20-Meter Parasitic 3-Element Array

1) Fixed Array	
Director	15 ft 8 in.
Driven Element	16 ft
Reflector	17 ft 7 in.
Spacing Between Elements	12-1/2 ft
2) Switched Array	
Director and Reflector	15 ft
Driven Element	16 ft
Spacing Between Elements	12-1/2 ft
Loading Coil	2 ft No. 12 wire wound 3 turns with 3 in. dia. Length adjusted for max. F/B ratio

Fig. 21-52 — Base hardware of the driven element and the matching transformer.

Fig. 21-53 — Geometry of the image plane used in this investigation. The pattern was chosen to approximate lines of current flow.

Fig. 21-54 — Base of one of the parasitic elements showing the relay enclosure, loading coil, and the indicator meter of the field-strength detector, which was located 2 wavelengths away.

STANDARD SIZES OF ALUMINUM TUBING

Many hams like to experiment with antennas but one problem in making antennas using aluminum tubing is knowing what sizes of tubing are available. If you want to build a beam, many questions about tubing sizes, weights, what size tubing fits into what other size, and so forth must be answered.

Table 21-V gives the standard sizes of aluminum tubing that are stocked by most aluminum suppliers or distributors in the United States and Canada. Note that all tubing comes in 12-foot lengths and also that any diameter tubing will fit into the next larger size, if the larger size has a 0.058-inch wall thickness. For example, 5/8-inch tubing has an outside diameter of 0.625 inches and will fit into 3/4-inch tubing with a 0.058-inch wall which has an inside diameter of 0.634 inches. Having used quite a bit of this type tubing it is possible to state that 0.009-inch clearance is just right for a slip fit or for slotting the tubing and then using hose clamps. To repeat, always get the next larger size and specify a 0.058-inch wall to obtain the 0.009-inch clearance.

With the chart, a little figuring will provide all the information needed to build a beam, including what the antenna will weigh. The 6061-T6 type of aluminum is a relatively high strength and has good workability, plus being highly resistant to corrosion and will bend without taking a "set."

Check the Yellow Pages for aluminum dealers.

TABLE 21-V

6061-T6 (61S-T6) ROUND ALUMINUM TUBE

In 12-Foot Lengths

O. D. Inches	WALL THICKNESS Inches	Stubs Ga.	I. D. Inches	APPROX. WEIGHT Per Foot	Per Length
3/16"	.035	(No. 20)	.117	.019 lbs.	.228 lbs.
	.049	(No. 18)	.089	.025 lbs.	.330 lbs.
1/4"	.035	(No. 20)	.180	.027 lbs.	.324 lbs.
	.049	(No. 18)	.152	.036 lbs.	.432 lbs.
	.058	(No. 17)	.134	.041 lbs.	.492 lbs.
5/16"	.035	(No. 20)	.242	.036 lbs.	.432 lbs.
	.049	(No. 18)	.214	.047 lbs.	.564 lbs.
	.058	(No. 17)	.196	.055 lbs.	.660 lbs.
3/8"	.035	(No. 20)	.305	.043 lbs.	.516 lbs.
	.049	(No. 18)	.277	.060 lbs.	.720 lbs.
	.058	(No. 17)	.259	.068 lbs.	.816 lbs.
	.065	(No. 16)	.245	.074 lbs.	.888 lbs.
7/16"	.035	(No. 20)	.367	.051 lbs.	.612 lbs.
	.049	(No. 18)	.339	.070 lbs.	.840 lbs.
	.065	(No. 16)	.307	.089 lbs.	1.068 lbs.
1/2"	.028	(No. 22)	.444	.049 lbs.	.588 lbs.
	.035	(No. 20)	.430	.059 lbs.	.708 lbs.
	.049	(No. 18)	.402	.082 lbs.	.984 lbs.
	.058	(No. 17)	.384	.095 lbs.	1.040 lbs.
	.065	(No. 16)	.370	.107 lbs.	1.284 lbs.
5/8"	.028	(No. 22)	.569	.061 lbs.	.732 lbs.
	.035	(No. 20)	.555	.075 lbs.	.900 lbs.
	.049	(No. 18)	.527	.106 lbs.	1.272 lbs.
	.058	(No. 17)	.509	.121 lbs.	1.452 lbs.
	.065	(No. 16)	.495	.137 lbs.	1.644 lbs.
3/4"	.035	(No. 20)	.680	.091 lbs.	1.092 lbs.
	.049	(No. 18)	.652	.125 lbs.	1.500 lbs.
	.058	(No. 17)	.634	.148 lbs.	1.776 lbs.
	.065	(No. 16)	.620	.160 lbs.	1.920 lbs.
	.083	(No. 14)	.584	.204 lbs.	2.448 lbs.
7/8"	.035	(No. 20)	.805	.108 lbs.	1.308 lbs.
	.049	(No. 18)	.777	.151 lbs.	1.810 lbs.
	.058	(No. 17)	.759	.175 lbs.	2.100 lbs.
	.065	(No. 16)	.745	.199 lbs.	2.399 lbs.
1"	.035	(No. 20)	.930	.123 lbs.	1.476 lbs.
	.049	(No. 18)	.902	.170 lbs.	2.040 lbs.
	.058	(No. 17)	.884	.202 lbs.	2.424 lbs.
	.065	(No. 16)	.870	.220 lbs.	2.640 lbs.
1"	.083	(No. 14)	.834	.281 lbs.	3.372 lbs.
1 1/8"	.035	(No. 20)	1.055	.139 lbs.	1.668 lbs.
	.058	(No. 17)	1.009	.228 lbs.	2.736 lbs.
1 1/4"	.035	(No. 20)	1.180	.155 lbs.	1.860 lbs.
	.049	(No. 18)	1.152	.210 lbs.	2.520 lbs.
	.058	(No. 17)	1.134	.256 lbs.	3.072 lbs.
	.065	(No. 16)	1.120	.284 lbs.	3.408 lbs.
	.083	(No. 14)	1.084	.357 lbs.	4.284 lbs.
1 3/8"	.035	(No. 20)	1.305	.173 lbs.	2.076 lbs.
	.058	(No. 17)	1.259	.282 lbs.	3.384 lbs.
1 1/2"	.035	(No. 20)	1.430	.180 lbs.	2.160 lbs.
	.049	(No. 18)	1.402	.260 lbs.	3.120 lbs.
	.058	(No. 17)	1.384	.309 lbs.	3.708 lbs.
	.065	(No. 16)	1.370	.344 lbs.	4.128 lbs.
	.083	(No. 14)	1.334	.434 lbs.	5.208 lbs.
	*.125	1/8"	1.250	.630 lbs.	7.416 lbs.
	*.250	1/4"	1.000	1.150 lbs.	14.832 lbs.
1 5/8"	.035	(No. 20)	1.555	.206 lbs.	2.472 lbs.
	.058	(No. 17)	1.509	.336 lbs.	4.032 lbs.
1 3/4"	.058	(No. 17)	1.634	.363 lbs.	4.356 lbs.
	.083	(No. 14)	1.584	.510 lbs.	6.120 lbs.
1 7/8"	.058	(No. 17)	1.759	.389 lbs.	4.668 lbs.
2"	.049	(No. 18)	1.902	.350 lbs.	4.200 lbs.
	.065	(No. 16)	1.870	.450 lbs.	5.400 lbs.
	.083	(No. 14)	1.834	.590 lbs.	7.080 lbs.
	*.125	1/8"	1.750	.870 lbs.	9.960 lbs.
	*.250	1/4"	1.500	1.620 lbs.	19.920 lbs.
2 1/4"	.049	(No. 18)	2.152	.398 lbs.	4.776 lbs.
	.065	(No. 16)	2.120	.520 lbs.	6.240 lbs.
	.083	(No. 14)	2.084	.660 lbs.	7.920 lbs.
2 1/2"	.065	(No. 16)	2.370	.587 lbs.	7.044 lbs.
	.083	(No. 14)	2.334	.740 lbs.	8.880 lbs.
	*.125	1/8"	2.250	1.100 lbs.	12.720 lbs.
	*.250	1/4"	2.000	2.080 lbs.	25.440 lbs.
3"	.065	(No. 16)	2.870	.710 lbs.	8.520 lbs.
	*.125	1/8"	2.700	1.330 lbs.	15.600 lbs.
	*.250	1/4"	2.500	2.540 lbs.	31.200 lbs.

*These sizes are extruded. All other sizes are drawn tubes.

ANTENNA SUPPORTS

"A"-FRAME MAST

The simple and inexpensive mast shown in Fig. 21-55 is satisfactory for heights up to 35 or 40 feet. Clear, sound lumber should be selected. The completed mast may be protected by two or three coats of house paint.

If the mast is to be erected on the ground, a couple of stakes should be driven to keep the bottom from slipping and it may then be "walked up" by a pair of helpers. If it is to go on a roof, first stand it up against the side of the building and then hoist it from the roof, keeping it vertical. The whole assembly is light enough for two men to perform the complete operation – lifting the mast, carrying it to its permanent berth, and fastening the guys – with the mast vertical all the while. It is entirely practicable, therefore, to erect this type of mast on any small, flat area of roof.

By using 2 X 3s or 2 X 4s, the height may be extended up to about 50 feet. The 2 X 2 is too flexible to be satisfactory at such heights.

SIMPLE 40-FOOT MAST

The mast shown in Fig. 21-56 is relatively strong, easy to construct, readily dismantled, and costs very little. Like the "A"-frame, it is suitable for heights of the order of 40 feet.

The top section is a single 2 X 3, bolted at the bottom between a pair of 2 X 3s with an overlap of about two feet. The lower section thus has two legs spaced the width of the narrow side of a 2 X 3. At the bottom the two legs are bolted to a length of 2 X 4 which is set in the ground. A short length of 2 X 3 is placed between the two legs about halfway up the bottom section, to maintain the spacing.

The two back guys at the top pull against the antenna, while the three lower guys prevent buckling at the center of the pole.

The 2 X 4 section should be set in the ground so that it faces the proper direction, and then made vertical by lining it up with a plumb bob. The holes for the bolts should be drilled beforehand. With the lower section laid on the ground, bolt *A* should be slipped in place through the three pieces of wood and tightened just enough so that the section can turn freely on the bolt. Then the top section may be bolted in place and the mast pushed up, using a ladder or another 20-foot 2 X 3 for the job. As the mast goes up, the slack in the guys can be taken up so that the whole structure is in some measure continually supported. When the mast is vertical, bolt *B* should be slipped in place and both *A* and *B* tightened. The lower guys can then be given a final tightening, leaving those at the top a little slack until the antenna is pulled up, when they should be adjusted to pull the top section into line.

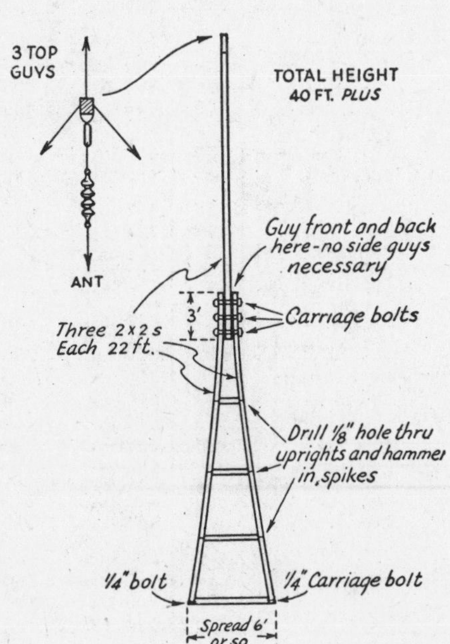

Fig. 21-55 – Details of a simple 40-foot "A"-frame mast suitable for erection in locations where space is limited.

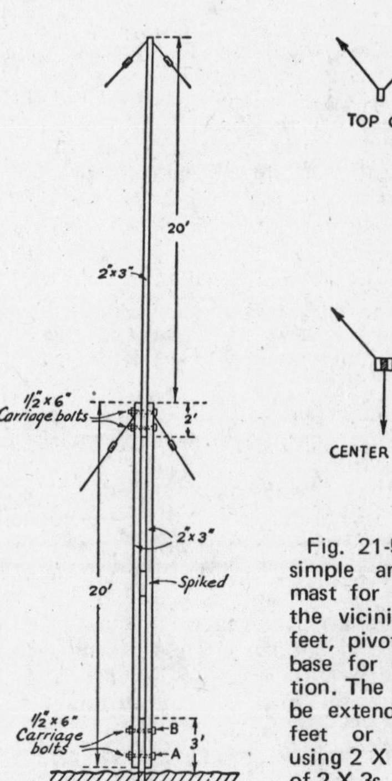

Fig. 21-56 – A simple and sturdy mast for heights in the vicinity of 40 feet, pivoted at the base for easy erection. The height can be extended to 50 feet or more by using 2 X 4s instead of 2 X 3s.

Fig. 21-57 – While guys are not normally required for the homemade tower, they provide an extra measure of protection against high winds. An inverted V can serve here as two of the guy lines.

A LOW COST TILT-OVER TOWER

Shown in Fig. 21-57 is a low-cost 30-foot tilt-over tower that can be made from readily available lumber. The tower will easily support a small triband beam or quad, and it can also serve as the midpoint connection for an inverted V. Fig. 21-60 shows the fixed section of the tower, anchored at the bottom in concrete (poured to a depth of 3 feet) and attached at the eaves with lag bolts. The sides of the fixed section are made from 12-foot-long 2 X 6s with 1 X 4 cross members. The inside dimension of the support is given in Fig. 21-58.

The tilt-over portion of the tower is made from 2 X 4s 30-feet long. Local lumber companies can order 30-foot (or longer) 2 X 4s. The complete tower cost was less than $35. The cross members of the tilt-over section are 2 X 4s, 9 inches long. These cross members are installed 25 inches apart, center-to-center. Additional bracing is provided by diagonally mounted stringers made from 1 X 2 stock. In the installation shown, the tower is tilted over from the bottom. One-inch diameter bolts installed at the bottom serve as the hinge. Bolts are also used near the eaves to secure the tower when it is in the upright position.

In the installation shown (at W1CUT) the tower had to be mounted against the side of the house, rather than at the end which would be a preferable location. If installed at the end of the house, the tower could be hinged at the roof peak and then tilted over onto the roof (making antenna work a little easier). In the installation shown, two men are required to raise or lower the tower – one man to "walk" the tower down and another on the roof, with a rope or tackle, to lower the assembly.

As shown in Fig. 21-59, the beam rotator is mounted near eaves. TV masting is run up through the center of the tower both as a support for the beam and also as a drive shaft. This serves to reduce the amount of weight that the tower has to carry near the top. The rotator shown is a TV type and will easily turn a small triband beam or quad.

GUYS AND GUY ANCHORS

For masts or poles up to about 50 feet, No. 12 iron wire is a satisfactory guy-wire material. Heavier wire or stranded cable may be used for taller poles or poles installed in locations where the wind velocity is likely to be high.

More than three guy wires in any one set usually are unnecessary. If a horizontal antenna is to be supported, two guy wires in the top set will be sufficient in most cases. These should run to the rear of the mast about 100 degrees apart to offset the pull of the antenna. Intermediate guys should be used in sets of three, one running in a direction opposite to that of the antenna, while the other two are spaced 120 degrees either side. This leaves a clear space under the antenna. The guy wires should be adjusted to pull the pole slightly back from vertical before the antenna is hoisted so that when the antenna is pulled up tight the mast will be straight.

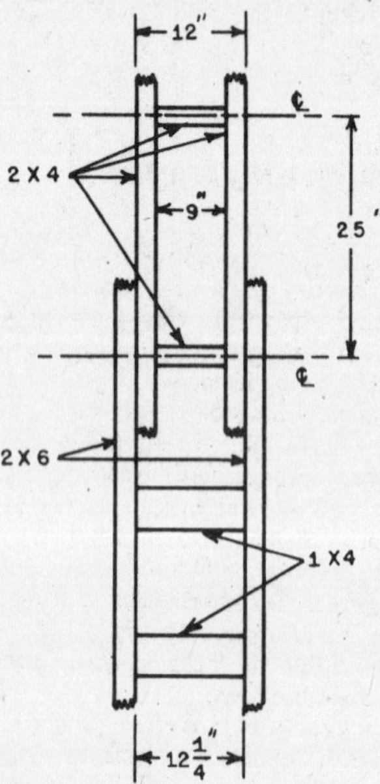

Fig. 21-58 – Constructional details of the fixed and tilt-over sections of the tower.

Guys and Guy Anchors

When raising a mast that is big enough to tax the available facilities, it is some advantage to know nearly exactly the length of the guys. Those on the side on which the pole is lying can then be fastened temporarily to the anchors beforehand, which assures that when the pole is raised, those holding opposite guys will be able to pull it into nearly vertical position with no danger of its getting out of control. The guy lengths can be figured by the right-angled-triangle rule that "the sum of the squares of the two sides is equal to the square of the hypotenuse." In other words, the distance from the base of the pole to the anchor should be measured and squared. To this should be added the square of the pole length to the point where the guy is fastened. The square root of this sum will be the length of the guy.

Guy wires should be broken up by strain insulators, to avoid the possibility of resonance at the transmitting frequency. Common practice is to insert an insulator near the top of each guy, within a few feet of the pole, and then cut each section of wire between the insulators to a length which will not be resonant either on the fundamental or harmonics. An insulator every 25 feet will be satisfactory for frequencies up to 30 MHz. The insulators should be of the "egg" type with the insulating material under compression, so that the guy will not part if the insulator breaks.

Twisting guy wires onto "egg" insulators may be a tedious job if the guy wires are long and of large gauge. A simple time- and finger-saving device (piece of heavy iron or steel) can be made by drilling a hole about twice the diameter of the guy wire about a half inch from one end of the piece. The wire is passed through the insulator, given a single turn by hand, and then held with a pair of pliers at the point shown in Fig. 21-61. By passing the wire through the hole in the iron and rotating the iron as shown, the wire may be quickly and neatly twisted.

HALYARDS AND PULLEYS

Halyards or ropes and pulleys are important items in the antenna-supporting system. Particular attention should be directed toward the choice of a pulley and halyards for a high mast since replacement, once the mast is in position, may be a major undertaking if not entirely impossible.

Galvanized-iron pulleys will have a life of only a year or so. Especially for coastal-area installations, marine-type pulleys with hardwood blocks and bronze wheels and bearings should be used.

For short antennas and temporary installations, heavy clothesline or window-sash cord may be used. However, for more permanent jobs, 3/8-inch or 1/2-inch waterproof hemp rope should be used. Even this should be replaced about once a year to insure against breakage.

It is advisable to carry the pulley rope back up to the top in "endless" fashion in the manner of a flag hoist so that if the antenna breaks close to the pole, there will be a means for pulling the hoisting rope back down.

Fig. 21-59 — This close-up shows the rotor and cable installations. A double 2 X 4 is used as the base support for the rotator.

Guy wires may be anchored to a tree or building when they happen to be in convenient spots. For small poles, a 6-foot length of 1-inch pipe driven into the ground at an angle will suffice.

Fig. 21-60 — The tower base support is made from 2 X 6s, the ends of which are in a 3-foot concrete base.

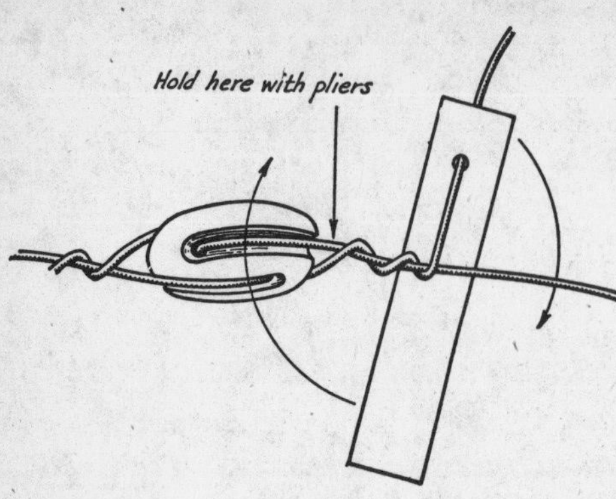

Fig. 21-61 – Using a lever for twisting heavy guy wires.

BRINGING THE FEED LINE INTO THE STATION

The antenna or transmission line should be anchored to the outside wall of the building, as shown in Fig. 21-63, to remove strain from the lead-in insulators. Holes cut through the walls of the building and fitted with feedthrough insulators are undoubtedly the best means of bringing the line into the station. The holes should have plenty of air clearance about the conducting rod, especially when using tuned lines that develop high voltages. Probably the best place to go through the walls is the trimming board at the top or bottom of a window frame which provides flat surfaces for lead-in insulators. Cement or rubber gaskets may be used to waterproof the exposed joints.

Where such a procedure is not permissible, the window itself usually offers the best opportunity. One satisfactory method is to drill holes in the glass near the top of the upper sash. If the glass is replaced by plate glass, a stronger job will result. Plate glass may be obtained from automobile junk yards, and drilled before placing in the frame. The glass itself provides insulation and the transmission line may be fastened to bolts fitting the holes. Rubber gaskets will render the holes waterproof. The lower sash should be provided with stops to prevent damage when it is raised. If the window has a full-length screen, the scheme shown in Fig. 21-63B may be used.

As a less permanent method, the window may be raised from the bottom or lowered from the top to permit insertion of a board which carries the feedthrough insulators. This lead-in arrangement can be made weatherproof by making an overlapping joint between the board and window sash, as shown in Fig. 21-62, or by using weatherstrip material where necessary.

Coaxial line can be brought through clearance holes without additional insulation.

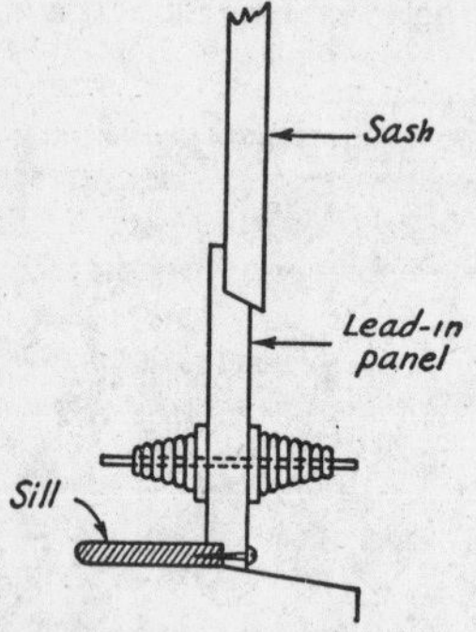

Fig. 21-62 – An antenna lead-in panel may be placed over the top sash or under the lower sash of a window. Substituting a smaller height sash in half the window will simplify the weatherproofing problem where the sash overlaps.

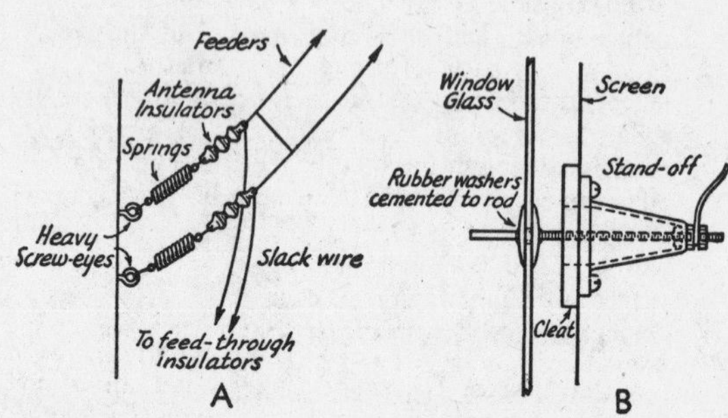

Fig. 21-63 – A – Anchoring feeders takes the strain from feed-through insulators or window glass. B – Going through a full-length screen, a cleat is fastened to the frame of the screen on the inside. Clearance holes are cut in the cleat and also in the screen.

Chapter 22

VHF and UHF Antennas

Improving his antenna system is one of the most productive moves open to the vhf enthusiast. It can increase transmitting range, improve reception, reduce interference problems, and bring other practical benefits. The work itself is by no means the least attractive part of the job. With even high-gain antennas, experimentation is greatly simplified, at vhf and uhf, because an array is a workable size, and much can be learned about the nature and adjustment of antennas. No large investment in test equipment is necessary.

Whether we buy or build our antennas, we soon find that there is no one "best" design for all purposes. Selecting the antenna best suited to our needs involves much more than scanning gain figures and prices in a manufacturer's catalog. The first step should be to establish priorities.

OBJECTIVES

Gain: Shaping the pattern of an antenna, to concentrate radiated energy, or received - signal pickup, in some directions at the expense of others is the only way to develop gain. This is best explained by starting with the hypothetical **isotropic antenna**, which would radiate equally in all directions. A point source of light illuminating the inside of a globe uniformly, from its center, is a visual analogy. No practical antenna can do this, so all antennas have "gain over isotropic" (**dBi**). A half-wave dipole in free space has 2.1 dBi. If we can plot the radiation pattern of antenna in all planes, we can compute its gain, so quoting it with respect to isotropic is a logical base for agreement and understanding. It is rarely possible to erect a half-wave antenna that has anything approaching a free-space pattern, and this fact is responsible for much of the confusion about true antenna gain.

Radiation patterns can be controlled in various ways. One is to use two or more driven elements, fed in phase. Such **collinear** arrays provide gain without markedly sharpening the frequency response, compared to that of a single element. More gain per element, but with a sacrifice in frequency coverage, is obtained by placing **parasitic elements** longer and shorter than the driven one, in the plane the first element, but not driven from the feedline. The reflector and directors of a **Yagi** array are highly frequency sensitive and such an antenna is at its best over frequency changes of less than one percent of the operating frequency.

Frequency Response: Ability to work over an entire vhf band may be important in some types of work. The response of an antenna element can be broadened somewhat by increasing the conductor diameter, and by tapering it to something approximating cigar shape, but this is done mainly with simple antennas. More practically, wide frequency coverage may be a reason to select a collinear array, rather than a Yagi. On the other hand, the growing tendency to channelize operations in small segments of our bands tends to place broad frequency coverage low on the priority list of most vhf stations.

Radiation Pattern: Antenna radiation can be made omnidirectional, bidirectional, practically unidirectional, or anything between these conditions. A vhf net operator may find an omnidirectional system almost a necessity, but it may be a poor choice otherwise. Noise pickup and other interference problems tend to be greater with such antennas, and those having some gain are especially bad in these respects. Maximum gain and low radiation angle are usually prime interests of the weak-signal DX aspirant. A clean pattern, with lowest possible pickup and radiation off the sides and back, may be important in high-activity areas, or where the noise level is high.

Height Gain: In general, the higher the better in vhf antenna installations. If raising the antenna clears its view over nearby obstructions, it may make dramatic improvements in coverage. Within reason greater height is almost always worth its cost, but height gain must be balanced against increased transmission-line loss. The latter is considerable, and it increases with frequency. The best available line may be none too good, if the run is long in terms of wavelength. Give line-loss information, shown in table form in Chapter 20, close scrutiny in any antenna planning.

Physical Size: A given antenna design for 432 MHz will have the same gain as one for 144 MHz, but being only one-third the size it will intercept only one-third as much energy in receiving. Thus, to be equal in communication effectiveness, the 432-MHz array should be at least equal in *size* to the 144-MHz one, which will require roughly three times as many elements. With all the extra difficulties involved in going higher in frequency, it is well to be on the big side, in building an antenna for the higher band.

DESIGN FACTORS

Having sorted out objectives in a general way, we face decisions on specifics, such as polarization, type of transmission line, matching methods and mechanical design.

Polarization: Whether to position the antenna elements vertical or horizontal has been a moot point since early vhf pioneering. Tests show little evidence on which to set up a uniform polarization policy. On long paths there is no consistent advantage, either way. Shorter paths tend to yield higher signal levels with horizontal in some kinds of terrain. Man-made noise, especially ignition interference, tends to be lower with horizontal. Verticals are markedly simpler to use in omnidirectional systems, and in mobile work.

Early vhf communication was largely vertical, but horizontal gained favor when directional arrays became widely used. The major trend to fm and repeaters, particularly in the 144-MHz band, has tipped the balance in favor of verticals in mobile work and for repeaters. Horizontal predominates in other communication, on 50 MHz and higher frequencies. It is well to check in advance in any new area in which you expect to operate, however, as some localities still use vertical almost exclusively. A circuit loss of 20 dB or more can be expected with cross-polarization.

Transmission Lines: There are two main categories of transmission lines: balanced and unbalanced. The former include open-wire lines separated by insulating spreaders, and Twin-Lead, in which the wires are embedded in solid or foamed insulation. Line losses result from ohmic resistance, radiation from the line, and deficiencies in the insulation. Large conductors, closely spaced in terms of wavelength, and using a minimum of insulation, make the best balanced lines. Impedances are mainly 300 to 500 ohms. Balanced lines are best in straight runs. If bends are unavoidable, the angles should be as obtuse as possible. Care should be taken to prevent one wire from coming closer to metal objects than the other. Wire spacing should be less than 1/20 wavelength.

Properly built, open-wire line can operate with very low loss in vhf and even uhf installations. A total line loss under 2 dB per hundred feet at 432 MHz is readily obtained. A line made of No. 12 wire, spaced 3/4 inch or less with Teflon spreaders, and running essentially straight from antenna to station, can be better than anything but the most expensive coax, at a fraction of the cost. This assumes use of baluns to match into and out of the line, with a short length of quality coax for the moving section from the top of the tower to the antenna. A similar 144-MHz setup could have a line loss under 1 dB.

Small coax such as RG-58 or 59 should never be used in vhf work if the run is more than a few feet. Half-inch lines (RG-8 or 11) work fairly well at 50 MHz, and are acceptable for 144-MHz runs of 50 feet or less. If these lines have foam rather than solid insulation they are about 30 percent better. Aluminum-jacket lines with large inner conductors and foam insulation are well worth their cost. They are readily water-proofed, and can last almost indefinitely. Beware of any "bargains" in coax for vhf or uhf uses. Lost transmitter power can be made up to some extent by increasing power, but once lost, a weak signal can never be recovered in the receiver.

Effects of weather should not be ignored. A well-constructed open-wire line works well in nearly any weather, and it stands up well. Twin-Lead is almost useless in heavy rain, wet snow or icing. The best grades of coax are impervious to weather. They can be run underground, fastened to metal towers without insulation, or bent into any convenient position, with no adverse effects on performance.

Impedance Matching

Theory and practice in impedance matching are given in detail in earlier chapters, and theory, at least, is the same for frequencies above 50 MHz. Practice may be similar, but physical size can be a major modifying factor in choice of methods. Only the matching devices used in practical construction examples later in this chapter will be discussed in detail here. This should not rule out consideration of other methods, however, and a reading of relevant portions of Chapters 20 and 21 is recommended.

Universal Stub: As its name implies, the double-adjustment stub of Fig. 22-1A is useful for many matching purposes. The stub length is varied to resonate the system, and the transmission line is tapped onto the stub at the point where line and stub impedances are equal. In practice this involves moving both the sliding short and the point of line connection for zero reflected power, as indicated on an SWR bridge connected in the line.

The universal stub allows for tuning out any small reactance present in the driven part of the

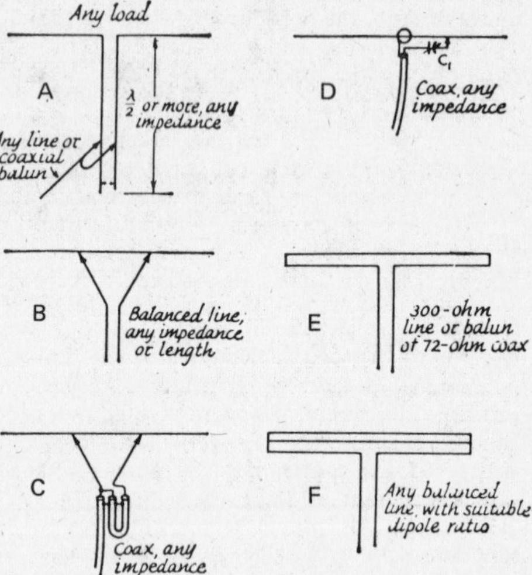

Fig. 22-1 — Matching methods commonly used in vhf antennas. The universal stub, A, combines tuning and matching. The adjustable short on the stub, and the points of connection of the transmission line, are adjusted for minimum reflected power in the line. In the delta match, B and C, the line is fanned out to tap on the dipole at the point of best impedance match. Impedances need not be known in A, B and C. The gamma-match, D, is for direct connection of coax. C1 tunes out inductance in the arm. Folded dipole of uniform conductor size, E, steps up antenna impedance by a factor of 4. Using a larger conductor in the unbroken portion of the folded dipole, E, gives higher orders of impedance transformation.

system. It permits matching antenna to line without knowledge of the actual impedances involved. The position of the short yielding the best match gives some indication of amount of reactance present. With little or no reactive component to be tuned out, the stub will be approximately a half-wavelength from load to short.

The stub should be stiff bare wire or rod, spaced no more than 1/20 wavelength. Preferably it should be mounted rigidly, on insulators. Once the position of the short is determined, the center of the short can be grounded, if desired, and the portion of the stub no longer needed can be removed.

It is not necessary that the stub be connected directly to the driven element. It can be made part of an open-wire line, as a device to match into or out of the line with coax. It can be connected to the lower end of a delta match, or placed at the feedpoint of a phased array. Examples of these uses are given later.

Delta Match: Probably the first impedance match was made when the ends of an open line were fanned out and tapped onto a half-wave antenna, at the point of most efficient power transfer, as in Fig. 22-1B. Both the side length and the points of connection either side of the center of the element must be adjusted for minimum reflected power in the line, but as with the universal stub, the impedances need not be known. The delta makes no provision for tuning out reactance, so the universal stub is often used as a termination for it, to this end.

Once thought to be inferior for vhf applications because of its tendency to radiate if improperly adjusted, the delta has come back to favor, now that we have good methods for measuring the effects of matching. It is very handy for phasing multiple-bay arrays with open lines, and its dimensions in this use are not particularly critical. It should be checked out carefully in applications like that of Fig. 22-1C, having no tuning device.

Gamma Match: An application of the same principle to direct connection of coax is the gamma match, Fig. 22-1D. There being no rf voltage at the center of a half-wave dipole, the outer conductor of the coax is connected to the element at this point, which may also be the junction with a metallic or wooden boom. The inner conductor, carrying the rf current, is tapped out on the element at the matching point. Inductance of the arm is tuned out by means of C1, resulting in electrical balance. Both the point of contact with the element and the setting of the capacitor are adjusted for zero reflected power, with a bridge connected in the coaxial line.

The capacitor can be made variable temporarily, then replaced with a suitable fixed unit when the required capacitance value is found, or C1 can be mounted in a waterproof box. Maximum should be about 100 pF for 50 MHz and 35 to 50 pF for 144. The capacitor and arm can be combined in one coaxial assembly, with the arm connecting to the driven element by means of a sliding clamp, and the inner end of the arm sliding inside a sleeve connected to the inner conductor of the coax. A commercially supplied assembly of this type is used in a 50-MHz array described later, or one can be constructed from concentric pieces of tubing, insulated by plastic sleeving. Rf voltage across the capacitor is low, once the match is adjusted properly, so with a good dielectric, insulation presents no great problem, if the initial adjustment is made with low power level. A clean, permanent high-conductivity bond between arm and element is important, as the rf current flow is high at this point.

Folded Dipole: The impedance of a half-wave antenna broken at its center is 72 ohms. If a single conductor of uniform size is folded to make a half-wave dipole as shown in Fig. 22-1E, the impedance is stepped up four times. Such a folded dipole can thus be fed directly with 300-ohm line with no appreciable mismatch. Coaxial line of 70 to 75 ohms impedance may also be used, if a 4:1 balun is added. (See balun information presented later in this chapter.) Higher impedance step up can be obtained if the unbroken portion is made larger in cross-section than the fed portion, as in 22-1F. For design information, see Chapter 20.

Baluns and Transmatches: Conversion from balanced loads to unbalanced lines, or vice versa, can be performed with electrical circuits, or their equivalents made of coaxial line. A balun made from flexible coax is shown in Fig. 22-2A. The looped portion is an electrical half-wavelength. The physical length depends on the propagation factor of the line used, so it is well to check its resonant frequency, as shown at B. The two ends are shorted, and the loop at one end is coupled to a dip-meter coil. This type of balun gives an impedance stepup of 4 to 1 in impedance, 50 to 200 ohms, or 75 to 300 ohms, typically.

Coaxial baluns giving 1-to-1 impedance transfer are shown in Fig. 22-3. The coaxial sleeve, open at the top and connected to the outer conductor of the line at the lower end (A) is the preferred type. A conductor of approximately the same size as the line is used with the outer conductor to form a quarter-wave stub, in B. Another piece of coax, using only the outer conductor, will serve this purpose. Both baluns are intended to present an infinite impedance to any rf current that might otherwise tend to flow on the outer conductor of the coax.

The functions of the balun and the impedance

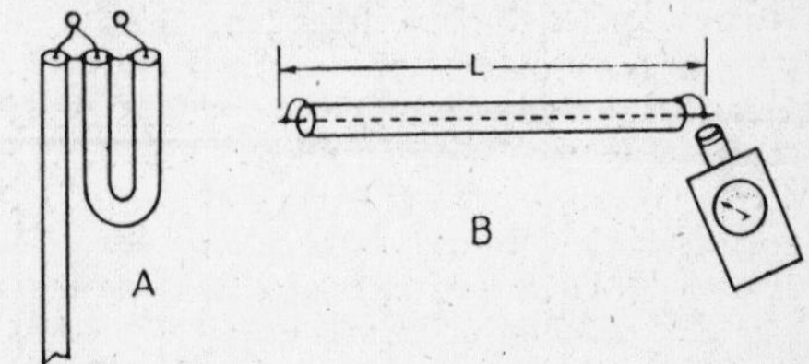

Fig. 22-2 – Conversion from unbalanced coax to a balanced load can be done with a half-wave coaxial balun, A. Electrical length of the looped section should be checked with a dip-meter, with ends shorted, B. The half-wave balun gives a 4:1 impedance step up.

transformer can be handled by various tuned circuits. Such a device, commonly called an antenna coupler or Transmatch, can provide a wide range of impedance transformations. A versatile example is described at the end of this chapter.

The *Q* Section: The impedance transforming property of a quarter-wave line is treated in Chapter 20. The parallel-bar Q section is not useful in low-impedance vhf matching situations, but Q sections of flexible coaxial line may be handy in phasing and matching vhf and uhf arrays. Such sections can be any odd multiple of a quarter-wavelength. An example of two 3/4-wave 75-ohm Q sections, used to phase and match a pair of Yagi bays, each of which has 50 ohms impedance, is given later in this chapter.

Mechanical Design

The small size of vhf and, especially, uhf arrays opens up a wide range of construction possibilities. Finding components is becoming difficult for home constructors of ham gear, but it should not hold back antenna work. Radio and TV distributors have many useful antenna parts and materials. Hardware stores, metals suppliers, lumber yards, welding-supply and plumbing-supply houses and even junkyards should not be overlooked. With a little imagination, the possibilities are endless.

Wood or Metal? Wood is very useful in antenna work, and it is almost universally available, in a great variety of shapes and sizes. Rug poles of wood or bamboo make fine booms. Round wood stock (dowelling) is found in many hardware stores in sizes suitable for small arrays. Square or rectangular boom and frame materials can be ripped to order in most lumber yards, if they are not available from the racks in suitable sizes.

There is no rf voltage at the center of a half-wave dipole or parasitic element, so no insulation is required in mounting elements that are centered in the support, whether the latter is wood or metal. Wood is good for the framework of multibay arrays for the higher bands, as it keeps down the amount of metal in the active area of the array.

Wood used for antenna construction should be well-seasoned and free of knots or damage. Available materials vary, depending on local sources. Your lumber dealer can help you better than anyone else in choosing suitable materials. Joining wood members at right angles is often done advantageously with gusset plates. These can be of thin outdoor-grade plywood or Masonite. Round materials can be handled in ways similar to those used with metal components, with U clamps and with other hardware.

Metal booms have a small "shorting effect" on elements that run through them. With materials sizes commonly employed, this is not more than one percent of the element length, and may not be noticeable in many applications. It is just perceptible with 1/2-inch tubing booms used on 432 MHz, for example. Formula lengths can be used as given, if the matching is adjusted in the frequency range one expects to use. The center frequency of an all-metal array will tend to be 0.5 to 1 percent higher than a similar system built of wooden supporting members.

Element Materials and Dimensions: Antennas for 50 MHz need not have elements larger than 1/2-inch diameter, though up to 1 inch is used occasionally. At 144 and 220 MHz the elements are usually 1/8 to 1/4 inch in diameter. For 420, elements as small as 1/16 inch in diameter work well, if made of stiff rod. Aluminum welding rod, 3/32 to 1/8 inch in diameter is fine for 420-MHz arrays, and 1/8 inch or larger is good for the 220 band. Aluminum rod or hard-drawn wire works well at 144 MHz. Very strong elements can be made with stiff-rod inserts in hollow tubing. If the latter is slotted, and tightened down with a small clamp, the element lengths can be adjusted experimentally with ease.

Sizes recommended above are usable with formula dimensions given in Table 22-I. Larger diameters broaden frequency response; smaller ones sharpen it. Much smaller diameters than those recommended will require longer elements, especially in 50-MHz arrays.

The driven element(s) of a vhf array may be cut from the formula

$$L \text{ (inches)} = \frac{5600}{\text{Freq. (MHz)}}$$

This is the basis for Table 22-I driven-element information. Reflectors are usually about 5 percent longer, and directors 5 percent shorter, though element spacing and desired antenna bandwidth affect parasitic-element lengths. The closer the reflector and director (especially the latter) are to the driven element the nearer they must be to the driven-element length to give optimum gain. This is another way of saying that close-spaced arrays tend to work effectively over narrower bandwidths than

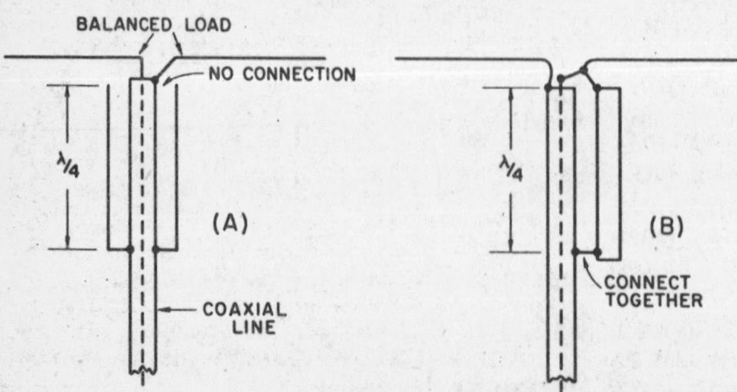

Fig. 22-3 — The balun conversion function, with no impedance change, is accomplished with quarter-wave lines, open at the top and connected to the coax outer conductor at the bottom. Coaxial sleeve, A, is the preferred type.

TABLE 22-I

Dimensions for VHF Arrays in Inches

*Freq. (MHz)**	*50**	*144**	*220**	*432**
Driven Element	111	38 5/8	25 7/16	13
Change per MHz	2	1/4	1/8	1/32
Reflector	116 1/2	40 1/2	26 3/4	13 1/2
1st Director	105 1/2	36 5/8	24 1/8	12 11/32
2nd Director	103 1/2	36 3/8	24	12 9/32
3rd Director	101 1/2	36 1/8	23 7/8	12 7/32
1.0 Wavelength	236	81 1/2	53 5/8	27 1/4
0.625 Wavelength	149	51	33 1/2	17
0.5 Wavelength	118	40 3/4	26 13/16	13 5/8
0.25 Wavelength	59	20 3/8	13 7/8	6 13/16
0.2 Wavelength	47 3/4	16 1/4	10 3/4	5 7/16
0.15 Wavelength	35 1/2	12 1/4	8	4

* Dimensions are for the *most-used* section of each band: 50 to 50.6 MHz, 144 to 145.5 MHz, 220 to 222 MHz, and 432 to 434 MHz. The element lengths should be adjusted for each megahertz difference in frequency by the amount given in the third line of the table. Example: If optimum performance is wanted much above 145 MHz, shorten all elements by about ¼ inch. For above 146 MHz, shorten by ½ inch. See text.

Element spacings are not critical, and table figures may be used, regardless of element lengths chosen. Parasitic element lengths are optimum for collinear arrays and small Yagis, having 0.2-wavelength spacing.

wide-spaced ones, though maximum gain may be possible with many different combinations of lengths and spacings.

Parasitic-element lengths of Table 22-I are based on spacings of about 0.2 wavelength, common in relatively short Yagis and collinear arrays. Dimensions given later in the individual descriptions of antennas may be at variance with those of the table. Where this is evident, the length differences result from use of different element spacings, for the most part. Some designs are for maximum gain, without consideration of bandwidth. Still others have slightly modified spacings, to give optimum results with a particular boom length.

ANTENNAS FOR 50 MHz

Simple antennas such as dipoles, groundplanes, mobile whips and the like are covered adequately elsewhere in this *Handbook.* Adaptation of them to vhf work involves mainly reference to Table 22-I for length information. We will be concerned here with arrays that give appreciable gain, or other properties needed in vhf communication.

Yagis, Short and Long: The Yagi array is practically standard for 50-MHz directive use. Usual sizes are three to six elements, though up to eight or nine in line are seen in ambitious installations. Director spacing, after the first three, must be very wide to be worthwhile, so boom lengths of 30 feet or more are needed for more than 6 elements. Though long Yagis certainly are desirable, it should be emphasized that the first two or three elements provide very high gain per unit of space. Even a 3-element Yagi, on as short a boom as 6 feet, is good for 7.5 dB over a dipole. To double the gain (add 3 dB) requires going to only 6 elements – but it takes a boom more than 20 feet long. If it is possible to put up a rotatable antenna at all, there is usually room for at least a 3-element structure, and the gain such an antenna provides is very helpful. Dimensions can follow those given for the first three elements of larger arrays described here.

Stacking Yagis: Where suitable provision can be made for supporting them, two Yagis mounted one above the other and fed in phase may be preferable to one long Yagi having the same theoretical or measured gain. The pair will require a much smaller turning space, for the same gain, and their lower radiation angle can provide interesting results. On long ionospheric paths a stacked pair occasionally may show an *apparent* gain much greater than the 2 to 3 dB that can be measured locally as the gain due to stacking.

Optimum spacing for Yagis of 5 elements or more is one wavelength, but this may be too much for many builders of 50-MHz antennas to handle. Worthwhile results can be obtained with as little as one half-wavelength (10 feet), and 5/8 wavelength (12 feet) is markedly better. The difference between 12 and 20 feet may not be worth the added structural problems involved in the wider spacing, at 50 MHz, at least. The closer spacings give lower measured gain, but the antenna patterns are cleaner than will be obtained with one-wavelength spacing. The extra gain with wider spacings

Fig. 22-4 – 5-over-5 stacked-Yagi array for 50 MHz, with all-coax feed.

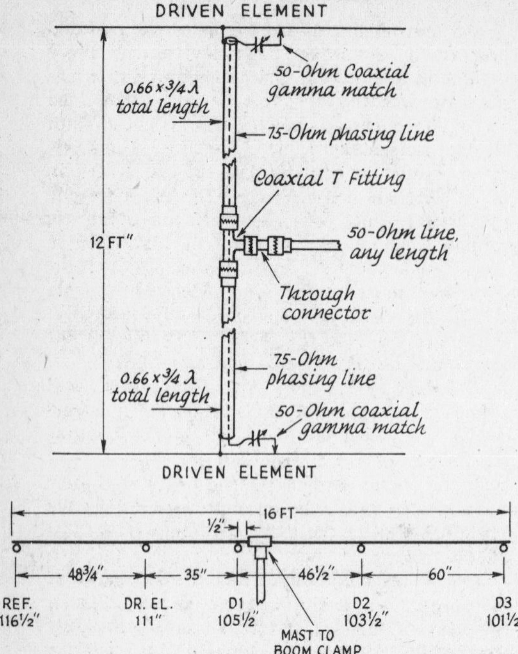

Fig. 22-5 – Principal dimensions of the 50-MHz 5-over-5, with details of the 3/4-wavelength *Q*-section matching system. The propagation factor of 0.66 applies only with solid-dielectric coax. Gamma-matching assemblies are coaxial-capacitor units (Kirk Electronics C6M).

is usually the objective on 144 MHz and higher bands, where the structural problems are not severe.

5-OVER-5 FOR 50 MHz

The information provided in Fig. 22-5 is useful for a single 5-element Yagi, or for the stacked pair of Fig. 22-4, either to be fed with a 50-ohm line. The phasing and matching arrangement may be used for any pair of Yagis designed for 50-ohm feed individually. With slight modification it will serve with Yagis designed for 200-ohm balanced feed.

Mechanical Details

Construction of the single Yagi bay or a stacked pair is simplified by use of components that should be available to most builders. Element-to-boom and boom-to-mast mounts are aluminum castings designed for these applications by Kirk Electronics, 134 Westpark Road, Dayton, Ohio 45459. The gamma matches shown schematically in Fig. 22-5 are of coaxial construction, waterproofed for long life, available from the same supplier.

Booms are made of two 8-foot lengths of 1 1/-4-inch aluminum (Reynolds) found in many hardware stores. Reynolds makes a special fitting for joining sections of the tubing, but these are not widely available from the usual hardware-store stocks, so a handmade splice was substituted. A piece of the same-diameter tubing as the booms, 12 inches or more in length, is slotted with a hacksaw, and then compressed to fit inside the ends of the two 8-foot lengths, as seen in Fig. 22-6.If the splice is held in the compressed position with large pipe pliers or a hose clamp, the ends will slide inside the boom sections readily. When the splice is released from compression, the two tubes can be driven together. Self-tapping screws should be run through the tubes and the splice, to hold the assembly firm. Use at least two on each side of the splice.

Elements are 1/2-inch aluminum tubing, Alcoa alloy 6061-T6. Almost any aluminum should be suitable. Kirk Yagi clamps, one-piece aluminum castings designed for this job, are available for 3/8 as well as 1/2-inch elements, and 1 1/4-inch boom. The eyes through which the elements pass are drilled, but must be tapped for 10-32 setscrews to tighten the elements firmly in place, two screws per element. The portion of the clamp that surrounds the boom can be spread slightly to allow the clamp to slide along the boom to the desired point. The interior surface is slightly rough, so tightening the yoke with the screw provided with the clamps makes the element set firmly on the boom. The reflector, driven element and first director are all in back of the boom splice.

The vertical member of the stacked array is 1 1/4-inch thick-wall anodized steel tubing, commonly used in large antenna installations for home TV. Do not use thin-wall aluminum or light galvanized steel masting. The aluminum is not strong enough, and inexpensive steel masting rusts inside, weakening the structure and inviting failure.

Spacing between bays can be a half wavelength (10 feet), 5/8 wavelength (12 feet), or a full wavelength (20 feet), though the wide spacing imposes mechanical problems that may not be worth the effort for most builders. The 5/8-wave spacing is a good compromise between stacking gain and severe support problems, and is recommended with the materials used here.

The 10-foot lengths of steel masting could be used, with the bottom 8 feet running through the tower bearing to the rotator. A heavier main support is preferable, however, and it is "1-inch water pipe" in this installation. This is iron, about 1 3/8-inch outside diameter, extending about 8 feet out of the tower. The steel masting between the Yagi bays is fastened to the pipe with four TV-type U-clamps, spaced evenly in the overlapping area of the two supports.

The booms are braced to the mast fore and aft, using the longest pieces of element stock left over when the forward directors are cut from 12-foot lengths. Ends of the braces are flattened about one inch, and bent to the proper angle. Outer ends fasten to the booms with two self-tapping screws each. The mast ends are clamped to the support with one TV U-clamp for each pair. This bracing is good insurance against fluttering of the booms and elements, which can cause failures after long periods, even though a structure appears adequately strong.

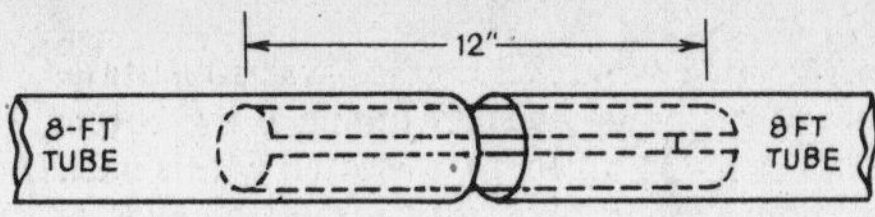

Fig. 22-6 – Details of the boom splices used in the 5-element 50-MHz Yagis. Two 8-foot lengths of 1 1/4-inch tubing are joined to make the 16-foot booms.

Phasing and Matching

A single 5-element Yagi can be fed directly with 50-ohm coax, through the Kirk coaxial gamma-match assembly (Type C6M). This has an adjustable coaxial capacitor, and an arm that connects to the driven element with a sliding clip. Both the capacitor and the point of connection should be adjusted for minimum reflected power, at the center of the frequency range most used. Doing this between 50.2 and 50.4 MHz is suitable for most operators, other than those using fm above 52.5 MHz. Each bay of the stacked pair should be set in this way. The pair can then be fed through a double *Q*-section of 75-ohm coax, as shown in Fig. 22-5.

The Kirk gamma-match assembly has an SO-239 coaxial fitting built in, so the phasing lines are fitted with PL-259 coaxial connectors at both ends. The inner ends attach to a matching coaxial T fitting. The main run of 50-ohm line connects to the center of the T, with a coaxial through-connector and a PL-259 fitting. When the antenna is installed all connectors should be wrapped tightly with plastic tape, and sprayed with Krylon or other protective spray. Dow-Corning Silastic RTV-732 sealant is also good for this use. If the coaxial phasing sections are wrapped around the booms and vertical support a few times, they will just reach the T-fitting, when 12-foot spacing is used.

The lines should be any odd multiple of a quarter-wavelength. If both are the same length the gamma arms should attach to the same side of the driven elements. If there is a half-wavelength difference in the lines, the arms should connect to opposite sides. The length given in Fig. 22-5 is nominal for solid-dielectric coax. If foam-dielectric line is used, the propagation factor given by the maker should be substituted for the 0.66 figure. It is best to grid-dip the line sections for resonant frequency, in any case. Cut the line three inches or more longer than the expected length. Solder a loop of wire between the center pin and the mounting flange of an SO-239 connector. Attach this to the PL-259 connector at one end of the line, and couple it to the dip-meter coil. Trim the line length until resonance at the midpoint of the intended frequency range is indicated. This will not change appreciably when the other coaxial connector is attached.

The line used in the model described is RG-59A/U, which is satisfactory for any amateur power level, so long as the SWR is kept low. Larger coax, such as RG-11A/U, is recommended for a greater margin of safety.

Adjustment and Testing

An individual Yagi can be tested and matched properly by mounting it a half-wavelength above ground, in a large area that is clear of obstructions for many wavelengths. The boom can also be tilted up, until the ground-reflected wave is not a factor in the field-strength meter reading. The SWR bridge should be connected at the gamma match, or an electrical half-wavelength therefrom. Apply low power (not over 10 watts) and adjust the gamma capacitor and the point of connection to the driven element for zero reflected power, at the desired frequency range. The model was flat from 50.2 to 50.4 with just perceptible reflected power showing at 50.1 to 50.5. Adjusted in this way the array should work well up to about 51 MHz.

The best way to check operation of the stacked pair is to support the array with the reflectors resting on the ground and the booms pointing straight up. A 6-foot step-ladder can be used for a temporary support. The bays can be fed separately with 50-ohm line, in this position, and the gamma settings should be the same as obtained in the first check, described above. Now connect the two 75-ohm phasing lines, and insert the SWR bridge in the 50-ohm line to the T fitting. The SWR should be the same as when the bays are fed separately through the 50-ohm line; close to 1:1. The array can be dismantled and reassembled atop the tower, and matching should remain correct.

The matching-phasing system described is useful for any two loads designed for 50-ohm feed. The 5/8-wave spacing is usable with up to at least 6-element bays, though wider bay spacing is needed for maximum gain with long Yagis. Individual antennas intended for 200-ohm balanced feed can be matched with 75-ohm coax in the phasing harness and baluns at each load.

Bay spacing is not critical. Close spacing gives somewhat lower gain, but a very clean pattern. The main lobe gets sharper and larger as spacing is increased, but minor lobes also increase. These take over from the main lobe if spacing of bays is carried too far. The effect of increasing bay spacing is shown graphically in Fig. 8-11 of *The Radio Amateur's VHF Manual*, and associated text.

144 OVER 50

Four phased 144-MHz Yagis are shown mounted above a 50-MHz 6-element Yagi in Fig. 22-7. The latter can be mechanically similar to the 5-element antennas of Fig. 22-4, though this two-band system was built almost entirely by hand. Element spacings are closer than in the 5-element 6-meter arrays, in order to fit 6 elements onto a 20-foot boom. The individual bays of the 2-meter array can be used singly, in pairs, or in the 4-bay system shown. Feed details are given for each application.

6-Element 50-MHz Yagi

The 6-meter elements were designed for light weight, with 1/2-inch tubing for half their length and thin-wall fuel-line tubing inserts for the outer

Fig. 22-7 – Antennas for two bands on a single support. Four 5-element Yagis for 144 MHz, top, have one-wavelength spacing each way. The 50-MHz Yagi is set up to make optimum use of 6 elements on a 20-foot boom.

portions. One-piece half-inch elements are equally good, though a bit bulkier. Elements can be run through the boom and held in place with clamps, as in Fig. 22-8, or mounted in Kirk castings. (See 5-element array description.) Lengths are 116, 110 1/2, 105 1/2, 104, 102 3/4, and 101 1/2 inches. Spacings, in the same order, are 36, 36, 42, 56 and 66 inches. The boom is made of two 10-foot aluminum mast sections, braced from above with 3/4-inch tubing. See Fig. 22-8.

The gamma matching was handled in two different ways. A coaxial capacitor and moving arm was hand-made, as shown in Fig. 22-9 using 1/2-inch and 1/4-inch tubes, insulated from one another by plastic sleeves that just fit inside the 1/2-inch fixed portion. The inner tubing can be wrapped with plastic tape to build up the needed thickness, to the same end. The arm is supported at two points with 1-inch ceramic pillars.

A second and simplier matching arrangement uses merely an extension of the main coaxial line, with a 100-pF fixed transmitting-type capacitor in series with the inner conductor and the sliding contact. The matching point was about 20 inches

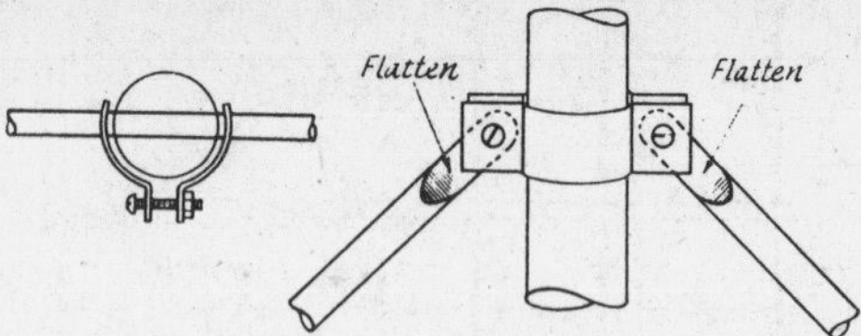

Fig. 22-8 – Elements may be run through a wood or metal boom, and held in place with simple aluminum clamps, left. At the right is a clamp for holding boom braces on the vertical support in the 50-MHz 6-element array.

out from the boom with a 100-pF capacitor. It is suggested that the matching be done first with a variable capacitor, substituting a fixed one when the desired value is found.

An element-mounting clamp no longer available appears in Fig. 22-9. The Kirk 1/2-to-1 1/4-inch element-mounting clamps (see 5-over-5 description) do this job nicely.

5-Element 144-MHz Yagis

An optimum design for 5-element 2-meter Yagis, to be used singly or combined in stacked systems, is shown in Fig. 22-10. Dimensions given work well from 144 to 146 MHz, if the matching is adjusted at 145. Lengths should be reduced 1/4 inch for each megahertz higher center frequency than 145 MHz. The original elements have center sections of 1/4-inch aluminum tubing, with 5/32-inch rod inserts that slide into the center members. One-piece elements of 1/8 to 1/4-inch tubing or rod will work equally well. The larger size will permit fastening in place with self-tapping screws bearing on the elements. For smaller sizes, use a clamp like that of Fig. 22-8. The booms are 3/4- or 1-inch diameter aluminum. Wood dowelling could be used equally well.

Feed Methods: A delta match is used in conjunction with a coaxial-line balun to feed a single 5-element Yagi. Some experimentation with delta dimensions may be required to achieve the best match. (See Fig. 22-1C and detailed description of the delta match earlier in this chapter.) This arrangement makes a fine small Yagi that can be dismantled readily, for carrying about in portable work.

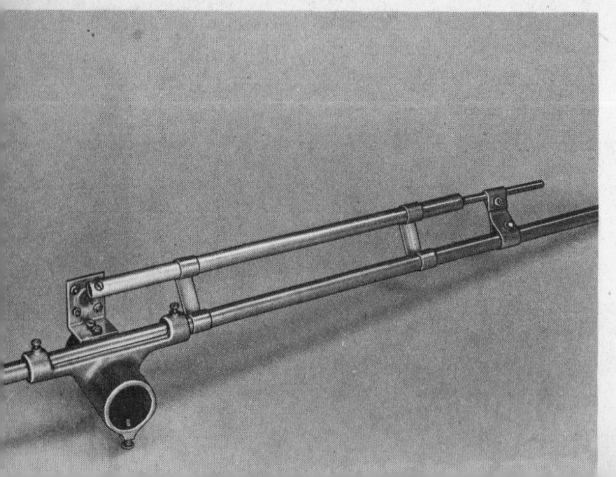

Fig. 22-9 – A hand-made coaxial gamma match for 50-MHz arrays. A 1/4-inch rod or tube 14 inches or longer slides inside a 1/2-inch sleeve that is connected to the coaxial fitting above the boom. The rod slides on plastic sleeves inside the larger section. Separation is maintained with two ceramic pillars mounted with wrap-around clips. Both the coaxial capacitor and the sliding clip between rod and element are adjusted for minimum reflected power in the coaxial line.

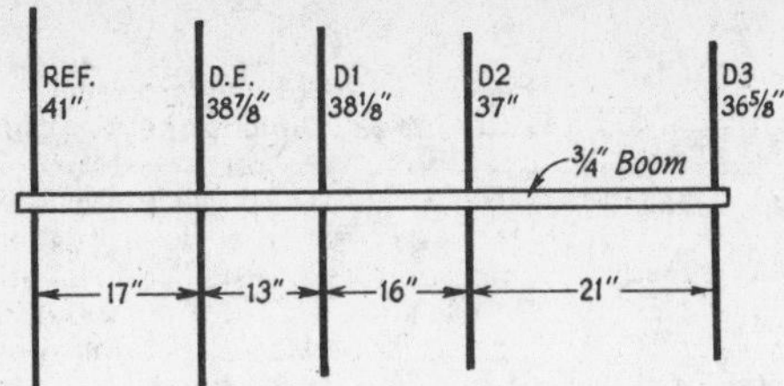

Fig. 22-10 – Optimum design for a 2-meter Yagi, using 5 elements on a 6-foot boom. When used singly, this antenna can be fed as shown in Fig. 22-1C, with 4-inch delta arms connected 3 inches either side of center. The balun loop would be about 27 inches long. With lengths shown, the antenna works well from 144 to above 146 MHz, but gain drops sharply above 147 MHz.

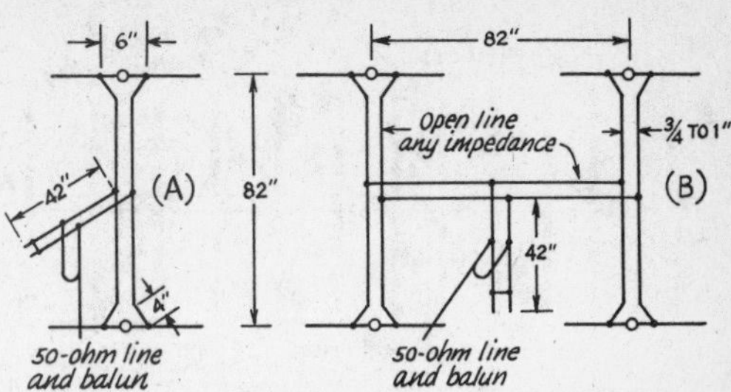

Fig. 22-11 – Stacking details for the 5-element Yagis of Fig. 22-7 and 22-10. The short on the universal stub, and the point of connection of the main transmission line, are adjusted for minimum reflected power in the latter. Balanced line could be connected similarly for the main turn.

Use of two 5-element Yagis with 1-wavelength spacing is shown in Fig. 22-11A. The phasing harness can be any open-wire line, preferably not spaced more than one inch. Delta dimensions are not critical in this application, as the matching is done with the universal stub at the center of the harness.

The 4-bay 20-element system in Fig. 22-7 and 22-11B uses two sets of 5-over-5, connected between centers with another 1-wavelength line. The universal stub is connected at the center of the horizontal section. In each case, the stub length and line-connection point are adjusted for minimum reflected power in the main line.

An interesting phasing method was used in the 4-bay array. Common electric zipcord, available in any hardware store, was split into its two parts. The insulation was left on, and spreaders made of ordinary 1/2-inch wood dowel were used to hold the wires one inch apart. Holes were drilled in these of such size that the zipcord could just be pulled through them. They are held in place with any good cement. If supported with TV-type screweyes that grip the spreaders, such a low-cost line is very durable. The array shown was taken down after two years of use in a very exposed location, and no deterioration was apparent. There was no breakage, even under several heavy ice loads each winter. Using several supports on each harness section is the key to this long life.

The transmission line was switched between the six- and two-meter arrays by means of a waterproofed antenna relay. To avoid the dangers of a 115-volt line run, 6.3-volt transformers were used at each end. This one-line hookup makes it possible to use a single rather expensive line to its fullest potential on two bands.

13-ELEMENT YAGI FOR 144 MHz

Many combinations of element lengths and spacings work well in long Yagis. The 13-element array detailed in Fig. 22-12 is the product of many months of joint experimental work by W2NLY and W6QKI. First described in *QST* for January, 1956, it has been a winner ever since. Elements are 1/8-inch hard-drawn aluminum wire, except for the folded-dipole driven element. This is the step up variety, intended to give a feed impedance of 200 ohms, for feeding with 50-ohm line and a coaxial balun.

The 24-foot boom carries a light load, and can

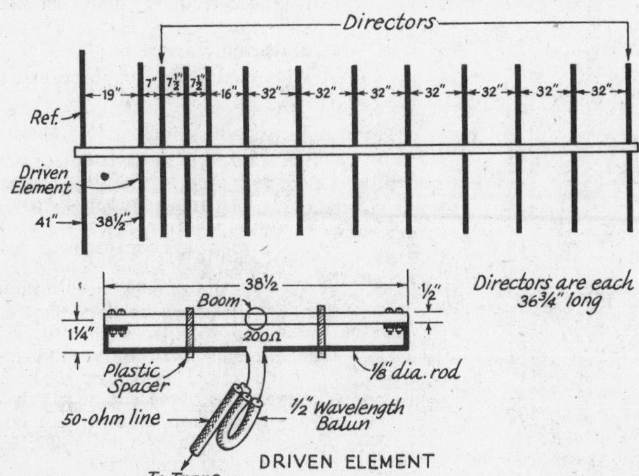

Fig. 22-12 – High-performance long Yagi for 144 MHz, from experimental work by W2NLY and W6QKI. Dimensions are for maximum gain between 144 and 145 MHz.

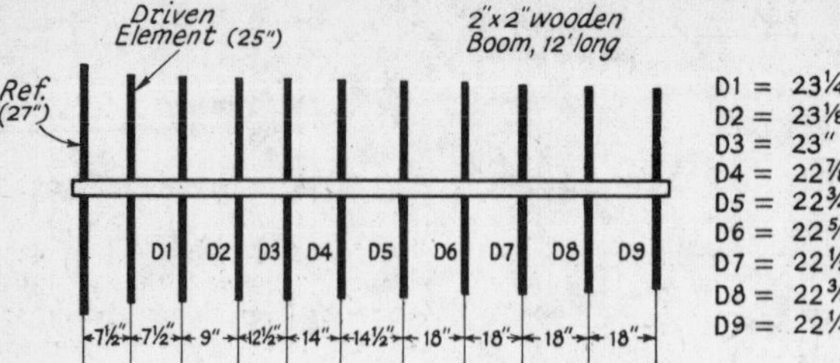

D1 = 23¼"
D2 = 23⅛"
D3 = 23"
D4 = 22⅞"
D5 = 22¾"
D6 = 22⅝"
D7 = 22½"
D8 = 22⅜"
D9 = 22¼"

Fig. 22-13 – 11-element Yagi for 220 MHz. Dimensions are for maximum gain in the lower 2 MHz of the band. Recommended feed method is a delta match, with universal stub and balun. Delta sides should be about 3 inches, tapped 2 inches either side of the element midpoint.

be made of thin-wall tubing if braced in the manner of the 50-MHz arrays previously described. Elements run through the boom and are held in place with clamps, as in Fig. 22-8. Lengths are for optimum gain between 144 and 145 MHz. Gain drops rapidly above 145.2 MHz. For a center frequency of 145 MHz, cut element lengths 1/8 inch. Broader frequency response can be obtained by tapering element lengths 1/8 inch per element, beginning with the second director.

Effective stacking of such long Yagis requires bay spacing of 1 1/2 to 2 wavelengths. Pairs or pairs of pairs can be fed in the manner of Fig. 22-15, using dimensions of Table 22-I.

11-ELEMENT YAGIS FOR 220 AND 432 MHz

High-gain antennas are almost a necessity for any serious work on 220 MHz and higher frequencies. The 11-element Yagis shown in Figs. 22-13 and 14 were worked out experimentally for maximum gain per element. They are intended primarily to be used in stacked pairs or sets of four, as shown (for 432 MHz) in Fig. 22-15.

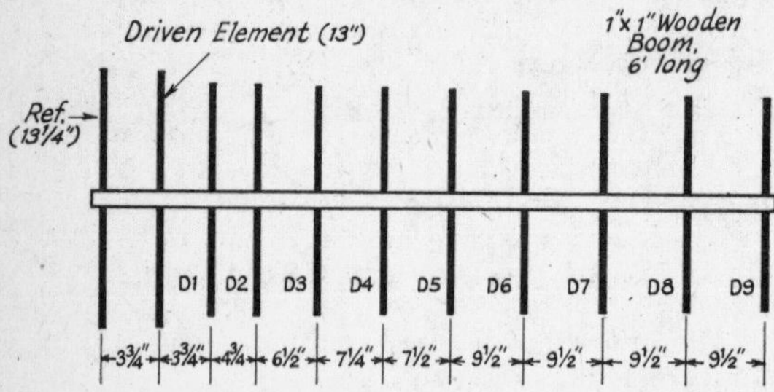

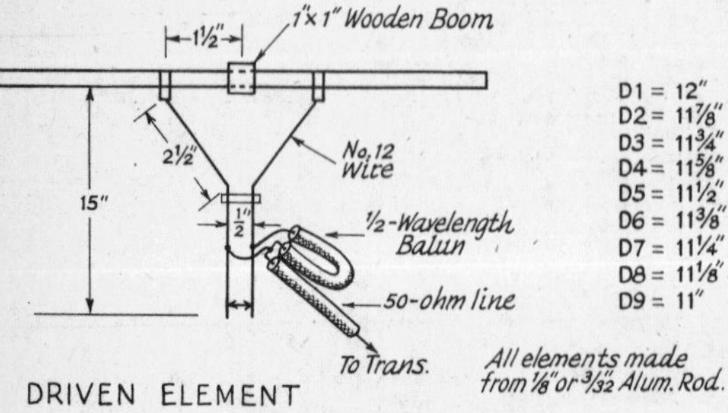

Fig. 22-14 – 11-element Yagi for 432 MHz, designed for optimum performance on a 6-foot boom. Operation should be uniform between 432 and 436 MHz, if the stub matching is adjusted when moving more than one megahertz in frequency.

Elements are stiff wire or welding rod, 1/8-inch diameter for 220, 3/32 or 1/8 inch for 432. Wood booms are shown, and are recommended for stacked arrays, particulary for 432. Metal booms should be 1/2-inch diameter for 432 and 3/4 to 1 inch for 220. Element lengths should be increased 0.5 to 1 percent if metal booms are used.

Frequency coverage without appreciable loss of gain, and no readjustment of matching, is about 1 percent of the operating frequency. Lengths of elements given are for 220 to 222 MHz and 432 to 434 MHz. Coverage can be extended somewhat higher by readjusting the matching for the desired higher frequency.

Recommended phasing is by open-wire line two wavelengths long each way. No. 12 wire spaced 1/2 to 3/4 inch with Teflon spreaders is ideal. If a metal supporting structure is used, it should preferably be entirely in back of the plane of the reflector elements.

COLLINEAR ANTENNAS

Information given thus far is mainly on parasitic arrays, but the collinear antenna has much to recommend it. Inherently broad in frequency response, it is a logical choice where coverage of an entire band is wanted. This tolerance also makes a collinear easy to build and adjust for any vhf application, and the use of many driven elements is popular in very large phased arrays, such as may be required for moonbounce (EME) communication.

Omnidirectional Verticals

Two or more half-wave elements mounted in a vertical line and fed in phase are often used to build up some gain, without directivity. A simple omnidirectional collinear of rugged construction is shown in Fig. 22-16. It is made entirely of copper pipe and matching elbow fittings, obtainable from plumbing supply houses and some hardware stores.

Initially the phasing stub was operated in the manner of Fig. 22-1A. When the optimum dimensions were found, the assembly was completed by making the angles with plumbing fittings, and the balun connections with bolts, nuts and star lugs.

Preferably the antenna should be mounted on a wooden support, though the center of the stub can be grounded for lightning protection. Dimensions given are for the upper half of the 2-meter band,

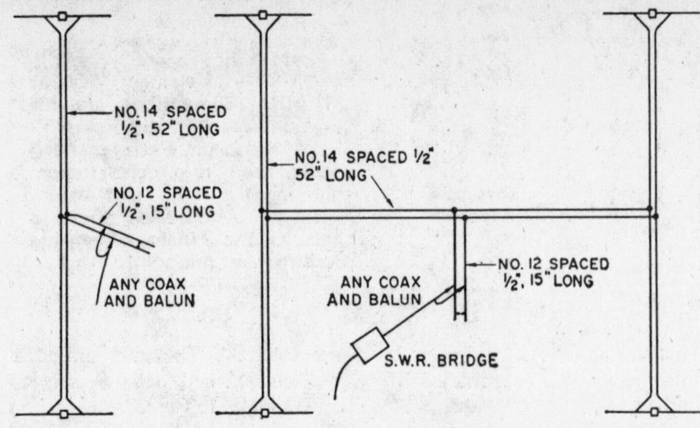

Fig. 22-15 – Phasing methods for using two or four 11-element Yagis for 432 MHz, with 2-wavelength spacing. Universal-stub match permits use of any type of transmission line.

though it works well enough all the way down to 144 MHz.

Any number of radiators can be used, if quarter-wave phasing stubs are connected between them. Commonly an odd number is used, and the center radiator is broken at its midpoint and fed with a universal stub. This type of antenna can be made of wire and strung up in a horizontal position. The pattern is bidirectional when this type of collinear is mounted horizontally.

Large Collinear Arrays

Bidirectional curtain arrays of 4, 6 and 8 half-waves in phase are shown in Fig. 22-17. Usually reflector elements are added, normally at about 0.2 wavelength in back of each driven element, for more gain and a unidirectional pattern. Such parasitic elements are omitted from the sketch in the interest of clarity. Dimensions are not critical, and may be taken from Table 22-I.

When parasitic elements are added, the feed impedance is low enough for direct connection open line or Twin-Lead, connected at the points indicated by black dots. With coaxial line and a balun, it is suggested that the universal stub match, Fig. 22-1A, be used at the feedpoint. All elements should be mounted at their electrical centers, as indicated by open circles in Fig. 22-17. The framework can be metal or insulating material, with equally good results. A model showing the preferred method of assembling an all-metal antenna is pictured in Fig. 22-18. Note that the metal supporting structure is entirely in back of the plane of the reflector elements. Sheet-metal clamps can be cut from scraps of aluminum to make this kind of assembly, which is very light in weight and rugged as well. Collinear elements should always be mounted at their centers, where rf voltage is zero – never at their ends, where the voltage is high and insulation losses and detuning can be very harmful.

Collinear arrays of 32, 48, 64 and even 128 elements can be made to give outstanding performance. Any collinear should be fed at the center of the system, for balanced current distribution. This is very important in large arrays, which are treated as sets of 6 or 8 driven elements each, and fed through a balanced harness, each section of which is a resonant length, usually of open-wire line. A 48-element collinear array for 432 MHz, Fig. 22-19, illustrates this principle.

PLANE AND PARABOLIC REFLECTORS

A reflecting plane, which may be sheet metal, wire mesh, or even closely-spaced elements of tubing or wire, can be used in place of parasitic reflectors. To be effective, the plane reflector must extend on all sides to at least a quarter-wavelength beyond the area occupied by the driven elements. The plane reflector provides high front-to-back ratio, a clean pattern, and somewhat more gain than parasitic elements, but large physical size rules it out for amateur use below 420 MHz. An interesting space-saving possibility lies in using a

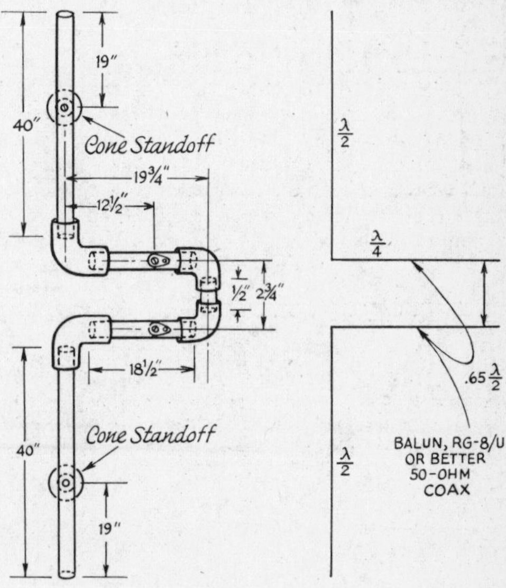

Fig. 22-16 – Rugged 2-meter omnidirectional vertical antenna made entirely of 1/2-inch copper pipe and elbows. The midpoint of the stub can be grounded, for lightning protection.

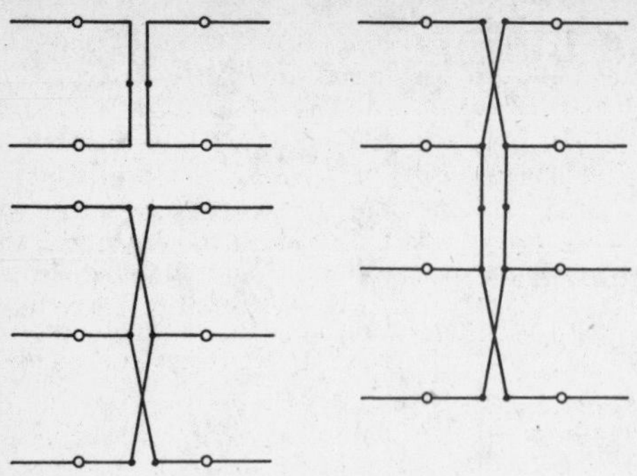

Fig. 22-17 – Element arrangements for 8, 12 and 16-element collinear arrays. Parasitic reflectors, omitted here for clarity, are 5 percent longer and 0.2 wavelength in back of the driven elements. Feed points are indicated by black dots. Open circles are recommended support points. The elements can run through wood or metal booms, without insulation, if supported at their centers in this way. Insulators at the element ends (points of high rf voltage) tend to detune and unbalance the system.

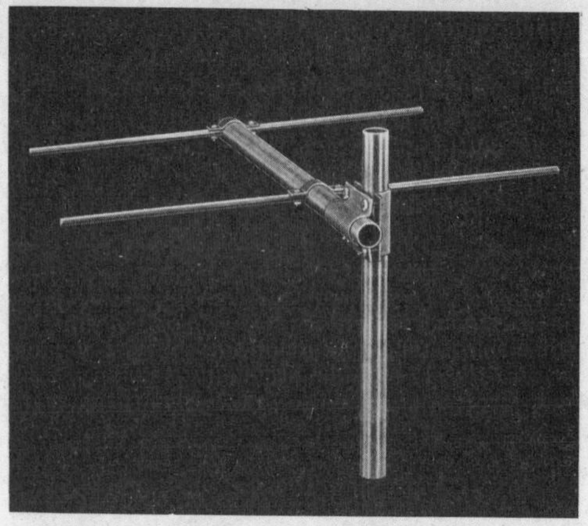

Fig. 22-18 – Model showing recommended method for assembling all-metal arrays. Suitable assembling clips can be cut and bent from sheet aluminum. Supporting structure should be in back of all active elements of the array.

single plane reflector with elements for two different bands mounted on opposite sides. Reflector spacing from the driven element is not critical. About 0.2 wavelength is common.

The reflector can be formed into parabolic shape for a focussing effect, similar to that in a searchlight. Parabolic reflectors must be very large in terms of wavelength. Principles involved in parabolic reflector design are discussed by WA9HUV in *QST* for June, 1971, page 100.

CIRCULAR POLARIZATION

Polarization is described as "horizontal" or "vertical," but these terms have no meaning once the reference of the earth's surface is lost. Many propagation factors can cause polarization change: reflection or refraction, passage through magnetic fields (Faraday rotation) and, satellite rolling, for examples. Polarization of vhf waves is often random, so an antenna capable of accepting any polarization is useful. Circular polarization, generated with helical antennas or with crossed elements fed 90 degrees out of phase, has this quality.

The circularly-polarized wave, in effect, threads its way through space, and it can be left- or right-hand polarized. These polarization "senses" are mutually exclusive, but either will respond to any plane polarization. A wave generated with right-hand polarization comes back with left-hand, when reflected from the moon, a fact to be borne in mind in setting up EME circuits. Stations communicating on direct paths should have the same polarization sense.

Both senses can be generated with crossed dipoles, with the aid of a switchable phasing harness. With helical arrays, both senses are provided with two antennas, wound in opposite directions.

Helical Antenna for 432 MHz

The 8-turn helix of Fig. 22-20 is designed for 432 MHz, with left-hand polarization. It is made

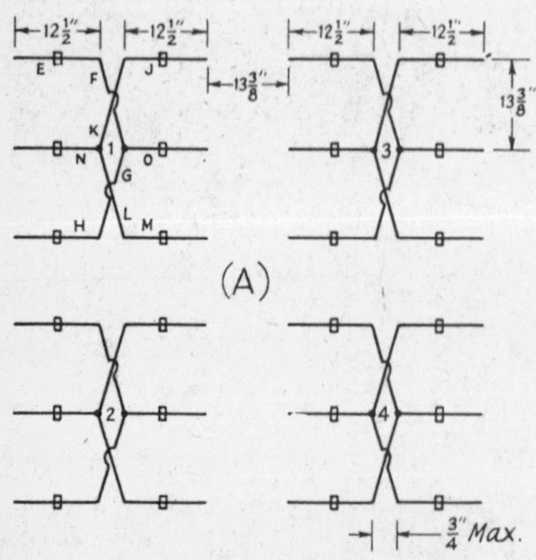

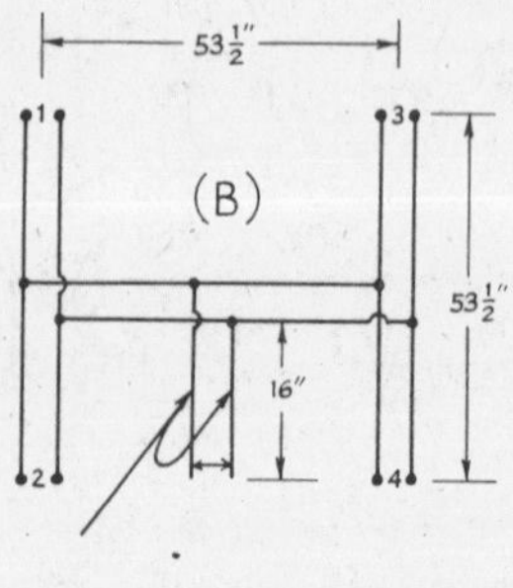

Fig. 22-19 – Large collinear arrays should be fed as sets of no more than 8 driven elements each, interconnected by phasing lines. This 48-element array for 432 MHz (A) is treated as if it were four 12-element collinears. Reflector elements are omitted for clarity. Phasing harness is shown at B.

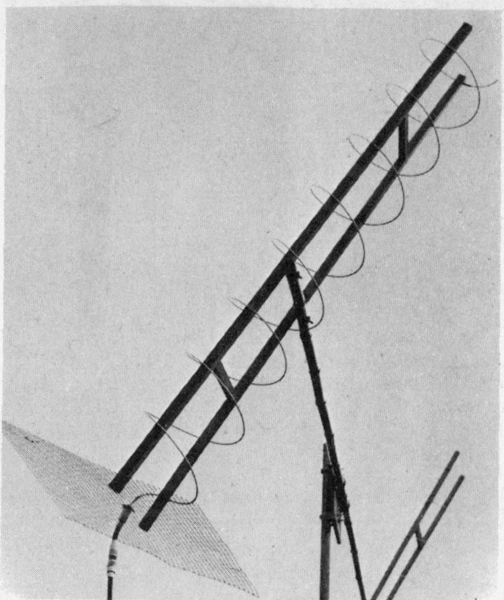

Fig. 22-20 – An 8-turn 432-MHz helical array, wound from aluminum clothesline wire. Left-hand polarization is shown. Each turn is one wavelength, with a pitch of 0.25 wavelength. Feed is with 50-ohm coax, through an 84-ohm Q section.

from 213 inches of aluminum clothesline wire, including 6 inches that are used for cutting back to adjust the feed impedance.

Each turn is one wavelength long, and the pitch is about 0.25 wavelength. Turns are stapled to the wooden supports, which should be water-proofed with liquid fiber glass or exterior varnish. The reflecting screen is one wavelength square, with a Type N coaxial fitting soldered at its center, for connection of the required coaxial Q section.

The nominal impedance of a helical antenna is 140 ohms, calling for an 84-ohm matching section to match to a 50-ohm line. This can be approximated with copper tubing of 0.4-inch inside diameter, with No. 10 inner conductor, both 6 1/2 inches long. With the antenna and transformer connected, apply power and trim the outer end of the helix until reflected power approaches zero.

The support arms are made from sections of 1 X 1 wood and are each 60 inches long. The spacing between them is 8.25 inches, outer dimension. The screen of the antenna in Fig. 22-20 is tacked to the support arms for temporary use. A wooden framework for the screen would provide a more rugged antenna structure. The theoretical gain of an 8-turn helical is approximately 14 decibels. Where both right- and left-hand circularity is desired, two antennas can be mounted on a common framework, a few wavelengths apart, and wound for opposite sense.

A TRANSMATCH FOR 50 AND 144 MHz

The antenna couplers as shown in Fig. 22-21 will permit unbalanced transmitter output lines (50-75 ohms) to be matched to balanced feeders in the 300 to 450-ohm impedance range. Also, "coax-to-coax" matching is possible with this circuit, permitting 50-ohm lines to be matched to 75-ohm lines, or vice versa. In situations where a high SWR condition exists where an antenna is being used in a part of the band to which it has not been tuned, this coupler will enable the transmitter to look into a flat load, thus permitting maximum loading for better efficiency.

Couplers of this type are beneficial in the reduction of harmonic energy from the transmitter, an aid to TVI reduction. It should be possible to realize a 30-dB or greater decrease in harmonic level by using this Transmatch between the transmitter and the feed line. When connected ahead of the receiver as well – a common arrangement – the added selectivity of the coupler's tuned circuits will help to reduce images and other undesired receiver responses from out-of-band signals. It is wise to remember that the use of devices of this kind will not correct for any mismatch that exists at the antenna end of the line. Although it assures a good match between the transmitter and the line, it can only disguise the fact that a mismatch exists at the antenna.

The Circuit

Balanced circuits are used for both bands, Fig. 22-22. Butterfly capacitors are employed to aid in securing good circuit symmetry. The links of each tuned circuit, L2 and L3, are series tuned by single-ended capacitors to help tune out reactance in the line.

Construction

A 4-1/2 X 4-1/2 X 2-inch homemade cabinet houses the 2-meter Transmatch; A Ten-Tec JW-5 is used as an enclosure for the 50-MHz unit. Other commercially made cabinets would be suitable, also. The two tuning controls are mounted in a line across the front of each cabinet. The main coil in each Transmatch is supported by a ceramic standoff insulator on one end and by the connection to the TUNING capacitor on the other. The links are self supporting. The coil taps are effected by bending standard No.6 solder lugs

Fig. 22-21 – These 6- and 2-meter Transmatches may be used with powers up to 500 watts. They can be employed with either balanced or unbalanced feeders.

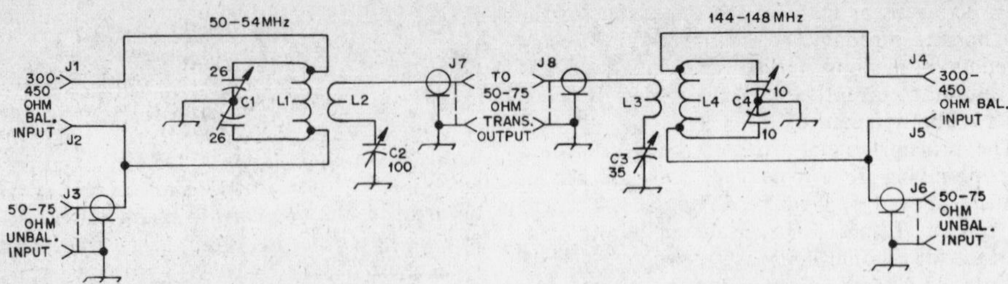

Fig. 22-22 – The schematic diagram of the vhf Transmatches. Capacitance is in pF unless otherwise noted. Resistance is in ohms, k = 1000.

C1 – 26-pF per section butterfly (E.F. Johnson 167-22).
C2 – 100-pF miniature variable (Millen 20100).
C3 – 35-pF miniature variable (Millen 20035).
C4 – 10-pF per section butterfly (E.F. Johnson 167-21).
J1-J4, incl. – Insulated binding post.
J5-J8, incl. – SO-239-style chassis connector.
L1 – 7 turns No. 10 copper wire, 1 1/2-inch dia, spaced one wire thickness between turns. Tap 2 1/2 turns from each end.
L2 – 2 turns No. 14 enam. or spaghetti-covered bare wire, 2-inch dia, over center of L1.
L3 – 2 turns No. 14 enam. or spaghetti-covered bare wire, 1 1/2-inch dia. over center of L4.
L4 – 5 turns No. 10 copper wire, 1-inch dia, spaced one wire thickness between turns. Tap 1 1/2 turns from each end.

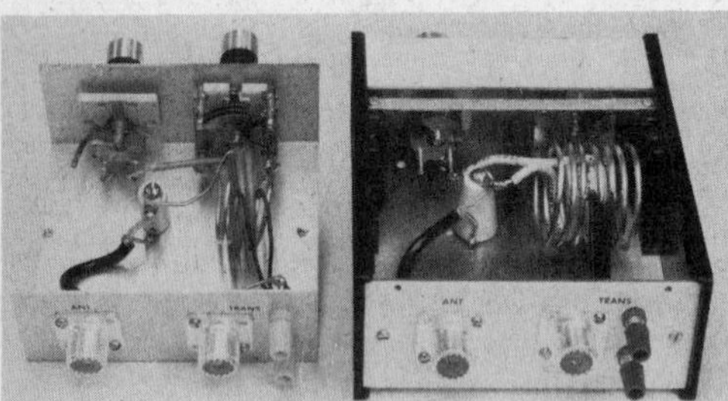

Fig. 22-23 – Inside view of the two Transmatches.

around the coil wire at the proper spots, then soldering the lugs in place. No. 20 bus wire is used to connect the taps of L1 to jacks J1 and J2. When operating coax-to-coax style, a short jumper wire connects J1 to its ground lug, or J4 to its ground lug, depending on the band being operated. The jumper must be removed for balanced-feeder operations.

Operation

Attach the vhf transmitter to J7 or J8 with a short length of coax cable. Connect a balanced feeder to J1 and J2 (for 50-MHz operation), or to J4 and J5 (for 144-MHz operation). A reflected-power meter or SWR bridge connected between the Transmatch and the transmitter will aid in the adjustment process. Adjust C1 and C2, alternately (for 50-MHz operation) for minimum meter reading on the SWR indicator. For 144-MHz operation, tune C3 and C4 in the same manner. Repeat the tuning until no further reduction in reflected power is possible. The meter should fall to zero, indicating a 1:1 match. No further adjustments will be needed until the transmitter frequency is moved 50 kHz or more. The tuning procedure is identical for matching coax to coax. In doing so, however, the antenna feed line (coax) is connected to either J3 or J6 and the shorting strap (discussed earlier) must be connected to J1 or J4. In some situations, it may be possible to get a better match by leaving the shorting strap off.

After the coupler is tuned up, the transmitter power can be increased to its normal level. These units will handle power levels up to 500 watts (transmitter output power) provided the coupler is tuned for a matched condition at all times. Reduced power (less than 50 watts) should be used during initial tune up, thus preventing parts from being damaged by heating or arcing. The coupler should never be operated without a load connected to its output terminals.

AN INEXPENSIVE DIRECTIONAL COUPLER

Precision in-line metering devices that are capable of reading forward and reflected power over a wide range of frequencies are very useful in amateur vhf and uhf work, but their rather high cost puts them out of the reach of many vhf enthusiasts. The device shown in Fig. 22-25 is an inexpensive adaptation of their basic principles. You can make it yourself for the cost of a meter, a few small parts, and bits of copper pipe and fittings that can be found in the plumbing stocks at many hardware stores.

Construction

The sampler consists of a short section of hand-made coaxial line, in this instance of 50 ohms impedance, with a reversible probe coupled to it. A small pickup loop built into the probe is terminated with a resistor at one end and a diode at the other. The resistor matches the impedance of the loop, not the impedance of the line section. Energy picked up by the loop is rectified by the diode, and the resultant current is fed to a meter equipped with a calibration control.

The principal metal parts of the device are a brass plumbing T, a pipe cap, short pieces of 3/4-inch ID and 5/16-inch OD copper pipe, and two coaxial fittings. Other available tubing combinations for 50-ohm line may be usable. The ratio of outer-conductor ID to inner-conductor OD should be 2.4/1. For a sampler to be used with other impedances of transmission line, see Chapter 20 for suitable ratios of conductor sizes. The photographs and Fig. 22-26 just about tell the rest of the story.

Soldering of the large parts can be done with a 300-watt iron or a small torch. A neat job can be done if the inside of the T and the outside of the pipe are tinned before assembling. When the pieces are reheated and pushed together, a good mechanical and electrical bond will result. If a torch is used, go easy with the heat, as an over-heated and discolored fitting will not accept solder well.

Coaxial connectors with Teflon or other heat-resistant insulation are recommended. Type N, with split-ring retainers for the center conductors, are preferred. Pry the split-ring washers out with a knife point or small screwdriver. Don't lose them, as they'll be needed in the final assembly.

The inner conductor is prepared by making eight radial cuts in one end, using a coping saw with a fine-toothed blade, to a depth of 1/2 inch. The fingers so made are then bent together, forming a tapered end, as seen in Fig. 22-26. Solder the center pin of a coaxial fitting into this, again being careful not to overheat the work.

In preparation for soldering the body of the coax connector to the copper pipe, it is convenient to use a similar fitting clamped into a vise as a holding fixture, with the T assembly resting on top, held in place by its own weight. Use the partially prepared center conductor to assure that the coax connector is concentric with the outer conductor. After being sure that the ends of the pipe are cut exactly perpendicular to the axis, apply heat to the coax fitting, using just enough so that a smooth fillet of solder can be formed where the flange and pipe meet.

Before completing the center conductor, check its length. It should clear the inner surface of the connector by the thickness of the split ring on the center pin. File to length; if necessary, slot as with the other end, and solder the center pin in place. The fitting can now be soldered onto the pipe, to complete the 50-ohm line section.

The probe assembly is made from a 1-1/2-inch length of the copper pipe, with a pipe cap on the top to support the upper feedthrough capacitor, C2. The coupling loop is mounted by means of small Teflon standoffs on a copper disk, cut to fit inside the pipe. The disk has four small tabs around

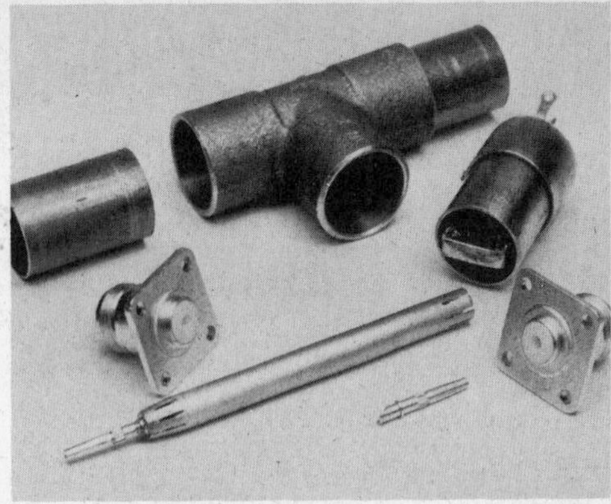

Fig. 22-24 — Major components of the line sampler. The brass T and two end sections are at the back of the picture. A completed probe assembly is at the right. The N connectors have their center pins removed. The pins are shown with one inserted in the left end of the inner conductor and the other lying in the right foreground.

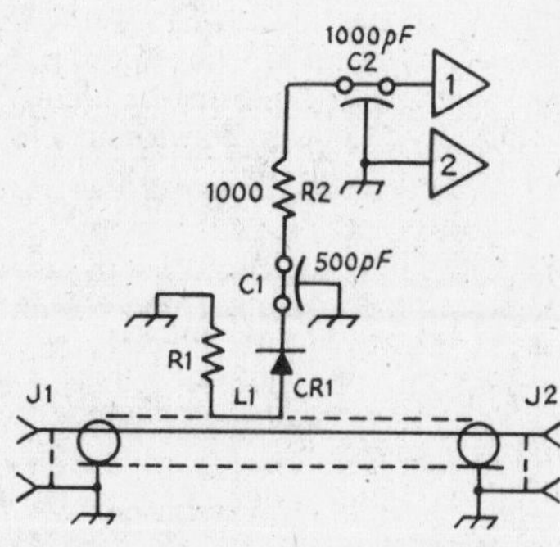

Fig. 22-25 — Circuit diagram for the line sampler.
C1 — 500-pF feedthrough capacitor, solder-in type.
C2 — 1000-pF feedthrough capacitor, threaded type.
CR1 — Germanium diode 1N34, 1N60, 1N270, 1N295, or similar.
J1,J2 — Coaxial connector, type N (UG-58A/U).
L1 — Pickup loop, copper strap 1 inch long × 3/16 inch wide. Bend into "C" shape with flat portion 5/8-inch long.
M1 — 0-100-μA meter.
R1 — Composition resistor, 82 to 100 ohms. See text.
R3 — 50,000-ohm composition control, linear taper.

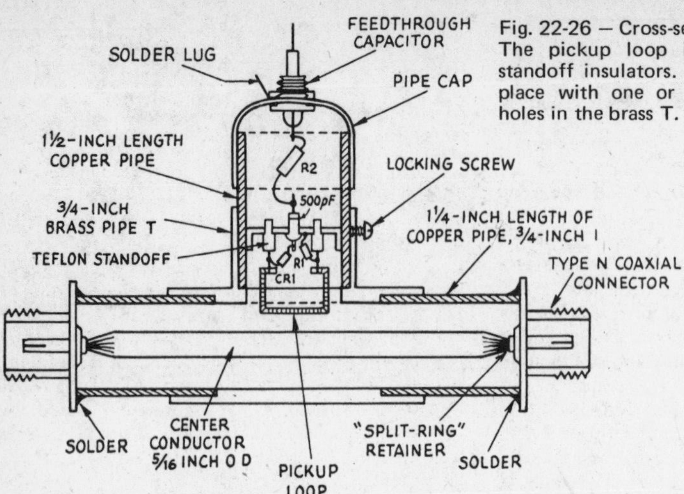

Fig. 22-26 – Cross-section view of the line sampler. The pickup loop is supported by two Teflon standoff insulators. The probe body is secured in place with one or more locking screws through holes in the brass T.

the edge for soldering inside the pipe. The diode, CR1, is connected between one end of the loop and a 500-pF feedthrough capacitor, C1, soldered into the disk. The terminating resistor, R1, is connected between the other end of the loop and ground, as directly as possible.

When the disk assembly is completed, insert it into the pipe, apply heat to the outside, and solder the tabs in place by melting solder into the assembly at the tabs. The position of the loop with respect to the end of the pipe will determine the sensitivity of a given probe. For power levels up to 200 watts the loop should extend beyond the face of the pipe about 5/32 inch. For use at higher power levels the loop should protrude only 3/32 inch. For operation with very low power levels the probe position can be determined by experiment.

The decoupling resistor, R2, and feedthrough capacitor, C2, can be connected, and the pipe cap put in place. The threaded portion of the capacitor extends through the cap. Put a solder lug over it before tightening its nut in place. Fasten the cap with two small screws that go into threaded holes in the pipe.

Calibration

The sampler is very useful for many jobs, even if it is not accurately calibrated, though it is desirable to calibrate it against a wattmeter of known accuracy. A good 50-ohm dummy load is a must.

The first step is to adjust the inductance of the loop or the value of the terminating resistor, for lowest reflected-power reading. The loop is the easier to change. Filing it to reduce its width will increase its impedance. Increasing the cross-section of the loop will lower it, and this can be done by coating it with solder. When the reflected-power reading is reduced as far as possible, reverse the probe and calibrate for forward power, by increasing the transmitter power output in steps and making a graph of the meter readings obtained. Use the calibration control, R3, to set the maximum reading.

Variations

Rather than use one sampler for monitoring both forward and reflected power by repeatedly reversing the probe, it is better to make two assemblies by mounting two T fittings end-to-end, using one for forward and one for reflected power. The meter can be switched between the probes, or two meters can be used.

The sampler described was calibrated at 146 MHz, as it was intended for 2-meter repeater use. On higher bands the meter reading will be higher for a given power level, and it will be lower for lower-frequency bands. Calibration for two or three adjacent bands can be achieved by making the probe depth adjustable, with stops or marks to aid in resetting for a given band. And, of course, more probes can be made, with each calibrated for a given band, as is done in some of the commercially available units.

Other sizes of pipe and fittings can be used, by making use of information given in Chapter 20 to select conductor sizes required for the desired impedances. (Since it is occasionally possible to pick up good bargains in 72-ohm line, you might like to make up a sampler for this impedance.)

Type N fittings were used because of their constant impedance, and their ease of assembly. Most have the split-ring retainer, which is simple to use in this application. Some have a crimping method, as do apparently all BNC connectors. If a fitting must be used that cannot be taken apart, drill a hole large enough to clear a soldering iron tip in the copper-pipe outer conductor. A hole of up to 3/8-inch diameter will have very little effect on the operation of the sampler.

Chapter 23

Assembling a Station

The actual location inside the house of the "shack" – the room where the transmitter and receiver are located – depends, of course, on the free space available for amateur activities. Fortunate indeed is the amateur with a separate room that he can reserve for his hobby, or the few who can have a special small building separate from the main house. However, most amateurs must share a room with other domestic activities, and amateur stations will be found tucked away in a corner of the living room, a bedroom, or even a large closet! A spot in the cellar or the attic can almost be classed as a separate room, although it may lack the "finish" of a normal room.

Regardless of the location of the station, however, it should be designed for maximum operating convenience and safety. It is foolish to have the station arranged so that the throwing of several switches is required to go from "receive" to "transmit," just as it is silly to have the equipment arranged so that the operator is in an uncomfortable and cramped position during his operating hours. The reason for building the station as safe as possible is obvious, if you are interested in spending a number of years with your hobby!

CONVENIENCE

The first consideration in any amateur station is the operating position, which includes the operator's table and chair and the pieces of equipment that are in constant use (the receiver, send-receive switch, and key or microphone). The table should be as large as possible, to allow sufficient room for the receiver or receivers, transmitter frequency control, frequency-measuring equipment, monitoring equipment, control switches, and keys and microphones, with enough space left over for the logbook, a pad and pencil. Suitable space should be included for radiogram blanks and a Callbook, if these accessories are in frequent use. If the table is small, or the number of pieces of equipment is large, it is often necessary to build a shelf or rack for the auxiliary equipment, or to mount it in some less convenient location in or under the table. If one has the facilities, a semicircular "console" can be built of wood, or a simpler solution is to use two small wooden cabinets to support a table top of wood or Masonite. A flush-type door will make an excellent table top. Homebuilt tables or consoles can be finished in any of the available oil stains, varnishes, paints or lacquers. Many operators use a large piece of plate glass over part of their table, since it furnishes a good writing surface and can cover miscellaneous charts and tables, prefix lists, operating aids, calendar, and similar accessories.

If the major interests never require frequent band changing, or frequency changing within a band, the transmitter can be located some distance from the operator, in a location where the meters can be observed from time to time. If frequent band or frequency changes are a part of the usual operating procedure, the transmitter should be mounted close to the operator, either along one side or above the receiver, so that the controls are easily accessible without the need for leaving the operating position.

A compromise arrangement would place the VFO or exciter at the operating position and the transmitter proper in some convenient location not adjacent to the operator. Since it is usually possible to operate over a portion of a band without retuning the transmitter stages, an operating position of this type is an advantage over one in which the operator must leave his position to change frequency.

Controls

The operator has an excellent chance to exercise his ingenuity in the location of the operating

This modern-day operating position was built by KØGKB, of Boulder Colorado. Installing a desk in a corner allows a large amount of table-top area, to be within reach of the operator. Shelves mounted above the operating position provide convenient storage space for books and station accessories.

controls. The most important controls in the station are the receiver tuning dial and the send-receive switch. The receiver tuning dial should be located four to eight inches above the operating table, and if this requires mounting the receiver off the table, a small shelf or bracket will do the trick. With the single exception of the amateur whose work is almost entirely in traffic or rag-chew nets, which require little or no attention to the receiver, it will be found that the operator's hand is on the receiver tuning dial most of the time. If the tuning knob is too high or too low, the hand gets cramped after an extended period of operating, hence the importance of a properly located receiver. The majority of cw operators tune with the left hand, preferring to leave the right hand free for copying messages and handling the key, and so the receiver should be mounted where the knob can be reached by the left hand. Phone operators aren't tied down this way, and tune the communications receiver with the hand that is more convenient.

The hand key should be fastened securely to the table, in a line just outside the right shoulder and far enough back from the front edge of the table so that the elbow can rest on the table. A good location for the semiautomatic or "bug" key is right next to the hand-key, although some operators prefer to mount the automatic key in front of them on the left, so that the right forearm rests on the table parallel to the front edge.

The best location for the microphone is directly in front of the operator, so that he doesn't have to shout across the table into it, or run up the speech-amplifier gain so high that all manner of external sounds are picked up. If the microphone is supported by a boom or by a flexible "goose neck" it can be placed in front of the operator without its base taking up valuable table space.

In any amateur station worthy of the name, it should be necessary to throw no more than one switch to go from the "receive" to the "transmit" condition. In phone stations, this switch should be located where it can be easily reached by the hand that isn't on the receiver. In the case of cw operation, this switch is most conveniently located to the right or left of the key, although some operators prefer to have it mounted on the left-hand side of the operating position and work it with the left hand while the right hand is on the key. Either location is satisfactory, of course, and the choice depends upon personal preference. Some operators use a foot- or knee-controlled switch, which is a convenience but doesn't allow too much freedom of position during long operating periods.

If the microphone is hand held during phone operation a "push-to-talk" switch on the microphone is convenient, but hand-held microphones tie up the use of one hand and are not too desirable, although they are widely used in mobile and portable work.

The location of other switches, such as those used to control power supplies, and phone/cw changeover, is of no particular importance, and they can be located on the unit with which they are associated. This is not strictly true in the case of the phone/cw DX man, who sometimes has need to change in a hurry from cw to phone. In this case, the changeover switch should be at the operating table, although the actual changeover may be done by a relay controlled by the switch.

If a rotary beam is used the control of the beam should be convenient to the operator. The direction indicator, however, can be located anywhere within sight of the operator, and does not have to be located on the operating table unless it is included with the control.

Frequency Spotting

The operator should be able to turn on only the oscillator of his transmitter, so that he can spot accurately his location in the band with respect to other stations. This allows him to see if he has anything like a clear channel, or to see what his frequency is with respect to another station. Such a provision can be part of the "send-receive" switch. Switches are available with a center "off" position, a "hold" position on one side, for turning on the oscillator only, and a "lock" position on the other side for turning on the transmitter and antenna relay. If oscillator keying is used, the key serves the same purpose, provided a "send-receive" switch is available to disable the rest of the transmitter and prevent a signal going out on the air during adjustment of the oscillator frequency.

For phone operation, the telegraph key or an auxiliary switch can control the transmitter oscillator, and the "send-receive" switch can then be wired into the control system so as to control the oscillator as well as the other circuits.

Comfort

Of prime importance is the comfort of the operator. If you find yourself getting tired after a short period of operating, examine your station to find what causes the fatigue. It may be that the chair is too soft or hasn't a straight back or is the wrong height for you. The key or receiver may be located so that you assume an uncomfortable position while using them. If you get sleepy fast, the ventilation may be at fault.

POWER CONNECTIONS AND CONTROL

Following a few simple rules in wiring your power outlets and control circuits will make it an easy job to change units in the station. If the station is planned in this way from the start, or if the rules are recalled when you are rebuilding, you will find it a simple matter to revise your station from time to time without a major rewiring job.

It is neater and safer to run a single pair of wires from the outlet over to the operating table or some central point, rather than to use a number of adapters at the wall outlet.

Interconnections

The ac wiring of most stations will entail little more than finding sufficient wall outlets to accept the power-cable plugs from the several units. However, a more sophisticated station would provide the various outlets at some inconspicuous area at the operating table or console. If the transmitter power is in excess of 500 watts it is advisable to provide 230 volts for its power supply (if it will work from 230 volts) rather than the more common 117-volt source. The higher voltage source will provide better regulation, and the house lights are less likely to "blink" with keying or modulation. A single switch, either on the wall of the "shack" or at the operating position, should control all of the 117- and 230-volt outlets; this makes it a simple matter to turn on the station to the "standby" condition.

The nature of the send-receive control circuitry depends so much upon the equipment in use that it is impossible to give anything but the broadest principles to follow. With commercial equipment, the instruction books usually provide some suggestions. In some cases the antenna-transfer relay is provided also, so that the antenna is connected to the transmitter and a cable from the transmitter is connected to the receiver. Normally the receiver is connected to the antenna through this relay. When the transmitter is "on" the relay transfers the antenna to the transmitter output circuit.

Lacking a built-in antenna transfer relay, many amateurs make do with a short separate wire for the receiving antenna. While this is acceptable in many instances, it is seldom as effective (on receiving) as using the same antenna for transmitting and receiving. A separate antenna relay can be used; several models are available, for use with coaxial or open-wire line. Models are available for use with 117-volt ac or 12-volt dc. Some have an auxiliary set of contacts that can be used to control the transmitter "on" function and the receiver "mute" circuit.

Break-In and Push-To-Talk

In cw operation, "break-in" is any system that allows the transmitting operator to hear the other station's signal during the "key-up" periods between characters and letters. This allows the sending station to be "broken" by the receiving station at any time, to shorten calls, ask for "fills" in messages, and speed up operation in general. With present techniques, it requires the use of a separate receiving antenna or an electronic "T-R" switch and, with high power, some means for protecting the receiver from the transmitter when the key is "down." If the transmitter is low-powered (50 watts or so), no special equipment is required except the separate receiving antenna and a receiver that "recovers" fast. Where break-in operation is used, the output stage should be disabled when adjusting the oscillator to a new frequency, to avoid radiating an unnecessary signal.

"Push-to-talk" is an expression derived from the "PUSH" switch on some microphones, and it means a phone station with a single control for all changeover functions. Strictly speaking, it should apply only to a station where this single send-receive switch must be held in place during transmission periods, but any fast-acting switch will give practically the same effect. A control switch with a center "OFF" position, will give more flexibility than a straight "push" switch. The one switch must control the transmitter, the receiver "on-off" circuit and, if one is used, the antenna changeover relay. The receiver control is necessary to disable its output during transmit periods, to avoid acoustic feedback. A "foot switch" on the floor at the operating position is a convenient control.

Many ssb transmitters provide for "VOX" (voice-controlled) operation, where the transmitter is turned on automatically at the first voice syllable and is held on for a half second or more after the voice stops. Operation with a VOX-operated ssb transmitter is similar to cw break-in, in that a separate receiving antenna or an antenna transfer relay or an electronic T-R switch is required.

Switches and Relays

It is dangerous to use an overloaded switch in the power circuits. After it has been used for some time, it may fail, leaving the power on the circuit even after the switch is thrown to the "OFF" position. For this reason, large switches, or relays with adequate ratings, should be used to control the plate power. Relays are rated by coil voltages (for their control circuits) and by their current and voltage ratings. Any switch or relay for the power-control circuits of an amateur station should be conservatively rated; overloading a switch or relay is very poor economy. Switches rated at 20

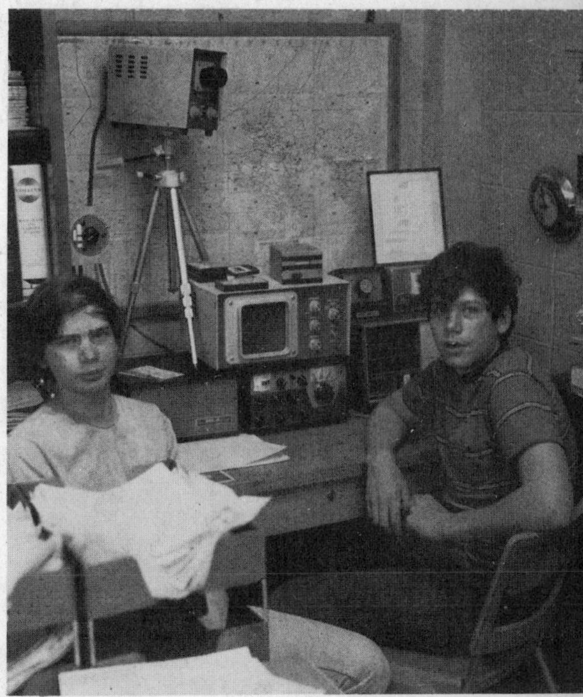

WBØFMH and WBØDMX are shown at the operating position of their high school club station. This very active radio club is equipped for all bands from 1.8 MHz through 450 MHz on several modes, including SSTV.

This modern amateur radio station is equipped for use in the hf bands. The gear is neatly arranged to provide the operator (K1ZND) with easy access to the various units. The foundation is made from plywood fashioned in the form of a console. The station belongs to K1THQ.

ampers at 125 volts will handle the switching of circuits at the kilowatt level, but the small toggle switches rated 3 ampers at 125 volts should be used only in circuits up to about 150 watts.

When relays are used, the send-receive switch closes the circuits to their coils. The energized relays close the heavy-duty relay contacts. Since the relay contacts are in the power circuit being controlled, the switch handles only the relay-coil current. As a consequence, this switch can have a low current rating.

SAFETY

Of prime importance in the layout of the station is the personal safety of the operator and of visitors, invited or otherwise, during normal operating practice. If there are small children in the house, every step must be taken to prevent their accidental contact with power leads of any voltage. A locked room is a fine idea, if it is possible, otherwise housing the transmitter and power supplies in metal cabinets is an excellent, although expensive solution. Lacking a metal cabinet, a wood cabinet or a wooden framework covered with wire screen is the next-best solution. Many stations have the power supplies housed in metal cabinets in the operating room or in a closet or basement, and this cabinet or entry is kept locked – with the key out of reach of everyone but the operator. The power leads are run through conduit to the transmitter, using ignition cable for the high-voltage leads. If the power supplies and transmitter are in the same cabinet, a lock-type main switch for the incoming line power is a good precaution.

A simple substitute for a lock-type main switch is an ordinary line plug with a short connecting wire between the two pins. By wiring a female receptacle in series with the main power line in the transmitter, the shorting plug will act as the main safety lock. When the plug is removed and hidden, it will be impossible to energize the transmitter, and a stranger or child isn't likely to spot or suspect the open receptacle.

An essential adjunct to any station is a **shorting stick** for discharging any high voltage to ground before any work is done in the transmitter. Even if interlocks and power-supply bleeders are used, the failure of one or more of these components may leave the transmitter in a dangerous condition. The shorting stick is made by mounting a small metal hook, of wire or rod, on one end of a dry stick or bakelite rod. A piece of ignition cable or other well-insulated wire is then run from the hook on the stick to the chassis or common ground of the transmitter, and the stick is hung alongside the transmitter. Whenever the power is turned off in the transmitter to permit work on the rig, the shorting stick is first used to touch the several high-voltage leads (plate rf choke, filter capacitor, tube plate connection) to insure that there is no high voltage at any of these points.

Fusing

A minor hazard in the amateur station is the possibility of fire through the failure of a component. If the failure is complete and the component is large, the house fuses will generally blow. However, it is unwise and inconvenient to depend upon the house fuses to protect the lines running to the radio equipment, and every power supply should have its primary circuit individually fused, at about 150 to 200 percent of the maximum rating of the supply. Circuit breakers can be used instead of fuses if desired.

Wiring

Control-circuit wires running between the operating position and a transmitter in another part of the room should be hidden, if possible. This can be done by running the wires under the floor or behind the base molding, bringing the wires out to terminal boxes or regular wall fixtures. Such construction, however, is generally only possible in elaborate installations, and the average amateur must content himself with trying to make the wires as inconspicuous as possible. If several pairs of leads must be run from the operating table to the transmitter, as is generally the case, a single piece of rubber- or vinyl-covered multiconductor cable will always look neater than several pieces of rubber-covered lamp cord, and it is much easier to sweep around or dust.

Solid or standard wire connected to a screw terminal (ac plug, antenna binding posts) should either be "hooked" around a *clockwise* direction, or, better yet, be terminated in a soldering lug. If the wire is hooked in a counter-clockwise position, it will tend to move out from under the screw head as the screw is tightened.

The antenna wires always present a problem, unless coaxial-line feed is used. Open-wire line from the point of entry of the antenna line should always be arranged neatly, and it is generally best to support it at several points. Many operators

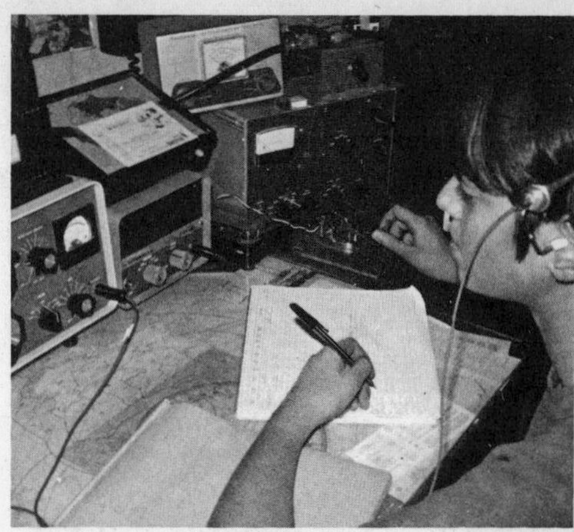

A world map can be placed under a large sheet of glass to provide a convenient position for reference. A skill, which has been developed by many amateurs, is the ability to write with one hand while operating the key with the other. Shown here is WA1NNC.

prefer to mount any antenna-tuning assemblies right at the point of entry of the feedline, together with an antenna changeover relay (if one is used), and then link from the tuning assembly to the transmitter can be made of inconspicuous coaxial line. If the transmitter is mounted near the point of entry of the line, it simplifies the problem of "What to do with the feeders?"

Lightning and Fire Protection

The National Electrical Code (NFPA No. 70) adopted by the National Fire Protection Association, although purely advisory as far as the NFPA is concerned, is of interest because it is widely used in law and for legal regulatory purposes. Article 810 deals with radio and television equipment, and Section C treats specifically amateur transmitting and receiving stations. Pertinent paragraphs are reprinted below:

810-11. Material. Antenna and lead-in conductors shall be of hard-drawn copper, bronze, aluminum alloy, copper-clad steel or other high-strength, corrosion-resistant material. Soft-drawn or medium-drawn copper may be used for lead-in conductors where the maximum span between points of support is less than 35 feet.

810-12. Supports. Outdoor antenna and lead-in conductors shall be securely supported. They shall not be attached to poles or similar structures carrying electric light or power wires or trolley wires of more than 250 volts between conductors. Insulators supporting the antenna conductors shall have sufficient mechanical strength to safely support the conductors. Lead-in conductors shall be securely attached to the antenna.

810-13. Avoidance of Contacts with Conductors of Other Systems. Outdoor antenna and lead-in conductors from an antenna to a building shall not cross over electric light or power circuits and shall be kept well away from all such circuits so as to avoid the possibility of accidental contact. Where proximity to electric light and power service conductors of less than 250 volts between conductors cannot be avoided, the installation shall be such as to provide a clearance of at least two feet. It is recommended that antenna conductors be so installed as not to cross under electric light or power conductors.

810-14. Splices. Splices and joints in antenna span shall be made with approved splicing devices or by such other means as will not appreciably weaken the conductors.

Soldering may ordinarily be expected to weaken the conductor. Therefore, the joint should be mechanically secure before soldering.

810-15. Grounding. Masts and metal structures supporting antennas shall be permanently and effectively grounded, without intervening splice or connection.

810-21. Grounding Material. The grounding conductor shall, unless otherwise specified, be of copper, aluminum, copper-clad steel, bronze, or other corrosion-resistant material.

810-22. Insulation. The grounding conductors may be uninsulated.

810-23. Supports. The grounding conductors shall be securily fastened in place and may be directly attached to the surface wired over without the use of insulating supports. Where proper support cannot be provided the size of the grounding conductor shall be increased proportionately.

810-24. Mechanical Protection. The grounding conductor shall be protected where exposed to physical damage or the size of the grounding conductor shall be increased proportionately to compensate for the lack of protection.

810-25. Run in Straight Line. The grounding conductor shall be run in as straight a line as practicable from the antenna mast and/or lightning arrestor to the grounding electrode.

810-26. Grounding Electrode. The grounding conductor shall be connected to a metallic underground water piping system. Where the building is not supplied with a (suitable) water system (one buried deeper than ten feet) the connection shall be made to the metal frame of the building when effectively grounded or to a grounding electrode. At a penthouse or similar location the ground conductor may be connected to a water pipe or rigid conduit.

810-27. Grounding Conductor. The grounding conductor may be run either inside or outside the building.

810-52. Size of Antenna. Antennas for amateur transmitting and receiving stations shall be of a size not less than given in Table 810-52.

Table 810-52

Size of Amateur-Station Outdoor Antenna Conductors

Material	Minimum Size of Conductors When Maximum Open Span Length Is: Less than 150 feet	Over 150 feet
Hard-drawn copper	14	10
Copper-clad steel, bronze or other high-strength material	14	12

810-53. Size of Lead-In Conductors. Lead-in conductors for transmitting stations shall, for various maximum span lengths, be of a size at least as great as that of conductors for antenna specified in 810-52.

810-54. Clearance on Building. Antenna conductors for transmitting stations, attached to buildings, shall be firmly mounted at least 3 inches clear of the surface of the building on nonabsorptive insulating supports, such as treated pins or brackets, equipped with insulators having not less than 3-inch creepage and airgap distances. Lead-in conductors attached to buildings shall also conform to these requirements, except when they are enclosed in a continuous metal shield which is permanently and effectively grounded. In this latter case the metallic shield may also be used as a conductor.

810-55. Entrance to Building. Except where protected with a continuous metal shield which is permanently and effectively grounded, lead-in conductors for transmitting stations shall enter building by one of the following methods:

(a) Through a rigid, noncombustible, nonabsorptive insulating tube or bushing.

(b) Through an opening provided for the purpose in which the entrance conductors are firmly secured so as to provide a clearance of at least 2 inches.

(c) Through a drilled window pane.

810-56. Protection Against Accidental Contact. Lead-in conductors to radio transmitters shall be so located or installed as to make accidental contact with them difficult.

810-57. Lightning Arrestors – Transmitting Stations. Each conductor of a lead-in for outdoor antenna shall be provided with a lightning arrestor or other suitable means which will drain static charges from the antenna system.

Exception No. 1. When protected by a continuous metallic shield which is permanetly and effectively grounded.

Exception No. 2. Where the antenna is permanently and effectively grounded.

810-59. Size of Protective Ground. The protective ground conductor for transmitting stations shall be as large as the lead-in, but not smaller than No. 10 copper, bronze or copper-clad steel.

810-60. Size of Operating Grounding Conductor. The operating grounding conductor for transmitting stations shall be not less than No. 14 copper or its equivalent.

810-70. Clearance from Other Conductors. All conductors inside the building shall be separated at least 4 inches from the conductors of other light or signal circuit unless separated therefrom by conduit or some firmly fixed non conductor such as porcelain tubes or flexible tubing.

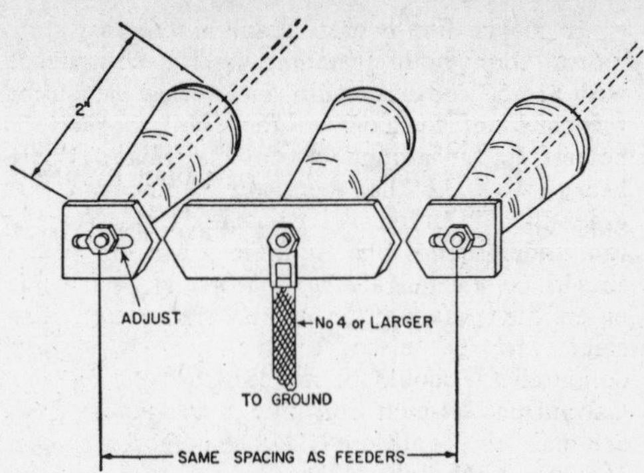

Fig. 23-1 — A simple lightning arrester made from three stand-off or feedthrough insulators and sections of a 1/8 X 1/2-inch brass or copper strap. It should be installed in the open-wire or Twin-Lead line at the point where it is nearest the ground outside the house. The heavy ground lead should be as short and direct as possible. Gap setting should be minimum for transmitter power.

810-71. General. Transmitters shall comply with the following:

(a) **Enclosing.** The transmitter shall be enclosed in a metal frame or grille, or separated from the operating space by a barrier or other equivalent means, all metallic parts of which are effectually connected to ground.

(b) **Grounding of Controls.** All external metallic handles and controls accessible to the operating personnel shall be effectually grounded.

No circuit in excess of 150 volts between conductors should have any parts exposed to direct contact. A complete dead-front type of switchboard is preferred.

(c) **Interlocks on Doors.** All access doors shall be provided with interlocks which will disconnect all voltages in excess of 350 volts between conductors when any access door is opened.

(d) **Audio Amplifiers.** Audio amplifiers which are located outside the transmitter housing shall be suitably housed and shall be so located as to be readily accessible and adequately ventilated.

This station, owned by the Talcott Mountain UHF Society, WA1IOX, is designed expressly for moonbounce and advanced amateur satellite work. The operator (WA1JLD) is able to control simultaneously the several receivers, "steer" the antennas, and still have access to the peripheral equipment for data recording and measurement.

The basic equipment is located on a table with homemade wooden shelves. Accessory equipment is located at either side on stands or in racks. This arrangement provides room for operation of the station by more than one operator at the same time — an important consideration for an advanced club station such a WA1IOX.

If coaxial line is used and an antenna has a dc return throughout (gamma match), compliance with 810-57 above is readily achieved by grounding the shield of the coax at the point where it is nearest to the ground outside the house. Use a heavy wire – the aluminum wire sold for grounding TV antennas is good. If the cable can be run underground, one or more grounding stakes should be located at the point where the cable enters the ground, at the antenna end. A grounding stake, to be effective in soils of average conductivity, should be not less than 8 feet long. Galvanized 3/4-inch iron pipe is acceptable, as is 5/8-inch steel rod or 1/2-inch nonferrous rod. Making connection to the outside of the outer conductor of the coaxial line will normally have no effect on the SWR in the line, and consequently it can be done at any point or points. A commercial model of a lightning arrester for coaxial line is available.

In some areas the probability of lightning surges entering the home via the 117/230-volt line may be high. A portion of the lightning surges originating on an overhead primary feeder can pass through the distribution transformer by electrostatic and electromagnetic coupling to the secondary circuit, even though the primary is protected by distribution-class lightning arresters. Radio equipment can be protected from these surges by the use of a "secondary service lightning arrester." A typical unit is the G.E. Model 9L15CCB007, marketed as the Home Lightning Protector. It is mounted at the weatherhead or in the service entrance box.

Rotary beams using a T or gamma match and with each element connected to the boom will usually be grounded through the supporting metal tower. If the antenna is mounted on a wooden pole or on the top of the house, a No. 4 or larger wire should be connected from the beam to the ground by the shortest and most direct route possible, using insulators where the wire comes close to the building. From a lightning-protection standpoint, it is desirable to run the coaxial and control lines from a beam down a metal tower and underground to the shack. If the tower is well grounded and the antenna is higher than any surrounding objects, the combination will serve well as a lightning rod.

A blackboard mounted near the operating position allows members of this club station, W8SH, to list operating information for the benefit of other club members.

The sole purpose of lightning rods or grounded roofs is to protect a building in case a lightning strike occurs; there is no accepted evidence that any form of protection can prevent a stroke.*

Experiments have indicated that a high vertical conductor will generally divert to itself direct hits that might otherwise fall within a cone-shaped space of which the apex is the top of the conductor and the base a circle of radius approximately two times the height of the conductor. Thus a radio mast may afford some protection to low adjacent structures, but only when low-impedance grounds are provided.

*See "Code for Protection Against Lightning," *National Bureau of Standards Handbook 46,* for sale by the Superintendent of Documents, Washington DC 20402.

Chapter 24

Operating a Station

Good on-the-air operating practices are important to every amateur for at least three good reasons: to assure compliance with regulations, to permit a large volume of activity to be conducted as efficiently and as simply as possible, and as a matter of personal pride and competence. Good practices is a very bewildering subject at first to many new amateurs, but as in so many other fields, it soon becomes apparent that there is a sound basis of custom and tradition which has produced a body of standard practices. These have evolved over more than a half-century of experience. One of the League's important functions has been to formalize, to foster and to encourage good standard practices so that they have become universal and accepted. Some of our standard practices go back a long time; others have been developed to meet changing circumstances, requirements and technology.

It used to be that one standard was all that was required. Today, things are different. There are standard operating practices for cw, voice, RTTY and repeaters, with additional standards for ATV not too far away. Those for cw and voice are pretty firmly established, but RTTY is newer and repeater operation newer still. Your League will take a crack at all of them. If its recommendations don't "take hold," they will be changed until they become acceptable to a majority in a particular operating specialty. This has been the pattern on cw and phone and will be the pattern on RTTY, repeaters, satellites and whatever else comes along in the future. Operating is better than 50% of most amateurs' lives. Better learn to do it *right.*

Initially, we'll talk about phone and cw, because they can be covered together. RTTY and repeaters will be handled separately.

ESTABLISHING A CONTACT

The best way to do this, especially at first, is to *listen* until you hear someone calling CQ, and call *them.* This requires a little patience, but that's something else all amateurs must learn if we are to share our bands in harmony. Tune around near your own frequency. If you hear a CQ, put your vfo on that frequency (*without* putting a signal on the air), wait until he indicates he is listening, then call him, thus: "W6ZRJ, W6ZRJ, this is W7PGY, W7 Papa Golf Yankee calling, Over" On cw: W6ZRJ W6ZRJ DE W7PGY W7PGY $\overline{\text{AR}}$. If no answer (to anyone) this may be repeated; brief, repeated calls are preferred to long drawn out ones. Chances are, if he is to hear you at all, he will hear your first brief call; most amateurs seldom tune far from their transmitting frequency to listen after a CQ. Note the ending signals. These have a special significance of their own to indicate to a casual listener the "status of the contact."

In answer to your call (assuming you are heard), the called station will reply: "W7PGY from W6ZRJ, roger . . ." and then go into conversation. On cw, it would be W7PGY DE W6ZRJ R . . . . That "roger" (R) means that he has received your call correctly. That's *all* it means – RECEIVED. It does not mean correct, I agree, I will comply. It is not sent unless everything was received correctly. Note also that "roger" is the phonetic equivalent of the letter R only in this usage. The regular phonetic for R is "Romeo."

Perhaps W6ZRJ heard W7PGY but did not catch his call. In this case, he might come back with "The W7 station, please repeat your call, this is W6ZRJ, over." On cw: QRZ? W7? DE W6ZRJ $\overline{\text{AR}}$. The presence of interference (QRM) and atmospherics (QRN) in the amateur bands makes use of this procedure fairly frequent. The contact (QSO) can then continue. Please note the FCC requirements on identification (97.87).

CALLING CQ

If you hear no CQ, you may wish to make such a call yourself. Refrain from CQing unless you are willing to establish contact with whoever calls. CQ means "I wish to contact *any* amateur station." If this is not your desire, then don't CQ, or be specific in doing so. A CQ call can be somewhat longer than a call to a specific station, because you are trying to attract the attention of casual listeners, including those tuning around looking for someone to call. However, please avoid the common operating discrepancy of calling CQ endlessly; it clutters up the air and drives off potential "customers." The average call would go something like this: "Hello CQ, CQ, CQ, calling CQ, this is WØPAN, W zero Papa Alpha November, Bloomington, Minnesota, calling CQ and listening, go." On cw: CQ CQ CQ DE WØPAN WØPAN WØPAN K. After a brief standby for replies, if no

OPERATING ABBREVIATIONS AND PREFIXES

Q SIGNALS

Given below are a number of Q signals whose meanings most often need to be expressed with brevity and clearness in amateur work. (Q abbreviations take the form of questions only when each is sent followed by a question mark.)

QRG Will you tell me my exact frequency (or that of . . .)? Your exact frequency (or that of . . .) is . . . kHz.
QRH Does my frequency vary? Your frequency varies.
QRI How is the tone of my transmission? The tone of your transmission is . . . (1. Good; 2. Variable; 3. Bad).
QRK What is the intelligibility of my signals (or those of . . .)? The intelligibility of your signals (or those of . . .) is . . . (1. bad; 2. poor; 3. fair; 4. good; 5. excellent.
QRL Are you busy? I am busy (or I am busy with . . .). Please do not interfere.
QRM Is my transmission being interfered with? Your transmission is being interfered with . . . (1. nil; 2. slightly; 3. moderately; 4. severely; 5. extremely.
QRN Are you troubled by static? I am troubled by static . . . (1-5 as under QRM).
QRO Shall I increase power? Increase power.
QRP Shall I decrease power? Decrease power.
QRQ Shall I send faster? Send faster (. . . wpm).
QRS Shall I send more slowly? Send more slowly (. . . wpm).
QRT Shall I stop sending? Stop sending.
QRU Have you anything for me? I have nothing for you.
QRV Are you ready? I am ready.
QRW Shall I inform . . . that you are calling him on . . . kHz? Please inform . . . that I am calling on . . . kHz.
QRX When will you call me again? I will call you again at . . . hours (on . . . kHz).
QRY What is my turn? Your turn is number . . .
QRZ Who is calling me? You are being called by . . . (on . . . kHz).
QSA What is the strength of my signals (or those of . . .)? The strength of your signals (or those of . . .) is . . . (1. Scarcely perceptible; 2. Weak; 3. Fairly good; 4. Good; 5. Very good).
QSB Are my signals fading? Your signals are fading.
QSD Are my signals mutilated? Your signals are mutilated.
QSG Shall I send . . . messages at a time? Send . . . messages at a time.
QSK Can you hear me between your signals and if so can I break in on your transmission? I can hear you between my signals; break in on my transmission.
QSL Can you acknowledge receipt? I am acknowledging receipt.
QSM Shall I repeat the last message which I sent you, or some previous message? Repeat the last message which you sent me [or message(s) number(s) . . .].
QSN Did you hear me (*or* . . .) on . . . kHz? I did hear you (*or* . . .) on . . . kHz.
QSO Can you communicate with . . . direct or by relay? I can communicate with . . . direct (or by relay through . . .).
QSP Will you relay to . . . ? I will relay to . . .
QSU Shall I send or reply on this frequency (*or* on . . . kHz)? Send or reply on this frequency (*or* on . . . kHz).
QSV Shall I send a series of Vs on this frequency (or . . . kHz)? Send a series of Vs on this frequency (or . . . kHz).
QSW Will you send on this frequency (or on . . . kHz)? I am going to send on this frequency (or on . . . kHz).
QSX Will you listen to . . . on . . . kHz? I am listening to . . . on . . . kHz.
QSY Shall I change to transmission on another frequency? Change to transmission on another frequency (or on . . . kHz).
QSZ Shall I send each word or group more than once? Send each word or group twice (or . . . times).
QTA Shall I cancel message number . . . ? Cancel message number . . .
QTB Do you agree with my counting of words? I do not agree with your counting of words; I will repeat the first letter or digit of each word or group.
QTC How many messages have you to send? I have . . . messages for you (or for . . .).
QTH What is your location? My location is . . .
QTR What is the correct time? The time is . . .

Special abbreviations adopted by ARRL:

QST General call preceding a message addressed to all amateurs and ARRL members. This is in effect "CQ ARRL."

THE R-S-T SYSTEM

READABILITY

1–Unreadable.
2–Barely readable, occasional words distinguishable.
3–Readable with considerable difficulty.
4–Readable with practically no difficulty.
5–Perfectly readable.

SIGNAL STRENGTH

1–Faint signals barely perceptible.
2–Very weak signals.
3–Weak signals.
4–Fair signals.
5–Fairly good signals.
6–Good signals.
7–Moderately strong signals.
8–Strong signals.
9–Extremely strong signals.

TONE

1–Sixty-cycle a.c. or less, very rough and broad.
2–Very rough a.c., very harsh and broad.
3–Rough a.c. tone, rectified but not filtered.
4–Rough note, some trace of filtering.
5–Filtered rectified a.c. but strongly ripple-modulated.
6–Filtered tone, definite trace of ripple modulation.
7–Near pure tone, trace of ripple modulation.
8–Near perfect tone, slight trace of modulation.
9–Perfect tone, no trace of ripple or modulation of any kind.

The "tone" report refers only to the purity of the signal, and has no connection with its stability or freedom from clicks or chirps. If the signal has the characteristic steadiness of crystal control, add X to the report (e.g., RST 469X). If it has a chirp or "tail" (either on "make" or "break"), add C (e.g., 469C). If it has clicks or noticeable other keying transients, add K (e.g., 469K). Of course a signal could have both chirps and clicks, in which case both C and K could be used (e.g., RST 469CK).

one answers and the frequency is still clear, you can try again. Short calls and frequent standbys are the best way to establish contact with the minimum QRM. This kind of procedure is easy to use when using VOX or keying through your VOX relay, or using cw break-in procedure.

THE QSO

During the contact, be sure to observe the FCC identification rules (see ARRL *License Manual*) Aside from that, there are no legal limits to what you can talk about, although it is recommended that controversial subjects connected with politics and morality be avoided. Keep everything on a friendly and cordial level, remembering that the conversation is not private and many others, including possibly members of the lay public, may be listening. Try to avoid the habitual utterances, procedures and inanities which so often make amateur radio contacts boring – things such as the drawn out 'ahhhhhh' to keep the VOX relay closed, or repeated "double dash" (dahdidididah) sign on cw, or hackneyed expressions such as "there" (referring to the other fellow) and "here" referring to yourself, or "we" when you mean "I." Both on cw and voice it is possible to be informal, friendly and conversational, and this is what makes an amateur radio QSO enjoyable. During the QSO, when you stand by the recommended signal is "go only" on voice, $\overline{\text{KN}}$ on cw, meaning that you want only the contacted station to come back to you. If you don't mind someone else breaking in, just "go" or K is sufficient. Of course, using VOX or break-in the conversation can proceed as it would face to face, without ending signals after each transmission; this is more normal in a voice contact than in a cw QSO.

ENDING THE QSO

When you decide to end the contact, *end* it. If the other fellow indicates a desire to end it, don't keep on talking, don't say "I won't hold you," then hold him. Express your pleasure at having contacted him and sign out, thus "W1QV from W6KW, clear." If you don't want further contacts, say "clear and leaving the air." On cw, it's $\overline{\text{SK}}$ W1QV DE W6KW, and, if leaving the air, CL.

All these things establish amateur radio as a cordial and fraternal hobby at the same time they foster orderliness and denote organization. Most of them have no legal standing; FCC regs say little about our internal procedures. The procedures we ourselves adopt are even more important than that, because they indicate that we are not just a bunch of hobbyists playing around in random fashion, but that we are an established communications *service* with distinct and distinctive procedures tailored to our special needs.

COURTESY

One thing that is considered the height of ill manners and "liddy" procedure in amateur radio is to tune up or make any transmission on a frequency which is already occupied. In some cases this is necessary, in others inadvertent; but it should always be avoided where possible. For example, if you are committed to a legal one-way transmission or schedule with a friend on a certain frequency at a certain time, it is sometimes unavoidable to cause temporary inconvenience to a going contact or even a net. In another situation, you may not hear another station on the frequency because of "skip," in which case an inquiry "Is the frequency in use?" or, on cw, the Morse letter C (didit dit) should bring a response if you are interfering with a station which you cannot hear. Use the same procedure in tuning up your antenna (use a dummy antenna for testing your rig) – don't *ever* fire up the rig and start tuning it without first turning on the receiver and checking the frequency. The amateur bands are crowded; consideration for the other guy will make things better for everybody.

RTTY PROCEDURES

On radioteletype, the methods of transmission and reception are somewhat different, so slightly different procedures are required. Voice is seldom a "written" mode and cw need not be, but RTTY always is. You type your transmission on a keyboard and it is received at the other end in printed form. Thus, most cw abbreviations can be used to good effect. In addition, such things as line feeds and carriage returns must be considered, as well as shifts for "letters" and "figures." These are nonprinting functions nevertheless essential for teleprinter operation.

Because of wide variations in RTTY machines, different mechanical procedures can often be used, but if you don't know the machine at the other end it is best to assume that it has none of the refinements.

As in other operating, the best thing to do is *listen*. The typical beadle-beadle of RTTY is familiar enough that it can be tuned in with an ordinary communications receiver, then put through the converter to copy on your printer. Some typical calls can be identified just by their sound, such as RY (the RTTY "test") and CQ and even your own call. The procedure is much the same as for cw – zero your vfo while copying and call your station on the same frequency. Even though he finishes his CQ with a carriage return (CR) and line feed (LF), it is a good idea to get into the habit of transmitting these functions, to "clear the machine." Thus: (2CR) (LF) K6DYX K6DYX K6DYX DE W1AW W1AW $\overline{\text{AR}}$ (2CR) (LF).

To initiate a CQ, find an unused point in the band, activate your carrier and transmit: (2CR) (LF) CQ CQ CQ DE K6DYX K6DYX K6DYX K (CR) (LF).

During the QSO, when you come to the end of a line (or the end-of-line indicator on tape equipment), send 2CR, LF, 2LTRS. That is, after your carriage return and line feed at the end of a line, the two nonprinting "letter" pulses serve to allow sluggish machines to get ready for the next line, and take less than a second to send. This is especially important with tape transmissions at the higher machine speeds – 75 and 100 wpm.

Most stations equipped for RTTY are also equipped with tape equipment. While RTTY can be sent manually from a keyboard, the use of tape for material which can be prepared ahead of time is much preferable, since it allows the machine to run at an even speed, faster than it could be typed by hand even by an expert typist. The tape is punched on a perforator and fed into a transmitter-distributor (TD) which is motor-driven. Thus, CQ calls or other prepared text (including message traffic) can be made up in advance. It is also fairly common practice to punch tape in ordinary QSOs, keeping ahead of the TD with the perforator. Many operators start punching their reply tape while they are still receiving from the operator at the other end, thus getting ahead far enough so that even if their typing speed is below the speed of the machine (usually 60 wpm) there is enough leeway to allow for the difference. Taped transmissions have no pauses, which can be irksome in manual transmissions.

RTTY equipments operate at different speeds and with different frequency shifts, depending on the sophistication of the equipment. Most amateurs, however, operate at a standard 60 wpm and 850-hertz shift, and those with 100 wpm and 170-hertz shift capability can usually switch to the standard. The considerate RTTY operator will be glad to do so whenever called upon, just as a considerate cw operator will slow down to the speed of his QSO.

REPEATER OPERATING

While repeater operation is voice operation, it has some ramifications that are not present in the type of operation used in direct contact on phone. Most repeaters are of the "open" type – that is any signal appearing on the repeater's input frequency is automatically repeated on its output frequency. Some repeaters have limited access, such as by means of a tone, a series of tones or pulses, or some other means to prevent their being triggered by a casual signal as described in Chapter 13. In either case, a repeater has to be built by somebody, installed by somebody, and maintained by somebody, usually at considerable expense and trouble. In some cases this "somebody" is an individual but more often a group, either organized for the purpose or an already-existing club undertaking repeater operation as a project. So a first point of repeater operating not exactly an on-the-air concept is to lend some kind of support to the group or individual that sponsors the repeater you use regularly.

Being somewhat new, no specific standards have yet been developed for repeater operating procedures, but certain customs are being observed which tend in this direction. Here are a few "dos" and "don'ts" put forward by repeater groups that may serve as useful guidelines:

1. Monitor the repeater you plan to use. Each system has its own peculiarities. Don't "key up" a repeater until you're familiar with its operation.

2. Don't activate the repeater without identifying yourself. Just by pressing your transmitter button you can tell if the repeater is being keyed (and therefore if it is active). It is considered poor practice (indeed, it is illegal!) to do this without identifying yourself.

3. Don't call CQ through a repeater. It isn't necessary, because all reception is done on the same frequency. If you want a QSO, all you have to do is key the repeater, identify yourself and stand by, thus: "This is W1UED mobile one monitoring the WA1KGR repeater."

4. During a repeater QSO, always pause momentarily before transmitting, after your contact has stood by for you. Two or three seconds seems to be the rule. This permits hearing "breakers."

5. Keep transmissions short. Most repeaters go off automatically after a certain length of transmission and must be rekeyed. If the repeater you are using does this, it's a sign you're talking too much. Keep transmissions under a minute in length.

6. Don't interrupt a going QSO unless you have reason for doing so, or unless participants invite breakers. When you do break in, don't say "break," just announce your call. "Break" means you have time-factor traffic. A double break ("break-break") means you have urgent traffic. A triple break ("break-break-break") signifies a disaster situation and should immediately stop all other operation.

7. It is most discourteous to use the pause between transmissions to call another station not in the QSO. Proper procedure is to request the channel. When or if granted, make your call, complete your business promptly, and return the channel to those who were using it.

8. Use a dummy load for tuning if possible. If you must tune up on the air, don't do so on a repeater input or output frequency.

9. Present logging rules for mobiles do not require that you log each individual QSO, only the beginning and ending of on-the-air operation for a given operating period. Your log must show however, such basic information as frequency band used, power input, signature of the operator, type of emission, and an indication of the location of the station. Mobile stations can comply with this latter item simply by noting "local" if within 100 miles of the address shown on the license. If on an extended trip, your log must show the location of the first and last QSO of each day, and must, if appropriate show compliance with the rule about notice of operation away from the authorized location.

ARRL makes available a repeater directory without charge to anyone requesting it If you want a copy, send three units of first-class postage (or a self-addressed stamped envelope, 7 × 9-inch).

CW PROCEDURE

Cw operating procedure has been developing for over a century, for our present International (Continental) Code had its beginnings on the telegraph wire lines. There is more to talk about in cw procedures than any other mode for this reason, not because it is the most popular mode. Phone many years ago outstripped cw as the most popular mode. But cw is far from dead. A listen to a rare DX pileup in the cw bands, or the cw section of any contest will demonstrate that conclusively. And it has many advantages over any other mode. Any amateur who avoids the use of cw because he is too lazy to become proficient enough in the code to realize its full benefits is missing almost half of amateur radio pleasure.

Good Sending

In many ways, cw can be compared with the spoken word. For the proficient cw man, it is indeed equivalent to this. But just as enunciation must be precise for best understanding in speaking, proper character formation and spacing is required in sending the code. And the learning processes are also similar. The beginning cw operator is subject to the same stresses and pressures as the child learning to talk, and can learn bad habits. He becomes subject to outside influences to his own possible detriment in everyday operating

Actually, it is far easier to learn code today than it was, say, forty years ago when nearly all amateur operation was by cw, because there are more helps available. On the other hand, there is less reason to learn it today than there was then. True, the licensing requirement still exists, but once you have your license if you prefer (and many amateurs do), you can spend 100 percent of your amateur operating time on voice or other modes that require no knowledge of the code. In the 1930s, you needed the code to communicate, not just to get your license. There are also, today, a great many gadgets on the market that, while seeming to make code easier only serve really to instill bad habits on the operator. Some teachers for example, would have you start out with an electronic keyer, but this weds you to such a device forever more. The best way to start is with an ordinary straight key, learning characters by their sound, and striving to imitate machine sending by learning to control the muscles used in manipulating this key. This makes "graduating" to a bug or an electronic key much easier at a later date.

In order to make your sending good, you have to know what good sending sounds like. The way to acquire this is to copy W1AW's bulletins and code practice, or other perfect sending, then strive to imitate it Sometimes you can get a copy of the practice text (it's listed in advance in *QST*), and try to send along with W1AW. Most amateur cw operators today have difficulty maintaining proper spacing, probably because so much equipment in use demands that we key through a VOX relay. On cw the control for this relay is usually set for minimum delay, so it will close quickly and open just as quickly; but on most equipments it still doesn't close quickly enough, so a part of the first dit or dah of the first character is cut off. This has a tendency to cause the operator to run his words together so the relay will stay closed while he is sending but open immediately when he stops, making his sending very difficult to copy.

Nobody's sending is perfect, and therefore *every* operator should continually strive for improvement. Watch out for the customary pitfalls as your cw proficiency develops. Do you ever send Q for MA, or P for AN? Do you have a "swing?" Yes, even on an electronic key you can develop personal idiosyncrasies. Be your own worst critic, and make sure your sending, at whatever speed, is beyond reproach.

Voice-Operating Hints

1) Listen before calling.
2) Make short calls with breaks to listen. Avoid long CQs; do not answer over-long CQs.
3) Use push-to-talk or voice control. Give essential data concisely in first transmission.
4) Make reports honest. Use definitions of strength and readability for reference. Make your reports informative and useful. Honest reports and *full* word description of signals save amateur operators from FCC trouble.
5) Limit transmission length. Two minutes or less will convey much information. When three or more stations converse in round tables, brevity is essential.
6) Display sportsmanship and courtesy. Bands are congested . . . make transmissions meaningful . . . give others a break.
7) Check transmitter adjustment . . . avoid a-m overmodulation and splatter. On ssb check carrier balance carefully. Do not radiate when moving VFO frequency or checking nfm swing. Use receiver BFO to check stability of signal. Complete testing before busy hours!

Break-In

On cw can you have true break-in – the ability to hear the signal of the other station while you are keying your transmitter. Technical considerations are covered elsewhere in this manual. Once this part of it has been accomplished, the full advantages and benefits of break-in can be realized. Long calls are unnecessary, because you can hear immediately if the station being called comes back to someone else. Much QRM is thus eliminated. If both stations in a QSO are using break-in, no station transmits unnecessarily; if the transmitting station is not being received, the receiving station "breaks" him and transmission stops. If another signal comes on the frequency, it can be heard immediately and any appropriate action taken. If message or other recorded traffic is being transmitted, any material missed can be filled immediately because the transmission can be interrupted just by the tap of a key. You can even call a CQ using break-in, and stop the moment someone hears you and starts calling. The customary procedure is CQ CQ CQ DE WØPAN WØPAN BK (pause) CQ CQ CQ . . ., until someone breaks or until it seems obvious no one is going to. Alternatively, the Q signal QSK can be used, either in sending CQ or at the beginning of a QSO to indicate to the other station that you are equipped for break-in and invite him to use it. QSK is the mark of a well-equipped and well-operated cw station.

VOICE OPERATING

The use of proper procedure to get best results is just as important as in using code. In telegraphy words must be spelled out letter by letter. It is therefore but natural that abbreviations and shortcuts have come into use. In voice work, however, abbreviations are not necessary, and have less importance in our operating procedure.

The letter "K" is used in telegraphic practice so that the operator will not have to pound out the separate letters. The voice operator can *say* the words "go" or "over."

One laughs on cw by sending HI. On phone, *laugh* when one is called for.

The matter of reporting *readability* and *strength* is as important to phone operators as to those using code. With telegraph nomenclature, it is necessary to spell out words to describe signals or use abbreviated signal reports. But on voice, we have the ability to "say it with words." "Readability four, strength eight" is the best way to give a quantitative report, but reporting can be done so much more meaningfully with ordinary words: "You are weak but I can understand you, so go ahead," or "Your signal is strong but you are buried under local interference."

Voice Equivalents to Code Procedure

Voice	*Code*	*Meaning*
Over	$\overline{AR}$	After call to specific station
End of message	$\overline{AR}$	End of transmission or record message
Wait; stand by	$\overline{AS}$	Self-explanatory
Roger	R	*All* received correctly
Go	K	Any station transmit
Go only	$\overline{KN}$	Addressed station only transmit
Clear	$\overline{SK}$	End of contact or communication
Closing station	CL	Going off the air

Phone-Operating Practice

Efficient voice communication, like good cw communication, demands good operating. Adherence to certain points "on getting results" will go a long way toward improving our phone-band operating conditions.

Use VOX or push-to-talk. If you use VOX (most home stations do), don't defeat its purpose by saying "aaahhh" to keep the relay closed. If you use push-to-talk (common on mobiles so traffic noises won't affect transmission), let go of the button every so often to make sure you aren't "doubling" with the other fellow. Don't be a monologuist – a guy who likes to hear himself talk.

Listen with care. It's natural enough to answer the loudest signal who calls, but do a little digging, if necessary, to answer the *best* signal instead, where there is a choice. Every amateur can't run a kilowatt, but there is no reason why every amateur cannot have a signal of the highest quality. Don't reward the guy who cranks up his gain and splatters by answering his call if another station is calling.

Interpose your call frequently. Say it often and distinctly, in measured tones. Too often, identification is muffled or slurred. The fastest voice communication doesn't come from the guy who talks fastest; it comes from the operator who speaks distinctly. Your call especially is important, you can be cited for improper identification if it cannot be understood.

Listen before transmitting. Make sure the frequency isn't being used before you come barging onto it. Our voice bands are pretty crowded and QRM is inevitable. But this is a reason for *more* courtesy, not less.

Keep modulation constant. By turning your gain "wide open" you are subjecting anyone listening to all kinds of extraneous noises that don't belong on the air. Speak as closely to the mike as you can without breath modulation, turn your gain down so that only your voice can be heard. A good stunt is to hold the mike at the corner of your mouth and talk across it, rather than into it. If you use a stationary mike, turn it so that your breath goes across it, not into if; otherwise, your "explosives" will distort your speech.

Have a pencil and paper always handy. Take notes on the other guy's conversation while he's talking, so you can answer him or comment on the things he has said; otherwise he might get the wrong impression that you are deliberately ignoring some of his remarks.

Avoid repetition. Don't repeat back what the other fellow has just said. Just *say* you received everything, don't try to prove it.

Avoid inanities. There are many of them in phone operation, and they are contagious. "That's a roger." "Yeeeaaah!" "By golly." The phoney laugh. The affected speech. If you must parrot, parrot the polished operator, not the affected or idiotic one.

Steer clear of such controversial or suggestive subjects as politics and sex, and of profanities, even those considered acceptable in today's permissive society.

Use phonetics only as required. When clarifying genuinely doubtful expressions and in getting your call identified positively we suggest use of the International Civil Aviation Organization list. However, don't overdo its use.

The speed of radiotelephone transmission (with perfect accuracy) depends almost entirely upon the skill of the two operators involved. One must learn to speak at a rate allowing perfect understanding as well as permitting the receiving operator to copy down the message text, if that is necessary. Because of the similarity of many English speech sounds, the use of word lists has been found necessary. All voice-operated stations should use a *standard* list as needed to identify call signals or unfamiliar expressions.

A – ALFA	N – NOVEMBER
B – BRAVO	O – OSCAR
C – CHARLIE	P – PAPA
D – DELTA	Q – QUEBEC
E – ECHO	R – ROMEO
F – FOXTROT	S – SIERRA
G – GOLF	T – TANGO
H – HOTEL	U – UNIFORM
I – INDIA	V – VICTOR
J – JULIETT	W – WHISKEY
K – KILO	X – X-RAY
L – LIMA	Y – YANKEE
M – MIKE	Z – ZULU

Example: W1AW . . . W 1 ALFA WHISKEY . . . W1AW

Round Tables. The round table has many advantages if run properly. It clears frequencies of interference, especially if all stations involved are on the same frequency, while the enjoyment value remains the same, if not greater. By use of push-to-talk, or vox, the conversation can be kept lively and interesting, giving each station operator ample opportunity to participate without waiting overlong for his turn.

Round tables can become very unpopular if they are not conducted properly. The monologuist, off on a long spiel about nothing in particular, cannot be interrupted; *make your transmissions short and to the point.* "Butting in" is discourteous and unsportsmanlike; *don't enter a round table, or any contact between two other amateurs, unless you are invited.* It is bad enough trying to copy through prevailing interference without the added difficulty of poor voice quality; *check your transmitter adjustments frequently.* In general, follow the precepts as hereinbefore outlined for the most enjoyment in round tables as well as any other form of radiotelephone communication.

DX OPERATING CODE

(For W/VE Amateurs)

Some amateurs interested in DX work have caused considerable confusion and QRM in their efforts to work DX stations. The points below, if observed by all W/VE amateurs, will go a long way toward making DX more enjoyable for everybody.

1. Call DX only after he calls CQ, QRZ?, signs $\overline{\text{SK}}$, or phone equivalent thereof.

2. Do *not* call a DX station:

a. On the frequency of the station he is working until you are *sure* the QSO is over. This is indicated by the ending signal $\overline{\text{SK}}$ on cw and any indication that the operator is listening, on phone.

b. Because you hear someone else calling him.

c. When he signs $\overline{\text{KN}}$, $\overline{\text{AR}}$, CL, or phone equivalents.

d. Exactly on his frequency.

e. After he calls a directional CQ, unless of course you are in the right direction or area.

3. Keep within frequency-band limits. Some DX stations operate outside. Perhaps they can get away with it, but you cannot.

4. Observe calling instructions of DX stations. "10U" means call ten kHz *up* from his frequency, "15D" means 15 kHz *down*, etc.

5. Give honest reports. Many foreign stations *depend* on W and VE reports for adjustment of station and equipment.

6. Keep your signal clean. Key clicks, chirps, hum or splatter give you a bad reputation and may get you a citation from FCC.

7. *Listen* for and *call* the station you want. Calling CQ DX is not the best assurance that the *rare* DX will reply.

8. When there are several W or VE stations waiting to work a DX station, avoid asking him to "listen for a friend." Let your friend take his chances with the rest. Also avoid engaging DX stations in rag-chews against their wishes.

WORKING DX

Most amateurs at one time or another make "working DX" a major aim. As in every other phase of amateur work, there are right and wrong ways to go about getting best results in working foreign stations, and it is the intention of this section to outline a few of them.

The ham who has trouble raising DX stations readily may find that poor transmitter efficiency is not the reason. He may find that his sending is poor, his calls ill timed, or his judgment in error. Working DX requires the know-how that comes with experience. If you just call CQ DX you may get a call from a foreign station, but it isn't likely to be a "rare one." On the other hand, unless you are experienced enough to know that conditions are right, your receiver is sensitive and selective enough and your transmitter and antenna properly tuned and oriented, you may get no calls at all, and succeed only in causing some unnecessary QRM.

The call CQ DX means slightly different things to amateurs on different bands:

a) On vhf, CQ DX is a general call ordinarily used only when the band is open, under favorable "skip" conditions. For vhf work, such a call is used for looking for new states and countries, also for distances beyond the customary "line-of-sight" range on most vhf bands.

b) CQ DX on our 7-, 14-, 21-, and 28-MHz bands may be taken to mean "General call to any foreign station." The term "foreign station" usually refers to any station on a different continent. If you do call CQ DX, remember that it implies you will answer any DX who calls. If you don't mean "general call to any DX station," then listen and call the station you do want.

Snagging the Rare Ones

Once in a while a CQ DX will result in snagging a rare DX contact, if you're lucky. This seldom happens, however; usually, what you have to do is listen – and listen – and then listen some more. *You gotta hear 'em before you can work 'em!* If everybody transmits, nobody is going to hear anything. Be a snooper. Usually, unless you are lucky enough to be among the first to hear him, a rare DX station will be found under a pileup, with stations swarming all over him like worker bees over a queen. The bedlam will subside when the DX station is transmitting (although some stations keep right on calling him), and you can hear him. Don't immediately join the pack, be a little cagey. Listen a while, get an idea of his habits, find out where he is listening (if not zero on himself), bide your time and wait your chance. Sometimes "tail-ending" works. This is the practice of waiting until the station your DX is working starts his sign-off, then just transmitting your own call. Be careful however; this could backfire. If your DX station doesn't respond to such tactics, best to avoid it. Some of them don't like it

Make your calls short, snappy. No need to repeat his call (he knows it very well, all he needs to know is that you are calling him), but send your own call a couple of times. Try to find a time when few stations are calling him and he is not transmitting; then get in there! With experience, you'll learn all kinds of tricks, some of them clever some just plain dirty. You'll have no trouble discerning which is which. Learn to use the clever ones, and shun the dirty ones. More than you think depends on the impressions we make on our foreign friends!

Codes and Ethics

One of the most effective ways to work DX is to know the operating habits of the DX stations sought, and to abide by the procedures they use. Know when and where to call, and for how long, and when to remain silent waiting your chance. DXing has certain understood codes of ethics and procedures that will make this popular amateur pursuit more fun for everybody if everybody follows them. One of the sad things about DXing is to listen to some of the vituperation and abuse that goes on, mostly by station on "this" side, as they trample on each other trying to raise their quarry. DX stations have been known to QRT in disgust at some of the tactics.

If W and VE stations will use the procedure in the "DX Operating Code" detailed elsewhere on these pages, we can all make a good impression on the air. ARRL has also recommended some operating procedures for DX stations aimed at controlling some of the thoughtless practices sometimes used by W/VE amateurs A copy of these recommendations (Op Aid No. 5) can be obtained free of charge from ARRL Headquarters .

Choosing Your Band

If it does nothing else in furthering your education, striving to work DX will certainly teach you a few things about propagation. You will find that four principal factors determine propagation characteristics. (1) The frequency of the band in which you do your operating. (2) The time of day or night. (3) the season of the year (4) The sunspot cycle. The proper choice of band depends pretty much on the other three factors. For example, the 3.5-4.0-MHz band at high noon in the summertime at the "node" part of the sunspot cycle is the poorest possible choice, while the same band at midnight during the wintertime at the 'null' part of the cycle might produce some very exciting DX. Similarly, you will learn by experience when to operate on which band for the best DX by juggling the above factors using both long-range and other indications of band conditions. WWV transmissions can also be helpful in indicating both current and immediate-forecast band conditions.

Conditions in the transmission medium often make it possible for the signals from low-powered transmitters to be received at great distances. In general, the higher the frequency band the less important power considerations become, for occasional DX work. This accounts in part for the relative popularity of the 14-, 21- and 28-MHz bands among amateurs who like to work DX.

QSL CARDS AND BUREAUS

Most amateurs who work another station for the first time, especially a foreign station, will later send the station a postcard confirming the contact. These cards are known as QSLs, taken from the international signal meaning, "I acknowledge receipt." A number of printing firms specialize in producing these postcards, following standard designs, or following the directions of an individual amateur. Advertisements of these printers appear each month in *QST*, ARRL's official journal.

Since it is rather expensive, for a foreign station especially, to send a QSL separately to each U.S. or Canadian station he's worked, ARRL has set up a system of QSL Bureaus, manned by amateur volunteers in each call area. The bureaus get packages of cards from overseas, which are sorted by call. Individual amateurs may claim their cards by sending a supply of stamped, self-addressed envelopes to the QSL manager in their call area. *QST* carries the addresses of these bureaus nearly every issue. Or write to ARRL Hq. for information.

Similarly, U.S. and Canadian amateurs may send QSLs in bulk to bureaus overseas rather than direct. Addresses for overseas bureaus appear in the IARU News department of *QST* each June and December.

KEEPING AN AMATEUR STATION LOG

The FCC requires every amateur to keep a complete station operating record (log) that shows (1) the date and time of each transmission, (2) all calls and transmissions made, whether contacts resulted or not, (3) the input power to the last stage of the transmitter, (4) the frequency band used, (5) the time of ending each contact (QSO), and (6) the signature of the licensed operator. Written messages handled in standard form must be included in the log or kept on file for a period of at least one year.

But a log can be more than just a legal record of station operation. It can be a "diary" of your amateur experience. Make it a habit to enter thoughts and comments, changes in equipment, operating experiences and reactions, anything that might make enjoyable reminiscences in years to come. Your log is a reflection of your personal

DATE TIME (GMT)	STATION CALLED	CALLED BY	HIS SIGNAL RST	MY SIGNAL RST	FREQ.	EMISSION TYPE	POWER INPUT WATTS	TIME OF ENDING QSO	OTHER DATA	NAME	QSLs S	QSLs R
16MAR.												
2300	W3EML	X	589	579	3.5	A1	250	2309	RCD 5	BILL	—	
2315	CQ	X			7							
16	X	W5NW	469	479	"	"	"	2330	CNDX POOR	SOUPY	✓	
35	K2SJO	X	57	59	3.8	A3	150	2355	SKED			
17MAR												
0005	UA9OH	X	579	589	14	A1	25	0012	NOVOSIBIRSK	VLADIS	✓	
0013	X	UW9FT	579	579	"	"	"	0020	"	VIK	✓	
1200	CQ	X			"	"	"					
02	X	VK3NR	579	579	"	"	"	1217	MELBOURNE	NOEL	✓	

KEEP AN ACCURATE AND COMPLETE STATION LOG AT ALL TIMES. FCC REQUIRES IT.

A page from the official ARRL log is shown above, answering every FCC requirement in respect to station records. Bound logs made up in accord with the above form can be obtained from Headquarters for a nominal sum or you can prepare your own, in which case we offer this form as a suggestion. The ARRL log has a special wire binding and lies perfectly flat on the table.

experience in amateur radio. Make it both neat and complete.

ARRL headquarters stocks log books and message blanks for the convenience of amateurs.

PUBLIC SERVICE OPERATING

Amateurs interested in rendering public service in operating under ARRL sponsorship have formed the Amateur Radio Public Service Corps (ARPSC). This organization has two principal divisions. One is the Amateur Radio Emergency Corps (AREC), an emergency-preparedness group of approximately 30,000 amateur operators signed up voluntarily to keep amateur radio in the forefront along preparedness lines. The other is the National Traffic System (NTS), a message-handling facility which operates daily (including weekends and holidays) for systematic handling of third-party traffic.

Also recognized by ARRL as a part of the organized amateur radio public service effort are the Radio Amateur Civil Emergency Service (RACES), a part of the amateur service serving civil defense under a separate sub-part of the amateur regulations; the Military Affiliate Radio Service, sponsored by the armed services to provide military training for amateurs; and numerous amateur groups organized into nets by individuals, clubs or other amateur entitites for public service and registered with the League. The detailed workings of ARPSC and RACES are covered briefly herein and explained in somewhat more detail in *Public Service Communications, Operating an Amateur Radio Station,* available to interested amateurs without charge, and *The Radio Amateur's Operating Manual.*

THE AMERICAN RADIO RELAY LEAGUE
RADIOGRAM
VIA AMATEUR RADIO

NUMBER	PRECEDENCE	HX	STATION OF ORIGIN	CHECK	PLACE OF ORIGIN	TIME FILED	DATE
73	R	C	W6LRU	11	SAN DIEGO CA	2330Z	APR 25

To
DAGMAR JOHNSON
26 WEST MULBERRY AVE
SACO ME

THIS RADIO MESSAGE WAS RECEIVED AT
AMATEUR STATION W1BJG PHONE 513-0811
OWNER F. D. Wilson
STREET ADDRESS Old Limerick Road
CITY AND STATE Biddeford, Maine

PLEASE LET US KNOW YOUR PLANS FOR SUMMER VISIT X LOVE

RITA

SENDER'S ADDRESS AND PHONE NUMBER FOR REFERENCE

REC'D	FROM	DATE	TIME	SENT	TO	DATE	TIME

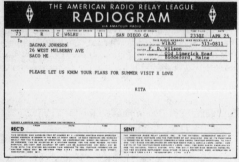

Here is an example of a plain-language message as it would be prepared for delivery. If the message were for relay instead of delivery, the information at the bottom would be filled in instead of that in the box.

MESSAGE HANDLING

Amateur operators in the United States and a few other countries enjoy a privilege not available to amateurs in most countries – that of handling third-party message traffic. In the early history of amateur radio in this country, some amateurs who were among the first to take advantage of this privilege formed an extensive relay organization which became the ARRL.

Thus, amateur message-handling has had a long and honorable history, and like most services, has gone through many periods of development and change. Those amateurs who handled traffic in 1914 would hardly recognize it the way some of us do it today, just as equipment in those days was far different from that in use now. Progress has been made and new methods have been developed in step with advancement in communication techniques of all kinds. Amateurs who handled a lot of traffic found that organized operating schedules were more effective than random relays, and as techniques advanced and messages increased in number, trunk lines were organized, spot frequencies began to be used, and there came into existence a number of traffic nets in which many stations operated on the same frequency to effect wider coverage in less time with fewer relays; but the old methods are still available to the amateur who handles only an occasional message.

Although message handling is as old an art as is amateur radio itself, there are many amateurs who do not know how to handle a formal message and have never done so. As each amateur grows older and gains experience in the amateur service, there is bound to come a time when he will be called upon to handle a written message, during a communications emergency, in casual contact with one of his many acquaintances on the air, or as a result of a request from a non-amateur friend. Regardless of the occasion, if it comes to you, you will want to rise to it! Considerable embarrassment is likely to be experienced by the amateur who finds he not only does not know the form in which the message should be prepared, but does not know how to go about putting it on the air.

Traffic work need not be a complicated or time-consuming activity for the casual or occasional message-handler. Amateurs may participate in traffic work to whatever extent they wish, from an occasional message now and then to becoming a part of organized traffic systems. This chapter explains some principles so the reader may know where to find out more about the subject and may exercise the message-handling privilege to best effect as the spirit and opportunity arise.

Responsibility

Amateurs who originate messages for transmission or who receive messages for relay or delivery should first consider that in doing so they are accepting the responsibility of clearing the message from their station on its way to its destination in the shortest possible time. Forty-eight hours after filing or receipt is the generally-accepted rule among traffic-handling amateurs, but it is obvious that if every amateur who relayed the message allowed it to remain in his station this long it might be a long time reaching its destination. Traffic should be relayed or delivered as quickly as possible.

Message Form

Once this responsibility is realized and accepted, handling the message becomes a matter of following generally-accepted standards of form and transmission. For this purpose, each message is divided into four parts: the preamble, the address, the text and the signature. Some of these parts themselves are subdivided. It is necessary in preparing the message for transmission and in actually transmitting it to know not only what each part is and what it is for, but to know in what *order* it should be transmitted, and to know the various procedure signals used with it when sent by cw. If you are going to send a message, you may as well send it right.

Standardization is important! There is a great deal of room for expressing originality and individuality in amateur radio, but there are also times and places where such expression can only cause confusion and inefficiency. Recognizing the need for standardization in message form and message transmitting procedures, ARRL has long since recommended such standards, and most traffic-interested amateurs have followed them. In general, these recommendations, and the various changes they have undergone from year to year, have been at the request of amateurs participating in this activity, and they are completely outlined and explained in *Operating an Amateur Radio Station* a copy of which is available upon request or by use of the coupon at the end of this chapter.

Clearing a Message

The best way to clear a message is to put it into one of the many organized traffic networks, or to give it to a station that can do so. There are many amateurs who make the handling of traffic their principal operating activity, and many more still who participate in this activity to a greater or lesser extent. The result is a traffic system which spreads to all corners of the United States and covers most U.S. possessions and Canada. Once a message gets into an organized net, regardless of the net's size or coverage, it is systematically routed toward its destination in the shortest possible time.

Amateurs not experienced in message handling should depend on the experienced message-handler to get a message through, if it is important; but the average amateur can enjoy operating with a message to be handled either through a local traffic net or by free-lancing. The latter may be accomplished by careful listening for an amateur station at desired points, directional CQs, use of recognized calling and net frequencies, or by making and keeping a schedule with another amateur for regular work between specified points. He may well aim at learning and enjoying through doing. The joy and accomplishment in thus developing one's operating skill to the peak of perfection has a reward all its own.

If you decide to "take the bull by the horns" and put the message into a traffic net yourself (and more power to you if you do!), you will need to know something about how nets operate, and if on cw, the special Q signals and procedure they use to dispatch all traffic with a maximum of efficiency. The frequency and operating time of the net in your section, or of other nets into which your message can go, is given in ARRL's Net Directory. This annually-revised publication is available on request. Listening for a few minutes at the time and frequency indicated should acquaint you with enough fundamentals to enable you to report into the net and report your traffic. From that time on you follow the instructions of the net control station, who will tell you when and to whom (and on what frequency, if different from the net frequency) to send your message. Cw nets use the special "QN" signals, so it may be helpful to have a list of these before you (available from ARRL Hq., Operating Aid No. 9B).

Network Operation

About this time, you may find that you are enjoying this type of operating activity and want to know more about it and increase your proficiency. Many amateurs are happily "addicted" to traffic handled after only one or two brief exposures to it. Much traffic is at present being conducted by cw, since this mode of communication seems to be popular for record purposes – but this does not mean that high code speed is a necessary prerequisite to working in traffic networks. There are many nets organized specifically for the slow-speed amateur, and most of the so-called "fast" nets are usually glad to slow down to accommodate slower operators.

It is a significant operating fact that code speed alone does *not* make for efficiency – sometimes the contrary! A high-speed operator who does not know procedure can "foul up" a net much more completely and more quickly than can a slow operator It is a proven fact that a bunch of high-speed operators who are not "savvy" in net operation cannot accomplish as much during a specified period as an equal number of slow operators who *know* net procedure. Don't let low code speed deter you from getting into traffic work. Given a little time your speed will reach the point where you can easily hold your own. Concentrate first on learning the net procedures

Voice modes are exceptionally well suited to short-range traffic work and require knowledge of phonetics and procedure peculiar to voice operation. Procedure is of paramount importance on phone, since the public may be listening.

Teamwork is the theme of all net operation. The net which functions most efficiently is the net in which all participants are thoroughly familiar with the procedure used, and in which operators refrain from transmitting except at the direction of the net control station, and do not occupy time with extraneous comments, even the exchange of pleasantries. There is a time and place for everything. When a net is in session it should concentrate on handling traffic until all traffic is cleared. Before or after the net is the time for rag-chewing and discussion. Some further details of net operation are included in *Operating an Amateur Radio Station*, mentioned earlier, but there is no substitute for actual participation.

The National Traffic System

To facilitate and speed the movement of message traffic, there is in existence an integrated national system by means of which originated traffic can normally reach its destination area the same day the message is originated. This system uses the state or section net as a basis. Each section net sends a representative to a "region" net (normally covering a call area) and each "region" net sends a representative to an "area" net (normally covering a time zone). After the area net has cleared all its traffic, its members then go back to their respective region nets, where they clear traffic to the various section net representatives. By means of connecting schedules between the area nets, traffic can flow both ways so that traffic originated on the West Coast reaches the East Coast with a maximum of dispatch, and vice versa. In general section nets function at 1900, region nets at 1945, area nets at 2030 and the same or different regional personnel again at 2130. Some section nets conduct a late session at 2200 to effect traffic delivery the same night. Local standard time is referred to in each case.

A system of daytime nets similar to the above is also in the initial stages at this writing. It is called "Daytime NTS" (DNTS). *QST* will cover details as they unfold.

The NTS plan somewhat spreads traffic opportunity so that casual traffic may be reported into nets for efficient handling one or two nights per week, early or late; or the ardent traffic man can operate in *both* early and late groups and in between to roll up impressive totals and speed traffic reliably to its destination. Old-time traffic men who prefer a high degree of organization and teamwork have returned to the traffic game as a result of the new system. Beginners have shown more interest in becoming part of a system nationwide in scope, in which *anyone* can participate. The National Traffic System has vast and intriguing possibilities as an amateur service. It is open to any amateur who wishes to participate.

The above is but the briefest resume of what is of necessity a rather complicated arrangement of nets and schedules. Complete details of the System and its operation are included in the ARRL *Public Service Communications Manual.*

EMERGENCY COMMUNICATION

One of the most important ways in which the amateur serves the public, thus making his existence a national asset, is by his preparation for and his participation in communications emergencies. Every amateur, regardless of the extent of his normal operating activities, should give some thought to the possibility of his being the only means of communication should his community be cut off from the outside world. It has happened many times, often in the most unlikely places; it has happened without warning, finding some amateurs totally unprepared; it can happen to *you*. Are you ready?

There are two principal ways in which any amateur can prepare himself for such an eventuality. One is to provide himself with equipment capable of operating on any type of emergency power (i.e., either ac or dc), and equipment which can readily be transported to the scene of disaster. Mobile equipment is especially desirable in most emergency situations.

Such equipment, regardless of how elaborate or how modern, is of little use, however, if it is not used properly and at the right times; and so another way for an amateur to prepare himself for emergencies, by no means less important than the first, is to *learn to operate efficiently*. There are many amateurs who feel that they know how to operate efficiently but who find themselves considerably handicapped at the crucial time by not knowing proper procedure, by being unable, due to years of casual amateur operation, to adapt themselves to snappy, abbreviated transmissions, and by being unfamiliar with message form and procedures. It is dangerous to overrate your ability in this; it is better to assume you have things to learn.

In general it can be said that there is more emergency equipment available than there are operators who know properly how to operate during emergency conditions, for such conditions require clipped, terse procedure with complete break-in on cw and fast push-to-talk or VOX on phone. The casual rag-chewing aspect of amateur radio, however enjoyable and worth-while in its place, must be forgotten at such times in favor of the business at hand. There is only one way to gain experience in this type of operation, and that is by practie. During an emergency is no time for practice; it should be done beforehand, as often as possible, on a regular basis.

This leads up to the necessity for emergency organization and preparedness. ARRL has long recognized this necessity and has provided for it. The Section Communications Manager (whose address appears on page 6 of every issue of *QST*) is empowered to appoint certain qualified amateurs in his section for the purpose of coordinating emergency communication organization and preparedness in specified areas or communities. This appointee is known as an Emergency Coordinator for the city or town. One should be specified for each community. For coordination and promotion at section level a Section Emergency Coordinator arranges for and recommends the appointments of various Emergency Coordinators at activity points throughout the section. Emergency Coordinators organize amateurs in their communities according to local needs for emergency communication facilities.

The community amateurs taking part in the local organization are members of the Amateur Radio Emergency Corps (AREC). *All* amateurs are invited to register in the AREC, whether they are able to play an active part in their local organization or only a supporting role. Application blanks are available from your EC, SEC, SCM or direct from ARRL Headquarters. In the event that inquiry reveals no Emergency Coordinator appointed for your community, your SCM would welcome a recommendation either from yourself or from a radio club of which you are a member. By holding an amateur operator license, you have the responsibility to your community and to amateur radio to uphold the traditions of the service.

Among the League's publications is a booklet entitled *Public Service Communications.* This booklet, while small in size, contains a wealth of information on AREC organization and functions and is invaluable to any amateur participating in emergency or civil defense work. It is free to AREC members and should be in every amateur's shack. Drop a line to the ARRL Communications Department if you want a copy, or use the coupon at the end of this chapter.

The Radio Amateur Civil Emergency Service

Following World War II there was established within our government the Federal Civil Defense Administration (FCDA), which, at the behest of ARRL and other amateurs, considered the role of the amateur in civil defense communication should the U.S. become embroiled in another war. This resulted, in 1951, in the establishment of the Radio Amateur Civil Emergency Service (RACES) with rules promulgated by FCC as a part of the Amateur Radio Service. FCDA has evolved into the present Defense Civil Preparedness Agency, part of the Department of Defense, and although the RACES rules have undergone several minor changes they are still essentially the same as originally put into effect.

RACES is intended solely for civil defense communication during civil emergencies, through the medium of amateur radio, and is designed to continue operation during any extreme national emergency such as war. It shares certain segments of frequencies with the regular (i.e., normal) Amateur Service on a nonexclusive basis. Its regulations are a subpart of the familiar amateur regulations (Part 97) and are included in full in the ARRL *License Manual*.

If *every* amateur participated, we would still be short of the total operating personnel required properly to implement RACES. As the service which bears the responsibility for the successful

Before Emergency

PREPARE yourself by providing emergency power for your station.

TEST your emergency equipment and operating ability in the annual Simulated Emergency Test and Field Day.

REGISTER with your ARRL Emergency Coordinator. If none, offer your services to local and civic relief agencies and explain what amateur radio can do during disasters.

In Emergency

LISTEN before you transmit, *always*!

REPORT to your Emergency Coordinator so he will have latest data on your facilities. Offer local civic and relief agencies your services directly in the absence of an EC.

RESTRICT all on-the-air work in accordance with FCC regulations, Sec. 97.107.

SOS is the International Distress Call for a dire emergency. The phone equivalent is MAYDAY. Use these calls for *emergency only*. False distress calls are unlawful.

RESPECT the fact that success in emergency depends on circuit discipline. The net control station is the supreme authority.

COOPERATE with those we serve. Be ready to help, but stay off the air unless there is a specific job to be done that you can handle more efficiently than any other station.

COPY bulletins from W1AW. During emergencies, special bulletins are transmitted.

After Emergency

REPORT to ARRL Headquarters promptly and fully so that the Amateur Service can receive full credit.

implementation of this important function, we face not only the task of installing (and in some cases building) the necessary equipment, but also of the training of thousands of additional people. This can and should be a function of the local unit of the Amateur Radio Emergency Corps under its EC and his assistants, working in close collaboration with the local civil defense organization.

The first step in organizing RACES locally is the appointment of a radio officer by the local civil defense director, possibly on the recommendation of his communications officer. A complete and detailed communications plan must be approved successively by local, state and DCPA regional directors, and by FCC. Once this has been accomplished, applications for station authorizations under this plan can be submitted direct to FCC. A complete bibliography of *QST* articles dealing with the subject of civil defense and RACES is available upon request from the ARRL Communications Department.

In the event of war, civil defense will place great reliance on RACES for back-up radio communication. Even in peacetime, RACES can be of great value in natural disaster communications. As a part of our total amateur public service effort, it deserves our whole-hearted and enthusiastic support and will permit us to continue to function in the public service, as amateurs, in RACES in wartime as we function in AREC and NTS during peacetime. If interested, inquire of your local civil defense agency and get sighed up with your radio officer.

ARRL OPERATING ORGANIZATION

Amateur operation must have point and constructive purpose to win public respect. Each individual amateur is the ambassador of the entire fraternity in his public relations and attitude toward his hobby. ARRL field organization adds point and purpose to amateur operating.

The Communications Department of the League is concerned with the practical operation of stations in all branches of amateur activity. Appointments or awards are available for rag-chewer, traffic enthusiast, phone operator, DX man and experimenter.

There are seventy-four ARRL Sections in the League's field organization, which embraces the United States, Canada, and certain other territory. Operating affairs in each Section are supervised by a Section Communications Manager (SCM) elected by members in that section for a two-year term of office. Organization appointments are made by the SCMs, elected as provided in the Rules and Regulations of the Communications Department, which accompany the League's By-Laws and Articles of Association. SCM addresses for all sections are given in full in each issue of *QST*. SCMs welcome monthly activity reports from all amateurs in their sections, regardless of status.

Whether your activity embraces phone or telegraphy, or both, there is a place for you in the League organization.

LEADERSHIP POSTS

To advance each type of station work and group interest in amateur radio, and to develop practical communications plans with the greatest success, appointments of ARRL members holding Conditional Class licenses or better to serve as leaders and organizers in particular single-interest fields are made by the SCM. Each leadership post is important. Each provides activities and assistance for appointee groups and individual members along the lines of natural interest. Some posts further the general ability of amateurs to communicate efficiently at all times by pointing activity toward networks and round tables; others are aimed specifically at establishment of provisions for organizing the amateur service as a standby communications group to serve the public in disaster, civil defense need or emergency of any sort. The SCM appoints the following in accordance with section needs and individual qualifications:

PAM Phone Activities Manager. Organizes activities for voice operators in his section. Promotes phone nets and recruits Official Phone Station appointees. The appointment of VHF-PAM is open to Technician licensees.

RM Route Manager. Organizes and coordinates cw traffic activities. Supervises and promotes nets and recruits Official Relay Station appointees.

SEC Section Emergency Coordinator. Promotes and administers section emergency radio organization.

EC Emergency Coordinator. Organizes amateurs of a community or other local areas for emergency radio service; maintains liaison with officials and agencies served, also with other local communication facilities. Sponsors tests, recruits for AREC and encourages alignment with RACES. A Technician Class licensee may receive this appointment if a qualified higher class licensee is not available.

STATION APPOINTMENTS

ARRL's field organization has a place for every active amateur who has a station. The Communications Department organization exists to increase individual enjoyment and station effectiveness in amateur radio work, and we extend a cordial invitation to every amateur to participate fully in the activities, to report results monthly, and to apply to the SCM for one of the following station appointments. ARRL membership and the conditional class or higher license or VE equivalent is prerequisite to all appointments, except where otherwise indicated.

OPS Official Phone Station. Sets high voice operating standards and procedures, furthers phone nets and traffic.

ORS Official Relay Station. Traffic service, operates cw nets; noted for 15 wpm and procedure ability. Open to RTTY traffickers.

OBS Official Bulletin Station. Transmits ARRL and FCC bulletin information to amateurs. Open to Technician licensees.

OVS Official VHF Station. Collects and reports vhf-uhf-shf propagation data, may engage in facsimile, TT, TV, work on 50 MHz and/or above. Takes part as feasible in vhf traffic work, reports same, supports vhf nets, observes procedure standards. Open to both Novice and Technician licensees.

OO Official Observer. Sends cooperative notices to amateurs to assist in frequency observance, insures high-quality signals, and prevents FCC trouble.

Emblem Colors

Members may wear the ARRL emblem with black-enamel background. A red background will indicate that the wearer is or has been SCM. SECs, ECs, RMs and PAMs may wear the emblem with green background. Observers and all *station* appointees are entitled to wear blue background emblems.

RADIO CLUB AFFILIATION

ARRL affiliation is available to any amateur society having (1) at least 51 percent of the voting club membership as full members of the League, and (2) at least 51 percent of members government-licensed radio amateurs. In high school and college radio clubs *bearing the school name,* the above requirements are modified to require only that the trustee or sponsor (for example) is a licensed amateur and a full member of ARRL. Where a society has common aims and wishes to add strength to that of other club groups and strengthen amateur radio by affiliation with the national amateur organization, a request addressed to the Communications Manager will bring the necessary forms and information to initiate the application for affiliation. Such clubs receive field-organization bulletins and special information at intervals for posting on club bulletin boards or for relay to their memberships. A travel plan providing communications, technical and secretarial contact from the Headquarters is worked out seasonally to give maximum benefits to as many as possible of the *active* affiliated radio clubs Papers on club work, suggestions for organizing, for constitutions, for radio courses of study, etc., are available on request.

Club Training Aids

One section of the ARRL Communications Department handles the Training Aids Program. This program is primarily a service to ARRL affiliated clubs. Material is aimed at education, training and entertainment of club members.

Training Aids include such items as motion-picture films, slides, audio tapes, lecture outlines and quizzes. Bookings are limited to ARRL-affiliated clubs primarily although bookings can be made to other groups on a non-priority basis.

All Training Aids materials are loaned free (except for shipping charges). If your club is affiliated but has not yet taken advantage of this service, you are missing a good chance to add the available features to your meeting programs and general club activities. Watch club bulletins and *QST* or write the ARRL Communications Department for TA-21.

W1AW

The Maxim Memorial Station, W1AW, is dedicated to fraternity and service. Operated by the League headquarters, W1AW is located adjacent to the Headquarters offices on a seven-acre site. The station is on the air daily, except holidays, and available time is divided between the different bands and modes. Facilities for all commonly used amateur modes are provided for all bands from 1.8 to 144 MHz.

Operation is roughly proportional to amateur interest in different bands and modes with maximum legal power on most bands. W1AW's daily bulletins and code practice aim to give operational help to the largest number.

W1AW was established as a living memorial to Hiram Percy Maxim, to carry on the work and traditions of amateur radio. The station is on the air daily and is open to visitors at all times it is in operation. The W1AW schedule of operation and visiting hours is printed each month in the *Operating News* section of *QST.*

OPERATING ACTIVITIES

Within the ARRL field organization there are many special activities. For all appointees and officials quarterly CD (Communications Department) Parties are scheduled to develop operating ability and a spirit of fraternalism.

In addition, ARRL sponsors various other activities open to all amateurs. The DX-minded amateur may participate in the Annual ARRL International DX Competition during February and March. This popular contest may bring you the thrill of working new countries and building up your DXCC totals; certificate awards are offered to top scorers in each country and ARRL section (see page 6 of any *QST*) and to club leaders. Then there is the very-popular Sweepstakes in November. Of domestic scope, the SS affords the opportunity to work new states for that WAS award. A Novice activity is planned annually. A 160-Meter Contest is scheduled for early December. The interests of vhf enthusiasts are also provided for in contests held in January, June and September of each year. Where enough logs (three) are received to constitute minimum "competition" a certificate in spot activities, such as the "SS" and vhf party, is awarded the leading newcomer for his work considered only in competition with other newcomers.

As in all our operating, the idea of having a good time is combined in the Annual June Field Day with the more serious thought of preparing ourselves to render public service in times of emergency. A premium is placed on the use of equipment without connection to commercial power sources. Clubs and individual groups always enjoy themselves in the "FD" and learn much about the requirements for operating under knockabout conditions afield.

ARRL contest activities are diversified to appeal to all operating interest, and will be found announced in detail in issues of *QST* preceding the different events.

AWARDS

The League-sponsored operating activities, heretofore mentioned, have useful objectives and provide much enjoyment for members of the fraternity. Achievement in amateur radio is also recognized by various certificates offered through the League and detailed below.

WAS Award

WAS means "Worked All States." An amateur, anywhere in the world, who succeeds in getting confirmed contacts with all fifty U.S. states and sends them in for examination, may receive this award from the League. There is a nominal service charge to those amateurs located within the League's operating territory (U.S., possessions, Puerto Rico and Canada) who are not ARRL members. For others, there is no charge except postage, which is expected to accompany the cards.

You can make the contacts over any period of time and on any or all amateur bands. If you wish, you may have your WAS award issued for some special way in which you made it, such as all cw, all phone, all on one band, all with lower power, etc. – only providing all cards submitted plainly show that a contact took place under the special circumstances for which you wish the award issued.

Before you send your cards, drop the ARRL Communications Department a line requesting a copy of the rules and an application blank.

5BWAS

The Five Band Worked All States Award became effective January 1, 1970. Only contacts made after that date count. Contacts must be confirmed with all 50 states on each of five amateur bands. Rules require applicants in the U.S. and possessions, Puerto Rico and Canada, to be a full member of ARRL. Basic WAS rules apply, with the addition of an application form fee of $10 (U.S.). This fee covers cost of return of the cards by first-class registered mail and a personalized plaque.

DX Century Club Award

The DXCC is one of the most popular and sought-after awards in all of amateur radio, and among the most difficult to acquire. Its issuance is carefully supervised at ARRL headquarters by a staff member who spends full time on this function alone.

To obtain DXCC, an amateur must make two-way contact with 100 "countries" listed on ARRL Operating Aid No. 7, which also contains the complete rules. Written confirmations are required for proof of contact. Such confirmations must be sent to ARRL headquarters, where each one is carefully scrutinized to make sure it actually confirms a contact with the applying amateur, that it was not altered or tampered with, and that the "country" claimed is actually on the ARRL list. Further safeguards are applied to maintain the high standards of this award. A handsome king-size certificate is sent to each amateur qualifying.

The term "country" is an arbitrary one not necessarily agreeing with the dictionary definition of such. For DXCC purposes, many bodies of land not having independent status politically are classified as countries. For example, Alaska and Hawaii, while states of the U.S., are considered separate "countries" because of their distance from the mainland. There are over 300 such designations on the ARRL list. Once a basic DXCC is issued, the certificate can be endorsed, by sticker, for additional countries by sending the additional cards in to headquarters for checking.

A separate DXCC award is also available for stations making all contacts by phone.

Because of the meticulous care in checking cards and handling this award, amateurs in the U.S., its possessions (including P.R.) and Canada who are not League members, are charged a nominal service fee both for basic DXCC and endorsements.

Before sending in your cards, be sure you are familiar with the rules (ARRL Operating Aid No. 7), which are quite detailed. In addition, get a copy of the DXCC application form (CD-164).

Five-Band DXCC

Entirely separate from DXCC, ARRL also offers a Five-Band DXCC (5BDXCC) Award for those amateurs who submit written proof of having made two-way contact with 100 or more countries on each of five amateur bands since January 1, 1969. Only full ARRL members are eligible in the U.S., possessions and Canada; elsewhere, any amateur may apply.

A charge of $10 (U.S.) is made for application forms; this covers the cost of returning cards by first class registered mail and issuance of a personalized engraved plaque for those qualifying.

For a copy of the complete rules, drop a line to ARRL Headquarters, 225 Main St., Newington, CT 06111.

WAC Award

The WAC award, Worked All Continents, is issued by the International Amateur Radio Union (IARU) upon proof of contact with each of the six continents. Amateurs in the U.S.A., Possessions and Canada should apply for the award through ARRL, headquarters society of the IARU. Those elsewhere must submit direct to their own IARU member-society. Residents of countries not represented in the Union may apply directly to ARRL for the award. Two basic types of WAC certificates are issued. One contains no endorsements and is awarded for cw, or a combination of cw and phone contacts; the other is awarded when all work is done on phone. There is a special endorsement to the phone WAC when all the confirmations submitted clearly indicate that the work was done on two-way ssb. Special endorsements are also available for RTTY and SSTV. The *only* special band endorsements are for 1.8, 3.5, and 50 MHz.

Code Proficiency Award

Many hams can follow the general idea of a contact "by ear" but when pressed to "write it down" they "muff" the copy. The Code Proficiency Award permits each amateur to prove himself as a proficient operator, and sets up a system of awards for step-by-step gains in copying proficiency. It enables every amateur to check his code proficiency, to better that proficiency, and to receive a certification of his receiving speed.

This program is a whale of a lot of fun. The League will give a certificate to any interested individual who demonstrates that he can copy perfectly, for at least one minute, plain-language Continental code at 10, 15, 20, 25, 30 or 35 words per minute, as transmitted monthly from W1AW and W6OWP.

As part of the ARRL Code Proficiency program W1AW transmits plain-language practice material each evening and week-day morning at speeds from 5 to 35 wpm, occasionally in reverse order. All amateurs are invited to use these transmissions to increase their code-copying ability. Non-amateurs are invited to utilize the lower speeds, 5, 7 1/2 and 10 wpm, which are transmitted for the benefit of persons studying the code in preparation for the amateur license examination. Refer to any issue of *QST* for details.

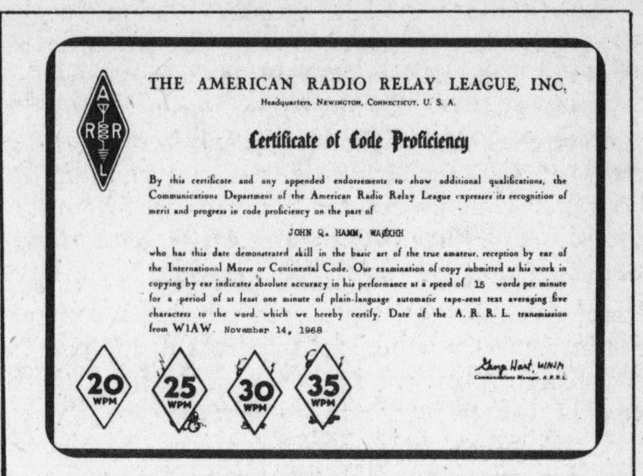

THE AMERICAN RADIO RELAY LEAGUE, INC.
Headquarters, Newington, Connecticut, U. S. A.

Certificate of Code Proficiency

By this certificate and any appended endorsements to show additional qualifications, the Communications Department of the American Radio Relay League expresses its recognition of merit and progress in code proficiency on the part of

JOHN Q. HAMM, WAØXHH

who has this date demonstrated skill in the basic art of the true amateur, reception by ear of the International Morse or Continental Code. Our examination of copy submitted as his work in copying by ear indicates absolute accuracy in his performance at a speed of 15 words per minute for a period of at least one minute of plain-language automatic tape-sent text averaging five characters to the word, which we hereby certify. Date of the A. R. R. L. transmission from W1AW. November 14, 1968

20 WPM 25 WPM 30 WPM 35 WPM

George Hart, W1NJM
Communications Manager, A.R.R.L.

Rag Chewers Club

The Rag Chewers Club is designed to encourage friendly contacts and discourage the "hello-good-bye" type of QSO. It furthers fraternalism through amateur radio.

Membership certificates are awarded to amateurs who report a fraternal-type contact with another amateur lasting a half hour or longer. This does not mean a half hour spent trying to get a message through or in trying to work a rare DX station, but a solid half hour of pleasant "visiting" with another amateur discussing subjects of mutual interest and getting to know each other. If nominating someone for RCC, please send the information to the nominee who will (in turn) apply to Headquarters for RCC.

Members sign "RCC" after their calls to indicate that they are interested in a chat, not just a contact.

Operating Aids

The following Operating Aids are available free, upon request: 4) Emergency Operating. 5) DX Operating Code. 6) Contest Duplicate Contact Record. 7) DXCC Countries List. 8) W.A.S. Record. 9b) ARRL Message Form. 13) Ready Reference Information. 14) A composite aid; Ending Signals, Time Conversion, Phonetic Alphabets, RST System and Steps in an Emergency.

A-1 Operator Club

The A-1 Operator Club should include in its ranks every good operator. To become a member, one must be nominated by at least two operators who already belong. General keying or voice technique, procedure, copying ability, judgment and courtesy all count in rating candidates under the club rules detailed at length in *Operating an Amateur Radio Station.* Aim to make yourself a fine operator, and one of these days you may be pleasantly surprised by an invitation to belong to the A-1 Operator Club, which carries a worthwhile certificate in its own right.

Brass Pounders League

Every individual reporting more than a specified minimum of official monthly traffic totals is given an honor place in the *QST* listing known as the Brass Pounders League and a certificate to recognize his performance is furnished by the SCM. In addition, a *BPL Traffic Award* (medallion) is given to individual amateurs working at their own stations after the third time they "make BPL" provided it is duly reported to the SCM and recorded in *QST*.

Public Service Honor Roll

A new listing, supplementing the BPL, was started in 1970. It takes into account the many public service functions of amateurs in addition to the handling of record messages. Points can be claimed for checking into and participating in nets, for serving as net control stations, as liaison between nets, for handling phone patches, for making BPL, for handling real emergency traffic and for serving as a net manager. Each such function has a maximum number of points per month so that nobody can make the PSHR by performing a single type of function, except handling emergency traffic. Versatility in public service is encouraged and rewarded. See *QST* for details.

Old Timers Club

The Old Timers Club is open to anyone who holds an amateur call at the present time, and who held an amateur license (operator or station) 20-or-more years ago. Lapses in activity during the intervening years are permitted.

If you can qualify as an "Old Timer," send an outline of your ham career. Indicate the date of your first amateur license and your present call. If eligible for the OTC, you will be added to the roster and will receive a membership certificate.

INTERNATIONAL PREFIXES

AAA-ALZ	United States of America
AMA-AOZ	Spain
APA-ASZ	Pakistan
ATA-AWZ	India
AXA-AXZ	Commonwealth of Australia
AYA-AZZ	Argentine Republic
BAA-BZZ	China
CAA-CEZ	Chile
CFA-CKZ	Canada
CLA-CMZ	Cuba
CNA-CNZ	Morocco
COA-COZ	Cuba
CPA-CPZ	Bolivia
CQA-CRZ	Portuguese Overseas Provinces
CSA-CUZ	Portugal
CVA-CXZ	Uruguay
CYA-CZZ	Canada
DAA-DTZ	Germany
DUA-DZZ	Republic of the Philippines
EAA-EHZ	Spain
EIA-EJZ	Ireland
EKA-EKZ	Union of Soviet Socialist Rep.
ELA-ELZ	Liberia
EMA-EOZ	Union of Soviet Socialist Rep.
EPA-EQZ	Iran
ERA-ERZ	Union of Soviet Socialist Rep.
ESA-ESZ	Estonia
ETA-ETZ	Ethiopia
EUA-EWZ	Bielorussian Soviet Socialist Rep.
EXA-EZZ	Union of Soviet Socialist Rep.
FAA-FZZ	France and French Community
GAA-GZZ	United Kingdom
HAA-HAZ	Hungarian People's Republic
HBA-HBZ	Switzerland
HCA-HDZ	Ecuador
HEA-HEZ	Switzerland
HFA-HFZ	People's Republic of Poland
HGA-HGZ	Hungarian People's Republic
HHA-HHZ	Republic of Haiti
HIA-HIZ	Dominican Republic
HJA-HKZ	Republic of Colombia
HLA-HMZ	Korea
HNA-HNZ	Iraq
HOA-HPZ	Republic of Panama
HQA-HRZ	Republic of Honduras
HSA-HSZ	Thailand
HTA-HTZ	Nicaragua
HUA-HUZ	Republic of El Salvador
HVA-HVZ	Vatican City State
HWA-HYZ	France and French Community
HZA-HZZ	Saudi Arabia
IAA-IZZ	Italy
JAA-JSZ	Japan
JTA-JVZ	Mongolian People's Republic
JWA-JXZ	Norway
JYA-JYZ	Jordan
JZA-JZZ	Western New Guinea
KAA-KZZ	United States of America
LAA-LNZ	Norway
LOA-LWZ	Argentine Republic
LXA-LXZ	Luxembourg
LYA-LYZ	Lithuania
LZA-LZZ	People's Republic of Bulgaria
MAA-MZZ	United Kingdom
NAA-NZZ	United States of America
OAA-OCZ	Peru
ODA-ODZ	Lebanon
OEA-OEZ	Austria
OFA-OJZ	Finland
OKA-OMZ	Czechoslovakia
ONA-OTZ	Belgium
OUA-OZZ	Denmark
PAA-PIZ	Netherlands
PJA-PJZ	Netherlands Antilles
PKA-POZ	Republic of Indonesia
PPA-PYZ	Brazil
PZA-PZZ	Surinam
QAA-QZZ	(Service abbreviations)
RAA-RZZ	Union of Soviet Socialist Rep.
SAA-SMZ	Sweden
SNA-SRZ	People's Republic of Poland
SSA-SSM	United Arab Republic
SSN-STZ	Sudan
SUA-SUZ	Arab Republic of Egypt
SVA-SZZ	Greece
TAA-TCZ	Turkey
TDA-TDZ	Guatemala
TEA-TEZ	Costa Rica
TFA-TFZ	Iceland
TGA-TGZ	Guatemala
THA-THZ	France and French Community
TIA-TIZ	Costa Rica
TJA-TJZ	Republic of Cameroon
TKA-TKZ	France and French Community
TLA-TLZ	Central African Republic
TMA-TMZ	France and French Community
TNA-TNZ	Republic of Congo (Brazzaville)
TOA-TQZ	France, French Community
TRA-TRZ	Republic of Gabon
TSA-TSZ	Tunisia
TTA-TTZ	Republic of Chad
TUA-TUZ	Republic of the Ivory Coast
TVA-TXZ	France and French Community
TYA-TYZ	Republic of Dahomey
TZA-TZZ	Republic of Mali
UAA-UQZ	Union of Soviet Socialist Republics
URA-UTZ	Ukrainian Soviet Socialist Rep.
UUA-UZZ	Union of Soviet Socialist Republics
VAA-VGZ	Canada
VHA-VNZ	Commonwealth of Australia
VOA-VOZ	Canada
VPA-VSZ	British Overseas Territories
VTA-VWZ	India
VXA-VYZ	Canada
VZA-VZZ	Commonwealth of Australia
WAA-WZZ	United States of America
XAA-XIZ	Mexico
XJA-XOZ	Canada
XPA-XPZ	Denmark
XQA-XRZ	Chile
XSA-XSZ	China
XTA-XTZ	Republic of the Upper Volta
XUA-XUZ	Khmer Republic
XVA-XVZ	Viet Nam
XWA-XWZ	Laos
XXA-XXZ	Portuguese Overseas Provinces
XYA-XZZ	Burma
YAA-YAZ	Afghanistan
YBA-YHA	Republic of Indonesia
YIA-YIZ	Iraq
YJA-YJZ	New Hebrides
YKA-YKZ	Syria
YLA-YLZ	Latvia
YMA-YMZ	Turkey
YNA-YNZ	Nicaragua
YOA-YRZ	Roumanian People's Republic
YSA-YSZ	Republic of El Salvador
YTA-YUZ	Yugoslavia

YVA-YYZ	Venezuela
YZA-YZZ	Yugoslavia
ZAA-ZAZ	Albania
ZBA-ZJZ	British Overseas Territories
ZKA-ZMZ	New Zealand
ZNA-ZOZ	British Overseas Territories
ZPA-ZPZ	Paraguay
ZQA-ZQZ	British Overseas Territories
ZRA-ZUZ	Republic of South Africa
ZVA-ZZZ	Brazil
2AA-2ZZ	Great Britain
3AA-3AZ	Monaco
3BA-3BZ	Mauritius
3CA-3CZ	Equatorial Guinea
3DA-3DM	Swaziland
3DN-3DZ	Fiji
3EA-3FZ	Panama
3GA-3GZ	Chile
3HA-3UZ	China
3VA-3VZ	Tunisia
3WA-3WZ	Viet Nam
3XA-3XZ	Guinea
3YA-3YZ	Norway
3ZA-3ZZ	People's Republic of Poland
4AA-4CZ	Mexico
4DA-4IZ	Republic of the Philippines
4JA-4LZ	Union of Soviet Socialist Rep.
4MA-4MZ	Venezuela
4NA-4OZ	Yugoslavia
4PA-4SZ	Ceylon
4TA-4TZ	Peru
4UA-4UZ	United Nations
4VA-4VZ	Republic of Haiti
4WA-4WZ	Yemen
4XA-4XZ	State of Israel
4YA-4YZ	International Civil Aviation Org.
4ZA-4ZZ	State of Israel
5AA-5AZ	Libya
5BA-5BZ	Republic of Cyprus
5CA-5GZ	Morocco
5HA-5IZ	Tanzania
5JA-5KZ	Colombia
5LA-5MZ	Liberia
5NA-5OZ	Nigeria
5PA-5QZ	Denmark
5RA-5SZ	Malagasy Republic
5TA-5TZ	Islamic Republic of Mauritania
5UA-5UZ	Republic of the Niger
5VA-5VZ	Togolese Republic
5WA-5WZ	Western Samoa
5XA-5XZ	Uganda
5YA-5ZZ	Kenya
6AA-6BZ	Arab Republic of Egypt
6CA-6CZ	Syria
6DA-6JZ	Mexico
6KA-6NZ	Korea
6OA-6OZ	Somalia
6PA-6SZ	Pakistan
6TA-6UZ	Sudan
6VA-6WZ	Republic of the Senegal
6XA-6XZ	Malagasy Republic
6YA-6YZ	Jamaica
6ZA-6ZZ	Liberia
7AA-7IZ	Indonesia
7JA-7NZ	Japan
7OA-7OZ	South Yemen Popular Republic
7PA-7PZ	Lesotho
7QA-7QZ	Malawi
7RA-7RZ	Algeria
7SA-7SZ	Sweden
7TA-7YZ	Algeria
7ZA-7ZZ	Saudi Arabia
8AA-8IZ	Indonesia
8JA-8NZ	Japan
8OA-8OZ	Botswana
8PA-8PZ	Barbados
8QA-8QZ	Maldive Islands
8RA-8RZ	Guyana
8SA-8SZ	Sweden
8TA-8YZ	India
8ZA-8ZZ	Saudi Arabia
9AA-9AZ	San Marino
9BA-9DZ	Iran
9EA-9FZ	Ethiopia
9GA-9GZ	Ghana
9HA-9HZ	Malta
9IA-9JZ	Zambia
9KA-9KZ	Kuwait
9LA-9LZ	Sierra Leone
9MA-9MZ	Malaysia
9NA-9NZ	Nepal
9OA-9TZ	Republic of Zaire
9UA-9UZ	Burundi
9VA-9VZ	Singapore
9WA-9WZ	Malaysia
9XA-9XZ	Rwanda
9YA-9ZZ	Trinidad and Tobago
A2A-A2Z	Republic of Botswana
A3A-A3Z	Kingdom of Tonga
A4A-A4Z	Oman
A5A-A5Z	Bhutan
A6A-A6Z	United Arab Emirates
C2A-C2Z	Republic of Nauru
C3A-C3Z	Principality of Andorra
L2A-L9Z	Argentina
S2A-S3Z	Bangladesh

ABBREVIATIONS FOR CW WORK

Abbreviations help to cut down unnecessary transmission. However, make it a rule not to abbreviate unnecessarily when working an operator of unknown experience.

AA	All after
AB	All before
ABT	About
ADR	Address
AGN	Again
ANT	Antenna
BCI	Broadcast interference
BCL	Broadcast listener
BK	Break; break me; break in
BN	All between; been
BUG	Semi-automatic key
C	Yes
CFM	Confirm; I confirm
CK	Check
CL	I am closing my station; call
CLD-CLG	Called; calling
CQ	Calling any station
CUD	Could
CUL	See you later
CUM	Come
CW	Continuous wave (i.e., radiotelegraph)
DLD-DLVD	Delivered
DX	Distance, foreign countries
ES	And, &
FB	Fine business; excellent
GA	Go ahead (or resume sending)
GB	Good-by
GBA	Give better address
GE	Good evening
GG	Going
GM	Good morning
GN	Good night
GND	Ground
GUD	Good
HI	The telegraphic laugh; high
HR	Here; hear
HV	Have
HW	How
LID	A poor operator
MA, MILS	Milliamperes
MSG	Message; prefix to radiogram
N	No
NCS	Net control station
ND	Nothing doing
NIL	Nothing; I have nothing for you
NM	No more
NR	Number
NW	Now; I resume transmission
OB	Old boy
OM	Old man
OP-OPR	Operator
OT	Old timer; old top
PBL	Preamble
PSE	Please
PWR	Power
PX	Press
R	Received as transmitted; are
RCD	Received
RCVR (RX)	Receiver
REF	Refer to; referring to; reference
RFI	Radio frequency interference
RIG	Station equipment
RPT	Repeat; I repeat
RTTY	Radioteletype
SASE	Self-addressed, stamped envelope
SED	Said
SIG	Signature; signal
SINE	Operator's personal initials or nickname
SKED	Schedule
SRI	Sorry
SVC	Service; prefix to service message
TFC	Traffic
TMW	Tomorrow
TNX-TKS	Thanks
TT	That
TU	Thank you
TVI	Television interference
TXT	Text
UR-URS	Your; you're; yours
VFO	Variable-frequency oscillator
VY	Very
WA	Word after
WB	Word before
WD-WDS	Word; words
WKD-WKG	Worked; working
WL	Well; will
WUD	Would
WX	Weather
XMTR (TX)	Transmitter
XTAL	Crystal
XYL (YF)	Wife
YL	Young lady
73	Best regards
88	Love and kisses

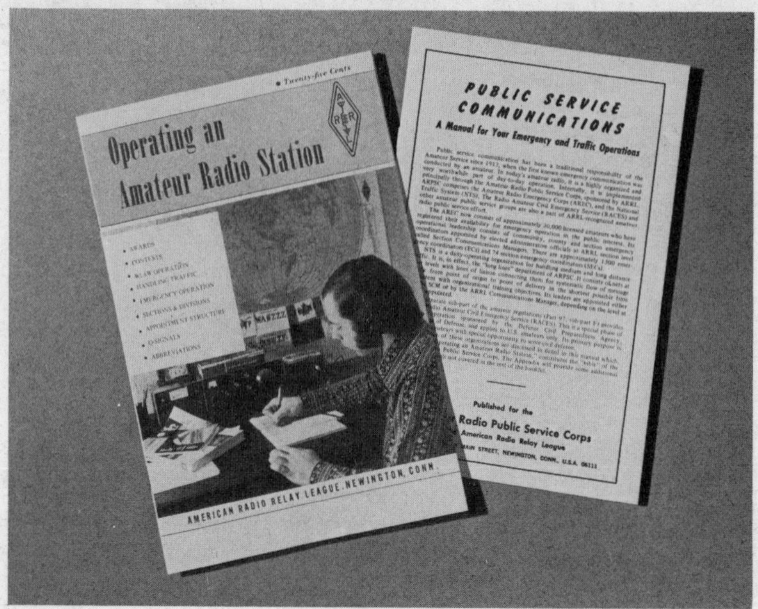

▲ *Operating an Amateur Radio Station* covers the details of practical amateur operating. In it you will find information on Operating Practices, Emergency Communication, ARRL Operating Activities and Awards, the ARRL Field Organization, Handling Messages, Network Organization, "Q" Signals and Abbreviations used in amateur operating, and other helpful material. It's a handy reference that will serve to answer many of the questions concerning operating that arise during your activities on the air.

▲ *Public Service Communications* is the "bible" of the Amateur Radio Public Service Corps. Within its pages are contained the fundamentals of operation of the Amateur Radio Emergency Corps (AREC), the National Traffic System (NTS), and the Radio Amateur Civil Emergency Service (RACES), including diagrams of how each is organized and how it operates. The role of the American Red Cross and FCC's regulations concerning amateur operation in emergencies also come in for some special attention.

The two publications described above may be obtained without charge by any *Handbook* reader. Either or both will be sent upon request.

AMERICAN RADIO RELAY LEAGUE
225 Main Street
Newington, CT 06111

Please send me, without charge, the following:

☐ **OPERATING AN AMATEUR RADIO STATION**
☐ **PUBLIC SERVICE COMMUNICATIONS**

Name ....
(Please Print)

Address ....

.... **Zip**

Chapter 25

Vacuum Tubes and Semiconductors

For the convenience of the designer, the receiving-type tubes listed in this chapter are grouped by filament voltages and construction types (glass, metal, miniature, etc.). For example, all miniature tubes are listed in Table I, all metal tubes are in Table II, and so on.

Transmitting tubes are divided into triodes and tetrodes-pentodes, then listed according to rated plate dissipation. This permits direct comparison of ratings of tubes in the same power classification.

For quick reference, all tubes are listed in numerical-alphabetical order in the index. Types having no table reference are either obsolete or of little use in amateur equipment. Base diagrams for these tubes are listed.

Tube Ratings

Vacuum tubes are designed to be operated within definite maximum (and minimum) ratings. These ratings are the maximum safe operating voltages and currents for the electrodes, based on inherent limiting factors such as permissible cathode temperature, emission, and power dissipation in electrodes.

In the transmitting-tube tables, maximum ratings for electrode voltage, current and dissipation are given separately from the typical operating conditions for the recommended classes of operation. In the receiving-tube tables, ratings and operating data are combined. Where only one set of operating conditions appears, the positive electrode voltages shown (plate, screen, etc.) are, in general, also the maximum rated voltages.

For certain air-cooled transmitting tubes, there are two sets of maximum values, one designated as CCS (Continuous Commercial Service) ratings, the other ICAS (Intermittent Commercial and Amateur Service) ratings. Continuous Commercial Service is defined as that type of service in which long tube life and reliability of performance under continuous operating conditions are the prime consideration. Intermittent Commercial and Amateur Service is defined to include the many applications where the transmitter design factors of minimum size, light weight, and maximum power output are more important than long tube life. ICAS ratings are considerably higher than CCS ratings. They permit the handling of greater power, and although such use involves some sacrifice in tube life, the period over which tubes give satisfactory performance in intermittent service can be extremely long.

The plate dissipation values given for transmitting tubes should not be exceeded during normal operation. In plate modulated amplifier applications, the maximum allowable carrier-condition plate dissipation is approximately 66 percent of the value listed and will rise to the maximum value under 100 percent sinusoidal modulation.

Typical Operating Conditions

The typical operating conditions given for transmitting tubes represent, in general, maximum ICAS ratings where such ratings have been given by the manufacturer. They do not represent the *only* possible method of operation of a particular tube type. Other values of plate voltage, plate current, etc., may be used so long as the maximum ratings for a particular voltage or current are not exceeded.

Detailed information and characteristic curves are available from tube and semiconductor manufacutrers, in books sold through radio dealers or direct from the factory.

Semiconductors

The semiconductor tablulation in this chapter is restricted to some of the more common diodes and transistors. The units listed were selected to represent those types that are useful for most amateur radio experimental applications. These diodes and transistors were chosen for their low cost and availability. Most of them can be obtained from the large mail-order houses or from the local manufacturer's distributor. Because there are thousands of diode and transistor types on today's market, this list is by no means complete.

INDEX TO TUBE TABLES

INDEX TO VACUUM-TUBE TYPES

Base-diagram section pages V5-V15. Classified data pages V16-V34.

Type	Page	Base
00-A	—	4D
01-A	—	4D
0A2	V19	5BO
0A3A	V19	4AJ
0A4G	—	4V
0A5	—	Fig. 19
0B2	V19	5BO
0B3	V19	4AJ
0C2	V19	5BO
0C3A	V19	4AJ
0D3A	V19	4AJ
0G3	—	5BO
0Y4	—	4BU
0Z4	—	4R
0Z4A	—	4R
0Z4G	V19	4R
1	—	4G
1A3	—	5AP
1A4P	—	4M
1A4T	—	4K
1A5GT	—	6X
1A6	—	6L
1A7GT	—	7Z
1AB5	—	5BF
1AB6	—	7DH
1AC6	—	7DH
1AE4	—	6AR
1AF4	—	6AR
1AF5	—	6AU
1AH5	—	6AU
1AJ4	—	6AR
1AX2	—	9Y
1B3GT	V19	3C
1B4	—	4M
1B5	—	6M
1B7GT	—	7Z
1B8GT	—	8AW
1C3	—	5CF
1C5GT	—	6X
1C6	—	6L
1C7G	—	7Z
1C21	—	4V
1D5GP	—	5Y
1D5GT	—	5R
1D7G	—	7Z
1D8GT	—	8AJ
1DN5	—	6BW
1E3	—	9BG
1E4G	—	5S
1E5GP	—	5Y
1E7G	—	8C
1EP1-2-11	—	11V
1F4	—	5K
1F5G	—	6X
1F6	—	6W
1F7G	—	7AD
1G3-GT/1B3-GT	V19	3C
1G4GT	—	5S
1G5G	—	6X
1G6GT	—	7AB
1H4G	—	5S
1H5GT	—	5Z
1H6G	—	7AA
1J3	V19	3C
1J5G	—	6X
1J6GT	—	7AB
1K3	—	3C
1K3	V19	3C
1L4	—	6AR
1L6	—	7DC
1LA4	—	5AD
1LA6	—	7AK
1LB4	—	5AD
1LB6	—	8AX
1LC5	—	7AO
1LC6	—	7AK
1LD5	—	6AX
1LE3	—	4AA
1LF3	—	4AA
1LG5	—	7AO
1LH4	—	5AG
1LN5	—	7AO
1N5GT	—	5Y
1N6G	—	7AM
1P5GT	—	5Y
1Q5GT	—	6AF
1R4	—	4AH
1R5	—	7AT
1S4	—	7AV
1S5	—	6AU
1SA6GT	—	6CA
1SB6GT	—	6CB
1T4	—	6AR
1T5GT	—	6X
1U4	—	6A
1U5	—	6BR
1U6	—	7DW
1-V	—	4G
1V2	V19	9U
1W4	—	5BZ
1X2	—	9Y
1X2A	—	9Y
1X2B	—	9Y
1Y2	—	4P
1Z2	—	7CB
2A3	—	4D
2A4G	—	5S
2A5	—	6B
2A6	—	6G
2A7	—	7C
2AP1A	—	11L
2B4	—	5A
2B6	—	7J
2B7	—	7D
2B22	—	Fig. 22
2B25	—	3T
2BP1-11	—	12E
2C4	—	5AS
2C21	—	7BH
2C22	—	4AM
2C25	—	4D
2C26A	—	4BB
2C34	—	Fig. 70
2C36	—	Fig. 21
2C37	—	Fig. 21
2C39	V21	—
2C40	V20	Fig. 11
2C43	V20	Fig. 11
2C51	—	8CJ
2C52	—	8BD
2D21	—	7BN
2E5	—	6R
2E22	V22	5J
2E24	—	7CL
2E25	V22	5BJ
2E26	V22	7CK
2E30	—	7CQ

Type	Page	Base
2EA5	—	7EW
2EN5	—	7FL
2G5	—	6R
2S/4S	—	5D
2V2	—	8FV
2V3G	—	4Y
2W3	—	4X
2X2-A	V19	4AB
2Y2	V19	4AB
2Z2	V19	4B
3A2	—	9DT
3A3	—	8EZ
3A4	—	7BB
3A5	—	7BC
3A8GT	—	8AS
3ACP1-7-11	—	14J
3AP1-4	—	7AN
3AP1A	—	7CE
3AQP1	—	12E
3B4	—	7CY
3B5GT	—	7AP
3B7	—	7BE
3B24	V20	Fig. 49
3B25	—	4P
3B26	—	Fig. 18
3B27	—	4P
3B28	V20	4P
3BP1-4-11	—	14A
3BP1A	—	14G
3C4	—	6BX
3C5GT	—	7AQ
3C6	—	7BW
3C22	—	Fig. 17
3C23	—	3G
3C24	V20	2D
3CP1	—	11C
3CX100A5	V21	—
3D6	—	6BB
3D23	—	Fig. 30
3D24	V22	Fig. 75
3DK6	—	7CM
3DX3	—	Fig. 24
3E5	—	6BX
3E6	—	7CJ
3E22	—	8BY
3E29	V22	7BP
3EA5	—	7EW
3EP1	—	11N
3FP7	—	14B
3FP7A	—	14J
3GP1-4-5-11	—	11A
3GP1A	—	11N
3GP4A	—	11N
3JP1—12	—	14J
3JP1A—11A	—	14J
3KP1-4-11	—	11M
3LE4	—	6BA
3LF4	—	6BB
3MP1	—	12F
3Q4	—	7BA
3Q5GT	—	7AP
3RP1-4	—	12E
3RP1A	—	12E
3S4	—	7BA
3SP1-4-7	—	12E
3UP1	—	12F
3V4	—	6BX
3WP1-2-11	—	12T
3-25A3	—	3G
3-50A4	—	3G
3-50D4	—	2D
3-50G2	—	2D
3-75A3	—	2D
3-100A2	V21	2D
3-400Z	V21	Fig. 3
3-500Z	V21	Fig. 3
3-1000Z	V21	Fig. 3
4A6G	—	8L
4C32	—	2N
4C34	—	2N
4C36	—	Fig. 31
4CX250	—	Fig. 75
4CX300A	V23	—
4CX1000A	V23	—
4D21	V23	5BK
4D22	V22	Fig. 26
4D23	—	5BK
4D32	V22	Fig. 27
4DK6	—	7CM
4E27	V22	7BM
4E27A	V23	7BM
4EW6	—	7CM
4X150A	V23	Fig. 75
4X150D	V23	Fig. 75
4X150G	V23	—
4X250B	V23	Fig. 75
4-65A	V22	Fig. 25
4-125A	V23	5BK
4-250A	V23	5BK
4-400A	V23	5BK
4-1000A/8166	V23	—
5A6	—	9L
5ABP1-7-11	—	14J
5ADP1-7-11	—	14J
5AMP1	—	14U
5AP1-4	—	11A
5AQP1	—	14G
5AS4A	V20	5T
5AT4	V20	5L
5ATP1-11	—	14V
5AU4	V20	5T
5AW4	V20	5T
5AX4GT	—	5T
5AZ4	—	5T
5BC3	—	9NT
5BP1	—	11A
5BP1A	—	11N
5BP7A	—	11N
5CP1-11	—	14B
5CP1A	—	14J
5CP1B-11B	—	14J
5CP7A	—	14J
5CP11A	—	14J
5CP12	—	14J
5D22	V23	5BK
5DJ4	—	8KS
5EA8	—	9AE
5FV8	—	9FA
5GP1	—	11A
5HP1-4	—	11A
5HP1A	—	11N
5JP1A-4A	—	11S
5LP1A-4A	—	11T
5MP1-11	—	7AN
5NP1-4	—	11A
5R4GY	V20	5T
5R4GYA	V20	5T

Type	Page	Base
5RP1A-4A	—	14P
5SP1-4	—	14K
5T4	—	5T
5U4G	V20	5T
5U4GA-GB	V20	5T
5UP1-11	—	12E
5V3A	V20	5T
5V4GA	V20	5L
5VP7	—	11N
5W4GT	—	5T
5X3	—	4C
5X4G	—	5Q
5XP1	—	14P
5XP1A-11A	—	14P
5Y3-G-GT	V20	5T
5Y4-G-GT	—	5Q
5Z3	V20	4C
5Z4	V20	5L
5-125B	V23	7BM
5-500A	V23	—
6A3	—	4D
6A4	—	5B
6A5GT	—	6T
6A6	—	7B
6A7	—	7C
6A8	V18	8A
6AB4	—	5CE
6AB5	—	6R
6AB6G	—	7AU
6AB7	—	8N
6AB8	—	9AT
6AC5GT	—	6Q
6AC6G	—	7AU
6AC7	V18	8N
6AD5G	—	6Q
6AD6G	—	7AG
6AD7G	—	8AY
6AD8	—	9T
6AE5G	—	6Q
6AE6G	—	7AH
6AE7GT	—	7AX
6AE8	V24	8DU
6AF3	—	9CB
6AF4A	V16	7DK
6AF5G	—	6Q
6AF6G	—	7AG
6AF7G	—	8AG
6AG5	V16	7BD
6AG6G	—	7S
6AG7	V18	8Y
6AH4GT	—	8EL
6AH5G	—	6AP
6AH6	V16	7BK
6AH7GT	—	8BE
6AJ4	V16	9BX
6AJ5	—	7BD
6AJ7	—	8N
6AJ8	—	9CA
6AK5	V16	7BD
6AK6	V16	7BK
6AK7	—	8Y
6AK8	—	9E
6AL3	—	9CB
6AL5	V16	6BT
6AL6G	—	6AM
6AL7GT	V19	8CH
6AM4	V16	9BX
6AM5	—	6CH
6AM6	—	7DB
6AM8A	—	9CY
6AN4	—	7DK
6AN5	V16	7BD
6AN6	—	7BJ
6AN7	—	9Q
6AN8A	V16	9DA
6AQ4	—	7DT
6AQ5A	V16	7BZ
6AQ6	V16	7BT
6AQ7GT	V19	8CK
6AQ8	—	9AJ
6AR5	V16	6CC
6AR6	V19	6BQ
6AR7GT	V19	7DE
6AR8	—	9DP
6AS5	—	7CV
6AS6	V16	7CM
6AS7GA	V19	8BD
6AS8	—	9DS
6AT6	V16	7BT
6AT8A	—	9DW
6AU4GT	—	4CG
6AU5GT	V19	6CK
6AU6A	V16	7BK
6AU7	—	9A
6AU8A	—	9DX
6AV4	V20	5BS
6AV5GA	—	6CK
6AV5GT	—	6CK
6AV6	V16	7BT
6AV11	—	12BY
6AW7GT	—	8CQ
6AW8A	—	9DX
6AX4GT	—	4CG
6AX5GT	V20	6S
6AX6G	—	7Q
6AX7	—	9A
6AX8	—	9AE
6AZ8	V16	9ED
6B4G	—	5S
6B5	—	6AS
6B6G	—	7V
6B7	—	7D
6B8	V18	8E
6B10	—	12BF
6BA6	V16	7BK
6BA7	V16	8CT
6BA8A	—	9DX
6BC4	V16	9DR
6BC5	—	7BD
6BC7	—	9AX
6BC8	—	9AJ
6BD4A	—	Fig. 80
6BD5GT	—	6CK
6BD6	—	7BK
6BD7	—	9Z
6BE6	V16	7CH
6BE7	—	9AA
6BE8A	V16	9EG
6BF5	V16	7BZ
6BF6	V16	7BT
6BG6GA	—	5BT
6BH5	—	9AZ
6BH6	V16	7CM
6BH8	V16	9DX
6BJ5	—	6CH
6BJ6A	V16	7CM
6BJ7	V16	9AX
6BJ8	V16	9ER

Type	Page	Base
6BK5	—	9BQ
6BK6	V16	7BT
6BK7A	—	9AJ
6BK7B	V16	9AJ
6BL7GTA	V19	8BD
6BL8	V16	9DC
6BM5	—	7BZ
6BN4A	V16	7EG
6BN6	V16	7DF
6BN7	—	9AJ
6BN8	V16	9ER
6BQ5	V16	9CV
6BQ6GTB/6CU6	V19	6AM
6BQ7A	V16	9AJ
6BR7	—	9BC
6BR8A	V16	9FA
6BS5	—	9BK
6BS7	—	9BB
6BS8	V16	9AJ
6BT6	—	7BT
6BT8	—	9FE
6BU5	—	8FP
6BU6	—	7BT
6BU8	—	9FG
6BV7	—	9BU
6BV8	—	9FJ
6BW4	V20	9DJ
6BW6	—	9AM
6BW7	—	9AQ
6BW8	—	9HK
6BW11	—	12HD
6BX4	V20	5BS
6BX6	—	9AQ
6BX7GT	V19	8BD
6BX8	V16	9AJ
6BY5G	V20	6CN
6BY6	—	7CH
6BY7	—	9AQ
6BY8	—	9FN
6BZ6	V16	7CM
6BZ7	V16	9AJ
6BZ8	V16	9AJ
6C4	V16	6BG
6C4	V20	6BG
6C5	—	6Q
6C6	—	6F
6C7	—	7G
6C8G	—	8G
6C10	—	12BQ
6CA4	V20	9M
6CA5	—	7CV
6CB5A	V19	8GD
6CB6A	V16	7CM
6CD6GA	V19	5BT
6CE5	V16	7BD
6CF6	—	7CM
6CG6	V16	7BK
6CG7	V16	9AJ
6CG8A	—	9GF
6CH6	—	9BA
6CH7	—	9EW
6CH8	—	9F
6CJ6	—	9AS
6CK4	V19	8JB
6CK6	—	9AR
6CL5	V19	8GD
6CL6	V16	9BV
6CL8A	—	9FX
6CM6	—	9CK
6CM7	—	9ES
6CM8	—	9FZ
6CN7	—	9EN
6CQ6	—	7DB
6CQ8	—	9GE
6CR6	—	7EA
6CR8	—	9GJ
6CS5	—	9CK
6CS6	—	7CH
6CS7	—	F9E
6CS8	—	9FZ
6CU5	—	7CV
6CU6	V19	6AM
6CU8	—	9GM
6CW4	V16	12AQ
6CW5	—	9CV
6CX7	—	9FC
6CX8	V16	9DX
6CY5	V16	7EW
6CY7	—	9EF
6CZ5	—	9HN
6D4	—	5AY
6D6	—	6F
6D7	—	7H
6D8G	—	8A
6D10	—	12BQ
6DA4A	—	4CQ
6DB5	—	9GR
6DB6	—	7CM
6DC6	—	7CM
6DE4	V20	4CG
6DE6	—	7CM
6DE7	—	9HF
6DG6GT	—	7S
6DJ8	V16	9AJ
6DK6	V16	7CM
6DN6	V19	5BT
6DN7	V19	8BD
6DQ5	V19	8JC
6DQ6B	V19	6AM
6DR7	—	9HF
6DS4	V16	12AQ
6DS5	—	7BZ
6DT5	—	9HN
6DT6	V16	7EN
6DT8	—	9DE
6DV4	—	12EA
6DW5	V16	9CK
6DX4	—	7DK
6DX8	—	9HX
6DZ4	—	7DK
6DZ7	V19	8JP
6E5	V19	6R
6E6	—	7B
6E7	—	7H
6E8G	—	8O
6EA5	—	7EW
6EA7	V19	8BD
6EA8	V16	9AE
6EB5	—	6BT
6EB8	V16	9DX
6EF6	V19	7S
6EH5	V16	7CV
6EH7	V16	9AQ
6EH8	V16	9JG
6EJ7	V16	9AQ
6ER5	V16	7FN
6ES5	—	7FP

Type	Page	Base
6ES8	V17	9DE
6EU7	V17	9LS
6EU8	V17	9JF
6EV5	—	7EW
6EW6	—	7CM
6EW7	—	9HF
6EX6	—	5BT
6EY6	V19	7AC
6EZ5	V19	7AC
6EZ8	V17	9KA
6F4	V20	7BR
6F4	V25	7BR
6F5	—	5M
6F6	V18	7S
6F7	—	7E
6F8G	—	8G
6FD7	—	9HF
6FG5	—	7GA
6FG7	—	9GF
6FH5	—	7FP
6FH6	V19	6AM
6FJ7	—	12BM
6FM7	—	12BJ
6FM8	—	9KR
6FQ5A	—	7FP
6FS5	—	7GA
6FV6	V17	7FQ
6FV8A	—	9FA
6FW8	—	9AJ
6FY5	—	7FN
6G5	—	6R
6G6G	—	7S
6GC5	V17	9EU
6GE5	—	12BJ
6GF5	—	12BJ
6GH8A	—	9AE
6GJ5	—	9NM
6GJ8	V17	9AE
6GK5	V17	7FP
6GK6	V17	9GK
6GM6	V17	7CM
6GM8	—	9DE
6GN8	V17	9DX
6GS8	—	9LW
6GT5	—	9NZ
6GU5	—	7GA
6GV8	—	9LY
6GW5	—	7GK
6GW6	V19	6AM
6GY8	—	9MB
6GZ5	—	7CV
6H4GT	—	5AF
6H5	—	6R
6H6	—	7Q
6H8G	—	8E
6HA5	—	76M
6HB5	—	12BJ
6HB6	V17	9PU
6HB7	—	9QA
6HF5	—	12FB
6HF8	—	9DX
6HG5	—	7BZ
6HJ8	—	9CY
6HK5	—	7GM
6HM5	—	76M
6HQ5	—	7GM
6HS6	—	7BK
6HS8	—	9LW
6HZ6	—	7EN
6HZ8	—	9DX
6J4	V17	7BQ
6J5	V18	6Q
6J6A	V17	7BF
6J6A	V20	7BF
6J7	V18	7R
6J8G	—	8H
6J11	—	12BW
6JB6	—	9QL
6JC6A	—	9PM
6JC8	—	9PA
6JD6	—	9PM
6JE6	—	9QL
6JE6A	—	9QL
6JF6	—	9QL
6JH6	—	7CM
6JH8	—	9DP
6JK8	—	9AJ
6JN8	—	9FA
6JT8	—	9DX
6JV8	—	9DX
6K5GT	—	5U
6K6GT	V19	7S
6K7	V18	7R
6K8	V18	8K
6K11	—	12BY
6KD6	—	12GW
6KD8	V17	9AE
6KE8	V17	9DC
6KM6	—	9QL
6KR8	V17	9DX
6KT6	V17	9PM
6KT8	V17	9QP
6KV8	—	9DX
6KY6	—	9GK
6KZ8	V17	9FZ
6L4	—	7BR
6L5G	—	6Q
6L6GA	—	7S
6L6GB	V18	7S
6L6GX	—	7S
6L7	V18	7T
6LF6	—	12GW
6LJ8	V17	9GF
6LM8	—	9AE
6LQ6	—	9QL
6LY8	V17	9DX
6M5	—	9N
6M6G	—	7S
6M7G	—	7R
6M8GT	—	8AU
6M11	—	12CA
6MQ8	—	9AE
6MU8	V17	9AE
6N4	—	7CA
6N5	—	6R
6N6G	—	7AU
6N7GT	V18	8B
6N7GT	V20	8B
6N8	—	9T
6P5GT	—	6Q
6P7G	—	7U
6P8G	—	8K
6Q4	—	9S
6Q5G	—	6Q
6Q6G	—	6Y
6Q7	V18	7V
6Q11	—	12BY
6R4	—	9R

Type	Page	Base
6R6G	—	6AW
6R7	V18	7V
6R8	—	9E
6S4	—	9AC
6S4A	—	9AC
6S6GT	—	5AK
6S7	—	7R
6S8GT	—	8CB
6SA7GT	V18	8R
6SB7Y	V18	8R
6SC7	V18	8S
6SD7GT	—	8N
6SE7GT	—	8N
6SF5	—	6AB
6SF7	V18	7AZ
6SG7	V18	8BK
6SH7	V18	8BK
6SH7L	—	8BK
6SJ7	V18	8N
6SJ7Y	V21	8N
6SK7	V18	8N
6SL7GT	V19	8BD
6SN7GTA	—	8BD
6SN7GTB	V19	8BD
6SQ7GT	V18	8Q
6SR7	V18	8Q
6SS7	—	8N
6ST7	—	8Q
6SU7GTY	—	8BD
6SV7	—	7AZ
6SZ7	—	8Q
6T4	V17	7DK
6T5	—	6R
6T6GM	—	6Z
6T7	—	7V
6T8	—	9E
6T8A	V17	9E
6T9	—	12FM
6U3	—	9BM
6U4GT	—	4CG
6U5	—	6R
6U6GT	—	7S
6U7G	—	7R
6U8	—	9AE
6U8A	V17	9AE
6V3	—	9BD
6V3A	—	9BD
6V4	V20	9M
6V5GT	—	6AO
6V6GTA	V18	7S
6V7G	—	7V
6V8	—	9AH
6W4GT	—	4CG
6W5G	—	6S
6W6GT	V19	7S
6W7G	—	7R
6X4/6063	V20	7CF
6X5GT	V20	6S
6X6G	—	7AL
6X8	—	9AK
6X8A	V17	9AK
6Y3G	—	4AC
6Y5	—	6J
6Y6G	—	7S
6Y6GA	V19	7S
6Y6GT	—	7S
6Y7G	—	8B
6Z3	V20	4G
6Z4	—	5D
6Z5	—	6K
6Z7G	—	8B
6ZY5G	—	6S
7A4	—	5AC
7A5	—	6AA
7A6	—	7AJ
7A7	—	8V
7A8	—	8U
7AB7	—	8BO
7AD7	—	8V
7AF7	—	8AC
7AG7	—	8V
7AH7	—	8V
7AJ7	—	8V
7AK7	—	8V
7B4	—	5AC
7B5	—	6AE
7B6	—	8W
7B7	—	8V
7B8	—	8X
7C4	—	4AH
7C5	—	6AA
7C6	—	8W
7C7	—	8V
7D7	—	8AR
7E5	—	8BN
7E6	—	8W
7E7	—	8AE
7EP4	—	11N
7EV6	—	7AC
7EY6	—	7AC
7F7	—	8AC
7F8	—	8BW
7G7	—	8V
7G8	—	8BV
7GP4	—	14G
7H7	—	8V
7J7	—	8BL
7JP1-4-7	—	14R
7K7	—	8BF
7L7	—	8V
7N7	—	8AC
7Q7	—	8AL
7R7	—	8AE
7S7	—	8BL
7T7	—	8V
7V7	—	8V
7VP1	—	14R
7W7	—	8BJ
7X6	—	7AJ
7X7	—	8BZ
7Y4	—	5AB
7Z4	—	5AB
8BP4	—	14G
9BM5	—	7BZ
9BW6	—	9AM
9NP1	—	6BN
10	—	4D
10EB8	—	9DX
10GP4	—	14G
10HP4	—	14G
10Y	—	4D
11/12	—	4F
12A4	—	9AG
12A5	—	7F
12A6	—	7S
12A7	—	7K
12A8GT	—	8A
12AB5	V17	9EU
12AB6	—	7CC
12AC6	—	7BK
12AD6	—	7CH
12AD7	—	9A
12AE6A	—	7BT
12AE7	—	9A

Type	Page	Base
12AF6	—	7BK
12AG6	—	7CH
12AH7GT	—	8BE
12AH8	—	9BP
12AJ6	—	7BT
12AL5	—	6BT
12AL8	—	9GS
12AQ5	V17	7BZ
12AT6	—	7BT
12AT7	V17	9A
12AU6	—	7BK
12AU7A	V20	9A
12AU7A	V17	9A
12AV5GA	—	6CK
12AV6	—	7BT
12AV7	V17	9A
12AW6	—	7CM
12AW7	—	7CM
12AX4GT	—	4CG
12AX4GTA	—	4CG
12AX7A	V17	9A
12AY7	V17	9A
12AZ7A	V17	9A
12B4	—	9AG
12B4A	—	9AG
12B6M	—	6Y
12B7	—	8V
12B7ML	—	8V
12B8GT	—	8T
12BA6	—	7BK
12BA7	—	8CT
12BD6	—	7BK
12BE6	—	7CH
12BF6	—	7BT
12BH7	—	9A
12BH7A	V17	9A
12BK5	—	9BQ
12BK6	—	7BT
12BL6	—	7BK
12BN6	—	7DF
12BQ6GA	—	6AM
12BQ6GT	—	6AM
12BQ6GTB	—	6AM
12BR7A	—	9CF
12BT6	—	7BT
12BU6	—	7BT
12BW4	—	9DJ
12BV7	—	9BF
12BX6	—	9AQ
12BY7	—	9BF
12BY7A	V17	9BF
12BZ6	—	7CM
12BZ7	—	9A
12C5	—	7CV
12C8	—	8E
12CA5	—	7CV
12CM6	—	9CK
12CN5	—	7CV
12CR6	—	7EA
12CS5	—	9CK
12CS6	—	7CH
12CT8	—	9DA
12CU5	—	7CV
12CU6	—	6AM
12CX6	—	7BK
12DB5	—	9GR
12DE8	—	Fig. 81
12DF5	—	9BS
12DF7	—	9A
12DK7	—	9HZ
12DL8	—	9HR
12DM7	—	9A
12DQ6A	—	6AM
12DQ7	—	9BF
12DS7	—	9JU
12DT5	—	9HN
12DT6	—	7EN
12DT7	—	9A
12DT8	—	9DE
12DU7	—	9JX
12DV7	—	9JY
12DV8	—	9HR
12DW5	—	9CK
12DW7	—	9A
12DW8	—	9JC
12DY8	—	9JD
12DZ6	—	7BK
12E5GT	—	6Q
12EA6	—	7BK
12EC8	—	9FA
12ED5	—	7CV
12EF6	—	7S
12EG6	—	7CH
12EK6	—	7BK
12EL6	—	7FB
12EM6	—	9HV
12EN6	—	7S
12F5GT	—	5M
12F8	—	9FH
12FK6	—	7BT
12FM6	—	7BT
12FP7	—	14E
12FQ8	—	9KT
12FR8	—	9KU
12FT6	—	7BT
12FX5	—	7CV
12FX8A	—	9KV
12G4	—	6BG
12G7G	—	7V
12G8	—	9CZ
12GA6	—	7CH
12GE5	—	12BJ
12GJ5	—	9NM
12GW6	—	6AM
12GN7	—	9BF
12GP7	—	14S
12H4	—	7DW
12H6	—	7Q
12HP7	—	11J
12J5GT	—	6Q
12J7GT	—	7R
12J8	—	9GC
12K5	—	7EK
12K7GT	—	7R
12K8	—	8K
12L6GT	—	7S
12L8GT	—	8BU
12Q7GT	—	7V
12R5	—	7CV
12S8GT	—	8CB
12SA7	—	8R
12SC7	—	8S
12SF5	—	6AB
12SF7	—	7AZ
12SG7	—	8BK
12SH7	—	8BK
12SJ7	—	8N
12SK7	—	8N
12SL7GT	—	8BD
12SN7GT	—	8BD
12SN7GTA	—	8BD
12SQ7	—	8Q
12SR7	—	8Q
12SW7	—	8Q

Type	Page	Base
12SX7	—	8BD
12SY7	—	8R
12U7	—	9A
12V6GT	—	7S
12W6GT	—	7S
12X4	V20	5BS
12Z3	—	4G
12Z5	—	7L
14A4	—	5AC
14A5	—	6AA
14A7	—	8V
14AF7	—	8AC
14AP1-4	—	12A
14B6	—	8W
14B8	—	8X
14C5	—	6AA
14C7	—	8V
14E6	—	8W
14E7	—	8AE
14F7	—	8AC
14F8	—	8BW
14H7	—	8V
14J7	—	8BL
14N7	—	8AC
14Q7	—	8AL
14R7	—	8AE
14S7	—	8BL
14V7	—	8V
14W7	—	8BJ
14X7	—	8BZ
14Y4	—	5AB
14Z3	—	4G
15	—	5F
15A6	—	9AR
15E	—	Fig. 51
16A5	—	9BL
17	—	3G
17Z3	—	9CB
18	—	6B
18FW6A	—	7CC
18FX6A	—	7CH
18FY6A	—	7BT
19	—	6C
19CL8A	—	9FX
19X3	—	9BM
19Y3	—	9BM
20	—	4D
20AP1-4	—	12A
20J8GT	—	8H
21A6	—	9AS
21A7	—	8AR
21EX6	—	5BT
22	—	4K
24-A	—	5E
24-G	—	2D
24XH	—	Fig. 1
25A6	—	7S
25A7GT	—	8F
25AC5GT	—	6Q
25AV5GA	—	6CK
25AV5GT	—	6CK
25AX4GT	—	4CG
25B5	—	6D
25B6G	—	7S
25B8GT	—	8T
25BK5	—	9BQ
25BQ6GA	—	6AM
25BQ6GT	—	6AM
25BQ6GTB	—	6AM
25C5	—	7CV
25C6G	—	7AC
25C6GA	—	7S
25CA5	—	7CV
25CD6G	—	5BT
25CD6GA	—	5BT
25CD6GB	—	5BT
25CU6	—	6AM
25D8GT	—	8AF
25DN6	—	5BT
25DQ6	—	6AM
25EC6	—	5BT
25EH5	—	7CV
25F5	—	7CV
25L6GT	—	7S
25N6G	—	7W
25S	—	6M
25SA7GT	—	8AD
25T	—	3G
25W4GT	—	4CG
25W6GT	—	7S
25X6GT	—	7Q
25Y4GT	—	5AA
25Y5	—	6E
25Z3	—	4G
25Z4	—	5AA
25Z5	V20	6E
25Z6	—	7Q
26	—	4D
26A6	—	7BK
26A7GT	—	8BU
26BK6	—	7BT
26C6	—	7BT
26CG6	—	7BK
26D6	—	7CH
26Z5W	—	9BS
27	—	5A
28Z5	—	5AB
30	—	4D
31	—	4D
32	—	4K
32ET5	—	7CV
32L7GT	—	8Z
33	—	5K
34	—	4M
34GD5	—	7CV
35/51	—	5E
35A5	—	6AA
35B5	V17	7BZ
35C5	—	7CV
35L6GT	—	7S
35T	—	3G
35TG	—	2D
35W4	V20	5BQ
35Y4	—	5AL
35Z3	—	4Z
35Z4GT	V20	5AA
35Z5GT	V20	6AD
35Z6G	—	7Q
36	—	5E
36AM3	V20	5BQ
37	—	5A
38	—	5F
39/44	—	5F
40	—	4D
40Z5GT	—	6AD
41	—	6B
42	—	6B
43	—	6B
45	—	4D
45Z3	—	5AM
45Z5GT	—	6AD
46	—	5C
47	—	5B
48	—	6A

Type	Page	Base
49	—	5C
50	—	4D
50A5	—	6AA
50AX6G	—	7Q
50B5	V17	7BZ
50BK5	—	9BQ
50C5	—	7CV
50C6G	—	7S
50C6GA	—	7S
50DC4	V20	5BQ
50FK5	V17	7CV
50L6GT	—	7S
50T	—	2D
50X6	—	7AJ
50Y6GT	V20	7Q
50Y7GT	—	8AN
50Z6G	—	7Q
50Z7G	—	8AN
51	—	5E
52	—	5C
53	—	7B
53A	—	Fig. 53
55	—	6G
56	—	5A
56AS	—	5A
57	—	6F
57AS	—	6F
58	—	6F
58AS	—	6F
59	—	7A
70A7GT	—	8AB
70L7GT	—	8AA
71-A	—	4D
72	—	4P
73	—	4Y
75	—	6G
75TH	—	2D
75TL	—	2D
76	—	5A
77	—	6F
78	—	6F
79	—	6H
80	V20	4C
81	—	4B
82	—	4C
83	V20	4C
83-V	V20	4AD
84/6Z4	—	5D
85	—	6G
85AS	—	6G
89	—	6F
90C1	—	5BO
99	—	4D
100TH	V21	2D
100TL	V21	2D
111H	—	2D
112-A	—	4D
117L7GT	—	8AO
117M7GT	—	8AO
117N7GT	V20	8AV
117P7GT	—	8AV
117Z3	V20	4CB
117Z4GT	—	5AA
117Z6GT	—	7Q
128AS	—	5A
150T	—	2N
152TH	—	4BC
152TL	—	4BC
175A	V23	Fig. 78
182-B	—	4D
183	—	4D
203-A	—	4E
203-H	—	3N
204-A	—	Fig. 39
205-D	—	4D
211	—	4E
212-E	—	Fig. 43
217-A	—	4AT
217-C	—	4AT
227-A	—	Fig. 53
241-B	—	Fig. 44
242-A	—	4E
242-B	—	4E
242-C	—	4E
249-B	—	Fig. 29
250TH	V21	2N
250TL	V21	2N
254	—	2N
254-A	—	Fig. 57
254-B	—	Fig. 57
261-A	—	4E
270-A	—	Fig. 39
276-A	—	4E
282-A	—	Fig. 57
284-B	—	3N
284-D	—	4E
295-A	—	4E
300T	—	2N
303-A	—	4E
304-A	—	Fig. 39
304-B	—	2D
304TH	V21	4BC
304TL	V21	4BC
305-A	—	Fig. 59
306-A	—	Fig. 63
307-A	—	Fig. 61
308-B	—	Fig. 43
310	—	4D
311	—	4E
311CH	—	Fig. 32
312-A	—	Fig. 68
312-E	—	Fig. 44
327-A	—	Fig. 50
327-B	—	Fig. 50
342-B	—	4E
356-A	—	Fig. 55
361-A	—	4E
376-A	—	4E
408A	—	7BD
417-A	V17	9V
482-B	—	4D
483	—	4D
485	—	5A
527	—	Fig. 53
559	—	Fig. 10
572B	V21	3G
575-A	—	4AT
592	—	Fig. 28
705-A	—	Fig. 45
717-A	—	8BK
756	—	4D
800	—	2D
801A/801	—	4D
802	—	6BM
803	V23	5J
804	—	Fig. 61
805	—	3N
806	—	2N
807	V22	5AW
807W	V22	5AW
808	—	2D
809	—	3G
810	V21	2N
811	—	3G

Type	Page	Base
811A	V21	3G
812	—	3G
812A	V21	3G
812H	—	3G
813	V23	5BA
814	V22	Fig. 64
815	V22	8BY
816	V20	4P
822	—	3N
822S	—	2N
826	—	7BO
828	—	5JP
829	—	7BP
829A	—	7BP
829B	V22	7BP
830	—	4D
830B	—	3G
831	—	Fig. 40
832	—	7BP
832A	V22	7BP
833A	V21	Fig. 41
834	—	2D
835	—	4E
836	V20	4P
837	—	6BM
838	—	4E
840	—	5J
841	—	4D
841A	—	3G
841SW	—	3G
843	—	5A
844	—	5AW
849	—	Fig. 39
850	—	Fig. 47
852	—	2D
860	—	Fig. 58
861	—	Fig. 42
864	—	4D
865	—	Fig. 57
866	—	4P
866A-AX	V20	4P
866B	V20	4P
866jr	V20	4B
871	—	4P
872A/872	V20	4AT
874	—	4S
878	—	4P
879	—	4AB
884	—	6Q
885	—	5A
902A	—	8CD
906P1-11	—	7AN
908A	—	7CE
909	—	5BP
910	—	7AN
911	—	7AN
914A	—	6BF
930B	—	3G
938	—	4E
950	—	5K
951	—	4M
954	—	5BB
955	—	5BC
955	—	5BC
956	—	5BB
957	—	5BD
958	—	5BD
958A	—	5BD
958A	—	5BD
959	—	5BE
967	—	3G
975A	—	4AT
1003	—	4R
1005	—	5AQ
1006	—	4C
1201	—	8BN
1203	—	4AH
1204	—	8BO
1206	—	8BV
1218A	—	7DK
1221	—	6F
1223	—	7R
1229	—	4K
1230	—	4D
1231	—	8V
1232	—	8V
1265	—	4AJ
1266	—	4AJ
1267	—	4V
1273	—	8V
1274	—	6S
1275	—	4C
1276	—	4D
1280	—	8V
1284	—	8V
1291	—	7BE
1293	—	4AA
1294	—	4AH
1299	—	6BB
1602	—	4D
1603	—	6F
1608	—	4D
1609	—	5B
1610	—	Fig. 62
1611	—	7S
1612	—	7T
1613	—	7S
1614	V22	7AC
1616	—	4P
1619	—	Fig. 74
1620	V18	7R
1621	—	7S
1622	—	7AC
1623	V20	3G
1624	—	Fig. 66
1625	V22	5AZ
1626	—	6Q
1627	—	2N
1628	—	Fig. 54
1629	—	6RA
1631	—	7AC
1632	—	7S
1633	—	8BD
1634	—	8S
1635	V19	8B
1641	—	Fig. 52
1642	—	7BH
1644	—	Fig. 4
1654	—	2Z
1802P1-11	—	11A
1805P1-4	—	11A
1806P1	—	11N
1851	—	7R
1852	V18	8N
1853	—	8N
2002	—	Fig. 1
2005	—	Fig. 1
2050	—	8BA
2051	—	8BA
2523N/128A	—	5A
4604	—	7CL
4652	—	Fig. 51
5514	—	4BO
5516	—	7CL

Type	Page	Base
5517	—	5BU
5556	—	4D
5562	—	Fig. 30
5590	—	7BD
5591	—	7BD
5608	—	7BD
5608A	—	7B
5610	—	6CG
5618	—	7CU
5651	V19	5BO
5654	—	7BD
5656	—	9F
5662	V19	Fig. 79
5663	—	6CE
5670	—	8CJ
5675	V20	Fig. 21
5679	—	7CX
5686	V17	9G
5687	V17	9H
5690	—	Fig. 38
5691	—	8BD
5692	—	8BD
5693	V18	8N
5694	—	8CS
5696	V19	7BN
5722	V17	5CB
5725	—	7CM
5726	—	6BT
5727	V19	7BN
5731	—	5BC
5749	—	7BK
5750	—	7CH
5751	—	9A
5755	—	9J
5763	V22	9K
5764	—	Fig. 21
5765	—	Fig. 21
5766	See 2C37	
5767	See 2C37	
5768	—	Fig. 21
5794	—	Fig. 21
5812	—	7CQ
5814	—	9A
5823	V19	4CK
5824	—	7S
5825	—	4P
5839	—	6S
5842	V17	9V
5844	—	7BF
5845	—	5CA
5847	—	9X
5852	—	6S
5857	—	9AB
5866	V21	Fig. 3
5867	—	Fig. 3
5871	—	7AC
5876	—	Fig. 21
5879	V17	9AD
5881	—	7AC
5890	—	12J
5893	V20	Fig. 21
5894A	V22	Fig. 7
5910	—	6AR
5915	—	7CH
5920	—	7BF
5933	V22	5AW
5961	—	8R
5962	V19	2AG
5963	—	9A
5964	—	7BF
5965	—	9A
5993	—	Fig. 35
5998	V19	8BD
6005	—	7BZ
6023	—	9CD
6026	—	Fig. 16
6028	—	7BD
6045	—	7BF
6046	—	7AC
6057	—	9A
6058	—	6BT
6059	—	9BC
6060	—	9A
6061	—	9AM
6062	—	9K
6063	V20	7CF
6064	—	7DB
6065	—	7DB
6066	—	7BT
6067	—	9A
6072	—	9A
6073	V19	5BO
6074	V19	5BO
6080	—	8BD
6082	—	8BD
6083	—	Fig. 5
6084	—	9BJ
6085	—	9A
6086	—	9BK
6087	—	5L
6101	—	7BF
6132	—	9BA
6135	—	6BG
6136	—	7BK
6137	—	8N
6140	—	9BY
6141	—	9BZ
6146	V22	7CK
6146A	V22	7CK
6146B	V22	7CK
6155	V23	5BK
6156	V23	5BK
6157	—	Fig. 36
6158	—	9A
6159B	V22	7CK
6173	—	Fig. 34
6186	—	7BD
6197	—	9BV
6201	—	9A
6211	—	9A
6216	—	Fig. 37
6218	—	9CG
6227	—	9BA
6252	V22	Fig. 7
6263	—	—

Type	Page	Base
6264	—	—
6265	—	7CM
6287	—	9CT
6308	—	8EX
6336A	—	8BD
6350	—	9CZ
6354	—	Fig. 12
6360	V22	Fig. 13
6374	—	9BW
6386	V17	8CJ
6417	V22	9K
6443	—	9BW
6485	—	7BK
6524	V22	Fig. 76
6550	V19	7S
6627	—	5BO
6660	—	7CC
6661	—	7CM
6662	—	7CM
6663	—	6BT
6664	—	5CE
6669	—	7BZ
6676	—	7CM
6677	—	9BV
6678	—	9AE
6679	—	9A
6680	—	9A
6681	—	9A
6816	V23	Fig. 77
6829	—	9A
6850	V22	Fig. 76
6883	V22	7CK
6884	V23	Fig. 77
6887	V17	6BT
6893	V22	7CK
6897	—	—
6907	—	Fig. 7
6939	V22	Fig. 13
6973	V17	9EU
7000	—	7R
7025	—	9A
7027A	V19	8HY
7034	V23	Fig. 75
7035	V23	Fig. 75
7054	—	9BF
7055	—	6BT
7056	—	6CM
7057	—	9AJ
7058	—	9A
7059	—	9AE
7060	—	9DX
7061	—	9EU
7077	—	—
7094	V23	Fig. 82
7137	—	7BQ
7167	—	7EW
7189A	V17	9CV
7247	—	9A
7258	V17	9DA
7270	V22	Fig. 84
7271	V22	Fig. 84
7308	—	9DE
7360	—	9KS
7408	—	7AC
7543	—	7BK
7551	V22	9LK
7558	V22	9LK
7581A	—	7AC
7586	V17	12AQ
7587	V17	12AS
7591	V19	8KQ
7695	—	9PX
7700	—	6F
7701	—	9MS
7717	—	7EW
7854	V22	Fig. 7
7868	—	9NZ
7895	V17	12AQ
7905	—	9PB
7984	—	12EU
8000	—	2N
8001	V22	7BM
8003	—	3N
8005	—	3G
8008	—	Fig. 8
8012	—	Fig. 54
8013-A	—	4P
8016	—	3C
8020	—	4P
8025	—	4AQ
8032	V22	7CK
8042	—	Fig. 51
8056	V17	12AQ
8058	V18	12CT
8072	V22	Fig. 85
8117	V22	Fig. 7
8121	V23	Fig. 86
8122	V23	Fig. 85
8163	V21	Fig. 3
8166/ 4-1000A	V23	—
8203	V22	12AQ
8295/172	V23	—
8298A	V22	7CK
8334	—	7DK
8393	V18	12AQ
8458	—	Fig. 13
8627	—	12CT
8628	V18	12AQ
8646	—	—
8677	V18	12CT
8808	—	Fig. 15
8873	V21	Fig. 87
8874	V21	—
8875	V21	—
8877	V21	—
9001	V18	7BD
9002	V18	7BS
9003	V18	7BD
9004	—	4BJ
9005	—	5BG
9006	V18	6BH
AT-340	—	5BK
AX9900	V21	Fig. 3
AX9901	—	Fig. 3

Type	Page	Base
AX9903	V22	Fig. 7
AX9905	—	Fig. 2
AX9909	—	Fig. 5
AX9910	V22	Fig. 7
BA	—	4J
BH	—	4J
BR	—	4H
CE220	—	4P
CK1005	—	5AQ
CK1006	—	4C
CK1007	—	Fig. 73
DR3B27	—	4P
DR123C	—	Fig. 15
DR200	—	2N
ECC81	—	9A
ECC82	—	9A
ECC83	—	9A
EF50	—	9C
F123A	—	Fig. 15
F127A	—	Fig. 15
G84	V19	4B
GL2C44	—	Fig. 9
GL5C24	—	Fig. 15
GL146	—	Fig. 56
GL152	—	Fig. 56
GL159	—	Fig. 56
GL169	—	Fig. 56
GL446A	—	Fig. 11
GL446B	—	Fig. 11
GL464A	—	Fig. 9
GL559	—	Fig. 10
GL6442	—	—
GL6463	—	9CZ
GL8012A	—	Fig. 54
HD203A	—	3N
HF60	—	2D
HF75	—	2D
HF100	—	2D
HF120	—	4F
HF140	—	4F
HF175	—	Fig. 46
HF200	—	2N
HF201A	—	Fig. 15
HF250	—	2N
HF300	—	2N
HK24	—	3G
HK54	—	2D
HK57	—	Fig. 33
HK154	—	2D
HK158	—	2D
HK252L	—	4BC
HK253	—	4AT
HK254	—	2N
HK257	—	7BM
HK257B	—	7BM
HK304L	—	4BC
HK354	—	2N
HK354C	—	2N
HK354D	—	2N
HK354E	—	2N
HK354F	—	2N
HK454H	—	2N
HK454L	—	2N
HK654	—	2N
HV12	—	3N
HV18	—	2N
HV27	—	3N
HY6J5GTX	—	6Q
HY6L6GTX	—	7AC
HY24	—	4D
HY25	—	3G
HY30Z	—	4BO
HY31Z	—	Fig. 60
HY40	—	3G
HY40Z	—	3G
HY51A	—	3G
HY51B	—	3G
HY51Z	—	4BO
HY57	—	3G
HY60	—	5AW
HY61	—	5AW
HY63	—	Fig. 72
HY65	—	Fig. 72
HY67	—	Fig. 65
HY69	—	Fig. 64
HY75	—	2T
HY75A	—	2T
HY114B	—	2T
HY615	—	Fig. 71
HY801A	—	4D
HY866Jr	—	4P
HY1231Z	—	Fig. 60
HY1269	—	Fig. 65
HYE1148	—	Fig. 71
KT66	—	7AC
KY21	—	—
NU2C35	—	Fig. 23
PE340	—	5BK
PL172/8295	V28	—
PL177A	V22	Fig. 14
PL6549	—	Fig. 14
PL6569	V21	Fig. 3
PL6580	V21	5BK
RK10	—	4D
RK11	—	3G
RK12	—	3G
RK15	—	4D
RK16	—	5A
RK17	—	5F
RK18	—	3G
RK19	—	4AT
RK20	—	Fig. 61
RK20A	—	Fig. 61
RK21	—	4P
RK22	—	Fig. 52
RK23	—	6BM
RK24	—	4D
RK25	—	6BM
RK25B	—	6BM
RK28	—	5J
RK28A	—	5J
RK30	—	2D
RK31	—	3G
RK32	—	2D
RK33	—	Fig. 69

Type	Page	Base
RK34	—	Fig. 70
RK35	—	2D
RK36	—	2D
RK37	—	2D
RK38	—	2D
RK39	—	5AW
RK41	—	5AW
RK42	—	4D
RK43	—	6C
RK44	—	6BM
RK46	—	Fig. 61
RK47	—	Fig. 64
RK48	—	Fig. 64
RK48A	—	Fig. 64
RK49	—	6A
RK51	—	3G
RK52	—	3G
RK56	—	5AW
RK57	—	3N
RK58	—	3N
RK59	—	Fig. 60
RK61	—	—
RK62	—	4D
RK63	—	2N
RK63A	—	2N
RK64	—	5AW
RK65	—	Fig. 48
RK66	—	Fig. 61
RK75	—	Fig. 61
RK100	—	Fig. 67
RK705A	—	Fig. 45
RK866	—	4P
T20	—	3G
T21	—	6A
T40	—	3G
T55	—	3G
T60	—	2D
T100	—	2D
T125	—	2N
T160L	V21	3G
T200	—	2N
T300	—	—
T814	—	3N
T822	—	3N
TB35	—	Fig. 30
TUF20	—	2T
TW75	—	2D
TW150	—	2N
TZ20	—	3G
TZ40	—	3G
UE100	—	2D
UE468	—	Fig. 32
UH35	—	3G
UH50	—	2D
UH51	—	2D
V70	—	3N
V70A	—	3N
V70B	—	3G
V70C	—	3G
V70D	—	3G
VR75	V19	4AJ
VR90	V19	4AJ
VR105	V19	4AJ
VR150	V19	4AJ
VT52	—	4D
VT127A	—	Fig. 53
WE304A	—	2D
X6030	—	Fig. 2
XXB	—	Fig. 6
XXD	—	8AC
XXL	—	5AC
XXFM	—	8BZ
ZB60	—	2D
ZB120	—	4E

SEMICONDUCTORS

Type	Page
1N21F	V24
1N34A	V24
1N35	V24
1N52A	V24
1N60	V24
1N64	V24
1N64A	V24
1N67A	V24
1N82A	V24
1N94	V24
1N270	V24
1N458A	V24
1N634	V24
1N645A	V24
1N914	V24
1N3754	V24
1N4001	V24
1N4002	V24
1N4004	V24
1N4719	V24
2N406	V24
2N441	V25
2N706A	V24
2N718A	V24
2N1179	V24
2N1302	V24
2N1306	V24
2N1491	V25
2N1970	V25
2N2102	V25
2N2157	V25
2N2222	V24
2N2270	V25
2N2631	V25
2N2869	V25
2N2876	V25
2N2925	V24
2N3053	V25
2N3055	V25
2N3119	V25

Type	Page
2N3391A	V24
2N3394	V24
2N3512	V25
2N3553	V25
2N3565	V24
2N3568	V24
2N3583	V25
2N3632	V25
2N3638	V24
2N3663	V24
2N3733	V25
2N3772	V25
2N3866	V24
2N3904	V24
2N3906	V24
2N3924	V25
2N3948	V25
2N4012	V25
2N4037	V25
2N4123	V24
2N4124	V24
2N4126	V24
2N4275	V24
2N4396	V25
2N4401	V24
2N4410	V24
2N4416	V25
2N4417	V25
2N4427	V25
2N4957	V24
2N4959	V24
2N5016	V25
2N5032	V24
2N5070	V25
2N5071	V25
2N5087	V24
2N5089	V24
2N5109	V24
2N5179	V24
2N5183	V24
2N5222	V24
2N5457	V26
2N5458	V26
2N5459	V26
2N5460	V25
2N5461	V26
2N5463	V26
2N5465	V26
2N5470	V25
2N5484	V26
2N5486	V26
2N5635	V25
2N5636	V25
2N5637	V25
2N5641	V25
2N5642	V25
2N5643	V25
2N5669	V26
2N5670	V26
2N5829	V24
2N5913	V25
2N5914	V25
2N5915	V25
2N5919	V25
2N5921	V25
2N5941	V25
2N5942	V25
2N5944	V25
2N5945	V25
2N5946	V25
2N5995	V25
2N5996	V25
2N6136	V25
2N40675	V25
3N128	V26
3N187	V26
3N200	V26
E300	V26
HEP51	V24
HEP53	V24
HEP56	V24
HEP801	V26
HEP802	V26
MBD101	V24
MJ480	V25
MMT3823	V26
MPF102	V26
MPF103	V26
MPF104	V26
MPF105	V26
MPF106	V26
MPF107	V26
MPF120	V26
MPF121	V26
MPF122	V26
MPS918	V24
MPS2926	V24
MPS3394	V24
MPS3563	V24
MPS3693	V24
MPS3694	V24
MPS3702	V24
MPS3706	V24
MPS6513	V24
MPS6514	V25
MPS6530	V25
MPS6534	V25
MPS6543	V25
MPS6569	V25
MPSA12	V25
MPSA55	V25
MPSU01	V25
MPSU51	V25
MSD7000	V24
TIS48	V25
TIS54	V25
TIXM10	V25
40231	V24
40235	V24
40600	V26
40601	V26
40602	V26
40603	V26
40604	V26
40673	V26

E.I.A. VACUUM-TUBE BASE DIAGRAMS

Socket connections correspond to the base designations given in the column headed "Base" in the classified tube-data tables. Bottom views are shown throughout. Terminal designations are as follows:

A = Anode	D = Deflecting Plate	IS = Internal Shield	RC = Ray-Control Eelectrode
B = Beam	F = Filament	K = Cathode	Ref = Reflector
BP = Bayonet Pin	FE = Focus Elect.	NC = No Connection	S = Shell
BS = Base Sleeve	G = Grid	P = Plate (Anode)	TA = Target
C = Ext. Coating	H = Heater	P_I = Starter-Anode	U = Unit
CL = Collector	IC = Internal Con.	P_{BF} = Beam Plates	• = Gas-Type Tube

Alphabetical subscripts D, P, T and HX indicate, respectively, diode unit, pentode unit, triode unit or hexode unit in multi-unit types. Subscript CT indicates filament or heater tap.

Generally when the No. 1 pin of a metal-type tube in Table II, with the exception of all triodes, is shown connected to the shell, the No. 1 pin in the glass (G or GT) equivalent is connected to an internal shield.

* On 12AQ, 12AS and 12CT: index = large lug; • = pin cut off

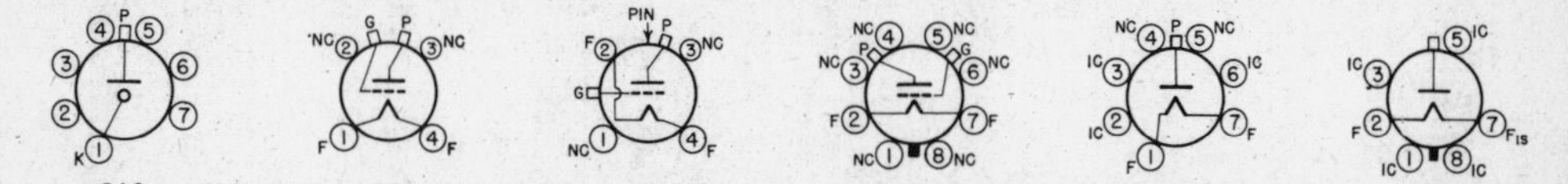

2AG 2D 2N 2T 2Z 3C

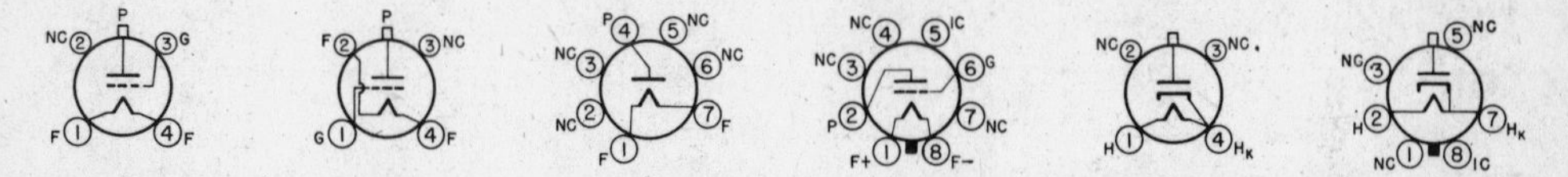

3G 3N 3T 4AA 4AB 4AC

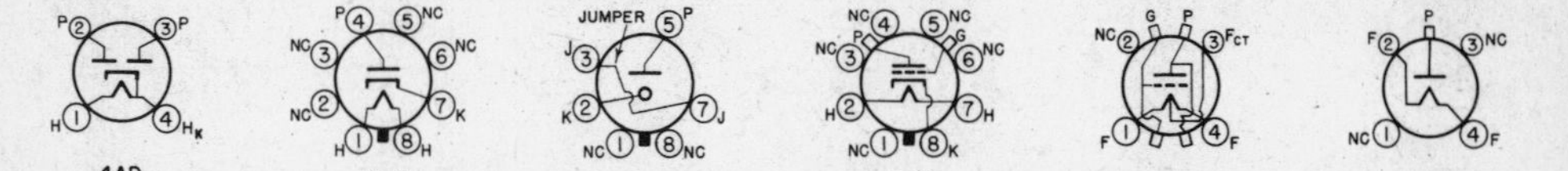

4AD 4AH 4AJ 4AM 4AQ 4AT

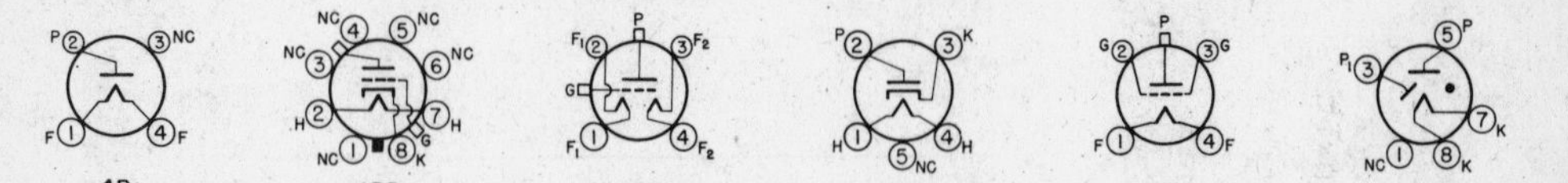

4B 4BB 4BC 4BJ 4BO 4BU

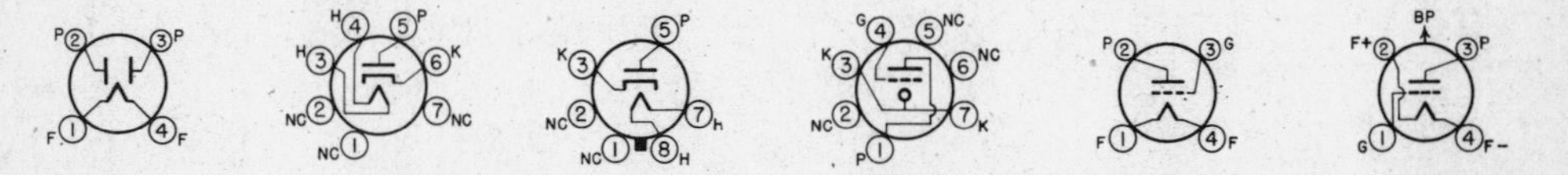

4C 4CB 4CG 4CK 4D 4E

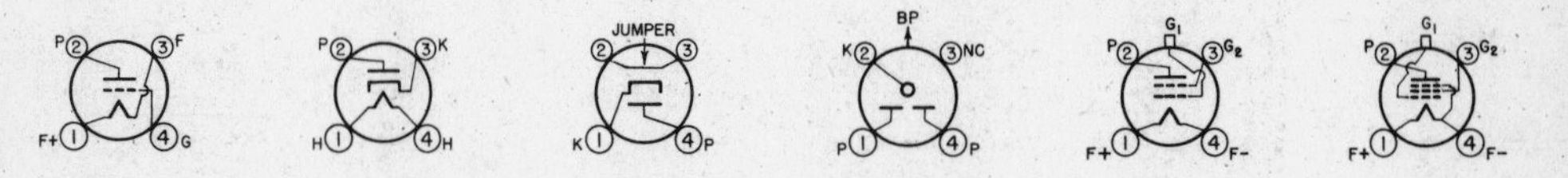

4F 4G 4H 4J 4K 4M

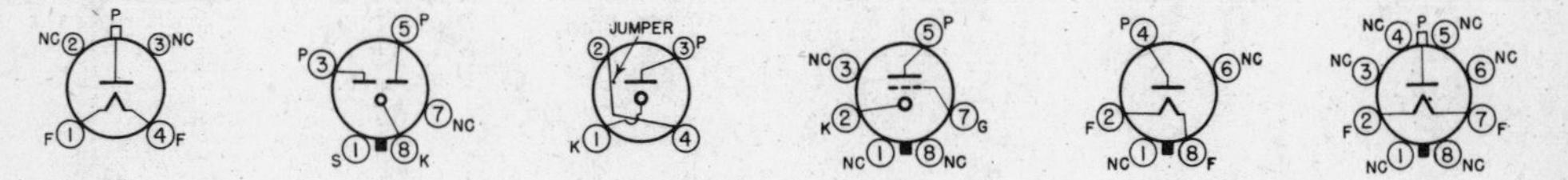

4P 4R 4S 4V 4X 4Y

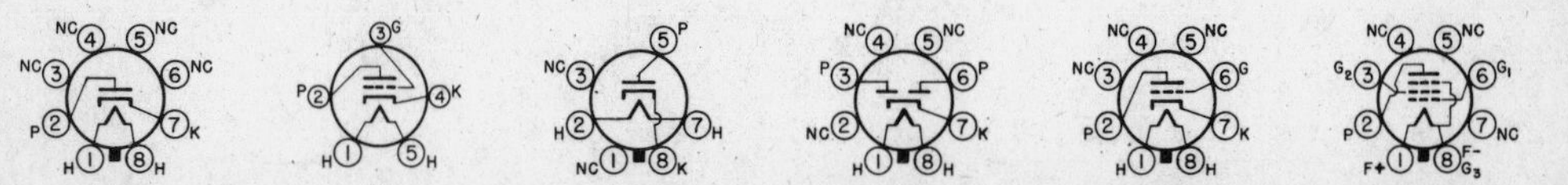

4Z 5A 5AA 5AB 5AC 5AD

TUBE BASE DIAGRAMS

Bottom views are shown. Terminal designations on sockets are given on page V5.

TUBE BASE DIAGRAMS

Bottom views are shown. Terminal designations on sockets are given on page V5.

TUBE BASE DIAGRAMS

Bottom views are shown. Terminal designations on sockets are given on page V5.

TUBE BASE DIAGRAMS

Bottom views are shown. Terminal designations on sockets are given on page V5.

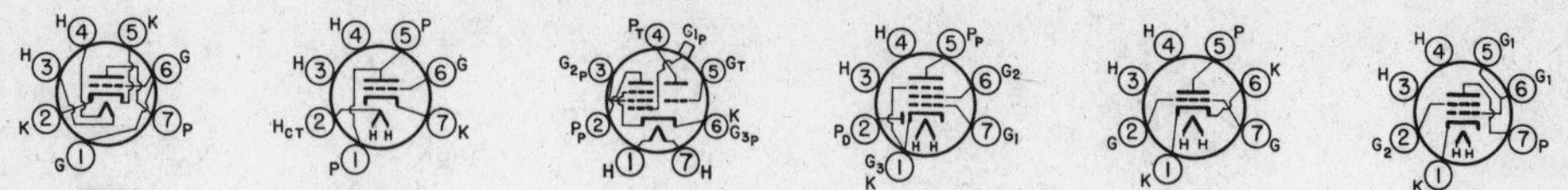

7DT 7DW 7E 7EA 7EG 7EK

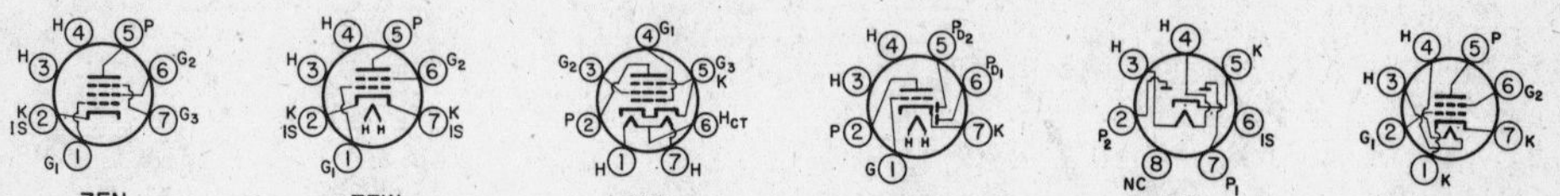

7EN 7EW 7F 7FB 7FL 7FN

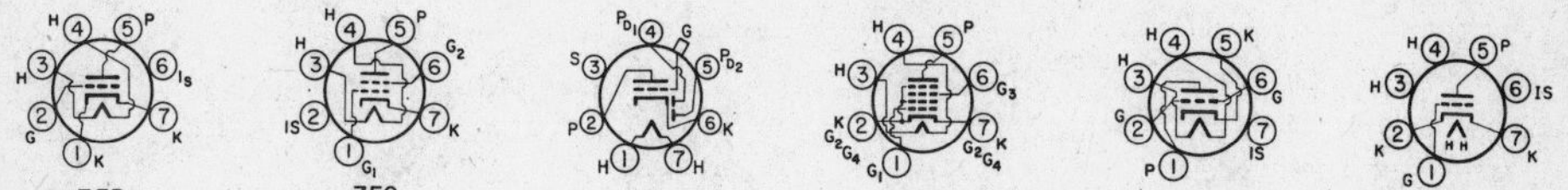

7FP 7FQ 7G 7GA 7GK 7GM

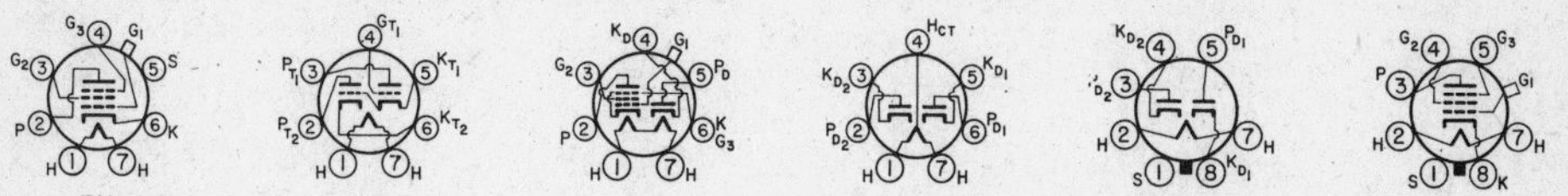

7H 7J 7K 7L 7Q 7R

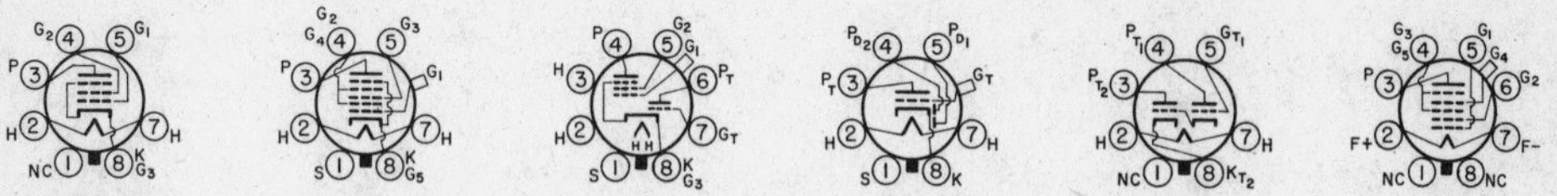

7S 7T 7U 7V 7W 7Z

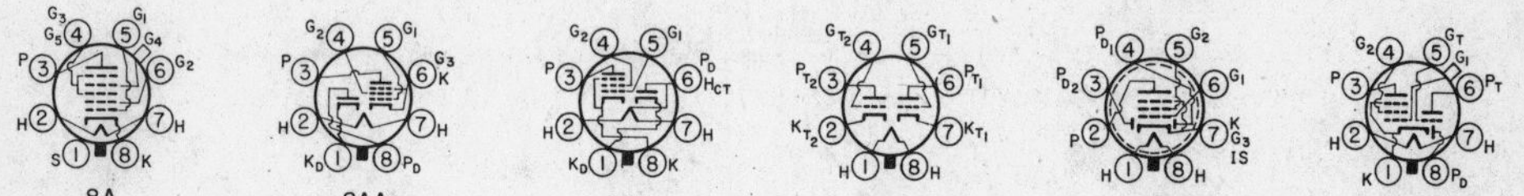

8A 8AA 8AB 8AC 8AE 8AF

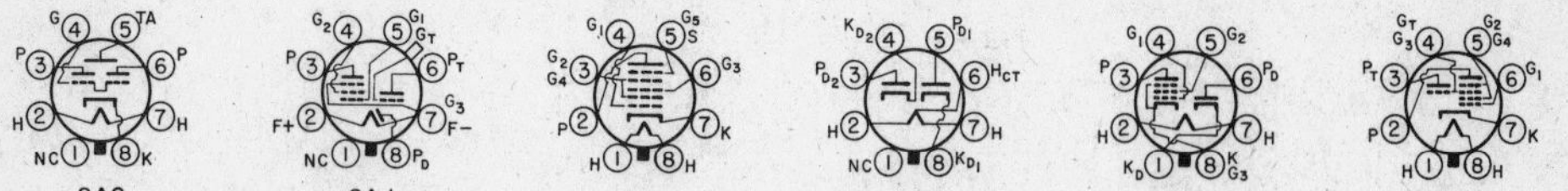

8AG 8AJ 8AL 8AN 8AO 8AR

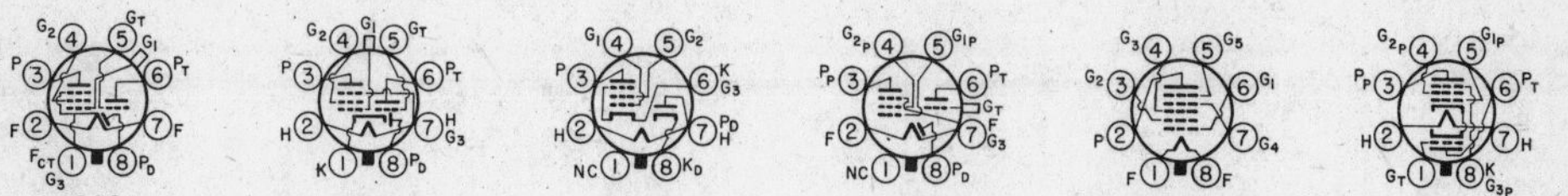

8AS 8AU 8AV 8AW 8AX 8AY

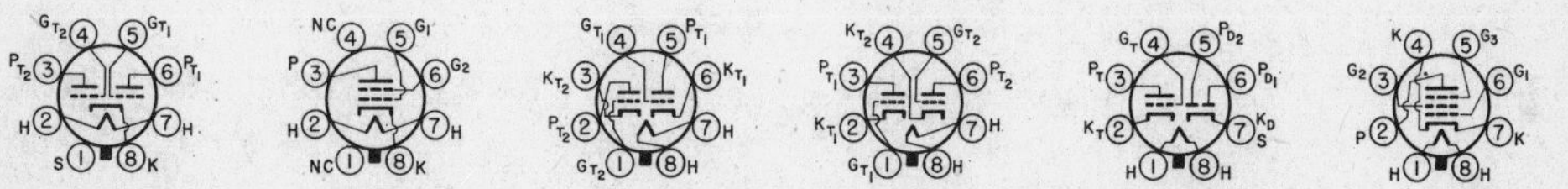

8B 8BA 8BD 8BE 8BF 8BJ

TUBE BASE DIAGRAMS

Bottom views are shown. Terminal designations on sockets are given on page V5.

TUBE BASE DIAGRAMS

Bottom views are shown. Terminal designations on sockets are given on page V5.

TUBE BASE DIAGRAMS

Bottom views are shown. Terminal designations on sockets are given on page V5.

TUBE BASE DIAGRAMS

Bottom views are shown. Terminal designations on sockets and * meaning are given on page V5.

TUBE BASE DIAGRAMS

Bottom views are shown. Terminal designations on sockets are given on page V5.

TUBE BASE DIAGRAMS

Bottom views are shown. Terminal designations on sockets are given on page V5.

FIG. 39 · FIG. 40 · FIG. 41 · FIG. 42 · FIG. 43 · FIG. 44 · FIG. 45 · FIG. 46 · FIG. 47 · FIG. 48 · FIG. 49 · FIG. 50 · FIG. 51 · FIG. 52 · FIG. 53 · FIG. 54 · FIG. 55 · FIG. 56 · FIG. 57 · FIG. 58 · FIG. 59 · FIG. 60 · FIG. 61 · FIG. 62 · FIG. 63 · FIG. 64 · FIG. 65 · FIG. 66 · FIG. 67 · FIG. 68 · FIG. 69 · FIG. 70 · FIG. 71 · FIG. 72 · FIG. 73 · FIG. 74 · FIG. 75 · FIG. 76 · FIG. 77 · FIG. 78 · FIG. 79 · FIG. 80 · FIG. 81 · FIG. 82 · FIG. 83 · FIG. 84 · FIG. 85 · FIG. 86 · FIG. 87

TABLE I—MINIATURE RECEIVING TUBES

Type	Name	Base	Fil. or Heater		Capacitances pF			Plate Supply V	Grid Bias	Screen Volts	Screen mA	Plate mA	Plate Res. Ohms	Transconductance[11]	Amp. Factor[4]	Load Res. Ohms	Watts Output
			V	Amp.	C_{in}	C_{out}	C_{gp}										
6AF4A	Uhf — Triode A_1 Amp.	7DK	6.3	0.225	2.2	0.45	1.9	80	150*	—	—	16	2.27K	6600	15	—	—
	Osc. 950 MHz							100	10KΩ	—	0.4[9]	22	—	—	—	—	—
6AG5	Sharp Cut-off Pent.	7BD	6.3	0.3	6.5	1.8	0.03	250	180*	150	2.0	6.5	800K	5000	—	—	—
								100	180*	100	1.4	4.5	600K	4500	—	—	—
6AH6	Sharp Cut-off Pent. Pent. Amp.	7BK	6.3	0.45	10.0	2.0	0.03	300	160*	150	2.5	10	500K	9600	—	—	—
	Triode Amp.							150	160*	—	—	12.5	3.6K	11K	40	—	—
6AJ4	Uhf Triode	9BX	6.3	0.225	4.4	0.18	2.4	125	68*	—	—	16	4.2K	10K	42	—	—
6AK5	Sharp Cut-off Pent.	7BD	6.3	0.175	4.0	2.8	0.02	180	200*	120	2.4	7.7	690K	5100	—	—	—
								150	330*	140	2.2	7	420K	4300	—	—	—
								120	200*	120	2.5	7.5	340K	5000	—	—	—
6AK6	Pwr. Amp. Pent.	7BK	6.3	0.15	3.6	4.2	0.12	180	−9	180	2.5	15	200K	2300	—	10K	1.1
6AL5	Dual Diode[10]	6BT	6.3	0.3	—	—	—	Max. rms voltage −117. Max. dc output current −9 mA.[1]									
6AM4	Uhf Triode	9BX	6.3	0.225	4.4	0.16	2.4	150	100*	—	—	7.5	10K	9000	90	—	—
6AN5	Beam Pwr. Pent.	7BD	6.3	0.45	9.0	4.8	0.075	120	120*	120	12.0	35	12.5K	8000	—	2.5K	1.3
6AN8A‡	Medium-μ Triode	9DA	6.3	0.45	2.0	2.7	1.5	200	−6	—	—	13	5.75K	3300	—	—	—
	Sharp Cut-off Pent.				7.0	2.3	0.04	200	180*	150	2.8	9.5	30K	6200	—	—	—
6AQ5A‡	Beam Pwr. Pent.	7BZ	6.3	0.45	8.3	8.2	0.35	180	−8.5	180	3/4	30[2]	58K	3700	29[5]	5.5K	2.0
								250	−12.5	250	4.5/7	47[2]	52K	4100	45[5]	5K	4.5
6AQ6	Dual Diode — High-μ Triode	7BT	6.3	0.15	1.7	1.5	1.8	100	−1	—	—	0.8	61K	1150	70	—	—
								250	−3	—	—	1	58K	1200	70	—	—
6AR5	Pwr. Amp. Pent.	6CC	6.3	0.4	—	—	—	250	−16.5	250	5.7/10	35[2]	65K	2400	34[5]	7K	3.2
								250	−18	250	5.5/10	33[2]	68K	2300	32[5]	7.6K	3.4
6AS6	Sharp Cut-off Pent.	7CM	6.3	0.175	4	3	0.2	120	−2	120	3.5	5.2	110K	3200	—	—	—
6AT6	Duplex Diode — High-μ Triode	7BT	6.3	0.3	2.3	1.1	2.1	250	−3	—	—	1	58K	1200	70	—	—
6AU6A‡	Sharp Cut-off Pent.	7BK	6.3	0.3	5.5	5	0.0035	250	68*	150	4.3	10.6	1 meg.	5200	—	—	—
6AV6	Dual Diode — High-μ Triode	7BT	6.3	0.3	2.2	0.8	2.0	250	−2	—	—	1.2	62.5K	1600	100	—	—
6AZ8	Medium-μ Triode	9ED	6.3	0.45	2	1.7	1.7	200	−6	—	—	13	5.75K	3300	19	—	—
	Semiremote Cut-off Pent.				6.5	2.2	0.02	200	180*	150	3	9.5	300K	6000	—	—	—
6BA6	Remote Cut-off Pent.	7BK	6.3	0.3	5.5	5	0.0035	250	68*	100	4.2	11	1 meg.	4400	—	—	—
6BA7	Pentagrid Conv.	8CT	6.3	0.3	Osc. 20kΩ			250	−1	100	10	3.8	1 meg.	950	—	—	—
6BC4	Uhf Medium-μ Triode	9DR	6.3	0.225	2.9	0.26	1.6	150	100*	—	—	14.5	4.8K	10K	48	—	—
6BE6	Pentagrid Conv.	7CH	6.3	0.3	Osc. 20kΩ			250	−1.5	100	6.8	2.9	1 meg.	475	—	—	—
6BE8A‡	Medium-μ Triode	9EG	6.3	0.45	2.8	1.5	1.8	150	56*	—	—	18	5K	8500	40	—	—
	Sharp Cut-off Pent.				4.4	2.6	0.04	250	68*	110	3.5	10	400K	5200	—	—	—
6BF5	Beam Pwr. Amp.	7BZ	6.3	1.2	14	6	0.65	110	−7.5	110	4/10.5	39[2]	12K	7500	36[5]	2.5K	1.9
6BF6	Dual Diode — Medium-μ Triode	7BT	6.3	0.3	1.8	0.8	2	250	−9	—	—	9.5	8.5K	1900	16	10K	0.3
6BH6	Sharp Cut-off Pent.	7CM	6.3	0.15	5.4	4.4	0.0035	250	−1	150	2.9	7.4	1.4 meg.	4600	—	—	—
6BH8‡	Medium-μ Triode	9DX	6.3	0.6	2.6	0.38	2.4	150	−5	—	—	9.5	5.15K	3300	17	—	—
	Sharp Cut-off Pent.				7	2.4	0.046	200	82*	125	3.4	15	150K	7000	—	—	—
6BJ6A	Remote Cut-off Pent.	7CM	6.3	0.15	4.5	5.5	0.0035	250	−1	100	3.3	9.2	1.3 meg.	3800	—	—	—
6BJ7	Triple Diode	9AX	6.3	0.45	Max. peak inverse plate voltage = 330 V. Max. dc plate current each diode = 1.0 mA												
6BJ8‡	Dual Diode — Medium-μ Triode	9ER	6.3	0.6	2.8	0.38	2.6	250	−9	—	—	8	7.15K	2800	20	—	—
6BK6	Dual Diode — High-μ Triode	7BT	6.3	0.3	—	—	—	250	−2	—	—	1.2	62.5K	1600	100	—	—
6BK7B	Medium-μ Dual Triode[10]	9AJ	6.3	0.4	3	1	1.8	150	56*	—	—	18	4.6K	9300	43	—	—
6BL8	Triode	9DC	6.3	0.43	2.5	1.8	1.5	250	−1.3	—	—	14	—	5000	20	—	—
	Pentode				5.2	3.4	0.025	250	−1.3	175	2.8	10	400K	6200	47	—	—
6BN4A	Medium-μ Triode	7EG	6.3	0.2	3.2	1.4	1.2	150	220*	—	—	9	6.3K	6800	43	—	—
6BN6	Gated-Beam Pent.	7DF	6.3	0.3	4.2	3.3	0.004	80	−1.3	60	5	0.23	—	—	—	68K	—
6BN8‡	Dual Diode — High-μ Triode	9ER	6.3	0.6	3.6	0.25	2.5	250	−3	—	—	1.6	28K	2500	70	—	—
6BQ5	Pwr. Amp. Pent.	9CV	6.3	0.76	10.8	6.5	0.5	300	−7.3	200	10.8	49.5[2]	38K	—	—	5.2K	17[3]
6BQ7A	Medium-μ Dual Triode[10]	9AJ	6.3	0.4	2.85	1.35	1.15	150	220*	—	—	9	6.1K	6400	39	—	—
6BR8A‡	Medium-μ Triode	9FA	6.3	0.45	2.5	0.4	1.8	150	56*	—	—	18	5K	8500	40	—	—
	Sharp Cut-off Pent.				5	2.6	0.015	250	68*	110	3.5	10	400K	5200	—	—	—
6BS8	Low-Noise Dual Triode[10]	9AJ	6.3	0.4	2.6	1.35	1.15	150	220*	—	—	10	5K	7200	36	—	—
6BX8	Dual Triode[10]	9AJ	6.3	0.4	—	—	1.4	65	−1	—	—	9	—	6700	25	—	—
6BZ6	Semiremote Cut-off Pent.	7CM	6.3	0.3	7.5	1.8	0.02	200	180*	150	2.6	11	600K	6100	—	—	—
6BZ7	Medium-μ Dual Triode[10]	9AJ	6.3	0.4	2.5	1.35	1.15	150	220*	—	—	10	5.6K	6800	38	—	—
6BZ8	Dual Triode[10]	9AJ	6.3	0.4	—	—	—	125	100*	—	—	10[1]	5.6K	8000	45	—	—
6C4	Medium-μ Triode	6BG	6.3	0.15	1.8	1.3	1.6	250	−8.5	—	—	10.5	7.7K	2200	17	—	—
6CB6A‡	Sharp Cut-off Pent.	7CM	6.3	0.3	6.5	1.9	0.02	200	180*	150	2.8	9.5	600K	6200	—	—	—
6CE5‡	Rf Pent.	7BD	6.3	0.3	6.5	1.9	0.03	200	180*	150	2.8	9.5	600K	6200	—	—	—
6CG6	Semiremote Cut-off Pent.	7BK	6.3	0.3	5	5	0.008	250	−8	150	2.3	9	720K	2000	—	—	—
6CG7‡	Medium-μ Dual Triode[10]	9AJ	6.3	0.6	2.3	2.2	4	250	−8	—	—	9	7.7K	2600	20	—	—
6CL6	Pwr. Amp. Pent.	9BV	6.3	0.65	11	5.5	0.12	250	−3	150	7/7.2	31[2]	150K	11K	30[5]	7500	2.8
6CW4	Triode	12AQ	6.3	0.13	4.1	1.7	0.92	70	0	—	—	8	5.44K	12.5K	68	—	—
6CX8	Medium-μ Triode	9DX	6.3	0.75	2.2	0.38	4.4	150	150*	—	—	9.2	8.7K	4600	40	—	—
	Sharp Cut-off Pent.				9	4.4	0.06	200	68*	125	5.2	24	70K	10K	—	—	—
6CY5	Sharp Cut-off Tetrode	7EW	6.3	0.2	4.5	3	0.03	125	−7	80	1.5	10	100K	8000	—	—	—
6DJ8	Twin Triode	9AJ	6.3	0.365	3.3	1.8	1.4	90	−1.3	—	—	15	—	12.5K	33	—	—
6DK6	Sharp Cut-off Pent.	7CM	6.3	0.3	6.3	1.9	0.02	300	−6.5	150	3.8	12	—	9800	—	—	—
6DS4	High-μ Triode	12AQ	6.3	0.135	4.1	1.7	.92	70	0	—	—	8	5.44K	12.5K	68	—	—
6DT6	Sharp Cut-off Pent.	7EN	6.3	0.3	5.8	—	0.02	150	560*	100	2.1	1.1	150K	615	—	—	—
6DW5	Beam Pwr. Amp.	9CK	6.3	1.2	14	9	0.5	200	−22.5	150	2	55	15K	5500	—	—	—
6EA8‡	Triode	9AE	6.3	0.45	3	0.3	1.7	330	−12	—	—	18	5K	8500	40	—	—
	Sharp Cut-off Pent.				5	2.6	0.02	330	−9	330	4	12	80K	6400	—	—	—
6EB8	High-μ Triode	9DX	6.3	0.75	2.4	.36	4.4	330	−5	—	—	2	37K	2700	100	—	—
	Sharp Cut-off Pent.				11	4.2	0.1	330	−9	—	7	25	75K	12.5K	—	—	—
6EH5	Power Pentode	7CV	6.3	1.2	17	9	0.65	135	0	117	14.5	42	11K	14.6K	—	3K	1.4
6EH7	Remote Cut-off Pent.	9AQ	6.3	0.3	9	3	.005	200	−2	90	4.5	12	500K	12.5K	—	—	—
6EH8	Triode	9JG	6.3	0.45	2.8	1.7	1.8	125	−1	—	—	13.5	—	7500	40	—	—
	Pentagrid Conv.				4.8	2.4	0.02	125	−1	125	4	12	170K	6000	—	—	—
6EJ7	Sharp Cut-off Pent.	9AQ	6.3	0.3	10	3	.005	200	−2.5	200	4.7	10	350K	15K	—	—	—
6ER5	Tetrode	7FN	6.3	0.18	4.4	3.0	0.38	200	−1.2	0	0	10	8K	10.5K	80	—	—

Type	Name	Base	Fil. or Heater V	Fil. or Heater Amp.	Capacitances pF C_{in}	Capacitances pF C_{out}	Capacitances pF C_{gp}	Plate Supply V	Grid Bias	Screen Volts	Screen mA	Plate mA	Plate Res. Ohms	Transcon-ductance[11]	Amp. Factor[4]	Load Res. Ohms	Watts Output
6ES8	Dual Triode	9DE	6.3	0.365	3.4	1.7	1.9	130	−1.2	—	—	15	—	12.5K	34	—	—
6EU7	Twin Triode	9LS	6.3	0.3	1.6	0.2	1.5	100	−1	—	—	0.5	80K	1250	100	—	—
6EU8	Triode	9JF	6.3	0.45	5.0	2.6	0.02	150	—	—	—	18	5K	8500	40	—	—
	Pentode				3.0	1.6	1.7	125	−1	125	4	12	80K	6400	—	—	—
6EZ8	Triple Triode — Triode No. 1	9KA	6.3	0.45	2.6	1.4	1.5	330	−4	—	—	4.2	13.6K	4200	57	—	—
	Triple Triode — Triodes No. 2 & 3					1.2											
6FV6	Sharp Cut-off Tetrode	7FQ	6.3	0.2	4.5	3	0.03	125	−1	80	1.5	10	100K	8000	—	—	—
6GC5	Pwr. Pent.	9EU	6.3	1.2	18.0	7.0	0.9	110	−7.5	110	4	50	13K	8000	—	2K	2.1
6GJ8	Triode	9AE	6.3	0.6	3.4	1.6	2.6	125	−1	—	—	13.5	5K	8500	40	—	—
	Pentode				8	2.4	0.36	125	−1	125	4.5	12	150K	7500	—	—	—
6GK5	High-μ Triode	7FP	6.3	0.18	5	3.5	0.52	135	−1	—	—	11.5	5400	15K	78	—	—
6GK6	Power Pentode	9GK	6.3	0.76	10	7.0	0.14	250	−7.3	250	5.5	48	38K	11.3K	—	5.2K	5.7
6GM6	Pentode	7CM	6.3	0.4	10	2.4	0.036	125	—	125	3.4	14	200K	13K	—	—	—
6GN8	High-μ Triode	9DX	6.3	0.75	2.4	0.36	4.4	250	−2	—	—	2	37K	2700	100	—	—
	Sharp Cut-off Pent.				11	4.2	0.1	200	—	150	5.5	25	60K	11.5K	—	—	—
6HB6	Power Pentode	9PU	6.3	0.76	13	8.0	0.18	250	100*	250	6.2	40	24K	20K	—	—	—
6J4	Grounded-Grid Triode	7BQ	6.3	0.4	7.5	3.9	0.12	150	100*	—	—	15	4.5K	12K	55	—	—
6J6A‡	Medium-μ Dual Triode — A_1 Amp.[10]	7BF	6.3	0.45	2.2	0.4	1.6	100	50*	—	—	8.5	7.1K	5300	38	—	—
	Medium-μ Dual Triode — Mixer							150	810*	—	—	4.8	10.2K	1900	Osc. peak voltage = 3 V		
6KD8	Sharp Cut-off Pent.	9AE	6.3	0.4	5.0	2.6	0.015	125	−1	110	3.5	9.5	200K	5000	—	—	—
	Medium-μ Triode				1.5	2.8	1.8	125	−1	—	—	13.5	—	7500	40	—	—
6KE8	Medium-μ Triode	9DC	6.3	0.4	2.4	2.0	1.3	125	68*	—	—	13	5.0K	8000	40	—	—
	Sharp Cut-off Pent.				5.0	3.4	.015	125	33*	125	2.8	10	125K	12K	—	—	—
6KR8	Sharp Cut-off Pent.	9DX	6.3	0.75	13	4.4	0.075	200	82*	100	3.0	19.5	60K	20K	—	—	—
	Medium-μ Triode				4.2	3.0	2.6	125	68*	—	—	15	4400	10.4K	46	—	—
6KT6	Remote Cut-off Pent.	9PM	6.3	0.3	9.5	3	0.19	125	56*	125	4.2	17	—	18K	—	—	—
6KT8	High-μ Triode	9QP	6.3	0.6	32	1.6	3.0	250	−2	—	—	1.8	31.5K	3200	100	—	—
	Sharp Cut-off Pent.				7.5	2.2	0.046	125	−1	125	4.5	12	150K	10K	—	—	—
6KZ8	Sharp Cut-off Pent.	9FZ	6.3	0.45	5.5	3.4	0.01	125	−1	125	4	12	200K	7500	—	—	—
	Medium-μ Triode				3.2	1.8	1.6	125	−1	—	—	13.5	5400	8500	46	—	—
6LJ8	Sharp Cut-off Pent.	9GF	6.3	0.4	5.5	3.4	0.015	125	33*	125	3.5	12	125K	13K	—	—	—
	Medium-μ Triode				2.4	2.0	1.4	125	68*	—	—	13	5K	8000	40	—	—
6LY8	High-μ Triode	9DX	6.3	0.75	2.6	2.8	3.8	200	−2.0	—	—	1.0	59K	1700	100	—	—
	Sharp Cut-off Pent.				13.0	4.4	0.75	200	—	100	3	19.5	60K	20K	—	—	—
6MU8	Medium-μ Triode	9AE	6.3	0.6	3	2.2	2.2	330	0	—	—	11.5	5.8K	6000	35	—	—
	Sharp Cut-off Pent.							330	0	150	4.2	19	165K	9000	—	—	—
6T4	Uhf Triode	7DK	6.3	0.225	2.6	0.25	1.7	80	150*	—	—	18	1.86K	7000	13	—	—
6T8A‡	Triple Diode-High-μ Triode	9E	6.3	0.45	1.6	1	2.2	100	−1	—	—	0.8	54K	1300	70	—	—
								250	−3	—	—	1	58K	1200	70	—	—
6U8A‡	Medium-μ Triode	9AE	6.3	0.45	2.5	0.4	1.8	150	56*	—	—	18	5K	8500	40	—	—
	Sharp Cut-off Pent.				5	2.6	0.01	250	68*	110	3.5	10	400K	5200	—	—	—
6X8A‡	Medium-μ Triode	9AK	6.3	0.45	2.0	0.5	1.4	100	100*	—	—	8.5	6.9K	—	40	—	—
	Sharp Cut-off Pent.				4.3	0.7	0.09	250	200*	150	1.6	7.7	750K	—	—	—	—
12AB5	Beam Pwr. Amp. — A_1 Amp.	9EU	12.6	0.2	8	8.5	0.7	250	−12.5	250	4.5/7	47[2]	50K	4100	45[5]	5K	4.5
	Beam Pwr. Amp. — AB_1 Amp.[3]							250	−15	250	5/13	79[2]	60K[1]	3750	70[5]	10K[6]	10
12AQ5	Beam Pwr. Amp. — A_1 Amp.	7BZ	12.6	0.225	8.3	8.2	0.35	250	−12.5	250	4.5/7	47[2]	52K	4100	45[5]	5K	4.5
	Beam Pwr. Amp. — AB_1 Amp.[3]							250	−15	250	5/13	79[2]	60K[1]	3750[1]	70[5]	10K[6]	10
12AT7	High-μ Dual Triode[10]	9A	12.6	0.15	2.2[7]	0.5[7]	1.5[7]	100	270*	—	—	3.7	15K	4000	60	—	—
			6.3	0.3	2.2[8]	0.4[8]	1.5[8]	250	200*	—	—	10	10.9K	5500	60	—	—
12AU7A	Medium-μ Dual Triode[10]	9A	12.6	0.15	1.6[7]	0.5[7]	1.5[7]	100	0	—	—	11.8	6.25K	3100	19.5	—	—
			6.3	0.3	1.6[8]	0.35[8]	1.5[8]	250	−8.5	—	—	10.5	7.7K	2200	17	—	—
12AV7	Medium-μ Dual Triode[10]	9A	12.6	0.225	3.1[7]	0.5[7]	1.9[7]	100	120*	—	—	9	6.1K	6100	37	—	—
			6.3	0.45	3.1[8]	0.4[8]	1.9[8]	150	56*	—	—	18	4.8K	8500	41	—	—
12AX7A	High-μ Dual Triode — A_1 Amp.[10]	9A	12.6	0.15	1.6[7]	0.46[7]	1.7[7]	250	−2	—	—	1.2	62.5K	1600	100	—	—
	High-μ Dual Triode — Class B		6.3	0.3	1.6[8]	0.34[8]	1.7[8]	300	0	—	—	40[2]	—	—	14[5]	16K[6]	7.5
12AY7	Medium-μ Dual Triode[10] — A_1 Amp.	9A	12.6	0.15	1.3	0.6	1.3	250	−4	—	—	3	—	1750	40	—	—
	Medium-μ Dual Triode[10] — Low-Level Amp.		6.3	0.3				150	2700*	Plate resistor = 20K. Grid resistor = 0.1 meg. V. G. = 12.5							
12AZ7A‡	High-μ Dual Triode[10]	9A	12.6	0.225	3.1[7]	0.5[7]	1.9[7]	100	270*	—	—	3.7	15K	4000	60	—	—
			6.3	0.45	3.1[8]	0.4[8]	1.9[8]	250	200*	—	—	10	10.9K	5500	60	—	—
12BH7A‡	Medium-μ Dual Triode[10]	9A	12.6	0.3	3.2[7]	0.5[7]	2.6[7]	250	−10.5	—	—	11.5	5.3K	3100	16.5	—	—
			6.3	0.6	3.2[8]	0.4[8]	2.6[8]										
12BY7A‡	Sharp Cut-off Pent.	9BF	12.6	0.3	11.1	3	0.055	250	68*	150	6	25	90K	12K	1200	—	—
			6.3	0.6													
35B5	Beam Pwr. Amp.	7BZ	35	0.15	11	6.5	0.4	110	−7.5	110	3/7	41[2]	—	5800	40[5]	2.5K	1.5
50B5	Beam Pwr. Amp.	7BZ	50	0.15	13	6.5	0.5	110	−7.5	110	4/8.5	50[2]	14K	7500	49[5]	2.5K	1.9
50FK5	Pwr. Pent.	7CV	50	0.1	17	9	0.65	110	62*	115	12	32	14K	12.8K	—	3K	1.2
5686	Beam Pwr. Pent.	9G	6.3	0.35	6.4	8.5	0.11	250	−12.5	250	3[5]	27[5]	45K	3100	—	9K	2.7
5687	Medium-μ Dual Triode[10]	9H	12.6	0.45	4[7]	0.6[7]	4[7]	120	−2	—	—	36	1.7K	11K	18.5	—	—
			6.3	0.9	4[8]	0.5[8]	4[8]	250	−12.5	—	—	12.5	3K	5500	16.5	—	—
5722	Noise Generating Diode	5CB	6.3	1.5	—	2.2	—	200	—	—	—	35	—	—	—	—	—
4A2 / 15874	High-μ Triode	9V	6.3	0.3	9.0	1.8	0.55	150	62*	—	—	26	1.8K	24K	43	—	—
5879	Sharp Cut-off Pent.	9AD	6.3	0.15	2.7	2.4	0.15	250	−3	100	0.4	1.8	2 meg.	1000	—	—	—
6386	Medium-μ Dual Triode[10]	8CJ	6.3	0.35	2	1.1	1.2	100	200*	—	—	9.6	4.25K	4000	17	—	—
6887	Dual Diode	6BT	6.3	0.2	Max. peak inverse plate voltage = 360 V. Max. dc plate current each diode = 10 mA.												
6973	Pwr. Pentode	9EU	6.3	0.45	6	6	0.4	440	−15	300	—	—	73K	4800	—	—	—
7189A	Pwr. Pentode	9CV	6.3	0.76	10.8	6.5	0.5	250	−7.3	250	5.5	48	40K	11.3K	—	—	—
7258	Sharp Cut-off	9DA	12.6	0.195	7	2.4	0.4	330	—	125	3.8	12	170K	7800	—	—	—
	Medium-μ Triode				2	0.26	1.5	330	−3	—	—	15	4.7K	4500	21	—	—
7586	Medium-μ Triode	12AQ	6.3	0.135	4.2	1.6	2.2	75	100*	—	—	10.5	3000	11.5K	35	—	—
7587	Sharp Cut-off Tet.	12AS	6.3	0.15	6.5	1.4	0.01	125	68*	50	2.7	10	200K	10.5K	—	—	—
7895	High-μ Triode	12AQ	6.3	0.135	4.2	1.7	0.9	110	0	—	—	7	6800	9400	64	—	—
8056	Medium-μ Triode	12AQ	6.3	0.135	4.0	1.7	2.1	12	0	—	—	5.8	1.6K	8000	12.5	—	—

TABLE I—MINIATURE RECEIVING TUBES—*Continued*

Type	Name	Base	Fil. or Heater V	Fil. or Heater Amp.	Capacitances pF C_{in}	Capacitances pF C_{out}	Capacitances pF C_{gp}	Plate Supply V	Grid Bias	Screen Volts	Screen mA	Plate mA	Plate Res. Ohms	Transconductance[11]	Amp. Factor[4]	Load Res. Ohms	Watts Output
8058	High-μ Triode	12CT	6.3	0.135	6.0	0.046	1.3	110	47*	—	—	10	—	10K	—	—	—
8393	Medium-μ Triode	12AQ	13.5	0.060	4.4	1.7	2.4	75	100*	—	—	10.5	3000	11.5K	35	—	—
8628	High-μ Triode	12AQ	6.3	0.10	10	3.4	1.7	150	3.3K*	—	—	0.3	41K	3100	127	7K	—
8677	Power Triode	12CT	6.3	0.15	6.0	1.2	—	180	1.2K*	—	—	20	3K	5400	70	—	1.4
9001	Sharp Cut-off Pent.	7BD	6.3	0.15	3.6	3	0.01	250	−3	100	0.7	2	1 meg.	1400	—	—	—
9002	Uhf Triode	7BS	6.3	0.15	1.2	1.1	1.4	250	−7	—	—	6.3	11.4K	2200	25	—	—
9003	Remote Cut-off Pent.	7BD	6.3	0.15	3.4	3	0.1	250	−3	100	2.7	6.7	700K	1800	—	—	—
9006	Uhf Diode	6BH	6.3	0.15	Max. ac voltage = 270. Max. dc output current = 5 mA.												

‡ Controlled heater warm-up characteristic.
Ω Oscillator gridleak or screen-dropping resistor ohms.
* Cathode resistor ohms.
** Space-charge grid.
[1] Per Plate.
[2] Maximum-signal current for full-power output.
[3] Values are for two tubes in push-pull.
[4] Unless otherwise noted.
[5] No signal plate mA.
[6] Effective plate-to-plate.
[7] Triode No. 1.
[8] Triode No. 2.
[9] Oscillator grid current mA.
[10] Values for each section.
[11] Micromhos.
[12] Through 33K.

TABLE II—METAL RECEIVING TUBES

Characteristics given in this table apply to all tubes having type numbers shown, including metal tubes, glass tubes with "G" suffix, and bantam tubes with "GT" suffix. For "G" and "GT"-tubes not listed (not having metal counterparts), see Tables III and V.

Type	Name	Base	Fil. or Heater V	Fil. or Heater Amp.	Capacitances pF C_{in}	Capacitances pF C_{out}	Capacitances pF C_{gp}	Plate Supply V	Grid Bias	Screen Volts	Screen mA	Plate mA	Plate Res. Ohms	Transconductance[12]	Amp. Factor[13]	Load Res. Ohms	Watts Output
6A8	Pentagrid Conv.	8A	6.3	0.3	—	—	—	250	−3	100	2.7	3.5	360K	550	—	—	—
								E_{bb} (Osc.) 250 V through 20K. Grid resistor (Osc.) 50K. I_b = 4 mA. I_{g1} = 0.4 mA.									
6AC7 1852	Sharp Cut-off Pent.	8N	6.3	0.45	11	5	0.15	300	160*	150	2.5	10	1 meg.	9000	—	—	—
								300	160*	60K[8]	2.5	10	1 meg.	9000	—	—	—
6AG7	Pwr. Amp. Pent.	8Y	6.3	0.65	13	7.5	0.06	300	3	150	7/9	30/31	130K	11K	—	10K	3
6B8	Dual-Diode — Pent.	8E	6.3	0.3	6	9	0.005	250	—3	125	2.3	10	600K	1325	—	—	—
6F6	Pwr. Amp. Pent. A_1 Amp.[1,5]	7S	6.3	0.7	6.5	13	0.2	250	20	20[10]	—	31/34	2.6K	2600	6.8	4K	0.85
	AB_2 Amp.[1,6]							350	730*	132[11]	—	50/60	—	—	—	10K[7]	9
								350	−38	123[11]	—	48/92	—	—	—	6K[7]	13
	A_1 Amp.[5]							250	−16.5	250	6/11	34/36	80K	2500	—	7K	3.2
								285	−20	285	7/13	38/40	78K	2500	—	7K	4.8
	AB_2 Amp.[6]							375	26	250	5/20	34/82	—	—	82[11]	10K[7]	18.5
								375	340*	250	8/18	54/77	—	—	94[11]	10K[7]	19
6J5	Medium-μ Triode	6Q	6.3	0.3	3.4	3.6	3.4	250	−8	—	—	9	7.7K	2600	20	—	—
6J7	Sharp Cut-off Pent. A_1 Amp.	7R	6.3	0.3	7	12	0.005	250	−3	100	0.5	2	1 meg.	1225	—	—	—
	Biased Detector							250	10K*	100	Zero signal cathode current = 0.43 mA.					0.5 meg.	
6K7	Variable-μ Pent. R.f. Amp.	7R	6.3	0.3	7	12	0.005	250	−3	125	2.6	10.5	600K	1650	990	—	—
	Mixer							250	−10	100	Osc. peak volts = 7						
6K8	Triode — Hexode Conv. Hexode	8K	6.3	0.3	—	—	—	250	−3	100	6	2.5	600K	350	—	—	—
	Triode							100	50K[8]	—	—	3.8	I_{g1} (Osc.) = 0.15 mA.				
6L6-GB[2]	Beam Pwr. Amp. A_1 Amp.[1,5]	7AC	6.3	0.9	11.5	9.5	0.9	250	−20	20[10]	—	40/44	1.7K	4700	8	5K	1.4
	A_1 Amp.[5] Self Bias							250	167*	250	5.4/7.2	75/78	—	—	14[10]	2.5K	6.5
								300	218*	200	3/4.6	51/55	—	—	12.7[10]	4.5K	6.5
	A_1 Amp.[5] Fixed Bias							250	−14	250	5/7.3	72/79	22.5K	6000	14[10]	2.5K	6.5
								350	−18	250	2.5/7	54/66	33K	5200	18[10]	4.2K	10.8
	A_1 Amp.[6] Self Bias							250	125*	250	10/15	120/130	—	—	35.6[11]	5K[7]	13.8
								270	125*	270	11/17	134/145	—	—	28.2[11]	5K[7]	18.5
	A_1 Amp.[6] Fixed Bias							250	−16	250	10/16	120/140	24.5[5]	5500[5]	32[11]	5K[7]	14.5
								270	−17.5	270	11/17	134/155	23.5[5]	5700[5]	35[11]	5K[7]	17.5
	AB_1 Amp.[6] Self Bias							360	270*	270	5/17	88/100	—	—	40.6[11]	9K[7]	24.5
	AB_1 Amp.[6] Fixed Bias							360	−22.5	270	5/11	88/140	—	—	45[11]	3.8K[7]	18
								360	−22.5	270	5/15	88/132	—	—	45[11]	6.6K[7]	26.5
	AB_2 Amp.[6] Fixed Bias							360	−18	225	3.5/11	78/142	—	—	52[11]	6K[7]	31
								360	−22.5	270	5/16	88/205	—	—	72[11]	3.8K[7]	47
6L7	Pentagrid — Mixer Amp. A_1 Amp.	7T	6.3	0.3	—	—	—	250	−3	100	6.5	5.3	600K	1100	−3[14]	—	—
	Mixer							250	−6	150	9.2	3.3	1 meg.	350	−15[14]	—	—
6N7GT	Class-B Twin Triode B Amp.[9]	8B	6.3	0.8	—	—	—	300	0	—	—	35/70	—	—	82[11]	8K[7]	10
	A_1 Amp.[15]							250	−5	—	—	6	11.3K	3100	—	—	—
6Q7	Dual Diode — High-μ Triode	7V[2]	6.3	0.3	5	3.8	1.4	250	−3	—	—	1	58K	1200	70	—	—
6R7	Dual Diode — Triode	7V[2]	6.3	0.3	4.8	3.8	2.4	250	−9	—	—	9.5	8.5K	1900	16	10K	0.28
6SA7GT	Pentagrid Conv.	8R[2]	6.3	0.3	9.5	12	0.13	250	0[3]	100	8	3.4	800K	Grid No. 1 resistor 20K.			
6SB7Y	Pentagrid Conv.	8R	6.3	0.3	9.6	9.2	0.13	100	−1	100	10.2	3.6	50K	900	—	—	—
								250	−1	100	10	3.8	1 meg.	950	—	—	—
								250	22K[8]	12K[8]	12/13	6.8/6.5	Osc. Section in 88—108 MHz. Service.				
6SC7	High-μ Dual Triode[5]	8S	6.3	0.3	2	3	2	250	−2	—	—	2	53K	1325	70	—	—
6SF7	Diode — Variable-μ Pent.	7AZ	6.3	0.3	5.5	6	0.004	250	−1	100	3.3	12.4	700K	2050	—	—	—
6SG7	Hf Amp. Pent.	8BK	6.3	0.3	8.5	7	0.003	250	−2.5	150	3.4	9.2	1 meg.	4000	—	—	—
6SH7	Hf Amp. Pent.	8BK	6.3	0.3	8.5	7	0.003	250	−1	150	4.1	10.8	900K	4900	—	—	—
6SJ7[4]	Sharp Cut-off Pent.	8N	6.3	0.3	6	7	0.005	250	−3	100	0.8	3	1 meg.	1650	—	—	—
6SK7	Variable-μ Pent.	8N	6.3	0.3	6	7	0.003	250	−3	100	2.6	9.2	800K	2000	—	—	—
6SQ7GT	Dual Diode — High-μ Triode	8Q	6.3	0.3	3.2	3	1.6	250	−2	—	—	0.9	91K	1100	100	—	—
6SR7	Dual Diode — Triode	8Q	6.3	0.3	3.6	2.8	2.4	250	−9	—	—	9.5	8.5K	1900	16	—	—
6V6GTA	Beam Pwr. Amp. A_1 Amp.[5]	7AC	6.3	0.45	10	11	0.3	180	−8.5	180	3/4	29/30	50K	3700	8.5[10]	5.5K	2
								250	−12.5	250	4.5/7	45/47	50K	4100	12.5[10]	5K	4.5
								315	−13	225	2.2/6	34/35	80K	3750	13[10]	8.5K	5.5
	AB_1 Amp.[6]							250	−15	250	5/13	70/79	60K	3750	30[11]	10K[7]	10
								285	−19	285	4/13.5	70/92	70K	3600	38[11]	8K[7]	14
1620	Sharp Cut-off Pent.	7R	6.3	0.3	7	12	0.005	250	−3	100	0.5	2	1 meg.	1225	—	—	—
5693	Sharp Cut-off Pent.	8N	6.3	0.3	5.3	6.2	0.005	250	−3	100	0.85	3	1 meg.	1650	—	—	—

* Cathode resistor-ohms.
[1] Screen tied to plate.
[2] No connection to Pin No. 1 for 6L6G, 6Q7G, 6RGT/G, 6S7G, 6SA7GT/G and 6SF5-GT.
[3] Grid bias = 2 volts if separate oscillator excitation is used.
[4] Also type 6SJ7Y.
[5] Values are for single tube or section.
[6] Values are for two tubes in push-pull.
[7] Plate-to-plate value.
[8] Osc. grid leak — Scrn. res.
[9] Values for two units.
[10] Peak af grid voltage.
[11] Peak af G-G voltage.
[12] Micromhos.
[13] Unless otherwise noted.
[14] G_3 voltage.
[15] Units connected in parallel.

TABLE III—6.3-VOLT GLASS TUBES WITH OCTAL BASES

(For "G" and "GT"-type tubes not listed here, see equivalent type in Tables II and V; characteristics and connections will be similar)

Type	Name	Plate Dissipation (Watts)	Base	Fil. or Heater		Capacitances pF			Plate Supply V	Grid Bias	Screen Volts	Screen mA	Plate mA	Plate Res. Ohms	Transconductance[4]	Amp. Factor	Load Res. Ohms	Watts Output
				V	Amp.	C_{in}	C_{out}	C_{gp}										
6AL7GT	Electron-Ray Indicator	—	8CH	6.3	0.15	—	—	—	Outer edge of any of the three illuminated areas displaced 1/16 in. min. outward with +5 volts to its electrode. Similar inward disp. with −5 volts. No pattern with −6 volts grid.									
6AQ7GT	Dual Diode — High-μ Triode	—	8CK	6.3	0.3	2.8	3.2	3	250	−2	—	—	2.3	44K	1600	70	—	—
6AR6	Beam Pent.	—	6BQ	6.3	1.2	11	7	0.55	250	−22.5	250	5	77	21K	5400	—	—	—
6AR7GT	Dual Diode — Remote Pent.	—	7DE	6.3	0.3	5.5	7.5	0.003	250	−2	100	1.8	7	1.2 meg.	2500	—	—	—
6AS7GA	Low-μ Twin Triode — DC Amp.[1]	—	8BD	6.3	2.5	6.5	2.2	7.5	135	250*	—	—	125	0.28K	7000	2	—	—
6AU5GT	Beam Pwr. Amp.[3]	10	6CK	6.3	1.25	11.3	7	0.5	115	−20	175	6.8	60	6K	5600	—	—	—
6BL7GTA	Medium-μ Dual Triode[1]	—	8BD	6.3	1.5	4.4	0.9	6	250	−9	—	—	40	2.15K	7000	15	—	—
6BQ6GTB 6CU6	Beam Pwr. Amp.[3]	11	6AM	6.3	1.2	15	7	0.6	250	−22.5	150	2.1	57	14.5K	5900	—	—	—
6BX7GT	Dual Triode[1]	—	8BD	6.3	1.5	5	3.4	4.2	250	390*	—	—	42	1.3K	7600	10	—	—
6CB5A	Beam Pwr. Amp.[3]	26	8GD	6.3	2.5	22	10	0.4	175	−30	175	6	90	5K	8800	—	—	—
6CD6GA	Beam Pwr. Amp.[3]	20	5BT	6.3	2.5	24	9.5	0.8	175	−30	175	5.5	75	7.2K	7700	—	—	—
6CK4	Low-μ Triode	—	8JB	6.3	1.25	8	1.8	6.5	550	−26	—	—	55	1.0K	6500	6.7	—	—
6CL5	Beam Pwr. Amp.[3]	25	8GD	6.3	2.5	20	11.5	0.7	175	−40	175	7	90	6K	6500	—	—	—
6DN6	Beam Pwr. Pent.[3]	15	5BT	6.3	2.5	22	11.5	0.8	125	−18	125	6.3	70	4K	9000	—	—	—
6DN7	Dissimilar Dual Triode	—	8BD	6.3	0.9	2.2	0.7	4	350	−8	—	—	8	9K	2500	22	—	—
						4.6	1	5.5	550	−9.5	—	—	68	2K	7700	15	—	—
6DQ5	Beam Pwr. Amp.[3]	24	8JC	6.3	2.5	23	11	0.5	175	−25	125	5	110	5.5K	10.5K	—	—	—
6DQ6B	Beam Pwr. Amp.[3]	18	6AM	6.3	1.2	15	7	0.55	250	−22.5	150	2.4	75	20K	6600	—	—	—
6DZ7	Twin Pwr. Pent.[1]	13.2	8JP	6.3	1.52	11	5	0.6	300	120*	250	15	80	—	—	—	9K[2]	12
6E5	Electron Ray — Triode	—	6R	6.3	0.3	—	—	—	250	—	—	—	—	—	—	—	—	—
6EA7	Dissimilar — Dual Triode	—	8BD	6.3	1.05	2.2	0.6	4	350	−3	—	—	1.5	34K	1900	65	—	—
						6	1.3	8	550	−25	—	—	95	770	6500	5	—	—
6EF6	Beam Pwr. Amp.[5]	—	7S	6.3	0.9	11.5	9	0.8	250	−18	250	2	50	—	5000	—	—	—
6EY6	Beam Pwr. Pent.	—	7AC	6.3	0.68	8.5	7	0.7	350	−17.5	300	3	44	60K	4400	—	—	—
6EZ5	Beam Pwr. Pent.	—	7AC	6.3	0.8	9	7	0.6	350	−20	300	3.5	43	50K	4100	—	—	—
6FH6	Beam Pwr. Pent.	—	6AM	6.3	1.2	33	8	0.4	770	−22.5	220	1.7	75	12K	6000	—	—	—
6GW6	Beam Power Amp.[3]	17.5	6AM	6.3	1.2	17	7	0.5	250	−22.5	150	2.1	70	15K	7100	—	—	—
6K6GT	Pwr. Amp. Pent.	—	7S	6.3	0.4	5.5	6	0.5	315	−21	250	4/9	25/28	110K	2100	—	9K	4.5
6SL7GT	High-μ Dual Triode[1]	—	8BD	6.3	0.3	3.4	3.8	2.8	250	−2	—	—	2.3	44K	1600	70	—	—
6SN7GTB	Medium-μ Dual Triode[1]	—	8BD	6.3	0.6	3	1.2	4	250	−8	—	—	9	7.7K	2600	20	—	—
6W6GT	Beam Pwr. Amp.	—	7S	6.3	1.2	15	9	0.5	200	180*	125	2/8.5	46/47	28K	8000	—	4K	3.8
6Y6GA	Beam Pwr. Amp.	—	7S	6.3	1.25	15	1	0.7	200	−14	135	2.2/9	61/66	18.3K	7100	—	2.6K	6
1635	High-μ Dual Triode	—	8B	6.3	0.6	—	—	—	300	0	—	—	6.6/54	—	—	—	12K[2]	10.4
6550	Power Pentode	35	7S	6.3	1.6	14	12	0.85	400	−16.5	225	18	105	27K	9000	—	3K	20
7027A	Beam Pwr. Amp.	—	8HY	6.3	0.9	10	7.5	1.5	450	−30	350	19.2	194	—	6000	—	6K[2]	50
7591	Beam Pwr. Amp.	19	8KQ	6.3	0.8	10	5	0.25	450	200*	400	22	94	—	—	—	9K[2]	28

* Cathode resistor-ohms.
[1] Per section.
[2] Plate-to-plate value.
[3] Horz. Deflection Amp.
[4] Micromhos. A
[5] Vert. Deflection mp.

TABLE IV—CONTROL AND REGULATOR TUBES

Type	Name	Base	Cathode	Fil. or Heater		Peak Anode Voltage	Max. Anode mA	Minimum Supply Voltage	Operating Voltage	Operating mA	Grid Resistor	Tube Voltage Drop
				Volts	Amp.							
0A2 6073	Voltage Regulator	5BO	Cold	—	—	—	—	185	150	5–30	—	—
0A3A/VR75	Voltage Regulator	4AJ	Cold	—	—	—	—	105	75	5–40	—	—
0B2 6074	Voltage Regulator	5BO	Cold	—	—	—	—	133	108	5–30	—	—
0B3/VR90	Voltage Regulator	4AJ	Cold	—	—	—	—	125	90	5–40	—	—
0C2	Voltage Regulator	5BO	Cold	—	—	—	—	105	75	5–30	—	—
0C3A/VR105	Voltage Regulator	4AJ	Cold	—	—	—	—	135	105	5–40	—	—
0D3A/VR150	Voltage Regulator	4AJ	Cold	—	—	—	—	185	150	5–40	—	—
5651	Voltage Regulator	5BO	Cold	—	—	115	—	115	87	1.5–3.5	—	—
5662	Thyratron — Fuse	Fig. 79	Htr.	6.3	1.5	200[1]	I_k to fuse — 150 Amp., 60 cycle, half-wave					50 V
5696	Relay Service	7BN	Htr.	6.3	0.15	500[1]	100 ma. peak current; 25-ma. average.					
5727	Gas Thyratron	7BN	Htr.	6.3	0.6	650	—	—	—	—	—	—
5823	Relay or Trigger	4CK	Cold	—	—	Max. peak inv. volts = 200; Peak mA = 100; Avg. mA = 25.						
5962	Voltage Regulator	2AG	Cold	—	—	—	—	730	700	5/55[2]	—	—
5998	Series Regulator	8BD	Htr.	6.3	2.4	250	125	—	110	100	350[6]	—

[1] Peak inverse voltage.
[2] Values in microamperes.

TABLE V—RECTIFIERS—RECEIVING AND TRANSMITTING

See Also Table IV—Controls and Regulator Tubes

Type	Name	Base	Cathode	Fil. or Heater		Max. AC Voltage Per Plate	DC Output Current mA	Max. Inverse Peak Voltage	Peak Plate Current mA	Type
				Volts	Amp.					
0Z4-G	Full-Wave Rectifier	4R	Cold	—	—	300	75	1000	200	GAS
1G3-GT/ 1B3-GT	Half-Wave Rectifier	3C	Fil.	1.25	0.2	—	1.0	33000	30	HV
1K3/1J3	Half-Wave Rectifier	3C	Fil.	1.25	0.2	—	0.5	26000	50	HV
1V2	Half-Wave Rectifier	9U	Fil.	0.625	0.3	—	0.5	7500	10	HV
2X2-A	Half-Wave Rectifier	4AB	Htr.	2.5	1.75	4500	7.5	—	—	HV
2Y2	Half-Wave Rectifier	4AB	Fil.	2.5	1.75	4400	5.0	—	—	HV
2Z2/G84	Half-Wave Rectifier	4B	Fil.	2.5	1.5	350	50	—	—	HV

TABLE V — RECTIFIERS — RECEIVING AND TRANSMITTING — *Continued*

See Also Table IV — Controls and Regulator Tubes

Type	Name	Base	Cathode	Fil. or Heater Volts	Fil. or Heater Amp.	Max. AC Voltage Per Plate	D.C. Output Current mA	Max. Inverse Peak Voltage	Peak Plate Current mA	Type
3B24	Half-Wave Rectifier	Fig. 49	Fil.	5.0	3.0	—	60	20000	300	HV
				2.5[5]	3.0	—	30	20000	150	
3B28	Half-Wave Rectifier	4P	Fil.	2.5	5.0	—	250	10000	1000	GAS
5AT4	Full-Wave Rectifier	5L	Htr.	5.0	2.25	550	800	1550	—	HV
5AU4	Full-Wave Rectifier	5T	Fil.	5.0	4.5	300[3]	350[3]	1400	1075	HV
						400[3]	325[3]			
						500[4]	325[4]			
5AW4	Full-Wave Rectifier	5T	Fil.	5.0	4.0	450[3]	250[3]	1550	750	HV
						550[4]	250[4]			
5R4GY 5R4GYA	Full-Wave Rectifier	5T	Fil.	5.0	2.0	900[3]	150[3]	2800	650	HV
						950[4]	175[4]			
5U4G	Full-Wave Rectifier	5T	Fil.	5.0	3.0	Same as Type 5Z3				HV
5U4GA	Full-Wave Rectifier	5T	Fil.	5.0	3.0	300[3]	275[3]	1550	900	HV
						450[3]	250[3]			
						550[4]	250[4]			
5U4GB 5AS4A	Full-Wave Rectifier	5T	Fil.	5.0	3.0	300[3]	300[3]	1550	1000	HV
						450[3]	275[3]			
						550[4]	275[4]			
5V3A	Full-Wave Rectifier	5T	Htr.	5.0	3.8	425[3] 500[4]	350	1400	1200	HV
5V4GA	Full-Wave Rectifier	5L	Htr.	5.0	2.0	375[3]	175	1400	525	HV
5Y3-G-GT	Full-Wave Rectifier	5T	Fil.	5.0	2.0	Same as Type 80				HV
5Z3	Full-Wave Rectifier	4C	Fil.	5.0	3.0	500	250	1400	—	HV
5Z4	Full-Wave Rectifier	5L	Htr.	5.0	2.0	400	125	1100	—	HV
6AV4	Full-Wave Rectifier	5BS	Htr.	6.3	0.95	—	90	1250	250	HV
6AX5GT	Full-Wave Rectifier	6S	Htr.	6.3	1.2	450	125	1250	375	HV
6BW4	Full-Wave Rectifier	9DJ	Htr.	6.3	0.9	450	100	1275	350	HV
6BX4	Full-Wave Rectifier	5BS	Htr.	6.3	0.6	—	90	1350	270	HV
6BY5G	Full-Wave Rectifier	6CN	Htr.	6.3	1.6	375[3]	175	1400	525	HV
6CA4	Full-Wave Rectifier	9M	Htr.	6.3	1.0	350[3]	150	1000	450	HV
6DE4	Half-Wave Rectifier	4CG	Fil.	6.3	1.6	—	175	5000	1100	HV
6V4	Full-Wave Rectifier	9M	Htr.	6.3	0.6	350	90	—	—	HV
6X4/6063 6X5GT	Full-Wave Rectifier	7CF 6S	Htr.	6.3	0.3	325[3] 450[4]	70	1250	210	HV
6Z3	Half-Wave Rectifier	4G	Fil.	6.3	0.3	350	50	—	—	HV
12X4	Full-Wave Rectifier	5BS	Htr.	12.6	0.3	650[3]	70	1250	210	HV
						900[4]	70	1250	210	
25Z5	Rectifier-Doubler	6E	Htr.	25	0.3	125	100	—	500	HV
35W4	Half-Wave Rectifier	5BQ	Htr.	35[1]	0.15	125	60	330	600	HV
35Z4GT	Half-Wave Rectifier	5AA	Htr.	35	0.15	250	100	700	600	HV
35Z5G	Half-Wave Rectifier	6AD	Htr.	35[1]	0.15	125	60	—	—	HV
36AM3	Half-Wave Rectifier	5BQ	Htr.	36	0.1	117	75	365	530	HV
50DC4	Half-Wave Rectifier	5BQ	Htr.	50	0.15	117	100	330	720	HV
50Y6GT	Full-Wave Rectifier	7Q	Htr.	50	0.15	125	85	—	—	HV
80	Full-Wave Rectifier	4C	Fil.	5.0	2.0	350[3]	125	1400	375	HV
						500[4]	125			
83	Full-Wave Rectifier	4C	Fil.	5.0	3.0	500	250	1400	800	MV
83-V	Full-Wave Rectifier	4AD	Htr.	5.0	2.0	400	200	1100	—	HV
117N7GT	Rectifier-Tetrode	8AV	Htr.	117	0.09	117	75	350	450	HV
117Z3	Half-Wave Rectifier	4CB	Htr.	117	0.04	117	90	300	—	HV
816	Half-Wave Rectifier	4P	Fil.	2.5	2.0	2200	125	7500	500	MV
836	Half-Wave Rectifier	4P	Htr.	2.5	5.0	—	—	5000	1000	HV
866-A-AX	Half-Wave Rectifier	4P	Fil.	2.5	5.0	3500	250	10000	1000	MV
866B	Half-Wave Rectifier	4P	Fil.	5.0	5.0	—	—	8500	1000	MV
866 Jr.	Half-Wave Rectifier	4B	Fil.	2.5	2.5	1250	250[2]	—	—	MV
872A/872	Half-Wave Rectifier	4AT	Fil.	5.0	7.5	—	1250	10000	5000	MV

[1] Tapped for pilot lamps.
[2] Per pair with choke input.
[3] Capacitor input.
[4] Choke input.
[5] Using only one-half of filament.

TABLE VI — TRIODE TRANSMITTING TUBES

Type	Maximum Ratings: Plate Dissipation Watts	Maximum Ratings: Plate Voltage	Maximum Ratings: Plate Current mA	Maximum Ratings: DC Grid Current mA	Maximum Ratings: Freq. MHz. Full Ratings	Amplification Factor	Cathode: Volts	Cathode: Amperes	Capacitances: C_{in} pF	Capacitances: C_{gp} pF	Capacitances: C_{out} pF	Base	Typical Operation: Class of Service	Typical Operation: Plate Voltage	Typical Operation: Grid Voltage	Typical Operation: Plate Current mA	Typical Operation: DC Grid Current mA	Typical Operation: Approx. Driving Power Watts	Typical Operation: P-to-P Load Ohms	Typical Operation: Approx. Output Power Watts
6J6A‡[2]	1.5	300	30	16	250	32	6.3	0.45	2.2	1.6	0.4	7BF	C·T	150	−10	30	1.6	0.035	—	3.5
6F4	2.0	150	20	8.0	500	17	6.3	0.225	2.0	1.9	0.6	7BR	C·T·O	150	−15 550* 2000[4]	20	7.5	0.2	—	1.8
12AU7A[2]	2.76[6]	350	12[6]	3.5[6]	54	18	6.3	0.3	1.5	1.5	0.5	9A	C·T·O	350	−100	24	7	—	—	6.0
6C4	5.0	350	25	8.0	54	18	6.3	0.15	1.8	1.6	1.3	6BG	C·T·O	300	−27	25	7.0	0.35	—	5.5
5675	5	165	30	8	3000	20	6.3	0.135	2.3	1.3	0.09	Fig. 21	G·G·O	120	−8	25	4	—	—	0.05
6N7GT[2]	5.5[6]	350	30[6]	5.0[6]	10	35	6.3	0.8	—	—	—	8B	C·T·O	350	−100	60	10	—	—	14.5
2C40	6.5	500	25	—	500	36	6.3	0.75	2.1	1.3	0.05	Fig. 11	C·T·O	250	−5	20	0.3	—	—	0.075
5893	8.0	400	40	13	1000	27	6.0	0.33	2.5	1.75	0.07	Fig. 21	C·T	350	−33	35	13	2.4	—	6.5
													C·P	300	−45	30	12	2.0	—	6.5
2C43	12	500	40	—	1250	48	6.3	0.9	2.9	1.7	0.05	Fig. 11	C·T·O	470	—	38[7]	—	—	—	9[7]
3C24	25	2000	75	7[13]	60	24	6.3	3.0	1.7	1.6	0.2	2D	C·T	2000	−130	63	18	4	—	100
	17	1600	60										C·P	1600	−170	53	11	3.1	—	68
	25	2000	75										AB_2[7]	1250	−42	24/130	270[9]	3.4[8]	21.4K	112
1623	30	1000	100	25	60	20	6.3	2.5	5.7	6.7	0.9	3G	C·T·O	1000	−90	100	20	3.1	—	75
													C·P	750	−125	100	20	4.0	—	55
													B[7]	1000	−40	30/200	230[9]	4.2[8]	12K	145

TABLE VI—TRIODE TRANSMITTING TUBES—*Continued*

Type	Maximum Ratings: Plate Dissipation Watts	Plate Voltage	Plate Current mA	DC Grid Current mA	Freq. MHz Full Ratings	Amplification Factor	Cathode: Volts	Amperes	Capacitances: C_{in} pF	C_{gp} pF	C_{out} pF	Base	Typical Operation: Class of Service	Plate Voltage	Grid Voltage	Plate Current mA	DC Grid Current mA	Approx. Driving Power Watts	P-to-P Load Ohms	Approx. Output Power Watts
811-A	65	1500	175	50	60	160	6.3	4.0	5.9	5.6	0.7	3G	C·T	1500	−70	173	40	7.1	—	200
													C·P	1250	−120	140	45	10.0	—	135
													G·G·B	1250	0	27/175	28	12	—	165
													AB_1	1250	0	27/175	13	3.0	—	155
812-A	65	1500	175	35	60	29	6.3	4.0	5.4	5.5	0.77	3G	C·T	1500	−120	173	30	6.5	—	190
													C·P	1250	−115	140	35	7.6	—	130
													B[7]	1500	−48	28/310	270[9]	5.0	13.2K	340
100TH	100	3000	225	60	40	40	5.0	6.3	2.9	2.0	0.4	2D	C·T / C·P	3000	−200	165	51	18	—	400
													B[7]	3000	−65	40/215	335[9]	5.0[8]	31K	650
3-100A2 100TL	100	3000	225	50	40	14	5.0	6.3	2.3	2.0	0.4	2D	C·T / C·P	3000	−400	165	30	20	—	400
													G·M·A	3000	−560	60	2.0	7.0	—	90
													B[7]	3000	−185	40/215	640[9]	6.0[8]	30K	450
3CX100A5[15]	100	1000	125[14]	50	2500	100	6.0	1.05	7.0	2.15	0.035	—	G·G·A	800	−20	80	30	6	—	27
	70	600	100[14]										C·P	600	−15	75	40	6	—	18
2C39	100	1000	60	40	500	100	6.3	1.1	6.5	1.95	0.03	—	G·I·C	600	−35	60	40	5.0	—	20
													C·T·O	900	−40	90	30	—	—	40
													C·P	600	−150	100[14]	50	—	—	—
AX9900/5866[15]	135	2500	200	40	150	25	6.3	5.4	5.8	5.5	0.1	Fig. 3	C·T	2500	−200	200	40	16	—	390
													C·P	2000	−225	127	40	16	—	204
													B[7]	2500	−90	80/330	350[9]	14[8]	15.68K	560
572B/T160L	160	2750	275	—	—	170	6.3	4.0	—	—	—	3G	C·T	1650	−70	165	32	6	—	205
													G·G·B[7]	2400	−2.0	90/500	—	100	—	600
810	175	2500	300	75	30	36	10	4.5	8.7	4.8	12	2N	C·T	2500	−180	300	60	19	—	575
													C·P	2000	−350	250	70	35	—	380
													G·M·A	2250	−140	100	2.0	4	—	75
													B[7]	2250	−60	70/450	380[9]	13[8]	11.6K	725
8873	200	2200	250	—	500	160	6.3	3.2	19.5	7.0	0.03	Fig. 87	AB_2	2000	—	22/500	98[8]	27[8]	—	505
250TH	250	4000	350	40[13]	40	37	5.0	10.5	4.6	2.9	0.5	2N	C·T·O	2000	−100	357	94	29	—	464
													C·T·O	3000	−150	333	90	32	—	750
													C·P	2000	−160	250	60	22	—	335
													C·P	2500	−180	225	45	17	—	400
													C·P	3000	−200	200	38	14	—	435
													AB_2[7]	1500	0	220/700	460[9]	46[8]	4.2K	630
250TL	250	4000	350	35[13]	40	14	5.0	10.5	3.7	3.0	0.7	2N	C·T·O	2000	−200	350	45	22	—	455
													C·T·O	3000	−350	335	45	29	—	750
													C·P	2000	−520	250	29	24	—	335
													C·P	2500	−520	225	20	16	—	400
													C·P	3000	−520	200	14	11	—	435
													AB_2[7]	1500	−40	200/700	780[9]	38[8]	3.8K	580
PL-6569	250	4000	300	120	30	45	5.0	14.5	7.6	3.7	0.1	Fig. 3	G·G·A	2500	−70	300	85	75[11]	—	555
													G·G·A	3000	−95	300	110	85[11]	—	710
													G·G·A	3500	−110	285	90	85[11]	—	805
													G·G·A	4000	−120	250	50	70[11]	—	820
8875	300	2200	250	—	500	160	6.3	3.2	19.5	7.0	0.03	—	AB_2	2000	—	22/500	98[8]	27[8]	—	505
304TH	300	3000	900	60[13]	40	20	5.0	25	13.5	10.2	0.7	4BC	C·T·O	1500	−125	665	115	25	—	700
							10	12.5					C·T·O	2000	−200	600	125	39	—	900
													C·P	1500	−200	420	55	18	—	500
													C·P	2000	−300	440	60	26	—	680
													C·P	2500	−350	400	60	29	—	800
													AB_2[7]	1500	−65	1065[8]	330[9]	25[8]	2.84K	1000
304TL	300	3000	900	50[13]	40	12	5.0	25	12.1	8.6	0.8	4BC	C·T·O	1500	−250	665	90	33	—	700
							10	12.5					C·T·O	2000	−300	600	85	36	—	900
													C·P	2000	−500	250	30	18	—	410
													C·P	2000	−500	500	75	52	—	810
													C·P	2500	−525	200	18	11	—	425
													C·P	2500	−550	400	50	36	—	830
													AB_1[7]	1500	−118	270/572	236[9]	0	2.54K	256
													AB_1[7]	2500	−230	160/483	460[9]	0	8.5K	610
													AB_2[7]	1500	−118	1140[8]	490[9]	39[8]	2.75K	1100
833A	350	3300	500	100	30	35	10	10	12.3	6.3	8.5	Fig. 41	C·T·O	2250	−125	445	85	23	—	780
	450[15]	4000[15]			20[15]								C·T·O	3000	−160	335	70	20	—	800
													C·P	2500	−300	335	75	30	—	635
													C·P	3000	−240	335	70	26	—	800
													B[7]	3000	−70	100/750	400[9]	20[8]	9.5K	1650
8874	400	2200	250	—	500	160	6.3	3.2	19.5	7.0	0.03	—	AB_2	2000	—	22/500	98[8]	27[8]	—	505
3-400Z	400	3000	400	—	110	200	5	14.5	7.4	4.1	0.07	Fig. 3	G·G·B	3000	0	100/333	120	32	—	655
PL-6580	400	4000[15]	350	120	—	45	5.0	14.5	7.6	3.9	0.1	5BK	G·G·A	4000	−110	350	92	105[11]	—	1080
													G·G·A	2500	−70	350	95	85	—	660
8163	400	3000	400	20[13]	30	350	5.0	14.1	8.0	5.0	0.3	Fig. 3	G·G·B	2500	0	72/400	140	35	—	640
3-500Z	500	4000	400	—	110	160	5	14.5	7.4	4.1	0.07	Fig. 3	G·G·B	3000	—	370	115	30	5K	750
													C·T	3500	−75	300	115	22	—	850
3-1000Z	1000	3000	800	—	110	200	7.5	21.3	17	6.9	0.12	Fig. 3	G·G·B	3000	0	180/670	300	65	—	1360
8877	1500	4000	1000	—	250	200	5.0	10	42	10	0.1	—	AB_2	2500	−8.2	1000	—	57	—	1520

* Cathode resistor in ohms.

[1] KEY TO CLASS-OF-SERVICE ABBREVIATIONS
- A_1 = Class-A_1 af modulator.
- AB_1 = Class-AB_1 push-pull af modulator.
- AB_2 = Class-AB_2 push-pull af modulator.
- B = Class-B push-pull af modulator.
- C·M = Frequency multiplier.
- C·P = Class-C plate-modulated telephone.
- C·T = Class-C telegraph.
- C·T·O = Class-C amplifier-osc.
- G·G·A = Grounded-grid class-C amp.
- G·G·B = Grounded-grid class-B amp. (Single Tone).
- G·G·O = Grounded-grid osc.
- G·I·C = Grid-isolation circuit.
- G·M·A = Grid-modulated amp.

[2] Twin triode. Values, except interelectrode capacitances, are for both sections in push-pull.
[3] Output at 112 MHz.
[4] Grid leak resistor in ohms.
[5] Peak values.
[6] Per section.
[7] Values are for two tubes in push-pull.
[8] Max. signal value.
[9] Peak af grid-to-grid volts.
[10] Plate-pulsed 1000-MHz. osc.
[11] Includes bias loss, grid dissipation, and feed-through power.
[12] 1000-MHz. cw osc.
[13] Max. grid dissipation in watts.
[14] Max. cathode current in mA.
[15] Forced-air cooling required.
[16] Plate-pulsed 3300-MHz. osc.
[17] 1900-MHz. cw osc.
[18] No Class-B data available.

TABLE VII — TETRODE AND PENTODE TRANSMITTING TUBES

Type	Maximum Ratings					Cathode		Capacitances			Base	Typical Operation										
	Plate Dissipation Watts	Plate Voltage	Screen Dissipation Watts	Screen Voltage	Freq. MHz, Full Ratings	Volts	Amperes	C_{in} pF	C_{gp} pF	C_{out} pF		Class of Service[14]	Plate Voltage	Screen Voltage	Suppressor Voltage	Grid Voltage	Plate Current mA	Screen Current mA	Grid Current mA	Approx. Driving Power Watts	P-to-P Load Ohms	Approx. Output Power Watts
8203	1.8	400	—	—	250	6.3	0.16	4.2	2.2	1.6	12AQ	C·P/C·T	155	—	—	14/2700[1]	21	—	5	0.4	—	1.55
6939[3]	7.5	275	3	200	500	6.3 12.6	0.75 0.375	6.6	0.15	1.55	Fig. 13	C·T	200	200	—	−20	60	13	2	1.0	—	7.5
												C·P	180	180	—	−20	55	11.5	1.7	1.0	—	6
												C·M	200	190	—	68K[1]	46	10	2.2	0.9	—	—
7551 7558	12	300	2	250	175	12.6 6.3	0.38 0.8	10	0.15	5.5	9LK	C·T	300	250	—	−55	80	5.1	1.6	1.5	—	10
												C·P	250	250	—	−75	70	3.0	2.3	1.0	—	7.5
5763 6417	13.5	350	2	250	50	6.3 12.6	0.75 0.375	9.5	0.3	4.5	9K	C·T	350	250	—	−28.5	48.5	6.2	1.6	0.1	—	12
												C·P	300	250	—	−42.5	50	6	2.4	0.15	—	10
												C·M[2]	300	250	—	−75	40	4	1	0.6	—	2.1
												C·M[4]	300	235	—	−100	35	5	1	0.6	—	1.3
2E26 6893	13.5	600	2.5	200	125	6.3 12.6	0.8 0.4	12.5	0.2	7	7CK	C·T	600	185	—	−45	66	10	3	0.17	—	27
												C·P	500	180	—	−50	54	9	2.5	0.15	—	18
												AB$_1$	500	200	—	−25	9/45	10[7]	0	0	—	15
6360[3]	14	300	2	200	200	6.3 12.6	0.82 0.41	6.2	0.1	2.6	Fig. 13	C·T	300	200	—	−45	100	3	3	0.2	—	18.5
												C·P	200	100	—	15K[1]	86	3.1	3.3	0.2	—	9.8
												C·M[11]	300	150	—	−100	65	3.5	3.8	0.45	—	4.8
												AB$_2$	300	200	—	−21.5	30/100	1/11.4	64[8]	0.04	6.5K	17.5
2E25	15	450	4	250	125	6	0.8	8.5	0.15	6.7	5BJ	C·T·O	450	250	—	−45	75	15	3	0.4	—	24
												C·P	400	200	—	−45	60	12	3	0.4	—	16
												AB$_2$[6]	450	250	—	−30	44/150	10/40	3	0.9[7]	6K	40
832A[3]	15	750	5	250	200	6.3 12.6	1.6 0.8	8	0.07	3.8	7BP	C·T	750	200	—	−65	48	15	2.8	0.19	—	26
												C·P	600	200	—	−65	36	16	2.6	0.16	—	17
6252/ AX9910[3]	20	750	4	300	300	6.3 12.6	1.3 0.65	6.5	—	2.5	Fig. 7	C·T	600	250	—	−60	140	14	4	2.0	—	—
												C·P	500	250	—	−80	100	12	3	4.0	—	—
												B	500	250	—	−26	25/73	0.7/16	52[8]	—	20K	23.5
1614	25	450	3.5	300	80	6.3	0.9	10	0.4	12.5	7AC	C·T	450	250	—	−45	100	8	2	0.15	—	31
												C·P	375	250	—	−50	93	7	2	0.15	—	24.5
												AB$_1$[6]	530	340	—	−36	60/160	20[7]	—	—	7.2K	50
815[3]	25	500	4	200	125	6.3 12.6	1.6 0.8	13.3	0.2	8.5	8BY	C·T·O	500	200	—	−45	150	17	2.5	0.13	—	56
												AB$_2$	500	125	—	−15	22/150	32[7]	—	0.36[7]	8K	54
6146 6146A	25	750	3	250	60	6.3	1.25	13	0.24	8.5	7CK	C·T	500	170	—	−66	135	9	2.5	0.2	—	48
												C·T	750	160	—	−62	120	11	3.1	0.2	—	70
												C·T[12]	400	190	—	−54	150	10.4	2.2	3.0	—	35
8032 6883						12.6	0.585					C·P	400	150	—	−87	112	7.8	3.4	0.4	—	32
												C·P	600	150	—	−87	112	7.8	3.4	0.4	—	52
												AB$_2$[6]	600	190	—	−48	28/270	1.2/20	2[7]	0.3	5K	113
6159B						26.5	0.3					AB$_2$[6]	750	165	—	−46	22/240	0.3/20	2.6[7]	0.4	7.4K	131
												AB$_1$[6]	750	195	—	−50	23/220	1/26	100[8]	0	8K	120
6524[3] 6850	25	600	—	300	100	6.3 12.6	1.25 0.625	7	0.11	3.4	Fig. 76	C·T	600	200	—	−44	120	8	3.7	0.2	—	56
												C·P	500	200	—	−61	100	7	2.5	0.2	—	40
												AB$_2$	500	200	—	−26	20/116	0.1/10	2.6	0.1	11.1K	40
807 807W 5933	30	750	3.5	300	60	6.3	0.9	12	0.2	7	5AW	C·T	750	250	—	−45	100	6	3.5	0.22	—	50
												C·P	600	275	—	−90	100	6.5	4	0.4	—	42.5
												AB$_1$	750	300	—	−35	15/70	3/8	75[8]	0	—	72
1625						12.6	0.45				5AZ	B[10]	750	—	—	0	15/240	—	555[8]	5.3[7]	6.65K	120
2E22	30	750	10	250	—	6.3	1.5	13	0.2	8	5J	C·T·O	750	250	22.5	−60	100	16	6	0.55	—	53
6146B/ 8298A	35	750	3	250	60	6.3	1.125	13	0.22	8.5	7CK	C·T	750	200	—	−77	160	10	2.7	0.3	—	85
												C·P	600	175	—	−92	140	9.5	3.4	0.5	—	62
												AB$_1$	750	200	—	−48	25/125	6.3	—	—	3.6K	61
AX- 9903[3] 5894A	40	600	7	250	250	6.3 12.6	1.8 0.9	6.7	0.08	2.1	Fig. 7	C·T	600	250	—	−80	200	16	2	0.2	—	80
829B[3] 3E29[3]	40	750	7	240	200	6.3 12.6	2.25 1.125	14.5	0.12	7	7BP	C·T	500	200	—	−45	240	32	12	0.7	—	83
												C·P	425	200	—	−60	212	35	11	0.8	—	63
												B	500	200	—	−18	27/230	—	56[8]	0.39	4.8K	76
3D24	45	2000	10	400	125	6.3	3	6.5	0.2	2.4	Fig. 75	C·T·O	2000	375	—	−300	90	20	10	4.0	—	140
													1500	375	—	−300	90	22	10	4.0	—	105
4D22	50	750	14	350	60	12.6 25.2	1.6 0.8	28	0.27	13	Fig. 26	C·T	750	300	—	−100	240	26	12	1.5	—	135
													600	300	—	−100	215	30	10	1.25	—	100
4D32						6.3	3.75				Fig. 27	C·P	600	—	—	−100	220	28	10	1.25	—	100
													550	—	—	−100	175	17	6	0.6	—	70
												AB$_2$[6]	600	250	—	−25	100/365	26[7]	70[8]	0.45[7]	3K	125
8117[3]	60	750	7	300	175	6.3 12.6	1.8 0.9	11.8	3.7	0.09	Fig. 7	AB$_1$	600	250	—	−32.5	60/212	1.9/25	—	—	1410	76
814	65	1500	10	300	30	10	3.25	13.5	0.1	13.5	Fig. 64	C·T	1500	300	—	−90	150	24	10	1.5	—	160
												C·P	1250	300	—	−150	145	20	10	3.2	—	130
4-65A	65	3000	10	600	150	6	3.5	8	0.08	2.1	Fig. 25	C·T·O	1500	250	—	−85	150	40	18	3.2	—	165
													3000	250	—	−100	115	22	10	1.7	—	280
												C·P	1500	250	—	−125	120	40	16	3.5	—	140
													2500	250	—	−135	110	25	12	2.6	—	230
												AB$_1$	2500	400	—	−85	15/66	3[7]	—	—	—	100
7854[3]	68	1000	8	300	175	6.3 12.6	1.8 0.9	6.7	2.1	0.09	Fig. 7	C·T	750	260	—	−75	240	12.7	5.5	3.5	—	123
												C·P	600	225	—	−75	200	7.8	5.5	3.5	—	85
4E27/ 8001	75	4000	30	750	75	5	7.5	12	0.06	6.5	7BM	C·T	2000	500	60	−200	150	11	6	1.4	—	230
												C·P	1800	400	60	−130	135	11	8	1.7	—	178
PL-177A	75	2000	10	600	175	6	3.2	7.5	0.06	4.2	Fig. 14	C·T·C·P	2000	400	0	−125	150	12	5	0.8	—	220
													1000	400	0	−105	150	16	5	0.7	—	100
												AB$_1$	2000	600	—	−115	25/175	0/7	0	0	—	210
7270 7271	80	1350	—	425	175	6.3 13.5	3.1 1.25	8	0.4	0.14	Fig. 84	C·T	850	400	—	−100	275	15	8	10	—	135
												AB$_1$	665	400	—	−119	220	15	6	10	—	85
8072	100	2200	8	400	500	13.5	1.3	16	0.13	0.011	Fig. 85	C·T·O	700	200	—	−30	300	10	20	5	—	85

Type	Maximum Ratings: Plate Dissipation Watts	Plate Voltage	Screen Dissipation Watts	Screen Voltage	Freq. MHz. Full Ratings	Cathode: Volts	Amperes	Capacitances: C_{in} pF	C_{gp} pF	C_{out} pF	Base	Typical Operation: Class of Service[14]	Plate Voltage	Screen Voltage	Suppressor Voltage	Grid Voltage	Plate Current mA	Screen Current mA	Grid Current mA	Approx. Driving Power Watts	P-to-P Load Ohms	Approx. Output Power Watts
6816[9] / 6884	115	1000	4.5	300	400	6.3 / 26.5	2.1 / 0.52	14	0.085	0.015	Fig. 77	C·T·O	900	300	—	−30	170	1	10	3	—	80
												C·P	700	250	—	−50	130	10	10	3	—	45
												AB_1[6]	850	300	—	−15	80/200	0/20	30[8]	0	7K	80
												AB_2[6]	850	300	—	−15	80/335	0/25	46[8]	0.3	3.96K	140
813[13]	125	2500	20	800	30	10	5	16.3	0.25	14	5BA	C·T·O	1250	300	0	−75	180	35	12	1.7	—	170
													2250	400	0	−155	220	40	15	4	—	375
												AB_1	2500	750	0	−95	25/145	27[7]	0	0	—	245
												AB_2[6]	2000	750	0	−90	40/315	1.5/58	230[8]	0.1[7]	16K	455
													2500	750	0	−95	35/360	1.2/55	235[8]	0.35[7]	17K	650
4-125A 4D21 6155	125	3000	20	600	120	5	6.5	10.8	0.07	3.1	5BK	C·T·O	2000	350	—	−100	200	50	12	2.8	—	275
													3000	350	—	−150	167	30	9	2.5	—	375
												AB_2[6]	2500	350	—	−43	93/260	0/6	178[8]	1.0[7]	22K	400
												AB_1[6]	2500	600	—	−96	50/232	0.3/8.5	192[8]	0	20.3K	330
												GG	2000	0	—	0	10/105[17]	30[17]	55[17]	16[17]	10.5K	145
4E27A/ 5-125B	125	4000	20	750	75	5	7.5	10.5	0.08	4.7	7BM	C·	3000	500	60	−200	167	5	6	1.6	—	375
													1000	750	0	−170	160	21	3	0.6	—	115
803	125	2000	30	600	20	10	5	17.5	0.15	29	5J	C·T	2000	500	40	−90	160	45	12	2	—	210
												C·P	1600	400	100	−80	150	45	25	5	—	155
7094	125	2000	20	400	60	6.3	3.2	9.0	0.5	1.8	Fig. 82	C·T	1500	400	—	−100	330	20	5	4	—	340
												C·P	1200	400	—	−130	275	20	5	5	—	240
												AB_1	2000	400	—	−65	30/200	35[7]	60[8]	0	12K	250
4X150A / 4X150G[15]	150[9]	2000	12	400	500	6 / 2.5	2.6 / 6.25	15.5 / 27	0.03 / 0.035	4.5 / 4.5	Fig. 75 / —	C·T·O	1250	250	—	−90	200	20	10	0.8	—	195
												C·P	1000	250	—	−105	200	20	15	2	—	140
												AB_2[6]	1250	300	—	−44	475[7]	0/65	100[8]	0.15[7]	5.6K	425
8121	150	2200	8	400	500	13.5	1.3	16	0.13	0.011	Fig. 5	C·T·O	1000	200	—	−30	300	10	30	5	—	165
4-250A 5D22 6156	250[9]	4000	35	600	110	5	14.5	12.7	0.12	4.5	5BK	C·T·O	2500	500	—	−150	300	60	9	1.7	—	575
													3000	500	—	−180	345	60	10	2.6	—	800
												C·P	2500	400	—	−200	200	30	9	2.2	—	375
													3000	400	—	−310	225	30	9	3.2	—	510
												AB_2[6]	2000	300	—	−48	510[7]	0/26	198[8]	5.5[7]	8K	650
												AB_1[6]	2500	600	—	−110	430[7]	0.3/13	180[8]	0	11.4K	625
4X250B	250[9]	2000	12	400	175	6	2.1	18.5	0.04	4.7	Fig. 75	C·T·O	2000	250	—	−90	250	25	27	2.8	—	410
												C·P	1500	250	—	−100	200	25	17	2.1	—	250
												AB_1[6]	2000	350	—	−50	500[7]	30[7]	100[8]	0	8.26K	650
7034/[9] 4X150A / 7035/ 4X150D	250 / 250	2000 / 2000	12 / 12	300 / 400	150	6 / 26.5	2.6 / 0.58	16	0.03	4.4	Fig. 75	C·T·O	2000	250	—	−88	250	24	8	2.5	—	370
												C·P	1600	250	—	−118	200	23	5	3	—	230
												AB_2[6]	2000	300	—	−50	100/500	0/36	106[8]	0.2	8.1K	630
												AB_1[6]	2000	300	—	−50	100/470	0/36	100[8]	0	8.76K	580
4CX-300A	300[9]	2000	12	400	500	6	2.75	29.5	0.04	4.8	—	C·T	2000	250	—	−90	250	25	27	2.8	—	410
												C·P	1500	250	—	−100	200	25	17	2.1	—	250
												AB_1[6]	2000	350	—	−50	500[7]	30[7]	100[8]	0	8.26K	650
175A	400	4000	25	600	—	5	14.5	15.1	0.06	9.8	Fig. 86	C·T·C·P	4000	600	0	−200	350	29	6	1.4	—	960
													2500	600	0	−180	350	40	7	1.6	—	600
												AB_1	2500	750	—	−143	100/350	1/35	0	0	—	570
4-400A	400[9]	4000	35	600	110	5	14.5	12.5	0.12	4.7	5BK	C·T·C·P	4000	300	—	−170	270	22.5	10	10	—	720
												GG	2500	0	—	0	80/270[17]	55[17]	100[17]	38[17]	4.0K	325
												AB_1	2500	750	—	−130	95/317	0/14	0	0	—	425
8122	400	2200	8	400	500	13.5	1.3	16	0.13	0.011	Fig. 86	C·T·O	2000	200	—	−30	300	5	30	5	—	300
5-500A	500	4000	35	600	30	10	10.2	19	0.10	12	—	C·T	3000	500	0	−220	432	65	35	12	—	805
												C·T	3100	470	0	−310	260	50	15	6	—	580
												AB_1	3000	750	0	−112	320	26	—	—	—	612
8166/ 4-1000A	1000	6000	75	1000	—	7.5	21	27.2	.24	7.6	—	C·T	3000	500	—	−150	700	146	38	11	—	1430
												C·P	3000	500	—	−200	600	145	36	12	—	1390
												AB_2	4000	500	—	−60	300/1200	0/95	—	11	7K	3000
												GG	3000	0	—	0	100/700[17]	105[17]	170[17]	130[17]	2.5K	1475
4CX1000A	1000	3000	12	400	400	6	12.5	35	.005	12	—	AB_1[6]	2000	325	—	−55	500/2000	−4/60	—	—	2.8K	2160
													2500	325	—	−55	500/2000	−4/60	—	—	3.1K	2920
													3000	325	—	−55	500/1800	−4/60	—	—	3.85K	3360
8295/ 172	1000	3000	30	600	—	6	8.2	38	.09	18	—	C·T	2000	500	35	−175	850	42	10	1.9	—	1155
													2500	500	35	−200	840	40	10	2.1	—	1440
													3000	500	35	−200	820	42	10	2.1	—	1770
												AB_1	2000	500	35	−110	200/800	12/43	110[8]	—	2.65K	1040
													2500	500	35	−110	200/800	11/40	115[8]	—	3.5K	1260
													3000	500	35	−115	220/800	11/39	115[8]	—	4.6K	1590

[1] Grid-resistor.
[2] Doubler to 175 MHz.
[3] Dual tube. Values for both sections, in push-pull. Interelectrode capacitances, however, are for each section.
[4] Tripler to 175 MHz.
[5] Filament limited to intermittent operation.
[6] Values are for two tubes
[7] Max.-signal value.
[8] Peak grid-to-grid volts.
[9] Forced-air cooling required.
[10] Two tubes triode connected, G_2 to G_1 through 20K Ω. Input to G_2.
[11] Tripler to 200 MHz.
[12] Typical Operation at 175 MHz.
[13] ±1.5 volts.

[14] KEY TO CLASS-OF-SERVICE ABBREVIATIONS
- AB_1 = Class-AB_1.
- AB_2 = Class-AB_2.
- B = Class-B push-pull af modulator.
- C·M = Frequency multiplier.
- C·P = Class-C plate-modulated telephone.
- C·T = Class-C telegraph.
- C·T·O = Class-C amplifier-osc.
- GG = Grounded-grid (grid and screen connected together).

[15] No Class B data available.
[16] HK257B 120 MHz. full rating.
[17] Single tone.

TABLE VIII — SEMICONDUCTOR DIODES[1]

This list contains but a small percentage of the available diode types. A complete listing would be impractical.

Small-Signal General-Purpose Diodes

Type	Material[2]	Use	Peak Reverse Volts	Max. Forward Voltage at Max. mA	Max. Forward mA at Max. V	Max. Reverse μ-amp
1N34A	G	General Purpose	75	50	5.0	30
1N35	G	General Purpose	50	—	—	2000
1N52A	G	General Purpose	85	50	5.0	100
1N60	G	Video Detector	25	50	5.0	40
1N67A	G	General Purpose	100	1	4.0	5
1N64A	G	General Purpose	100	1.0	4.0	5
1N94	S	High-Speed	75	1.0	10.0	5
1N270	G	General Purpose	100	90	—	100
1N458A	S	Signal Diode	125	1	100	25
1N634	G	60-Volt Very Low Z	120	—	50.0	45
1N645A	S	Signal Diode	225	1	400	.05
1N914	S	Fast Logic/HF Det.	75	1	75	.025
1N3754	S	Rectifier	100	1.2	150	300
1N4001	S	Rectifier	50	1.1	1000	30
1N4002	S	Rectifier	100	1.1	1000	30
1N4004	S	Rectifier	400	1.1	1000	30
1N4719	S	Rectifier	50	1.0	3000	1500
MSD7000	S	Dual Series Diode	100	1.1	200	100

Microwave Mixer and UHF Diodes

Type	Material[2]	Use	Average Freq.	Noise Figure
1N21F[3]	G	Mixer	3060 MHz	6dB
1N82A	S	Mixer	1000 MHz	14dB
MBD101	S	Mixer ($V_R = 4v$)	1000 MHz ($C_T = 1pF$ @ 0V)	7dB

[1] A bar, plus sign, or color dot usually denotes the cathode end of crystal diodes. Diode color code rings are grouped toward the cathode end.

[2] S = Silicon. G = Germanium.

[3] Polarity is such that the base is the anode and the tip is the cathode, R-types have opposite polarity.

TABLE IX — SEMICONDUCTORS

SMALL-SIGNAL TYPES

No.	Type	Maximum Ratings: Mate-rial[1]	Maximum Ratings: Diss. (Watts)	Maximum Ratings: V_{CEO} (Volts)	Maximum Ratings: I_C (dc)	Characteristics: h_{FE} (Min.)	Characteristics: f_T (Typ.)	Characteristics: Noise Fig. (dB)	Characteristics: Use (Typ.)	Other Data: Case Style	Other Data: Base Conn.	Other Data: Manu-facturer[2]	Application
2N406	PNP	G	0.15	—18	—	34	0.65 MHz	—	Gen. Purpose	TO-1	7	R	Gen. Purpose
2N706A	NPN	S	0.3*	20	50 mA	20	400 MHz	—	rf	TO-18	8	M	rf, Switching
2N718A	NPN	S	0.5	50	150 mA	40	60 MHz	—	—	TO-18	8	R	Switching
2N1179	PNP	G	0.080*	—30	—10 mA	100	—	—	hf Amp.	TO-45	5	R	rf Mixer
2N1302	NPN	G	0.15	25	0.3A	20	—	—	Computer	TO-5	8	R	Osc., Amp.
2N1306	NPN	G	0.15	25	0.3A	60	—	—	Computer	TO-5	8	R	Osc., Amp.
2N2222	NPN	S	1.8	30	800 mA	35	250 MHz	—	Gen. Purpose	TO-18	8	M	vhf Amp., Osc.
2N2925	NPN	S	0.2*	25	100 mA	170	160 MHz	2.8	Gen. Purpose	—	1	GE	Osc., rf, i-f, af
2N3391A	NPN	S	0.2*	25	100 mA	250	160 MHz	1.9	Audio	—	1	GE	Low-noise Preamps.
2N3394	NPN	S	0.31	25	100 mA	55	—	—	Gen. Purpose	TO-92	2	M	Audio Amp.
2N3565	NPN	S	0.2	25	50 mA	150	—	—	—	TO-106	7	—	—
2N3568	NPN	S	0.3	60	500 mA	120	60 MHz	—	—	TO-105	—	—	—
2N3638	PNP	S	0.3	—25	—500 mA	100	150 MHz	—	—	TO-105	—	—	Switching
2N3663	NPN	S	0.12*	12	25 mA	20	900 MHz	4	rf	—	1	GE	vhf/uhf Osc., Amp., Mix.
2N3702	PNP	S	0.31	—25	—200 mA	60	100 MHz	—	Gen. Purpose	TO-92	2	M	vhf Osc., Amp.
2N3866	NPN	S	5	3	400 mA	5	800 MHz	—	Gen. Purpose	TO-39	8	M	uhf Amp., Osc.
2N3904	NPN	S	0.21	40	200 mA	40	300 MHz	—	Gen. Purpose	TO-92	2	M	vhf Amp., Osc.
2N3906	NPN	G	0.15	25	300 mA	60	—	—	Computer	TO-5	8	R	Osc., Amp.
2N4123	NPN	S	0.21	30	200 mA	50	250 MHz	—	Gen. Purpose	TO-92	2	M	vhf Amp., Osc.
2N4124	NPN	S	0.3	25	200 mA	120	250 MHz	5	Audio-rf	—	2	M	—
2N4126	PNP	S	0.3	—25	200 mA	120	250 MHz	4	Audio-rf	—	2	M	—
2N4275	NPN	S	0.28	15	—	18	—	—	—	—	—	—	Switching
2N4401	NPN	S	0.31*	40	600 mA	20	250 MHz	—	Gen. Purpose	TO-92	2	M	Osc., rf, i-f, af
2N4410	NPN	S	0.31*	80	250 mA	60	250 MHz	—	Gen. Purpose	TO-92	2	M	Osc., rf, i-f, af
2N4957	PNP	S	.2	30	30 mA	20	1600 MHz	2.6	rf Amp.	TO-72	9	M	rf Amp., Mix., Osc.
2N4959	PNP	S	.2	30	30 mA	20	1500 MHz	3.2	rf Amp.	TO-72	9	M	rf Amp., Mix., Osc.
2N5032	NPN	S	.2	10	20 mA	25	2000 MHz	3.0	rf Amp.	TO-72	9	M	Low-noise rf Amp.
2N5087	PNP	S	0.310*	—50	—50 mA	200	150 MHz	1	rf Amp.	TO-92	2	M	Low-noise rf Amp.
2N5089	PNP	S	0.310*	—25	—50 mA	450	175 MHz	2	rf Amp.	TO-92	2	M	Low-noise rf Amp.
2N5109	NPN	S	3.5*	40	0.4 A	70	—	3	vhf Amp.	TO-39	8	R	Wide-band Amp.
2N5179	NPN	S	0.200*	12	50 mA	25	900 MHz	4.5	rf Amp.	TO-72	9	M	uhf Amp., Osc., Mix.
2N5183	NPN	S	0.5	18	1 A	120	200 MHz	—	Gen. Purpose	TO-104	8	R	vhf Osc., Amp.
2N5222	PNP	S	0.310*	—15	—50 mA	20	450 MHz	—	rf Amp.	TO-92	18	M	rf Amp., Mix., Video i-f
2N5829	PNP	S	.2	30	30 mA	20	1600 MHz	2.3	rf Amp.	TO-72	9	M	rf Amp., Mix., Osc.
40231	NPN	S	0.5*	18	100 mA	55	60 MHz	2.8	Audio	TO-104	7	R	Preamps. and Drivers
40235	NPN	S	0.18*	35	50 mA	40	1200 MHz	3.3	rf	TO-104	9	R	vhf/uhf Amp., Osc., Mix.
HEP51	PNP	S	0.6	—25	—600 mA	80	150 MHz	—	—	TO-5	8	M	rf Amp.
HEP53	NPN	S	0.6	30	600 mA	85	200 MH	—	—	TO-5	8	M	rf Amp.
HEP56	NPN	S	0.31	20	100 mA	70	750 MHz	—	—	TO-92	18	M	uhf Osc.
MPS918	NPN	S	0.310*	15	—	20	200 MHz	6	Amp. Osc.	TO-92	2	M	uhf Amp., Osc.
MPS2926	NPN	S	0.31	18	100 mA	35	300 MHz	—	Gen. Purpose	TO-92	2	M	vhf Osc., Amp.
MPS3394	NPN	S	0.31	25	100 mA	55	—	—	Gen. Purpose	TO-92	2	M	Audio Amp.
MPS3563	NPN	S	0.310*	12	—	20	200 MHz	—	Amp. Osc.	TO-92	2	M	uhf Amp., Osc.
MPS3693	NPN	S	0.310*	45	—	40	200 MHz	4	rf Amp.	TO-92	2	M	50 MHz Amp.
MPS3694	NPN	S	0.310*	45	—	100	200 MHz	4	rf Amp.	TO-92	2	M	50 MHz Amp.
MPS3702	PNP	S	0.31	—25	—200 mA	60	100 MHz	—	Gen. Purpose	TO-92	2	M	vhf Osc., Amp.
MPS3706	NPN	S	0.310*	20	600 mA	600	100 MHz	—	af Amp.	TO-92	2	M	Audio Amp.

SMALL-SIGNAL TYPES — *Continued*

No.	Type	Maximum Ratings				Characteristics				Other Data			
		Material[1]	Diss. (Watts)	V_{CEO} (Volts)	I_C (dc)	h_{FE} (Min.)	f_T (Typ.)	Noise Fig. (dB)	Use (Typ.)	Case Style	Base Conn.	Manufacturer[2]	Application
MPS6514	NPN	S	.3	25	100 mA	150	480 MHz	2.0	Audio-rf	TO-92	2	M	af-rf Amp.
MPS6530	NPN	S	0.310*	40	600 mA	30	390 MHz	—	Amp.	TO-92	2	M	Complementary Amp
MPS6534	PNP	S	0.310*	–40	–600 mA	60	260 MHz	—	µhf Amp.	TO-92	2	M	Complementary Amp.
MPS6543	NPN	S	0.310*	25	—	25	750 MHz	—	Osc.	TO-92	2	M	uhf Osc.
MPS6569	NPN	S	0.310*	20	—	20	300 MHz	6	i-f Amp.	TO-92	18	M	vhf Amp., Video i-f
MPSA12	NPN	S	0.310*	20	—	35	—	—	Audio Amp.	TO-92	2	M	High-Z Pre-amp.
MPSA55	PNP	S	0.5	–60	–500 mA	50	50 MHz	—	Audio Amp.	TO-92	2	M	Audio Amp.
TIS48	NPN	—	1.2*	40	500 mA	40	500 MHz	—	rf	TO-92	3	TI	rf, Switching
TIS54	PNP	—	0.25*	–12	–80 mA	30	300 MHz	—	rf	TO-92	3	TI	rf, Switching
TIXM10	PNP	—	0.075*	–20	–30 mA	20	630 MHz	4	rf	TO-72	4	TI	rf, Preamp., vhf/uhf

LARGE-SIGNAL TYPES

No.	Type	Maximum Ratings				Characteristics				Other Data			
		Material[1]	Diss. (Watts)	V_{CEO} (Volts)	I_C (dc)	h_{FE} (Min.)	f_T (Typ.)	Noise Fig. (dB)	Use (Typ.)	Case Style	Base Conn.	Manufacturer[2]	Application
2N441	PNP	G	150	–40	–15 A	20	—	—	Gen. Purpose	TO-36	13	M	Switch, Amp.
2N1491	NPN	S	3.0*	30	100 mA	15	300 MHz	—	rf Amp.	TO-39	8	R	vhf Amp., Mix.
2N1970	PNP	G	170	–50	–15 A	17	—	—	Gen. Purpose	TO-36	13	M	Switch, Amp.
2N2102	NPN	S	5†	65	1 A	20	100 MHz	6	Gen. Purpose	TO-5	8	R	af, rf Amps. (Linear)
2N2157	PNP	—	170†	–60	–30 A	40	100 kHz	—	af	TO-36	13	M	af, dc Amp., Switch.
2N2270	NPN	S	5†	—	1 A	10	—	6	Amp.	TO-5	9	R	Low-noise Amp.
2N2631	NPN	S	8.75†	60	1.5 A	—	200 MHz	—	rf	TO-39	8	R	Class C rf Amp., Osc.
2N2869	PNP	—	30†	–50	–10 A	50	200 kHz	—	Gen. Purpose	TO-3	11	R	af, Osc., Amp., Switch.
2N2876	NPN	S	17.5†	60	1.5 A	—	200 MHz	—	rf	TO-60	12	R	vhf Class-C Amp.
2N3053	NPN	S	5	60	700 mA	50	—	—	—	TO-5	8	R	Pwr. Switch
2N3055	NPN	S	115	60	15 A	20–70	—	—	Gen. Purpose	TO-3	11	R	Switch, Reg., Amp.
2N3119	NPN	S	4†	80	500 mA	50	450 MHz	—	Amp.	TO-5	8	R	Switch, Pulse Amp.
2N3512	NPN	—	4	35	500 mA	10	250 MHz	—	Audio-rf	—	7	R	—
2N3553	NPN	S	7†	40	1 A	10	500 MHz	—	rf	TO-39	8	M	Class A, B, C rf Mult., Amp., Osc.
2N3583	NPN	S	35†	175	2 A	10	15 MHz	—	hV Gen. Purp.	TO-66	11	R	rf, af Osc., Amp. dc Amp.
2N3632	NPN	S	23*	65	3 A	—	400 MHz	—	rf Amp.	TO-60	12	R	uhf Pwr. Amp., Osc.
2N3733	NPN	S	23*	65	3 A	—	400 MHz	—	rf Amp.	TO-60	12	R	uhf Pwr. Amp., Osc.
2N3772	NPN	S	150	60	20 A	15–60	800 kHz	—	Pwr. Amp.	TO-3	11	R	Pwr. Amp.
2N3866	NPN	S	5†	30	0.4 A	—	800 MHz	—	rf	TO-39	8	R	Class A, B, C rf Mult., Amp., Osc.
2N3924	NPN	S	7*	18	500 mA	—	350 MHz	—	rf Amp.	TO-39	8	M	uhf Pwr. Amp., Osc.
2N3948	NPN	S	1*	20	400 mA	15	700 MHz	—	rf Amp.	TO-39	8	M	uhf Pwr. Amp., Osc.
2N4012	NPN	S	11.6*	40	1.5 A	—	500 MHz	—	rf Amp.	TO-60	12	R	uhf Pwr. Amp., Osc.
2N4037	PNP	S	7†	–40	–1 A	50	60 MHz	—	Gen. Purpose	TO-5	8	R	Amp., Switching
2N4396	NPN	S	62†	60	5 A	60	4 MHz	—	Gen. Purpose	TO-3	11	R	rf, af Osc., Amp. dc Amp.
2N4427	NPN	S	3.5*	20	400 mA	—	500 MHz	—	rf Amp.	TO-39	8	R	uhf Amp.
2N5016	NPN	S	30*	65	4.5 A	—	600 MHz	—	rf Amp.	TO-60	12	R	uhf Pwr., rf Amp.
2N5070	NPN	S	70†	65	3.3 A	—	30 MHz	—	Amp.	TO-60	12	R	30 MHz Amp.
2N5071	NPN	S	70†	65	3.3 A	—	76 MHz	—	Amp.	TO-60	12	R	50 MHz Amp.
2N5470	NPN	S	3.5†	55	200 mA	—	2GHz	—	uhf Amp.	—	—	R	Microwave Osc., Amp.
2N5635	NPN	S	7.5*	35	1 A	5	—	—	rf Amp.	—	23	M	400 MHz, rf Amp.
2N5636	NPN	S	15*	35	1.5 A	5	—	—	rf Amp.	—	23	M	400 MHz, rf Amp.
2N5637	NPN	S	30*	35	3 A	5	—	—	rf Amp.	—	23	M	400 MHz rf Amp.
2N5641	NPN	S	15*	35	1 A	5	—	—	rf Amp.	—	23	M	400 MHz, rf Amp.
2N5642	NPN	S	30*	35	3 A	5	—	—	rf Amp.	—	23	M	400 MHz, rf Amp.
2N5643	NPN	S	60*	35	5 A	5	—	—	rf Amp.	—	23	M	400 MHz, rf Amp.
2N5913	NPN	S	3.5†	14	330 mA	—	900 MHz	—	uhf Amp.	TO-39	8	R	432 MHz Amp.
2N5914	NPN	S	10.7†	14	1.5 A	—	900 MHz	—	uhf Amp.	—	—	R	432 MHz Amp.
2N5915	NPN	S	10.7†	14	1.5 A	—	800 MHz	—	uhf Amp.	—	—	R	432 MHz Amp.
2N5919	NPN	S	25†	30	4.5 A	—	400 MHz	—	uhf Amp.	—	—	R	220 MHz Amp.
2N5921	NPN	S	8.3†	50	700 mA	—	2.3 GHz	—	uhf Amp.	—	—	R	Microwave Osc., Amp.
2N5941	NPN	S	80	35	6.0A	10	50 MHz	—	rf Amp.	—	25	M	30 MHz rf Amp.
2N5942	NPN	S	140	35	12 A	10	50 MHz	—	rf Amp.	—	26	M	30 MHz rf Amp.
2N5944	NPN	S	5	16	0.4A	20	470 MHz	—	uhf Amp.	—	27	M	432 MHz rf Amp.
2N5945	NPN	S	15	16	0.8 A	20	470 MHz	—	uhf Amp.	—	27	M	432 MHz rf Amp.
2N5946	NPN	S	37.5	16	2.0 A	20	470 MHz	—	uhf Amp.	—	27	M	432 MHz rf Amp.
2N5995	NPN	S	10.7	14	1.5 A	—	175 MHz	—	vhf Amp.	—	23	R	vhf rf Amp.
2N5996	NPN	S	35.7	18	5.0 A	—	175 MHz	—	vhf Amp.	—	23	R	vhf rf Amp.
2N6136	NPN	S	60	18	6.0 A	20	470 MHz	—	uhf Amp.	—	27	M	432 MHz rf Amp.
MJ480	NPN	S	87†	40	1 A	30	4 MHz	—	Gen. Purpose	TO-3	11	M	af, rf Amp., Osc.
MPS-U01	NPN	S	1.0*	30	1.5 A	70	50 MHz	—	af Amp.	—	20	M	Audio Amp.
MPS-U51	PNP	S	1.0*	–30	–1.5 A	70	50 MHz	—	Gen. Purpose	—	20	M	af Amp.

FIELD-EFFECT TRANSISTORS

No.	Type	Diss. (mW)	V_{DS}	V_{GS}	MIN. µ MHOS	C_{ISS} (pF)	MAX. IDSS (mA)	Top Freq. (MHz)	Case Style	Base Conn.	Manufacturer	Application
2N4416	N JFET	175	30	–6.0	4000	4	15	450	TO-72	15	M	vhf/uhf rf Amp , Mix., Osc.
2N4417	N FET	175	30	–30	4500	3.5	15	400	—	22	UC	vhf uhf Amp.
2N5460	P JFET	310	—	40	1000	5	5	—	TO-92	19	M	Gen. Purpose Audio

FIELD-EFFECT TRANSISTORS — *Continued*

No.	Type	Diss. (mW)	V_{DS}	V_{GS}	MIN. μ MHOS	C_{ISS} (pF)	MAX. I_{DSS} (mA)	Top Freq. (MHz)	Case Style	Base Conn.	Manu-facturer	Application
2N5461	P JFET	310	—	40	1500	5	9	—	TO-92	19	M	Gen. Purpose Audio
2N5463	P JFET	310	—	40	1000	5	5	—	TO-92	19	M	Gen. Purpose Audio
2N5465	P FET	310	—	60	2000	5	16	—	TO-92	19	M	Gen. Purpose Amp.
2N5669	N JFET	310	25	1.0	1600	4.7	4	—	TO-92	6	M	Amp. Switching
2N5670	N JFET	310	25	2.0	2500	4.7	8	—	TO-92	6	M	Amp. Switching
3N128	N IGFET	100	20	—	5000	5.8	—	200	TO-72	14	R	af, rf, Amp., Mix., Osc.
3N187	MOS n-channel Depletion type	330	20	−6+6	7000	4	8.5	300	TO-72	16	R	—
3N200	MOS n-channel Depletion type	330	20	−6+6	10,000	8.5	—	500	TO-72	16	R	uhf rf Amp.
40600	N Dual-Gate FET	400	20	−8	10,000	5.5	18	250	TO-72	16	R	uhf rf Amp.
40601	N Dual-Gate FET	400	20	−8	10,000	5.5	18	250	TO-72	16	R	vhf Mixer
40602	N Dual-Gate FET	400	20	−8	10,000	5.5	18	250	TO-72	16	R	vhf Amp.
40603	N Dual-Gate FET	400	20	−8	10,000	5.5	18	—	TO-72	16	R	rf Amp.
40604	N Dual-Gate FET	400	20	−8	10,000	5.5	18	—	TO-72	16	R	rf Mix.
40673	N Dual-Gate FET	330	20	−6	12,000	6	35	400	TO-72	16	R	rf Amp.
E300	N JFET	250	—	1	9000	5.5	30	100	—	4	SI	vhf Amp.
HEP801	N JFET	200	20	—	3000	—	9	—	TO-72	14	M	af Amp.
HEP802	N JFET	200	25	—	2000	—	20	—	TO-92	6	M	rf Amp.
MMT3823	N JFET	225	30	−30	3000	4.0	20	—	—	21	M	rf Amp., Mix.
MPF102	N JFET	200	25	−2.5	2000	4.5	20	200	TO-92	6	M	af, rf Amp., Mix., Osc.
MPF103/ 2N5457	N JFET	310	25	−25	1000	4.5	5	—	TO-92	6	M	Gen. Purpose Audio
MPF104/ 2N5458	N JFET	310	25	−25	1500	4.5	9	—	TO-92	6	M	Gen Purpose Audio
MPF105/ 2N5459	N JFET	200	25	−4.5	2000	4.5	16	100	TO-92	6	M	af, rf Amp., Mix., Osc.
MPF106/ 2N5484	N JFET	200	25	−25	2500	5	30	432	TO-92	6	M	af, rf Amp., Mix., Osc.
MPF107/ 2N5486	N JFET	310	—	−25	1000	5	20	400	TO-92	6	M	vhf-uhf rf Amp.
MPF120	N Dual-Gate MOS FET	500	25	±20	8000	4.5	18	105	—	24	M	rf Amp.
MPF121	N Dual-Gate MOS FET	500	25	±20	10,000	4.5	30	200	—	24	M	rf Amp.
MPF122	N Dual-Gate MOS FET	500	25	±20	8000	4.5	20	200	—	24	M	rf Mix.

* = Ambient Temp. of 25°C (No heat sink). † = Case Temp. of 25°C (with heat sink).
[1] S = Silicon. G = Germanium. [2] GE = General Electric. M = Motorola. R = RCA. SI = Siliconix. TI = Texas Instuments. UC = Union Carbide.

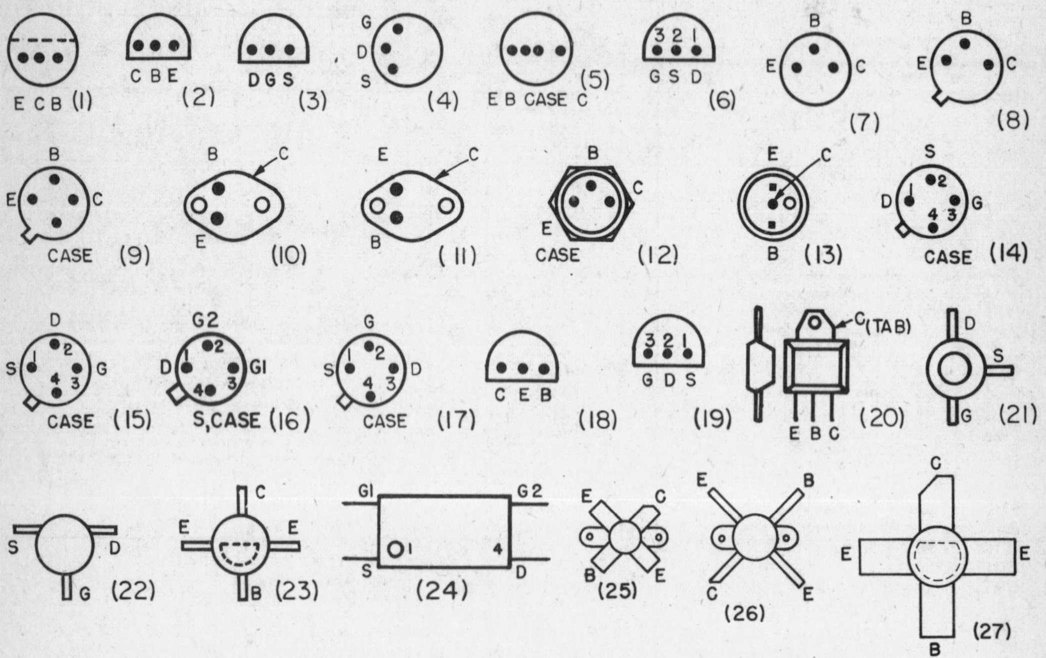

The leads are marked C - collector, B - base, E - emitter, G - gate, D - drain, and S - source.

Some Abbreviations used in Text and Drawings

A – ampere
ac – alternating current
A/D – analog-to-digital
af – audio frequency
afc – automatic frequency control
afsk – audio frequency-shift keying
agc – automatic gain control
alc – automatic load (or level) control
a-m – amplitude modulation
anl – automatic noise limiter
ARC – amateur radio club
AREC – Amateur Radio Emergency Corps
ARPSC – Amateur Radio Public Service Corps
ATV – amateur television
avc – automatic volume control
bc – broadcast
BCD – binary-coded decimal
bci – broadcast interference
bcl – broadcast listener
BFO – beat-frequency oscillator
BPL – Brass Pounders League
CB – Citizens band
CCIR – International Radio Consultative Committee
ccw – counterclockwise
c.d. – civil defense
CD – Communications Department (ARRL)
CMOS or COSMOS – complimentary-symmetry metal-oxide semiconductor
coax – coaxial cable, connector
COR – carrier-operated relay
CP – Code Proficiency (award)
CR – cathode ray
CRT – cathode-ray tube
ct – center tap
CTCSS – continuous tone-controlled squelch system
cw – continuous wave (code), clockwise
D/A – digital-to-analog
dB – decibel
dc – direct current
DF – direction finder
DOC – Department of Communications (Canadian)
dpdt – double-pole double-throw
dpst – double-pole single-throw
dsb – double sideband
DTL – diode-transistor logic
DX – long distance
DXCC – DX Century Club
EC – Emergency Coordinator
ECO – electron-coupled oscillator
ECL – emitter-coupled logic
EME – earth-moon-earth
emf – electromotive force (voltage)
FAX – facsimile
FCC – Federal Communications Commission
FD – Field Day
FET – field-effect transistor
FF – flip-flop
fm – frequency modulation
FMT – frequency measuring test
fsk – frequency-shift keying
GDO – grid-dip oscillator
GHz – gigahertz
GMT – Greenwich Mean Time
gnd – ground
H – henry
hf – high frequency
HFO – heterodyne frequency oscillator
Hz – hertz
IARU – International Amateur Radio Union
IC – integrated circuit
ID – inside diameter
i-f – intermediate frequency
in./s – inch per second
IRC – International Reply Coupon
ITU – International Telecommunication Union
IW – Intruder Watch
JFET – junction field-effect transistor
k – kilo
kc – kilocycle
kHz – kilohertz
kW – kilowatt
LED – light-emitting diode
lf – low frequency
LMO – linear master oscillator
LO – local oscillator
lsb – lower sideband
LSB – least-significant bit
LSD – least-significant digit
LSI – large-scale integration
luf – lowest usable frequency
mA – milliampere
MARS – Military Affiliate Radio System
Mc – Megacycle
mf – medium frequency
MG – motor-generator
mH – millihenry
MHz – Megahertz
mic – microphone
mix – mixer
MO – master oscillator
MOSFET – metal-oxide semiconductor field-effect transistor
MOX – manually-operated switching
ms – millisecond
m.s. – meteor scatter
MSB – most-significant bit
MSD – most-significant digit
MSI – medium-scale integration
muf – maximum usable frequency
MUX – multiplex
mV – millivolt
mW – milliwatt
nbfm – narrow-band frequency modulation
n.c. – no connection
NC – normally closed
NCS – net control station
NO – normally open
npn – negative-positive-negative
NTS – National Traffic System (ARRL)
OBS – Official Bulletin Station
OD – outside diameter
OO – Official Observer
op amp – operational amplifier
OPS – Official Phone Station
ORS – Official Relay Station
osc – oscillator
OVS – Official VHF Station
oz – ounce
PA – power amplifier
pc – printed or etched circuit board
PEP – peak-envelope power
PEV – peak-envelope voltage
pF – picofarad
PIV – peak-inverse voltage
pk – peak
pk-pk – peak-to-peak
PL – private line
PLL – phase-locked loop
pm – phase modulation
pnp – positive-negative-positive
pot – potentiometer
PRV – peak-reverse voltage
PSHR – Public Service Honor Roll
PTO – permeability-tuned oscillator
PTT – push-to-talk
RACES – Radio Amateur Civil Emergency Service
RCC – Rag Chewers Club
rcvr – receiver
rf – radio frequency
rfc – radio-frequency choke
RFI – radio-frequency interference
RM – Route Manager
RM-(number) – FCC rulemaking
rms – root-mean-square
RO – Radio Officer (c.d.)
RST – readability-strength-tone
RTL – resistor-transistor logic
RTTY – radio teletype
s.a.e. – self-addressed envelope
s.a.s.e. – stamped s.a.e.
SCM – Section Communications Manager
SCR – silicon-controlled rectifier
SEC – Section Emergency Coordinator
SET – simulated emergency test
S.M. – silver mica (capacitor)
SNR – signal-to-noise ratio
spdt – single-pole double-throw
spst – single-pole single-throw
SS – Sweepstakes (contest)
ssb – single sideband
SSTV – slow-scan TV
SWL – short-wave listener
SWR – standing wave ratio
sync – synchronous, synchronizing
TCC – Transcontinental Corps
TD – transmitting distributor
TE – transequatorial (propagation)
tfc – traffic
tpi – turns per inch
T-R – transmit-receive
TTL or T^2L – transistor-transistor logic
TTY – Teletype
TV – television
TVI – television interference
UJT – unijunction transistor
usb – upper sideband
uhf – ultra-high frequency
V – volt
VCO – voltage-controlled oscillator
VCXO – voltage-controlled crystal oscillator
VFO – variable frequency oscillator
vhf – very high frequency
vlf – very low frequency
VOM – volt-ohm-milliammeter
VOX – voice-operated break-in
VR – voltage regulator
VTVM – vacuum-tube voltmeter
VXO – variable crystal oscillator
W – watt
WAC – Worked All Continents
WAS – Worked All States
wbfm – wide-band fm
wpm – words per minute
ww – wire wound
wv – working voltage
xtal – crystal
μ – micro (10^{-6})

Application for Membership

AMERICAN RADIO RELAY LEAGUE

Administrative Headquarters: Newington, Connecticut, U. S. A. 06111

........................19....

AMERICAN RADIO RELAY LEAGUE,
Newington, Conn., U. S. A. 06111

Being genuinely interested in Amateur Radio, I hereby apply for membership* in the American Radio Relay League. I enclose remittance ($9.00 in the U. S., $10.00 in Canada, $10.50 elsewhere, U. S. funds) in payment of dues for........ ....year(s), including subscription to *QST* for the same period. Please begin *QST* with the................. issue. Amount enclosed: $..............................

The call of my station is..............................

The class of my operator's license is......................

I belong to the following radio societies.................

....

Send Membership Certificate ☐ or Membership Card ☐

....
Name

....
Address

....
City, State, Zip Code

A bona fide interest in amateur radio is the only essential requirement, but full voting membership is granted only to licensed radio amateurs of the United States and Canada. Therefore, if you have a license, please be sure to indicate it above.

*Membership is available only to individuals. Life Membership is granted to Full Members for $180 ($200 Canada, $210 elsewhere). Write the Secretary for details.

Any member of the immediate family, living at the same address, may also become a League member, without QST, at the special rate of $2.00 per year. Such family membership must run concurrently with that of the member receiving QST.

Index

A

B

C

D

E

F

G

H

O

P

Q

R

S

U

V

W

XYZ